A DESCRIPTIVE CHECK LIST

Describing Almost 7500 Items OF

WESTERN AMERICANA

View of the rear of the George W. Soliday library, facing Lake Washington. The entrance door is behind the chair in right foreground. The late Mrs. Soliday stands overlooking her garden.

A DESCRIPTIVE CHECK LIST

Together With

SHORT TITLE INDEX

Describing Almost 7500 Items of

WESTERN AMERICANA

Comprising

BOOKS, MAPS AND PAMPHLETS

OF THE IMPORTANT LIBRARY
(In Four Parts)

FORMED BY

GEORGE W. SOLIDAY
Seattle, Wash.

COMPILED WITH NOTES BY

PETER DECKER [pseud.]

1940-1945

ANTIQUARIAN PRESS, LTD.
NEW YORK
1960

First Published
1940-1945

Reprinted With Corrections 1960
By
ANTIQUARIAN PRESS, LTD.
New York, N.Y.

This Edition Limited To 550 Copies
Of Which
500 Numbered Copies Are For Sale

This Is No. . . . . . .

Printed in U.S.A.

Noble Offset Printers, Inc.
New York, N.Y.

Foreword

More than fifteen years have passed since the George W. Soliday catalogue of books relating to the Northwestern region of the United States and Canada was issued under my imprint. Although envisaged as a commercial venture wherein Mr. Soliday's books might be sold at the prices then prevailing, it was not until the fourth part of the catalogue was printed and distributed that I was solicited by numerous booksellers, collectors and librarians to supply an index to all the four parts. As I had held back only 100 copies each of the four parts, an index which would exceed more than one hundred double column pages seemed to me at the time, to be unrealistic.

My first reaction was to decline the suggestion to make the index and underwrite its printing and publication. It was not until I sought the advice of the late Lathrop C. Harper, Edward W. Eberstadt, Roland Tree of Henry Stevens, Son and Stiles, and Wright Howes, the historically minded bookseller of Chicago, that I was induced to go through with the project. It had not immediately occurred to me that the Soliday collection, while it contained the usual voyages to Northwest Coast and the obvious Overlands which had been aptly annotated previously, did also comprise a large group of important but less scarce books relating to American travel, which had not been described in one volume elsewhere. Also, there was a large segment of valuable Russian historical literature relating to the Northwest Coast that had only been sparsely offered prior to the appearance of the Soliday Catalogue. These then were the compelling factors that influenced me in my decision to go ahead with the project.

This publication, per se, was not originally intended to be a commercial undertaking. The index to all four parts entailed a cost of more than one thousand dollars, and the buckram bindings, three dollars and fifty cents per volume. The one hundred copies, which were all I had available, were sold out almost immediately at seven dollars and fifty cents each. Fortunately, I kept one copy for myself. And now, down through the years, hardly a week or month goes by, that I do not receive an inquiry or order for this catalogue. The prices, as of other historical and bibliographical material, have greatly increased. So it is with considerable satisfaction to me, that the Antiquarian Press Ltd. has offered to make this book available again for booksellers, librarians and collectors.

This is primarily a catalogue for booksellers, as the requests for copies have come mainly from them. Prices as then offered obviously do not obtain today. Their inclusion therefore in this new issue is only academic. Errors in the original text will be found relating to binding, format, and in a few cases, date of issue since I worked mainly from cards. I have tried to correct most of the mistakes in this new edition and have listed them on each page. Nontheless I would advise the reader to check for himself. He will derive bibliographical satisfaction and experience in doing this. Also, he should mark any errors we may have overlooked, for his own guidance and ours.

As for the late Mr. Soliday and his collection, I covered this briefly in the original work, and have included that sketch in this edition. Since the complete bound catalogue in its first form was an afterthought, the lack of continuous pagination for the four parts obviously made the original unwieldy for convenient use. It will be far simpler therefore, to be able to use this much handier and attractively sturdier volume, in which a thumb index has been supplied for each part.

PETER DECKER

Foreword

More than fifteen years have passed since the George W. Soliday States and Canada was issued under my imprint. Although envisaged as catalogue of books relating to the Northwestern region of the United a commercial venture wherein Mr. Soliday's books might be sold at the prices then prevailing, it was not until the fourth part of the catalogue was printed and distributed that I was solicited by numerous booksellers, collectors and librarians to supply an index to all the four parts. As I had held back only 100 copies each of the four parts, an index which would exceed more than one hundred double column pages seemed to me at the time, to be unrealistic.

My first reaction was to decline the suggestion to make the index and underwrite its printing and publication. It was not until I sought the advice of the late Lathrop C. Harper, Edward W. Eberstadt, Roland Tree of Henry Stevens, Son and Stiles, and Wright Howes, the historically minded bookseller of Chicago, that I was induced to go through with the project. It had not immediately occurred to me that the Soliday collection, while it contained the usual voyages to Northwest Coast and the obvious Overlands which had been aptly annotated previously, did also comprise a large group of important but less scarce books relating to American travel, which had not been described in one volume elsewhere. Also, there was a large segment of valuable Russian historical literature relating to the Northwest Coast that had only been sparsely offered prior to the appearance of the Soliday Catalogue. These then were the compelling factors that influenced me in my decision to go ahead with the project.

This publication, per se, was not originally intended to be a commercial undertaking. The index to all four parts entailed a cost of more than one thousand dollars, and the buckram bindings, three dollars and fifty cents per volume. The one hundred copies, which were all I had available, were sold out almost immediately at seven dollars and fifty cents each. Fortunately, I kept one copy for myself. And now, down through the years, hardly a week or month goes by, that I do not receive an inquiry or order for this catalogue. The prices, as of other historical and bibliographical material, have greatly increased. So it is with considerable satisfaction to me, that the Antiquarian Press Ltd. has offered to make this book available again for booksellers, librarians and collectors.

This is primarily a catalogue for booksellers, as the requests for copies have come mainly from them. Prices as then offered obviously do not obtain today. Their inclusion therefore in this new issue is only academic. Errors in the original text will be found relating to binding, format, and in a few cases, date of issue since I worked mainly from cards. I have tried to correct most of the mistakes in this new edition and have listed them on each page. Nontheless I would advise the reader to check for himself. He will derive bibliographical satisfaction and experience in doing this. Also, he should mark any errors we may have overlooked, for his own guidance and ours.

As for the late Mr. Soliday and his collection, I covered this briefly in the original work, and have included that sketch in this edition. Since the complete bound catalogue in its first form was an afterthought, the lack of continuous pagination for the four parts obviously made the original unwieldy for convenient use. It will be far simpler therefore, to be able to use this much handier and attractively sturdier volume, in which a thumb index has been supplied for each part.

PETER DECKER

* MR. SOLIDAY AND HIS LIBRARY

The items in this catalogue, as well as those in my catalogues 17 and 18 are from the collection of George W. Soliday, of Seattle, Washington. It has required more than two years to list the 25,000 volumes in this collection, and now that the work is drawing to a close, we can do no more than put a mark of finality on our work by acceding to the request of many of our clients for some brief account of a man who, for the past fifty years, has foraged world-wide to gather what may be described as perhaps the most diversified collection of Northwestern Americana ever assembled by a private citizen.

Our task in dispersing the collection has been a pleasurable one for both Mr. Soliday and myself, one that has been rather a new experience in American bookselling. Hitherto, libraries of such proportions as this have quite properly been dispersed by the heirs and executors of estates in the larger auction rooms. The business is usually terminated in a few hours of feverish bidding and everything pertaining thereto is quite competently rendered to the satisfaction of all.

However, there are not always executors and heirs. For fifty years Mr. Soliday has enjoyed "a constant source of pleasure", not only for himself and the late Mrs. Soliday, but for the numerous friends and students who were graciously welcomed to their library "Sanctuary" on High Lane. And now, at 73, still robust and still the philosopher, Mr. Soliday is permitting himself the one pleasure that he has always looked forward to—the recapitulation of all he has gained "as an amateur collector". Mr. Soliday will not admit it, but one has the right to suspect that he is enjoying to the fullest the "bibliographical fun" he is having in going back over his collection, item by item. One completes the full cycle by reversing the hour glass of collecting. One is wise, one has learned something, perhaps one could have done better. And, as the sand runs out in that final recapitulation of all that has gone before, one knows then that one has not only suitably prolonged one's love for books but has made one's last footnotes and gained on's best knowledge.

Mr. Soliday is of the great prairies, the son of a pioneer. Born in Ohio in 1869, he was removed by his parents to the northern part of the Dakota Territory, then largely inhabited by Indians, traders and homesteaders. The prairies were still in their natural state, there was still no public school system and the nearest town was more than fifty miles distant. When a public school system was established Mr. Soliday attended during the latter part of his childhood and youth. During 1887-1888 he attended the Jamestown College "very irregularly".

---

* This brief sketch is reprinted exactly as it appeared in the first issue of the bound catalogue preceding part III. Mr. Soliday died on August 23, 1950.

In 1890 the Dakota Territory was divided into its present states of North and South Dakota, and Mr. Soliday was appointed County Auditor of Foster County. Later, he was able to fulfill his ambition for the law by graduating from the Law School of Northwestern University, being admitted to practice before the Supreme Courts of both Illinois and North Dakota. He is now admitted to appear before the Supreme Court of Washington and the United States Supreme Court.

As a young man, only a short time out of Law School, Mr. Soliday was elected States Attorney of Foster County, North Dakota, a position which he held during four terms until his resignation in 1902. Meanwhile, he had married Miss Virginia Rutledge Warren of Jacksonville, Illinois. Upon his resignation as States Attorney, Mr. and Mrs. Soliday removed to Chicago where they continued to reside until 1907. In that year Mr. Soliday retired from further law practice and has passed the remaining years in traveling and collecting.

A collector from early youth, Mr. Soliday now found the leisure to build a library of the proportions he had always envisaged. With a sure foundation of good books already acquired, Mr. and Mrs. Soliday, with their niece Virginia R. Orton, in 1907, began a two-year tour of the world during which they acquired some of the most important items in their library. They visited London, Paris, Madrid, Rome and Florence, Berlin and Vienna, Moscow and St. Petersburg, Tokyo, Shanghai, and finally settled for a brief sojourn at Ipoh far up on the Malay Peninsula.

Returning to the United States in 1909, Mr. and Mrs. Soliday settled down in their modest home in Seattle. There, surrounded by their rapidly expanding collection which was soon to become carefully installed in a modest fireproof library, known then as now as "our sanctuary where care, worry or trouble was never permitted to enter", Mr. and Mrs. Soliday, until her death last year, continued to reside among friends, students, and the not infrequent bibliographer who continued to drop in for a chat. It must be said that no one who knew and loved books rarely passed through Seattle without dropping in for a chat with the Solidays. These visits were always welcomed.

For diversion there was the rock garden with its myriad of flowers, the long trellis-laden wistaria, the hedges to be trimmed, the setting out of new bulbs, the feeding of the pheasants down by the lake, or merely sitting upon the verandah viewing the distant snow-covered Mt. Ranier or the mighty Olympics. It was and is a good life, a life which Mr. Soliday too modestly claims is "without adventure, danger, or romance, but with plenty of romancers. These latter explain my fondness for Western Americana, books of Adventure, Discovery, Exploration, and Pioneering".

PETER DECKER.

THE GEORGE W. SOLIDAY COLLECTION OF WESTERN AMERICANA

PART I

1 ABBOTT, T(WYMAN) O(SMAND). Real Property Statutes of Washington Territory from 1843 to 1839 . . . 1232 pp. 8vo, Olympia, Washington, 1892. $7.50

Contains much valuable material relating to the Territory of Washington, including treaties, proclamations and special laws of Congress, such as the Donation Acts, private acts and Indian treaties.

2 ABERCROMBIE, W. R. Alaska, 1899. Copper River Exploring Expedition. Capt. W. R. Abercrombie, Second U. S. Infantry Commanding. 169 pp., 127 plates, map. 8vo. Washington, 1900. $4.50

Vivid scenes at Valdez, the dreaded Scurvy, destitution among the miners, the Valdez Glacier sufferings, Wilson Mining Co. sufferings, exploration of Quartz Creek and Tonsea Lake, the Wrangell Mt. District, difficulties traveling through unknown wilderness with a pack train, etc.

3 ADAMS, G. MERCER. From Savagery to Civilization; the Canadian Northwest, its History and its Troubles . . . 390 pp., 11 ports. 8vo, original wrappers. Toronto, 1885. $7.50

An interesting book. Has chapters on The Hudson's Bay, The North-West Fur Co., Early Discoveries, Alexander McKenzie, Alexander Henry, Selkirk Settlement, Massacre at Red River, The Amalgamation of River Fur Companies, etc.

4 ADAMS, G. MERCER. Makers of American History. The Lewis and Clark Exploring Expedition, 1804-1806. 189 pp. 8vo, cloth. New York, 1904. $4.00

Not listed in Smith. An excellent account of this historical expedition.

5 ADAMS, JACOB. A Survivor's Story of the Custer Massacre. 227 pp. The Journal of American History, Vol. 3, No. 2, 1909. 8vo. 1909. $3.75

6 ADAMS, JOHN QUINCY. The Oregon Question; War or Peace. North American Review, Vol. 45, Feb., 1846. 8vo. Boston, 1846. $3.50

7 [AERONAUTICS.] The Great Steam Duck, or a Concise Description of a most Useful and Extraordinary Invention for Aerial Navigation. [Frontis.] By a Member of the L. L. B. B. [Louisville Literary Brass Band] Louisville, 1841. 4to, cloth. New York, 1928. $7.50

Earliest published work in the western states on the subject of aviation .

8 AIMARD, GUSTAVE. The Frontiersmen. 254 pp. 12mo, cloth. N. Y. (c. 1854). $4.75

9 AKIN, JAMES R. The Journal of James Akin, Jr. (Day-by-Day Narrative of the Richey-Akin party, across the plains by ox-team from Iowa to Oregon in 1842). Map of the route and photographic facsimiles. 32 pp. 8vo, original printed wrappers. Norman, Okla., 1919. $8.50

Never before printed. Original text has been preserved throughout. Important for facts in regard to the road, the settlements, the relations between the whites and Indians. Plain recital of hardships and dangers on the route. Seven of the party died on the way.

10 [ALASKA.] (Adney, Tappan). Klondike Stampede. 417 pp., illus., 2 maps. 8vo, cloth. New York, 1900. $3.50

11 [ALASKA.] An Album of Newspaper Clippings Relating to all phases of Alaska from 1894. 515 pp. Album, cloth. V.p.,V.d. $25.00

Contains an uncommon amount of material expertly collated for the advantage of the research student.

12 [ALASKA.] The Apostle of Alaska. The Story of William Duncan of Mellokahtla by John W. Arctander. 395 pp. 8vo, cloth. Chicago, (1909). $3.75

DOCUMENTS RELATING TO ALASKAN PURCHASE

13 [ALASKA.] Acquisition of Alaska. (1) Russian America. Message from the President of the U. S. transmitting Correspondence in relation to Russian America. Feb. 19, 1868. 40th Cong., 2nd Session., H. R., Ex. Doc. 177. 359 pp, (2) Message of the President transmitting Information relative to Russian America. April 21, 1868. 40th Cong., 2nd Sess., H, R., Ex. Doc. 177, Part 2. 19 pp., Map. (3) Suffering Soldiers in Alaska. Letter from the Secretary of War relative to the alleged Suffering of the U. S. Soldiers in Alaska, Jan. 27, 1868. 40th Cong., 2nd Sess., H. R., Ex. Doc., 117. 4 pp. (4) Message from the President in relation to the transfer of Territory from Russia to the U S., Jan. 28, 1868, 40th Cong., 2nd Sess., H. R., Ex. Doc. 1255. 14 pp. Together four related items. 8vo, blue cloth and calf. Washington, 1868. $27.50

14 [ALASKA.] Affairs in Alaska. Report of Commander L. A. Beardslee, U. S. Ship Jamestown, June 1879 to Jan. 1880. Letter from the Sec'y of the Navy. 46th Cong., 2nd Sess., Ex. Doc. 105. Washington, 1880. $4.00

15 [ALASKA.] A Bill to Authorize the President of the U. S. to locate, construct and operate Railroads in the Territory of Alaska, and for other Purposes. Reports made by the Committee. 155 pp., map. 4to, ¾ mor. Washington, 1912. $7.50

16 [ALASKA.] The Building of Railroads in Alaska. Hearings on Same. 459 pp. 8vo, ¾ mor. Washington, 1913. $7.50

17 [ALASKA.] (Chapman, John W.) Alaska's Great Highway. 15 pp., 8vo, original wrappers. Hartford, 1909. $3.00

18 [ALASKA.] Chugach National Forest Lands in Alaska. Message of the President. 62nd Cong., 1st Sess., Sen. Doc. 77. 409 pp. 8vo, 3/4 mor. Washington, 1911. $5.00

Bound in with the above is "Report on coal in Alaska for use in the U. S. Navy". 123 pp., illus., maps. Washington, 1914.

19 [ALASKA.] Alaska Coal Lands. Hearings before the Committee on Public Lands of the United States Senate. 486 pp. 8vo, 3/4 mor. Washington, 1913. $7.50

20 [ALASKA.] A collection of works relating to Alaska. Six collected items bound in a single 8vo volume. (1) Alaska and Northwest Quarterly, Vol. 1, Jan., Feb., March, 1909; (2) The Alaska Frontier, by Thomas W. Balch. Phila., 1902; (3) Boundary Disputes, by Judge C. H. Hanford, 1899; (4) The Gold Fields of Alaska, 1901; (5) Salmon Fisheries of Alaska, 1902; (6) Annual Report of Alaskan Agriculture, 1902. The six items, 8vo, mor. V.p.,V.d. $18.00

21 [ALASKA.] A collection of works relating to Alaska. 3 vols., V.p., V.d., all bound in one volume, 3/4 mor. The collection includes: (a) The Forty Mile Quadrangle, Yukon-Tanana Region, Alaska. 52 pp., illus., maps. 1909; (b) The Petroleum Fields of the Pacific Coast of Alaska, with an Account of the Bering River Coal Deposits. 64 pp., illus., maps. 1905; (c) Report of the Progress of Investigation of Mineral Resources of Alaska in 1905. 169 pp., illus., maps. 1906. $7.50

22 [ALASKA.] A collection of four works relating to Alaska, viz; (1) Matanuska and Talkeetna Basins. Washington, 1907; (2) Berners Bay Region, Washington, 1907; (3) Prince William Sound, Washington, 1910; (4) Solomon and Casadepaga Quadrangle. Washington, 1911. 8vo, 3/4 mor., Illus., fldg. maps. Washington, 1907-1911. $12.50

23 [ALASKA.] Collection of works relating to Alaskan mines: (1) Ketchikan and Wrangle Mining Districts; (2) Rampart Gold Placer Region; (3) Fairbanks and Rampart Quadrangles; Yukon-Tanana Region. 8vo, 3/4 mor. V.p., V.d. (All bound in one volume). $7.50

24 [ALASKA.] Commercial Alaska, 1867-1903. 117 pp. 4to, 3/4 mor. Washington, 1903. $4.50

25 [ALASKA.] The Alaska Commercial Company. To the Klondike and Alaska Gold Fields. 73 pp., illus., fldg. map. 8vo. San Francisco, 1898. $6.50

26 [ALASKA.] The Alaska Boundary. By George Davidson, President Geographical Society of the Pacific. 4to, cloth, port. map. San Francisco, 1903. $17.50

This is the most complete and exhaustive work ever undertaken on the subject. It gives a complete history of Alaska from its earliest discovery and occupation, and includes a description of the disputed boundary lines down to the decision of the Alaska Boundary Tribunal, Oct. 20, 1903. This work was printed for private circulation only and the original issue consisted of but few copies.

27 [ALASKA.] Document relating to the Customs of Alaska. 46th Cong., 2nd Sess., Ex. Doc. 192. 8vo. Washington, 1880. $3.50

28 [ALASKA.] (Elliott, Henry M.) Report upon the Present Condition of the Fur-Seal Rookeries of the Pribolov Islands of Alaska, 240 pp., illus., maps. 8vo, ¾ mor., fine. Washington, 1896. $4.50

29 [ALASKA.] (Elliott, Henry M.). Report on the Seal Industries of Alaska. 188 pp., illus. 8vo, cloth. Washington, 1884. $4.75

30 [ALASKA.] Exploration in Alaska in 1898. Twentieth Annual Report of the U. S. Geological Survey to the Secretary of the Interior, 1898-99. Charles D. Walcott, Director. In Seven Parts. 509 pp., illus., maps. 8vo. Washington, 1900. $7.50

31 [ALASKA.] Alaska Fisheries; Hearings before the Sub-Committee of the Committee on Fisheries, U. S. Senate. Printed for the Use of the Committee. 62nd Cong., 2nd Sess. 536 pp. 8vo. Washington, 1912. $7.50

32 [ALASKA.] The Fur and Seal and Other Fisheries of Alaska, Investigation of. Report from the Committee on Merchant Marine and Fisheries of the House of Representatives. 50th Cong., 2nd Sess. 8vo. Washington, 1889. $3.00

33 [ALASKA.] Fur Seals of Alaska. Hearings before a Committee on Ways and Means, House of Rep. 58th Cong., 2nd Sess., March 9 and 10, 1904. 76 pp. ¾ mor. Washington, 1904. $5.00

34 [ALASKA.] Alaska Gold Placers. (a) Forty Mile Birch Creek, Fairbanks Region; (b) Fairhaven, Seward Peninsula. 8vo, ¾ mor., fine. Washington, 1905. $3.75

35 [ALASKA|] Governor's Report of Personal Outrages in Alaska. 50th Cong., 2nd Sess., Ex. Doc. 141. 8vo. Washington, 1889. $4.50

36 [ALASKA.] (Hallock, Charles.) Our New Alaska; or the Seward Purchase Vindicated. 209 pp., 2 plates, fldg. map. 8vo, cloth. New York, 1886. $3.75

37 [ALASKA.] Harriman Alaska Expedition with cooperation of Washington Academy of Sciences. Vol. 1. Narrative, Glaciers, Natives by John Burroughs, John Muir and George Bird Grinnell. Vol. 2. History, Geography, and Resources by William Dall, Chas. Keeler, Henry Garnett, Wm. H. Brewer, C. Hart Merriman, Geo. Bird Grinnell and M. L. Washburn. 2 vols., 8vo, cloth, maps, illus. (numerous photogravures and colored plates of animals, birds and plants). N. Y., 1901. $12.50

38 [ALASKA.] (Harris, A. C.) Alaska and the Klondike Gold Fields. 528 pp., illus., map. 8vo, cloth. Chicago, c. 1897. $3.00

39 [ALASKA.] Henderson, Lester D. Alaska, its Scenic Features, Geography, History and Government. 112 pp., illus. 8vo, cloth. June, 1928. $3.00

40 [ALASKA.] (Herron, Jos. S.) Explorations in Alaska, 1899, for an All-American Overland Route from Cook Inlet, Pacific Ocean, to the Yukon. 77 pp., illus., fldg. map. 8vo. Washington, 1901. $6.50

Presentation copy.

41 [ALASKA.] (Herron, Jos. S.) Exploration in Alaska, 1899, for an All American Overland Route from Cook Inlet, Pacific Ocean to the Yukon. 71 pp., illus. 8vo, half mor., fine copy. Washington, 1909. $4.50

42 [ALASKA.] (Hitchcock, Mary E.) Two Women in the Klondike; the Story of a Journey to the Gold Fields of Alaska. 485 pp., illus., 1 pl., map. 8vo, cloth. N. Y., 1899. $3.50

43 [ALASKA.] Alaska Indian Mythology, their Legends and Traditions; History of the Totem Pole; Description of a Potlach. 12 pp., 8vo, sewn, illus. San Francisco, N.d. $2.50

44 [ALASKA.] Compiled Laws on Alaska. 8vo, cloth. Washington, 1913. $7.50

45 [ALASKA.] Alaska Magazine and Canadian Yukoner. Vol. 1, No. 1, March, 1900; Vol. 1., No. 3, June, 1900. 8vo, cloth. Tacoma, 1900. $7.50

Smith locates but the University of Washington as reporting copies of this scarce work. The work contains articles on transportation in Alaska; discovery of quartz; review of Atlan; a Botanist's trip on the Upper Yukon; scenes in the mines; an article on Seattle by Prosch, etc.

46 [ALASKA.] Mineral Resources, 1908. (a) Kotsina-Chitina District; (b) Nabesna-White River District; (c) Kenai Peninsula. Fldg. map., illus., 8vo, ¾ mor., fine. Washington, 1909. $5.00

47 [ALASKA.] Portfolio of 34 large Folding Maps of the Chugach National Forest Lands. All in a Morocco Solander Case. Washington, 1911. $12.50

48 [ALASKA.] Protection of Fur Seals and Sea Otter. Hearings before the Committee on Foreign Affairs of the House of Representatives. 150 pp., 8vo, half mor. Washington, 1912. $2.50

49 [ALASKA.] Construction of Railroads in Alaska. Hearings before the Committee on Territories, U. S. Senate (with addenda and index). 718 pp. 8vo, ¾ mor. Washington, 1913. $7.50

50 [ALASKA.] Railway Construction. Report on. 49th Cong., 2nd Sess., Misc. Doc. 22. 8vo,. Washington, 1886. $4.00

51 [ALASKA.] Railway Routes in Alaska. A collection of 19 maps and plates in a portfolio. Half morocco binding. All maps fine. 1913. $17.50

52 [ALASKA.] Railroad Routes in Alaska. Message from the President, transmitting a Report of Alaska Railroad Commission. 172 pp., maps. 62nd Cong., 3rd Sess., H. R., Doc. 1346. 8vo, half mor. Washington, 1913. $3.00

53 [ALASKA.] Railway Routes in Alaska. Report of the Alaska Railroad Commission, 172 pp., fldg. maps. 8vo, half mor. Washington, 1913. $4.00

54 [ALASKA.] Report of Agents, Officers and Persons acting under the Authority of the Secretary of the Treasury in Relation to the condition of Seal Life on the Rookeries of the Pribilof, and to the Pelagic Sealing in Bering Sea and the North Pacific Ocean, in the Years 1893-1895. In two Parts, 379 and 154 pp., 11 maps and illus. 8vo, half mor. Washington, 1896. $10.00

55 [ALASKA.] Report of the Conditions in Alaska. 46th Cong., 2nd Sess., Ex. Doc. 179. 8vo. Washington, 1880. $3.00

56 [ALASKA.] Report on Education in Alaska. 4 vols. 8vo, half mor. Washington, 1907, 1908, 1909, 1910-11. $10.00

57 [ALASKA.] Report of the Alaska Engineering Commission. Portfolio of Maps. 1914-1915. ¾ mor. Washington, 1915. $10.00

58 [ALASKA.] Reports of the Alaska Engineering Commission from March 12, 1914 to Dec. 31, 1915. 210 pp., illus. (18 maps in separate portfolio). 2 vols., half mor., fine. Washington, 1916. $15.00

59 [ALASKA.] Report of Alaska Investigations in 1914 by E. Lester Jones. 155 pp., illus. 8vo, half mor. Washington, 1915. $4.50

60 [ALASKA.] Report of Alaska Investigations in 1914. Department of Commerce, Bureau of Fisheries. 155 pp., maps, illus. 4to, cloth. Washington, 1915. $4.50

61 [ALASKA.] Report of the Alaska Road Commission, 1906. 114 pp., illus. 8vo, half mor. Washington, 1907. $3.00

62 [ALASKA.] Report on the Salmon Fisheries of Alaska, 1901, 1902, 1903, 1904, 1905. Together with a report on the Fisheries of Alaska in 1908, Bureau of Fisheries Document No. 645. 8vo, ¾ mor. Washington, V. p., v. d. $7.50

63 [ALASKA.] Report of the Special Agent for the Protection of the Alaska Salmon Fisheries. 77 pp., illus., maps. 8vo, half mor. Washington, 1900. $3.00

64 [ALASKA.] Report of the Sub-Committee of the Committee on Territories appointed to investigate conditions in Alaska. 32 Hearings before the sub-committee. 276 pp., fldg. map. 8vo, half mor. Washington, 1904. $3.75

65 [ALASKA.] Report of United States Naval Officers Cruising in Alaskan Waters. 47th Cong., 1st Sess., Ex. Doc. 81. 8vo. Washington, 1882. $5.00

66 [ALASKA.] San Francisco's Advantages as an Outfitting Point for the Alaska Gold Fields. 59 pp. 4to. Burns, Owen & Co., San Francisco, 1898. $7.50

67 [ALASKA.] Seal and Salmon Fisheries and General Resources of Alaska. Illus. and maps. 4 vols. 8vo, half mor. Washington, 1898. $22.50

68 [ALASKA.] Seal Islands in Alaska. 50th Cong., 1st Sess., Ex. Doc. 1. 8vo. Washington, 1887. $2.50

69 [ALASKA.] Seal Islands of Alaska. 1232 pp. 8vo, half mor. Washington, 1911. $7.50

70 [ALASKA.] Session Laws, Resolutions and Memorials Passed at the First Regular Session of the Territorial Legislature. 463 pp. 8vo. Juneau, 1913. $17.50

71 [ALASKA.] The Situation. Indian Rights Association. 7 pp. 8vo. Phila., 1914. $2.00

72 [ALASKA.] Territorial Government Agricultural Development. Hearings before the Committee on Territories of the House of Representatives. 8vo, half mor. Washington, 1906. $4.00

73 [ALASKA.] Thirteenth Annual Report of the U. S. Geological Survey, 1891-92. 8vo, half mor. Washington, 1893. $3.50

Contains a report of the second expedition to Mount Saint Elias by Israel C. Russell.

74 [ALASKA.] Twentieth Annual Report of the United States Geological Survey, 1898-99. Explorations in Alaska. 509 pp., maps, illus. 8vo, half mor. Washington, 1900. $7.50

75 [ALASKA.] Twenty-first Annual Report of the United States Geological Survey. Part 2. Contains: (a) Reconnaissance from Pyramid Harbor to Eagle City, Alaska, by Alfred H. Brooks (maps); (b) Reconnaissance of the Chitina River and Skolai Mountains, Alaska, by Oscar Rohn (maps); (c) Preliminary Report on a Reconnaissance along the Chandler and Koyukuk Rivers in Alaska in 1899 (maps and plates). 8vo, half mor. Washington, 1900. $7.50

76 [ALASKA.] The Wonders of Alaska. By Alexander Badlam. 152 pp., 29 plates, 8 maps. 8vo, cloth. San Francisco: Bancroft, 1890. $7.50

77 [ALASKA.] History of the Wrongs of Alaska; An Appeal to the People and Press of America. 8vo, 43 pp., original wrappers. San Francisco, 1875. $10.00

This is an important "behind the scenes" account of early Alaskan affairs.

78 [ALASKAN BOUNDARY.] Map to Accompany Correspondence Respecting the Alaska Boundary. (United States, No. 1, 1904). Presented to both Houses of Parliament by Command of His Majesty, Feb., 1904. 8vo. London, 1904. $10.00

79 [ALASKA LAWS.] (Carter, Thomas H.) Laws of Alaska; embracing the penal code, the code of criminal procedure, the political code, code of civil procedure, and the civil code with the treaty of cession, and all acts and parts of acts relating to the District . . . annotated with references to decisions by the courts of the U. S. and the Supreme Court of Oregon. 533 pp., 4to, calf. Chicago, 1900. $7.50

80 [ALASKA MAGAZINE.] Vol. 1, No. 1 to No. 5 inclusive, Jan., 1927 to May, 1927. A Complete issue (all that were published). 8vo, original printed wrappers. Juneau, Alaska, 1927. $22.50

A very scarce complete run of the only large scale magazine which has ever been published in Alaska and devoted mainly to Alaska and the Northwest.

LARGEST AND FINEST MAP OF ALASKA TERRITORY

81 [ALASKA MAP.] Map of Russian America, or Alaska Territory compiled from Russian Charts and Surveys of Western Union Telegraph Company. Col. C. S. Bulkley, Engineer-in-Chief. By J. F. Lewis, Chief Draftsman, M. Cadin, Assistant. Lithographed by Britton and Rey. Size, 5 feet 9 inches by 4 feet 2 inches. San Francisco, 1867. $75.00

One of the largest and finest maps ever issued of Alaska and one of excessive rarity.

ALCALA-GALIANO'S VOYAGE TO PUGET SOUND, 1792

82 ALCALA-GALIANO (Don Dionysio). Relacion del Viage hecho por las Goletas y Mexicana en el ano en el ano de 1792 para reconocer el Estrecho de Fuca; con una Introduccion en que se da Noticia de la Expeciones executadas anterioramente por los Espanoles en Busca del Paso del Noroeste de la America. De Orden del Rey. Madrid en la Imprenta Real, 1812. Complete with the folding sheet of the missions of California, and accompanied by the folio atlas of 9 maps and 8 curious plates. Small 4to, full polished calf, and Folio. $165.00

One of the most important Voyages to the Northwest Coast of America. The Commander of the expedition, Don. Dionysio Alcala-Galiano, was probably the author of the work. It contains several Indian vocabularies, notably those of the Eslen, Runsien and Nutka. The 9 maps (4 of which are folding ones) delineate the Western Coast of North America from Acapulco to Unalaska; and the coast of California on a larger scale; with Plans of the harbours of S. Diego, Monte Rey, Cala de los Amigos (Nootka), Mulgrave, & Desengano. The plates include portraits of Macuina, chief of Nootka, Tetacus, chief of Juan de Fuca and his wife, a large folding aquatint view of the Cala de los Amigos (the Spanish Establishment on the Bay of Nootka), and a curious folding plate of the Feast celebrating the attainment of marriageable age of the Chief of Nootka's son.

Cowan says this work of great importance is rendered more valuable by the Introduction, which is a masterly resume of Spanish Voyages to the coast, written by Martin Fernandez de Navarette, whose name does not appear in the work.

83 ALDRITCH, HERBERT L. Arctic Alaska and Siberia, or Eight Months with the Arctic Whalemen. 234 pp., map. 8vo, cloth. Chicago, 1889. $4.00

84 ALEXANDER, CHARLES. "Bobbie," a Great Collie. 114 pp., illus. 8vo. N. Y., 1926. $3.75

Story of a collie who found his way through 3000 miles of strange country to return to his Oregon home.

Item 82, Insert in line 2 Sutil after Goletas. In sixth line of this title date should read 1802.

85 ALEXANDER, HARTLEY B. The Religious Spirit of the American Indian. 51 pp., 8vo. Chocago, 1910. $2.50

COPY OF AN UNRECORDED OVERLAND, 1863

86 ALEXANDER, R. H. Narrative of Incidents and Personal Adventure in a Journey Across the Rocky Mountains. 1862. Original manuscript, 21 pp. typewritten copy. 8vo. N.p., N.d. $10.00

87 ALEXANDER, T. Experiences of a Trapper and Hunter from Youth to Old Age. 118 p., illus. 8vo, original printed wrappers. Linton, Ore., 1924. $4.75

88 [ALLEN, ETHAN.] Ethan Allen, the Robin Hood of Vermont. By Henry Hall. 207 pp. 12mo, cloth. N. Y., 1897. $2.50

89 ALLEN, EDWARD WEBER. North Pacific: Japan, Siberia, Alaska, Canada. 282 pp., illus. 12mo, cloth. N. Y., 1936. $2.00

90 ALLEN, WILLIAM A. Adventures with Indians and Game, or Twenty Years in the Rocky Mountains. Portrait and 28 full-page plates. 302 pp. 8vo, half roan. Chicago, 1903. $12.50

The life story of "Montana Allen", one of the founders of Billings. He spent upwards of a quarter of a century hunting both game and Indians. A typical old plainsman, herewith sets down his many thrilling adventures not only as scout and plainsman and leader of the plains migrations but also gives interesting accounts of his experiences as express messenger, stock raiser, blacksmith, dentist, crack rifle shot and Indian fighter.

91 ALLEN, WILLIAM. The Army of Northern Virginia in 1862. 537 pp. 8vo, cloth. Boston, 1892. $5.00

Has material on Governor Stevens of Oregon.

92 ALLEN, WILLIS BOYD. The Red Mountain of Alaska. 348 pp., illus. 8vo, cloth. Boston, (1889). $3.50

93 ALLING, HORATIO. Why We Vote; a Discussion of the Government of the State of Washington. 163 pp., map. 8vo, cloth. Olympia, 1900. $5.00

94 ALLEN, W. W. and AVERY, R. B. California Gold Book. First Nugget, its Discovery and Discoverers and some of the Results Proceeding therefrom. Illus. 8vo, cloth. San Francisco, 1893. $4.50

An authoritative history of the gold discovery and of those associated with it. Also contains some account of the Harlan-Wimmer overland expedition in 1846; life of James Marshall; Indian adventures, etc.

95 ALVORD, CLARENCE W., and BIDGOOD, LEE. The First Explorations of the Trans-Allegheny Region by the Virginians, 1650-1674. Maps and facsimiles. 8vo, cloth. Cleveland, 1912. $12.50

Contains accounts of the discovery of New Brittaine, John Lederer, expeditions of Batts and Fallan, Needham and Arthur, etc., etc.

96 [AMERICAN NORTHWEST.] Apple Growing in the Pacific Northwest. 8vo, cloth, illus., 215 pp. Portland (c. 1911). $3.50

Compilation of lectures, experiments and discussions of the subject conducted by the Educational Dept. of the Portland U. M. C. A.

MAPS SHOWING PROTESTANT MISSIONS OF THE NORTHWEST

97 [AMERICAN BOARD OF COMMISSIONERS FOR FOREIGN MISSIONS.] Maps and Illustrations of the Missions of the American Board of Commissioners for Foreign Missions, 1843, 26 plates (plate 26 is a map of the Oregon Mission). 8vo. Boston: A. B. C. F. M., 1843. $22.50

98 [AMERICAN JOURNAL OF SCIENCE AND ARTS. Six Consecutive Numbers from July, 1848 to May, 1849, forming Volumes 6 and 7 of the New Series. 8vo, original wrappers. New Haven, 1848-49. $30.00

An interesting collection containing Dana's "Notes on Upper California" (day by day journal of Emmon's division of Wilkes expedition from Ft. Vancouver to San Francisco in 1841); extracts from 3 California letters by C. S. Lyman, 1847-48, and two other long letters from Lyman describing the mines. Lyman's letter of March, 1848, was possibly the first account of the gold discovery to reach the east, being probably received by Dr. Silliman about Aug. 15 with mail dated up to March 30th of that year. It was not published until Sept. 1st. In the meantime the New York Herald announced the discovery on Aug. 15, but not from an original communication as it was probably "pilfered" from the Mormon "California Star" of Aug. 1. In any event Lyman's was certainly the first authentic account by a man of science of the reception of news that thrilled the world.

99 [AMERICAN POPULISM.] Errors of Populism. By Herman W. Craven. 113 pp. 8vo, original wrappers. Seattle, 1906. $3.75

JOSHUA HETT SMITH'S NARRATIVE ON CAPTURE OF ANDRE

100 [AMERICAN REVOLUTION.] An Authentic Narrative of the Causes which led to the Death of Major Andre, Adjutant General of His Majesty's Forces in North America. By Joshua Hett Smith. 8vo, half calf, fldg. map. Portraits. London, 1808. $15.00

The only eye witness authority on the Arnold-Andre treason meeting "amid a clump of firs' on the banks of the Hudson, near Haverstraw, N. Y. Will always be an important American book.

101 [AMERICAN REVOLUTION.] Major Andre's Journal. Operations of the British Army under Lieut.-Gen. Sir William Howe and Sir Henry Clinton, June 1777 to Nov. 1778. 8vo, cloth, colored portrait, fldg. map. Ltd. ed. Tarrytown, 1930. $6.00

101a [AMERICAN REVOLUTION.] (Wertenbaker, T. J.). Torchbearer of the Revolution. The Story of Bacon's Rebellion and its Leader. 250 pp. 8vo, cloth. Princeton, 1940. $2.50

EXTRA-ILLUSTRATED FOLIO REPOSITORY OF MAJOR ANDRE

102 [ANDREANA.] Containing the Trials, Execution and Various Matters connected with the History of Major John André. Folio, quarter turkey morocco. Phila., 1865. $12.50

Compiled by Horace W. Smith. Reprints the proceedings of the Board of Officers who tried André at Tappan and contains all the contemporary accounts of the execution. The material was gathered from many sources, many of which are now inaccessible. This edition is extra-illustrated with 12 fine engravings of the various characters implicated in the conspiracy.

EYE-WITNESS ACCOUNT OF THE YORKTOWN SIEGE

103 [AMERICAN REVOLUTION.] (Deux-Ponts, Count Wm. De.) My Campaign in America: a Journal kept by Count William de Deux-Ponts, 1780-81. Translated from the French by Sam'l Abbott Green. 8vo, ¾ mor. Boston, 1868. $10.00

Presentation copy from Mr. Green to Richard Frothingham. Also laid in is a letter from Mr. Green. The original journal kept by Count de Deux-Ponts, commander of a regiment in Rochambeau's army, was picked up in one of the little bookstalls on the Quais in Paris by the late Mr. Green, who later edited and published it.

104 [AMERICAN REVOLUTION.] History of the Fight at Concord, on the 19th of April, 1775. By Ezra Ripley, with other Citizens of Concord. 8vo, boards, calf back, 60 pp. Concord, 1867. $4.50

This was the book cited by Emerson in his celebrated "Concord Memories."

105 [AMERICAN REVOLUTION.] The Turning Point of the Revolution, or Burgoyne in America. By Hoffman Nickerson. 8vo, cloth. New York, 1928. $3.50

106 [AMERICAN REVOLUTION.] Soldier and Pioneer: a Biographical Sketch of Lt. Richard C. Anderson of the Continental Army. By E. L. Anderson. Small 4to, cloth. New York, 1879. $2.50

Col. Anderson, a Virginian ,was at the battle of Trenton, and took prominent part in the war in the south. Contains some account of Border Warfare in Kentucky and Ohio in 1783, while he was stationed at Louisville.

107 [AMERICAN REVOLUTION.] History of the War of the Independence of the U. S. A. By Charles Botta. 2 vols. 8vo, old sheep, fronts. (worn). New Haven, 1840. $2.25

108 [AMERICAN REVOLUTION.] Narrative of Lieut.-Gen'l Sir Henry Clinton Relative to his Conduct during part of the Command of the King's Troops in North America, Particularly in that part which respects the Unfortunate issue of the Campaign of 1781 &c. 8vo, calf-backed boards. Original Edition. London, 1783. $17.50

109 [AMERICAN REVOLUTION.] An Answer to that Part of the Narrative of Lieut.-Gen'l Sir Henry Clinton, which relates to the Conduct of Lieut.-Gen'l Earl Cornwallis during the Campaign in North America in the Year 1781. By Earl Cornwallis. 8vo, calf-backed boards. London, 1783. $17.50

110 [AMERICAN REVOLUTION.] The Fight at Diamond Island, Lake George [1777]. By B. F. De Costa. 4to, original boards. N. Y.: J. Sabin & Sons, 1872. $7.50

No. 33 of 200 copies, initialed by Sabin. A hitherto unpublished account of Col. Brown's attempt to cut Burgoyne's communication at the head of the Northern Lakes.

111 [AMERICAN REVOLUTION.] The Life of William Alexander, the Earl of Stirling, Major General in the Army of the United States during the Revolution. With Selections from his Correspondence. By His Grandson, William Alexander Duer. 8vo, cloth. Portrait. New York, 1847. $3.00

One of the five ranking generals, Lord Stirling's account is extremely important, especially as related to the campaign in New York, Long Island and New Jersey.

112 [AMERICAN REVOLUTION,] Diary of Capt. Jabez Fitch. Small 4to, orig. printed wrappers. Woodcuts [Brooklyn, N. Y., 1899]. [Text in facsimile]. $3.50

Best account of Prison life in N. Y. during the Revolution.

113 [AMERICAN REVOLUTION (Connecticut).] Ebenezer Foote. The Founder. Being an Epistolary Light upon his Time. By Katherine A. Foote. Portrait. 8vo, cloth. Delhi, N. Y., 1927. $2.50

Foote, a son of Connecticut, served through the Revolution. It was Capt. Foote, of the Commissary Dept., who stopped the garrulous Joshua Hett Smith on that memorable September night at Crompond, N. Y., when he was conducting the ill-fated Major Andre back through the American lines. The publication of these letters of Capt. Foote's (afterwards a Major) helped very much in explaining certain phases of the Revolution.

114 [AMERICAN REVOLUTION—LOYALISTS.] Orderly Book of the Maryland Royalists Regiment, June 18, 1778 to Oct. 12th, 1778. 111 pp. Edited by Paul Leicester Ford. 4to, wrappers, unopened. Brooklyn, 1891. $4.50

No. 111 of 250 copies printed from the original mss .discovered some years ago at Newton, L. I.

115 [AMERICAN REVOLUTION.] Memoirs of Major-General William Heath. By Himself. New Edition, with illustrations and notes. Edited by William Abbatt. To which is added the Accounts of the Battle of Bunker Hill by Generals Dearborn, Lee and Wilkinson. 8vo, cloth. N. Y., 1901. $2.50

116 [AMERICAN REVOLUTION.] Retrospect of the Boston Tea-Party, with a Memoir of George R. T. Hewes, a Survivor of the Little Band of Patriots who drowned the Tea in Boston Harbour in 1773. By a Citizen of New York. 12mo, original boards, paper label, frontispiece. First Ed., N. Y., 1834. $5.00

In a cloth slip-case and as near the original condition as one can find it.

MEMOIRS OF GENERAL CHARLES LEE

117 [AMERICAN REVOLUTION.] Memoirs of the Late Charles Lee, Esq., Lieut.-Col. of the 44th Regiment, Colonel in the Portuguese Service, Major General and Aide-de-Camp to the King of Poland, and Second in Command in the Service of the United States during the Revolution, etc. 8vo, half calf. London, 1792. $10.00

118 [AMERICAN REVOLUTION.] The Treason of Charles Lee, Major General. Second in Command in the American Army of the Revolution. By George H. Moore. 8vo, cloth. New York, 1860. $5.00

TRIAL OF GENERAL LEE AT NEW BRUNSWICK, N. J.

119 [AMERICAN REVOLUTION (New Jersey).] Proceedings of a General Court Martial, held at Brunswick in the State of New Jersey by order of his Excellency Gen. Washington, Commander-in-Chief of the Army of the U. S. A., for the Trial of Major General Lee, July 4th, 1778, Major General Lord Stirling, President. 8vo, sewn, 134 pp., uncut. Cooperstown [N. Y.], 1823. $17.50

Rare. In a cloth slip-case.

120 [AMERICAN REVOLUTION.] Proceedings on the Occasion of the Dedication of the Monument on the One Hundredth Anniversary of the Paoli Massacre in Chester County, Pa., Sept. 20, 1877. Illus. 8vo, ¾ mor. West Chester, Pa., 1877. $3.50

121 [AMERICAN REVOLUTION]. Memoirs, and Letters and Journals of Major General Riedesel, during his Residence in America. Translated from the original German . . . by William L. Stone. Illus. 2 vols. 8vo, cloth. Albany, 1868. $17.50

122 [AMERICAN REVOLUTION.] Officers of the Continental Army, who served to the end of the War and Acquired the Right to Commutation Pay and Bounty Land; also Officers Killed in Battle, or Died in Service. Compiled by Alexander Ray. Washington, 1849. $5.00

123 [AMERICAN REVOLUTION.] Narrative of Jonathan Rathbun, with Accurate Accounts of the Capture of Groton Fort, the Massacre that Followed, and the Sacking and Burning of New London, Sept. 6, 1781, by the British Forces, under the Command of the Traitor Benedict Arnold. By Rufus Avery and Stephen Hempstead. Together with an interesting Appendix. Small 12mo, ¾ calf. (New London, 1840). $7.50

This is the Original Edition of this scarce work.

124 [AMERICAN REVOLUTION.] Memoir of Col. Benjamin Tallmadge. 8vo. Portrait, original cloth. New York, 1858. $10.00

As Major of a detachment of "Light Horse" troops Tallmadge was assigned to Connecticut to guard the Sound and the lower passages to New York, where treason was rife. It was the sensible Tallmadge who countermanded his own superior officer's orders and had the captured Major Andre returned ot the Post at Armonk, New York, for questioning, after Col. Jameson was about to send him on up to traitor Arnold at West Point. Had Tallmadge not made this decision, perhaps, the identity of Andre would never have been revealed.

TRIAL OF JOSHUA HETT SMITH

125 [ARNOLD CONSPIRACY.] Record of the Trial of Joshua Hett Smith, Esq:, for Alleged Conspiracy in the Treason of Benedict Arnold, 1780. 116 pp. Roy. 8vo, original wrappers, paper label, uncut. Morrisiana, N. Y., 1866. $17.50

No. 18 of 50 copies printed. According to H. B. Dawson, the manuscript record of the trial of Smith has been lost. The above is apparently the first separate printing.

126 [AMERICAN REVOLUTION.] (Gordon, William.) The History of the Rise, Progress and Establishment of the Independence of the U. S. of America: Including an Account of the Late War. 4 vols. 8vo, calf. London, 1798. $17.50

Gordon is deservedly reckoned as one of the most impartial and reliable of the Numerous historians of the American Revolution. The Critical Review states: "There arises some suspicion that Dr. Gordon actually wrote under the influence of American prejudice". And as Sabin added: "A suspicion which might have been confirmed had the reviewer been aware that the author was aided by Thomas Jefferson."

127 [AMERICAN REVOLUTION.] An Accurate and Interesting Account of the Hardships and Sufferings of the Band of Heroes who traversed the Wilderness in the Campaign against Quebec in 1775. By John Joseph Henry. 12mo, calf. Lancaster, 1812. $12.50

"First and best edition of a narrative of rare interest'—Sabin.

128 [AMERICAN REVOLUTION.] The Sexagenary; or, Reminiscences of the American Revolution. By S. G. Bloodgood. 8vo, cloth. Portrait Engravings. Albany: J. Munsell, 1866. $5.00

129 [AMERICAN SPORT.] Hunting on the Kenai Peninsula; an Observation on the Increase of Big Game in North America. 90 pp.; illus. 8vo, cloth. Seattle, 1924. $3.75

130 [AMERICAN SPORT.] Wild Western Scenes: a Narrative of Adventures in the Western Wilderness, the nearest and Best California . . . Minute Accounts of Bear, Deer and Buffalo Hunts—Desperate Conflicts with the Savages . . . Wolf Hunts, Fishing and Fowling. By Luke Shortfield [John Beauchamp Jones]. Illus. 8vo, original cloth. Philadelphia, 1849. $7.50

131 [AMERICAN SUNDAY SCHOOL UNION.] History of the Sandwich Islands, with an Account of the American Mission established there in 1820. With a Supplement. 231 pp. 8vo, calf. Phila. (c. 1831). $7.50

132 ANDERSON, ALEXANDER CAULFIELD. Handbook and Map of the Gold Region of Fraser's and Thompson's Rivers, with Table of Distances. By Alexander C. Anderson, late Chief Trader of Hudson's Bay Company's service. To which is appended Chinook-Jargon Language used, etc., etc. 31 pp., fldg. map (in photostat). 8vo. San Francisco, 1858. $45.00

Very rare. Smith cites only one copy in Northwest libraries. The author, a Hudson Bay Co. official, describes the routes to the new gold fields from his own personal and accurate knowledge. In the appendix is the Chinook Jargon, the language used by the different Indian tribes, French, half-breeds, and sailors in this region.

ANDERSON' SCARCE HISTORY OF THE NORTHWEST

133 ANDERSON, ALEXANDER CAULFIELD. The Dominion of the West, a Brief Description of British Columbia, its Climate and Resources. The Government Prize Essay, 1872. 112 pp. 8vo, original printed wrappers. Victoria, 1872. $22.50

The author, a native of Calcutta and educated in England, came to Vancouver in the service of the H. B. Co. in 1832. He retired from the company in 1854 with the rank of Chief Trader, and was appointed by the Dominion Government as Commissioner on Indian Land Difficulties. Bancroft states that Anderson was the "most scholarly of all the Hudson's Bay Company officers . . . indeed without the information given me by Anderson, Tolmie and others I do not see how I could have written with any degree of correctness a history either of Oregon or of British Columbia."

134 ANDERSON, G. H. Vancouver and his Great Voyage: The Story of a Norfolk Sailor, Captain George Vancouver, R.N., 1757-98. Portrait and 7 Illustrations. 90 pp. 8vo, half calf. King Lynn, 1923. $7.50

One of a few copies reprinted from the "Lynn Advertiser". This is the only separate life of Vancouver which has been published up to the present time.

135 ANDERSON, JOHN J. Did the Louisiana Purchase extend to the Pacific Ocean and our Title to Oregon? 8 pp., map. 8vo, original wrappers. San Francisco, 1880. $4.50

136 ANDERSON, RUFUS. History of the Mission of the American Board of Commissioners for Foreign Missions to the Sandwich Islands. 3rd ed. 408 pp. 8vo, cloth. Boston, 1872. $5.00

Contains an account of the exploration of the northwest coast.

137 ANDREWS, C. L. The Story of Sitka, the Historic Outpost of the Northwest Coast. The Chief Factory of the Russian American Company. 108 pp., illus. 8vo, cloth. Seattle, (c. 1922). $3.50

138 ANDREWS, C. L. The Story of Alaska. 258 pp., front. 8vo, cloth. Seattle, (1931). $2.00

SOURCE WORK ON ESTABLISHMENT OF MISSIONS IN NORTHWEST

139 [ANNALES DE LA PROPAGATION DE LA FOI.] Complete run of 41 volumes from Vol. 1, No. 1, 1822 to 1863. 8vo, half calf. Lyon, France, 1822-1863. $125.00

A storehouse of research material covering reports of Catholic missions throughout the world. In each volume will be found communications from missions established in America, amongst which may be mentioned: Kentucky, Louisiana, New Orleans, Baltimore, Maryland, Ohio, Cincinnati, Michigan, Florida, Alabama, Momile, St. Louis, Indiana, New York, Charleston, Boston, Hudson Bay, Philadelphia, Red River, Dubuque, Texas, Nashville, Rocky Mts., Oregon, California, Buffalo Bill, etc., etc. The relations cover wars with the Indians, life and privations of the missioners, education of the natives, hunting, travel, letters of Father De Smet, gold-seekers and other historical material of vast importance.

Item 139, Fourth line of note should be "mobile" not "momile."

140 ANSON, GEORGE. A Voyage Round the World in the Years 1740-44, by George Anson, Esq., Commander-in-Chief of a Squadron of his Majesty's Ships, sent upon an Expedition to the South Seas, compiled from Papers and other Materials of the Right Hon. Lord Anson, and Published under his Direction, by Richard Walter, M.A., Chaplain of his Majesty's Ship and Centurion in that Expedition. 42 copper plates. 4to, full contemporary calf, gilt. London, 1748. $25.00

Original Edition. The engraved maps and plates include a large chart of the Pacific Ocean, views of Juan Fernandez Island, Brazil, Patagonia, Philippines, Sack of Payta, Capture of the Spanish Galleon, etc. On the outbreak of the war with Spain in 1739 Anson was recalled from Carolina and despatched with a fleet of eight vessels to harass Spanish shipping in the South Seas.

141 ANSON, GEORGE. Atlas. 15 maps, 27 large double page plates. 4to, cloth. N.p., N.d. $12.50

142. [ARIZONA.] (Hinton, Richard J.) The Hand-Book to Arizona; its Resources, Towns, Mines, Ruins and Scenery. Map and illus. 8vo, limp cloth. San Francisco and N. Y., 1878. $10.00

143 [ARIZONA AND NEW MEXICO.] (Cozzens, Samuel Woodworth). The Marvelous Country, or Three Years in Arizona and New Mexico, the Apaches Home, etc. 532 pp. 8vo, cloth. 100 engravings. London, 1874. $10.00

144 ARMSTRONG, A. N. Oregon: Comprising a Brief History and Full Description of the Territories of Oregon and Washington . . . interspersed with Incidents of Travel and Adventure. 147 pp. 12mo, cloth. Chicago, 1867. $22.50

145 ARMSTRONG, BENJ. G. Early Life among the Indians. Reminiscences of the life of Benjamin G. Armstrong. Treaties of 1835, 1837 and 1854., Habits and Customs of the Red Men of the Forest. Incidents, Biographical Sketches, Manners, etc. Dictated to and Written by Thomas P. Wentworth. 12mo, cloth. Ashland, Wis., 1892. $6.00

146 ARMSTRONG, M. The Early Empire Builders of the Great West. By a Pioneer. 456 pp. 8vo, cloth, illus. St. Paul, 1901. $7.50

Personal reminiscences of the early settlements, fur trade, gold fever, Indian Wars, travel and early hardships, etc.

147 [ARCTIC OCEAN.] Report of the Cruise of the Revenue Marine Steamer Corwin in Alaska and the Northwest Arctic Ocean in 1888. 4to, cloth. Washington, 1888. $5.00

Smith, 4155.

148 [ARCTIC OCEAN.] Report of the Cruise of the Revenue Marine Steamer Corwin in the Arctic Ocean in the Year 1885. 192 pp., maps, plates. 4to, cloth. Washington, 1887. $5.00

Smith, 4155.

Item 144, Date should read 1857.

149 [ARCTIC OCEAN.] Report of the Cruise of the Revenue Marine Steamer Corwin in the Arctic Ocean in the Year 1884, by Capt. M. A. Healy, U.S.R.M., Commander. 128 pp., illus. 4to, cloth. Washington, 1889. $5.00

Smith, 4155.

150 [ARKANSAS.] (Ross, W. P.). The Life and Times of Hon. Wm. P. Ross of the Cherokee Nation. 8vo, illus. Fort Smith, Ark., 1893. $7.50

151 [ASTOR, JOHN JACOB.] John Jacob Astor, Landlord of New York. By Arthur D. Howland Smith. 8vo, cloth 296 pp., illus. Phila., 1929 $3.50

152 [ASTOR, JOHN JACOB.] Studies in early American History. A Notable Lawsuit. By Franklin H. Head. Illus. 12mo, original printed wrappers. Chicago, 1898. $10.00

Presentation copy from the author. The work concerns a lawsuit brought by Frederic Olmstead against the Astor Estate on the claim that John Jacob Astor had obtained the treasures of Capt. Kidd, the Pirate.

153 ATKIN, BARTON. Modern Antiquities comprising Sketches of Early Buffalo and the Great Lakes. Also a Sketch of Alaska. 190 pp., 8vo, cloth. Buffalo, 1898. $3.75

154 ATKINSON, G. H. Fruits of the Oregon Mission. Contained in the Missionary Herald, March, 1869, pp. 76-82. 8vo, original wrappers. Boston, 1869. $5.00

This is a historical review of the discovery, occupation and missionary effort of the Oregon country.

155 ATKINSON, REV. G. H. Missions on the Pacific Coast. Letters and Journals, from May 8th, 1848 at Honolulu, which he left on May 22nd, for Columbia River, June 17 came in sight of Cape Disappointment. Arrival in Oregon; Physical Features; Banks of Columbia; Ft. Vancouver; Beating up the Williamette; Diary continues until July 4, 1848. The Home Missionary, Vol. 30 No. 11. 8vo, original wrappers. New York, 1849. $7.50

156 [APIANUS, PETRUS.] Cosmographia, siue Descriptio Universi Orbis. (Map of the World), Petri Apiani & Gemmai Frisii, iam denuum integritati suae restituta. Adjiecti sunt alii, tum Gemmae Frisii, tum aliorum Autorum Tractatus ac libelli varii. Antwerp. J. Berrelerum, 1584. $27.50

See Harisse B. A. V., p. 239. According to Clement this is the fullest and most important of all editions of Apianus. It contains many additions by Gemma Frisius, some appearing for the first time.

157 [ATLAS.] (Arrowsmith A.) Folio Atlas containing a number of Arrowsmith Maps of North America. N. p., N. d. (Baltimore). $10.00

158 [ATLAS.] (Bellin, J. M.) Le Petit Atlas Maritime. 577 plans and charts of Harbors, Bays, &c., throughout the world. 5 volumes, 4to, boards with calf backs, uncut. Paris, 1764. $67.50

Fine sound set of this rare work. See Phillips, 3508 for the full list of plates. The above includes the finest series of harbor plans that had been done at this time. It is a very necessary companion volume to the "Hydrographie Francois". The Plates are mostly double page with the coast lines and rivers colored throughout in blue, and with fine engraved titles.

BUACHE THE GREAT GEOGRAPHER AND INTERPRETER OF BERING'S VOYAGE TO DISCOVER N.W. AMERICA

159 [ATLAS.] (Bauche, Phillippe) Considerations Geographiques Physique sur les Nouvelles Decouvertes au Nord de la grand Mer, Appelles Vulgairement la Mer du Sud. 158 pp. Royal 8vo, calf. Paris, 1753. $90.00

Inserted is a large folding map by De L'Isle, 1750: "Carte des Nouvelles Decouvertes au Nord de la Mer du Sud, tant a l'est de la Siberie et du Kamchatka que a l'Ouest de la Nouvelle France". This is one of the rarest works on the Northwest Coast. The only other copy located is in the Bancroft Collection. The De L'Isle Map is also very rare.

Buache was the great geographer and interpreter of Bering's Voyages. The Delisle map mentioned above was done by Nicholas Delisle, one of three celebrated brothers, who drew up the chart for Bering's second voyage. Of the three Delisle brothers we give the following:

The Three Delisle brothers were quite prominent in Russian geographical affairs during the first half of the 18th century. Guillaume (1675-1726). the oldest and best known was regarded as one of the ablest biographers of his day. After 1718, he held in France the title of Premier Geograph Du Roi. Peter had an interview with him when that monarch visited Paris and it is supposed that Delisle was in some way responsible for the sending out of the Bering expedition. The Oldest Nicholas Delisle (1688-1768) was a well-known astronomer. At the invitation of Peter and Catherine he went to St. Petersburg in 1725. He remained in Russia busily engaged in astronomical and geographical problems until 1747. It was he who drew up the chart for Bering's second voyage. Delisle's memoir of 1750 on the Russian discoveries made him many enemies at St. Petersburg. Louis Delisle de la Croyere—half brother to the other two—became the pride of the family only after his death. Part of his life was spent on the frontier of Canada leading an irregular life and writing to his father for money with which to pay his debts. [Vide Delisle mss.] Nicholas found Louis a position at the Russian capital and from there he went with the Bering party as one of the scientists. He was on Chirocoff boats on his voyage to America and died on his return in 1741.

160 [ATLAS.] (Colton, J. H.). Colton's Atlas of America, illustrating the Physical and Political Geography of North and South America, accompanied by Descriptions, Statistical and Historical by Richard Swainson Fischer. 63 double-page maps each finely colored and with engraved title-page. 4to, cloth, roan back. N. Y., 1858. $22.50

The west was without railroads, but the trails and roads are located. Minnesota's western boundary is the Missouri river. Nebraska extends to the northern bounds of the United States, and it and Kansas extend westward to the Rockies. California shows the old trials, which are also marked for the proposed routes of the proposed Transcontinental Railway.

161 [ATLAS.] (Colton, J. H.) General Atlas. Folio. With Many fine maps. N. Y. and London, 1856. $10.00

D'ANVILLE'S FAMOUS BERING ATLAS

161a ATLAS. (D'Anville, J. B.). Nouvel Atlas de la Chine, de la Tartarie Chinoise et du Tibet. Grand folio, Mit 42 Karten (einige Kolorient). Schones, sehr breitrandiges Exemplar. Hlbrd. La Haye, 1737. $30.00

Mentions Bering's voyages and has maps relating to same. This is the Atlas which should accompany Du Halde. See Golder's "Bering," Vol. 5, p. 362. Also see item 162.

A FOUNDATION BOOK LEADING TOWARD ALASKA'S DISCOVERY

162 [ATLAS.] (Du Halde, J. B.) Description Geographique, Historique, Cheonol., Politique et Physique de l'Empire de la Chine et de la Tartarie Chinoise; enriche des cartes generales et particulieres de ces Pays, de la Carte generalex et des Cartes particulieres du Thibet, et de la Coree; & ornee d'un grandnombre de figures et de vignettes grav. en taille-douce. Avec un avertisement prelim 4 vols. La Haye, 1736. Mit 53 Taf., Planen a Vign. &c. 4 vols., 4to, calf. A La Haye, 1736. $90.00

Vol. 4 contains the "Relation Succinte du Voyage du Captain Taine Beetings dans Siberie", which is cited in Golder's "Bering". The above work is accompanied by D'Anvilles Atlas. This Atlas: "Nouvel Atlas de la Chine" dated La Haye, 1737, is priced separately at $30.00.

Whether it is "historical determinism" or not, history seems to have the right man at the right place and the right time to point the way toward the future and truth; and this occurs in spite of an opportunist Hitler or Mussolini. Du Halle, Bellin, D'Anville and Buache, all in the employ of Peter the Great, with what little rightful information they had, stood at the right road and pointed with great historical truth the right way. Du Halle certainly cast doubt on the mythical "Terra de Jeso" as being another continent [America.] It was Kamchatka or one of the Kurils. And while the early voyages were severely condemned, Bellin, Buache and D'Anville constructed their maps out of the charts and journals of the men of the early Russian Expansionist Movement. Du Halde cast doubt on the so-called "Terra de Jeso". D'Anville certainly proved that it was not in his maps. And Bering finally found the real "Terra de Jeso", which was the great country of Alaska and the continent of North America. So, a discerning student should have D'Anville Atlas to accompany the above work.

163 [ATLAS.] (Pallas, A. S.). Voyages du Proffesseur Pallas dans plueeurs Provinces de l'Empire de Russie et dans l'Asie Septentrionale. 8 vols. and Atlas, Nouvelle Edition. 8 volumes and Atlas in Folio, half calf, fine uncut copy. Paris, An 2. (1794). $60.00

Professor Pallas' monumental work is one of the most conclusive and accurate works on the Russian Expansionist movement which lead to the discovery of Northwest America. The above is the best edition.

164 ATWOOD, ALBERT. Glimpses in Pioneer Life on Puget Sound. 483 pp., illus., port. 8vo, cloth. Seattle: Denny-Coryell, 1903. $7.50

Smith, 138. History of Methodism in the Pacific Northwest.

165 AUBE, TH. Notes sur le Centre-Amerique (Costa Rica, Nicaragua, et San-Salvador) Vancouver et la Columbie Anglaises: Par Tr. Aube. 59 pp,. 8vo. Paris: Berger-Levrault et Cie, 1877. $27.50

Smith, 139, who locates but one copy, that in the Provincial Library of British Columbia.

166 AUDUBON, I. L. Scenes de la Nature dans les Etats Unis et le Nord de l'Amerique. Trad. avec preface et notes par E. Bazin. 2 vols, 8vo, cloth. Paris, 1857. $17.50

167 AUDUBON, MARIA R. Audubon and His Journals. 2 vols, 532 and 553 pp., 8vo, cloth, illus. London, 1898. $17.50

168 AUDUBON, J. W. Western Journal, 1849-1850: record of a trip from New York to Texas and an Overland Journey through Mexico and Arizona to the Gold-Fields of California; with Biographical Memoir by his daughter, Maria R. Audubon; edited with introduction, notes and index by Frank Hodder. 251 pp., 8vo, cloth. Cleveland, 1906. $10.00

169 [AUDUBON, J. J.] Life of John James Audubon. By Mrs. Audubon. 443 pp., illus. 8vo, cloth. N. Y., 1901. $5.00

170 [AUDUBON, J. J.] Delineations of American Scenery and Character. With an Introduction by Francis Hobart Herrick. 349 pp., 8vo, cloth. N. Y., 1926. $5.00

171 AUSTIN, OSCAR P. Steps in the Expansion of our Territory. 259 pp., 8vo, cloth. N. Y., 1903 $3.00

172 BACKUS, MANSON F. The Development of the Northwest. 12 pp., 8vo. wrappers. Seattle, 1927. $2.50

BACQUEVILLE'S RARE WORK ON EARLY FRENCH SETTLEMENTS

173 BACQUEVILLE, DE LA POTHERIE, C. C. Le R. Histoire de l'Amerique Septentrionale. 4 vols., 12mo, calf. Complete with all Maps and Plates. Paris: Chez Jean-Luc Nion et Francois Diot, 1722. $55.00

Sabin 2692. Jones 413. Rare First Edition. Vol. 1 contains a Relation of a voyage to Ft. Nelson in Hudson's Bay in 1697; the first establishment of the French in that part of North America; capture of Ft. Nelson from the English; with a description of the River St. Lawrence; the Government of Quebec, Three Rivers and Montreal from 1534 to 1701. Vol. 2 Consists of an account of the Indians of Canada, their manners and customs, Religion and Occupations, and of their relations with all the Nations, especially the Iroquois and those inhabiting the region round Lake Superior, including the Hurons and Illinois. Alliances between the French and Indians, with a relation of their transactions with Mons. Traci, Frontenac, de la Barre and Devonville. Vol. 3. Gives a history of the Iroquois and their relations with the English; an account of the wars with them (1689-1701), and of the negotiations for a general peace between them and the French and their Indian Allies. Vol. 4. Consists of a history of the Agenaguis, with an account of the general peace under the Administration of the Comte de Frontenac and Mons, le Chevalier de Callieres, etc.

The fine series of plates are beautifully engraved and mostly relate to Indian life, but in Vol. I there are views of Quebec and the taking of Ft. Nelson.

174 BAGLEY, CLARENCE B. Compiled Charters of the City of Seattle. 127 pp., 8vo, cloth. Seattle, 1910. $5.00

175 BAGLEY, CLARENCE B. History of Seattle. 623 pp., fine plates. 3 vols. 4to, cloth. Chicago, 1916. $10.00

176 BAGLEY, CLARENCE B. The Acquisition and Pioneering of Old Oregon. Portraits and Illus. 4to, half morocco., g. t. Seattle, 1924.

Privately printed account of the overland trip with the Bethel Company in 1852, the settlement of Oregon, pioneer Seattle and its founders, etc.

177 BAGLEY, CLARENCE B. Pioneer Seattle and Its Pioneers. 17pp. Illus. 8vo, sewn. Seattle, 1926. $3.50

178 BAGLEY, CLARENCE B. Indian Myths of the Northwest. 145 pp., illus., 8vo, cloth. Seattle, 1930. $5.00

Autographed by Mr. Bagley.

179 BAGLEY, CLARENCE B. Early Catholic Missions in Old Oregon. 2 vols, 8vo, cloth. Seattle, 1932. $5.00

180 BAILEY, FLORENCE MERRIAN. Handbook of Birds of the Western United States. 534 pp., colored plates, map 8vo, cloth. Boston, (1902). $7.50

Smith 158.

181 BAILEY, W. F. The First Trans-Continental Railroad, its Projectors, Construction and History. 164 pp., 12mo, cloth. Pittsburgh: Privately Printed, N. d. $10.00

Inside history of the Overland Railroad ,with valuable details of the builders and the Indian troubles incurred.

182 [BAKER, JIM.] The Life of. By Noli Mumey, M.D., Illustrated. 8vo, original boards, folding map, uncut and unopened. 234pp. Denver, 1931. $12.50

One of 200 copies distributed. Author's copy signed. Jim Baker was a great and picturesque figure of the old west, friend of Jim Bridges, colleague of Carson, scout for Fremont, Kearney and Marcy. Dr. Mumey gathered material for this work from pioneers and Jim Baker's descendants.

183 BAKER, ERNST EVERHART. The Heart of the Last Frontier 143 pp., 8vo, cloth. Salem, Ore., 1915. $4.75

Smith 170

184 BAKER, GEO. E. The Life of William E. Seward, with Selections from his Works. 410 pp., 8vo, cloth. N. Y., 1855. $4.50

185 BAKER, J. C. Baptist History of the North Pacific Coast, with special reference to Western Washington, British Columbia and Alaska. 472 pp., illus. 8vo, cloth. Phila. (c1912). $4.50

186 BAKER, MARCUS, and McCORMICK, JAMES. Geographic Dictionary of Alaska. 689 pp., 2nd ed. 8vo, half mor. Washington, 1906. $5.00

187 BAKER, MARCUS. Geographic Dictionary of Alaska. 446 pp., 8vo, half mor. Washington, 1902. $7.50

Smith 172.

188 BALCH, F. H. The Bridge of the Gods. A Romance of Indian Oregon. 280 pp., illus., 8vo, cloth. Chicago, 1890. $7.50

Original Edition.

189 BALCH, THOMAS WILLING. Alaska Frontier. 188 pp., maps in text. 4to, cloth. Phila., 1903. $7.50

Smith 182.

190 BALCH, THOMAS WILLING. Alaska-Canadian Frontier. 45 pp., maps in text. 4to. Phila., 1902. $5.00

Smith 183.

191 BALL, NICHOLAS. The Pioneers of '49. A History of the Excursion of the Society of California Pioneers of New England from Boston to the leading cities of the Golden State, April 10-May 17, 1890. With Reminiscenses and Descriptions by Nicholas Ball, 288 pp., illus., 8vo, cloth. Boston, 1891. $10.00

PRESENTATION COPY OF BALLANTYNE'S "HUDSON BAY"

192 BALLANTYNE, R. M. Hudson's Bay; or Everyday Life in the Wilds of North America during six years' residence in the Territories of the Honourable Hudson's Bay Company. 328 pp., illus., front. 8vo. Edinburgh: Blackwoods, 1848. $25.00

The rare Original Edition. Smith 187. Among the considerable number of men who served the Hudson's Bay Co. none have produced a more complete, interesting and evidently faithful narrative of the various phases of a fur-trader's life among the Indians than Mr. Ballantyne"—Field's Indian Bibliography. The above is a fine uncut Pressentation copy.

192a THE SAME. 2nd ed. Edinburgh, 1857. $5.00

193 BALLANTYNE, R. M. Away in the Wilderness, or Life among the Red Indians and Fur Hunters of the North America. 144 pp., 12mo, cloth. Phila., 1873. $4.50

194 BALLOU, MATURIN M. Ballou's Alaska, the New Eldorado. A Summer Journey to Alàska. 353 pp., maps. 12mo, cloth. Boston, 1891. $5.00

The best edition.

195 SAME. Boston, 1893. $2.50

196 (BANCROFT, HUBERT HOWE) Bancroft's Hand-Book Almanac for the Pacific States . . . ed by Wm H. Knight, 1862. 191 pp., 8vo. San Francisco, 1862. $10.00

197 BANCROFT, HUBERT HOWE. The Pacific Almanac. 107 pp., 8vo, original wrappers. San Francisco, 1865. $7.50

198 BANCROFT, HUBERT HOWE. The Native Races of the Pacific States of North America, with Folding Maps and Illustrations. 5 vols, thick 8vo, mor. N. Y., 1874. $27.50

199 BANCROFT, HUBERT HOWE. History of Central America. 3 vols, 8vo, full mor. San Francisco, 1886. $15.00

200 BANCROFT, HUBERT HOWE. History of Alaska, 1730-1885. Illus., map 8vo, mor. San Francisco, 1886. $8.50

201 BANCROFT, HUBERT HOWE. History of the Northwest Coast. Illus., map. 2 vols., full mor. 8vo. San Francisco, 1886. $15.00

Illustrated with maps of the early voyages, with early explorations and discoveries of the Northwest coast, fur trade, Mackenzie's and other voyages, overland expeditions. Fine copy of the best edition in full morocco.

202 BANCROFT, HUBERT HOWE. History of Oregon, Illus., map 8vo, full morocco. San Francisco, 1886. $15.00

203 BANCROFT, HUBERT HOWE. History of British Columbia, 1792-1887. 792 pp., illus., map. 8vo, mor. San Francisco, 1887. $7.50

204 BANCROFT, HUBERT HOWE. Popular Tribunals. 2 vols, map, fascms. 8vo, mor. San Francisco, 1887. $10.00

205 BANCROFT, HUBERT HOWE. History of California. 6 vols, 8vo, full mor. San Francisco, 1886-1890. $25.00

206 BANCROFT, HUBERT HOWE. History of Utah, 1540-1887. Maps in text. 8vo, sheep. San Francisco, 1889. $4.50

207 BANCROFT, HUBERT HOWE. Essays and Miscellany, 764 pp., 8vo, ¾ calf. San Francisco, 1890. $7.50

208 BANCROFT, HUBERT HOWE, Literary Industries. Port. 8vo, ¾ mor. San Francisco, 1890. $7.50

Account of historical explorations northward.

209 BANCROFT, HUBERT HOWE. History of Washington, Idaho, and Montana, 1845-1889. 8vo, cloth, illus. San Francisco, 1890. $5.00

210 BANCROFT, HUBERT HOWE. History of Nevada, Colorado Springs and Wyoming. 327 pp., 8vo, ¾ calf. San Francisco, 1890. $7.50

FINE SET OF BANCROFT'S "CHRONICLES OF THE BUILDERS"

211 BANCROFT, HUBERT HOWE. Chronicles of the Builders of the Commonwealth; Historical Character Study. 8 vols (1 v., Index), ports, map, tables. 8vo, cloth. San Francisco, 1891-92. $52.50

Smith 202.

212 BANCROFT, HUBERT HOWE. Chronicles of the Builders of the Commonwealth. Map. 8vo, 3/4 mor. San Francisco, 1892. $10.00

213 BANCROFT, HUBERT HOWE. The New Pacific. Map. 8vo, cloth. N. Y., 1900. $2.50

214 BANCROFT, HUBERT HOWE. In These Latter Days. 8vo, cloth. Chicago, 1917. $3.75

215 BANDEL, EUGENE. Frontier Life in the Army, 1854-1861. 330 pp., map. 8vo, cloth. Glendale, 1932. $2.50

RARE MONTANA MISSION PRINT

216 BANDINI, REV. J. (S. J.). Szmimeie-s Jesus Christ; a Catechism of the Christian Doctrine in the Flathead or Klaispel Language. Composed by the Missionaries of the Society of Jesus. 45 pp. Montana: St. Ignatius Print, 1880. $27.50

Smith 3909 locates but one copy.

217 BANKS, LOUIS A. Censor Echoes; or Words that Burned, and Speeches of some of the Prominent Temperance Workers of Oregon and Washington. With portraits and woodcuts. 12mo, 162 pp., original cloth. Portland, 1882. $12.50

Scarce northwest item. The above includes a sketch of Vancouver and short biographies of J. W. Watts, Mrs. Abigail S. Duniway, author of "Captain Gray's Company", Wm. R. Dunbar, etc.

RARE CATHOLIC MISSION PUBLICATION RELATING TO THE NORTHWEST

218 [BANNIERE de MARIE IMMACULATE, LA.] Publice fois par au par les Peres Oblats de Marie Immaculate. No. 1 through 20 annee, Mai 1893 to 1912. Twenty Volumes, Royal 8vo, original printed wrappers. Ottawa, 1893-1912. $40.00

A complete run of this scarce work which contains much valuable first-hand material relating to the Mountains and the Northwest.

219 BANNING, CAPT. Wm., and GEORGE, HUGH. Six Horses. 410 pp. 8vo, cloth. N. Y. (1930). $3.50

Early stage coach days.

220 BANNON, A. H. A Hunter's Summer in the Yukon Territory. [Interesting hunting plates.] 48 pp., 12mo, original printed wrappers. Columbus: F. B. Toothaker, 1911. $25.00

Narrative of thrilling adventures among the wild game of the Northwest. The author had with him as guide the celebrated old Montana prospector and hunter, Jim Blair, and together they brought down many specimens of Grizzly, Moose, Caribou, Mountain Sheep, etc. Not in Smith Check List.

221 BARBEAU, CHARLES MARIUS. The Downfall of Temlaham. 253 pp., colored plates. 8vo, cloth. Toronto, 1928. $3.50

The author is the Canadian Government ethnologist and folk-lorist. He here gives the legends of Temlaham, an Indian on the Skeena.

222 BARBEAU, CHARLES MARIUS. Totem Poles of the Gitksan, Upper Skeena River, British Columbia. 275 pp., 33 plates. 8vo, cloth. Ottawa, 1929. $3.50

223 BARCA, M. de la. Life in Mexico during a Residence of Two Years in the Country. By Madam c——de la B——, with a preface by W. H. Prescott. 437 pp., 8vo, cloth. London, 1843. $7.50

224 BARKER, FRED F. Compilation of the Acts of Congress and Treaties relating to Alaska, from March 30, 1867 to March 3, 1905. 496 pp., 4to, mor. Washington, 1906. $7.50

225 BARNEBY, W. HENRY. Life and Labour in the Far, Far West, being Notes of a Tour in the Western States, British Columbia, Menitoba, and the Northwest Territory. 432 pp., maps, cloth. London, 1884. $7.50

226 BARNEBY, W. HENRY. The New Far West and the Old Far West, being Notes of a Tour in North America, Japan, China, Ceylon, etc. 316 pp., map., illus. 8vo, cloth. London, 1889. $6.00

227 BARNES, DEMAS. From the Atlantic to the Pacific, Overland. A series of Letters. Port. 12mo, cloth. N. Y., 1866. $10.00

228 BARRA E. I. A Tale of Two Oceans. An Account of a Voyage from Philadelphia to San Francisico, around Cape Horn, in 1849-50. By an old California, n. d. 198 pp., 8vo, original prnited wrappers. San Francisco, 1893. $7.50

Scarce privately printed narrative, which is an actual diary of the voyage.

229 BARRINGTON, DAINES D. The Possibility of Approaching the North Pole. With Map and Vignette. A new edition with an appendix, containing papers on the same subject, and on a Northwest Passage, by Colonel Beaufoy. 8vo, original boards, uncut. 187pp. New York, 1818 $4.50

230 BARRINGGTON, DAINES. Miscellanies. . . . 558pp. 2 Portraits, 2 Maps, tables. 4to, calf (fine tall uncut copy). London: Nichols, 1781. $25.00

Pages 469-534 contain the Journal of a voyage in 1775 to explore the coast of America, northward of California, by the second pilot of the fleet. Don Francisco Antonio Maurelle, in the King's Schooner called the Sonora, and commanded by Don Juan Francisco de la Bodega. In the Northwest Boundary disputes (1825-26), Richard Rush referred the British Plenipotentiaries to the above work.

231 BARROW, JOHN A. Chronological History of Voyages into the Arctic Region; Undertaken Chiefly for the Purpose of Discovering a North-East, North-West, or Polar Passage between the Atlantic and the Pacific; From the Earliest Periods of Scandinavian Navigation, to the Departure of Recent Expeditions, Under the Orders of Captains Ross and Buchan. Folding map and woodcuts. 8vo, originial boards, uncut. London 1818. $25.00

Fine unopened copy in the original binding, with the label intact. "Through his (Barrow's) influence a measure for promoting Polar discovery became law in 1818"—Encyclopaedia Britannica.

232 BARROW, SIR JOHN. Voyages of Discovery and Research in the Arctic Regions, from the Year 1818 to the present time. . . . Search of a North-West Passage from the Atlantic to the Pacific; with two attempts to reach the North Pole. 530 pp., port, 2 maps. 8vo, cloth, London, 1846. $7.50

233 BARROWS, WILLIAM (Gen). To Idaho and Montana: Wanderings there: Returning. (Contained in the Boston Review, May, 1865). 8vo, cloth. Boston, 1865. $7.50

234 BARROWS, WILLIAM (Gen). Three Thousand Miles up the Missouri. (Containied in the Boston Review, April and May, 1865). 2 vols, 8vo, cloth. Boston, 1865. $10.00

235 BARRETT, S. M. Geronimo's Story of his Life. Taken Down and Edited by S. M. Barrett. Plates. 8vo, cloth. N. Y., 1915. $5.00

Contains papers on the origin of the Apache Indians- Geronimo's battles and his surrender, etc.

THE GREAT RUSSIAN MISSIONER TO ALASKA AND NORTH WEST COAST

236 BARSUKOV, I. P. (Innocent, Metropolitan of Moscow). Tvoreniia Innokentiia, Mitropolite Moskovskage. (The works of Innocent, Metropolitan of Moscow). 3 vols., calf. Moscow, 1886-88. $40.00

The rare collected work of Innocent, the great Russian Missioner to America. Vol. I contains sermons, speeches and shorter writings, including translations of his Aleutian works. (2) An account of the Russian Church in America and of Veniaminov's missionary travels and labors, 1828-1878. (3) Notes of the Unalaska District, with annotations.

237 BARTLETT, JOHN RUSSELL. Personal Narrative of Exploratiions and Incidents in Texas, New Mexico, California, Sonora, and Chihuahua, connected with the U. S. and Mexican Boundary Commission during the Years 1850, 51, 52 and 53. Map, illus. 2 vols, 8vo, original cloth. N. Y., 1854. $17.50

Wagner-Cump 234.

238 BARTLETT, LAURA B. DOWNEY. Dictionary of the Intertribunal Indian Language commonly called Chinook. 92 pp., 8 vo, original wrappers. Tacoma, 1924. $4.50

239 BARTLETT, LAURA B. DOWNEY. Chinook-English Songs. 40 pp., 8vo, original wrappers. Portland, (1914). $4.00

240 BASHFORD, HERBERT. Stories of Western Pioneers. 192 pp., illus. 8vo, cloth. San Francisco, N. d. $3.50

241 BASHFORD HERBERT, Songs from Puget Sound. 100 pp., 8vo, cloth. San Francisco, 1898. $3.50

242 BASHFORD, HERBERT. The Tenting of the Tillicums, a Story of Boy Life on Puget Sound. 200pp., illus. 8vo, cloth. N. Y., (1906). $3.75

243 BASS, FLORENCE. Stories of Early Times in the Great West. 203 pp., illus. 8vo, cloth. Indianapolis, (1927). $3.00

244 BASS, WILLIAM WALLACE. Adventures in the Canyons of the Colorado by two of its earliest Explorers, James White and W. W. Hawkins. Port., illus, 12mo, original printed wrappers. Grand Canyon, 1920. $750

Original edition. Privately printed for the author. The edition was withdrawn.

245 BATTAY, THOMAS. Life and Adventures of a Quaker among the Indians. 349 pp., 12mo, cloth. Boston, c1875. $7.50

Interesting first hand details of the Cheyennes, Comanches and Kiowas.

246 BAUDRY DES LOZIERES. (Louis Narcisse). Voyage a la Louisiane et sur le Continent de l'Amerique Septentrionale, 1794-98. Folding map. 382 pp., 8vo, calf. Paris, 1802. $15.00

Original edition. Braislin 119, Monaghan 149.

247 BAYLIES, FRANCIS. A Narrative of Major General Wood's Campaign in Mexico in the Years 1846, 1847 and 1848. 78 pp., original wrappers. Albany, 1851. $15.00

248 BEAUCHAMP, S. T. D. The Iroquois Trail, or Footprints of the Six Nations, in Customs, Traditions, and History. . . . To which are included David Cusick's Sketches of Ancient History of the Six Nations. 8vo, boards. Fayetteville, N. Y., 1892. $7.50

249 BEADLE, J. H. The Undeveloped West; or Five Years in the Territories. Life and Adventures on Praries, Mountains and the Pacific Coast. 832 pp., plates. 8vo, cloth. Phila., 1873. $6.00

Fine copy of the Original Edition.

250 BEADLE, J. H. Western Wilds and the Men who Redeem them. An authentic Narrative, embracing an account of Seven Years Travel and Adventures in the Far West: Wild Life in Arizona; Perils of the Plains; Life in the Canyon and Death on the Desert; Thrilling Scenes and Romantic Incidents in the Lives of Western Pioneers, etc. Folding map and plates. 624 pp. 8vo, cloth. Cincinnati, 1878. $5.00

251 BEADLE, J. H. Life in Utah; or the Mysteries and Crimes of Mormonism, being an Expose of the Latter Day Saints with a full and authentic History of Polygamy and the Mormon Sect from its Origin to the Present Time. 540 pp., map. 8vo, cloth. Phila., 1870. $3.50

252 BECHDOLT, FREDERICK R. When the West was Young. 309 pp., 8vo, cloth. N. Y., 1922. $2.75

253 BECHDOLT, FREDERICK R. Tales of Old-Timers. 367 pp., 8vo, cloth. N. Y., (c1924). $3.00

True narratives of the old west.

254 BECKNELL, (CAPT. Wm.) The Journals of Captain Thomas Becknell from Boone's Lick to Santa Fe, and from Santa Cruz to Green River. 8vo, wrappers. Missouri Historical Review. St. Louis, 1910. $4.00

255 BEECHEY, CAPTAIN F. W. Narrative of a Voyage to the Pacific and Behring's Strait, to co-operate with the Polar Expeditions: Performed in H. M. Ship "Blossom" in the Years 1825-28. With Folding Maps and 23 Plates. 2 vols. 4to, uncut. London, 1831. $20.00

Fine and perfect copy of the First Edition on large paper, with all the maps and plates. Field says of it: "One of the most interesting of modern voyages, this quarto edition is beautifully printed and illustrated." Native Indians in the vicinity of San Francisco are described, together with the Mexican Missions where the expedition spent two months in 1826.

256 —— Same. First American Ed. 493 pp., 8vo, cloth. Phila., 1832. $7.50

The above wos Com. James Biddle's copy with his autograph on title.

257 BEGG, ALEXANDER. The Creation of Manitoba; or a History of the Red River Troubles. Portraits. 408 pp., 12ho, cloth. Toronto, 1871 $7.50

257a BELSHAW, GEORGE. Journal from India to Oregon, March 23 to Sept. 27, 1853. Royal 8vo, 22 pp. of typewritten text copied from the orignial diary. $17.50

Interesting day-by-day journal of an overland journey by an early Oregon pioneer.

258 BELL, MAJOR HORACE. Reminiscences of a Ranger; or, Early Times in Southern California. 457 pp., 8vo, original cloth. Los Angeles, 1881. $20.00

Original Edition. Braislin 1436. An exceptionally interesting and factual narrative of events and conditions from 1851 on. Bell joined Walker's Filibustering Expedition of which he gives a lucid account. He was one of the band who captured Joaquin Murietta, whose history and career he recounts. He also narrates the exploits of Moreno, as well as those of other desperadoes of the region. He further gives the history of the Los Angeles Vigilance Committee; the fraudulent land grants; an account of Bandini's Revolution; Beckwourth, Sublette; in short Major Bell seems to draw in all the celebrated pioneer figures, good and bad.

259 BELL, ROBERT. Report on Hudson's Bay and some of the Lakes and Rivers lying to the West of it, 1879-80. 113 pp., plates. 8vo, cloth. Montreal: Dawson, 1881. $7.50

260 BELL, WILLIAM A. New Tracks in North America, a Journal of Travel and Adventure whilst engaged in the Survey of a Southern Railway to the Pacific Ocean during 1867-8. With large colored folding map, 20 colored plates and plans and woodcuts in text. 2 vols; 8vo, cloth. London, 1869. $17.50

Original Edition, fine copy. Contains accounts of the native Indian tribes of Arizona and New Mexico.

261 BELLINGHAM (WASHINGTON) HERALD. Chronological and Biographical History of Northwestern Washington. Illus. 58 pp. 8vo, cloth. Bellingham, 1910. $7.50

Not in Smith. A reference work for newspapers and public and private libraries.

262 BENNETT, EMERSON. The Border Rover. 524 pp., 8vo, 12mo, cloth, Philadelphia, (1857). $4.50

Wagner-Gamp 285. Region of Ft. Bent.

262a BENNETT, EMERSON. Prairie Flower; or Adventures in the Far West. 120 pp., 8vo, original printed wrappers. Cincinnati, n. d. Story of the Oregon Trail. (c. 1849). $7.50

Wagner-Camp 162. Story of the Oregon Trail.

263 BENOIST, CHARLES. Les Francais et la Nord-]uest Canadien. 128 pp. 8vo, cloth. Bar-le-Duc, Imprimerie de l'oeuvre de Saint Paul, 1895. $12.50

Smith 327 locates one copy.

264 BENSON, H. C. Life among the Choctaw Indians, and Sketches of the Southwest. 314 pp. 8vo, original cloth. Cincinnati, 1860. $15.00

An important book with details of over three years' residence among the Choctaws. "A veritable relation of personal experiences"—Field.

265 BENSON, N. P. The Log of the Eldorado. 66 pp., illus. 8vo, San Francisco, N. d. $7.50

Interesting narrative of the wreck of a lumber schooner from Astoria, 1913. Scarce

266 BENTON, THOMAS HART. Thirty Years View; or a History of the working of the American Government for Thirty Years, from 1820 to 1850, etc. 2 vols., port., plates, cloth. N. Y., 1854-6. $7.50

BENYOWSKY'S ACCOUNT OF NORTH WEST FUR TRADERS

267 BENYOWSKY, MAURITIUS AUGUSTUS COUNTE de. Memoirs and Travels, consisting of his Military Operations in Poland, his exile into Kamchatka, his Escape and Voyage from that Peninsula through the Northern Pacific Ocean. . . . 23 plates. 2 vols, calf. London: Robinson, 1790. $27.50

Smith 332. The Count was exiled to Siberia by the Russian Government for his part in the Polish troubles of 1769. The work is valuable in regard to the Russian fur traders, its description of Kamchatka and the various islands of the northern Pacific, including the Aleutians and Alaska.

268 BERGMAN, HANS. History of Scandinavians in Tacoma and Pierce County. 200 p., illus. 8vo, cloth. Tacoma, 1926. $10.00

Scarce. History of Tacoma and its early settlement.

THE MOST COMPLETE SET OF NORTHWEST FUR FISHERIES AWARD

269 [BERING SEA ARBITRATION.] Northwest Fishery. Bering Sea Arbitration. No. 1 Case presented on part of Her Brittanic Maj. to the Tribunal of Arb. between Her Brit. Majesty and the US London, 1893. 161pp. No. 2. Report of the Bering Sea Com. and the Report of the British Commissioners of June 1, 1892. With 5 maps, diagrams, appendices. 1893, 241 pp. No. 3 Counter case presented on the part of Her B. Maj. 1893. 315pp. No. 4 Argument of Her Majesty's Gov., 1893. 162pp. No. 5, Map of the northern portions of the North portions of the Pacific Ocean annexed as part of the appendix to the case of H. M. Gov., 1893. No. 6 The case of the US before the tribunal of arb. convened at Paris, 1893. 433pp., fldg, diagrams. No. 7. The counter case of the US, 1893. 153pp. No. 8 Argument of the US. 1893. 327 pp. 10. Bering Sea Arbitration. Regard Bering Sea. Together 10 pieces (lacking No. 9). 8vo and folio, original blue printed wrappers. London, 1893. $50.00

Smith 335. While Smith lists only 5 volumes, some of it relates to what took place previous to and following the actual award of 1893. This is probably one of the completest sets in existence of the actual arbitration proceedings, containing all the proceedings except No. 9.

270 [BERING SEA FISHERIES.] Further Correspondence Respecting. U. S. No. 2, (1891). 61 pp., 8vo, sewn. London, (1881). $3.75

271 [BERING SEA FISHERIES.] Correspondence Respecting . . . 1886-1890. 532 pp., 8vo, cloth. London, (1890). $4.00

272 [BERING SEA FISHERIES.] Further Correspondence. U. S., No. 3, (1892). 191 pp., map, 8vo, cloth. London, $4.00

273 [BERING SEA FISHERIES.] Telegraphic Correspondence Respecting. U. S. No. 1 (1892). $3.75

274 [BERING SEA FISHERIES.] Correspondence Respecting Claims for Compensation on account of British Vessels seized in Behring Sea by U. S. Cruisers. U. S., No. 1, (1895). 43 pp., 8vo, sewn. London, (1895). $3.75

275 [BERING SEA FISHERIES.] Report of Prof. D'Arcy Thompson on his Mission to Behring Sea in 1896. U. S., No. 3, (1897). 39 pp., 8vo, sewn. London, (1897). $3.75

276 [BERING SEA FISHERIES.] Correspondence with the United States Government. U. S. No. 4, (1897). 130 pp., 8vo, cloth. London, (1897). $3.75

277 [BERING SEA FISHERIES.] Despatches from Professor D'Arcy Thompson. U. S. No. 1, (1898). 15 pp., 8vo, sewn. London, (1898). $3.75

278 [BERING SEA FISHERIES.] Joint Statement of Conclusions U. S., No. 2 (1898). 5 pp., sewn. London, (1898). $3.75

279 BERCK, V. N. Viedomost Miekham Vyvezennym Chastnymi Ross-Amer. Komp. 169 pp., map., fldg. tables, 8vo, calf. St. Petersburg, 1823. $32.50

Important in part for its list of furs exported by the Russian-American Fur Company.

280 BERCK, V. N. Kronological Istoriia Vsiekh Put. v. Siev. Poliarnyia Strany s Prisovokupl. Obozriennia Fizicheskikh Avoistv togo Kraia. (Chronological History of all Voyages to Northern Polar Lands, with Surveys of the Physical Nature of that Country). 2 vols in one, 8vo, calf, folding map, plates. St. Petersburg, 1821-1823. $35.00

281 BERCK, V. N. (Bering and Chirikov). Pervoe Morskoe Puteschestvie Rossiian Predpriniatoe dlia Riesheniia Geogrzadachi pod nachal jstvom Flota, Kap. . . . I—go ranga Vitusa Beringa. 126 pp., fldg. map and table. 8vo, calf. St. Petersburg, 1823. $37.50

First sea voyage of the Russians undertaken to solve the geographical problem whether America and Asia were united.

282 BESANT, WALTER. Captain Cook. 191 pp. port. 8vo, cloth. London, 1894. $3.50

283 BIDWELL, JOHN. Reminiscences of the Conquest. From the Overland Monthly, Dec. 1890. 8vo. San Francisco, 1890. $1.50

Bidwell was a member of the Bartleson party which made an overland trip tc California in 1842.

284 BIDWELL, JOHN. The First Emigrant Train to California. (Contained in 4 numbers of the Century Magazine, 1890-91). Map of the Overland and many fine illus. 8vo, original wrappers as issued. N. Y., 1890-91. $7.50

Wagner-Camp 88. These articles were reprinted about 1914 as "Echoes of the Past".

285 BIDWELL, JOHN. Echoes of the Past; an Account of the First Emigrant Train to California, etc. 12mo, original printed wrappers. Chico. (1914). $3.50

286 BIEBER, RALPH P. Diary of a Journey to the Pike's Peak Gold Mines in 1859. 8vo, wrappers. Cleveland, 1927. $4.50

287 BIEBER, RALPH P. Diary of a Journey from Missouri to California in 1849. 42 pp., 8vo. Columbia, (Mo.), 1928. $4.00

This is the diary of Bennett C. Clark.

288 BIEBER, RALPH P. Exploring Southwestern Trails, 1846-1854 by Philip St. George Cooke, William Henry Chase Whiting, Francis Xavier Aubry. Ed. by Ralph H. Bieber and Averam B. Bender. 383 pp., illus., map. 8vo, cloth. Glendale, 1938. $5.00

289 BIEBER, RALPH P. Southern Trails to California in 1849, 386 pp., illus., map. 8vo, cloth. Glendale, 1937. $5.00

290 BIRD, GEORGE ROBERT. Tenderfoot Days in Territorial Utah, 221 pp., illus. 12mo, cloth. Boston, 1918. $3.75

Bird went to Utah in 1874 and describes conditions from that time on.

291 BISHOP, CAPT. H. P. Mackensie's Rock. With a Map showing the course followed by the Explorer from Bella Coola to the Rock. Illus of Views along the Route. 31 pp., 8vo, original wrappers. Ottowa, N. d. $4.50

292 BLAIKIE, WILLIAM GARDEN. Summer Suns in the Far West; a Holiday Trip to the Pacific Slope. 160 pp., front. 8vo, cloth. London, 1890. $3.50

293 BLAIR, EMMA HELEN. The Indian Tribes of the Upper Mississippi Valley and Region of the Great Lakes as described by Nicholas Perrot, Bacqueville de la Potherie, Morrell Marston and Thomas Forsyth, etc. Maps, ports, facs., and views. 2 vols, 8vo, cloth. Cleveland, 1911. $15.00

294 BLAKE, F. N. Report of the Management of the Indians in British North America by the British Government. 38 pp., 8vo. Washington, 1870. $5.00

295 BLAKE,, MARY E. On the Wing; rambling Notes of a Trip to the Pacific. 325 pp., 8vo, cloth. Boston, 1883. $4.50

BLANCHET'S REPORT ON OREGON AND CALIFORNIA

296 BLANCHET, FRANCOIS NORBERT. Memoire Presente a la Congregation de la Propagande sur the Territoire de l'Oregon. 129 pp., 8vo, original wrappers. Quebec, 1847. [Sold]

Wagner-Camp 127. An important collection of source material relating to the evangelization of both Oregon and California. The volume is seldom offered.

297 BLANCHET, FRANCOIS NORBERT. Mission de Walla-Walla. With Brouillet's Report of the Whitman Massacre and Answer to the Protestant Allegations against the Catholic. 105 pp., 8vo, original printed wrappers Quebec, 1849. [Sold]

Wagner-Camp 164. A short account of Bishop Blanchet's overland journey from Westport to Walla Walla in 1847, together with Brouillett's account of the Whitman massacre and his answer to Spalding's charges against the Catholic missionaries; correspondence with Col. Gilliam, Gov. Abernathy and Blanchet relating to the Waillapu tragedy is included.

298 BLANCHET, FRANCOIS NORBET. Voyage de l'Eveque de Walla Walla. (In: "Rapport sur les Missions du Diocese de Quebec, Mars, 1851, No. 9"). With a Map: "Trace de la Route de Westport, Etat de Missouri, a Walla Walla, Oregon." 8vo, original wrappers. Quebec . . . 1851. [Sold]

Wagner-Camp 195. The author left Montreal in April, 1847, and arrived at Walla Walla in Sept., 1847. He went via Pittsburgh to St. Louis, thence by steamer to Kansas Landing. The party left Westport May 8.

299 BLANCHET, FRANCOIS NORBERT. Dictionary of the Chinook Jargon, to which is added numerous conversations thereby enabling any person to speak Chinook Correctly. 4th ed. 8vo, Portland, Oregon: S. J. McCormick, Franklin Book Store, Front St. 1868. $75.00

Pilling states in his bibliography of Chinookan languages—"I put this title under Blanchet's name upon information furnished by J. B. Gill . . . " The work is excessively rare. Eames had the only copy Pilling was able to locate. Not in Smith.

300 BLANCHET, FRANCOIS NORBERT and St. Onge, L. N. J. M. J. Chinook Jargon. Dictionary, Catechism, Prayers and Hymns. Composed in 1838 and 1839 by Rt. Rev. Modeste Demers. Revised, corrected and completed in 1867 by most Rev. F. N. Blanchet. With modifications and additions by Rev. L. N. St. Onge, Missionary among the Yakimas and other Indian Tribes. 8vo, cloth. Montreal, 1871. $125.00

A very rare and important work. Smith does not locate a copy in any Northwest Library.

301 BLANCHET, FRANCOIS NORBERT. Historical Sketches of the Catholic Church during the past forty years. 186 pp., 8vo, original wrappers. Portland, 1878. $175.00

Smith was unable to locate a perfect copy. The above is a perfect copy of this excessively rare and important historical work. The title as published, No. 352, in Smith's Check List does not appear to be correct, as it was apparently taken from a copy in the Portland Library. The title page in the latter copy was inserted in 1884 as is shown by the following legend in the copy: "Washington, D. C. Title page printed for Edward Mallet by Gray and Clarkson, 339 Pa. Ave., 1884".

302 BLANCHET, FRANCOIS NORBERT. Historical Sketches of the Catholic Church in Oregon and the Northwest. 72 pp., 8vo, wrappers. Ferndale, Wash., 1910. $20.00

This is a rare reprint of the rare original edition, of which Smith locates but one copy.

303 BLANCHET, FRANCOIS-XAVIER. Dix Ans sur la cote du Pacifique par un Missionnaire Canadien, en faveur d une oeuvre. Prix 25 centimes. 8vo. Quebec, 1873. $17.50

Blanchet was a nephew of Mgr. Norbert Blanchet. He arrived in Oregon, July 24, 1863, and was stationed at Jacksonville, Ore. until 1888. He died in Portland in 1906. This work relates to the climate, productions, the state of religion, etc.

304 BLANCHET, RT. REV. A. M. A. (First Bishop of Nisqually). Illustrated Catholic Family Annual for 1888. 156 pp. 8vo, cloth. N. Y., and London, 1888. $7.50

305 BLANCHARD, RUFUS. Documentary History of the Cession of Louisiana to the U. S. 71 pp., map, 8vo, cloth. Chicago, 1903. $7.50

306 BLANCHARD, RUFUS. Discovery and Conquests of the Northwest. With the History of Chicago. 8vo, half mor. Wheaton, 1879. $15.00

307 BLANKENSHIP, GEORGE E. Lights and Shadows of Pioneer Life on Puget Sound. 90 pp., 8vo. Olympia, 1923. $4.50

Written by an early pioneer.

308 BLEDSOE, A. J. Indian Wars of the California Northwest: A California sketch, embracing the Overland Expedition of the Gregg Party in 1849, the suffering and terrible privations endured and the death by starvation of Dr. Josiah Gregg; the Redding Expedition and Events of the Klamath War, the War with the Win-Toons, the Two Years War, etc. 8vo, 505 pp. San Francisco, 1885 $30.00

A rare work, although but printed 55 years ago. Contains an account of the Overland Expedition of the Gregg Party in 1849, etc., etc.

309 BOAS, FRANZ. The Mythology of the Bella Coola Indians. The Jesup North Pacific Expedition 2. 11 plates. Folio. N. Y., 1900. $5.00
Smith 367.

309a BOAZ, FRANZ. Sketch of the Kwakiutl Language. 1900. Large 8vo. 13 pp. N. p., 1900. $3.75

310 BOAS, FRANZ. The Indians of British Columbia. 11 plates. Folio. (Montreal Royal Society of Canada). Toronto, 1883. $7.50

311 BODDAM-WHETHAM J. Western Wanderings. A Record of Travel in Utah, Nevada, California, Oregon and British Columbia. Plates. 364 pp., 8vo, cloth. London, 1874. $3.75

312 BODDY, ALEXANDER ALFRED. By Ocean Prairie and Peak; some Gleanings from an Emigrant Chaplin's Log on a Journey to British Columbia, Manitoba and Eastern Canada. Folding map, 204 pp., illus., 8vo, cloth. Society for Promoting Christian Knowledge. London, 1896. $5.00

313 BOILLOT, LEON. Aux Mines d'Or Klondike du Lac Bennett a Dawson City. 255 pp., folding map, illus. 8vo, ¾ mor. Paris, 1899. $17.50

A beautiful copy of this rare work of which Smith seems to locate but one copy. It is one of the best accounts of the gold stampede and perhaps the most beautifully illustrated of all the books on this subject.

314 BOIT, JOHN. Remarks on the Ship "Columbia's" Voyage from Boston (on a voyage round the globe). 8vo. Boston, 1920. $5.00

This log book which some years ago came into the possission of the Massachusetts Historical Society is extremely important as it is the fullest account extant of the voyage from the day the ship left Boston (Sept. 28, 1790), until it returned July 25, 1793. The original log of Capt. Gray was destroyed, only some extracts being preserved.

315 BOLDUC, JEAN-BAPTISTE ZACHARIE. Mission de la Colombie. Deuzieme Lettre et Journal de M.-J.-Z. Bolduc, Missionaire a la Colombie. 22 pp., 12mo, sewn, laid in folding protective case. Quebec, J. B. Frechette, Pere, 1845. [Sold]

Wagner-Camp 93. Cowan p. 21. The above work is of superlative rarity. While the first relation is rare and is described by Wagner this "Second Relation" is seldom offered.

316 BOLDUC, J. B. Z. Mission de la Colombie. Lettre et Journal de M. Bolduc, Missionaire de la Colombie. 95 pp., wrappers. Quebec, 1843. [Sold]

Wagner-Camp 93. Father Bolduc reached Oregon by sea in 1841 after experiencing considerable difficulty from the Hudson's Bay Company. He did, however, manage to make his observations among the Indians and the people of the Territory, which he sent back for publication. His narrative gives a detailed account of the missions established, notices of pioneer work and work still to be done. In 1845 he published the rarer "second relation" which is described above.

317 BOLTON, HERBERT EUGENE. Fray Juan Crespi; Missionary Explorer on the Pacific Coast, 1769-1774. 402 pp., 8vo, cloth, illus. Berkeley, 1927. $7.50

Now scarce. Contains a diary of a sea expedition to the North Pacific Coast in 1774.

318 BOND, J. W. Flatboating on the Yellowstone in 1877. Port. 22 pp., 8vo, wrappers. 1925. $2.00

Narrative of an 800-mile journey down the Yellowstone from Miles City to Ft. Lincoln with captured Indians of the Nez Perces War of 1876. Bond says the war was a religious one.

319 BONER, CHARLES. Guide for Travelers on the Plains and in the Mountains. 61 pp., 8vo. London, N. d. $12.50

320 BONISTEEL, MARY G. Army Boys and Girls. 248 pp., illus. 8vo, cloth. Baltimore, 1895. $7.50

321 BONNER, T. D. The Life and Adventures of James P. Beckwourth, Mountaineer, Scout, and Pioneer, and Chief of the Crow Nation of Indians. Plates. 537 pp., 12mo, cloth. N. Y., 1856. $15.00

Wagner-Camp 272. Fine copy of the Original Ed.

322 BONNEY, EDWARD. The Banditti of the Prairies. 248 pp., 12mo, cloth. Chicago, N. d. $3.50

323 BONSAL, STEPHEN. Edward Fitzgerald Beale. A Pioneer in the Path of Empire, 1822-1903. 17 illus. 312 pp., 8vo, cloth. N. Y., 1912. $7.50

Beale was an officer under Com. Stockton and fought with the army at San Pasqual and when night fell upon the indecisive action he, with Kit Carson, carried to Com. Stockton, at San Diego, the news of Gen. Kearney's desperate situation. Beale also carried the first gold east. Later he became an explorer, surveyor and builder of roads. This work also contains a narrative of Beale's trip across the plains in 1853.

324 [BORDER BANDITS.] Hawkeye Harry. Tracy the Outlaw King of Bandits. 184 pp., 8vo, cloth. Baltimore, c. 1908. $3.50

325 BORLAND, HAL G. Rocky Mountain Tipi Tales. 247 pp., colored illus. 8vo, cloth. N. Y., 1924. $3.75

326 BORTHWICK, J. D. Three Years in California. Eight tinted full page plates. 284 pp., 8vo, original cloth. London, 1857. $15.00

Original Edition. Cowan, p. 64: "Borthwick spent some time in 1851 as an actual miner at Weaver Creek. His book presents a faithful and graphic picture of those mining evperiences of the early days and is very agreeable reading. The tinted lithographs, after drawings by the author, give further attraction to this work."

327 BOSSU, M. Nouveaux Voyages aux Indes Occidentales contenant une differens Peuples qui habitent les environs dur Grand Fleuve St-Louis, appelle vulgurement le Mississippi. 4 plates by St. Aubin. 2 vols. in 1. 8vo, calf. Paris, 1768. $32.50

This is the Original Paris Edition and contains Bossu's first two voyages to Louisiana. The author was a captain in the French Marines. This is a superb copy of this rare work.

328 BOSSU, M. Nouveaux Voyages dans l'Amerique Septentrionale contenant une Collection de Lettres ecrites sur les lieux par l'Auteur, a son ami M. Douin le Nouveau-Monde. 4 engraved plates. 8vo, calf. Amsterdam, 1777. $15.00

Includes notices of Indian tribes on the Texas coast and travels and adventures into the Arkansas and Mississippi country.

329 BOUCHARD, A. Travels of a Naturalist; a Record of Adventures, Discoveries, History and Customs of Americas and Indians, Habits and Descriptions of Animals, chiefly made in North America, California, Mexico, Central America, Columbia, Chili, etc., during the last forty-two years. Portrait of Bouchard. 8vo, cloth. London, 1894. $20.00

A scarce work privately printed for the author.

RARE INDIAN MISSION PRESS ITEM

330 BOULET, J. B. Prayer Book and Catechism in the Snohomis Language. 32 pp., original wrappers. Tulalip Mission Press, 1879. $40.00

Excessively rare. Library of Congress PM2371Z787. Not mentioned by Pilling, Smith or any bibliography consulted. Probably the only printed text of the Snohomish language that can be found.

331 BOWEN, ALBERT D. Seattle and the Orient. 183 pp., illus. 8vo, original wrappers. Seattle, 1900. $4.50

332 BOWLES, SAMUEL. The Switzerland of America; or, A Summer Vacation in the Parks and Mountains of Colorado. 166 pp., 8vo, cloth. Springfield, 1869. $3.50

333 BOWLES, SAMUEL. Pacific Railroad—Open; How to go; Guide for Travel to and through Western America. 122 pp., 8vo cloth. Boston: Fields, 1869. $7.50

334 BOWMAN, JACOB. The Archives of the State of Washington. Reprint of the Annual Report of the American Historical Association, 1908. 8vo. Washington, 1910. $3.00

335 BOYD, ROBERT. History of the Synod of Washington of the Presbyterian Church in the United States of America, 1835-1909. 288 pp., 8vo. N. p., N. d. $5.C0

336 BRABRANT, A. J. Vancouver Island and its Missions, 1874-1900. Reminiscences of the Rev. A. J. Brabrant. 89 pp., illus., cloth. N. p., N. d. (c. 1900). $17.50

Rev. Moser who succeeded Father Brabant stated in 1910 that only about 70 copies of this book were printed on a hand press and either sold or given away. Contains much on the early events of Vancouver Island and Northern Washington.

BRADFORD'S RARE ATLAS OF AMERICA

338 [BRADFORD'S ATLAS, 1838.] An Illustrated Atlas of the United States and Adjacent Countries. 4to, half calf (loose covers). Boston, 1838. $50.00

Rare. Contains 40 American maps and plans, including a map of the Republic of Texas and one of the earliest descriptions of Oregon, or Columbia. Also included are plans of the City of Washington, New Orleans, Cincinnati, Boston, New York, Philadelphia, Baltimore. There are separate maps for each state. Only three copies have been offered during the past thirty years.

339 BRADFORD, W. J. A. Notes on the Northwest or Valley of the Upper Mississippi. 302 pp., 12mo, cloth. N. Y., 1846. $5.00

340 BRADBURY, JOHN. Travels in the Interior of America in the Years 1809-11. Including a Description of Upper Louisiana and the Western Territories. 8vo, half mor. London, 1817. $25.00

Original Edition.

341 BRADY, CYRUS TOWNSEND. Northwestern Fights and Fighters. 19 pp., 15 plates. 8vo. N. Y., 1913. $3.50

Nez Perce and Modoc Wars.

342 BRADLEY, THOMAS H. O'Toole's Mallet; or, The Resurrection of the Second National City of the United States of America. 65 pp., 8vo, wrappers. N. p., N. d. $75.00

Original Edition of an Important and Excessively Rare work. The history of the founding of Port Angeles, present thriving shipping center on the South shore of Puget Sound. The town was originally laid out on a federal reserve and lots were sold, hence the Port Angeles residents called it the "Second National City." However, the reserve proved detrimental to the development of the town and was not opened until Jan., 1894, when Capt. O'Toole, Register of the U. S. Land Office, acting under an Act of Congress, sold the lots to the highest bidders, of which Bradley has given an account in the above work. Smith did not seem to locate a copy of this rare work, nor can copies be located in any library on the Northwest Coast.

343 BRADY, CYRUS TOWNSEND. Indian Fights and Fighters. 423 pp., 8vo, cloth. N. Y., 1913. $3.00

344 BRANCH, E. DOUGLAS. Westward. The Romance of the American Frontier. 627 pp., maps, illus. 8vo, cloth. N. Y.. 1930. $6.00

345 BRATT, JOHN. Trails of Yesterday. Illus. 8vo, cloth. Chicago, 1921. $7.50

The author gives his experiences as bullwhacker, in Gallatin Valley, gold miner and cattleman, just before and after the Civil War. He relates the war with Dull Knife's Band, the massacre of Ft. Phil Kearney, Spotted Tail, Buffalo Bill, life at Ft. McPherson, etc.

346 BRERETON, ROBERT MAITLAND. Reminiscences of an old English Civil Engineer, 1858-1908. 111 pp., illus., port., maps, tables. 8vo, cloth. Portland: Privately Printed, 1908. $17.50

Original Edition of a work privately printed by the author without copyright. It contains personal recollections, observations and adventures in the mines of California, and other experiences in Oregon. An appendix is given over to correspondance with W. M. Stewart, Ralston and other noted pioneer figures.

347 BREWERTON, GEORGE DOUGLAS. A Ride with Kit Carson through the Great American Desert and the Rocky Mountains. (In Harper's New Monthly Magazine, Aug., 1853). (2) Incidents of Travel in New Mexico. (In Harper's New Monthly Magazine, April, 1854). (3) In the Buffalo Country). (Harper's New Monthly Magazine, Sept., 1862). 3 vols., 8vo, cloth. N. Y., 1853-1862. $10.00

Wagner-Camp 222. These articles, published at intervals, detail the author's trip from San Francisco via Los Angeles to Santa Fe and Independence in the summer of 1848. He gives an account of Aubry's ride from Santa Fe to Independence, having met that famous rider on his return. He also gives an account of the death of Bill Williams.

348 BRIDGES, WOODMAN. Shooting Skyward. 63 pp., illus. 8vo, cloth. Tacoma, 1912. $3.50

A story of Mt. Ranier. Not in Smith.

349 BRISTOL, S. The Pioneer Preacher; trip across the Plains to Oregon and California in time of Indian Wars, before Railroads; Three years in the Mining Camps of California and Idaho; 21 years in Southern California. Plates. 336 pp., 12mo, cloth. N. Y., 1898. $7.50

A source book by a '49er. Besides his own relation he gives a narrative of one of two survivors of the Van Zant Train. Presentation copy signed by the author.

RARE BRITISH-AMERICAN BOUNDARY CLAIMS DISPUTE

350 [BRITISH-AMERICAN JOINT COMMISSION.] (1) Treaty between Her Majestry and the United States of America for the Settlement of Claims of the Hudson's Bay and Puget Sound Agricultural Companies. Signed at Washington, July 1, 1863. Presented to both Houses of Parliament by Command of Her Majesty. Folio, London, 1864. (2) Evidence for the United States in the Matter of the Claim of the Hudson's Bay and Puget Sound Agricultural Companies. Presented before the British and American Joint Commissions for Final Settlement of Same. 397 pp., 8vo. Washington, 1867. (3) The same. 8vo, 562 pp. (bound with the above). (4) Evidence of the United States in the matter of the Claim before the British and American Joint Commission for the Final Settlement of the Claims of the Hudson's Bay and Puget Sound Agricultural Companies. 399 pp., 8vo. Washington, 1867. (This was not included in the Lib. of Cong. set). (5) Opinions and Award of the Commissioners under the Treaty of July 1, 1863, between Great Britain and the United States for the Final Settlement of the Claims of the Hudson's Bay and Puget Sound Agricultural Companies, Pronounced Sept. 19, 1869. 31 pp., original wrappers. Montreal, 1869. Together 5 vols., 8vo and folio. V. p., V. d. $500.00

See Smith 436-542 with note regarding this excessively rare work. There is apparently no entirely complete account of the proceedings known outside those in the Library of Congress. The above work contains all the evidence and argument, with the final award and the Treaty, all of which embrace the bulk of the importance of the commission's work. It required over forty years to assemble the numbers above described. The only set reported in the Northwest is the Photostat copies from the Lib. of Congress set in the University of Washington.

The Following Seven Items Are the Official Transactions of the Union of Vancouver and British Columbia

351 [BRITISH-COLUMBIA-VANCOUVER ISLAND.] Return to an Address of the Honourable House of Commons dated 24 June 1858:—for a "Return of all lands in Vancouver's Island sold to any individual or company, with the names of the Persons or Company to whom such lands have been sold, the extent to which such lands are under cultivation and the localities in which they are situated. 3 pp., folio. London, 1858. $15.00

352 [BRITISH-COLUMBIA-VANCOUVER ISLAND.] Copies or Extracts of any Correspondence between Mr. Langford and the Colonial Department relative to alleged abuses in the Government of Vancouver's Island; of any correspondence between the Colonial Department and Governor Douglas referring to Mr. Langford's charges; and of any correspondence with the Government of Vancouver's Island relative to the Appointment of Chief Justice Cameron and the Remonstrance against such appointment. 52 pp., folio. London, 1863. $47.50

Not in Smith's Check List. The above work contains grave charges against Governor Douglas and Chief Justice Cameron. Langford alleged that Mr. Cameron was a man of obscure origin, with no legal training, and had previously been an uncertified bankrupt in Scotland. It was further alleged that justice had been entirely overthrown in Vancouver's Island, etc. Governor Douglas admitted that the Chief Justice was not a professional lawyer and included a long letter from Cameron in which the latter submitted his personal history. The Duke of Newcastle replied to Governor Douglas in a long and acrimonious communication in which he questions the conduct of public servants in Vancouver Island. In short, this work gives much of early personal history of the founding of Vancouver and British Columbia.

353 [BRITISH COLUMBIA-VANCOUVER ISLAND.] Papers relative to the Proposed Union of British Columbia and Vancouver Island. Presented by both Houses of Parliament by Command of Her Majestry, 31st May 1866. 44 pp., folio. London, 1866. $22.50

A full relation of the antagonism and commercial rivalry and the events that finally lead to the union of the two colonies, British, Columbia and Vancouver Island. Smith 1490 locates but one copy.

354 [BRITISH COLUMBIA-VANCOUVER ISLAND.] Further Papers Relative to the Union of British Columbia and Vancouver's Island. 47 pp., folio. London, 1867. $22.50

Smith 1490. Contains 21 despatches from the Governor and 9 from the Secretary of State relative to the Union.

355 [BRITISH COLUMBIA-VANCOUVER ISLAND.] Further Papers relative to the Union of British Columbia and Vancouver Island (in continuation of Papers presented 25th of June, 1866). Presented to both Houses of Parliament by Command of Her Majesty, May 1867. 47 pp., folio. London, 1867. $22.50

Smith 1490.

356 [BRITISH COLUMBIA-VANCOUVER ISLAND.] Return to an Address of the Honourable the House of Commons, dated 2 July 1868; for—"Copy or Estract of Correspondence between Governor Kennedy of Vancouver's Island, Governor Seymour of British Columbia, and the Colonial Office, on the subject of a Site for the Capital of British Columbia. Ordered by the House of Commons to be printed, 28 July 1868. Folio. London, 1868. $15.00

The above work relates to the contest between Westminster and Victoria as to which should be selected the capital of the united provinces. The work contains the proclamation of Governor Seymour naming Victoria the capital. Not in Smith.

357 [BRITISH COLUMBIA-VANCOUVER ISLAND.] Return to the Address of the House of Commons, dated 1 June 1869;—for "Papers on the Union of British Columbia with the Dominion of Canada. Colonial Office, 2 August, 1869. Ordered by the House of Commons to be printed, 3 August 1869. 31 pp., folio. London, 1869. $15.00

This important document contains a relation of the various efforts and means to effect a union of British Columbia with the Dominion.

Smith 1489 locates one copy.

OFFICIAL RECORD OF NORTHWEST BOUNDARY DISPUTE

358 [BRITISH-UNITED STATES NORTHWEST BOUNDARY DISPUTE.] North-West America Water Boundary. (a) Case of the Government of Her Britannic Majesty submitted to the Arbitration and Award of His Majesty the Emperor of Germany, in accordance with Article 34 of the Treaty between Great Britain and the United States of America, signed at Washington, May 8, 1871. London, 1873. (b) Memorial of the Canal de Haro as the Boundary Line of the United States of America; presented in the name of the American Government to his Majesty William I, as arbitrator. London, 1873. (c) Second and Definite Statement on behalf of the Government of Her Britannic Majesty submitted to His Majesty the Emperor of Germany under the Treaty of Washington, May 8, 1873. (d) Reply to the United States to the Case of the Government of Her Britannic Majesty, presented to the Emperor of Germany under the provisions of the Treaty of Washington, London, 1873. (e) Maps annexed to the Case of the Government of Her Britannic Majesty. London, 1873. (f) Maps annexed to the Memorial and Reply of the United States Government submitted to the Arbitration and Award of the Emperor of Germany. London, 1873. (g) Correspondence respecting the Award of the Emperor of Germany in the matter of the Boundary Line between Great Britain and the U. S. London, 1873. Seven parts in one volume, complete with the 19 maps. Royal 8vo, half calf. London, 1873. $75.00

One cannot over-estimate the importance of the above work for the history of Oregon, Washington, British Columbia and Vancouver Island at this interesting period of its formative life. The maps are as follows: (a) Carta Esferica de los Reconocimeintos hechos en la Costa N. O. de America en 1791-2 por las goltros "Sutil" y "Mexicana"; (b) A chart showing part of N. W. America with the tracks of His Majesty's Sloop "Discovery," commanded by George Vancouver; (c) Haro and Rosario Straits, surveyed by Capt. G. H. Richards; (d) Strait of Juan de Fuca, surveyed by Richard Kellett; (e) Map of Oregon and Upper California from the surveys of J. C. Fremont and other Authorities.

The work also includes the following additional maps: (a) Map of de Haro, 1790; (b) Map of Eliza, 1791; (c) Map of Vancouver, 1798; (d) Map of Galiano and Valdez, 1802; (e) Map of Duflot de Mofras, 1844; (f) Map of Wilkes, 1845; (g) Map of W Sturgis, 1845; (h) U. S. Coast Survey of Washington Sound and approaches; (i) Spanish Chart published in 1795; (j) Cross Sections of Haro and Rosario Channels; (k) Sketch to illustrate the route of vessels of the Hudson's Bay Co.

359 [BRITISH-UNITED STATES NORTHWEST BOUNDARY DISPUTE.] Northwest Water Boundary, presented to both Houses of Parliament by Command of Her Majesty. 41 & 36 & 17 & 34 & 17 & 45 & 12 pp., 19 maps. London (1873). Together with (the addition of North America, No. 10. 1873). No. 10 being the Protocol signed at Washington on the 10th of March, 1873, defining the boundary line through the Channel of Haro, in accordance with the award. Together, 2 vols. in one. Roy. 8vo, half morocco. London, 1873. $45.00

Smith 1502 and 1503.

360 [BRITISH COLUMBIA-VANCOUVER.] Return to Three Addresses of the Honourable the House of Commons, dates 16 August 1848 and 6th Feb. and March 1, 1849: viz. Address, 16 Aug., 1848 for Copies or extracts of a Despatch to the Admiralty from Rear-Admiral Sir George Seymour, dated H.M.S. "Collingwood," Valparaiso, the 8th day of Feb., 1847; Copies of a Despatch from Commander Gordon, dated H.M. Steam Sloop "Cormorant," Nesqually, the 7th day of Oct., 1846 to Capt. J. A. Duntze of H.M.S. "Fisquard," being enclosed in last; of a letter dated Vancouver the 7th day of September, 1846, signed Peter Skene Ogden and James Douglas, addressed to Capt. Duntz, of H.M.S. "Fisquard"; copies of Extracts of a Report by Lieuts. Warre and Vavasour, dated the 1st day of Nov., 1845, addressed to the Secretary of State for Colonies relating to soil, climate, minerals and harbours; copies or extracts of a Report by Lieut. Vavasour, dated March, 1846, addressed to Col. Hollaway of the Royal Engineers, Canada, to the same effect; and of the Instructions sent by the Admiralty to the Commanding Officer or any other Officer on the Pacific Station relative to the Coals in Vancouver Island and of the Correspondence between the Colonial Office and the Admiralty on the same subject; Address, 6 Feb. 1849, for a copy of Charter of Grant of Vancouver's Island to the Hudson's Bay Company, and copies of any Correspondence which has passed between the Colonial Office and the Hudson's Bay Co. on that subject, since the last papers were laid on the table; Address, 1 March 1849 for a Copy of any Report from the Committee of Her Majesty's Privy Council for Trades and Plantations on Grant of Vancouver's Island to the Hudson's Bay Co. 20 pp., folio. London, 1849. $75.00

Smith 1495 devotes almost a column to this item. Not only it is very rare but important historically.

Fine copy of the Original Edition.

EARLY FOUNDING LAW OF BRITISH COLUMBIA AND VANCOUVER ISLAND, ON PUGET SOUND

361 [BRITISH COLUMBIA-VANCOUVER.] An Act to Provide for the Administration of Justice in Vancouver's Island. Ordered by the House of Commons to be Printed, 5 July 1849. 4 pp., folio. London, 1849. $12.50

Not in Smith. Early foundation law of British Columbia.

362 [BRITISH COLUMBIA.] A Complete Hand-Book replete with the latest Information concerning the newly discovered Gold Fields. With Map. 67 pp., 8vo, wrappers. London (1858). $37.50

A rare work which is not mentioned in Smith's Check List.

363 [BRITISH COLUMBIA.] British North American Act of 1867. Terms of Union with Canada. Rules and Orders of the Legislative Assembly. 189 pp., 8vo, cloth. Victoria, 1873. $17.50

Not in Smith.

364 [BRITISH COLUMBIA.] Papers connected with the Indian Land Question. 1850-1875. 167 plus 16 pp., 8vo. Victoria, 1875. $37.50

A rare work relating to the relations of the Hudson's Bay Company and the Indians. Here are some of the contents: Conveyance of Land to the Hudson's Bay by Indian Tribes; Conveyance between the Sec'y of State for the Colonies and Governor David Douglas; Correspondence between the Colonial Sec'y and the Chief Commissioner of Lands and Works; Correspondence between the Rev. J. B. Good and the Colonial Secretary; Correspondence between the Lieut. Governor and the Sec'y of State for the Provinces; Correspondence between the Indian Commission and the Provincial Governor. This work is not mentioned by Smith.

365 [BRITISH COLUMBIA.] Message relative to the Terms of the Union with the Province of British Columbia. Printed by order of Parliament. 66 pp., 8vo, original wrappers. Ottawa, 1875. $12.50

366 [BRITISH COLUMBIA.] Province of British Columbia, Canada. Its Climate and Resources. With Information for Emigrants. 136 pp., folding map. 8vo, original printed wrappers. Victoria, 1883. $10.00

Smith 463 reports one copy.

367 [BRITISH COLUMBIA.] Province of British Columbia. Information for Intending Settlers. Published by the Governor of Canada. 32 pp., 8vo, original wrappers. Ottawa, 1883. $4.00

368 [BRITISH COLUMBIA.] Report on an Exploratory Survey for a line of Railway to connect the Canadian Pacific Railway with Barkerville, Cariboo District. By H. P. Bell. 8 pp., 2 large folding maps., 8vo, original wrappers. Victoria (1887). $7.50

369 [BRITISH COLUMBIA.] Report of Select Committee Claims to Granville Town Lots. 65 pp., 8vo, original wrappers. Victoria, 1888. $4.75

370 [BRITISH COLUMBIA.] Its Resources and Capabilities. Reprinted from "Canada, a Memorial." 20 pp., 8vo, original printed wrappers. Montreal, 1889. $7.50

371 [BRITISH COLUMBIA.] British Association for the Advancement of Science. Committee Appointed to investigate the Physical Features, Languages, and Industrial and Social Conditions of the Northwestern Tribes of the Dominion of Canada. Fifth Report. 97 pp., 6 plates. 8vo. London: Spottiswoode, London, 1889. $10.00

Contains "Remarks on North American Ethnology," by Horatio Hale; "Report on the Indians of British Columbia," by Franz Boas, and other valuable reports. Smith seems to locate but 3 copies.

372 [BRITISH COLUMBIA.] Natural History Society. Papers and Transactions, Vol. 1, No. 1, 64 pp. 8vo, original wrappers. Victoria, 1891. $7.50

Contains Fannin's "Birds of British Columbia," etc. Smith does not mention this work.

373 [BRITISH COLUMBIA.] General View of Mining in British Columbia. Bulletin No. 19. 176 pp., illus. 8vo, original wrappers. Victoria, 1904. $4.50

374 [BRITISH COLUMBIA.] The Mineral Provinces of Canada. Being a Short History of Mining in the Provinces. A Synopsis of the Mining Laws, etc. 38 pp., illus., map. 8vo. Victoria, 1909. $2.50

375 [BRITISH COLUMBIA.] Report of the Provincial Archives Dep't for the year ending Dec. 31, 1913. 135 pp. 8vo. Victoria, 1914. $7.50

Contains copies of many historical documents and letters never before published. The documents are signed by Vancouver, Colville, Demers, McDonald, Ogden, Douglas, Tolmie-David Thompson.

376 [BRITISH COLUMBIA.] Report of the Provincial Archives Department. Annual Report for the Year ended Dec. 31st, 1913. 135 pp., 8vo, cloth. Victoria, 1914. $5.00

377 [BRITISH COLUMBIA.] Report of the Royal Commission on Indian Affairs for the Province of British Columbia. 4 vols., 8vo, original printed wrappers. Victoria, 1916. $37.50

A valuable and historical publication.

378 [BRITISH COLUMBIA.] Royal Commission on Indian Affairs for the Province of British Columbia. 4 vols., 8vo, cloth. Victoria, 1916. $30.00

As this was a rather expensive set of reports to publish it was issued in only a small edition.

379 [BRITISH COLUMBIA.] Days of Old and Days of Gold in British Columbia. A few Reminiscences of the early Gold Mining Days. 15 pp., illus. 8vo, original wrappers. Victoria, 1922. $4.75

Not mentioned by Smith.

380 [BRITISH COLUMBIA.] Historical Association. First Annual Report and Proceedings. 34 pp., 8vo, wrappers. Victoria, 1923. $4.75

Contains an address by Judge F. W. Howay, "Earliest Pages of the History of British Columbia"; "The Pioneer Press of British Columbia," by J. Forsyth; an article on Thomas Muir, Scottish political martyr and his connection with Vancouver's Island, etc.

381 [BRITISH COLUMBIA.] Second Annual Report of the British Columbia Historical Association. 45 pp., illus. 8vo, wrappers. (Victoria), 1924. $3.50

381a —— Same. 3rd Annual Report. 1925. $3.50

382 [BRITISH COLUMBIA.] Archives of British Columbia. Memoir No. 8. 210 pp., illus. 8vo, cloth. Victoria, 1928. $10.00

Already a scarce work relating to the Colonial Postal System. A sketch of the origin and early development of the postal service on the Pacific Coast of the Northwest, Vancouver Island, etc.

383 [BRITISH COLUMBIA ARCHIVES.] Minutes of the House of Assembly of Vancouver Island, Aug. 12, 1856 to Sept. 25, 1858. 78 pp. 8vo. Victoria, 1918. $15.00

384 [BRITISH COLUMBIA ARCHIVES.] Minutes of the Council of Vancouver Island, commencing Aug. 30, 1851 and continuing through 1861. Memoir No. 11. 93 pp., 8vo. Victoria, 1918. $12.50

385 [BRITISH COLUMBIA ARCHIVES.] House of Assembly Correspondence Book. Aug. 25th, 1856 to July 6, 1859. 63 pp. Memoir No. 4. 8vo. Victoria, 1918. $12.50

386 BRITON, DANIEL C. The American Race; a Linguistic Classification and Ethnographic Description of the Native Tribes of North and South America. 392 pp. 8vo, cloth. Phila., 1901. $3.50

387 BRITON, DANIEL C. The Myths of the New World, a Treatise on the Symbolism and Mythology of the Red Race of America. 360 pp., 8vo, cloth. Phila., 1896. $3.75

388 BRODERICK, THERESE. The Brand. 271 pp., 8vo, cloth. Seattle, 1909. $3.75

Narrative of the Flathead Indians.

388a BROGAN, JAMES, S. J. An Historical Landmark Old Mission Church of the Coeur d'Alene Indians. [Church of the Sacred Heart.] Built without nails . . . 1846, at Shootloty, near Cataldo, Idaho. 15 illus. Large 8vo, original wrappers. N. p., N. d. [Spokane.] $7.50

389 BROKE, GEORGE. With Sack and Stock in Alaska. 158 pp., 8vo, cloth. London, 1891. $5.00

390 BROMLEY, GEORGE TISDALE. The Long Ago and Later on; or, Recollections of Eighty Years. Portrait. 12mo, cloth. San Francisco, 1904. $7.50

Contains several chapters on California, the author having reached San Francisco in 1851.

391 BRONSON, E. B. Reminiscences of a Ranchman. 314 pp., 12mo, cloth. N. Y., 1918. $7.50

Original Edition. A classic on the cowboy.

392 [BROOK FARM.] Early Letters of George William Curtis to John S. Dwight. Brook Farm and Concord. 12mo, cloth, first ed. N. Y., 1896. $2.50

Letters from the first student at the colony to his Latin professor there.

393 [BROOK FARM.] Brook Farm, its Members, Scholars, Visitors. By Lindsay Swift. 12mo, original cloth. N. Y., 1900. $3.50

Item 391, Date should read 1908, not 1918.

BROUGHTON'S VOYAGE TO N. W. COAST

394 BROUGHTON, WM. R. Voyage of Discovery in the North Pacific Ocean in His Majesty's sloop Providence and her tender in 1795-1798; complete with all the Folding Maps and Plates in fine condition. 412 pp. 4to, original half calf. London: Cadell and Davis, 1804. $150.00

An unusually clean copy of this rare work. One of the most important of the voyages made to the Northwest coast of America. The work was the chief authority put forward by Great Britain in 1846, when making her claims to the Oregon territory. Broughton had previously been on the coast in command of the Chatham under Vancouver, when he surveyed Columbia. In 1793 he returned home across the Isthmus from San Blas to Vera Cruz with Vancouver's dispatches.

395 BROUGHTON, WM. R. Voyage de decouvertes dans la partie Septentrionale de l'Ocean Pacifique . . . pendant les annees 1795, 1796, 1797 et 1798 . . . traduit . . . par J. B. B. E. 7 plates, 3 maps, tables. 8vo, calf. Paris, 1807. $27.50

Smith 484.

BROUILLET'S ACCOUNT OF THE WHITMAN TRAGEDY

396 BROUILLET, J. B. A. Protestantism in Oregon. Account of the Murder of Dr. Whitman and the Ungrateful Calumnies of H. H. Spaulding, Protestant Missionary. 8vo, sewn. Washington, 1858. $27.50

397 BROUILLET, J. B. A. True Account of the Whitman Murder. 40 pp., original wrappers. Ferndale, Wash., 1912. $27.50

This exceedingly rare reprint was issued from a small mission press and a copy is seldom found.

398 BROUILLET, J. B. A. The Whitman Massacre. Contained in 9 numbers of "The Lewiston Catholic Monthly," Vol. 8, Oct., 1924 through Vol. 9, June, 1925. 8vo. Lewiston, 1924-25. $7.50

399 BROWER, J. V. The Missouri River and its utmost Source. A Narrative Description of the Evolution and Discovery of the River and its Headwaters. 206 pp., 8vo, original wrappers. St. Paul, 1897. $5.00

Braislin 224. Account of the Indian occupancy of the territory; Spanish and French discoveries; early traders and Montana mines; early explorations, etc.

400 BROWN, JENNIE BOUGHTON. Fort Hall—On the Oregon Trail. A Historical Study. 466 pp., illus., 8vo, cloth. Caldwell, 1932. $2.50

401 BROWN, JOHN. The Northwest Passage and the Plan for Sir John Franklin. 463 pp., plate, maps. 8vo, cloth. London, 1858. $7.50

Smith 492 locates but one copy.

402 BROWN, JOHN W. History of Alaska. With maps of "Inside Passage" and of "Alaska" and many interesting Illustrations. 96 pp., 8vo, original printed wrappers. Seattle, 1909. $7.50

A scarce work. Smith cites only two copies, although the work was printed on the west coast.

403 BROWN, R. C. LUNDIN. British Columbia; an Essay. 8vo, cloth. New Minister Royal Engineer Press, 1863. $32.50

404 BROWN, R. C. LUNDIN. Klatsassan and other Reminiscences of Missionary Life in British Columbia. 199 pp., front., folding map. 8vo, cloth. London, 1873. $15.00

Smith 494 locates but one copy. Rev. Brown went to British Columbia as a missioner to the Indians. He arrived there in 1861 and spent many years in that vicinity among the Indians. He is a recognized authority on the Pacific Northwest Indians.

BROWN'S HISTORY OF VANCOUVER, IN WRAPPERS

405 BROWN, ROBERT. Vancouver Island Exploration, 1864. 27 pp., 8vo, wrappers. Victoria (1865). $40.00

Smith 498. Rare and important Northwest history. The only copy located is that in the Seattle Public Library.

406 BROWN, VALENTINE. The Chieftan and Satires. 192 pp., 8vo, cloth. Portland, 1903. $3.75

Smith 499.

407 BROWNELL, CHARLES DEWOLF. The Indian Races of North and South America, including the Sioux War and Indian Massacres in Minnesota. Numerous colored plates. 8vo, cloth. Hartford, 1864. $3.75

Gives an account of the aboriginal races, costumes, mythology, religious ceremonies, etc.; also gives an account of the war with the Oregon Indians.

408 BROWNELL, HENRY HOWARD. The New World: Embracing American History. 2 vols. in 1. 8vo, cloth. N. Y., 1857. $7.50

Contains the discovery and history of Oregon.

409 BROWNE, J. ROSS. Adventures in the Apache Country; a Tour through Arizona and Sonora, with Notes on the Silver Regions of Nevada. Illus. 12mo, cloth. N. Y., 1869. $8.50

410 BRUFFEY, GEORGE A. Eighty-One Years in the West. Port. 12mo, wrappers. Butte, 1925. $6.50

The author was born in West Virginia in 1842. In 1844 his family moved to Missouri where his father fitted out wagons for the '49ers. At the age of twenty the author was prospecting for gold in Nevada and Montana

411 BRYANT, EDWIN. What I Saw in California; Being the Journal ot a Tour, by the Emigrant Route and South Pass of the Rocky Mountains, Across the Continent of North America, the Great Desert Basin, and through California, in the years 1846-1847. 455 pp., 12mo, cloth. N. Y., 1848. $12.50

Wagner-Camp 146. Original Edition. Cowan, p. 28: "An excellent authority both on the overland journey and events in California."

412 BRYANT, EDWIN. Rocky Mountain Adventure. Fearful Fights of American Hunters with Savage Indians, Mexicans, Racheros, etc. With a Full Account of the Bear Conquest of California. Front. 12mo, cloth. N. Y. (1885). $4.00

413 BRYCE, GEORGE. Remarkable History of the Hudson's Bay Company, including that of the French Traders of North-Western Canada and of the Northwest. Maps and illus. 8vo, cloth. N. Y., 1900. $10.00

414 BRYCE, GEORGE. The Life of Lord Selkirk, Colonizer of Western Canada. Illus. 8vo, cloth. Toronto, 1902. $3.75

414a BRYCE, GEORGE. The Scotsman in Canada, Western Canada, including Manitoba, Saskatchewan, Alberta, British Columbia and portions of Rupert's Land and Indian Territories. 2 vols., 8vo, cloth. Toronto (1911). $17.50

Vol. 1 contains: Scots of Eastern Canada, Vol. 2, of Western Canada; contains much on the Scottish fur traders, as well as the history and biography of the regions described.

415 BUCKLAND, A. R. John Horden, Missionary Bishop. A Life on the Shores of Hudson's Bay. 141 pp., illus. 8vo, cloth. London, N. d. $7.50

Horden arrived at Moose Factory, a Hudson's Bay Post, Aug. 25, 1851, and passed the remainder of his life, nearly forty years, in the Northwest. He was consecrated Bishop of Moosonee, Dec. 15, 1872.

ORIGINAL NARRATIVE OF "BUCKSKIN MOSE"

416 BUCKSKIN, MOSE; or, Life from the Lakes to the Pacific, as Ranger, Gold-Digger, Indian Scout, and Guide. Written by Himself. Edited by C. G. Rosenburg. Plates. 285 pp. (ex. lib., name on title). 12mo, cloth. N. Y., 1873. $20.00

Original Edition. Cowan, p. 28: "Buckskin Mose, whose real name is unknown, was one of the singular characters that belong to the past. He reached California in 1857 (1856) and seems to have spent much of his time at Honey Lake and Susanville, in Lassen County." The narrative is extremely interesting and reveals the author as a member of Capt. Crimm's Overland party of 1855, and late, Captain of the Buckskin Rangers of California. He gives a full account of the Crimms Emigration Co., which numbered 75 men, and of the adventurous journey across the plains from Saint Jo. He spent a year and a half at the diggins, then joined the Rangers; and from then until 1869, when the narrative ends, he followed the career of an Indian fighter.

417 BUFFUM, GEORGE T. Smith of Bear City and other Frontier Sketches. Illus. 249 pp., 8vo, cloth. N. Y., 1906. $7.50

Twenty sketches of actual characters of frontier days. Presentation copy.

418 BULFINCH, T. Oregon and Eldorado; or, Romance of the Rivers. 464 pp., 12mo, original cloth. Boston, 1866. $6.00

Original Edition, fine copy. Cited in Bancroft's "List of Authorities." Relates to the discovery of the Columbia River by Capt. Gray, and the expedition of Lewis and Clark.

UNRECORDED BRITISH COLUMBIA PAMPHLET IN WRAPPERS

419 BULKLEY, THOMAS A British Columbia. Correspondence on the Subject of a Graving Dock at Esquimalt, B. C.; Also a copy of Advertisement and Tender for its construction, and Report of the Chief Engineer to the Government on the Subject. 20 pp., original wrappers. Ottawa, 1873. $20.00

Unable to locate another copy.

420 BUMSTEAD, JOSEPH. A Voyage Round the World, 1785-88, performed by M. de la Peyrouse, to which are added (with separate titlepages) a Voyage to California by Don Antonio Maurelle; and an Abstract of the Voyage of Capt. George Vancouver. 333 pp., 12mo, sheep. Boston, 1801. $10.00

The earliest American printing of these important voyages.

421 BUNDY, HALLOCK C. The Valdez-Fairbanks Trail. 87 pp., illus., 8vo, cloth. N. p., 1910. $3.75

422 BUNNELL, LAFAYETTE HOUGHTON. Discovery of the Yosemite, and the Indian War of 1851, which lead to that Event. Illus., 12mo, cloth. Chicago (1880). $10.00

423 BURDETT, CHARLES. Life of Kit Carson. 328 pp., 12mo, cloth. 1869. $5.00

This edition contains an account of the death of Kit Carson.

BURGESS' RARE PRIVATELY PRINTED HISTORY OF THE NOOTKA SOUND CONTROVERSY

424 BURGESS, SIR JAMES BLAND. Narrative of the Negotiations occasioned by the Dispute between England and Spain in the Year 1790. 8vo, ¾ morocco. 307 pp. [Privately Printed, 1790-91.] $250.00

This was issued without a title page, printed but not published. Manning in his "Nootka Sound Controversy," in a note, P. 365, says: "This narrative is a very rare book, and very valuable for the subject in hand. No previous writer on the Nootka controversy has consulted it. Probably only a few copies were printed. The King's own copy is now in the British museum. That obtained for use in this study is the only copy that Messrs. Henry Stevens Son and Stiles have noted during the whole of their business experience. Neither date nor the name of publisher or author is given. The British Museum Cat. gives 1791? as the date. It is evidently an official account prepared in the Foreign Office especially for the King. In a letter from J. B. Burgess, Under Sec'y for Foreign Aàairs, to Lord Auckland, dated Nov. 12, 1790, he mentions an "interesting Narrative which, at leisure hours, I prepared for the King . . ."

This copy settles the much mooted question as to the authorship, as it is a presentation copy from J. B. Burgess to his good friend, J. W. Croker.

424a BURNET, JACOB. Notes on the Early Settlement of the Northwestern Territory. Port. 8vo, calf. Cincinnati, 1847. $7.50

An account of the Indian wars and pioneer life of the old Northwest. "A valuable original contribution to the early history of the Northwest and particularly of Hio," Prof. B. A. Hinsdale.

425 BURNETT, PETER H. Recollections and Opinions of an Old Pioneer. 12mo, cloth. N. Y., 1880. $15.00

Burnett made the Overland from Independence to Oregon in 1843. He later went to California in the fall of 1848 to look for gold, and the remainder of his book relates to California, of which he was the first governor.

425a —— The same. Original cloth. Cin., 1888. Ex. lib. stamp on title, front flyleaf missing. $7.50

FINE SET OF BURNEY'S N. W. "DISCOVERIES" IMPORTANT FOR CALIFORNIA HISTORY

426 BURNEY, CAPT. JAMES (R.N.). A Chronological History of the Discoveries in the South Sea or Pacific Ocean. 5 vols., 4to, complete with all the charts and plates, original boards, uncut, complete with labels. London, 1803-1817. $160.00

"The Great Reputation of this work has been consistently sustained for a century. Many of the early voyages to California, and the adjacent coast, would be nearly inaccessible were they not herein collected. Among these are the narratives or reports of Alarcon, Cabrillo, Salvatierra, Vizcaino and numerous others. The author has also included the discussions as to whether California was insular or a part of the mainland; dissertations upon the name of California; and an account of the expedition of the Spaniards to conquer California; all of which have been taken from original sources."—Cowan, Bib. of California.

427 BURNEY, CAPT. JAMES (R.N.). A Chronological History of the Northeastern Voyages of Discovery; and of the early Eastern Navigations of the Russians. Map. 8vo, calf. London, 1819. $15.00

Gives long accounts of the Russian explorations towards the Northwest Coast of America.

Bound up in the same volume is the following work, "An Abridgement of Portlock and Dixon's Voyage round the World, performed in 1785-88."—London, 1789.

428 BURNEY, RT. HON. VICOUNT. Balance Sheet of the Washington Treaty in 1872 in account with the People of Great Britain and her Colonies. 27 pp., map. 8vo, sewn. London, 1873. $10.00

Relates to the San Juan de Fuca (Puget Sound) boundary disputes.

429 BURNHAM, FREDERICK W. A Missionary Trip to Alaska. 30 pp., map. 8vo, wrappers. Cincinnati, N. d. $5.00

Not in Smith.

430 BURPEE, LAWRENCE J. The Search for the Western Sea. The Story of the Exploration of North-Western America. Maps and Plates. 8vo, original cloth, uncut. Toronto, 1908. $37.50

The rarest of Burpee's works. It is divided into three parts: (1) The northern gateway; (2) The southern gateway; (3) The road to the sea. The author has made an exhaustive study of his subject and his work is invaluable to the student. There are many excellent illustrations and a good index.

431 BURPEE, LAWRENCE J. Journal of Laroque from the Assiniboine to the Yellowstone. 82 pp., cloth. Ottawa, 1910. $20.00

First printing of this interesting narrative which is now quite scarce. Larocque was at the Mandan Village when Lewis and Clark were there. He is mentioned in the latter's journals.

432 BURPEE, LAWRENCE. A Chapter in the Literature of the Fur Trade. 8vo, cloth. Chicago, 1911. $4.75

By an authority.

433 BURPEE, LAWRENCE J. Among the Canadian Alps. 239 pp., colored plates, 5 maps. 8vo, cloth. N. Y., 1914. $5.00

434 BURPEE, LAWRENCE J. Pathfinders of the Great Plains. A Chronicle of La Verendrye and his Sons. 116 pp., illus., map. 8vo, cloth. Toronto, 1914. $4.75

435 BURPEE, LAWRENCE J. Sanford Fleming, Empire Builder. 8vo, cloth., illus. Toronto, 1915. $7.50

435a BURRALL, W. T. A Trip to the Far West of British Columbia (May-July, 1891). 26 pp. 8vo, original printed wrappers (woodcuts). Wisbech (1891). $27.50

No other copy has been located.

436 BURTON, RICHARD. The English Hero; or, Sir Francis Drake Reviv'd; being a Full Account of the Dangerous Voyages, etc. 175 pp., 8vo, calf. London, 1701. $12.50

Account of Drake's voyage up the California coast.

437 BURTON, CAPT. RICHARD FRANCIS. The City of the Saints and Across the Rocky Mountains to California. Maps, plan, 8 plates. 8vo, ¾ morocco. London, 1861. $12.50

Wagner-Camp 370. Fine copy of the Original Edition. The maps include the Wahsatch Mts. and Great Salt Lake. The route was from the Missouri River to the Pacific.

FIRST PUBLISHED NARRATIVE OF A TRIP OVERLAND TO THE NORTHWEST COAST

438 BUTEL-DUMON, G. M. Memoires historiques sur la Louisiane, contenant ce qui y est arrive, de plus memorable depuis l'annee 1687, jusqu'a present; avec l'establissement de la Colonie Francois dans cette Province, sous la Compagnie des Indes; le climate, les productions de ce pays; l'origine et la Religion des Sauvages; leur moeurs et leurs coutumes, etc. Large Map of Louisiana, a folding referenced plan of New Orleans; a folding plan of the concession to M. Le Blanc on the Yazoo River; a folding plan of Fort Rosalie and environs in the territory of the Natchez Indians. Natural History Plates, including the cotton plant, &c. 2 vols. in one. 12mo, original boards. Paris, 1753. $57.50

Museum Catalog. 1923. Said to have been written by L'Abbe Mercier (see Narrative and Critical History of America. Vol. 5, p. 65). This contains pp. 246, v. 2 a digest of the narrative of the journey of Moncact-Ape from Natchez, to the North Pacific Ocean, via the Missouri and Columbia rivers. Being the First Published Narrative of an Overland Trip to the North Pacific Coast.

439 BUTLER, CAPT. E. An Essay on our Indian Question. 49 pp., 8vo, wrappers. N. Y., 1882. $7.50

440 BUTLER, SIR WILLIAM FRANCIS. Far Out; Rovings Retold. 386 pp., 8vo, cloth. London, 1880. $7.50

Not in Smith. Relating to the author's adventures in Oregon, California and British Columbia.

441 BUTLER, SIR WILLIAM FRANCIS. An Autobiography. 476 pp., maps. 8vo, cloth. London, 1913. $7.50

The author was in the Far West in 1867.

442 BUTTERFIELD, C. W. History of Brule's Discoveries and Explorations, 1610-1626, being a Narrative of the Discovery by Stephen Brule, of Lakes Huron, Ontario and Superior; and of his explorations (the first made by civilized man) of Pennsylvania and Western New York; also of the Province of Ontario, Canada, with a biographical notice of the Discoverer and Explorer who was killed and eaten by savages. With map, portrait and illus. 8vo, cloth. Cleveland, 1892. $15.00

443 BUTTERFIELD, C. W. History of the Discovery of the Northwest by John Nicolet in 1634; with Sketch of his Life. 114 pp., 12mo, cloth. Cincinnati, 1881. $25.00

Original Edition. A fine copy of the scarcest of Butterfield's works. "A meritorious monograph on the first discoverer of the Northwest. A complete and exhaustive account of the life and explorations of Nicolet amply fortified by citations."—Larned's Bibliography.

444 BUTTERFIELD, C. W. History of the Girty's. 426 pp., 8vo, cloth. Cincinnati, 1890. $22.50

445 BUTTERWORTH, HEZIKIAH. The Log School House on the Columbia. A Tale of the Pioneers of the Great Northwest. 250 pp., 8vo, cloth, illus. N. Y., 1890. $7.50

Fine copy of the Original Edition.

446 BUTTERWORTH, HEZIKIAH. Zigzag Journeys in the Great Northwest; or, A Trip to the American Switzerland. 319 pp., illus., ports. 12mo, cloth. Boston (c. 1890). $4.75

447 BYRNE, P. E. Soldiers on the Plains. 260 pp., 8vo, cloth. N. Y., 1926. $3.75

An authentic story of the Indian campaigns of the 60's and 70's.

448 [BUFFALO BILL.] (Cody, W. F.). True Tales of the Plains. 259 pp., 8vo, cloth. N. Y., 1908. $3.50

449 BUCKINGHAM, J. S. America, Historical, Statistic and Descriptive. 3 vols., 8vo, cloth, ports., and illus. London (1841). $4.00

450 [CALIFORNIA.] (Brodie, Walter). Pitcairn's Island, and the Islanders, in 1850. Together with Extracts from his Private Journal and a few Hints upon California. Port. 12mo, original cloth. London, 1851. $12.50

Original Edition. The author arrived at San Francisco, which he calls "a horrid sink of iniquity," in 1850. After several weeks' stay at Pitcairn's Island, San Francisco does not shine by contrast.

451 [CALIFORNIA.) (Brooks, J. T.). Four Months among the Gold-Finders of Alta California: Being the Diary of an Expedition from San Francisco to the Gold Districts. Map. 207 pp., 8vo, cloth. London, 1849. $15.00

Original Edition. Cowan, p. 25: "One of the first works to give the results of actual experience in the newly discovered region. His party of five accumulated more than 100 pounds of gold, but unfortunately were relieved of the greater part of it by equally enterprising highwaymen."

452 [CALIFORNIA.] (Browne, J. Ross). Report of the Debates in the Convention of California on the Formation of the State Constitution in September and October, 1849. 479 pp., 8vo, cloth. Washington, 1850. $7.50

453 [CALIFORNIA.Q (Cappe d'Auteroche, Jean). Voyage en Siberia, fait par ordre du Roi en 1761; contenant les moeurs les usages des Russes et l'etat de cette puissance, etc. 2 vols., 8vo, calf. Amsterdam, 1769. $17.50

454 [CALIFORNIA.] (Chard, Thomas). California Sketches. 26 pp., 8vo, original boards. Chicago, 1888. $4.50

Cowan, p. 114: "The results of this expedition were feared by Spain and hastened the occupation and settlement of Alta California."

455 [CALIFORNIA.] The Big Trees of California. By Galen Clark. Port., illus., 104 pp., small 12mo, wrappers. Yosemite Valley, Calif., 1910. $1.00

Scarce little work, privately printed.

456 [CALIFORNIA.] (Clark, Susie C.). The Round Trip from the Hub to the Golden Gate. 293 pp., 8vo, cloth. Boston, 1890. $2.50

CLAVIGERO'S RARE WORK ON CALIFORNIA, WITH MAP

457 [CALIFORNIA.] (Clavigero, Francisco S.). Storia della California. Opera Postuma. 2 vols. in one. 8vo, half calf. Venezia, 1789. $50.00

Fine copy of this rare work with the rare map. Smith in his "Bibliotheca America Nova," says: "This work appears to be very little known, not being mentioned in any bibliographical work which I have seen."

458 [CALIFORNIA.] (Cole, Cornelius). Memoirs of. Port. 354 pp., 8vo, cloth, paper label. N. Y., 1908. $7.50

The greater part of this narrative relates to a trip across the plains in '49; Indians; Fort Laramie; Sutter's Fort and Sacramento in 1849; Life at the Mines; Vigilance Committee; Lynching; Fur Trade; and other events and conditions of the period.

459 [CALIFORNIA.] (Combier, C.). Voyage au Golfe de Californie, Description de la Sonora et de ses Minerales de la Basse Californie &c. Nuits de la Zone Torride. Map. 8vo, calf. Paris (c. 1832). $15.00

Not mentioned by Cowan.

460 [CALIFORNIA.] (Comerford, Mary Teresa). Memoir of Rev. Mother Mary Teresa Comerford, founder of the Convent of the Presentation Order of the Pacific Coast. 120 pp., 8vo, cloth. San Francisco, 1882. $15.00

Mother Mary Teresa arrived in San Francisco in 1854 and opened a school.

461 [CALIFORNIA.] The Last of the California Rangers. By Jill L. Batt-Cossley 299 pp,, 12mo, cloth N. Y., 1928. $3.50

462 [CALIFORNIA.] (Crane, Lauren E.). Newton Booth of California. 521 pp., 8vo, cloth. N. Y., 1894. $4.50

463 [CALIFORNIA.] (Cutts, James Madison). The Conquest of California and New Mexico, by the Forces of the U. S. in the Years 1846 and 1847. With engravings, Plans of battle, etc. 12mo, cloth. Phila., 1847. $22.50

464 [CALIFORNIA.] (Denison, E. S.). Pacific Coast Souvenir. 12 pp., 48 plates Roy. 8vo. Oakland, (1888). $3.50

465 [CALIFORNIA]. (Duboc, G.) Les Nuees Magellaniques. [Two Parts in one volume] Part 1: Voyage au Chili, au Perou et en California. Part 2: Le Requin ou le Mer du Sud. 8vo, calf. Paris, 1853. $22.50

Not in Sabin. Describes a voyage to California in 1835.

466 [CALIFORNIA.] (Dunbar, Edward E.) The Romance of the Age, or the Discovery of Gold in California. Portrait and Illus. 12mo, cloth (name stamp on title). 134 pp. New York, 1867. $5.00

DWINELLE'S HISTORY OF SAN FRANCISCO

467 [CALIFORNIA.] (Dwinelle, John W.). The Colonial History of the City of San Francisco; being a Narrative Argument in the Circuit Court of the U. S. for the State of California for four square leagues of land claimed by that city and confirmed to it by the Court. Third Edition. 8vo, orig. half mor., San Francisco; Town and Bacon, 1866. $120.00

Contains three views and two maps. A superb copy carefully collated and found complete. This is of excessive rarity and one of the high spots of California. Only 200 copies were printed, the "first" edition was a court brief. See Cowan, p. 75: "This work contains a large number of documents, most of which are now either inaccessible or destroyed."

468 [CALIFORNIA.] (Evans, Col. Albert S.). A La California. Sketches of Life in the Golden Gate. Illus. 8vo, cloth. San Francisco, 1873. $8.50

Cowan p. 80: "A very entertaining book. Some of the chapters are 'In the Mists of the Pacific', 'In the Streets of San Francisco', 'Around the Mountain Camp-Fire', 'The Chinese Feast of the Dead', and 'Early Times'. As the preface states, it embodies in a permanent and attractive form much that would otherwise have perished from sight and memory.' "

469 [CALIFORNIA.] (Farwell, Williard B.) The Chinese at Home and Abroad. Together with the Report of the Special Committee of the Board of Supervisors of San Francisco on the condition of the Chinese Quarters, of that City. 118 pp., folding map, 8vo, cloth. San Francisco, 1885. $12.50

Cowan: "Farwell's report contains vivid and extensive descriptions of the objectionable features of these sections in San Francisco and Sacramento'.'

470 [CALIFORNIA.] (Farnham, Eliza W.) California, In-doors and Out; or how we Farm, and Live in the Golden State. 12mo, cloth, 508 pp. N. Y., 1856. $5.00

Contains an original narrative of the Donner Party, gathered from several individuals of both sexes who were members of the unfortunate expedition; the Vigilance Committee of 1856, etc.

471 [CALIFORNIA.] The Transformation of Job. A Tale of the High Sierras. By Frederick Vining Fisher. Illus. 4to, boards. Chicago, 1900. $1,25

472 [CALIFORNIA.] (Fitzgerald, O. P.) California Sketches. 207 pp., cloth. Nashville, 1899. $4.75

The author was in California in 1855.

473 [CALIFORNIA.] (Ferguson, Chas. D.) The Experience of a Forty-Niner during Thirty-Four Years' Residence in California and Australia. Edited by Frederick T. Wallace. Port., illus. 8vo, cloth, 507 pp. Cleveland, 1888. $5.00

Story of the overland route, massacres, mining, etc.

474 [CALIFORNIA.] (Frizell, L.). Across the Plains to California in 1852. illus, maps. 8vo, wrappers. N. Y., 1915. $4.00

475 [CALIFORNIA.] (Foote, P. J.) Some Historical Notes of Men and Events that led to the Return of the Jesuits to California. 17 pp., 8vo, wrappers. San Francisco, N. d. $5.00

This work covers the activities of the Jesuits in Oregon also, as their return to California, after an absence of 75 years, was by the way of Oregon. The author was attached to St. Ignatius College of San Francisco.

476 [CALIFORNIA.] (Forbes, Alex.) California: A History of Upper and Lower California from their first Discovery to the Present Time, comprising an Account of the Climate, Soil, Natural Productions, Agriculture, Commerce, &c. 8vo, original cloth, map and plates. London, 1893. $17.50

Original Edition, presentation copy from William Forbes (son of the author). *This copy is defective in that it has one map and two plates missing, hence the price.*

477 [CALIFORNIA.] Geological Survey of California Botany. 2 vols, 8vo, cloth. Cambridge, 1880. $15.00

Scarce. Some slight stains in Vol. 1.

480 [CALIFORNIA.] (Gerstacker, Frederich). Reisen: (1) Sudamerika (2) California. 2 vols., 12mo, original half binding. Stuttgart, 1853. $17.50

Original Edition. Relates to California in 1849, San Francisco, Mission Dolores, Sacramento City, etc. The entire second volume relates to California. Cowan does not mention this work.

481 [CALIFORNIA.] (Gorley, H. A.) Selections from the Numerous Letters and Patriotic Speeches of my Husband. 134 pp., 8vo, cloth. San Francisco, 1876. $10.00

Scarce. Relates to California in the 50's and 60's to Oregon and the Whitman Massacre.

UNRECORDED CALIFORNIA GUIDE

482 [CALIFORNIA GUIDE.] California, en Skildring af Landet, dess Klimat, och Guildminor. Map of the gold regions of California, dated 1850, and plate of miners washing gold. 12mo, printed wrappers; entirely uncut. In a cloth case. Stockholm, 1850. $22.50

Braislin 297. Very Scarce. Unknown to Cowan and other bibliographers. The unknown author traversed California in 1846 and later met Dr. Marsh, Messrs. Livermore, Sutter and others.

483 [CALIFORNIA.] (Harrison, E. S.). Monterey County, its General Features, Resources, Attractions and Inducements to Investors and Homeseekers. 38 pp., illus., map. Small 4to, mor. San Francisco, N. d. $9.00

484 [CALIFORNIA.] California Immigration Union. All About California. 82 pp., 8vo, original wrappers. San Francisco, 1871. $5.00

485 [CALIFORNIA.] Incidents on Land and Water; or Four Years on the Pacific Coast. 336 pp., illus. 12mo, cloth. Boston, 1858. $5.00

California mining, gambling, society life, etc.

THE FOUNDATION VOLUME OF CALIFORNIA'S TERRITORIAL AND STATE HISTORY

486 [CALIFORNIA.] Journal of the Senate of the State of California; at their First Session begun and held at Puebla de San Jose, on the Fifteenth Day of December, 1849. 570 pp. 8vo, original half sheep and boards. San Jose; J. Winchester, Printer, 1850 (and also bound with the above) Journal of the Proceedings of the House of Assembly of the State of California; at its First Session begun and held at San Jose, etc. 777 pp. (the pagination continuous from Senate Journal). 8vo. San Jose: J. Winchester, 1850. $45.00

An absolutely complete copy, including both indices, and the "Appendix Reports of Committees, Executive Documents, Communications, and other Papers." It contains every official, executive and departmental action of every sort, out of which grew the organization of California, together with all the debates, petitions, discussions and votes leading to and determining those actions. For an account of the strange and unpleasant conditions under which this historic session was held, and of its troubles and circumstances, see Bancroft, Vol. 7, pp. 608-36.

487 [CALIFORNIA.] Journal of the Senate [and House of Assembly] of California at their Sixth Session, held at Sacramento. 8vo, sheep. (worn). Sacramento, 1855. $10.00

488 [CALIFORNIA.] Journal of the House of Assembly (and Senate Appendix) of California at their Seventh Session held at Sacramento, 1855. 8vo, sheep (worn). Sacramento, 1855. $10.00

489 [CALIFORNIA.] The Appendix of the Senate of California for the Eighth Session held at Sacramento, 1856, together with the Appendix of the House of Assembly, 1857. 8vo, sheep (worn). Sacramento, 1856-57. $7.50

490 [CALIFORNIA.] Appendix to the Senate of California at its Ninth Session held at Sacramento, 1858, together with the Appendix of the House of Assembly, 1857. 8vo, sheep (worn). Sacramento, 1857. $7.50

491 [CALIFORNIA.] Journal of the Senate of California at its Tenth Session held at Sacramento, 1859, together with the House Appendix, 1859. 8vo, sheep, (worn). Sacramento, 1859. $7.50

492 [CALIFORNIA.] Appendix of the Senate of California at its Eleventh Session held at Sacramento (San Francisco), 1860, together with the House Appendix for 1860, 8vo, sheep (worn). Sacramento, 1860. $7.50

493 [CALIFORNIA.] Journal of the House of Assembly of California at their Sixteenth Session held at Sacramento, 1866. 8vo, sheep (worn). Sacramento, 1866. $7.50

494 [CALIFORNIA.] Journal of the Senate of California at their Seventeenth Session held at Sacramento, (with the Appendix), 1868. 8vo, sheep (worn). Sacramento, 1868. $7.50

495 [CALIFORNIA.] Journal of the House of Assembly of California at their Eighteenth Session held at Sacramento, 1870, together with the Senate and House Appendix, 1870, 8vo, sheep (worn). Sacramento, 1870. $7.50

496 [CALIFORNIA.] Los Angeles Then and Now. By Atchison and Eshelman. Illus., 200 pp., 12mo, cloth. Los Angeles, 1897. $1.00

497 [CALIFORNIA.] In and About Los Angeles. full-page illus. Album, original wrappers, N. p., 1906. $1.00

498 [CALIFORNIA] La Riena. Los Angeles in Three Centuries. 108 pp., illus, ports. 8vo, wrappers. Los Angeles, 1929. $1.00

499 [CALIFORNIA.] (Mast, Isaac.) The Gun, Rod and Saddle; or Nine Months in California. Frontis. 278 pp. 12mo, cloth. Phila., 1875. $5.00

500 [CALIFORNIA.] Monterey and its Environs. With a Brief History, Legends, Views of the Past and Present. Maps. Small oblong 4to, original pictorial wrappers. Monterey, 1913. $1.50

501 [CALIFORNIA.] Who Made Oakland. By Florence B. Crocker. Illus. 8vo, stiff wrappers, 158 pp. Oakland, 1925. $1.00

502 [CALIFORNIA.] Papers of the California Society. Vol 1, Part 1 and 2, 2 vols. 4to, wrappers. San Francisco, 1887. $12.50

Part I contains "The first phase of the Conquest of California" by Wm. Carey Jones; the Local Units of History by Martin Kellogg, and other papers. Part II contains "A History of the College of "California" by Samuel H. Willey.

503 [CALIFORNIA.] The California Pilgrim, a series of Lectures. 261 pp., 8vo, cloth. Sacramento, 1853. $15.00

"Written in the form of an allegory, giving many details of California life. The author, a clergyman, was the founder of the Congregational Church in California, having arrived in 1849; the plates (six in number) are apparently of the earlier works of Charles Nahl, afterwards famous"—Cowan.

504 [CALIFORNIA.] California Pioneers. Constitution, bylaws and list of Members of the Society of California. 91 pp., 8vo, cloth. San Francisco, 1881. $3.00

505 [CALIFORNIA.] (Powers, Stephen.) Afoot and Alone; a Walk from Sea to Sea by the Southern Route. Adventures and Observations in Southern California, New Mexico, Arizona, Texas, etc. Illus. with numerous engravings. 8vo, cloth. Hartford, 1884. $10.00

Original Edition. Paullin 417. A scarce splendidly written and intensely interesting narrative. Powers made his journey of 5000 miles from Charleston to San Francisco in 1868.

506 [CALIFORNIA.] Ranch Life in California. Extracted from the Home Correspondence of E. M. H. 171 pp., 8vo, cloth. London, 1886. $7.50

507 [CALIFORNIA.] (Revere, Lieut. J. W.) Tour of Duty in California; including a Description of the Gold Region; and an Account of the Voyage around Cape Horn; with notice of the Principal Events attending the Conquest of California. Folding Map and Plates. 305 pp. 12mo, cloth. New York, 1849. $15.00

Original Edition. The author, grandson of Paul Revere, wrote here, according to Cowan "one of the most valuable works of the period."

508 [CALIFORNIA.] Mission Santa Barbara. Early Days in Alta California. Illus.. 32 pp. Small 4to, original wrappers. Santa Barbara, 1917. $1.00

509 [CALIFORNIA.] San Diego. A Comprehensive Plan for its Improvement. By John Nolen. Numerous illus. 8vo, original printed boards. Boston, 1908. $1.50

510 [CALIFORNIA.] Charter of the City of San Diego, adopted March 16, 1889. 121 pp., 8vo, cloth. San Diego, 1923. $1.00

511 [CALIFORNIA.] San Diego. A Brief History, 1542-1888. Illus. 12mo, wrappers. San Diego, 1929. $1.00

512 [CALIFORNIA.] San Diego County. Report of Research Studies. . . . 1935-37. Folio, wrappers. Los Angeles, 1937. $1.00

513 [CALIFORNIA.] History of the Rancheros. of San Diego County. Illus. 8vo, original wrappers. San Diego, 1939. $1.25

514 [CALIFORNIA.] The Story of Water in San Diego. By H. Austin Adams. Ports., illus. Roy. 8vo, wrappers. Chula Vista, Calif., N. d. $1.00

515 [CALIFORNIA.] Men and Memories of San Francisco in the "Spring of '50." 12mo, cloth. San Francisco, 1873. $10.00

516 [CALIFORNIA.] The City that Was. A Requiem of old San Francisco. By Will Irwin. 12mo, boards. N. Y., 1908. $1.00

517 [CALIFORNIA.] The Story of Mission San Luis Obispo de Tolosa in the Valley of the Bears. By Grace Therese Mitchell. 16 pp., illus. 8vo, wrappers. N. p, N. d. $1.00

518 [CALIFORNIA.] The Miracle Missions. By Vernon J. Selfridge. Illus. album, original wrappers. Los Angeles, 1915. $1.00

519 [CALIFORNIA.] (Zoeth Skinner.) The Beginnings of San Francisco from the Expedition of Anaz, 1774, to the City Charter of April 15, 1850. 2 vols, 8vo, cloth. San Francisco, 1912. $5.00

520 [CALIFORNIA.] The Tahquitch Maiden. A Tale of the San Jacintos. By Phebe Estelle Spalding. Illus. 26 pp., 12mo, boards. San Francisco, 1911. $1.00

521 [CALIFORNIA.] (Ella Sterling.) The Story of the Files. A Review of California Writers and Literature. Numerous portraits. 8vo, boards. San Francisco, 1893. $6.00

A history of the beginning and development of various western periodicals, the early press, etc.; with intimate particulars of the old-time writers that cannot be secured in any other form.

522 [CALIFORNIA.] The Vigilance Committee of 1856. By a Pioneer California Journalist. 12mo, 57 pp. Original printed wrappers. San Francisco: James H. Barry, 1887. $3.50

The anonymous pamphlet declaring that the Vigilantes Committee contained criminal characters similar to those hanged, and that among the rank and file there were "scores of scoundrels of every degree." Full of the frankest historical relations.

523 [CALIFORNIA AND OREGON.] James Clyman, American Frontiersman, 1792-1881. The Adventures of a Trapper and Covered Wagon Emigrant as told in his own Reminiscences and Diaries. Edited by Charles L. Camp. Portrait, 4to cloth, mint in d. w. San Francisco, 1928. $15.00

An original narrative of remarkable adventures in the early Rocky Mountain Fur Trade, Black Hawk War, California and the Oregon Trail in the 40's, and the Gold Rush, Clyman, a Virginian by birth, an early pioneer of Danville, Illinois, was one of Ashley's pathfinders, one of those indomnitable heroes who have not yet received their proper important place in American history. Jim Clyman, Edward Rose, Jedediah Smith, Jim Bridger, Hugh Glass, Thomas Fitzpatrick, W. L. Soublette—pathfinders, all of them. Clyman's is one of the best diaries relating to the opening of the West, and the California Historical Society and Mr. Camp are to be commended for making it available. Clyman's father was a tenant of George Washington.

524 CALKINS, FRANK W. Indian Tales; Frontier Sketches; Hunting Stories. Illus. 3 vols in one, 8vo, cloth. Chicago, N. d. $7.50

Now quite scarce. Authentic memoirs of wild adventures in the early days on the border.

525 CAMPBELL, ARCHIBALD. A Voyage Round the World from 1806 to 1812; In which Japan, Kamtschatka, the Aleutian Islands, and the Sandwich Islands were visited. Including a Narrative of the Author's shipwreck on the ship's Long Boat. With an Account of the Present State of the Sandwich Islands, and a Vocabulary of their language. 8vo, half calf, complete with Map. Edinburgh, 1861. $27.50

The whole of this interesting work relates to the Northwest coast of America and the Sandwich Islands. The author was shipwrecked on a reef to the southwest of Sannack or Halibut Islands. He gives an account of the country and natives of that part of the Northwest Coast, and also of the natives of the Sandwich Islands, and a vocabulary of their language. The work was edited by James Smith of Jordanhill.

526 CAMPBELL, JOHN. The Origins of the Haidahs of Queen Charlotte Islands. 112 pp., 8vo, original wrappers. Ottowa, 1897. $5.00

Smith 581. A signed presentation copy.

527 CAMPBELL, J. F. My Circulat Notes; Extracts from Journals, Letters sent home, Genealogical and other Notes, written while travelling round the World. Illus. 2 vols in one, 8vo, cloth, uncut. London, 1876. $7.50

First hand chats about things seen in California and Oregon.

528 CAMPBELL, ROBERT. Journal of Robert Campbell, 1801-1851. Typewritten manuscript of 99 pp. Sm. 4to, cloth. N. p., N. d. $75.00

Very important unpublished journal. Campbell entered the service of the Hudson's Bay Company, arriving at Ft. Garry, Sept., 1830. In 1832 he made a trip to Kentucky for sheep, which were driven overland to the Red River. Also in 1832 he went to York Factory and was there appointed to the Mackenzie River district, arriving at Ft. Simpson, Oct., 1834. He discovered the Upper Stikine in 1837, and also discovered the Upper Yukon or Pelly River in 1840. He was appointed Chief Factor in the Hudson Bay Co. This is one of the most interesting as well as historically important journals ever written by any fur trader. Publishing rights included.

529 CAMERON, CHARLOTTE. A Cheechako in Alaska and Yukon, 292 pp., map, illus. 8vo, cloth. London, 1920. $5.00

Contains a great amount of valuable information relating to Alaska and the Klondike. Scarce.

530 [CARSON, Kit.] (Camp, Chas L.) Kit Carson in California, Extracts from his Own Story. Port. 8vo, original wrappers. San Francisco, 1922. $3.75

531 [CANADIAN PACIFIC ROAD.] Description of the Country between Lake Superior and the Pacific Ocean, on the line of the Canadian Pacific Railway. 143 pp., 8vo. Ottawa, 1876. $5.00

Not in Smith.

532 [CANADIAN PACIFIC ROAD.] (Chapleau. l'Hon. M.) Discours de l'Hon. N. Chapleau sur les Resolutions du Chemin de Fer Canadian Pacifique. 68 pp. 8vo, original wrappers. Ottawa, 1885. $4.75

533 [CANADIAN PACIFIC ROAD.] The New Highway to the Orient across the Mountains, Prairies and Rivers of Canada. 48 pp., illus. 8vo, wrappers. N. p., N. d. (May, 1901). $3.75

Not in Smith.

534 [CANADA.] Report of the Delegates Appointed to Negotiate for the Acquisition of Ruperts Land and the North-West Territory. Laid before Parliament by Command of His Excellency the Governor General. 40 pp., 8vo. Ottawa, 1868. $17.50

535 [CANADA.] Report of the Select Committee of the Senate on the Subject of Rupert's Land, Red River and North-West Territories, together with the Minutes of Evidence. 38 pp., 8vo, sewn. Ottawa, 1870. $15.00

Important document relating to the Hudson's Bay Co., containing much original testimony.

536 [CANADA.] Notes sur le Canada. 129 pp., folding map. 8vo, cloth. Paris, 1878. $2.50

537 [CANADA.] The New West. Extending from the Great Lakes across the Plains and Mountains to the Golden Shores of the Pacific. Wealth and Growth, Manufacturing and Commercial Interests. Historical Statistical, Biographical, Illus, maps. 8vo, original wrappers. Winnepeg, 1882. $12.50

Rare. Many folding plates of towns and settlements in the country described. Not in Smith.

538 [CANADA.] (Carling, John) Canada: Its History, Productions and Natural Resources. 160 pp., folding map. 8vo, cloth. Ottawa, 1886. $3.75

539 [CANADA.] (Carrel, Frank). Canada's West and Farther West Illus. 8vo, cloth. Toronto, 1911. $3.50

540 CANE, COL. C. Summer and Fall in Western Alaska: the Record of a Trip to Cook's Inlet after Big Game. Illus. 8vo, cloth. London, 1903. $5.00

Seattle to Cook's Inlet, at Kenai and Kusseloff, Lake Tustamena, Nikolai Creek, etc.

541 [CANESTRELLI, PHILIP.] Catechism of Christian Doctrine prepared and enjoined by Order of the Third Plenary Council of Baltimore. Translated into Flathead by a Father of the Society of Jesus. 102 pp., 8vo. Woodstock College (Md.), 1891. $17.50

Not in Smith.

542 CANFIELD, C. L. The Diary of a Forty-Niner. Map, 231 pp., 8vo, original pictorial boards. San Francisco, 1906. $12.50

Original Edition, of which nearly all copies were destroyed in the great fire.

543 CANFIELD, CHAUNCEY. The City of Six. Illus. 12mo, boards, 366 pp. Chicago, 1910. $5.00

The author was general agent for the Pacific Coast for one of the largest railway systems in the west.

CANFIELD'S NORTHERN PACIFIC REPORT

544 CANFIELD, THOMAS L. Northern Pacific Railroad Partial Report to the Board of Directors, of the Reconnoissance made in the Summer of 1896, between Lake Superior and the Pacific Ocean. Accompanied with Notes on Puget Sound, by Samuel Wilkcson. Two large Folding Maps. For Private Circulation Only. 96 and 44 pp. 8vo, sewed, in cloth slip-case. N. p., 1870. $60.00

Excessively rare. The inside history of the Northern Pacific Railroad's delicate operations and negotiations, and embodies "Facts which ought not in the present state of the company's affairs to go to the public, but which at the same time should be known to the Directors, before they take action in respect to commencing operations upon the western portion of the line."

545 CANNON, M. Wailptu: Its Rise and Fall, 1836-1847. A Narrative of Pioneer Days in the Pacific Northwest. (Incidents of the Trail); Life among the Cayuse Indians; the two score women and girls and their treatment at the hands of the Savage Indians). Portraits and Plates. 171 pp., 8vo, original wrappers. Boise: Privately printed, 1915. $5.00

546 CANNON, FRANK J. AND KNAPP, GEO. L. Brigham Young and his Mormon Empire. 398 pp., illus. 8vo, cloth. Chicago, (1913). $3.00

547 CANTWELL, JOHN C. Report on the Operations of the U. S. Revenue Steamer Nunivak on the Yukon River Station, Alaska, 1888-1901. 325 pp., illus. 8vo. Washington, 1904. $3.75

548 CARDINELL, CHARLES. Adventures on the Plains. 8vo, cloth. San Francisco, 1922. $5.00

549 CARMICHAEL, ALFRED. Indian Legends of Vancouver Island. 97 pp., illus. 8vo, cloth. Toronto (c1922). $2.00

550 CARR, JOHN. Pioneer Days in California: Historical and Personal Sketches. (Narrative of the author's trip from Illinois arross the plains through Utah and Wyoming to California in 1850. With Reminiscences of life at the Mines, Pioneer Politics, Manners and Customs). Embracing many Facts never before given to the Public. Portrait. 452 pp., 8vo, cloth. Eureka, Times Print, 1891. $25.00

Original Edition. Cowan, p. 41: "In addition to the interesting narrative of this pioneer, his work contains valuable material concerning the biographies of many of the early Californians."

551 CARRINGTON, FRANCES C. My Army Life and Fort Phil. Kearney Massacre, with an Account of the Celebration of "Wyoming Opened." Maps and Illus. 8vo, cloth. Phila., 1910. $5.00

Mrs. Carrington went to Fort Phil Kearney in 1865 as the bride of Lieut. Grummond and was at the Fort when Major Fetterman's command was ambushed almost within sight of the fort. Both her husband and Fetterman were killed. This is a fine account of the frontier posts.

552 CARRINGTON, GENERAL H. B. The Indian Question. An Address. Map and Illus. 8vo, cloth. Boston, 1909. $10.00

Delivered before the Geographical and Biological Sections of the British Ass'n for the Advancement of Science, 1875. Supplemental to the address are: Official report of the Ft. Phil Kearney Massacre; Itinerary of the expedition of 1866 to open a wagon road to Montana.

553 CARTER, GEN. W. H. Old Army Sketches. 203 pp., 8vo, cloth. Baltimore, 1906. $5.00

554 [CARTHAGENA.] An Account of the Expedition to, with Explanatory Notes and Observations. 8vo, new calf-backed boards. London, 1743 $10.00

The first account of the celebrated siege of the French Fleet by Admiral Sir Charles Knowles on the mainland coast off the Caribbean in which Americans formed a large part of the expeditionary force. Rare.

555 CARVALHO, S. N. Incidents of Travel and Adventure in the Far west . . . 380 pp., illus. 12mo, cloth. N. Y., 1858. $5.00

FOUNDATION OF WISCONSIN AND MINNESOTA HISTORY

556 CARVER, JONATHAN. Travels through the Interior Parts of North America in the Years 1766-1767 and 1768. With 2 folding maps and 5 plates. Large paper copy. 8vo, old tree calf. London: Printed for the Author, 1778. $27.50

Carver originated the word "Oregon," reference to which may be found on page 9 of preface and page 542 of text. Fine tall copy of the Original Edition.

CASSIN'S "CALIFORNIA BIRDS" BEAUTIFULLY COLORED

557 CASSIN, J. Illustrations of the Birds of California, Texas, Oregon, British and Russian America. Containing Descriptions and Figures of all North American Birds not given by Former American Authors, and a General Synopsis of North American Ornithology. Illustrated with 50 beautiful full-page colored Plates. Large 8vo, handsomely bound in ¾ morocco, gilt panelled back, gold border, gilt top. Choice copy. Scarce. 1862 $50,00

This beautiful work is practically a supplement of Anderson's great work as it contains all the birds not mentioned in that famous work.

558 CASTLE, HENRY A. The Army Mule and other War Sketches. 269 pp., illus. 8vo, cloth, Indianapolis, 1898. $3.50

559 CATALDO, JOSEPH—S. J. Kuailks Metatcopun. Being a series of Interviews with Father Cataldo, S. J., last Surviving Member of the Original Jesuit Missionaries to the Indians of the Northwest. By Lawrence T. Crosby. Port and Plate. 16 pp., 4to, original wrappers. Wallace, 1925. $10.00

Apostle to the Coeur d'Alene, Spokane and Nez Perce Indians before the coming of the white men, Father Cataldo traversed the trails and camped on the sites of the Coeux d'Alenes district long before the diggings were discovered. These are his recollections of the early days; the Indians; gold rush days; Indian wars; etc.

560 CATALDO, JOSEPH—S. J. Lu Tel Kaimin tis Kolinzuten-Kuitlt Smiimii. Some Narratives from the Holy Bible in Kalispel. Complied by the Missionaries of the Society of Jesus. 140 pp., 8vo, original printed wrappers. St. Ignatius Print, Montana, 1879. $35.00

No other copy has been reported.

561 CATALDO, JOSEPH—S. J. Paradigma Verbi Activi. Lingua Numipu. Vulgo Nez-Perce. Missionarium S. J. in Monitibus Sexosis pro eorumdem privato usu. Typis Missionis SS. Cordis Indus Convictoribus Collaborantibus. 56 pp. 8vo. Desmet, Idaho, 1888. $25.00

Excessively rare. No other copy can be found in any bibliography consulted. The work was printed for private use of the Jesuit Fathers upon their own mission press.

562 CATALDO, JOSEPH—S. J. Gramatica Linguae Numipu Actore Presbytero Missionario E. Soc. Jesu in Montibus Sexosis. Typsis Puerorum Indorum. Desmet, Idaho, 1891. Second Title: A Numipu or Nez-Perce Grammar by a Missionary of the Society of Jesus in the Rocky Mountains. 255 pp., 8vo, cloth. Indian Boy's Press. Desmet, Idaho, 1891. $50.00

Smith 621 locates but one copy, that in the Library of the University of Washington.

563 CATALDO, JOSEPH—S. J. Prayers Catechism Hymns in Numipu Language (Nez Perce) for the use of St. Joseph's Mission, S. J. in Oregon and Idaho. 48 pp., 8vo, cloth. Pendleton, Ore., 1909. $17.50

No copy recorded in bibliographies consulted.

564 CATALDO, JOSEPH M. Jesus-Christ-Nim Kinne uetas-pa kut Ka-Kala Time-Nin I-Ues Piles-Eza-Pa Taz-pa Tamtai-pa Numipu-Timt-Ki. 1914. (The Life of Jesus Christ from the Four Gospels in the Nez Perces language by J. M. Cataldo, S. J. 386 pp., 8vo, cloth. Portland, Ore. (c1915). $10.00

Not mentioned by Smith or other bibliographies consulted.

565 [CATHOLIC CHURCH.] Progress of the Catholic Church in America and the Great Catholic Congress of 1893. 2 vols. in one. 8vo, cloth, illus. Chicago, N. d. $7.50

565a [CATHOLIC CHURCH.] (Liturgy and Ritual). A.M.D.G. Canotle Rannaga Kelekak Delochet Roka. Permissu Superiorum. 54 pp. 8vo. Winnipeg, 1904. $7.50
North America. [Text and 31 colored plates.] Folio, full morocco. Lon-

Wickersham, No. 1043.

566 [CATHOLIC CHURCH.] "Good Tidings"—A Monthly Periodical Devoted to giving valuable Information on Catholic Faith and Practice, and well Adapted for Sunday Reading, especially in Sections of the Country seldom Visited by a Priest. Vol. 1, January, 1906 through Vol. 6, Dec., 1911. 8vo, cloth. Ferndale, (Wash.,) 1906-1911. $30.00

Very scarce and important work, which contains, among other material, Brouillet's account of the Whitman Massacre and Blanchet's History of the Catholic Church in Oregon.

567 [CATHOLIC MISSIONS.] Circular of the Catholic Commissioner for Indian Missions to the Catholics of America. 14 pp., wrappers. Baltimore, 1874. $7.50

568 [CATHOLIC MISSIONS.] Kiahlik Iksa Nana-Aiyimmika I Katikisma. 200 pp., 8vo, cloth. Washington, D. C., N. d. $4.75

A catechism of the Catholic Religion published by the Catholic Indian Mission and translated into the Choctaw language.

569 CATLIN, GEORGE. Last Rambles Amongst the Indians of the Rocky Mountains. 361 pp., illus. 8vo, cloth. London, 1868. $7.50

570 CATLIN, GEORGE. Letters and Notes on the Manners, Customs and Condition of the North American Indians. Plates and maps. 2 vols, 8vo, original cloth, paper labels, errata slip. London, 1841. $15.00

Wagner-Camp 84. Loosely inserted is the rare "Folium Reservatum" (description of the Buffalo Dances).

570a [CATLIN'S NORTH AMERICAN INDIAN PORTFOLIO.] Hunting scenes and Amusements of the Rocky Mountains and Prairies of America. From Drawings and Notes of the Author, Made During Eight Years' Travel amongst Forty-eight of the Wildest and Most Remote Tribes of Savages in North America. [Text and 25 colored plates.] Folio, half morocco. London, 1844. $175.00

One of the most famous of all color-plate works on the American Indian, with all the 31 plates. It was also published with the plates uncolored. The illustrations portray aboriginal hunters, tribal dances and sports, and types of costume and character. Humboldt called Catlin "One of the most admirable observers of manners who ever lived among the aborigines of America."

571 CATON, JOHN D. Origin of the Praries. 30 pp., 8vo, wrappers. Ottawa, Illinois, 1869. $7.50

A scarce work by the well-known authority on the American deer and antelope and other wild life of the plains.

572 CATON, JOHN D. The Antelope and Deer of America. A comprehensive scientific treatise upon the natural history, including the characteristics, habits, affinities, and capacity for domestication of. Front., illus. 8vo, cloth. N. Y., 1877. $9.00

Braislin 524.

573 CATTERMOLE, E. G. Famous Frontiersmen, Pioneers and Scouts. illus. 8vo, cloth. Chicago, 1883. $4.50

574 CAWSTON, GEO. AND KEANE, A. H. The Early Chartered Companies (A. D. L296-1858). Front. 8vo, cloth. London, 1896. $7.50

Contains a long account of the Hudson's Bay Co., the Virginia and New England Companies, Massachusetts Bay Co., the Georgia Charter, and the London Company (originally called the South Virginia Company). Smith 638.

575 [CENTRAL PACIFIC RAILROAD.] The Central Pacific Railroad across the Continent, with an Account of the Central Pacific Railroad of California, a Description of the Route, the Progress and Character of the Work. 31 pp., 8vo, wrappers. N. Y., 1868. $6.00

576 [CHAMBERLAIN, E. J.] In the Beginning: Old Williamette Days. Portrait and Plates, including that of the first house built in Salem. 38 pp., 12mo, original printed wrappers. (Salem, 1905). $15.00

A scarce privately printed work is an autographed presentation copy "from the grand-daughter and only direct descendant of Jason Lee."

577 CHAMPNESS, W. To Cariboo and Back; Journey to the Gold-Fields in British Columbia. Map and 13 views from sketches made on the journey. 4to, boards. London, 1865. $7.50

An important narrative by a participant in the Cariboo gold rush of 1862. Contained in five numbers of "The Leisure Hour." The journal extends to no less than twenty chapters and was "prepared for publication from rough notes and sketches sent from Victoria, B. C." Eight of these views were reproduced in Scholefield and Howay's "History of British Columbia."

578 CHAPLIN, RALPH. The Centralia [Wash.] Conspiracy. 80 pp., 8vo, cloth. Seattle, N. d. $5.00

UNCUT COPY OF CHAPPELL'S HUDSON BAY

579 CHAPPELL, LIEUT. EDWARD. Narrative of a Voyage to Hudson's Bay in His Majesty's Ship Rosamund, containing some Account of the Northeastern Coast of America and of the Tribes inhabiting that remote Region. Map, 4 plates and vignettes. 8vo, calf. London, 1817. $17.50

Braislin 373. The large folding map shows the Great Nelson River from Lake Winnipeg to Cull Lake with all the portages, falls and rapids. The work also contains a minute description of the Esquimaux, Mountaineer and Micmacs of Labrador and the Red Indians of Newfoundland. There is a Cree vocabulary in the index.

580 CHAPMAN, W. O. Diary of an Amateur Explorer in Glacier National Park. 31 pp., illus, 8vo. wrappers. N. p. 1911. $2.75

Fur trade and the Hudsons Bay Co.

581 CHARLEVOIX, P. F. X., de. Journal of a Voyage to North America, undertaken by Order of the French King, containing the Geographical Description and Natural History of that Country, particularly Canada. Together with an Account of the Customs, Characters, Religion, Manners and Traditions of the Original Inhabitants. Folding Map. 2 vols, calf. London, 1761. $45.00

The Original Edition in English. The author, member of the Society of Jesus, visited North America in 1705 and again in 1720 during which he made a sort of grand tour, going up the St. Lawrence, through the Lakes and down the Mississippi to New Orleans, collecting material for the best contemporary account of the country.

582 CHASE, S. P. Relations between the U. S. and Northwest British America, embracing the Report of J. W. Taylor, Special Agent on the Red River of the North and the Saskatchewan; (2) Memoir of Northwest British America and its Relations to the U. S. from 1822 to 1861; (3) Physical Geography of the Regions; (4) History and Organization of the Hudson's Bay Co.; (5) Selkirk Settlement; (6) The Gold Discoveries; (7) Letters of Mactavish, etc. Large folding map. 8vo, cloth. Washington, 1862. $15.00

583 CHATEAUBRIAND, LE VICOMTE DE. Les Natchez. Suivis de la Description du Pays des Natchez. 446 pp., front. 8vo, cloth. Paris, 1864. $4.75

584 CHENEY, W. D. Central Oregon. 149 pp., 8vo, cloth. (Seattle), 1918. $3.00

585 [CHEYENNE MASSACRE.] (Chivington, Col. J. M.) Massacre of the Cheyenne Indians: An Inquiry into all Facts connected with the attack of the Colorado volunteers under Col. Chivington on the Cheyenne Indians near Fort Rounds. 108 pp. 8vo, boards. Washington, 1865 $12.50

The Committee was convened to investigate all the matters connected with the action between Col. Chivington and the Cheyenne Indians, known as the Sand Creek, or Chivington Massacre; and to ascertain who were the aggressors; whether the campaign was conducted by Chivington according to the recognized rules of civilized warfare; and whether or not it was forced upon the Indians by the whites. The investigation was virtually a court-martial of Chivington and Governor Evans and reveals in detail the acts of cruelty, barbarity and murder perpetrated upon the body of unoffending Indians by a gang of "beings in the form of men disgracing the uniform of the United States soldiers and officers." The proclamation and testimony of Evans; the official reports and examination of Chivington and other officers engaged in the bloody affair; as well as copies of documents in the War Department in relation thereto, together with Editorial articles and narratives from the Rocky Mountain News in defense of the butchery are all reproduced verbatim. See Field "Indian Bibliography."

586 [CHICAGO RECORD.] Klondike. The Chicago Record's Book for Gold Seekers. 555 pp., illus, maps. 8vo, cloth. Chicago (1897). $5.00

587 [CHICAGO AND NORTHWESTERN RAILROAD.] A History of the Origin of the Place Names connected with the Chicago and Northwest and Chicago, St. Paul, Minneapolis and Omaha Railways. 201 pp., map. 8vo, cloth. Chicago, 1908. $5.00

588 [CHICAGO AND NORTHWESTERN RAILROAD.] Yesterday and Today. A History. 124 pp., map. 8vo, cloth. Chicago, 1910. $5.00

EARLY "CHINOOK JARGON" IN WRAPPERS

589 [CHINOOK JARGON.] Vocabulary of the complete language used by the Indians of Oregon, Washington Territory and British Possessions. 8 pp., original wrappers. Published by Nutchings and Rosenfeld. San Francisco, 1860. $25.00

590 [CHINOOK JARGON.] A Dictionary of the Chinook Jargon or Indian Trade Language of the North Pacific Coast. 29 pp., original wrappers. Victoria: Hibben and Co., (1871). $20.00

Smith does not seem to report a copy in the Northwest libraries. According to Pilling this was printed in 1871.

591 CHIROUSE, EUGENE CASIMIR.] The Indian Sentinel. Chirouse Number, Vol. 1, No. 7, Jan. 1918. 48 pp., illus. By Charles Buchanan and others. Bureau of Catholic Indian Missions. Washington, 1918. $5.00

Chirouse, born in the Province of Dauphine, France, in 1821, became missionary to the Yakima Indians of the Pacific Northwest in 1848 and remained among them until 1856. He was then transferred to the Mission of Puget Sound, with headquarters at Olympia, where he served the Tulalip, Lummi, Swinomish, Ft. Madison and Muckleshoot Indians. He died in the Northwest in 1892, after having exercised a great influence over the Northwest tribes.

592 CHITTENDEN, NEWTON H. Settlers, Prospectors and Tourists Guide, or Travels through British Columbia. 8vo, original printed wrappers. Victoria, 1882. $15.00

The only copy located seems to be that in the University of Washington Library. The work describes the Salmon fisheries, building of the railroad through the Cascades, the Fraser River District, etc.

592a CHORIS (M. LOUIS). Voyage Pittoresque autour du Monde, avec des Portraits de Sauvages d'Amerique, d'Asie, d'Afrique, et des Isles du Grand Ocean, des Paysages, des vues Maritimes et plusieurs objects d'Histoire Naturelle; accompagne de Descriptions par M. le Baron Cuvier, et M. A. de Chamisso, et d'Observations sur les Cranes Humaine par M. le Docteur Gall. With Portraits, Maps, Colored Plates of natives, birds, animals, utensils, scenes of native life, &c. Folio, half calf. Paris, 1822-1826. $150.00

Extremely Rare. This is an account of an Independent voyage to the North Pacific of Lieut. Otto von Kotzebue made in the years 1815-18, Choris accompanying the expedition as an artist. There is a section of fourteen plates taken while staying at the port of San Francisco, including the view of the Presidio and dance of the inhabitants of California, both of which are in color. The above work contains 128 plates, all colored, and 3 maps. The work also contains the later work by Choris, "Vues et Paysages des Regions Equinoviales recuilles dans Voyage Autour du Monde," published in 1826, with plates in color. Because of a printer's error this was listed at $85.00 in our catalogue 14; it obviously should have been $185.00. We have herewith reduced the price.

CHRISTY'S "VOYAGES IN SEARCH OF N. W. PASSAGE"

593 CHRISTY, MILLER. Voyages of Luke Foxe of Hull and Captain James of Bristol, in Search of the Northwest Passage, in 1631-32, with Narratives of the Earlier Northwest Voyages of Frobisher, Davis, Weymouth, Hall, Knight, etc. Edited with Notes and an Introduction by Christy Miller. With folding maps and other illustrations. 2 vols, 8vo, cloth, uncut. London, 1844. $17.50

594 CHRISTY, MILLER. The Silver Map of the World's Contemporary Medallion commemorative of Drake's great voyage (1577-80). A Geographical Essay including some critical remarks on the Zeno Narrative and Chart of 1558, and on the curious misconception as to the position of the Discoveries made by Martin Frobisher in 1576-7-8, which crept into the Cartography of the North Atlantic &c. 8vo, cloth, uncut, maps. London, 1900. $7.50

Mr. Christy's work as Editor of the Hakluyt Society Series is the well-known authority on early voyages. His Zeno and Frobisher arguments are admirably illustrated by a facsimile of the actual chart of the Frobisher first voyage in 1576, the original of which is preserved in the library of the Marquis of Salisbury.

595 [CHURCH MISSIONARY SOCIETY.] The British Columbia Mission. 8vo, boards. London, 1905. $3.00

596 [CHURCH MISSIONARY SOCIETY.] Six Lessons on Missions in Alaska. 12 pp., original wrappers. Hartford: C. M. Pub. Co., 1907. $3.25

597 [CHURCH MISSIONARY SOCIETY.] Outline Histories of the Church Missionary Society Missions. 159 pp., 8vo, cloth. London, 1907. $5.00

598 [CHURCH MISSIONARY SOCIETY.] The Northwest Canada Missions. 79 pp., 8vo, boards. London, 1910. $3.25

599 [CHURCH MISSIONARY SOCIETY.] The Mission among the Eskimo. 20 pp., 8vo, boards. N. d., London. $3.25

600 CLAMPITT, J. W. Echoes from the Rocky Mountains; Reminiscences and Thrilling Incidents of the Golden Age and Settlement of the West. 8vo, original cloth, port, and plates. Chicago, 1888. Original Edition. $7.50

601—SAME. 8vo, orig. cloth. Chicago, 1890. $3.50

602 CLARKE, JOHN A. Gleanings by the Way. 352 pp., 12mo, half calf. N. Y., 1842. $12.50

Journal of a tour in the Mississippi Valley with a voyage up the Ohio to Illinois and Iowa; adventures on the plains crossing Michigan; and observations made west of Mississippi in 1837.

603 CLARK, JOSEPH BOURNE. Leavening the Nation; the Story of American Home Missions. 362 pp., port., map, tables. 8vo, cloth. N. Y. (1908) $350

Relates to the Pacific Northwest, Oregon and Washington.

604 CLARK, JOSEPH G. Lights and Shadows of a Sailor's Life, including the more thrilling events of the U. S. Exploring Expedition (including California and Northwest Coast). 5 fine woodcut plates. 12mo, cloth. Boston, 1847. $17.50

Fine copy of the scarce Original Edition, of which there seems to be no copy in the Northwest Coast libaries, Smith mentioning none, though locating 3 copies of the next (1848) edition.

605 —— Same. 12mo, half morocco. Boston, 1848. $12.50

606 CLARK, ADELE. Old Montreal. John Clarke: His Adventures, Friends and Family. By his Daughter, Adele Clarke of Westmount. 47 pp., illus., 4to, cloth. Montreal, 1906. $27.50

Rare. John Clarke was a partner of John Jacob Astor in the Astoria adventure, arriving there on the ship "Beaver." As the book was privately printed the work is already difficult to find. Smith does not seem to have located a copy.

607 CLARKE, S. A. Pioneer Days of Oregon History. Ports. and illus. 2 vols., 8vo, cloth. Portland, 1905. $7.50

The most interesting history of Oregon is that of the Provisional Government, when the pioneers, having in vain appealed to the general government to recognize Oregon as part of the national domain, met and organized a Provisional Government. Under it they not only enacted necessary laws but urged war against hostile Indians. The above work is an important contribution to this period.

608 CLAY, JOHN. My Life on the Range. With 17 plates. 8vo, cloth, uncut. Chicago, 1924. $25.00

Fine copy of the rare Original Edition of one of the best histories of the cattle ranges ever published. It contains a vast amount of information nowhere else obtainable.

609 CLEVELAND, RICHARD J. Voyage of a Merchant Navigator of the Days of the Past; compiled from (his) Journals and Letters. Port. 12mo, cloth. N. Y., 1886. $7.50

The above work is entirely different from the author's celebrated "Narrative of Voyages and Commercial Enterprises," as it contains reminiscences, letters, etc.

610 CODMAN, JOHN. Round Trip by way of Panama, through California, Oregon, Nevada, Utah, Idaho and Colorado with notes on Railroads, Commerce, Agriculture, Mining, Scenery and People. 331 pp., 8vo, cloth. N. Y., 1879. $3.75

611 COFFIN, CHARLES CARLETON. The Seat of Empire. 232 pp., 5 plates, large map, 12mo, cloth. Boston, 1870. $7.50

Relates to the Overland, the Northwest, Montana, Idaho, Oregon, etc. Unusual to find a copy with the map, as above.

612 COFFIN, CHARLES CARLETON. The Great Commercial Prize. 8vo, original printed wrappers (stained). Boston, 1858. $17.50

An account of Puget Sound, Fraser River, Oregon; exposes attempt of Britain to gain control of the Northwest and makes an impassioned appeal for all to "wake up!" Smith 730 locates one copy.

613 COLE, GILBERT L. In the Early Days along the Overland Trail in Nebraska Territory in 1852. Port. 12mo, cloth. Kansas City, Mo.: F. Hudson Pub. Co. (1905). $10.00

Rare, privately printed narrative of early overland pioneers. The expedition was headed by W. W. Wadsworth (Marshall of Placerville), which left Monroe, Michigan, and crossed the plains to Hangtown in 5 months. A carefully written narrative by an argonaut who took the time and trouble to make accurate notes along the way.

614 COLLINS, HUBERT E. The War Path and Cattle Trail. 296 pp., illus., 8vo, cloth. N. Y., 1928. $3.75

Ranch life, Cheyennes, Araphoes, Indian Territory.

COLNETT'S WHALING VOYAGE TO THE COAST OF OREGON AND CALIFORNIA, 1789

615 COLNETT (CAPT.) JAMES. A Voyage to the South Atlantic and Round Cape Horn into the Pacific Ccean, for the purpose of extending the Spermaceti Whale Fisheries, and other objects of Commerce, by Ascertaining the Ports, Bays, Harbors and Anchoring Births in Certain Islands and Coasts in those Seas. 3 full-page plates, including one of the whale, and 6 large folding maps. 179 pp. 4to, cloth. London, 1798. $85.00

For an extended account of this important work see Bancroft's "Northwest Coast," vol. 1, pp. 210-23. One of the chief results of the voyage was the Nootka Controversy, Colnett arrived at this place in 1789 and represented to the Spanish Commander, Martinez, "that he had come under authority of the King of England with orders to take possession of Nootka, construct a fort, establish a factory and plant a colony." The Spaniards resisted, Martinez informing him that he had already taken formal possession of the country for Spain. There followed an interview which waxed so exceedingly hot that both commanders forgot the exigencies of the situation and permitted something of the truth to escape them. The English, being sadly outnumbered, Colnett was arrested, his ship and cargo seized, himself placed in the stocks, his officers imprisoned and his crew put in arms. They were then transported to San Blas, where they were plundered of all they had, several dying of fever and one committing suicide. Colnett alleges he was the victim of the most inhuman treatment—"was carried from ship to ship like a criminal, frequently threatened with death by hanging as a pirate on the yardarm," etc. As may be imagined, the affair developed into a most dangerous situation, and relations between England and Spain were seriously strained. Through the negotiations of powerful diplomats war was narrowly averted, which, had it occurred, would in all probability have involved the United States, since the Americans were suspected of having instigated the seizure; Kendrick and Gray (discoverer of the Columbia River) were known to be on terms of close intimacy with Martinez.

616 [COLORADO.] (Greatorex, Eliza). Summer Etchings in Colorado. Introduction by Grace Greenwood. Royal 8vo, cloth. N. Y. (1873). $4.50

617 [COLTER, JOHN.] Discoverer of Yellowstone Park. An Account of His Exploration in 1807 and of His Further Adventures as Hunter, Trapper, Indian Fighter; Pathfinder and Member of Lewis and Clark Expedition. By Stallo Vinton. Royal 8vo, boards, large paper edition. N. Y., 1926. $17.50

618 COLQUHOUN, ARCHIBALD R. The Mastery of the Pacific. 440 pp., 41 plates, 2 maps. 8vo, cloth. N. Y., 1902. $4.75

619 COLTON, J. CALVIN. Colton's Guide. The Western Tourist and Emigrant's Guide through the States of Ohio, Michigan, Indiana, Illinois, Missouri, Iowa and Wisconsin, and the Territories of Minnesota, Missouri and Nebraska. Folding map. 16mo, cloth. N. Y., 1852. $8.50

620 COLVILLE, FREDERICK VERON. Botany of the Death Valley Expedition. Contributions of the U. S. National Herbarium, Vol. 4. 318 pp., plates, folding map. Royal 8vo. Washington, 1893. $7.50

621 COLVOCORESSES, LIEUT. G. M. Four Years in a Government Exploring Expedition to the Northwest Coast, Oregon and California. Plates. 371 pp. 12mo, cloth. N. Y., 1852. $12.50

Original Edition. The journal of an officer in Wilkes' Expedition, and one of the only sources for the overland trip through Oregon and California in 1841. Colvocoresses left the main party at Vancouver (Sept. 2, 1841) in company with Lieut. Emmons and a party of 37 others on an overland expedition to Alta California. Under dated entries he describes in detail the trip across the mountains; natural curiosities, Indian tribes; Sutter's Fort; San Francisco, etc. Other chapters are devoted to the Bear Flag Revolution, the Conquest of California, the Gold Discovery and affairs immediately thereafter.

622 COLYER, VINCENT. Bombardment of Wrangel, Alaska. Report of the Secretary of War, Secretary of Interior and a Letter to the President. 23 pp., 8vo, original wrappers. Washington, 1870. $12.50

Original Edition of an exceedingly scarce item in wrappers relating to the troubles in Alaska. Smith locates one copy.

623 COMAN, KATHERINE. The Industrial History of the U. S. 461 pp., 8vo, cloth. N. Y., 1910. $7.50

624 COMAN, KATHERINE. Economic Beginnings of the Far West. 2 vols., 8vo, cloth. N. Y., 1912. $7.50

625 COMAN, KATHERINE. Economic Beginnings of the War West. How we won the land beyond the Mississippi. 2 vols., 8vo, cloth, illus. N. Y., 1921. $7.50

626 [CONFERENCE OF WESTERN GOVERNORS.] Proceedings of the Conference held at Salt Lake City, Utah, June 5, 6, 7, 1913. 119 pp., cloth. Denver, 1913. $4.00

627 —— Same. Held at Seattle, May 18-19-20, 1915, and at Portland, Ore., Sept. 22, 1915. 97 pp., 8vo, cloth. Olympia, 1915. $4.00

628 [CONGRESSIONAL GLOBE AND APPENDIX.] 25th Cong., 3rd Sess., Vol. 7. 4to, cloth. Washington, 1839. $7.50

Contains the memorial of J. L. Whitcomb, and 35 other citizens of Oregon, dated March 16, 1838, asking the U. S. Government to take formal possession of the country. Also has first printing of a bill to provide for protection of citizens of the U. S. residing on the Columbia.

629 [CONGRESSIONAL GLOBE AND APPENDIX.] 2nd Sess., 26th Congress, Vol. 9. 4to, cloth. Washington, 1841. $6.00

Relates to Oregon and other western states.

630 [CONGRESSIONAL GLOBE AND APPENDIX.] 1st Sess., 27th Congress, Vol. 10. 4to, cloth. Washington, 1841. $6.00

631 [CONGRESSIONAL GLOBE AND APPENDIX.] 3rd Sess., 27th Congress, Vol. 12. 4to, cloth. Washington, 1843. $15.00

Contains material relating to the occupation of Oregon Territory; resolutions of the various state governors, and 71 speeches on the Oregon Question.

632 [CONGRESSIONAL GLOBE AND APPENDIX.] New Series containing Sketches of Debates and Proceedings at the First Session of the 29th Congress. 4to, cloth. Washington, 1846. $12.50

Contains an immense amount of valuable material on the Oregon country.

633 [CONGRESSIONAL GLOBE AND APPENDIX.] New Series, containing Sketches of Debates and Proceedings of the 2nd Session of the 29th Congress. 4to, cloth. Washington, 1847. $12.50

This and the preceding volume contain much material relating not only to the Oregon Territory but to California and Texas.

634 CONKEY, W. B. Official Guide to the Klondike Country and the Gold Fields of Alaska, with the Official Maps, Vivid Descriptions and Thrilling Experiences; the most complete and thoroughly exhaustive Collection of every known information necessary to a full realization of the immense Resources of the Gold Fields of Alaska . . . 296 pp., illus., maps., 12mo, cloth. Chicago: Conkey Co., 1897. $8.50

Smith seems to locate but one copy, that in the Provincial Library of British Columbia.

635 [CONNECTICUT.] Baker, Henry A. History of Montville, Conn., formerly the north parish of New London from 1640 to 1896. Illus. 8vo, cloth. Hartford, 1896. $7.50

636 [CONSTITUTION (THE).] Secret Proceedings and Debates of the Convention assembled at Philadelphia in the Year 1787 for the Purpose of forming the Constitution of the U. S. A. From Notes by Robert Yates, Chief Justice of New York and copies by John Lansing. 8vo, contemporary calf. Albany: Webster and Skinner, 1821. $7.50

Original Edition. Braislin 462. The appendix contains historical documents by Randolph Pinckney, A. Hamilton, the draft of a constitution submitted Aug. 6, and the constitution as amended and adopted; amendments thereto and list of members of the Federal Convention. At the end is a short sketch of Chief Justice Yates.

637 COOK, JAMES. Fifty Years on the Old Frontier, as Cowboy, Guide, Scout and Ranchman. Intro. by Gen. Charles King. Port. and 45 plates. 8vo, cloth. New Haven, 1923. $4.00

638 COOK, JOHN R. The Border and the Buffalo. An Untold Story of the Southwest Plains. Portrait and plates. 8vo, cloth. Topeka, 1907. $5.00

Braislin 472. Reminiscences of an old plainsman and hunter; fights with Kiowas, Commanches and Staked Plain Apaches in 1877, etc.

639 COOLEY, HARRIS REED. The First White Woman to Cross the Rocky Mountains. The Diary Kept by One of Them. (In Magazine of Western History, Sept., 1890). 8vo, wrappers. 1890. $3.00

DR. COOMBS'S RARE "CHINOOK DICTIONARY"

640 COOMBS, S. F. Dictionary of the Chinook Jargon as spoken on Puget Sound and the Northwest, with Original Indian Names for Prominent Places and Localities, with their Meetings, Historical Sketch, etc. 8vo, original printed wrappers. Lowman and Hanford Stationery and Printing Company, Seattle, Wash., 1891. $75.00

Smith 961 is only able to locate the copy in the Portland Library. Although printed about 40 years ago, copies are exceedingly hard to locate, as it stated that almost the entire edition was destroyed in the great Seattle fire. The cover title of this work reads: "Chinook Dictionary and Original Indian Names of Western Washington." (Picture). Mr. Coombs was a well-known authority on the history of the Northwest.

641 CORNEY, PETER. Voyages in the North Pacific: The Narrative of Several Trading Voyages from 1813 to 1818, between the Northwest Coast, the Hawaiian Islands and China, with a Description of the Russian Establishments on the Northwest Coast. Interesting Account of Kamehameha's Realm: Manners and Customs of the People, etc. And Sketch of a Cruise in the Service of the Independents of South America in 1819. With Preface and Appendix of valuable confirmatory Letters prepared by W. D. Alexander. 12mo, original wrappers. 138 pp. Honolulu: Thos. G. Thrum, 1896. $15.00

Valuable contribution to the history of California and the N. W. Coast. In particular it throws much light on the proceedings of the Russians from 1815 to 1817, and is one of the narratives by an eye-witness of the burning of Monterey. It even escaped Bancroft and Greenhow.

642 CORNWALLIS, KINAHAN. New Eldorado; or, British Columbia. Plate and map. 8vo, half morocco. London, 1858. $35.00

Rush from California to the Diggings; historical sketches; Indian life; future of British Columbia; scenery; life in the mines; ascent of the Fraser River. Apparently only two copies have been reported of this rare work.

643 COSTELLO, J. A. The Siwash, their Life, Legends and Tales; Puget Sound and Pacific Northwest. 169 pp., illus., 8vo, cloth. Seattle, 1895. $7.50

643a COTTERILL, GEORGE F. The Climax of a World Quest. The Story of Puget Sound, the Modern Mediterranean of the Pacific. Illus. 8vo, cloth, mint in dust wrappers. Seattle (1927). $2.50

Mr. Cotterill, former Mayor of Seattle and President of the Seattle Port Commission, arrived in the Northwest in the early 80's.

644 COUES, ELLIOT. Description of the original manuscript journals and Field Note Books of Lewis and Clark, etc. American Philosophical Society. 8vo, cloth. Phila., 1893. $3.50

645 COUES, ELLIOT. Journal of Jacob Fowler; Narrative of an Adventure from Arkansas through the Indian Territory, Oklahoma, Kansas, Colorado, and New Mexico, to the Sources of the Rio Grande del Norte, 1821-1822. Illus., 8vo, cloth. N. Y., 1898. $4.50

646 COUES, ELLIOT. Birds of the Northwest: a Hand-Book of American Ornithology. 791 pp. 8vo, cloth. Boston, 1877. $7.50

647 COUTANT, C. G. History of Wyoming and the Far West, embracing an Account of the Spanish, Canadian and American Explorations; the Experience and Adventures of Trappers and Traders in the Early Days; including Events of the Oregon Migration, the Mormon Movement and Settlements, the Indian Tribes and Manners and Customs, and their Wars and Depredations on the Overland Trail, etc., interspersed with Personal Reminiscences of Pioneers. 8vo, half mor. 2 maps and 76 plates, fine copy. Laramie, 1899. $10.00

647a COWIE, ISAAC. The Company of Adventurers. A Narrative of Seven Years in the Service of the Hudson's Bay Company, during 1867-74. On the Great Buffalo Plains, with Historical and Biographical Notes. 515 pp. 8vo, cloth., illus. Toronto, 1913. $12.50

648 COX, ROSS. Adventures on the Columbia River, including the Narrative of a Residence of Six Years in the Western Side of the Rocky Mountains. 2 vols., half calf. London: Colburn, 1831. $35.00

Braislin 498. The scarce Original Edition of a valuable work depicting Indian life, manners and customs, hardships of a western trader's life. Cox sailed in the Astor ship "The Beaver" and remained with the company on the Columbia until its dissolution, when he joined the English Northwest Fur Company, afterwards crossing the continent to Fort William.

649 —— Same. 8vo, original cloth, paper label, uncut. N. Y., 1832. $15.00

650 CRAIG, NEVILLE. Washington's First Campaign, Death of Jumonville and the Taking of Fort Necessary; also Braddock's Defeat . . . Folding map, illus. 8vo, original printed wrappers, entirely uncut. Pittsburgh, 1848. $17.50

Excessively rare in the state as above described.

651 CRAPO, THOMAS. Strange, but True. Life and Adventures of Captain Crapo and Wife. 151 pp., illus., 8vo. New Bedford, 1893. $7.50

Crapo was cabin boy on the "Marcie," commanded by Captain Billings, sailing from New Bedford for the North Pacific Ocean, where they arrived in 1858. A scarce privately printed narrative.

652 CRAWFORD, C. H. Scenes of Earlier Days in Crossing the Plains to Oregon and Experiences of Western Life. With portrait and plates. 12mo, original cloth. Petaluma, 1898. $27.50

Western Americana 323: "A rare narrative crudely printed and in a home-made original binding of equally "local quality." The personal narrative of an Argonaut of 1851 who traveled to Oregon and California, with details of adventures on the plains and among the Indians; the massacre of all but two of the wagon train; the Powder River Mines; outlawry, murder and wild times among the miners.

653 CRAWFORD, LEWIS F. Badlands and Broncho Trails. 114 pp., illus. 8vo, cloth. Bismarck, c. 1922. $3.50

654 CRAWFORD, LEWIS F. The Medora-Deadwood Stage Line. 17 pp., illus., 8vo, wrappers. Bismarck, 1925. $3.50

An interesting history of the stage route to the Black Hills.

655 CRAWFORD, LEWIS F. Rekindling Camp Fires. The Exploits of Ben Arnold Connor (Wa-si-cu-Tam-a-he-ca). An Authentic Narrative of Sixty Years in the Old West as Indian Righter, Gold Miner, Cowboy, Hunter and Army Scout. Map and port. 324 pp., 8vo, cloth. Bismarck, 1926. $4.75

History with the bark on.

656 CRAWFORD, LEWIS F. Idyl to Sentinel Butte. 8vo, cloth. N. p., n. d. (Sentinel Butte, N.D.). $2.50

Interesting historical description of Sentinel Butte.

657 CRAWFORD, LUCY. The History of the White Mountains, From the First Settlement of Upper Coos and Pequket. By Lucy, wife of Ethan Allen Crawford, Esq. 16mo, cloth (backstrip a little worn). White Hills, 1846. $17.50

Despite the wear on the backstrip, this is a good copy of a work that is scarce in any condition.

658 CRAWFORD, MEDOREM. Journal of the Expedition organized for the Protection of Emigrants to Oregon, under the Command of Medorem Crawford. 8vo, sewn. [Washington, 1863.] $37.50

Braislin 515. Original Edition. A copy in the Library Association of Portland and another in the Library of the University of Washington are the only copies known to Smith. Wagner-Camp 386 gives a summary of the day-by-day itinerary of this expedition from Ft. Lincoln, Neb., to Walla Walla. This is the only diary of the first large emigrant train to Washington.

659 CREMONY, JOHN C. Life Among the Apaches. 322 pp., 12mo, cloth. San Francisco, 1868. $17.50

Original Edition. Cremony was Bartlett's interpreter from 1849 to 1851, and Major of the California Cavalry operating in Arizona, New Mexico and Texas. His work to the present day remains one of the best upon the Apache and his aboriginal neighbors.

660 CROASDALE, HENRY E. Scenes on Pacific Shores with a Trip Across South America. 173 pp., plate., 8vo, cloth. London, 1873. $6.50

Relates to Vancouver's Island, British Columbia and the State of Washington.

661 CROSBY, THOMAS. Among the An-ko-me-nums; or, Flathead Tribes of Indians of the Pacific Coast. 243 pp., front., illus. 8vo, cloth. Toronto, 1907. $10.00

Original Edition of a scarce work on the various Indian tribes of the Northwest by a Methodist Missionary.

662 CROSBY, THOMAS. Up and Down the North Pacific Coast by Canoe and Mission Ship. 403 pp., illus. 8vo, cloth. Toronto, 1914. $5.00

Crosby was a Methodist missionary for fifty years on the Northwest coast.

663 CUMING, F. Sketches of a Tour to the Western Country, through Ohio, Kentucky, Mississippi and West Florida; with a Notice of an Expedition through Louisiana. 12mo, calf. Pittsburgh, 1810. $27.50

Original Edition. Thomson, No. 236: "One of the most interesting works relating to the West. A good, sound copy.

664 [CUSTER, GEN. A. GEORGE.] The Boy General. Story of the Life of Major-General George A. Custer. By Mary E. Burt. 8vo, cloth. N. Y., 1901. $3.50

CUTLER'S "TOPOGRAPHICAL DESCRIPTION," INCLUDING LE RAYE'S JOURNAL OF TRAVELS, 1801-5

665 CUTLER, JERVAISE. A Topographical Description of Ohio, Indiana and Louisiana. With an Account of the Indian Tribes west of the Mississippi, and the Interesting Journal of Mr. Charles LeRaye, while a Captive with the Sioux Nation. Complete with the 5 plates, including the first engraved view of Cincinnati. 12mo, calf. Boston, 1812. $75.00

Original Edition. Braislin 540. A good, sound copy of an important and valuable relation, being the earliest authentic relation of a captivity among the Sioux. There is a small library stamp on the title of this copy.

666 [DAKOTA.] (Carr, Robert). Black Hills Ballads. 175 pp., 8vo, cloth. Denver, 1922. $3.75

667 [DAKOTA.] (Coursey, O. W.). Beautiful Black Hills. A Comprehensive Treatise on the Black Hills of South Dakota. 8vo, cloth. Mitchell, S. D. (c. 1926). $3.00

668 [DAKOTA.] General Laws and Memorials and Resolutions of the Territory of Dakota, passed at the First Session of the Legislative Assembly. 561 pp., errata slip. Also bound in is the Private Laws. 31 pp., with errata. 8vo, sheep. Yankton, 1862. $12.50

669 [DAKOTA.] Standing Rules for the Government of the Legislative Assembly of Dakota: To which are Appended a List of the Members and Officers of both Houses, Lists of Committees and the Organic Act. First Session. 31 pp., 8vo, sewn. Yankton, 1863. $10.00

670 [DAKOTA.] History of Southeastern Dakota; its Settlement and Growth, Geological and Physical features, Counties, Cities, Towns and Villages, Incidents of Pioneer Life, Biographical Sketches of the Pioneers, with a Brief Outline of the History of the Territory in General. 8vo, cloth. Sioux City, 1881. $15.00

671 DALE, H. C. The Ashley Smith Explorations. 8vo, original cloth. Fine copy. 8vo, cloth, map and plates. Cleveland, 1918. $30.00

672 DALL, WM. H. Remains of later Pre-Historic Man obtained from caves in the Catherina Archipelego, Alaska Territory, and especially from the caves of the Aleutian Island. Illus., 40 pp. (Smithsonian Contributions to Knowledge, No. 318). Washington, 1878. $7.50

Smith 885.

673 DALL, WM. H. Alaska and its Resources. Map and numerous illus. Royal 8vo, cloth. 639 pp. Boston, 1897. $7.50

One of the best histories of Alaska. With a chronological list of expeditions, 1542-1867; travels on the Yukon; aboriginal inhabitants; list of works on Alaska, etc.

674 DALRYMPLE, ALEXANDER. Voyages dans la mer du Sud, par les Espagnols et les Hollandois. Trad. de l'Anglois par Freville. Avec 3 cartes. 8vo, calf. Paris, 1774. $27.50

675 DALRYMPLE, ALEXANDER. Plan for Promoting the Fur Trade and securing it to this country by uniting the operations of the East-India and Hudson's Bay Companies. 32 pp. 8vo. George Bigg, London, 1789. $20.00

A photostatic facsimile of this rare work of which but two copies are known. This contains extracts from Capt. Hanna's log, who visited the Northwest coast in the "Sea Otter" in 1786, and is nowhere else available.

676 DALRYMPLE, ALEXANDER. (a) Plan of Port San Diego, on the west coast of California, 1782. These plates were taken from Spanish Manuscripts communicated by John Henry Knox, Esq., to whom this plate is inscribed by his most obliged Dalrymple, 1786. (b) Fanya or Fango(?). Plan of Monterey in California by Don Josef Tobar y Tamariz. 7th Dec. 1786. By a Spanish Manuscript received from Dr. Robertson. The north is misplaced in this plan. (c) Plan of the Road Principe in the Channel of Santa Barbara. By Josef Tobar y Tamariz, 1786. Three plans on one plate (8½ by 11½ in.). Dalrymple, London, Jan. 7, 1789. $125.00

The above maps or plans were the first published in relation to the various places mentioned and are of the greatest rarity.

677 DALRYMPLE, ALEXANDER. Plan of San Francisco, on the Northwest coast of California. From a Spanish Manuscript communicated by John Henry Knox, Esq., to whom this plate is inscribed by his most obliged Dalrymple. (11½ by 18 in.). Dalrymple, London, Jan. 17, 1789. $100.00

678 DALRYMPLE, ALEXANDER. Sketch of Ahouset. By Capt. Duncan, Master in the Royal Navy, 1788. Dalrymple, London, Dec. 17, 1789. $40.00

679 DALRYMPLE, ALEXANDER. Plan of Calamity Harbour. By James Johnstone, a Master in the Royal Navy, 1787. (9½ by 20 in.). Dalrymple, London, Oct. 23, 1789. $35.00

680 DALRYMPLE, ALEXANDER. Plan of the Inlet of Bucareli, Latitude 55, 19′ N. Longitude 27, 9′ West from Cape San Lucar. Discovered in 1775 with the Sonora, by Don Juan Franco de la Quadra and Don Franco Anto Mourelle, and minutely examined in the expedition of 1789 by the same and other Officers. From a Spanish manuscript communicated by John Henry Knox, Esq., to whom this Plate is inscribed by his most obliged Dalrymple. 12 by 12 inches. Dalrymple, London, Jan. 17, 1789. $50.00

681 DALRYMPLE, ALEXANDER. (a) Plan of St. Patrick's Bay. By Capt. James Hanna, 1786. (b) Chart of part of Northwest Coast. By Capt. James Hanna, in "Snow Otter,' 1786. (c) Track of the Snow Experiment in company with the Capt. Cook. By S. Wedhbrough. All on one sheet (11¼ by 12½ in.). Dalrymple, London, March 19, 1789. $65.00

DALRYMPLE'S RARE SEPARATE CHARTS OF THE NORTHWEST COAST

682 DALRYMPLE, ALEXANDER. Sketch of the Entrance of the Strait of Juan de Fuca. By Charles Duncan, Master of the Royal Navy, Aug. 15, 1788. Plate showing entrance, with a map. 11¾ by 12 inches. Dalrymple, London, Jan. 14, 1790. $125.00

683 DALRYMPLE, ALEXANDER. Plan of Snug Harbor Cove in Prince William Sound. 8½ by 11½ inches. Dalrymple, London, March 24, 1789. $40.00

684 DALRYMPLE, ALEXANDER. Milbank's Sound. By Charles Duncan, Master of the Royal Navy, 1788. 6½ by 11 inches. Dalrymple, London, Dec. 24, 1789. $40.00

685 DAMON, S. C. "The Friend." The following volumes: Vol. 2 (unbound); Vol. 3, 1845 (boards); Vol. 4, 1846 (unbound); Vol. 5, 1847 (unbound); Vol. 6, 1847 (unbound); Vol. 8, 1850 (unbound. 4to, Honolulu, Oahu, H. I. V.d. (1844, 1845, 1846, 1847, 1848, 1850). Six years. $100.00

DAMON'S OREGON AND CALIFORNIA NARRATIVE, 1849

686 DAMON, S. C. A Trip from the Sandwich Islands to Lower Oregon and Upper California, 1848-1849. 56 pp., 4to, boards. Honolulu, Oahu, H. I. Printed at the Polynesia Office, 1849. $90.00

Original Edition of the earliest work printed in the Sandwich Islands on Oregon and California. The author was editor of the "Friend," but discontinued its publication to turn explorer and to verify the accounts of the new settlements in Oregon and California. A fine copy.

687 DAMPIER, CAPT. WILLIAM. Voyages: A complete collection of all his Voyages, edited by John Masefield. Handsomely printed in large antique type by Ballantyne with all the rare and curious folded maps and plates carefully reproduced, and photogravure portrait. 2 vols., 8vo, gilt. London, 1906. $37.50

Printed in an edition of 1000 copies and now long out of print. The volumes contain the complete unabridged account of all Dampier's voyages, including a life of Dampier by Masefield.

688 DANA, C. M. The Great West; or, Garden of the World: Its History, Wealth, Natural Advantages and Future, with complete Guide to Emigrants and Description of different Routes Westward, etc. 12mo, cloth. 396 pp. Boston, 1857. $7.50

A good copy of a scarce book. Ohio, Indiana, Illinois, Michigan, Wisconsin, Iowa, Missouri, etc.

689 DANA, JAMES D. Corals and Coral Islands. Illus. 398 pp., 8vo, cloth. N. Y., 1872. $8.50

Dana was a member of Wilkes' Expedition and in the wreck of the Peacock at the mouth of the Columbia.

690 DANA, JOHN COTTON. The Far Northwest. Illus. (65 full-page plates). Large 8vo, original wrappers. Newark, 1906. $7.50

EARLY 18th CENTURY MAP OF THE NORTHWEST

691 DANET, GUILE. Map: l'Amerique Meridonale et Septentrionale. (19 by 27 inches). Paris, 1731. $15.00

Shows the west coast of North America as far north as Detroit du Nord.

692 DANIELS, JOSEPH. Iron and Steel Manufacture in Washington, California and Utah. 8vo, original printed wrappers (Bulletin Univ. of Washington, Eng. Exp. Station, Report No. 2, 69 pp.). Seattle, 1929. $2.00

693 DAVENPORT, HOMER. The Country Boy, the Story of his Own Life. 191 pp. Embellished with 62 illus. made from his original drawings. Port. 8vo, cloth. N. Y. (c. 1910). $7.50

Davenport was a native of Oregon and in the above work he recounts his life and experiences in Oregon during pioneer days.

694 DAVENPORT, M. Under the Gridiron. A Summer in the United States and the Far West. 143 pp., 8vo, cloth. London, 1876. $5.00

695 DAVIDSON, GEORGE. The Alaskan Boundary. 235 pp., maps, ports. 8vo. San Francisco, 1903. $7.50

Author's presentation copy. Small portion of front wrapper damaged.

696 DAVIDSON, GEORGE. Identification of Sir Francis Drake's Anchorage on the coast of California in the Year 1579. 58 pp. 12 folding maps. San Francisco, 1890. $17.50

697 DAVIDSON, GEORGE. Methods and Results; Voyages of Discovery and Exploration on the Northwest Coast of America from 1539 to 1603. Appendix No. 7. Maps, original wrappers. Washington, 1887. $12.50

698 DAVIDSON, GEORGE. Pacific Coast Pilot of California, Oregon and Washington. Plates, maps, charts. 4to, cloth (entirely rewritten). Washington, 1889. $10.00

699 DAVIDSON, GEORGE. The name "Mt. Ranier." (Reprinted from the Sierra Club Bulletin, No. 35). 8vo, oiginal wrappers. Jan., 1907. $3.00

700 DAVIS, ANDREW McFARLAND. The Journey of Moncacht-Ape, an Indian of the Yazoo Tribe across the continent about the year 1700. 30 pp. Original Wrappers. Worcester, Mass., 1883. $22.50

In the "Histoire de la Louisane par Le Page du Pratz," v. 3, page 87 et seq., is recorded the story of Moncact-Ape's journey across the continent to the Pacific Northwest. The above is a study as to the probable truth of the narrative and it concludes with the thought that "there is nothing in the story to tax our credulity." True or false, the narrative is the first of an overland trip to the Oregon country. Author's presentation copy. Not in Smith.

701 DAVIS, GEO. T. B. Metlakahtla. A True Narrative of the Red Man. 128 pp., illus. 12 mo, cloth. Chicago, 1904. $4.50

Scarce. Not in Smith.

702 DAVIS, LEWIS. The Life of Rev. Daniel Edwards, D.D., late Bishop of the United Brethren of Christ. 322 pp. 8vo, cloth. Dayton, Ohio, 1883. $12.50

Pacific Coast, California, Oregon and the Cascade Conference.

703 [DAVYDOV, G. L.] Davydov and Khostov. Dvukratnoe Puteshestvie v. Ameriku Morskikh Ofitserov Kvostova i Davydova, Pisannoe sim Posliedmom. 2 vols, 12mo, 287 and 234 pp. St Petersburg, 1810-12. $90.00

An account of two voyages to America by these two naval officers. Description of Alaska, Aleutian Islands, Tlingit Indians, languages, glossary, vocabularies. Lib. of Cong. 1-21786. Wickersham 6152. Bancroft, vol. 33, p. 458.

704 DAWSON, GEO. M. Report on the Queen Charlotte Island, 1878. Published by Authority of Parliament. 239 pp., 14 plates, 2 maps. 8vo, cloth. Montreal, (Dawson) 1880. $13.50

Now very scarce.

705 DAWSON, GEO. M. Report on an Exploration from Fort Simpson on the Pacific Coast to Edmonton on the Saskatchewan, embracing a portion of the northern part of British Columbia and the Peace River country, 1879. 177 pp., 7 plates. 8vo, original wrappers, 1881. $10.00

The volume also contains many other items on the Northwest.

706 DAWSON, GEO. M. The Mineral Wealth of British Columbia, with an annotated list of local metals of economic value. 163 pp. 8vo, original wrappers. Montreal, 1888. $7.50

707 DAWSON, GEO. M. Notes on the Shuswap people of British Columbia. 44 pp., illus, map (Royal Society of Canada Transactions, v. 5, section 2, 1887). 8vo, original wrappers. Montreal, 1887. $4.00

708 DAWSON, GEO. M. Notes and Observations on the Kwakiool people of Vancouver Island and the adjacent coasts, made during the summer of 1885, with a vocabulary of about 700 words. 8vo. Montreal (Dawson), 1888. $6.00

709 DAWSON, GEO. M. Report on an Exploration in the Yukon District, N. W. T. and adjacent northern portion of British Columbia, 1887. Published by Authority of Parliament. 277 p. front., illus, map. 8vo, original wrappers. Montreal (Dawson), 1888. $4.50

DAWSON'S "BIRDS OF WASHINGTON"

710 DAWSON, WILLIAM LEON, AND BOWLES, J. H. The Birds of Washington; a complete Scientific and Popular Account of the 372 species of birds found in the state. 2 vols folio, 458 pp. and 29 full page illus. and 997 pp. and 29 full page illus. Seattle, 1909. $90.00

No. 26 of Patron's De Lux Edition limited to 85 sets. This is a beautiful clean set in full morocco.

710a DEBO, ANGIE. And Still the Waters Run. 390 pp., 8vo, cloth. Princeton, 1940. $4.00

This definite and courageous volume tells the story of the dissolution of the five Indian republics which maintained a separate existence as protectorates of the U. S. "Grafting off the Indians" has never been so completely described as in this work. The author won the Dunning Prize for her "Rize and Fall of the Choctaw Republic" (1934).

711 DE FONTE, ADMIRAL BARTHOLOMEW. A letter from Admiral Bartholomew e Fonte, the Admiral of New Spain and Peru, and now Prince of Chili; giving an Account of the most material Transactions in a Journal of his from the Calo of Lima, in Peru, on his Discoveries to find out if there was any Northwest Passage from the Atlantic Ocean into the South and Tartarian Sea. Contained in Pages 123-126 "Memorie for the Curious," April, 1708, and maps 149-151 for May, 1708. 8vo, calf (repaired at hinge). London, 1708 $57.50

This is the original appearance of this narrative in print.

712 DE HASS, WILLIS. History of the Early Settlement and Indian Wars of Western Virginia; embracing an Account of the various Expeditions in the West previous to 1795, &c. Fldg. Plate and Engravings. 416 pp. 8vo, cloth. Wheeling, 1851 $30.00

Thomson 318. Fine copy of the Original Edition.

713 DELANO, ALONZO. Life on the Plains and among the Diggins; Scenes and Adventures of an Overland Journey to California; with Incidents of the Route. Mistakes and Sufferings of the Emigrants, the Indian Tribes, etc. 12mo, cloth. Aurburn, 1854.

Wagner-Camp No. 238. Original Edition. "This is one of the most interesting of California books." The author left St. Joe in April, 1849 and arrived at the Feather River diggings September 9th. His book is one of the Big Bend of the Humboldt via the Lassen-Applegate trail across the Black Rock Desert and over the Sierra to Goose Lake, thence southward via the Pit and Sacramento Rivers to the mines.

714 DELANO, AMASA. Narrative of Voyages and Travels in the Northern and Southern Hemispheres: comprising Three Voyages Round the World; together with a Voyage of Survey and Discovery in the Pacific Ocean and Oriental Islands. Portrait and Map. 8vo, calf (one hinge repaired). Boston, 1817. $17.50

DELISLE'S HISTORY AND MAPS OF EARLY NORTHWEST VOYAGES

715 DELISLE, ADMIRAL JOSEPH NICHOLAS. Nouvelles Cartes des Decouvertes de L.Amiral De Fonte, et Authres Navigateurs Espognols, Portugais, Anglois, Hollandois, Francois & Russes, dans les meres Septentrionales avec leur Explication qui comparend, L'Histoire des Voyages, tant par Terre que par Mer, dans le partie Septentrionale de la Terre. les Routes de Navigation, les Extraits de Journaux de Marina, les Observations Astronomiques, & tout ce qui peut contribuer au progres de la Navigation; avec la Description des Pays, l'Histoire des Habitans, le Commerce que l'on y peut faire, &c. Par M. De L'Isle, Professeur de Mathematiques au College Royal, &c. 4to (out of binding). Map. A Paris, 1753. $150.00

716 DELLENBAUGH, F. S. North Americans of Yesterday; Comparative Study of North American Indian Life, Customs, and Productions on theory of Ethnic Unity of Race. Maps, plates. 8vo, cloth.. N. Y., 1901. $5.00

717 DELLENBAUGH, F. S. Freemont and '49. The story of a Remarkable Career and its Relation to the Exploration and Development of our Western Territory, especially California. Maps, illus. 8vo, cloth. N. Y., 1914. $4.50

718 DELLENBAUGH, F. S. A Canyon Voyage. The Narrative of the Second Powell Expedition down the Green-Colorado River from Wyoming, and the Explorations on Land, in the years 1871 and 1872. Illus., maps. 8vo, cloth. N. Y., 1905. $4.50

719 DELLENBAUGH, F. S. Breaking the Wilderness. The Story of the Conquest of the Far West, from the Wanderings of Cabeza de Vaca to the first descent of the Colorado by Powell, and the completion of the Union Pacific Railway, with some particular account of the exploits of Trappers and Traders . . . Illus., 8vo, cloth. N. Y., 1901. $4.50

720 DELLENBAUGH, F. S. The Romance of the Colorado River. The story of its discovery in 1540, etc. Illus. 8vo, cloth. N. Y., 1907. $4.50

DEMERS' JOURNEY FROM VANCOUVER TO ST. PAUL, 1846

721 DEMERS, MODESTE. Mission de Vancouver. Lettre de Monseigneur de Vancouver a un pretre de l'Archeveche. 105 pp. 8vo, original printed wrappers. Quebec, 1849. $27.50

Wagner-Camp 167 (also note No. 164). Contains Demers' account of his journey from Vancouver Island to St. Paul via the Hudson's Bay Company's route through Ft. Jasper and Ft. Carleton, and Red River in 1846.

722 DENNETT, JOHN FREDERICK. The Voyage and Travels of Captains Parry, Franklin, Ross and Belzoni, forming an interesting history of the Manners, Customs and Characteristics of various Natives. 2 vols., 8vo. London, 1826. $7.50

723 DENNY, EMILY INEZ. Blazing the Way; or, True Stories, Songs and Sketches of Puget Sound and other Pioneers. 504 pp., illus., 8vo. Seattle: Ranier Printing Co., 1909. $5.00

724 DENYS, FERDINAND. Les Californies, l'Oregon, et les Possessions Russes en Amerique, les Noutka et de la Reine Charlotte. 108 pp., 8vo, wrappers. Paris, 1849. $40.00

Fine copy of this rare account of California and Oregon, Vancouver and the Queen Charlotte Islands. The item contains many beautiful engravings of various places, Indians, beavers, etc.

725 DE VOUGONDY, M. An Atlas without any title-page, being Supplemental Maps, numbering from 1 to 10 inclusive, all relating to early voyages to the North Pacific Ocean. Size of each map, 12 by 15 inches. Folio. 1772. [Sold]

The maps are as follows: (1) Carte des parties nord et ouest de Amerique dressee d'apres les relations les plus autheritiques par . . . M en 1764. (2) Carte des parties nord and ouest de l'Asie, etc. Par . . . M en 1764. (3) Nouvelle representation des cote nord et est de l'asie. (4) Carte de la California et des Pays nord-ouest separes de l'asie par le detroit d'Anian. (5) Carte de la Californie: (a) La carte manuscrite de l'Amerique de Mathieu Neron Pecci olen dressee a Florence en 1604; (b) ditto, Sanson, 1655; (c) DeLisle Amerique. Sept., 1700; (d) ditto. Le Pere Kino, 1705; (e) ditto. Societe des Jesuites. 1767. (6) Carte des Nouvelles Descouvertes par P. Buach, 1752. (7) Carte Generale des Decouvertes de l'Amiral de Fonte. de Lisle. 1752. (8) Carte Generale des Decouvertes e l'Amiral de Fonte. Jefferys, 1768. (9) Carte Terres Artiques. De Vaugondy. (10) Partie de la Carte du Capt. Cluny, 1769.

726 DEWEY, HENRY B. History of Education in Washington. 68 pp., charts., 8vo. Olympia, 1909. $3.75

727 D'WOLF, CAPTAIN JOHN. A Voyage to the North Pacific and a Journey through Siberia more than half a century ago. 147 pp., 8vo, Original wrappers. [100 copies printed.] Cambridge, 1861. [Sold]

Excessively rare and important. D'Wolf was Herman Melville's uncle. The above work was printed but not published and is a presentation copy frim the author. Cannot be found among Library of Congress cards. D'Wolf was Captain of the Juno, 250 tons, from Bristol, Rhode Island. He was at Sitka in the summer of 1805, where he sold the "Juno" to Governor Van Varanoff and remained there until he accompanied Langsdorff across the Pacific Ocean, through Siberia, to St. Petersburg. Langsdorff mentions D'Wolf repeatedly and at v. 2, p. 95 says: "Capt. D'Wolf, one of the most compassionate and benevolent of men, who often made me the sharer of his joys and sorrows, sighing one day over the numbers that were constantly dying, said to me, 'It is indeed extraordinary that Christians can practice so little philanthropy towards each other. The body of Promuschlenik is thrown carelessly into the earth and all ceremony of internment is waived (and) with the Aleutian we scarcely see a friend or comrade follow his deceased countrymen.'"

728 [DICKINSON, JOHN.] The Life and Times of John Dickinson, 1732-1808. Prepared at the request of the Historical Society of Pennsylvania, by Chas. A. Stille. Portraits. 2 volumes, 8vo, original cloth, paper labels. Phila., 1891. $7.50

From the year 1760 until 1763, Dickinson was the most conspicuous person in the service of Pennsylvania, and that, of course, means one of the most prominent figures in American history. He was the first to advocate resistance to taxation on constitutional grounds. Mr. Stille had access to mss. of the family, of McKean, Tilghman, P. L. Ford, and others.

729 DILKE CHAS. WENTWORTH. Great Britain. A Record of travel in English-Speaking Countries during 1866 and 1867. 595 pp., 8vo, cloth. London, 1869. $7.50

Colorado, Rocky Mountains, Utah, California, etc.

MINT COPY OF DIMSDALE'S "VIGILANTES" IN WRAPPERS

730 DIMSDALE, THOMAS J. The Vigilantes of Montana, or Popular Justice in the Rocky Mountains. Being a Correct and Impartial Narrative of the Chase, Trial, Capture and Execution of Henry Plummer's Road Agent Band, together with Accounts of the Lives and Crimes of many of the Robbers and Desperadoes, the whole being intersperced with Sketches of life in the Mining Camps of the Far West. 12mo, Original Printed Wrappers. Virginia City, M. T. 1866. $180.00

Probably the finest copy extant of this rare work, the first book printed in Montana.

731 DIX, MORGAN. Memoirs of John Adams Dix. 2 vols., 8vo, cloth. New York, 1883. $6.00

Oregon Question, Oregon Government, etc. Not in Smith.

732 DIXON, GEORGE. Voyage autour du monde, et principalement a la cote nord-ouest de l'Amerique, fait en 1785, 1786, 1787 et 1788, a bord du King-George et de la Queen-Charlotte, par les Capitaines Portlock et Dixon; traduit de l'Anglois par M. Lebas. 2 vols., 8vo, calf. 17 plates, 5 maps, 13 tables. Par Maradan, Paris, 1789. $15.00

Smith 980.

Item 727, Omit "cannot be found among Library of Congress Cards."

732a DIXON, GEORGE. Remarks on the Voyages of John Meares, Esq., in a Letter to that Gentleman. Very fine uncut copy. London, 1790. $87.50

On page 7, Dixon says: "to point out half your absurdities would fill a volume as large as your own . . . I shall therefore without further preface point out some of your numerous errors." From this it is easy to judge the opinion that Dixon had formed of Meares' account of his voyages.

733 DODDRIDGE, JOSEPH. Notes on the Settlement and Indian Wars, of the Western Parts of Virginia & Pennsylvania, from the Year 1763 until the Year 1783 inclusive. Together with a View, of the state of society and manners of the first settlers of the Western Country. 12mo, original calf. Wellsburgh, Va., 1824. $50.00

Ayer No. 75. Fine copy of the Rare Original Edition. The facts were drawn from original sources, mostly of personal observations. Contains accounts of the captiivty of Mrs. Brown, Adam Poe, Col. Crawford, Col. Knight, death of Cornstalk, etc.

734 DODGE, GRENVILLE M. Union Pacific Railroad. Report of G. M. Dodge, Chief Engineer, with accompanying Reports of Chiefs of Parties for the Year 1867. 85 pp. Original Wrappers. Washington, 1868. $22.50

Fine copy of the rare Original Edition. Contains the journals of James A. Evans' explorations through Wyoming and the Black Hills and his passage through the Laramie Canyon. Evans is reported to be the first white man ever to pass through the Canyon. The volume also contains the report of P. T. Browne, detailing his reconnoissances in the Republican Valley to Ft. Morgan on the Platte, thence by the Platte Valley to Denver. Also included is Hill's report on the North Platte country, and the narrative of Thomas Bates' explorations in Utah, thence by way of the Humboldt to the Treckee and across to California.

735 DODGE, GRENVILLE, M. Personal Recollections of General William T. Sherman. 40 pp. 8vo, original wrappers. Des Moines, 1902. $7.50

Relates to the Civil War and Indian Campaigns of the west.

736 DODGE, GRENVILLE, M. The Indian Campaign of the Winter of 1864-65. 21 pp. 8vo, Original Wrappers. Denver, 1897. $7.50

An important contribution to the history of the Indian wars of the Northwest.

737 DODGE, GRENVILLE, M. The Battle of Atlanta and other campaigns, addresses, etc. 183 pp., illus. 8vo, cloth. Council Bluffs, 1910. $4.50

738 DODGE, GRENVILLE, M. How we built the Union Pacific Railway and other Railway Papers and Addresses. 30 Historical Plates. 171 pp., 8vo, original wrappers (Council Bluffs, 1911). $10.00

The authoritative account of the building of the first transcontinental railroad. The plates are from photographs and original drawings made at the time and are not found elsewhere.

739 DODGE, RICHARD IRVING. The Black Hills. A Minute Description of the Routes, Scenery, Soil, Climate, Timber, Gold, Geology, Zoology, etc. Map, sectional drawings, tinted lithos, views. 12mo, cloth. N. Y., 1876. $6.00

740 DOMENECH, ABBE EMANUEL. Seven Years Residence in the Great Deserts of North America. Plates, map. 2 vols., half mor. London, 1860.

741 DONAN, P. Where Rolls the Oregon, the Columbia River Empire. 72 pp. Illus., map. 8vo, original wrappers. Portland, 1902. $4.00

742 DOUGLAS, DAVID. Observations on some Species of the Genera and Ortyx, natives of North America; with descriptions of four other species of the former, and two of the later Genus. Together with: An Account of the Species of Calochortus; a genus of American Plants. 2 plates, one colored. 4to, calf. London, 1828. $60.00

Presentation copy by the author to Nicholas Garry, Deputy Governor of Hudson's Bay Co.

743 DOUGLAS, DAVID. Journal Kept by David Douglas during his Travels in North America, 1823-27. 364 pp. Illus. 8vo, cloth. London, 1914. $20.00

Although printed in 1914 this work is now quite scarce. Douglas, one of the world's great exploring botanists, arrived at the Columbia River April 7, 1825 and remained in the Oregon Territory several years botanizing and exploring the entire region. He was first to apply the name "Cascade" to the range now known by that name. The Douglas Fir was also named after him. He went overland to the Red River Settlement in 1827. In 1834 he went to Hawaii where he met his tragic death.

744 DOUGLAS, THOMAS. (Red River Occurrences). Statement respecting the Earl of Selkirk's Settlement upon the Red River in North America, its destruction in 1815 and 1816; and the Massacre of Governor Semple and his party; with observations upon the recent publication entitled "A Narrative of Occurrences in the Indian Country". vii-194-100 pp., map. 8vo. London, 1817. $32.50

SOURCE VOLUME OF SELKIRK'S RED RIVER TRAGEDY

745 DOUGLAS, THOMAS. (Red River Occurrences). Statement respecting the Earl of Selkirk's Settlement of Kildonan, upon the Red River in North America; its destruction in the years 1815 and 1816; and the Massacre of Governor Semple and his Party. 125 pp., map. 8vo. London, n.d. $75.00

The above is the rare privately printed first edition, with the preface dated January, 1817. The work was distributed only to Lord Selkirk's friends and a few who were interested in the enterprise.

746 DOUGLAS, WILLIAM. A Summary, Historical and Political, of the first planting, progressive improvements and present state of the British Settlements in North America. 2 vols., 8vo, ¾ mor. Boston, 1749-1751. $30.00

Contains an account of the establishment of the original thirteen colonies, of the Canadian and West Indian provinces, Hudson's Bay Co., the fur trade and the Newfoundland codfishery.

747 DRAKE, DANIEL. Pioneer Life in Kentucky; a series of reminiscential letters from Daniel Drake of Cincinnati to his children. Edited with notes by Charles D. Drake. 8vo, 317 pp., cloth, as new. Cincinnati, 1870. $7.50

DUFLOT DE MOFRAS' "OREGON AND CALIFORNIA"

748 DUFLOT DE MOFRAS, EUGENE. Exploration du Territoire de l'Oregon des Californies et de la Mer Vermeille, 1840-1842. 2 vols. and Atlas, together 3 vols. Folding maps, charts and plates, 8vo & folio, half morocco. Paris, 1844. $190.00

Original Edition. Cowan, p. 74: "Superior to any of the twenty within that decade". Wagner: "One of the twenty rarest and most important works dealing with the history of California". A magnificent set. The author was an attache at the French Legation in Mexico.

749 DUGAST, GEORGE. The Canadian West; its Discovery by the Sieur de la Verendrye; its development by the Fur-Trading Companies down to the year 1822. Translated from the French by Abbe G. Dugast. 12mo, half mor., original wrappers bound in. Montreal, 1905. $18.50

750 DUHAUT-CILLY, A. Viaggio intorno al globo principalmente alla California ed alla Isole Sandwich, 1826-1829. Full-page views of Monterey, San Luis Rey, the Russian Settlement at Bodega, etc. 2 vols., 296 and 394 pp. bound in one volume. 8vo, half calf. Torino, 1841. $37.50

No other navigator had ever visited so many California establishments. The author spent two years on the coast and in the interior exploring, trading, visiting towns, missions and collecting material on the inhabitants and the Indians. Cowan, p. 74.

751 DUMBELL, K. E. M. Seeing the West. 8vo, cloth, 206 pp. N. Y., 1920. $2.50

752 DUNBAR, WILLIAM. Louisiana. Documents relating to the purchase and exploration of Louisiana. (1) The limits and bounds of La. by Thomas Jefferson. (2) The exploration of the Red, the Black and Washita Rivers by William Dunbar. Folding map. 8vo, cloth, uncut. Boston and New York (Bruce Rogers typography), 1904. $12.50

One of 550 copies printed from the original manuscript in the American Philosophical Society.

753 DUNIWAY, A. S. David and Anna Matson. Plates. 8vo, cloth. N. Y., 1876. $4.50

Narrative poem of the early Oregon pioneers. The author's father died in Ft. Laramie in 1872.

754 DUNRAVEN (Earl of). The Great Divide: Travels in the Upper Yellowstone Country. Two large folding maps in color and numerous plates of Indians, etc. 8vo, half roan. N. Y., 1876. $6.00

Narrative of hunting and exploring adventures in Wyoming, etc.

755 DURHAM, N. W. History of the city of Spokane and Spokane County, Washington from its earliest settlement to the present time. 3 vols., 4to, cloth, illus. Chicago, 1912. $17.50

The best history of the region.

756 DURRIE, DANIEL S. A History of Madison, the Capital of Wisconsin; including the Four Lake Country, to July 1874. With an Appendix on Dane County and its Towns. Original Photographs tipped in. 8vo, cloth. Madison, 1874. $17.50

757 DURRIE, DANIEL S. Illustrated History of Missouri. 639 pp. Illus. 8vo, cloth. St. Louis, 1876. $12.50

Biographies of the fur traders and early navigators of the Missouri River.

758 EASTMAN, CHARLES A. Indian Boyhood. 289 pp., 8vo, cloth. Boston, 1902. $3.25

Fine description of Indian life among the tribes of the northwest.

759 EASTMAN, CHARLES A. The Soul of the Indian; an Interpretation. 171 p., 8vo, cloth. Boston, (1911). $3.00

760 EASTMAN, CHARLES A. From the Deep Woods to Civilization. Chapters in the autobiography of an Indian. 8vo, cloth. Boston, 1916. $3.00

EDWARDS' NEW MEXICAN CAMPAIGN

761 EDWARDS, FRANK S. A Campaign in New Mexico with Col. Doniphan. With a Map of the Route and Table of Distances. Folding map. 184 pp., 12mo, half mor. Phila., 1847. $24.50

Wagner-Camp 132. Original Edition. "This is the most entertaining account of the expedition". Contains much important material concerning General Houston and western Texas.

762 [EDWARDS, JOHN N.] Biography, Memoirs, Reminiscences and Recollections. With a reprint of Shelby's Expedition to Mexico. Compiled by his wife, Jennie Edwards. Portrait. 12mo, cloth. Kansas City, Mo., 1889. $5.00

Published by Jennie Edwards in a small edition. The pro-Confederate views of Edwards led him to defend the western bandits.

763 EDWARDS, JOHN N. Noted Guerrillas, or the Warfare of the Border. Illus. 488 pp., 8vo, cloth. St. Louis, 1877. $17.50

Paullin 879. Good copy of the Original Edition. Adventures of Quantrell, Bill Anderson, Todd, Poole, Clement, Gregg, James Brothers, Youngers, Art McCoy, etc.

FACSIMILE OF P. L. EDWARDS' NARRATIVE, 1842

764 EDWARDS, COL. PHILIP LEGET. Sketch of the Oregon Territory; or, Emigrant's Guide. 12mo. Liberty, Mo., 1842. $15.00

The above is a photostat copy of the Wagner-Jones copy, the only one known.

765 EATON, A. H. The Oregon System. Story of Direct Legislation in Oregon. 8vo, cloth. Chicago, 1912. $3.50

766 EELLS, CUSHING. Results of the Oregon Missionary. (Contained in the Missionary Herald, Dec. 1866 by one of the earliest missionaries to the Oregon Country.) 8vo, half calf. Boston, 1866. $3.75

767 EELLS, MYRON. The Twana Indians of the Snohomish Reservation in Washington Territory, by the Rev. Myron Eells, Missionary among the Indians. 8vo. Washington, 1877. $5.00

768 EELLS, MYRON. Hymns in the Chinook Jargon Language. Compiled by Rev. M. Eels (sic), missionary of the American Missionary Association. (Vignette). 12mo, original printed wrappers Portland, Publishing House of Geo. H. Himes, 1878. $27.50

Smith 1092 apparently locates but one copy in the Washington Historical Society. The cover title is the same as above with copyright notice on verso. The Jargon hymns have English translations.

769 EELLS, MYRON. History of the Congregational Association of Oregon and Washington Territory; the Home Society of Oregon and Adjoining Territories; and the Northwestern Association of Congregational Ministers. 8vo, original wrappers, 124 pp. Himes: Portland (Ore.), 1881. $17.50

Not only describes the organization of most of the early churches in Oregon and Washington, but gives considerable details relating to the early colleges, preachers, members of the Association, education, church work, etc.

770 EELLS, MYRON. History of the Indian Missions on the Pacific Coast, Oregon, Washington and Idaho. 270 pp., plates. 8vo, cloth. Phila., (1882). $7.50

Important history by an authority. Scarce.

771 EELLS, MYRON. Ten Years of Missionary Work among the Indians of Skokomish, Washington Territory, 1874-1884. Portrait and Plates. 271 pp., 12mo, cloth. Boston, (1886). $6.00

Appropos of accounts dealing with this particular subject, Rev. Eells comment is pertinent. He says: "It is surprising to find how few books can be obtained on Missionary work among the Indians. After ten years of effort the writer has been able to secure twenty-six books on such work in the U. S."

772 EELLS, MYRON. The Rapid Forming of Rock Stratas in Oregon. (Contained in the American Antiquarian, 1888). 8vo, 1888. $2.50

773 EELLS, MYRON. Hymn in the Chinook Jargon Language 2nd Ed., revised and enlarged. 8vo, cloth. Portland, 1889. $5.00

774 EELLS, Myron. Aboriginal Geographic Names in the State of Washington. (From the American Anthropologist for January, 1892.) 8vo, 1892. $3.00

775 EELLS, MYRON. Chinook Jargon. (From the American Anthropologist for July, 1894.) 8vo, cloth. 1894. $3.00

776 EELLS, MYRON. Father Eells: or the Results of Fifty-Five years of Missionary Labors in Washington and Oregon; a biography of Rev. Cushing Eells . . . 342 pp., ports, illus. 8vo, cloth. Boston, 1894. $5.00

777 EELLS, MYRON. 37 pp., excerpt from the Whitman College Quarterly, Oct. 1898. 8vo. Walla Walla, 1898. $4.50

778 EELLS, MYRON. Reply to Professor Bourne's "The Whitman Legend." 122 pp., 8vo, wrappers. Walla Walla: Statesman Pub.. Co., 1902. $4.50

779 EELLS, Myron. Marcus Whitman, Pathfinder and Patriot. 349 pp., 22 illus. 8vo, cloth. Seattle, 1909. $3.75

780 EELLS, MYRON. Stone Age of Oregon. 8vo, cloth. N. p., N. d. $3.50

781 EGAN (HOWARD R.) Pioneering in the West 1846-78. Major Howard Egan's Diary. Illus. cloth,, 303 pp. Richmond, Utah, 1917. $5.00

Thrilling experiences of pre-Frontier life among the Indians, their traits, civil and savage, and part of the Autobiography of the author interrelated to his fathers. One of a few copies privately printed.

782 ELIOT, SAMUEL A. Conditions among the Indians of the Northwest Coast. 28 pp., 8vo, original wrappers. Washington, 1915. $3.75

783 ELLIOTT, THOMAS COIT. The Earliest Travelers on the Oregon Trail. 16 pp., front., wrappers. Portland, 1912. $5.00

Privately printed and scarce little work by an acknowledged authority.

784 ELLIOTT, THOMAS COIT. Camels in the Inland Empire. 4 pp., 8vo, wrappers. N. p., n. d. $3.00

785 ELLIS, HENRY. Voyage to Hudson's Bay, by the Dobbs Gally and California, in 1746-47, for discovering a North West Passage; with an accurate survey of the Coast. Together with facts and arguments from which the future findings of such a passage is rendered probable. Map and plates. 8vo, calf. London, 1748. $25.00

Original edition. Braislin 671. A voyage made before the finding of the North-West Passage which contributed knowledge to its ultimate achievement.

786 —— The Same. French Edition. 2 vols., 12mo, calf. Maps and plates. Paris, 1749. $12.50

787 ELLISON, W. G. H. The Settlers of Vancouver Island. 154 pp., 2 plates., 8vo, original wrappers. London, n. d. $7.50

Smith 1135 locates but one copy.

788 EMMONS, GEORGE T. The Chilkat Blankets. (Memoirs of the American Museum of Natural History, Vol. 3, Part 4, pp. 329-400 plates.) 4to, original wrappers. N. Y., 1907. $5.00

789 EMORY, LIEUT. COL. W. H. Notes of a Military Reconnaissance from Fort Leavenworth, in Missouri, to San Diego, in California, including part of the Arkansas, Del Norte and Gila Rivers. 30th Cong., 1st Sess., Ex. Doc. 41. Folding maps, 67 plates, 614 pp., 8vo, cloth. Washington, 1848. $7.50

The House issue. Contains also the report of Lt. Col. St. George Cooke of his march from Santa Fe to San Diego, and also the Journal of Capt. A. R. Johnston, First Dragoons, who made a similar expedition.

790 ENGLISH, W. H. Conquest of the Country Northwest of River Ohio, 1778-1783, and Life of George Rogers Clark. With over 125 illus. 2 vols., royal 8vo, cloth. Indianapolis, 1896. $15.00

"This great work is a noble historical and biographical work of permanent value which at once takes first rank"—Elliott Coues. It is still the standard authority on Geo. Rogers Clark and is now scarce.

EARLY MAP OF THE GOLD REGIONS IN BRITISH COLUMBIA

791 EPNER, GUST. Map of the Gold Regions in British Columbia. Compiled from Sketches and Information by his Excellency James Douglas, C.B., Governor of British Columbia and Vancouver's Island, and from data obtained from most intelligent and reliable Miners. By Gust Epner. 16 by 20 inches, mounted on linen. Lithographed by Britton & Co., San Francisco (1862). $50.00

Excessively rare. An accurate map used by the miners.

792 ERSKINE, CHARLES. Twenty Years before the Mast. With the more thrilling Scenes and Incidents while circumnavigating the Globe under the command of the late Admiral Charles Wilkes, 1838-1842. Illus. 8vo, cloth. Phila., 1896. $7.50

Erskine was a member of the Wilkes' Expedition to Oregon. Smith reports one copy.

793 [ESPINOSA Y TELLO, JOSE.] A Spanish Voyage to Vancouver and the North West Coast of America Being the Narative of the Voyage made in the year 1792 by the Schooners Sutil and Mexicana to explore the Strait of Fuca. Translated from the Spanish with an Introduction by Cecil Jane. Illustrated with a folding map and six illustrations. The Argonaut Press: London, 1930. $7.50

794 ESTES, GEORGE. The Rawhide Railroad, with Portrait and typical Sketches of early Pioneer Conditions. 54 pp. Small 4to, cloth backed boards. Canby, Ore. (1916). $7.50

Story of a remarkable steam railroad operated in the Walla Walla Valley on which rawhide overlaying wooden beams was used in place of steel rails. The road came to an end when hungry wolves ate up the rawhide.

IMPORTANT WORK ON "NOOTKA SOUND" BY MEARES' SUPER CARGO

794a [ETCHES, JOHN.] An Authentic Statement of all the Facts relative to Nootka Sound; its Discovery, History, Settlement, Trade and the Probable Advantages to be derived from it; in an Address to the King. 26 pp. 12mo, ¾ morocco. London: Printed for J. Debrett, 1790. $150.00

Excessively rare. Smith locates but three copies. Etches was the Supercargo with Meares.

795 EVANS, ELWOOD. Oration by Hon. Elwood Evans, Portland, Oregon, July 4th, 1865. 16 pp. N. p., n. d. (Portland: Committee on Invitations, 1865). $22.50

Smith 1175 locates one copy in the library of Washington University. The work contains allusions to Oregon history. Evans, a Washington Territory pioneer, went to the Territory as Secretary to Governor Stevens and was an important character in the territory, as well as its most authoritative local historian.

ELWOOD EVANS' REPORT ON WASHINGTON TERRITORY

796 EVANS, ELWOOD. Puget Sound: Its Past, Present and Future. An address delivered at Port Townsend, Jan. 5, 1869. 16 pp., 8vo, original printed wrappers. Olympia, 1869. $27.50

Smith 1176.

797 EVANS, ELWOOD. The Re-Annexation of British Columbia to the United States, Right, Proper and Desirable. An Address before the Tacoma Library Association, Jan. 18, 1870. 24 pp., 8vo, double column, sewn. Olympia, 1870. $42.50

Not in Smith. A rare work on a topical question in the 60's and 70's among residents of the Northwest.

798 EVANS, ELWOOD. Annual Address before the Fourth Annual Exhibition held in Olympia, Friday, Oct. 9, 1874. 32 pp., 8vo, original printed wrappers. Olympia, 1875. $20.00

Not in Smith. Important historical address on the beginnings of Washington's industries.

799 EVANS, ELWOOD. Washington Territory; her Past, her Present, and the elements of Wealth which ensure her Future: Address delivered at the Centennial Exposition, Philadelphia, Sept. 2, 1876, and in joint convention of the Legislature of Washington Territory, Oct. 13, 1877. 51 pp., 8vo, wrappers. Olympia, 1877. $42.50

Smith 1178.

800 EVANS, ELWOOD. Puyallup Indian Reservation. Address delivered before the Tacoma Chamber of Commerce, May 17, 1892. 15 pp., 8vo, wrappers. Tacoma, 1892. $12.50

Not in Smith.

801 EVANS, ELWOOD, and Meany, E. S. State of Washington; a brief History of the Discovery, Settlement and Organization of Washington, the Evergreen State . . . 224 pp., illus., 8vo, original wrappers. Tacoma, 1893. $3.50

802 EVANS, ROBLEY D. A Sailor's Log; Recollections of Forty Years of Naval Life. 467 pp., 8vo, cloth. N. Y., 1901. $3.75

802a EWERS, G. & M. Englehardt, Bei trage zur Kenntniss Russlande und seiner Geschichte. Bd. 1 (all published). 8vo, cloth. Dorpat, 1818. $27.50

Contains: Dawudov, Nachrichten von der Insel Kadjak und den russischen Niederlassungen daselfst, 336 pp. Davydov and Khostor, Isle Kodiac, pp. 70-141. Vol. 2, pp. 337-716. Dorpat, 1818. All bound in one vol.

FALCONER'S REPORT ON "OREGON BOUNDARY CLAIM"

803 FALCONER, THOMAS. On the Discovery of the Mississippi, and on the Southwestern, Oregon, and Northwestern Boundary of the United States, with a Translation from the Original Manuscript of Memoirs, etc., relating to the Discovery of the Mississippi by Robert Cavalier de la Salle and the Chevalier Henry de Tonty. Folding map. 8vo, half calf, uncut London, 1844. $37.50

The most important of the English contributions to the celebrated "Oregon Boundary Question". Much of the work is based on documents in the Archives of the Marine at Paris. The author, an able lawyer, presents a strong case for the British contention to the Oregon country, hinging his claim on the broad territorial acquisition of La Salle and other French explorers, which he considers were acquired by Great Britain upon the cession of New France.

804 FALCONER, THOMAS. The Oregon Question; or, A Statement of the British Claims to the Oregon Territory, in opposition to the Pretensions of the Government of the U. S. of America. 48 pp., map, 8vo, half calf. London, 1845. $27.50

805 FANNING, CAPT. EDMUND. Voyages Round the World; with Selected Sketches of Voyages to the South Seas, North and South Pacific Oceans, Chnia, etc. Performed under the command and agency of the author . . . Plates. 8vo, orignial boards, uncut. N. Y., 1833. $22.50

Fine copy of the Original Edition. Contains three chapters not in the Marine Research Society edition. The plates, which include a number of ship views, are lithographed by Endicott.

806 FARIS, JOHN T. On the Trail of the Pioneers. Romance, Tragedy and Triumph on the Path of Empire. 319 pp., illus., 8vo, cloth. N. Y., 1920. $3.75

807 FARNHAM, ELIZA W. California—In-Doors and Out; or, How We Mine, Farm and Live. 12mo, cloth. N. Y., 1856. $5.00

Contains an original narrative of the Donner party gathered from several individuals of both sexes who were members of the tragic party; vigilance committee. The author was the wife of Thos. J. Farnham.

808 FARNHAM, THOMAS J. Travels in the Great Western Prairies, the Anahuac and Rocky Mountains, and in the Oregon Territory. 2 vols., 8vo, original cloth. London, 1843. $27.50

Braislin 707. Field calls this the Best Edition of this celebrated work. The party left Peoria, Illinois, May 1, 1839 and Independence Day, May 30, going by the Santa Fe Trail to Ft. Bent; but Farnham and 11 others turned north by way of the Arkansas to South Park; from there they crossed over to the Grand and over the Divide to the North Fork of the Platte, thence on to Brown's Hole; then on to Ft. Hall, thence, with an Indian guide to Whitman's Mission, arriving Sept. 23.

809 FARNHAM, THOMAS J. The Early Days of California: What I Saw and Heard. Port. and plates. 12mo, cloth. Phila., 1859. $6.00

810 —— The same. 8vo, cloth. Phila., 1860. $4.00

811 FARRAGUT, ADMIRAL DAVID G. The Life of, First Admiral of the U. S. Navy, embodying his Journal and Letters. By Loyall Farragut. 586 pp., illus., map, 8vo, cloth. N. Y., 1879. $7.50

Gives an account of his services in California, Vigilance Committee, etc.

812 FAWCETT, EDGAR. Some Reminiscences of Old Victoria. 294 pp., illus., 8vo, cloth. Toronto, 1912. $6.00

The author arrived in San Francisco as a child. The first part is devoted to his experiences in San Francisco in the early fifties. He witnessed the celebrated murder of James King. He went to Victoria in 1858. The work contains much of the pioneer history of Victoria.

813 FEARON, HENRY BRADSHAW. Sketches of America. A Narative of a Journey of Five Thousand Miles through the Eastern and Western States of America . . . with Remarks on Mr. Birkbeck's "Notes and Letters." 8vo, sheep. London, 1818. $7.50

Thomson p. 118: Buck 98. Original Edition. One of the most important source books on Illinois prior to statehood, and on conditions in America just after the war of 1812. Fearon was the advance agent for 39 English families who were contemplating moving to America. This original edition is scarce.

814 FEATHERSTONHAUGH, CAPT. G. W. Narrative of the Operations of the British North American Boundary Commission, 1872-76. 23-72 pp., 3 plates, map, tables, 8vo, cloth. Woolwich, 1876. $15.00

815 FELT, JOSEPH B. Memorial of William Smith Shaw. 346 pp., 8vo, cloth. Boston, 1852. $7.50

Relates to the writing of the history of the Lewis and Clark Expedition by Biddle and Dr. Barton. Scarce.

816 FERNAND-MICHEL, M. Dix-Huit Ans chez les Sauvages. Voyage et Missions dans l'Estreme Nord de l'Amerique Britannique. D'Apres les Documents de Mgr. Henry Faraud, Eveque, Vicare Apostolique de Mackensie. 364 pp., 8vo, cloth. Paris and Bruxelles, 1870. $12.50

Father Faraud arrived at Saint-Boniface on the Red River in 1846 and thereafter spent many years among the natives of the Northwest.

817 FERRER, MALDONADA LORENZO. Voyage de la mer Atlantique a l'Ocean Pacifique par le Nord-Ouest dans le mer Glaciale par le Capitaine Lourent Ferrer Maldoanado, l'an 1588, traduit d'une manuscript Espagnol . . . 84 and 19 pp., 3 folding maps. Plaisance, 1812. $45.00

Smith 1226 locates one copy in the Provincial Library of British Columbia. This is an important history of the geographical discoveries on the Northwest Coast of America. Only 600 copies of the work were originally printed.

818 FERRIS, MRS. B. G. The Mormons at Home; with some Incidents of Travel from Missouri to California, 1852-3. In a series of Letters. 12mo, cloth. N. Y., 1856. $6.50

Wagner-Camp 274. Original Edition. The author was the wife of the U. S. Secretary for Utah. Mrs. Ferris gives the narrative of her trip across the plains from Independence to Salt Lake in 1852, and from thence, via the Humboldt, to California in 1853.

819 FIELD, STEPHEN J. Personal Reminiscences of Early Days in California. To which is added the Story of his attempted Assassination by a Former Associate on the Supreme Bench of the State. 472 pp., 8vo, half mor. N. p. (San Francisco). [Sold]

Presentation copy "With Compliments of Stephen M. Field". Only a few copies of this scarce work were privately printed for friends.

820 FINCK, H. T. Pacific Coast Scenic Tour; from Southern California to Alaska, the Canadian Pacific Railway, Yellowstone Park and Grand Canyon. 309 pp., map, 8vo, cloth. N. Y., 1890. $3.50

821 FISHER, EZRA. Correspondence of Rev. Ezra Fisher, Pioneer Missionary of the American Baptist Home Mission Society in Indiana, Illinois, Iowa and Oregon. Edited by Sarah Fisher Henderson, et al. 8vo, cloth. N. p., n. d. [Portland, Ore., 1919.] $17.50

The experiences of one of the earliest missionaries to Oregon on the overland trail. He went as a member of the New London Emigrating Company in 1845. He writes carefully of the Indian wars of 1845-55. This work is excessively scarce.

822 FISK, CAPT. JAMES LIBERTY. Expedition of Capt. Fisk to the Rocky Mountains. Letter from the Sec'y of War in answer to a resolution of the House of Feb. 26, transmitting a report of Capt. Fisk of his late Expedition to the Rocky Mountains and Idaho. (Report dated St. Paul, Jan. 28, 1864). 38th Cong., 1st Sess., Sen Ex. Doc.—(no number). 38 pp., 8vo, sewn. $22.50

Wagner-Camp 399.

822a FISK, CAPT. JAMES LIBERTY. Expedition from Ft. Abercrombie to Ft. Benton. Letter from the Secretary of War, in answer to Resolution of the House of 19th Instant, transmitting report of Captain J. L. Fisk, of the expedition to escort Emigrants from Ft. Abercrombie to Ft. Benton . . . March 2, 1863. Ordered Printed. 37th Cong., 3rd Sess., H.R. Ex. Doc. 80. 36 pp., 8vo, sewn. (Washington, 1863). $22.50

Wagner-Camp 388.

823 FITZGIBON, MARY. A Trip to Manitoba; or, Roughing it on the Line. 267 pp., 8vo, cloth. Toronto, 1880. $6.50

Interesting narrative of a trip made in 1879 via the lakes to Duluth, thence to Fisher's Landing, thence down the Red River in a steamer.

824 [FITZPATRICK, THOMAS.] Broken Hand. The Story of Thomas Fitzpatrick, Chief of the Mountain Men. By Leroy R. Hafen and W. J. Ghent. Map and illus., 8vo, cloth, d. w. Denver, 1931. $10.00

Scarce limited edition.

825 FLAGG, EDMUND. The Far West; or, A Tour beyond the Mountains, embracing Outlines of Western Life and Scenery; Sketches of the Prairies, Rivers, Ancient Mounds, etc. 2 vols., 12mo, half mor. Fine set. N. Y., 1838. $15.00

826 FLANDRAU, GRACE. The Vendrye Overland Quest of the Pacific. 64 pp., 8vo, original wrappers. N. p., n. d. $2.00

827 FLANDRAU, GRACE. Seven Sunsets. 44 pp., illus., 8vo, original wrappers. N. p., n. d. $2.00

828 FLANDRAU, GRACE. Red River Trails. 27 pp., illus., 8vo, original wrappers. N. p., n. d. $2.00

829 FLANDRAU, GRACE. A Glance at the Lewis and Clark Expedition. 29 pp., illus., 8vo, original wrappers. N. p., n. d. $2.00

830 FLANDRAU, GRACE. The Story of the Marias Pass. 22 pp., illus., 8vo, original wrappers. N. p., n. d. $2.00

831 FLEMING, SANFORD. Expeditions to the Pacific. (Contained in the Royal Society of Canada Proceedings, Vol. 7, Series 2, pp. 89-141). 8vo, cloth. Ottawa, 187-. $5.00

Relates to explorations for a route for the railway.

832 FLEMING, SANFORD. (Canadian Pacific Railroad). Report of Progress on the Explorations and Surveys up to January, 1874. 286 pp., map, plates. 8vo, cloth. Ottawa, 1874. $15.00

Smith 1254. Original Edition, of which only two copies are reported in N. W. libraries. Fleming was Chief Engineer in charge of the survey and location of the Canadian Pacific Railroad.

833 FLEMING, SANFORD. Canadian Pacific Railway. Map and Charts to accompany Report on the Explorations and Surveys up to January, 1874. 6 maps and charts. 8vo, original wrappers. Ottawa, 1874. $20.00

Smith does not report a copy of this scarce work.

834 FLEMING, SANFORD. Report on Surveys and Preliminary Operations on the Canadian Pacific Railway. 431 pp., illus., maps., 8vo, cloth. Ottawa, 1877. $17.50

835 FLEMING, SANFORD. Railway Report and Documents in Reference to the Location of the Line and a Western Terminal, 1878. 104 pp., 8vo, original wrappers. Ottawa, 1878. $12.50

Smith 1259 locates but one copy.

836 FLEMING, SANFORD. Engineer in Chief, Canadian Pacific Railway. Report addressed to the Honorable Minister of Public Works, Canada, 1879. 142 pp., folding map. 8vo, original wrappers. Ottawa, 1879. $12.50

Smith 1257 reports one copy.

837 FLEMING, SANFORD. Report and Documents in Reference to the Canadian Pacific Railway, 1880. 373 pp., 8 maps. 4to, cloth. Ottawa, 1880. $15.00

838 FLEMING, SANFORD. England and Canada; a Summer Tour between Old and New Westminster, with Historical Notes. 449 pp., map. 8vo, cloth. London, 1884. $5.00

Contains account of Nova Scotia, Quebec, Montreal, Ottawa, Toronto, Lake Superior, Winnipeg, Hudson Bay Co., Lord Selkirk, Calgary, Rocky Mountains, Eagle Pass, Kicking Horse Valley, Kamloops, Fraser River, New Westminster, Victoria, British Columbia, etc.

839 FLINT, JAMES. Letters from America, containing Observations on the Climate and Agriculture of the Western States, the Manners of the People, the Prospects of Emigrants, &c. 8vo, half calf. Edinburgh, 1822. $13.50

Relates to Pennsylvania, Ohio, Kentucky, Indiana, the Great Lakes, etc.

840 FLINT, THOMAS. Diary of Dr. Thomas Flint. California to Maine and Return, 1851-1855. 78 pp., 8vo, cloth. Los Angeles, 1921. $3.75

An exceptionally interesting overland narrative.

ACCOUNT OF EARLY ENGLISH COLONIZATION OF FLORIDA

841 [FLORIDA.] (Stork, Wm.). An Extract from the Account of East Florida, published by Dr Stork, who resided a considerable Time in Augustine, the Metropolis of that Province. With Observations of Denys Rolle, who formed a Settlement on St. John's River, in the same Province. With his Proposals to such Persons as may be inclined to settle thereon. First Edition. 8vo, half calf. London: Privately printed in the Year 1766. $62.50

Rare. The work was designed to advertise Rolle's colonization scheme. Drake says of this work: "In 1766 he (Rolle) purchased a whole district in Florida, whither he proceeded with 1,000 persons to people the new possessions; but, through the unhealthiness of the climate and the desertion of those who escaped disease, he soon found himself without colonists and without money, and was compelled to work his passage back to England in an American vessel."

842 [FLORIDA.] Depredations in Florida, by U. S. Army, in 1814. April 20th, 1842. 27th Cong. 2nd Session. [Caption title.] 7 pp., 8vo, unopened. Washington, 1814. $2.50

843 FLORY, J. S. Thrilling Echoes from the Frontier: Personal Reminiscences. Plate. 248 pp., 12mo, cloth. Chicago, 1893. $10.00

An authentic and valuable narrative of a trip across the plains; Denver and the mines; lynch law; buffalo hunting; Yellowstone country; hunting; prospecting; ranch life; captivity and escape of the author; wild horses, etc.

843a FOI, MARIE DE LA. Letter of a Canadian Sister from Washington Territory to her Relatives. Tulalip, W. T., Nov., 1868. (Pp. 13-21 Annals of the Association of the Holy Childhood). 8vo, sewn. N. p., 1869. $12.50

844 FOLSOM, W. H. C. Fifty Years in the Northwest. 736 pp., illus., 8vo, cloth. St. Paul, 1888. $7.50

Folsom arrived at Prairie du Chien at the age of nineteen (1836). The place was then a military post known as Fort Crawford.

845 FOOTE, MARY HALLOCK. A Picked Company. 12mo, cloth. Boston, 1912. $3.50

An overland story.

846 FOOTNER, HULBERT. New Rivers of the North. The Yarn of two Amateur Explorers. 281 pp., illus., 8vo, cloth. N. Y., 1912. $4.75

Headwaters of the Fraser, Peace River and Hay River.

847 FORBES, CHARLES. Prize Essay; Vancouver Island, its Resources and Capabilities as a Colony. 8vo, original printed wrappers. In a cloth case. Vancouver, 1862. $17.50

Smith 1277 locates one copy, that in the Provincial Library of British Columbia. The work contains much information concerning the features of Vancouver Island, its Indian and White population, towns; indeed, it gives a complete picture of the island.

848 FORDHAM, ELIAS PYM. Personal Narrative of Travels in Virginia, Maryland, Pennsylvania, Ohio, Indiana, Kentucky; and a Residence in the Illinois Territory, 1817-1818. Edited by F. A. Ogg. 8vo, cloth. Cleveland, 1906. $7.50

849 [FOREIGN MISSIONS.] American Board of Commissioners for Foreign Missions Annual Reports. From 1834 through 1850. 16 vols., 8vo, original printed wrappers. N. Y., 1834-1850. $75.00

A fine run of this scarce work in the original wrappers. Like the Missionary Herald this work is indispensable if one wishes to gather accurate first-hand knowledge of the west from the pen of men who were on the ground. They saw it happen. Not only is there complete official reports of all the Oregon missions but other missions throughout the western territories.

850 FORSTER, JOHN R. History of the Voyages and Discoveries made in the North. Maps. 4to, half calf. Dublin, 1786. $10.00

Contains an account of the Island of Anticosti Newfoundland; William Baffin's Voyage; Bering's Voyage; Button's Voyage to Hudson's Bay; Cabot's Voyage; Dobbs' Voyage of Discovery; James Cook; Davis' Voyage; Voyage of Juan de Fuca; Hudson's Bay Co.; James' Voyage; Nova Scotia, etc.

851 FORSYTH, GEN. GEORGE A. The Story of the Soldier. Plates. 389 pp., 12mo, cloth. N. Y., 1900. $6.00

An accurate work on the wars and explorations of the western frontier from 1846 to the close of the Nez Perce campaign in 1877; with long and detailed accounts of the various Indian wars, including the troubles of 1866-67; the Sioux Campaigns of 1868-69; the Piegan Clash; Apache Battles; Modoc War; Sioux Campaign of 1876; Nez Perce War, etc.

852 FOSTER, JOHN W. A Century of American Diplomacy; Being a Brief Review of the Foreign Relations of the U. S., 1776-1876. 497 pp., 8vo, cloth. Boston, 1902. $4.75

Oregon boundary; project to concede to Great Britain the territory north of the Columbia River; History of the Oregon Question, etc.

853 FOUNTAIN, PAUL. The Eleven Eaglets of the West. 8vo, cloth, uncut. London, 1906. $4.75

Exceedingly interesting narrative of travels in California, Oregon, Washington, Idaho, Montana, Wyoming, Utah, Colorado, Arizona, New Mexico and Nevada when these states were still considered as "wild west".

854 FOURSIN, PIERRE. La Colonisation Francaise au Canada Manitoba Territories du Nord-Ouest Colombie Anglaise. 45 pp., original wrappers. Ottawa, 1891. $4.75

855 FOWLER, JACOB. The Journal of Jacob Fowler, Narrating an Adventure from Arkansas through the Indian Teritory, Oklahoma, Kansas, Colorado and New Mexico, to the sources of the Grande del Norte, in 1821-22. Edited with notes by Elliott Coues. Facs., 183 pp., 8vo, cloth. N. Y., 1898. $6.50

The original manuscript was discovered by Mr. Couees in the collection of Col. Durrett of Louisville. So far as is known Fowler was the first man to make the journey he describes.

856 FRANCE, GEO. W. The Struggles for Life and Home in the North-West. By a Pioneer Home-builder. Numerous illus., 607 pp., 8vo, original printed wrappers. N. Y., 1890. $10.00

Trip across the plains to Salt Lake City in '65; over the deserts to California; experience at the mines; settlement of Walla Walla; Indian wars; land jumping; seven years experience in the Seateo Bastile for murder; defending himslf against the claim jumpers; expose of the courts and laws of Montana, Oregon, Calif., and Alaska; how big land steals are worked, etc.

FINE TALL COPY OF FRANCHERE'S NARRATIVE

857 FRANCHERE, GABRIEL. Relation d'un voyage a la cote du nord-ouest inal calf. 284 pp., including half title. Montreal: De l'Imprimerie de C. B. Pasteur, 1820. $125.00

Fine copy of the Original Edition, from the library of J. Quinn Thornton, noted Oregon Pioneer and Author. Wagner-Camp 16. This narrative contains some account of Robert Stuart and Wm. Hunt, and of the establishment of Astor's trading post on the Columbia.

858 —— The same. 12mo, cloth. N. Y., 1854. $12.50

859 FRANKLIN, CAPT. SIR JOHN. Narrative of a Journey to the Shores of the Polar Sea, 1819-22. With an Appendix on Various Subjects relating to Science and Natural History. Also: Narrative of a Second Expedition to the Shores of the Polar Sea, 1825-27. Together, 2 vols., maps and plates (some colored), 4to, half calf. London, 1823-28. $20.00

Wagner-Camp 23 and 34. This expedition started overland from York Factory (Hudson Bay) to explore the northern coast of America, from the mouth of the Coppermine River to the eastern extremity of the continent. It passed up the Hayes, Steel and Hill Rivers, Jack River, Knee Lake, Trout River, Holy Lake, Windy Lake, White Fall Lake, Lake Winnipeg, the Saskatchewan, Cross Cedar and Pine Island Lakes, to Cumberland House. From there they went to Carlton House and Ft. Chipewyan, thence Slave Lake, Ft. Providence and the upper I rt of the Coppermine River, wintering at Ft. Enterprise. In June of the following year a fresh start was made up the Coppermine to its mouth. From there the Polar Sea was navigated for 550 miles. The party then journeyed back across the barren countries, arriving again at Ft. Enterprise after suffering extreme hardships.

860 FRASER, J. D. The Gold Feve.; , Two Years in Alaska. A True Narrative of Actual Events as Experienced by the Author. 100 pp., 8vo, original wrappers. N. p., n. d. (1923). $3.75

861 FREMONT, JOHN C. Report of the Exploring Expedition to the Rocky Mountains . . . 693 pp., 22 plates, 3 maps, tables. 8vo, cloth. Washington: Gales and Seaton, 1845. $5.00

862 FREMONT, JOHN C. Report of the Exploring Expedition to the Rocky Mountains in the Year 1842, and to Oregon and North California in the Years 1843-4. Numerous litho. views, folding plates, etc. 8vo, cloth. Washington, 1845. $5.00

863 FREMONT, JOHN C. Narrative of the Exploring Expedition to the Rocky Mountains in the Year 1842, and to Oregon and North California in the Years 1843-44. 185 pp., 8vo, cloth. N. Y., 1846. $4.50

864 FREMONT, JOHN C. Oregon and California; the Exploring Expedition to the Rocky Mountains, Oregon and California. 456 pp., 2 ports. 8vo, cloth. Buffalo, 1849. $5.00

865 FREMONT, JOHN C. Geographical Memoir upon Upper California in Illustration of the Map of Oregon and California. 67 pp., large folding map, original printed wrappers. Washington, 1848. $10.00

866 —— The same. 67 pp., 8vo, sewn. Washington, 1848. No map. $2.50

867 FREMONT, JOHN C. Col. Fremont's Religion. The Calumnies against him, exposed by Indisputable Proofs. 10 pp., 8vo, sewn. N. Y., 1856. $4.00

868 FREMONT, JOHN C. The Life of. 8vo, illus., original wrappers. N. Y., 1856. $8.50

A scarce biography apparently used as a campaign document.

869 FREMONT, JOHN C. Memoirs of My Life, including the Narative of Five Journeys of Western Exploration, 1842-54. Illustrated with original portraits, etc. 4to, one vol. (all published), original printed wrappers, uncut, map. Chicago, 1887. $10.00

Extremely rare.

870 FREMONT, JOHN C. The Fearful Issue to be Decided in November Next. Shall the Constitution and the Union Stand or Fall. Fremont, the Sectional Candidate of the advocates of Dissolution. 24 pp., 8vo, sewn. N. p., n. d. $6.50

Apparently a scarce campaign document.

871 FRENCH, L. H. Nome Nuggets: Some of the Experiences of a Party of Gold-Seekers in Northwestern Alaska. 102 pp., illus., 8vo, cloth. N. Y., 1901. $5.00

Smith 1335 reports one copy.

872 FROEBEL, JULIUS. Seven Years' Travel in Central America, Northern Mexico and the Far West of the U. S. Illus., 8vo, cloth. London, 1859. $7.50

Wagner-Camp 292. One of the most interesting books of travel through the southwest. He went to California by way of Santa Cruz, and down the Gila, arriving at Los Angeles Sept. 9, 1852.

873 —— Same. Rare Original German Edition. 2 vols., 12mo, cloth. Leipzig, 1857-58. $12.50

874 —— Same. French Edition. 3 vols., 8vo, cloth. Bruxelles, 1861. $12.50

875 FRY, F. Fry's Traveler's Guide and Descriptive Journal of the Great North-Western Territories of the U. S. of America; comprising the Territories of Idaho, Washington, Montana, and the state of Oregon, with sketches of Colorado, Utah, Nebraska and British America, &c. . . . 16mo, original cloth. 264 pp. Cincinnati, 1865. $40.00

Wagner-Camp 416. Author went from Council Bluffs, 1858, to South Pass, old Ft. Hall and Ft. Boise. He gives an account of the Boise placer mines, also of the Dalles, and considerable information on Montana.

876 FRY, JAMES B. Army Sacrifices; or, Briefs from Official Pigeon-Holes. 16mo, cloth. N. Y., 1879. $5.00

The Fetterman, Grattan and Canby Massacres, the Indian fights of Forsyth, Hartsuff, Powell; a voyage to Oregon in 1848; etc.

877 FULLER, GEO. W. History of the Pacific Northwest. 383 pp., 8vo, cloth. N. Y., 1931. $5.00

878 FURLONG, CHAS. W. Let 'Er Buck. A Story of the Passing of the Old West. 242 pp., illus., 8vo, cloth. N. Y., 1921. $3.00

Cowboy life in the west.

879 [FUR TRADE.] Chambers Repository. (Exhaustive accounts of the Fur Trade in North America, and the Hudson's Bay Co.). Vol. 5, No. 65. 8vo, calf. London, 1853-54. $7.50

880 [FUR TRADE.] (Elliott, Henry W.). Report on the Prybilov or Seal Islands of Alaska. First Edition. Illus. with many full-page tinted plates. 4to, half morocco. Washington, 1873. $35.00

One of the rarest of the American fur hunting books. For some reason, perhaps because of its frank statement, the book was suppressed and no other copy has been publicly sold since the Burton Sale of 1916. The original report can be distinguished in that it was printed the reverse way of the page and the plates tinted. The revised edition is quite common. The author gives more than a a statistical report, he gives the entire history of seal hunting, details of various methods, conservation, etc.

881 [FUR TRADE.] (Campbell, Robert). A History of the Scotch Presbyterian Church. 8vo, cloth. Illus. 801 pp. Montreal, 1887. $17.50

Contains many sketches of members of the church who were prominent in the fur trade in the Northwest among them being Simon Fraser, McDonald, Alexander Mackenzie, Simon McTavish and many more. This book was published in a small edition and is now quite scarce.

882 [FUR TRADE.] (Elliott, Thomas Coit). The Fur Tade in the Columbia River Basin prior to 1811. 16 pp., front., wrappers. Portland, 1915. $10.00

A scarce pamphlet on the subject. Smith 1125 cites but three copies.

883 [FUR TRADE.] The Home of the Wolverine and Beaver; or, Fur Hunting in the Wilds of Canada. By Chas. Henry Eden. 254 pp., 8vo, cloth. London, n. d. $4.75

884 [FUR SEALING.] (Great Britain-Foreign Office). Russia No. 1 (1893). Correspondence respecting an Agreement for the Protection of Russian Sealing interests in the North Pacific Ocean during the Year 1893. 29 pp., folio. London (1893). $7.50

Smith 1505 locates one copy.

885 [FUR SEALING.] (Great Britain-Foreign Office). Russia No. 2 (1893). Correspondence respecting the Seizure of British Sailing Vessels by Russian Cruisers in the North Pacific Ocean. 116 pp., map, folio. London (1893). $7.50

Smith 1506 locates one copy.

886 [FUR SEALING.] (Great Britain-Foreign Office). Russia No. 3 (1893). Despatches from Sir R. Morier, inclosing Reply to the Russian Government in regard to the Seizure of British Sealing Vessels by Russian Cruisers in the North Pacific Ocean. 15 pp., folio. London (1893). $7.50

Smith 1507 cites one copy.

887 [FUR SEALING.] (Great Britain-Foreign Office). Russia, No. 1 (1895). Correspondence respecting the Agreement with Russia relative to the Seal Fishery in the North Pacific. 52 pp., folio. London (1895). $7.50

Smith 1508 locates one copy.

888 [FUR SEALING.] (Great Britain-Foreign Office). Russia, No. 1 (1890). Correspondence respecting the Seizure of the British Schooner "Araunah" by the Russian Authorities. 25 pp., map, folio. London, n. d. $7.50

Smith 1504 locates one copy.

888a GALLATIN, ALBERT. Views of the Public Debt, Receipts and Expenditures of the United States. 61 pp. First Edition. 8vo, unbound. N. Y., 1800. $7.50

889 GALLATIN, ALBERT). The Oregon Question. 75 pp., 8vo, wrappers. N. Y., 1846. $7.50

Cowan, p. 94: States that this is the best edition of Gallatin's masterly statement of the controversy which at the time was engaging the entire attention of both Great Britain and the United States.

890 GALLATIN, ALBERT. Synopsis of the Indian Tribes within the U. S. East of the Rocky Mountains and in the British and Russian Possessions in North America. 8vo, half morocco. Cambridge, 1836. $17.50

A fine uncut copy as issued in the Transactions and Collections of the American Antiquarian Society. It includes Dookin's Historical Account of the Christian Indians in New England, etc. This volume is the scarcest of the series, as a large portion of the edition was burned at the Stationer's Hall fire in Boston in 1836.

891 GALLATIN, ALBERT. Letters . . . on the Oregon Question, originally published in the National Intelligencer, Jan., 1846. 30 pp., 8vo, sewn. Washington: Gideon, 1846. $4.75

892 GALLATIN, ALBERT. The Oregon Question (Five Papers and Appendix). 75 pp., 8vo, original wrappers. N. Y., 1876. $4.00

893 GARCES, FRANCISCO. On the Trail of a Spanish Pioneer. The Diary and Itinerary of Francisco Garces, in his Travels through Sonora, Arizona and California, 1775-1776. Translated from a contemporary copy of the Original Spanish Manuscript by Elliott Coues. Maps, views and facsimiles. 2 vols., royal 8vo, cloth, uncut. N. Y., 1900. $15.00

Original edition. This diary describes the fifth and last journey of Garces as a missionary priest among the wild tribes from his station near Tucson, Arizona. He accompanied the expedition of Lt. Col. Anza to the San Gabriel Mission near Los Angeles, thence journeyed eastward as far as Zuni. A priest named Font accompanied Anza to San Francisco, making a very creditable map of the country which is published in the above work. The diary is aided by the critical notes of Mr. F. W. Hodge.

894 GARFIELD, HON. S. Climates of the Northwest; being condensed Notes of a Lecture. 20 pp., map, 8vo, original printed wrappers. Phila., 1872. $3.75

The author was delegate in Congress from Washington Territory. His work, as above noted, is devoted to proclaiming the superiorities of the Northwest over California and the inland states.

895 GARLAND, HAMLIN. Trail of the Goldseekers. 264 pp., 8vo, cloth. N. Y., 1899. First Edition. Fine. $7.50

896 GARLAND, HAMLIN. The Book of the American Indian. 274 pp., illus. by Remington. 8vo, cloth. N. Y., 1923. $6.00

TALL COPY OF GARRARD'S "WAH-TO-YAH", 1850

897 GARRARD, LEWIS H. Wah-To-Yah and the Taos Trail; or, Prairie Travel and Scalp Dances with a look at Los Rancheros and the Rocky Mountain Campfire. 349 pp., 8vo, original cloth. N. Y., 1850. $32.50

Wagner-Camp 182. Original Edition, with page No. 269 misnumbered 26. This is one of the most important narratives of the Overland trail.

898 GARRY, NICHOLAS. Diary of Nicholas Garry, Deputy Governor of the Hudson's Bay Company from 1822-1835. A detailed narrative of his Travels in the Northwest Territories of British North America in 1821. 8vo, cloth. Ottawa, 1900. $10.00

ORIGINAL EDITION OF GASS' NARRATIVE

899 GASS, PATRICK. Journal of Travels under Lewis and Clark, through the Interior of America to the Pacific Ocean, 1804-06. With a Description of the Country and an Account of its Inhabitants. 12mo, boards. Pittsburgh, 1807. $47.50

900 [GASS, PATRICK.] Geographical, Commercial and Political Essays, including Statistical Details of Various Countries. 321 pp., 8vo, calf. London, 1812. $5.00

Contains remarks on Patrick Gass' Journal of his voyage from the mouth of the Columbia to the Pacific Ocean.

901 GAYARRE, CHARLES. Essai Historique sur la Louisiane. 2 vols. in one 231 pp., half morocco. New Orleans, 1830-31. $22.50

Important and rare account of early Louisiana.

902 [GEORGIA.] Report Respecting the Operations for the Improvement of Brunswick Harbor, in the State of Georgia. Feb. 1, 1837 . . . 24th Cong. 2nd Session. 8vo, stitched. 5 pp. and folding map of Brunswick Harbor. Caption title. [Washington, 1837.] $3.00

903 [GEORGIA.] Discourse Concerning the Design'd Establishment of a New Colony to the South of Carolina in the Most Delightful Country in the Universe. By Sir Robert Mountgomery, Baronet. London, 1717. Reprinted 4to, cloth, folding plan. N. Y., 1914. $7.50

The original is of utmost rarity, being the first book published on the Present State of Georgia. Having obtained a grant along the Savannah River the author issued the above Proposals for settling the Colony (which he called Azilia)—Rich.

GEORGIA-FLORIDA BOUNDARY DISPUTE

904 [GEORGIA-FLORIDA.] Resolution of the Legislature of Georgia, with a Correspondence of the Governor of that State, Relating to the Boundary Line Between the State of Georgia and the Territory of Florida, March 17, 1826. 8vo, 8 pp., uncut and unopened. Washington: Printed by Gales and Seaton, 1826. $4.00

905 GERRISH, THEODORE. Life in the World's Wonderland: The Ranches of Dakota; the Wonders of the Yellowstone; the Mines of the Rockies; and the Stories of Old Trappers, Miners and Indian Fighters. Plates, 421 pp., 8vo, cloth. Biddeford, 1887. $5.00

GERSTNER'S TRIP THROUGH KENTUCKY AND OHIO

906 GERSTNER, C. VON. Beschreibung einer Reise durch die Vereinigten Staaten in 1838-40. 12mo, cloth. Leipzig, 1842. $30.00

Buck 335. The author traveled through Virginia, the Carolinas and Georgia to Louisiana, thence northward through Mississippi, Illinois, Kentucky and Ohio.

907 GHENT, W. J. The Road to Oregon. A Chronicle of the Great Emigrant Trail. 274 pp., illus., 8vo, cloth, d. w. N. Y., 1929. $3.75

908 GIBBON, JOHN MURRAY. Scots in Canada. A History of the Settlement of the Dominion from the Earliest Days to the Present Time. 162 pp., illus., 8vo, cloth. London, 1911. $4.75

Relates to the Northwest Coast, Hudson's Bay Co., and the Northwest Fur Company.

909 GIBBS, GEORGE. Dictionary of the Chinook Jargon; or, Trade Language of Oregon. 43 pp., 4to. Cramoisy Press, N. Y., 1863. $17.50

Smith 1394. This 4to edition of this work is rare, according to Cowan, who states that only 100 copies were printed.

910 GIBBS, GEORGE. Alphabetical Vocabulary of the Chinook Language. Small 4to, cloth. N. Y., 1863. $10.00

911 GIBBS, GEORGE. Physical Geography of the North-West Boundary of the U. S. (Journal of the American Geographical Society, 1870-1871). 8vo, cloth. Washington, 1871. $4.00

912 GIBBS, JOSIAH F. The Mountain Meadow Massacre. Illus., 8vo, wrappers. (Salt Lake City), 1910. $5.00

Scarce. A hostile attack on Mormonism, with new material on the massacre.

913 GIBBS, J. WATT. Recollections of a Pioneer: The Narrative of an Overland Trip to California in 1849 and 1850. Back Across the Plains in '51, with Accounts of Cattle Driving and Bear Hunting, and a Final Expedition Across the Plains through Wyoming, Idaho, Utah, etc., in Sixty-Five. 12mo, cloth. [St. Joseph, 1912.] $7.50

Original Edition of this scarce privately printed work. Gibson made the overland to California from Missouri in 1849, and had two years of adventure and mining there. The party, comprising Robert Gilmore and his son, Mat, James Gilmore and his son, Dave, Ben Poteet, Charles and Henry McCray, the author and his three brothers, left Missouri in May of '49. Gibson returned eastward across the plains in '51, and in '64 made another trip overland with cattle.

913a GIBBS, MIFFLIN WISTER. Shadow and Light. An Autobiography with Reminiscences of the Last and Present Century. 372 pp. Illus. 12mo, cloth. Washington, 1902. $75.00

The above work is a very scarce and uncommon book by an educated Negro who had many varied experiences in California and the Pacific Northwest. Born in Philadelphia, Gibbs was influenced at an early age by Frederic Douglas for whom he lectured and carried on propaganda work for the betterment of the Negro. He later went overland to California in the gold rush, arriving in San Francisco in Sept., 1850. He first worked as a carpenter and then founded the firm of Lester and Gibbs, dealer in fine boots and shoes. In 1851, Gibbs, with Jonas P. Townsend and W. W. Newby, published in the "Alta California," a public protest against being disfranchised and denied their right of oath. It was the first pronouncement of the colored people of the state of California. The protest caused much excitement at the time. Gibbs later published the first periodical in the state, "The Mirror of the Times," which advocated equal rights. In 1865, when gold was discovered on the Fraser River, he went there with a stock of goods. He resided in Victoria, B. C., for several years, being elected to the Common Council there in 1866. He later went to Florida, was appointed U. S. Consul to Madagascar; and in 1872 settled down to the practice of law in Little Rock, Ark., where he became a municipal judge. The above little work is an important contribution to the times and is seldom offered.

914 GILDER, WM. H. Schwatka's Search. Sledging in the Arctic for the Franklin Records. 316 pp., illus., map, 8vo, cloth. N. Y., 1881. $5.00

915 GILL, J. A Complete Dictionary of the Chinook Jargon. English-Chinook and Chinook-English. 12mo, 84 pp., original wrappers. Portland, 1909. $3.00

916 GILLIAM, ALBERT M. Travels in Mexico, during the Years 1843 and '44; including a Description of California, the Principal Cities and Mining Districts of that Republic, the Oregon Territory, etc. 12mo, cloth. Aberdeen, 1847. $4.50

917 GILLMORE, PARKER. Prairie and Forest: a Description of the Game of North America, with Personal Adventures in their Pursuits. By "Ubique." 378 pp., illus., 8vo, cloth. N. Y., 1874. $5.00

918 GILPIN, WM. The Central Gold Regions. The Grain, Pastoral and Gold Regions of North America, with some Views of its Physical Geography and Observations on the Pacific Railroad. 6 folding maps. 8vo, cloth. Phila., 1860. $7.50

Wagner-Camp 358. Gilpin first crossed the plains to Oregon in 1843. Contains 3 speeches on the Pacific Railroad.

919 GILMAN, DANIEL C. The Life of James Dwight Dane, Scientific Explorer, Minerologist, Geologist, Zologist, Professor in Yale University. 409 pp., 8vo, cloth. N. Y., 1899. $4.00

Dana was with the Wilkes' Exploring Expedition.

920 GILMAN, ISABELL AMBLER. Alaskaland, a Curious Contradiction. 110 pp., front., 8vo, cloth. Seattle (1914). $3.75

921 GILPIN, WM. Notes on Colorado Territory; and its Inscription in the Physical Geography of the North American Continent. 12mo, 52 pp., original wrappers. London, 1870. $12.50

Presentation copy from the author.

RARE GIORDA DICTIONARY OF THE "FLATHEAD INDIAN LANGUAGE"

922 GIORDE, JOSEPH. A Dictionary of the Kalispel; or, Flathead Indian Language. Compiled by the Missionaries of the Society of Jesus. Kalispel-English, English-Kalispel and Appendix. 3 vols. in one. 8vo, half green morocco, uncut. St. Ignatius Print, Montana, 1877-1878-1879. $35.00

Fine copy of the Original Edition. This, one of the most important works issued by any missionary press, was based on the manuscript dictionary of Rev. C. Mengarini. Owing to its large size, the labor of printing and difficulty of getting supplies, it must be self-evident that but few copies could have been printed or issued. The work is of utmost importance to the northwest and of extreme rarity. Smith 1422. Also see Pilling.

923 GIORDA, JOSEPH. Szmimeie-s Jesus Christ. A Catechism of the Christian Doctrine in the Flat-Head or Kalispel Language composed by the Missionaries of the Society of Jesus. 45 pp., 8vo, cloth. St. Ignatius Print, Montana, (Missoula) 1880. $40.00

The work is copyrighted by the Rev. J. Bandini, S. J. who stated that it was composed by Father Giorda. See Pilling Biography of the Salishan Language. Not in Smith.

924 GIST, CHRISTOPHER. Journals, with Historical, Geographical and Ethnological Notes; and Biographies of his Contemporaries. By William M. Darlington. Folding maps on Japan paper. 296 pp., 8vo, cloth, uncut. Fine. Pittsburgh, 1893. $15.00

First Edition, large paper copy. The journal of 1750 being a private report of the Ohio Co. has hitherto never appeared complete. The second journal of 1751 to 1752 has never been printed. The third journal is herein given complete. The journals contain much valuable material such as descriptions of the French Forts, biographical notes of the Montours, George Croghan, Tom Cresap, etc.

925 GLISAN, RODNEY. Journal of Army Life. Illus., 12mo, cloth. San Francisco, 1874. $7.50

The author joined the army as a surgeon in 1850. He relates of Indian service in Arkansas, on the Missouri, and the Southwest. He visited California in 1855. There is a further relation of Indian wars in Oregon and Washington in 1855-58.

ORIGINAL NARRATIVE OF BERING'S SECOND EXPEDITION TO N. W. COAST

926 GMELIN, JOHAN GEORG. Reise durch Eibirien von dem Jahr 1733 bis 1743. 4 vols., full vellum. Gottingen, 1751-52. $75.00

Original Edition of a rare and important work relating to Alaska and the Northwest. Gmelin was one of the scientists with Bering's second expedition, the largest and most extensive expedition ever sent out by any government.

927 GOLDER, FRANK A. Russian Expansion on the Pacific, 1641-1850; An Account of the earlier and later Expeditions made by the Russians along the Pacific Coast of Asia and North America; including some related expeditions to the Arctic Regions; with Bibliography and Analytical Index. Facsimiles and maps. 8vo, cloth. 368 pp. Cleveland: Clark, 1914. $7.50

The only authoritative study of the Russian expansion on the Pacific published in any language during the past century. The work is of such importance that the Russsian government has already translated and issued the volume in Russian.

928 GOLDER, FRANK A. Guide to Materials for American History in Russian Archives. 177 pp., 8vo, cloth. N. Y., 1917. $4.50

929 GOLDER, F. A. Bering's Voyages; an Account of the Efforts of the Russians to Determine the Relation of Asia and America. 2 vols., 8vo, cloth. N. Y., 1922-1925. $7.50

930 GOLOVININ, V. M. Begebenheiten des Capt. Golovinin in der Gefangenschaft bei den Japanern, 1811-13 nebst Bemerkungen uber das Japanische Reich und Volk und einen Anhange des Capt. Rikord. Aus dem Russische von C. Schultz. 2 Bde mit 7 Karten und Kupfern. 8vo, half calf. Leipzig, 1817-1818. $17.50

Wickersham 6170.

931 GOLOVININ, V. M. Sokrashchennyia zapiski flote Kap. Lieut. Golo vina o plavanii ego na shliepie Dianie dlia opisi Kuriljskukh ostrovov v 1811 godu. 146 pp., 3 folding maps, 4to, calf. St. Petersburg, 1819. $37.50

This is an epitome of the memoranda of Capt.-Lieut. Golovinin on his voyage in the Sloop Diana for inspection of the Kuril Islands in 1811. Not in Smith. Relates to the Northwest coast.

932 GOLOVININ, V. M. Puteshestvie vokrug svieta po poveleniiu Gosudaria v 1817-19. g. flote Kap. Golovinin. 3 folding maps and plates. 2 vols., 8vo, calf. St. Petersburg, 1822. $55.00

Wickersham 6164. Relates to the Aleutian Islands, Novo Archangel, Albion, San Francisco, Monterey, Sandwich Islands, etc.

933 GOLOVININ, VASILII MIKAILOVICH (Capt. of the Russian Navy). Memoirs of a Captivity in Japan during the Years 1811, 1812 and 1813, with observations on the country and the people. 3 vols., 8vo, cloth. London, 1824. $30.00

Smith 1433 locates one copy, that in the library of the University of Washington. The work gives an account of the voyages of Messrs. Chvstoff and Davidoff to the Northwest coast of America. The author also has much to say concerning Krusensten, Langsdorff ànd Broughton.

934 GOODE, REV. WILLIAM H. Outposts of Zion, with Limnings of Mission Life. 464 pp., port., 12mo, original cloth. Cincinnati, 1863. $17.50

Wagner-Camp 390. Fine copy of this scarce work by a pastor who for ten years was a member of the frontier conferences of his church. It relates to early scenes and events in Kansas and Nebraska from 1854-69.

935 [GOODLANDER, G. W.] Memoirs and Recollections of G. W. Goodlander of the Early Days of Fort Scott. From April 29, 1858 to Jan. 1, 1870 . . . And Biographies of Col. H. T. Wilson and George A. Crawford, the fathers of Fort Scott. Illus., 16mo., .cloth. Ft. Scott, Kansas, 1900. $6.00

936 [GOODNIGHT, CHARLES.] Pioneer Days in the Southwest. From 1850-1879. Thrilling descriptions of Buffalo Hunting, Indian Fighting and Massacres, Cowboy Life, etc. Illus., 12mo, cloth. Guthrie, 1909. $5.00

937 GOODWIN, C. C. As I Remember Them. 355 pp., 8vo, cloth. Salt Lake City, 1913. $4.50

Intimate personal sketches of many prominent western men.

938 GOODWIN, CARDINAL. The Trans-Mississippi West, 1803-1853. 528 pp., 8vo, cloth. N. Y., 1922. $3.75

939 GOODYEAR, W. A. Coal Mines of the Western Coast of the U. S. 162 pp., 8vo, cloth. San Francisco, 1877. $7.50

Relates to coal mines in Oregon and Washington Territory.

940 GORDON, LIEUT. A. R. Rapport de la dieuxeme Expedition de la Baia-d'Hudson. 114 pp., map, 8vo, cloth. Toronto, 1885. $3.75

941 GORDON, DANIEL M. Mountain and Prairie; a Journey from Victoria to Columbia. 310 pp., 4 maps, plates, 8vo, cloth. Montreal, 1880. $5.00

942 GORDON, GEORGE BYRON. In the Alaskan Wilderness. 247 pp., front., maps, facsimiles, 8vo, cloth. Phila., 1917.

Smith 1447.

Item 932, Size sould read 4to.

FINE COPY OF GORLINSKI'S MAP OF U. S.

943 GORLINSKI, JOSEPH. Map of the United States and Territories showing the extent of Public Surveys and other Details, constructed from Plates and Official Survey of the General Land Office, under the Direction of the Hon. Jos. S. Wilson, Commissioner. By Joseph Gorlinski, Draughtsman. 29 by 76 inches. Lithographed by Bowen and Co., Philadelphia, 1867. Folded and mounted in case. $22.50

The Gorlinski Map is without doubt one of the finest ever issued by the government.

944 GOSNELL, R. E. British Columbia, a Digest of Reliable Information regarding its Natural Resources and Industrial Possibilities. 48 pp., original wrappers. Vancouver, 1890. $7.50

Smith 1453 reports one copy.

945 GOSNELL, R. E. British Columbia, compiled from the year book of British Columbia and Manual of Provincial Information to which is added a chapter containing much special information respecting the Canadian Yukon and Northern Territory generally. 285 pp., illus., map., 8vo, cloth. Victoria, 1897. $3.50

946 GOSNELL, R. E. The Year Book of British Columbia, and Manual of Provincial Information. 406 pp., illus., 8vo, cloth. Victoria, 1911. $3.75

947 GOSNELL, R. E. The Story of Confederation, with Postscript on the Quebec Situation. 156 pp., illus., 8vo, cloth. N. p., n. d. $3.75

948 GOTTFREDSON, PETER. History of the Depredations in Utah. 12mo, illus., original decorated cloth. (Salt Lake City, 1919). $7.50

Original edition of an important work long out of print and now scarce. The author arrived in Utah with his parents in 1858 at the age of 12 years. They were pioneers of Mt. Pleasant and Sevier counties. Gottfredson was a herd boy from 1863-72 and took part in the Indian wars. The work contains many narratives relating to Utah that have never been published.

949 GOULDER, W. Reminiscences: Incidents in the Life of a Pioneer of Oregon and Idaho. Port. 12mo, cloth. Boise, Privately Printed, 1909. $12.50

An extremely valuable narrative. The author started overland in 1844 with Robidoux, went up the Missouri with both Benton and Robidoux (founder of St. Joe); he then joined the Waymire Oregon Train and reached the Boise Valley in '45; here his party were induced to take the "Meek-Cut-Off" to the Dalles, and because of this they only reached Oregon after much privation and hardships.

950 GOVE, CAPT. JAMES. The Utah Expedition, 1857-8. Letters of Capt. A. Gove to Mrs. Gove, and Special Correspondence of the New York Herald. 4to, original boards. Concord, N. H., 1928. $20.00

Wagner-Camp 298, note. One of 50 copies privately printed on large paper. Gove was a member of the Utah Expedition sent across the Plains in 1857 to "preserve order" and "obedience to law" among "recalcitrant and marauding" Mormons. The author's narrative, written in the form of letters, is a primary source and almost the only one aside from governmental records, for the history of the Mormon War and events of the overland during the years 1857-58.

951 GOWAN, HERBERT H. Church Work in British Columbia, being a Memoir of the Episcopate of Acton Windeyer Sillitoe, D.D.D.C.L. 232 pp., illus., 8vo, cloth. London, 1899. $6.00

952 GRAHAM, MAJOR W. A. The Story of the Little Big Horn. Custer's Last Fight. 174 pp., illus., 8vo, cloth. N. Y., 1926. $3.00

953 GRAINER, M. ALLERDALE. Woodsmen of the West. 206 pp., 8vo, cloth. London, 1908. $2.50

954 GRANT, G. Ocean to Ocean; being a Diary kept during a Journey from the Atlantic to the Pacific. 60 full-page plates. 371 pp., 12mo, original cloth. Toronto, 1873. $5.00

The author was a member of the Fleming Exploring Expedition. His narrative contains valuable particulars of the country traversed and of its Indian tribes.

955 GRANT, W. COLQUHOUN. Description of Vancouver Island by its First Colonist . . . Map. 8vo, cloth. London, 1857. $6.00

Smith 1473.

GRAVES RARE ACCOUNT OF ALASKA AND THE BUILDING OF ITS FIRST RAILWAY

956 GRAVES, S. H. On the White Pass Pay-Roll, by the President of the White Pass and Yukon Route; with Illustrations. 258 pp., 8vo cloth. Chicago, 1908. $50.00

Excessively rare. Smith does not seem to locate a single copy. The work was privately printed for private circulation. A delightfully written book giving the inside history of the first railroad constructed in Alaska. Contains a vivid picture of the conditions at Skagway, the lawlessness of the camps, vigilantes, Soapy Smith Tragedy, etc.

957 GRAY, WILLIAM CUNNINGHAM. Musings by Camps, Fire and Wayside. 337 pp., illus., 8vo, cloth. Chicago, 1902. $3.75

958 GRAY, W. H. A History of Oregon, 1792-1849. Drawn from the Personal Observation and Authentic Information. View of Astoria and slip of Errata. 8vo, cloth, 624 pp. Portland, 1870. $7.50

Original Edition of a work by one of the first Oregon pioneers. Gives a long account of the journey across the plains with Whitman and Spalding in 1836.

959 [GREAT NORTHERN RAILWAY.] Valley, Plain and Peak, Scenes on the line of the Great Northern Railway. 94 pp., illus., 8vo, cloth. St. Paul, 1898. $3.00

960 [GREAT NORTHERN RAILWAY.] The Oriental and Captain Palmer. 19 pp., illus. N. p. (1924). $1.50

961 [GREAT NORTHERN RAILROAD.] Editorial Comment on the Upper Missouri Historical Expedition of 1925. 30 pp., wrappers. St. Paul, 1925. $2.50

962 [GREAT NORTHERN RAILROAD.] Red River Trails. 27 pp., wrappers. N. p., 1925. $2.50

This charming little historical monograph, written by Miss Flandrau, portrays the romance of the beginning of the Great Northern.

963 [GREAT NORTHERN RAILROAD.] Oregon, the Twentieth State. 32 pp., map, illus., 8vo, wrappers. St. Paul, n. d. $3.50

Smith 1521.

964 [GREAT NORTHERN RAILROAD.] Last Year of the "Switchback." 19 pp., illus., 8vo, wrappers. N. p., n. d. $3.00

Railroading in the Cascades.

965 [GREAT NORTHERN RAILROAD.] Atlas of the Northwest. Royal 8vo, cloth. N. p., n. d. $2.50

Early atlas with large maps of the various states and territories.

966 [GREAT NORTHERN RAILROAD.] An Important Visit. Zebulon Montgomery Pike, 1805. 12 pp., wrappers. N. p., n. d. $2.50

967 [GREAT NORTHERN RAILROAD AND NORTHERN STEAMSHIP CO.] The Great Northern Country; being the Chronicles of the Happy Travellers Club in their pilgrimage across the American Continent as traversed by the Great Northern Railway Line and Northern Steamship Company from Buffalo to the Pacific Coast. 169 pp., illus., map, 8vo, original wrappers. (St. Paul), n.d. $7.50

Smith 1523 reports a copy in the Tacoma library.

968 GREEN, JONATHAN S. Journal of a Tour on the Northwest Coast of America, 829. 8vo, boards, 105 pp. N. Y., 1929. $7.50

Wagner-Camp 70, note. Heartman Historical Series, of which 160 copies were printed. Relates to Oregon, California, Northwest Coast and Sandwich Islands. The journal was first printed in the Missionary Herald, of which this is the first separate publication.

969 GREEN, WM. SPOTSWOOD. Among the Selkirk Glaciers, being the account of a rough survey in the Rocky Mountain Region of British Columbia. 251 pp., illus., map. London, 1890. $3.75

970 GREELY, ADOLPHUS W. Explorers and Travelers. 337 pp., front., illus., maps, 12mo, cloth. N. Y., 1893. $3.50

Includes accounts of Carver, Robert Gray, Lewis and Clark, Wilkes, Fremont, etc.

971 GREELEY, HORACE. An Overland Journey from New York to San Francsico in 1859. 386 pp., 12mo, cloth. N. Y., 1859. $7.50

Wagner-Camp 359. The above work relates the overland trip which inspired Greeley to make his celebrated advice: "Young man, go west!.' Greeley went up the Solomon Fork and Republican River to Cherry Creek, thence to Denver and Salt Lake, thence by Pleasant Valley and the Carson to California. He argues at the end for government aid to a transcontinental railroad.

972 GREENHOUGH, G. B. Address to the Royal Geographical Society, 27th May, 1840. 41 pp., 8vo, sewn. Ottawa, 1840. $7.50

Refers to the first journey of Dease and Simpson, to the Townsend expedition and to that of Prince Maximilian of Wied.

973 GREGG, JOSIAH. Commerce of the Prairies; or, The Journal of a Santa Fe Trader during Eight Years' Expeditions across the Great Western Prairies, and a Residence of nearly Nine Years in Northern Mexico. Two maps, six plates and woodcuts in text. 2 vols., 12mo, original cloth. N. Y., 1844. $50.00

Original Edition.

973a —— Same. 2 vols., 12mo, half roan, ex-lib. Phila., 1857. $15.00

974 GREENHOW, ROBERT. Memoir, Historical and Political on the Northwest Coast of America and the Adjacent Territories. Folding map. 228 pp., 8vo, sewn. Washington, 1840. $10.00

Among contemporary writers on the Oregon Question and on the events of Oregon history on which that question depended Greenhow should be deservedly mentioned in first place. His "Memoir" was prepared under the direction of the Secretary of State while the author was librarian of the State Department at Washington. It was published by order of the Senate at the request of the celebrated Linn, champion of Oregon occupation and settlement.

975 GREENHOW, ROBERT. The History of Oregon and California and other Territories on the Northwest Coast of North America; accompanied by a Geographical View and Map of those Countries. And a Number of Documents as Proofs and Illustration of the History. 8vo, cloth. Boston, 1844. $15.00

Original Edition. Cowan: "The ablest and most important work of its time. Greenhow has long been regarded as an eminent historian and his work is of permanent value."

975a —— Same. Enlarged, half calf. Boston, 1845. $15.00

Contains Falconer's "Strictures".

976 GREENHOW, ROBERT. Answer to the Strictures of Mr. Thomas Falconer of Lincoln's Inn, on the History of Oregon and California. Also Mr. Falconer's Reply to Mr. Greenhow's Answer; also Mr. Greenhow's Rejoinder. 2 volumes, 8vo, sewn, 7 pp., and 4 pp. (Washington, 1845). $12.50

Two rare pamphlets on the Oregon Question, which are seldom found together.

977 GRIEVE, JAMES. History of Kamchatka and the Kurilski Island, with the Countries Adjacent. Published at Petersbourg in the Russian Language and translated by J. Grieve. Maps and Views. 4to, half calf. Gloucester, 1764. $17.50

Relates to the northwest coast of America and the adjacent islands. The author also has much to say about the fur trade.

978 GRIFFIN, GEO. BUTLER. Documents from the Sutro Collection. 214 pp., 8vo. Los Angeles, 1891. $5.00

979 GRINNELL, GEORGE BIRD. Pawnee Hero Stories and Folk Tales, with Notes on the Origin, Customs and Character of the Pawnee People. 12mo, cloth, illus. N. Y., 1889. $5.00

980 GRINNELL, GEORGE BIRD. The Indians of Today. 185 pp., illus. 8vo, cloth. Chicago, 1900. $7.50

Smith 1544.

981 GRINNELL, GEORGE BIRD. The Punishment of Stingy and other Indian Tales. 235 pp., front. 12mo, cloth. N. Y., 1901. $7.50

982 GRINNELL, GEORGE BIRD. Jack in the Rockies; or, A Boy's Adventures with a Pack Train. 272 pp., 12mo, cloth. N. Y., 1904. $3.00

983 GRINNELL, GEORE BIRD. Beyond the Old Frontier; Adventures of Indian-Fighters, Hunters and Fur Traders. 286 pp., port., illus. 8vo, cloth. N. Y., 1913. $7.50

984 GRINNELL, GEORGE BIRD. The Fighting Cheyennes. Port., map, illus. 8vo, cloth. N. Y., 1915. $7.50

985 GRINNELL, GEORGE BIRD. Two real Scouts and their Pawnee Battalion. The Experiences of Frank J. North and Luther H. North, Pioneers in the Great West, 1856-1882, and their defense of the building of the Union Pacific Railroad. 299 pp., map, illus. 8vo, cloth. Cleveland, 1928. $7.50

986 GROVER, LÀ FAYETTE. Speech on the Oregon Question delivered in the House of Representatives, Jan. 26, 1846. 8vo, 16 pp., sewn. Washington, 1846. $3.00

Not in Smith.

GROVER'S EARLY OREGON ARCHIVES

987 GROVER, LA FAYETTE. Oregon Archives: Including the Journals, Governor's Messages and Public Papers of Oregon from the earliest attempt to form a Government down to and inclusive of the Session of the Territorial Legislature held in 1849. 8vo, new half calf binding. Salem, Oregon, 1853. $125.00

Smith was able to locate only two copies. The work is of the highest importance for the early history of the Oregon country, as it contains documents and papers nowhere else to be found. This is the George H. Himes copy with his notations.

988 GROVER, LA FAYETTE. Inaugural Address of Governor Grover. 8vo, 18 and 11 pp., original wrappers. Salem, Ore., 1870. $12.50

GROVER'S CAMPAIGN AGAINST THE MODOC'S

989 GROVER, LA FAYETTE. The Modoc War: Report of Governor Grover to General Schofield on the Modoc War and the Reports from the Field of Major General John F. Miller and General John E. Ross. Also a letter on the Indian Title and Rights of Settlers in the Wallowa Valley. 68 pp. 8vo, original printed wrappers. Salem, 1874. $37.50

Original Edition of a rare work unrecorded by either Bancroft or Cowan. An elaborate, comprehensive and amazingly frank statement of the causes of the Modoc War, with vivid accounts of the Lava Beds Tragedy and other brutalities and depredations made upon the whites. Gen. Ross' reports, which are included, give a detailed narrative of the campaign from the outbreak of hostilities to the end of the war with the capture of "Captain Jack."

990 GUNNISON, LIEUT. J. W. The Mormons; or, Latter Day Saints in the Valley of the Great Salt Lake: A History of their Rise and Progress, Present Condition and Prospects, derived from Personal Observations during a Residence among them. Plate. 8vo, cloth. Phila., 1856. $7.50

Contains also material on Jim Bridger and the Yellowstone country.

991 GUPTIL, A. B. A Practical Guide to the Yellowstone National Park. 122 pp., map. St. Paul (1890). $2.50

991a HABERSHAM, A. W. The North Pacific Surveying and Exploring Expedition; or, My Last Cruise. 507 pp., illus. 8vo. Phila., 1857. $12.50

Habersham was a lieut. in the U. S. Navy. The expedition sailed from Norfolk in June, 1853 and arrived in San Francisco, Oct. 1855.

992 HAFEN, LEROY. The Overland Mail, 1849-1869. Promoter of Settlement, Precursor of Railroads. 261 pp. 8vo, cloth. Cleveland, 1926. $7.50

993 HAGERTY, J. M. The Story of Okanogan. 32 pp., map. 8vo. Nighthawk, Wash. (1905). $3.00

994 HALCOMBE, JOHN JOSEPH. Stranger than Fiction. 275 pp., pl. and ports. 8vo. London Society for Promoting Christian Knowledge. London, 1873. $10.00

Recounts the missionary labors of William Duncan in British Columbia. The above copy was that of J. G. Swan with his notes.

995 HALE, CHARLES R. Innocent of Moscow. The Apostle of Kamchatka and Alaska. 23 pp. 8vo, original wrappers. N. P., n. d. (1888). $22.50

Innocent, Archbishop of Kamchatka, afterwards Metropolitan of Moscow, has been called the "Russian Selwyn", but he began his missionary labors much earlier than the Bishop of New Zealand and was called to a higher position of dignity than that held by the Bishop of Litchfield. John Vaniaminoff was born in 1797 and was graduated from the Seminary of Irkutsk in 1817, entering the ministry that year. He was consecrated Bishop of Kamchatka at St. Petersburg in 1840 and thereafter was known as Innocent. He spent 20 odd years in Kamchatka and Northwest America. This copy contains letters written by Innocent from Alaska. No other copy of this work has been located.

996 HALE, HORATIO. Was America peopled from Polynesia? A study in Comparative Philology. 15 pp. 8vo. Berlin, 1890. $5.00

Not in Smith. This work contains comparative pronouns in the language of Polynesia and Western America.

997 HALE, HORATIO. An International Idiom. A Manual of the Oregon trade language, or Chinook Jargon. 63 pp. 8vo. London: Whittaker & Co., 1890. $7.50

Hale was the philologist of the Wilkes Expedition; he was born in Newport, N. H. and was graduated from Harvard. For critical reviews of this work see those of H. de Charency, C. G. Leland, and J. Reade.

998 HALE, HORATIO. The Development of Languages. A paper read before the Canadian Institute. Toronto, April, 1888. 45 pp. 8vo. Toronto, 1888. $17.50

Presentation copy from the author. "When many years ago it fell to my charge to make the first ethnological survey of Oregon, I found in that region several families of languages remarkable for the great number, variety and expressiveness of their grammatical variations, among those the most striking . . . was the Sahaptin . . . commonly known among the Whites as the Nez-Perces. I was so fortunate as to obtain a complete account from a very able and accomplished American missionary, Rev. A. B. Smith, who had resided three years among them and who kindly placed in my hands his manuscript grammar, comprising one of the most thorough and profound analyses ever made of an unwritten tongue . . . with the aid of another highly educated and indefatigable missionary, the Rev. Dr. Whitman". The Sahaptin verb far surpasses both the Aryan and Semetic in the variety of its forms and the precision and nicety of its distinctions. There is much in this work about the Nez-Perces. No copy was located by Smith. Excessively rare.

999 HALL, ALFRED A. A Grammar of the Kwaguith Language. From Transactions of the Royal Society of Canada. Vol. 6, Sec. 2, 1888. 8vo, wrappers. Montreal, 1889. $5.00

1000 HALL, EDWARD HEPPLE. Lands of Plenty. British North America for Health, Sport and Profit. 192 pp., 2 maps. 8vo. London, 1879. $5.00

A considerable section is devoted to British Columbia, its position, boundaries and divisions, the gold region, Vancouver's Island; its mountains and shore scenery, forests, Puget Sound, salmon fishing, game sporting, etc.

1001 HALL, F. S. Studies in the History of Ornithology in the State of Washington (1792-1832) with special reference to the Discovery of New Species. (Contains David Douglas, pioneer naturalist on the Columbia River, 1825-1833). 8vo, original wrappers. (Seattle), 1934. $3.50

1002 HALL, F. S. A Historical Resume of Exploration and Survey—Mammal Types and their Collectors in the State of Washington. 8vo, original wrappers. Seattle, 1932. $3.50

1003 HALL, JAMES. Notes on the Western States; containing Sketches of their Soil, Climate, Resources and Scenery. 304 pp., 12mo, cloth. Phila., 1838. $5.00

Anecdotes of the first settlers, navigation of the western rivers, western steamboats, origin and early history, some accounts of the first boats, Cincinnati in 1826, etc.

1004 (HALL, JAMES A.). Starving on a Bed of Gold; or, The World's Longest Fast. 149 pp. 8vo, cloth. San Cruz, 1909. $10.00

A rare Alaska item.

1005 HALL, McCREARY. Explorations of the Northwest, the Louisiana Territory, the Oregon Territory. 8vo, original wrappers. Chicago, n. d. $5.0C

Not in Smith.

1006 HALL, RINALDO M. Oregon, Washington, Idaho and their Resources. 88 pp., folding map. 8vo, original wrappers. N. P., 1905. $3.50

1007 HALLER, GRANVILLE C. San Juan and Secession; Possible relations to the War of the Rebellion; Did General Harney try to make trouble with England to aid the Conspiracy? A careful review of his Orders and the Circumstances attending the disputed possessions during the Year 1859. 16 pp. 8vo, wrappers. N. p., n. d. $22.50

Smith, 1577, who locates but two copies. The above first appeared in the Tacoma Sunday Ledger of Jan. 19, 1896.

1008 HALLOWAY, W. L. Wild Life on the Plains and Horrors of Indian Warfare. 592 pp. 8vo, cloth. St. Louis, n. d. $2.50

1009 HALSEY, FRANCIS WHITING and Gaius Leonard Halsey. The Pioneers of Unadilla Village, 1784-1840, by F. W. Halsey, and Reminiscences of the Village Life of Panama and California from 1840-1850. By G. L. Halsey. 323 pp., illus. 8vo, cloth. Unadilla, N. Y., 1902. $7.50

Dr. Halsey sailed for California from N. Y., in Feb., 1849, a member of the Bristol and California Company. He worked in the mines during his stay in California and this work contains his diary from Feb. 12, 1849, to Nov. 11, 1849.

1010 HAMILTON, J. C. The Prairie Province; Sketches of Travel from Lake Ontario to Lake Winnipeg, and an Account of the Geographical Position, Climate, Civil Institutions, Inhabitants, Productions and Resources of the Red River Valley, with a Map of Manitoba, plan of Winnipeg, a view of Ft. Garry and others. 259 pp. 8vo, cloth. Toronto (1876). $7.50

Thunder Bay to Red River, down the Red River, Winnipeg, Ft. Garry, Hudson's Bay Co., portages, Indians and half breeds, Selkirk Settlement, Assinibije Crown Colony, etc.

1011 HAMILTON, W. R. Address to the Royal Geographical Society, 27th May, 1830. 8vo, 42 pp., sewn. Ottawa, 1839. $5.00

Has a fine tribute to the triumph of Dease and Simpson, and refers to Russian America.

1012 HAMILTON, W. T. My Sixty Years on the Plains, Trapping, Trading and Indian Fighting. Edited by E. T. Seiber. With illustrations by Charles M. Russell. 8vo, cloth. N. Y., 1905. $12.50

1013 HAMMOND, I. B. Reminiscences of Frontier Life: (Narrative of my Trip across the Plains in '65; Adventures among the Wild Animals and Pioneers of Wyoming, Montana, Idaho: Outlawry on the Frontier; Mine Salting, etc.). Port. and plates. 135 pp. 8vo, original wrappers. N. p.: Privately Printed for the Author's friends, 1904. $15.00

Owing to the author's death while the book was in press the whole edition was "scrapped," a few copies only escaping the paper mill.

1014 HANBURY, DAVID T. Sport and Travel in the Northland of Canada. Folding map and plates (some colored) and illus. 8vo, cloth. London, 1904. $10.00

A fine uncut copy.

1015 HANCOCK, SAMUEL. The Narrative of Samuel Hancock. With an Introduction by A. D. Snowden Smith. Folding map. 8vo, cloth. N. Y., 1927. $3.50

Detailed narrative of Hancock's overland trip to Oregon in 1845; his adventures and sufferings; his escape from the Indians; his gold seeking expedition to California; his life as a trader among the Indians on Puget Sound; together with an account of his captivity among the savages, and a recital of the Whitman massacre.

1016 HANDSACKER, SAMUEL. Pioneer Life, by "Uncle Sam" Handsacker, Pioneer '53, Private Co. B, 2nd Regt., Oregon Mounted Volunteers Rouge River Indian Wars, '55-'56. 104 pp., illus. 8vo, cloth. Eugene, Ore., 1908. $10.00

Smith No. 1591, who locates but two copies. The work was privately printed and is important in its relation to the Northwest.

1017 HANFORD, C. H. Seattle and Environs, 1852-1924. 3 vols. 8vo, illus. Chicago and Seattle, 1924. $12.50

Judge Hanford, an early pioneer, and at one time Judge of the U. S. District Court, in this work has written a reliable history of Seattle and vicinity.

1018 HANFORD, C. H., and Shepard, Charles E. Celebration of John Marshall Day, Feb. 4, 1901. Report of Proceedings, including orations by C. H. Hanford and Chas. E. Shepard. 60 pp. 8vo. Seattle, 1901. $3.00

1019 HANFORD, C. H. Halcyon Days in Port Townsend. 118 pp., illus. 8vo. Seattle, 1925. $22.50

Privately printed in a small edition. The author, a pioneer Judge of the Northwest, relates many incidents concerning men and events of the Pacific Northwest, especially Washington and Oregon. The work is extremely rare.

1020 HANFORD, C. H. General Claxton. Portrait. 8vo. N. Y., 1917. $3.50

This is really a narrative of pioneer days in early Oregon. Starting with the burning of his father's cabin at Seattle by the Indians, the narrative runs on to the end of the Civil War.

1021 HANS, FRED M. The Great Sioux Nation. A Complete History of Indian Life and Warfare in America. Illus. 8vo, cloth. Chicago, n. d. $4.00

1022 HANSON, MARCUS L. Old Fort Snelling, 1819-1858. 270 pp. 8vo, cloth. Iowa City, 1916. $3.50

1023 HANSON, JOHN. Map of South Eastern Washington compiled from Official Surveys and Published by Eastwick, Morris and Co. Size 20 by 40 inches, in a cloth folding cover. Seattle, Washington, 1878. $7.50

1024 HANSON, JOS. M. Conquest of the Missouri. Life and Exploits of Capt. Grant Marsh. Map and illus. 472 pp. 8vo, cloth. Chicago, 1909. $7.50

An authoritative work dealing with the period of conquest of the Upper Mississippi River Valley.

1025 HARDY, LADY DUFFUS. Through Cities and Prairie Lands. 8vo, cloth. Chicago, 1882. $3.50

Salt Lake City, Mormons, Nevada, California.

1026 HARDY, R. Travels in the Interior and West Coast of Mexico, Arizona, New Mexico and Lower California in 1825-1828. Folding map and 7 plates in aquatint. 540 pp. 8vo, original boards, uncut. London, 1829. $7.50

Narrative of the first exploration of the Southwest by a European. It contains valuable material relating to the Indian tribes; the Yaqui War; the Opate's; exploration of the Rio Colorado; pearl fisheries; River Gila; the mines, Sonora, etc.

1027 HARGRAVE, JOS. JAMES. Red River. 506 pp. 8vo, cloth. Montreal: Printed for the Author, 1871. $10.00

The author was the son of Chief Factor James Hargrave, who served principally in command of York Factory. His mother was a sister of Governor McTavish, to whom he became private secretary. As such he had access to all fur-trade and colonial records and came into personal contact, at Ft. Garry, with all the notables and veteran officers in the country. Consequently he had unique facilities for acquiring information, which he had the natural ability and education to make use of, and the moral courage to state without fear or favor. He was the most painstakingly accurate historian of the Red River and his book is one of the best on the Northwest.

1028 HARGRAVES, EDWARD HAMMOND. Australia and its Gold Fields; a Historical Sketch of the Progress of the Australian Colonies, with a Particular Account of the Recent Gold Discoveries. (Narrative of the Author's Travels and Experiences in California 1849-50; with an Account of the Discovery of Gold there). Folding map and port. 240 pp., 12mo, original cloth. London, 1855. $15.00

The author was the discoverer of gold in Australia and the original of Charles Reade's celebrated character in "It's Never Too Late to Mend." His explorations in Australia were induced by his experiences in the mines of California, and herein he gives a narrative of his trip to San Francisco in 1849; adventures on the overland journey to the "diggings"; life at the mines; experiences on the Sacramento and San Joaquin; trip to Maysville; Sutter's Fort; etc.

1029 HARMON, S. W. Hell on the Border, He Hanged Eighty-Eight Men! A History of the Great U. S. Criminal Court in the Indian Territory, and the Trials and Punishment thereof before Judge Isaac C. Parker, besides much other lore of untold value and interest to readers in every walk of life. Portraits and gruesome illus. 720 pp. 8vo, wrappers. Fort Smith, 1898. $7.50

1030 HARNETT (Legh, Esq. of California). Two Lectures on British Columbia. 50 pp. 8vo original wrappers. Victoria: Higgings and Long, 1868. $27.50

Not in Smith, Cowan, etc. Harnett, who had been a prominent mining expert in California for 17 years, was invited to B. C. to study the gold deposits and possible gold fields there. He spent upwards of a year in exploring, and these "lectures" are a description of his travels, work and discoveries. He visited all the diggings, describes them and their output, and discusses them in comparison with the mines of California and Idaho.

1031 HARNEY, W. D. Art Works of Seattle and Western Washington. 78 plates. Folio. Racine, 1910. $9.00

Smith 1600. Scarce.

1032 HARNEY, W. D. Art Works of Seattle and Alaska. 26 pp., 78 plates. Folio. Racine, 1907. $7.50

Contains fine plates of scenery in Seattle and Alaska.

1033 HARPENDING, ASBURY. The Great Diamond Hoax and other stirring Incidents in the Life of. Edited by James H. Wilkins. Portraits. 8vo, cloth. 283 pp. San Francisco, 1913. $3.50

The life story of a famous California character and early pioneer.

1034 HARPER, FRANK B. Fort Union and its Neighbors on the Upper Missouri. A chronological record of Events. 36 pp., illus., original wrappers. N. p., N. d. $3.00

1035 HARRIMAN, ALICE. A Man of Two Countries. 301 pp. 8vo, cloth. Seattle, 1910. $3.50

A narrative of Montana.

1036 HARRIMAN, ALICE. Songs O' the Olympics. 69 pp., illus. 8vo, boards. Seattle, 1909. $3.25

1037 HARRISON, CARTER. A Summer's Outing and the Old Man's Story. 12mo, cloth. Chicago, 1891. $4.50

Dakota and the Missouri River, the National Park, Helena, Vancouver, etc.

1038 HARRINGTON, DOSSIE ELMER. Diary of Basil Nelson Longworth, March 15, 1853 to Jan. 22, 1854, covering the period of his migration from Ohio to Oregon. 43 pp., original wrappers. Denver, 1927. $5.00

1039 HARRIS, MARTHA DOUGLAS. History and Folklore of the Cowichan Indians. 90 pp., illus. 8vo, original wrappers. Victoria, 1901. $5.00

Mrs. Harris was a daughter of Governor James Douglas.

1040 HARRISON, E. S. Alaska Almanac, 1909. Small 4to. 168 pp., wrappers. Seattle, 1909. $3.50

1041 HARRISON, E. S. Nome and Seward Peninsula. 112 pp. illus., folding map. 8vo, cloth. Seattle, c. 1905. $3.00

1042 HARRISON, E. S. Industrial Progress in Alaska. 32 pp., illus. 8vo, original wrappers. Seattle, 1909. $3.00

1043 HARRISON, E. S. Alaska, the Sportsman's Paradise. 12 pp. 8vo, original wrappers. Seattle, N. d. $3.00

1044 HARRISON, E. S. Alaska Geography, Physiography, Climate, History and Government. 8 pp. 8vo. Seattle, 1909. $2.00

1045 HARRISON, E. S. Scenic Alaska. 8 pp., sewn. Seattle, 1909. $2.00

1046 HARRISON, E. S. Resources of Alaska. 32 pp., original wrappers. Seattle, 1909. $2.50

1047 HARRISON, E. S. Nome and the Seward Peninsula. A Book of Information about Northwestern Alaska. 132 pp., maps, illus. 8vo, original wrappers. Seattle (c. 1905). $3.75

1048 HARRISON, J. T. Eulogy pronounced by J. T. Harrison over the Remains of his friend Griffith Davies. 12mo, sewn. Seattle, 1924. $3.75

Davies was an old pioneer in Seattle.

1049 HARRISON, C. Haida Grammar. Edited by A. F. Chamberlain. Royal Society of Canada Proceedings, pp. 123-226, Series 2, vol. 1, 1895. Cloth, 8vo. Montreal, 1895. $4.50

1050 HASKELL, WILLIAM B. Two Years in the Klondike and Alaska Gold-Fields. A thrilling Narrative of Personal Experiences and Adventure in the Wonderful Gold Regions of Alaska and the Klondike, etc. 558 pp., illus. 8vo, cloth. Hartford, 1898. $3.50

1051 HASKINS, C. W. The Argonauts of California, being Reminiscences of Scenes and Incidents that occurred in the Early Mining Days. By a Pioneer. Numerous Plates. 501 pp., 8vo, cloth. N. Y.: Published for the Author, 1890. $12.50

An interesting narrative of the life, adventures and experiences during the early days of the gold rush. A particularly valuable feature is its "Pioneer Index," which occupies no less than 142 pages and lists upwards of 35,000 argonauts who had reached the state by Dec. 31, 1849. These include the various pioneer expeditions by sea and across the plains, with names of companies, individuals and vessels, and places and dates of departure.

1052 HASTINGS, L. B. Typewritten Manuscript of an Overland Journey from Hancock County, Illinois to Oregon in 1847. Folio. 39 typesheets. N.p., N.d. $17.50

1053 HART, ADOLPHUS M. History of the Valley of the Mississippi. Crown 8vo. Cloth. Cincinnati, 1853. $5.00

1054 HARTE, BRET. Tales of the Argonauts and other Sketches. 293 pp., 8vo, cloth. Boston, 1875. $4.50

HASTING'S RARE GUIDE TO OREGON AND CALIFORNIA

1055 HASTINGS, LANSFORD W. The Emigrant's Guide, to Oregon and California, containing Scenes and Incidents of a Party of California Emigrants; and a Description of California; with a Description of Different Routes to those Countries; and all necessary Information relative to Equipment, Supplies and Method of Traveling. By Lansford W. Hastings, Leader of the Oregon and California Emigrants of 1842. 8vo, [with remnants of the Original Wrappers.] Cincinnati: George Conclin. 1845. [Sold]

1056 HAUPT, H. The Yellowstone National Park. Large map and Illus. 8vo, cloth. N. Y., 1883. $7.50

Not in Smith.

THE FIRST HAWAIIAN VOCABULARY IN ENGLISH

1057 [HAWAII.] (Andrews, Louvin). Vocabulary of Words in the Hawaiian Language. 32 pp., boards. Lahainaluna: Press of the High School, 1836. $35.00

The very rare first Hawaiian Vocabulary.

1058 HAWKES, ERNEST WILLIAM. The "Inviting-in" Feast of the Alaska Eskimos. 29 pp., 13 full page plates. 8vo, wrappers. Ottawa, 1913. $3.75

Not in Smith.

1059 HAWLEY, A. T. Portland, Oregon, the Metropolis of the Pacific Northwest. Illus. 8vo, original wrappers, N.p., N.d. (Portland). $2.75

1060 HAWORTH, PAUL LELAND. Trailmakers of the Northwest. 277 pp., 8vo, cloth, front., and illus. N. Y., 1921. $3.00

1061 HAWORTH, PAUL LELAND. On the Headwaters of the Peace River. A Narrative of a Thousand Mile Canoe trip to a little known Range of the Canadian Rockies. 295 pp., front., illus., maps. 8vo, cloth. N. Y., 1921. $4.00

1062 HAWTHORNE, JULIAN and BREWERTON, G. DOUGLAS. History of Washington . . . the Evergreen State, from Early Dawn to Daylight. 4to, cloth. N. Y., 1893. $7.50

Contains many full page portraits paged as text.

1063 HAYDEN, F. V. Sun Pictures of Rocky Mountain Scenery, with a Description of the Geographical and Geological Features, and some Account of the Resources of the Great West . . . Illus. 4to, half mor. N. Y., 1870. $12.50

The illustrations consist of 30 views along the line of the Pacific Railroad from Omaha to Sacramento. The author was U. S. geologist and author of important contributions to the geology of the West.

1064 HAYDEN, F. V. Twelfth Annual Report of the U. S. Geological and Geographical Survey of the Territories. A report of the progress of Exploration in Wyoming and Idaho for the Year 1878. 2 vols., 8vo, cloth. Washington, 1883. $7.50

1065 HAYDON, A. L. Riders of the Plains. Illus. 8vo, cloth. Chicago (1910). $3.00

Adventures and romance with the Northwest Mounted Police, 1873-1910.

HAYMOND'S HISTORICAL ARGUMENT IN BEHALF OF THE PACIFIC RAILROAD BEFORE THE SENATE COMMITTEE

1066 HAYMOND, CREED. The Central Pacific Railroad. Its Relations with the Government. It has Performed all its Obligations. Arguments of Creed Haymond, its General Solicitor, made to a Select Committee of the U. S. Senate, Consisting of Senators Frye, Dawes, Hiscock, Davis, Morgan, Butler and Hearst. 181 pp., 8vo, original front wrapper. Washington (1888). $17.50

The Original Issue privately printed. The argument occupied three days in its delivery. An exhaustive review of the overland railroad project and its development, prepared by the head of the law department of the road in defense of Huntington, Crocker and Stanford in vindication of their work in connection with the building of the Central Pacific Railway and in reply to "slanders of twenty years". Haymond discusses the purposes in hand; denounces certain "railroad wreckers"; recites directors and their upbuilding; the surveys and construction of the road; the acquisition of additional roads; and much other early information. This is an essential volume of railroad history.

1067 HAYS, JEFF W. Portland and Oregon, A.D. 1999, and other Sketches. 112 pp., 8vo, original wrappers. Portland, 1915. $3.00

Smith No. 1636.

1068 HAYES, JEFF W. Looking Backward at Portland. Devoted to the Old-Timers of the early '80's with humorous stories and Historical Data. 101 pp. 8vo, original wrappers. Portland, 1911. $4.50

1069 HAZARD, JOSEPH. Snow Sentinels of the Pacific Northwest. 248 pp. 8vo, cloth. Seattle, 1932. $2.50

1070 HAZARD, JOSEPH. The Glacier Playfields of the Mt. Ranier National Park. 96 pp. 8vo, original wrappers. (Seattle), 1920. $3.50

1071 HAZLITT, W. C. British Columbia and Vancouver Island; comprising a Historical Sketch of the British Settlements in the North-West Coast of America. And a Survey of the Character, Capabilities, Topography, Ethnology, etc., of that Region. Folding map, original pictorial boards. London, 1858. $17.50

The appendix contains a Vocabulary of the Chinook Jargon as used by the Indians on the Fraser and Thompson rivers and the surrounding country. First discovery of the coast by the Spaniards; voyages of Capt. Cook; discoveries of the fur traders; voyage of Vancouver; Fraser's voyages; gold discoveries; languages, etc.

1072 HEAD, GEORGE. Forest Scenes and Incidents in the Wilds of North America, being the Diary of a Winter's Route from Halifax to the Canadas. 362 pp. 8vo, cloth. London, 1929. $3.50

1073 HEALY, W. J. Women of the Red River, being a Book written from the Red River Era. 162 pp., illus. 8vo, cloth. Winnipeg, 1923. $4.50

A valuable contribution to the history of the Red River country. Contains numerous narratives contributed by early pioneers.

FIRST OVERLAND TO THE ARCTIC REGION

1074 HEARNE, SAMUEL A. A Journey from Prince of Wales Fort in Hudson's Bay to the Northern Ocean, undertaken by order of the Hudson's Bay Co., for the Discovery of Copper Mines, a North West Passage, &c., in the Years 1769-1772. Large folding chart of Hearne's and 8 plans and views. 4to, half calf. London, 1795. $80.00

First edition of the account of the first overland journey to the Arctic Ocean. Hearne gives much attention to the Natural History and the Indian tribes of the region traversed. He was sent by the Hudson's Bay Co., at their expense, to discover copper mines and a northwest passage. He dedicates his work to Samuel Wegg, Governor, Sir James Winterlake, Deputy Governor, and the Committee of the Hudson's Bay Company.

1075 HEBARD, GRACE RAYMOND. Sacajawea—A Guide and Interpreter of the Lewis and Clark Expedition, etc. 340 pp., illus. 8vo, cloth. Glendale, 1933. $5.00

1076 HEBARD, GRACE RAYMOND., and BRININSTOOL, E. A. The Bozeman Trail; Historical Accounts of the Blazing of the Overland Routes into the Northwest, and the fights with Red Cloud's Warriors. With Introduction by General Charles King. Handsomely printed in large type on handmade paper and extensively illustrated with maps (some colored), plans, views, etc. 2 vols. Large 8vo, cloth, uncut, gilt tops. Cleveland, 1922. $10.00

1077 HEBARD, GRACE RAYMOND. The Pathbreakers from River to Ocean; the Story of the Great West from the Time of Coronado to the Present. 263 pp., illus., 4 maps. 12mo, cloth. Chicago, 1911. $4.50

1078 HECKEWELDER, JOHN. Narrative of a Mission of United Brethren among the Delaware and Mohegan Indians, from its commencement, 1740 to 1808. Reprinted from the original manuscript, to which are added other documents are noted below: edited by W. E. Connelly. Thick 4to, cloth. Map, portraits and facsimiles. Cleveland, 1907. $17.50

Only 160 copies printed, each numbered and signed. Contains much of historic importance to Mich., Ohio, Pa., W. Va., Md., Del., N. J., Conn., Mass., and N. Y.

Field 946: "The narrative of this mission is one of the noblest labors of the human race. Heckewelder's narrative is a full and faithful record of the details of the mission, its wonderful success, and its appalling destruction . . ."

1079 HEDGES, JAMES BLAINE. Henry Villard and the Railways of the Northwest. 224 pp., maps. 8vo, cloth. New Haven, 1930. $2.75

1080 HEER, OSWALD. Flora Fossilis Alaskana. Fossile Flora von Alaska. Von Oswald Heer, mit 10 Taflen. 41 pp. Folio. Stockholm, 1869. $15.00

1081 HEGG, E. A. Souvenir of Alaska and Yukon Territory. 104 pp., illus. 8vo, wrappers. Skagway (Alaska), 1900. $7.50

1082 HELMS, LUDVIG VERNER. Pioneering in the Far East and Journeys to California in 1849, etc. 408 pp., map. 8vo, cloth. London, 1882. $4.50

1083 HENDERSON, LESTER D. Historical Sketch of Alaska, with Brief Outline of Resources and Civil Government. 39 pp. Original wrappers. Juneau, 1923. $5.00

1084 HENN, BERNHART, and WILLIAMS, JESSE. A Township Map of the State of Iowa compiled from the U. S. Surveys, official Information and Personal Reconnaissance, showing the Streams, Roads, Towns, Post Offices, County Seats, Works of Internal Improvements, etc., etc. A large and fine folio lithographic map in colors, 22 inches high by 35½ inches wide, folded in the original stamped cloth covers, gilt. Fairfield, Iowa and Philadelphia, 1855. $15.00

Rare. The best map of the state up to the date named. Shows the Emigrant Road to the Pacific; the Great Western Mail Route; Land Offices, main and common roads; railroads, completed and projected; the military road to St. Paul; etc. Henn and Williams were the principal land dealers in the state, with offices at Fairfield, Charitan, Sioux City and Ft. Dodge. A fine clean map.

1085 HENRY, ALEXANDER. Travels and Adventures in Canada and the Indian Territories, Between the Years 1760 and 1776 . . . 8vo, old calf. N. Y., 1809. $25.00

Wagner-Camp 7. This copy contains a leaf of errata at the end.

1086 HENRY, ALEXANDER. Travels and Adventures in Canada and the Indian Territories between the Years 1760 and 1776. New Edition, edited by James Bain. 347 pp. 8vo, cloth. Boston, 1907. $7.50

1087 HENRY, ALEXANDER, and THOMPSON, DAVID. New Light on the Early History of the Greater Northwest; the Manuscript Journals of Alexander Henry . . . and of David Thompson . . . 1799-1814; Explorations and Adventures among the Indians on the Red, Saskatchewan, Missouri, and Columbia Rivers. Ed. by Elliott Coues. 3 vols. Port., facsimiles, maps. Cloth. N. Y., 1897. $15.00

This is an entirely new and original work printed from the original manuscripts, and contains the daily journal of the author's travels, explorations and adventures in the fur trade throughout the vast territory west of the Great Lakes.

FIRST POEMS PUBLISHED IN WASHINGTON TERRITORY

1088 HENRY, FRANCIS. Lodge Odes of the Independent Order of U. F. F. U. Published by Authority under Dispensation 12347-001. And the Odes of Dennis, the Shoemaker. 16 pp. 8vo. Washington Standard: Olympia, 1858. $27.50

The above, which is probably the only known copy, is not mentioned by Smith.

1089 HENRY, FRANCIS. Address of Francis Henry, G.C., U.F. of F.U., delivered in the Methodist Episcopal Church at Olympia, Feb. 23, 1865. 16 pp. 8vo, sewn. U. E. Hicks, Printer: Olympia, 1865. $15.00

Not in Smith.

1090 HERIOT, GEORGE. Travels through the Canadas, containing a Description of the Picturesque Scenery on some of the Rivers and Lakes, with an Account of the Productions, Commerce and Inhabitants of those Provinces; to which is subjoined a Comparative View of the Manners and Customs of several of the Indian Nations of North and South America. Maps and plates. 4to, half morocco, by Morrell. London, 1807. $17.50

Contains large folding view of Quebec, map of the St. Lawrence, view of St. Paul's Bay, Quebec from Cape Diamond, Quebec from Beauport, Falls of Montmorenci, view of the City of Montreal, Fall of the Niagara, etc.

1091 [HERMAN, FATHER.] Ascetic and Enlightener of Alaska. 12 pp., front. 8vo, wrappers. N. p., N. d. $15.00

This interesting pamphlet was published at a missionary press in Alaska, in a very small edition. It is excessively rare. Not listed in Smith or other bibliographies.

1092 HERMANN, BINGER. The Louisiana Purchase and our Title west of the Rocky Mountains, with a Review of Annexation by the United States. 87 pp., 7 ports., 5 maps. 4to, calf. Washington, 1898. $4.75

SARAH HERNDON'S MONTANA MIGRATION OF 1865

1093 HERNDON, SARAH RAYMOND. Days on the Road: Crossing the Plains in 1865. Portrait. 12mo, cloth. N. Y.: Privately Printed, 1902. $15.00

Braislin 944. Sarah Raymond was a member of the Hardinbrooke oxtrain, and this is her day-by-day narrative of the journey. She drove one of the wagons, baked the best bread, and wrote one of the best overland journals extant. The Hardinbrooke outfit was constantly in close touch with the McMahan train, and both—much to their mystification—escaped all attack from the Indians. The secret of the immunity lay in the fact that McMahan's party carried a big portable engine and a lot of iron piping in plain sight, and the Indians thought it was a new and horrific engine of war. So they devoted their attention to trains in front and behind. The route was along the North Platte, through Bridger's Pass, Green River, and Wyoming Territory. Among others in Hardinbrooke's party who became prominent in Montana and the Northwest were Dr. Howard, Hillhouse, Winthrop, Kerfoot, Walker, Bower, Kennedy, Morrison, and Curry. Sarah herself married and settled in Virginia City, her first home being a log cabin with a dirt roof.

1094 HERNE, PEREGRINE. Perils and Pleasures of a Hunter's Life; or, The Romance of Hunting. Hand colored plates. 8vo, cloth. Phila., 1857. $10.00

The personal narrative of a St. Louis fur hunter, dealing with life and adventure on the plains and Rockies; trapping on the Yellowstone; wolf and sheep hunting in the South Pass country; Brown's Hole; Camp with Palliser on the Big Sandy; Life at the Rendezvous; Old Bill Williams, Fitzpatrick, Marceline, "Chabonard", etc. Journey from the Rendezvous southward across New Mexico to Texas and return to Brown's Hole.

1095 HERRIFF, E. L. Pocket Map of Tacoma and Puget Sound. Size 13 by 18 inches. Folded in cloth cover. C. 1889. $1.50

1096 HERRING, FRANCIS B. Among the People of British Columbia, Red, White and Brown. 229 pp., illus. 8vo, cloth. London, 1903. $7.50

1097 HERRING, FRANCIS B. In the Pathless West with Soldiers, Pioneers, Miners and Savages. 240 pp., illus. 8vo, cloth. London, 1904. $7.50

Early British Columbia with many early plates.

1098 HEWES, JOSHUA. Lieutenant Joshua Hewes, a New England Pioneer, and some of his Descendants, etc. Edited by Eben Putnam. 636 pp., illus. 8vo, cloth. Privately Printed. N. p., 1913. $22.50

The above work is quite rare. It contains a chapter on David Hewes of California, a pioneer of 1850, and also contains an account of the first locomotive used in Oregon, also a plate of same.

1099 HEWITT, RANDALL H. Across the Plains and Over the Divide. A Mule Train Journey from East to West in 1862, and Incidents Connected Therewith. Map and Illus. 12mo, cloth. N. Y., 1906. $35.00

Fine presentation copy by the author. A well-written and detailed account of an overland journey from St. Joseph, Mo., to Olympia, Wash., in 1862. The narrative is mainly in diary form. The author was at Ft. Kearney on June 24, at Ft. Laramie in Mid-July, South Pass end of July, the Yellowstone end of August, Walla Walla, first of October, thence to Portland and Olympia, arriving the first of November. He experienced most of the adventures and hardships of the overland pioneer—Indian raids, terrible desert crossings, buffaloes, grizzlies, etc. Part of the end of the journey was made on the Columbia River.

1100 HEYLYN, PETER. Cosmographie in Four Books: containing the Chorographie and Historie of the Whole World, and all the Principal Kingdoms, Provinces, Seas and Isles thereof. 2nd ed. 1098 plus (1089-1095) plus 21 unnumbered pages. 4 maps, tab. Folio, calf. London: Selle, 1657. $40.00

This work was quoted in Bancroft's "Northwest Coast." The above is the best edition of this rare work. Sabin 13278.

1101 HIATT, ISAAC. Thirty-One Years in Baker County. A History of the County from 1861 to 1893. 208 pp. 8vo, original printed wrappers. Baker City: Abbott and Foster Job Print, 1893. $22.50

A fine old narrative, much of which relates to the early gold strikes, life in the diggings, the Boise mines, the Powder River discoveries, Indian troubles, and travels and adventures on the plains and in the mountains.

1102 HIBBEN, T. N. A Dictionary of the Chinook Jargon; or, Indian Trade Language of the North Pacific Coast. 29 pp. 8vo, wrappers. Victoria (1871). $7.50

See Pilling.

1103 HIBBEN, T. N. Picturesque British Columbia from the Rockies to the Capital. Illus. 8vo, wrappers. N. pub. Victoria, n. d. $2.00

1104 HIBBEN, T. N. Guide to the Province of British Columbia for 1877-78. Compiled from the latest and most authentic sources of information. 410 pp. 8vo, cloth. Victoria, 1877. $7.50

Contains a dictionary of the "Chinook Jargon."

1105 HICKMAN, W. H. Brigham's Destroying Angel; the Life, Confession, and Startling Disclosures of the Notorious Bill Hickman, the Danite Chief of Utah. Written by Himself. Portrait and plates. 218 pp. 12mo, original pictorial cloth. N. Y., 1872. $8.50

Original Edition. Despite the title (which, together with some explanatory notes, was the contribution of Hickman's editor), this autobiography is one of the essential documents of western history. The author here narrates his trip across the plains to Salt Lake in 1849; thence to California with the Watson train; experiences among the miners and mining camps to 1852; return to Salt Lake and work during the Mormon War; massacre of the Aiken Party; trip into the Montana country in 1862; gold discoveries there; and his services as guide to Gen. Connor in the Snake River Region.

1106 HIGGINS, BETH BELL. Memory Pictures of Puget Sound. 53 pp. 8vo. New York, 1900. $4.00

Smith 1675.

1107 HIGGINSON, ELLA. Alaska, the Great Country. 537 pp. 8vo, cloth. Illus., map. N. Y., 1908. $4.00

Smith 1679.

1108 HIGGINSON, ELLA. The Vanishing Race and Other Poems. 28 pp. 8vo, wrappers. Bellingham, 1911. $2.50

1109 HIGGINSON, ELLA. From the Land of the Snow Pearls. Tales from Puget Sound. 269 pp. 8vo, cloth. N. Y., 1897. $3.00

1110 HIGGINSON, ELLA. Mariella: of Out-West. 8vo, cloth. N. Y., 1902. $3.50

Original Edition. Narrative of the Puget Sound country.

1111 HIGGINSON, ELLA. The Voice of April-Land and other Poems. 121 pp. 8vo, cloth. N. Y., 1903. $2.50

Smith 1686.

1112 [HILDRETH, JAMES.] Dragoon Campaigns to the Rocky Mountains; being a history of the Enlistment, Organization, and First Campaigns of the Regiment of U. S. Dragoons; together with Incidents of a Soldier's life, and Sketches of Scenery and Indian Character. By a Dragoon. 12mo, cloth. N. Y., 1836. $25.00

Wagner-Camp 59.

1113 HILDRETH, S. P. Pioneer History: Being an Account of the First Examinations of the Ohio Valley and the early Settlement of the Northwest Territory. Map and illus. 8vo, cloth. Cincinnati, 1848. $7.50

The above copy lacks map.

1114 HILL, ALICE POLK. Tales of the Colorado Pioneers. 12mo, cloth. 319 pp. Denver, 1884. $5.00

Original Edition. Relates the killing of Gantz by Gordon, the great flood, Indians on war path, coming of the railroads, the Bonanza Tunnel, Leadville, bandits of Colorado, etc., etc.

1115 HILL, JAMES J. Highways of Progress. 353 pp. 8vo, cloth. N. Y., 1910. $3.50

1116 HILL, GEO. W. Vocabulary of the Shosone Language. 36 pp. 12mo, half morocco. Salt Lake, 1877. $37.50

A much sought item. As far back as 1893, M. E. Jones, a Salt Lake collector, described this book as "the only copy I could find anywhere".

1117 HILL, JAMES J. Addresses. Thirty-four separate Addresses delivered at various times and places, from 1902 to 1916. Assembled and bound in one volume. 8vo, cloth. V. p., V. d. $22.50

The above work is probably the only copy of James A. Hill's collected speeches.

1118 HILL, J. L. The Passing of the Indian and Buffalo. 8vo, original wrappers. 47 pp. Long Beach, Calif., N. d. $4.50

Fine copy of a scarce item.

1119 HILLIARD, HENRY WASHINGTON. Speech of Mr. Hilliard of Alabama on the Oregon Question, delivered in the House of Representatives of the U. S., Jan. 6, 1846. 15 pp. 8vo. Washington: Gideon, 1846. $3.00

1120 HILL-TOUT, CHARLES. Notes on the Cosmogony and History of the Squamish Indians of British Columbia. 8vo, original wrappers. Toronto, 1897. $3.75

1121 HILL-TOUT, CHARLES. Notes on the Cosmogony and History of the Spanish Indians of British Columbia. Transactions of the Royal Society of Canada, Second Series, 1897-98, Vol. 3, Sec. 2. 8vo, original wrappers. London, 1897. $3.75

1122 HILL-TOUT, CHARLES. British North America; the Home of the Salish and Dene. With map and 33 plates. 278 pp. 8vo, cloth. London, 1907. $5.00

Relates almost exclusively to native races of British Columbia, Vancouver Island, Queen Charlotte Island, Northern Oregon and Southern Alaska, their inhabitants, dress and personal adornment; food and cooking, bark vessels, implements of war, social organisation; religion, social customs, folktales and myths. A work of much value in regard to this region.

1123 HILL-TOUT, CHARLES. Later Prehistoric Man in British Columbia. 103 pp. Royal Society of Canada, Ser. 2, Vol. 1, 1895. Ottawa, 1895. $2.50

1124 HILL-TOUT, CHARLES. Oceanic Origin of the Kwakintl-Nootka and Salish Stocks of British Columbia and Fundamental Unity of Same with additional Notes on the Dene. Royal Society of Canada, Proclamations and Transactions, Vol. 4, Ser. 2, pp. 187-231. Ottawa. $3.00

1125 [HIMES, GEO. H., Publisher.] Wa'amet or Williamette. 66 pp. N. p., N. d. 8vo, original printed wrappers. Portland: Himes, 1875. $22.50

This is a very rare Himes item. Fine copy.

1126 HINES, GUSTAVUS. Oregon and its Institutions; comprising a full History of the Williamette University. the first established on the Pacific Coast. 8vo. 326 pp., illus. N. Y. (1868). $4.75

1127 HINES, GUSTAVUS. Voyage Round the World; with a History of the Oregon Mission, and Notes of several Years' Residence on the Plains, bordering on the Pacific Ocean; comprising an Account of Interesting Adventures among the Indians west of the Rocky Mountains (with) a full description of Oregon Territory. 437 pp. 8vo, cloth. Buffalo, 1850. $5.00

Gives the results of several exploring tours among the Indians, their manners and customs gained from years of mission life.

1128 HINES, GUSTAVUS. Life on the Plains of the Pacific, Oregon; its Condition and Prospects. Containing a description of the Geography, Climate and Productions, with the Personal Adventures among the Indians. Portrait. 8vo, origial cloth, uncut. Buffalo, 1851. $7.50

1129 HINES, HARVEY KIMBALL. Missionary History of the Pacific Northwest, containing the wonderful story of Jason Lee, with Sketches of many of his Co-Laborers, all illustrating life on the Plains and in the Mountains in Pioneer Days. 510 pp., 17 ports., 2 plates. 8vo, cloth. Portland, (c. 1899). $7.50

1130 HINES, HARVEY KIMBALL. Jason Lee. 43 pp., wrappers. 8vo. San Francisco, 1896. $12.50

Smith 1717.

1131 HINES, HARVEY KIMBALL. Illustrated History of the State of Washington: Containing a History of the State of Washington from earliest period of its Discovery to the Present Time, etc. 933 pp., illus. 8vo, cloth. Chicago, 1893. $7.50

This work is now scarce.

1132 HINES, HARVEY KIMBALL. At Sea and In Port; or, Life Experiences of William S. Fletcher for Thirty Years Seaman's Missionary in Portland, Oregon. 251 pp. 8vo, cloth. Portland, N. d. $4.00

1133 HINES, HARVEY KIMBALL. Ascent of Mt. Hood, Oregon, Sept., 1864 and July, 1866. Proceedings of the Royal Geographical Society. 80-84 pp. 8vo. London, April 10, 1867. $5.00

1134 HITCHCOCK, ETHAN ALLEN. (Major Gen., U. S. A.). Fifty Years in Camp and Field, being his Diary. Edited by W. A. Crofut. Port. 8vo, cloth. 514 pp. N. Y., 1909. $7.50

This biography, covering the eventful years from 1814 to 1867, contains a stirring account of the memorable achievements in which this grandson of Ethan Allen played a conspicuous part. All the wars in which the nation engaged during these years, from the Indian troubles in Florida through the struggle for the preservation of the Union, are vividly presented. Gen. Hitchcock was born in Virginia and gives some notes of early times in Vermont; also he gives some account of Indian wars in California and Oregon in 1851.

1135 HITTELL, JOHN S. Commerce and Industries of the Pacific Coast of North America. 819 pp. 8vo, illus., 2 maps. San Francisco: Bancroft, 1882. $3.75

1136 HITTELL, JOHN S. Mining in the Pacific States of North America. 12mo, cloth. San Francisco, 1861. $7.50

Not in Cowan. Practically the entire book relates to mining in California. Full account of the rush to the mines; the Washoe River fever; and a full description of the mining districts of California. The scarcest of Hittell's works and one of the most valuable.

FIRST ISSUE OF "OLD GRIZZLY ADAMS"

1137 HITTELL, THEODORE H. The Adventures of James Capen Adams, Mountaineer and Grizzly Bear Hunter of California. Illus. 12mo, cloth. Boston and San Francisco, 1860. $12.50

Wagner-Camp 348. Original edition of a work which, according to Cowan, was "probably the most popular work of its time issued in California." The illustrations are by the celebrated San Francisco artist, Charles Nahl.

1138 [H. L. (JUNIOR).] A letter written from Ft. Scott, Indian Territory, Sept. 16, 1845. 8vo. In the London Athenaeum, Dec. 13, 1845. London, 1845. $7.50

The letter is a long three-column article. The writer joined Col. Kearney on the expedition to the Rocky Mountains and went with the U. S. Dragoons to Ft. Laramie, arriving there on the 17th of September. The command then started for the South Pass, etc., etc. Not mentioned by Wagner.

1139 HOBBS, CAPT. JAMES. Wild Life in the Far West; Personal Adventures of a Border Mountain Man. Comprising Hunting and Trapping Adventures with Kit Carson; Captivity and Life among the Commanches; Service under Doniphan in the War with Mexico; Desperate Combats with Apaches, Grizzly Bears, etc., etc. Illus. 8vo, cloth. Hartford, 1872. $25.00

Original Edition. Rare in the 1872 edition.

1140 HODGE, F. W. Handbook of American Indians, north of Mexico. 2 vols. 8vo. Map, ports., illus. Washington, 1912. $14.50

1141 HODGES, L. K. Mining in the Pacific Northwest; a complete Review of the Mineral Resources of Washington and British Columbia. 192 pp., 28 maps. 8vo, cloth. Seattle: Post Intelligencer, 1897. $12.50

Smith 1740. This work has become exceedingly scarce.

1142 HOITT, IRA G. Pacific Coast Guide and Programs of the Knights Templar Triennial Conclave, at San Francisco, August, 1883. 230 pp. 8vo, cloth. San Francisco, 1883. $2.50

1143 HOLBROOK, SAMUEL F. Treescore Years; an Autobiography containing Incidents of Voyages and Travels, including Six Years in a Man-of-War . . . Also two years in California . . . Illus. 12mo, cloth. Boston, 1857. $10.00

1144 HOLLEY, FRANCES CHAMBERLAIN. Once Their Home; or, Our Legacy from the Dahkotahs, Historical, Biographical and Incidental from Far-Off Days, Down to the Present. Illus. 8vo, cloth. Chicago, 1891. $10.00

RARE ACCOUNT OF LIFE ON THE PLAINS IN 1865

1145 HOLLIDAY, GEO. H. On the Plains in '65, by George H. Holliday, late Sergeant Co. G., 6th West Virginia Volunteer Cavalry. Twelve Months in the Volunteer Cavalry Service among the Indians of Nebraska, Colorado, Dakota, Wyoming and Montana. Crude woodcut frontispiece and other woodcut illus. 8vo, original printed wrappers. N. p., n. d. (1883). $47.50

Fine copy of the Original Edition. Perhaps the most interesting of all the post Civil War narratives. The author enlisted in the Union Army at the age of 15 and served through the rebellion. Mustered out in Washington he re-enlisted and his regiment was sent to the Rocky Mountains to protect the frontier, guard the overland mail and the government posts on the North Platte and elsewhere. A member of the 6th West Virginia Veteran Cavalry he served in Dakota, Wyoming and Montana. The Indians had had their way during the war years and this regiment was sent to enforce the law again. The regiment went from Washington to St. Louis, thence by steamer to Ft. Leavenworth, and on up the Missouri to Ft. Kearney. And the author is discerning enough in both major and minor details. There is some account of the Sioux Wars, of wild horses, hunting on the Powder River; fight at Horseshoe Station; buffalo in Wind River Valley, etc. This is both an interesting and intelligent narrative.

1146 HOLLINGSWORTH, LIEUT. JOHN McHENRY. The Journal of Lieut. John McHenry Hollingsworth of the First New York Volunteers (Stevenson's Regiment), Sept., 1846-August, 1849, being the Recital of the Voyage of the Susan Drew to California; the arrival of the Regiment in 1847; its military movements and adventures during 1847-49; Incidents of daily life and Adventures of the author in the Gold Mines. 61 pp. Royal 8vo. One of 50 copies issued on large paper and specially bound. San Francisco, 1923. $7.50

1146a HOLLISTER, O. J. Life of Schuyler Colfax. 535 pp., 8vo, cloth. N. Y., 1886. $4.75

Rare Account of Life on the Plains in 1865.

1148 HOLMAN, FREDERICK VAN VORHEES. Dr. John McLoughlin, the Father of Oregon. 301 pp., illus. 8vo, cloth. Cleveland, 1907. $7.50

1149 HOLMAN, FREDERICK V. Some Instances of Unsatisfactory Results under Initiative Amendments of the Oregon Constitution. 8vo. Portland: Privately Printed, 1910. $3.75

1150 HOLT, JOSEPH. The Relation of Music to the Civilization of the Northwest; a Lecture delivered before the Young Men's Hebrew Association of Portland, Oregon, by Joseph Holt, Friday Evening, October 24th, 1890. 26 pp. 8vo, original wrappers. Portland: Himes, 1890. $7.50

Not in Smith.

1151 HOOD, MARGARET GRAHAM. Tales of Discovery on the Pacific Slope. 172 pp. 8vo, cloth. San Francisco, 1898. $3.50

1152 HOOKER, WM. FRANCIS. The Prairie Schooner. 156 pp. 8vo, cloth. Chicago, 1918. $5.00

Fascinating history of the old days, written by a freighter.

1152a HODSON, JOHN MILTON, et al. Masonic History of the Northwest; a Graphic Recital of the Organization and Growth of Freemasonry in the Northwest States. 574 pp. 8vo, cloth. San Francisco (c. 1902). $7.50

Smith 1745.

1153 HOOKER, WM. FRANCIS, and DRIGGS, HOWARD R. The Bull-Whacker—Adventures of a Frontier Freighter. 167 pp., illus. 8vo, cloth. N. p. 1924. $4.50

Personal adventures of an ox-team driver and freighter in the early days of Wyoming and the Northwest.

HOOKER'S RARE "BOTANICAL MISCELLANY" WITH ALL THE BEAUTIFULLY COLORED PLATES

1154 HOOKER, SIR WM. JACKSON. Botanical Miscellany, Containing Figures and Descriptions of Such Plants as Recommend themselves by their Novelty, Rarity, or History, or by the Uses to which they are Applied in the Arts, in Medicine, and in Domestic Economy; together with occasional Botanical Notices and Information. 3 vols. 4to, 356 pp., 421 pp., 390 pp. London: Murray, 1830, 1831, 1833. [Sold]

The collation is as follows: Vol. 1: Title, Ded., 356pp., and 75 full page colored plates, including frontis.; Vol. 2, Title, 421pp., and plates numbered from 74 to 94, nineteen of which are colored. Vol. 3: Title, 390pp., plates numbered from 95 to 112, plus 19 full page colored plates. At p. 178, vol. 1, appears "Sketch of a Journey to the Rocky Mountains and the Columbia River in North America, by Thomas Drummond, Assistant Naturalist to the Second Land Arctic Expedition, under the Command of Sir John Franklin, R.N." There are also other references to Mensie, Scouler and Douglas.

The above work is a fine set of the Original Edition; it is extremely rare and important. Mr. Wagner, in his withdrawn edition, states, "I have never been able to locate a copy of this book."

1155 HOOKER, SIR WILLIAM JACKSON. Flora Boreali-Americana; or, The Botany of the Northern Parts of British America; compiled principally from the Plants collected by Dr. Richardson and Dr. Drummond . . . Illustrated with folding map and 238 plates. 2 vols. 4to, cloth. London, 1840. $125.00

Vol. 1. Fldg. map, 118 plates. Vol. 2, 328pp., 120 plates; 238 plates in both vols.

1156 HOOKER, SIR WILLIAM JACKSON. Companion to the Botanical Magazine; Being a Journal containing such interesting information, as does not come within the Prescribed Limits of the Magazine. Edited by W. J. Hooker. Portrait, colored lithographed plates and views. 384 and 381 pp. 2 vols., cloth. London, 1835-36. [Sold]

Wagner-Camp 60. The above appeared at "Companion to the Botanical Magazine", vol. 2, published in London for the proprietor, Samuel Curtis. The frontispiece to the volume is a portrait of Douglas. Vol. 1 collates 384pp., plus 18 folding plates, 17 of which are colored. Also at p. 16, vol. 1 appears an account of Mr. Drummond's departure from New Orleans to Texas, the particulars of his stay in Texas, etc. Vol. 2 collates 381pp., with 32 plates, most of them colored. This is probably one of the best sets of this rare work with all the beautiful large plates in splendid state.

1157 HOOPER, S. K. Rhymes of the Rockies; or, What the Poets have found to Say of the Beautiful Scenery. 64 pp. 8vo, wrappers. Chicago, 1898. $3.75

1158 HOOPER, WILLIAM HULME. Ten Months among the Tuski, with Incidents of an Arctic boat expedition in search of Sir John Franklin, as far as the Mackenzie River and Cape Bathurst. 417 pp., illus., 5 plates, map. 8vo, cloth. London, 1853. $7.50

This work is filled with relations of encounters with the Esquimaux, their mode of life, appearance and character. The author's long journey up the Mackenzie furnished many particulars of the Red Indians of the Coppermine and other tribes, of the wars with the Esquimaux and the horrible massacres of these unwarlike people.

1159 [HOPE, LOG OF THE SHIP.] (Ingraham, Capt. Joseph). Journal of the Brigantine "Hope" from Boston to the North-West Coast of America, 1790-1792, by Joseph Ingraham, Captain of the "Hope" and formerly Mate of the "Columbia." 241 pp. 11-14 inches in positive photostatic copy of the four original manuscript volumes forming this journal which appear to have been obtained during the discussion of the "Oregon Question." They were used by Mr. Greenhow in the preparation of his "The History of Oregon and California." See pp. 226-228. A valuable, interesting and human document. Ingraham was an officer in the American navy during the Revolutionary War. 241 pp. Folio. N. p., N. d. $75.00

The original log books are in the Library of Congress.

1160 HOPKINS, C. T. Common Sense applied to the Immigration Question showing why the "California Immigrants Union" was founded and what it expects to do. 64 pp., sewn. 8vo. San Francisco (c. 1869). $5.00

1161 HOPKINS, MRS. SARAH (WINNEMUCCA). Life among the Plutes; their Wrongs and Claims; ed. by Mrs. Horace Mann . . . 268 pp. 8vo, cloth. Boston, 1883. $4.75

Relates to the Bannock War, Yakima Affair, etc.

1162 HOPPE, J. Californiens Gegenwart und Zukunft. Nebst Beitragen von A. Erman, ueber die Klimatologie von Californien und Ueber die geographische Verbreitung des Goldes. 8vo, original printed wrappers, uncut and unopened. Maps. Berlin, 1849. $15.00

Item 1156, First line of note should read appeared "as" not "at."

1163 HORETZKY, CHARLES. Canada on the Pacific; being an account of a Journey from Edmonton to the Pacific by the Peace River Valley, and of a Winter Voyage along the Western Coast of the Dominion; with remarks on the Physical Features of the Pacific Railway Route and Notices of the Indian Tribes of British Columbia. 244 pp., pl., map. 8vo, cloth. Montreal, 1874. $10.00

The author organized and conducted the Overland Expedition of Mt. Sanford Fleming in 1872. His narrative is both interesting and reliable. The route was from Edmonton to Assiniboine, thence to Lesser Slave Lake Dunvegen, Ft. St. John, Rocky Mt. Portage, Stewart's Lake, Hazetton, Naas, Ft. Simpson, Nanaimo, San Francisco.

1164 HORETZKY, CHARLES. Some Startling Facts Relating to the Canadian Pacific Railway and the North-West Lands, also a Brief Discussion regarding the Route, the Western Terminus and the Lands Available for Settlement. 76 pp. 8vo, wrappers. Ottawa, 1880. $10.00

Attacking Fleming and the Engineers of the Canadian Pacific, Horetzky claims to have seen and examined more of the northwestern country "than any engineer of Fleming's staff", and presents herein results of nine years' investigation.

1165 HORNADAY, WM. T. Our Vanishing Wild Life. 411 pp., illus., map. 8vo, cloth. N. Y., 1913. $3.75

1166 HORNADAY, WM. T. Camp-Fires in the Canadian Rockies. 350 pp., illus., maps. 8vo, cloth. N. Y., 1907. $4.50

1167 HOSMER, JAMES K. The History of the Louisiana Purchase. 230 pp. 8vo, cloth. N. Y., 1902. $3.75

1168 HOUGH, EMERSON. The Story of the Cowboy. Illus. by Wm. L. Wells and Charles M. Russell. 8vo, cloth. N. Y., 1903. $4.50

1169 HOUGH, EMERSON. The Way to the West and the Lives of Three Early Americans, Boone-Crockett-Carson. Illus. 8vo, cloth. Indianapolis (1903). $4.50

1170 HOUGH, EMERSON. The Story of the Outlaw. A Study of the Western Desperado. Illus. 12mo, boards. N. Y., 1907. $10.00

The scarce first edition. John A. Murrell, the Harps, Plummer, Slade, the Lincoln Co., War and Billy the Kid, the Stevens Co., War, Vigilantes of California, etc.

1171 HOUGH, EMERSON. 54-40 or Fight. 402 pp. 8vo, cloth. Indianapolis, 1909. $4.50

Fine copy of the Original Edition.

1172 HOUGH, EMERSON. The Young Alaskans and the Trail. 8vo, cloth. N. Y., 1911. $3.00

1173 HOUGH, EMERSON. Magnificent Adventure; story of the World's Greatest Explorations. Illus. 8vo, cloth. First ed. N. Y., 1916. $4.00

A story of the Lewis and Clark expedition.

1174 HOWARD, D. F. Oregon's First White Men. A Complete Historical Novel. New Light on Oregon History. Facts uncovered hitherto unknown. Read who first Discovered Oregon and gave it its Name, etc. 8vo. 72 pp., wrappers. Ranier (Ore.), 1927. $4.50

EARLY GUIDE AND DIRECTORY FOR VICTORIA, B. C.

1175 HOWARD, F. P., and BARNETT, GEO. The British Columbian and Victoria Guide and Directory for 1863, under Patronage of His Excellency, Governor Douglas, C.B., and the Executive of the British Colonies. 216 pp. 8vo, original boards. Victoria, 1863. $50.00

Smith 1789 locates one copy on the coast lacking pp. 215-16. Although bearing the imprint of Victoria, this book was actually printed in San Francisco. In addition to the "Guide and Directory," the book contains historical sketches of the various settlements, including Victoria, New Westminster, Douglas, Lilloet, Yale, Caribbo and Sticken; Descriptive accounts of the Fraser and Peace River mines; tables of distances; Act of the Hudson's Bay Co. Stations; etc.

1176 HOWARD, JACOB. San Juan Island. Speech in the House of Representatives, April 16, 1869. 13 pp. 8vo. Washington, 1870. $3.50

Smith 1790 reports one copy.

1177 HOWARD, JAMES Q. History of the Louisiana Purchase. 170 pp. 8vo, cloth. Chicago, 1902. $7.50

An important historical contribution based upon unimpeachable sources. The popular view of Jefferson as the master-strategist and far-seeing statesman of the negotiation is shown to be a conception not entirely in accord with the facts.

1178 [HOWARD, OLIVER OTIS.] Autobiography of O. O. Howard, Major General, U. S. Army. 2 vols., 8vo, illus., cloth. N. Y., 1908. $6.00

1179 HOWARD, OLIVER OTIS. Famous Indian Chiefs I Have Known. 364 pp. 8vo, cloth. N. Y., 1912. $3.50

1180 HOWARD, OLIVER OTIS. My Life and Experiences among our Hostile Indians. A Record of Personal Observations, Adventures and Campaigns among the Indians of the Great West; with some account of their Life, Habits, Traits and Religion, Ceremonies, Dress, Savage Instincts, and Customs in Peace and War. 570 pp., illus. 8vo, cloth. Hartford (1907). $7.50

Sioux massacre; among the Apaches and Pimas; Modoc War; among the Alaska Indians; adventures among the Bannocks; Sheep Eaters; Flatheads and Cheyennes, etc.

1181 HOWARD, OLIVER OTIS. Nez Perce Joseph; an Account of his Ancestors, his enemies, his murders, his war, his pursuit and capture. 274 pp., illus. 8vo, cloth. Boston, 1881. $6.50

1182 HOWAY, F. W. The Work of the Royal Engineers in British Columbia, 1858 to 1863. Early Historical Plates and Views. 17 pp., folio, wrappers. Victoria, 1910. $4.75

A valuable addition to the authentic literature relating to the early history of British Columbia. McBride, The Ned McGowan War; the San Juan Trouble; Fraser River and Cariboo; etc.

1183 HOWAY, F. W. The Overland Journey of the Argonauts of 1862. Transactions of the Royal Society of Canada. 8vo, wrappers. Ottawa, 1919. $3.25

1184 HOWAY, F. W. The Origin and History of the Great Canyon of Fraser River. Transactions Royal Society of Canada, Sec. 4, 1920. 8vo, wrappers. Toronto, 1920. $3.50

1185 HOWAY, F. W. The Attitude of Governor Seymour Towards Confederation. Transactions of the Royal Society of Canada, Sec. 2, 1920. 8vo, wrappers. Ottawa, 1920. $3.25

1186 HOWAY, F. W. Governor Musgrave and Confederation. Transactions of the Royal Society of Canada, Series 2, 1921. 8vo, wrappers. Ottawa, 1921. $3.50

1187 HOWAY, F. W. The Raison d'Etre of Forts Yale and Hope. Transactions of the Royal Society of Canada, Sec. 2. 8vo, wrappers. Ottawa, 1922. $3.50

1188 HOWAY, F. W. The Early History of the Fraser River Mines. 126 pp., illus. Archives of British Columbia, No. 6 8vo. Victoria, 1926. $7.50

This is an important contribution to the history of the mines on the Fraser River, 1858 and later, by an acknowledged authority.

1189 HOWAY, F. W. British Columbia, the Making of a Province. 289 pp., 24 illus. 8vo, cloth. Toronto (c. 1928). $3.25

1190 HOWAY, F. W. The Dixon-Mears Controversy. Containing remarks on the Voyage of John Meares by George Dixon, and Answer to Mr. George Dixon by John Meares, and further Remarks on the Voyages of John Meares by George Dixon. 156 pp., illus. 8vo, cloth. Toronto (c. 1929). $12.50

No. 72 of a limited edition of 250 copies.

1191 HOWAY, F. W. Zimmerman's Captain Cook. An Account of the Third Voyage of Captain Cook Around the World, 1776-1780 by Henry Zimmerman of Wissloch, in the Palitinate, and translated from the Mannheim Edition of 1781 by Elsa Michaelis and Cecil French. Edited with an introduction and notes by F. W. Holway. 120 pp., illus. 8vo, cloth. Toronto (1930). $10.00

No. 34 of a limited edition of 250 copies.

1192 HOWE, M. A. DEWOLF. The Life and Letters of George Bancroft. 2 vols. 8vo, cloth. N. Y., 1908. $6.50

1193 HOWE, OCTAVIUS T. Argonauts of '49. 221 pp. 8vo, cloth. Cambridge, 1923. $4.00

1194 HOWELL, THOMAS. A Flora of Northwest America Containing brief descriptions of all the known indigenous and naturalized Plants growing without cultivation north of California, west of Utah, and south of British Columbia. 792 pp. and Index (Vol. 1, all published). 8vo, cloth. Portland (Ore.), 1903. $27.50

1195 HOWISON, JOHN. Sketches in Upper Canada, Domestic, Local and Characteristic; to which are added Practical Details for the Information of every Class, and some Recollections of the U. S. of A. 8vo, half calf. Edinburgh, 1825. $7.50

Glengary settlement, Lake Ontario, view of Kingston Bay, York, Queenston, Death of Brock, Lake Erie, Talbot Settlement, Northwest Country, Lake Superior, etc.

1196 HOWISON, LIEUT. N. M. Oregon; Report of an Examination in 1846 of the Coasts, Harbors, Rivers, Soil, Production, Climate and Population of Oregon. 36 pp. 8vo, sewn. Washington, 1848. $17.50

One of the sources used by Bancroft. Howison spent nearly a year in the Oregon country, exploring the interior, living among the Indians, pioneers, etc. His vessel, the "Shark," was wrecked in the Columbia, and the flag taken therefrom was the first to float over the Territory.

1197 HUBBARD, BELA. Memorials of a Half Century. 581 pp. 8vo, cloth. N. Y., 1887. $3.75

1198 [HUDSON'S BAY COMPANY.] Report of the Select Committee on., together with the Proceedings of the Committee, Minutes of Evidence, Appendix and Index (18), 547 pp., 1857—Plans referred to the Report from the Select Committee on Hudson's Bay Company, title and 3 maps, 1857—in one vol., folio. Original wrappers. Ordered to be Printed, 31 July and 11 Aug., 1857. $87.50

One of the most important volumes in existence on the development of the great western lands of the Dominion. After going over six thousand questions here printed, the Committee recommended that the districts on the Red River, Saskatchewan and Mackenzie should be withdrawn from the jurisdiction of the Hudson's Bay Co., and be ceded to Canada, or formed into a separate colony, also that it should be proper to terminate the connection of the Company with Vancouver Island, and means provided to extend the colony to the west of the Rocky Mts. Evidence was given by Sir Geo. Simpson, Sir John Richardson, Col. Lefroy, Col. Crofton, Rev. G. O. Corbet, John Miles, John McLaughlin, James Cooper, and others, relating to conditions in the districts of Red River, Saskatchewan and the Mackenzie regarding the Indians. The matter relating to the Red River Settlement is of great historical importance.

1199 [HUDSON'S BAY COMPANY.] "A Million": Shall We Take It? Addressed to the Shareholders of the Company by One of Themselves. 8vo. 38 pp., ¾ morocco. London, 1866. $17.50

Smith 1811, who locates one copy in the Library of the Legislative Assembly of British Columbia.

1200 [HUDSON'S BAY COMPANY.] Certain Confidential Correspondence of the Foreign Office and of the Hudson's Bay Company copied from Original Documents. 8vo, original wrappers. 36-77-85-26-12 pp. Ottawa, 1899. $17.50

This correspondence, copied by Dr. Klotz, Director of the Dominion Observatory, contains a large amount of material relating to the Hudson's Bay Company's stations in the Pacific Northwest, Alaska, International Boundary Line, etc. Smith does not mention this item.

1201 [HUDSON'S BAY COMPANY.] Fur Animals, Fur Skins, Their Grade, Their Size, Their Value, Their Habits, and How they should be Handled. 18 pp., illus., wrappers. N. p., N. d. $4.00

1202 [HUDSON'S BAY COMPANY.] Edward Ermatinger's York Factory Express Journal, being a Record of Journeys made between Ft. Vancouver and Hudson Bay in the Years 1827-28. 8vo, cloth. Ottawa, 1912. $8.50

1203 [HUDSON'S BAY COMPANY.] An Act for Regulating the Fur Trade and Establishing a Criminal and Civil Jurisdiction within certain parts of America. 7 pp., sewn, folio. 2nd of July, 1821. London, 1821. $47.50

Behind this act lies the history of the struggle between the Hudson's Bay Co. and the Northwest Co. of Montreal. From the year 1803 the struggle between the two companies for supremacy in the west and on the Pacific had been a series of murder and robbery. This act gave jurisdiction in all the territories west to the Pacific to the Hudson's Bay Co., which meant that all the vast territory from New York to the Pacific, and from the Arctic Sea down to Oregon and North California became the possession of that company. Further, the act made all free traders and members of the Northwest Company outlaws.

RARE EARLY LAW AFFECTING OREGON AND WASHINGTON TERRITORIES

1204 [HUDSON'S BAY COMPANY.] A Bill for Regulating the Fur Trade and establishing a Criminal and Civil Jurisdiction within certain parts of North America. Folio, half calf. London, 1821. $50.00

This bill was introduced on account of the competition in the Fur Trade between the Hudson's Bay Co. and certain persons of Montreal trading under the name of the Northwest Company. The competition became so bitter that great loss was incurred, not only to the companies inovlved but to the fur trade generally and to the Indians. It was deemed necessary to put an end to the constant feuds and disturbances by the regulations set forth in the above bill. The last clause ,however, emphatically states: "That nothing in this Act shall be taken to affect any right which the Governor and Adventurers trading to Hudson's Bay are by law entitled to claim and exercise under their Charter, but all Rights, Privileges, etc., shall remain in full force as if this Act had never been made." Not in Smith.

1205 [HUDSON'S BAY COMPANY.] An Act for Extending the Jurisdiction of the Courts of Justice in the Provinces of Upper and Lower Canada to the Trial and Punishment of Persons Guilty of Crimes and Offenses within certain parts of North America adjoining said Provinces. 3 pp., folio, 11th Aug., 1803. London, 1803. $32.50

A rare unrecorded early law relating to the Northwest. The act was passed so that the Hudson's Bay Co. could remain absolute lords of the Northwest, and thus bring to justice any members of the rival fur companies or free traders whom the company reckoned had infringed their charter in any way.

THE RARE "BLUE BOOK" RELATING TO THE DESTRUCTION OF SELKIRK'S RED RIVER COLONY

1206 [HUDSON'S BAY COMPANY.] Papers relating to the Red River Settlement; Return to an Address from the Honourable House of Commons to H.R.H. the Prince Regent, dated 24th of June, 1819. 287 pp., 3 folding maps. Folio, wrappers, uncut. London, 1819. $100.00

No record of a sale found in any lists consulted. The work contains copies of the official communications which may have taken place between the Secretary of State for Foreign Affairs and the Provincial Government of Upper and Lower Canada, relative to the destruction of the Settlement on the Red River; to the legal proceedings thereon in the Courts of Upper and Lower Canada, or to any complaints made of those proceedings by Lord Selkirk, or the agents of the Hudson's Bay Co., or the Northwest Company; also for copies of extracts of the reports made by the Commissioners for Special Inquiry appointed to inquire into the offences committed in the Indian Territory, so far as the same could be made public without prejudice to the public service or to the judicial proceedings then pending in Canada. The above work is known as the celebrated "Blue Book." It is an extremely rare and important historical document.

1207 [HUDSON'S BAY COMPANY.] Canada and Pacific Telegraph. Return to an Address of the Honourable The House of Commons, dated May 10, 1864. Copy of Extracts on any Correspondence between the Colonial Office and the Authorities in Canada and British Columbia on the subject of the proposed Telegraphic Communication between Canada and the Pacific (in continuation of Parliamentary Paper No. 438, of Session 1863). Ordered by the House of Commons to be Printed, 17 June, 1864. Folio. London, 1864. $27.50

This is a continuation of the Return dated 10 July, 1863 on overland transportation and communication. Not in Smith.

1208 [HUDSON'S BAY COMPANY.] Return to the Address of the Honourable the House of Commons, dated 10 July, 1863; for "Copy of all correspondence, from the 1st of Jan., 1862 to the present time, between the Colonial Office and the Hudson's Bay Co., or other Parties, relative to a Road and Telegraph from Canada to British Columbia, and the transfer of the property and rights of the Hudson's Bay Co. to other parties. Ordered by the House of Commons to be printed, 15th of July, 1863. Folio. 21 pp. London, 1863. $30.00

Rare original issue. Smith locates no copy.

Important official history of the proposal for all Canadian lines of communication between Canada and British Columbia. It shows with what reluctance the Hudson's Bay Company yielded to the "Progress of the British Empire in America by trying to discourage the movement." Governor Berens, among other objections, says: "Beyond the Red River to the base of the Rocky Mountains, the line will pass through a vast desert, in some places without wood, or water, exposed to the incursions of roving bands of Indians, and entirely destitute of any means of subsistence for emigrants, save herds of Buffalo, which roam at large through the plain, and whose presence on any particular portion of these prairies can never be reckoned on.

1209 [HUDSON'S BAY CO.] (Fitzgerald, James Edward). An Examination of the Charter and Proceedings of the Hudson's Bay Company, with Reference to the Grant of Vancouver's Island. Map. 16mo, cloth. London, 1849. $7.50

Argues against the policy of granting the company extensive tracts of lands. The dedicatory letter is addressed to Gladstone.

1210 [HUDSON'S BAY COMPANY.] (Vancouver Island). Governor Blanchard to the Secretary of State, 26th December, 1849 to August 30th, 1851. Royal 8vo, wrappers. New Westminster, N. d. $37.50

Smith seems to have located no copy.

An important historical work relating to the foundation of Vancouver Island on Puget Sound. Blanchard was the first governor of Vancouver and this is an official history of his administration. He gives the condition of the settlement, his relation to the servants of the Hudson's Bay Co., Indians, etc. Not only is the work of utmost importance for the period, it is also a rare early imprint of the British Columbia Press.

1211 [HUDSON'S BAY COMPANY.] (Vancouver's Island). Copy of Correspondence between the Chairman of the Hudson's Bay Company (Sir J. H. Pelly) and the Secretary of State for the Colonies (Earl Grey) relative to the colonization of Vancouver's Island. 17 pp. Folio, sewn. London, 1848. $75.00

Smith 1491 locates one copy in the Provincial Library of British Columbia. Hidden under the title of the above work is the inside history of the duel between the Hudson's Bay Company and the British Government. The territory at issue and the stakes played for by the company were no less than control, government and colonization of all territories belonging to the Crown in North America. The effrontery of this proposal woke the government from its dream of nearly two centuries regarding the designs of the "Company of Adventurers" and the negotiations then were suspended. The company thereupon altered its pretensions and humbly pleaded for only the territory west of the Rocky Mountains, or, failing that, for Vancouver's Island. Upon this basis an agreement was reached whereby the company was given the Island only, but with a stipulation that the government might buy it back within ten years. Bancroft says of the settlement: "There was probably never so irrational an agreement by a British Minister professing to have his wits about him." Nevertheless, by this agreement Grey dealt the final blow to the company's monopolistic regime on the mainland, limited its sway to the island, and enabled the government to take advantage of the purchase clause, by which, for a payment of less than 60,000 pounds the company's sovereignty was forever annulled. In addition to this material and the text of the original draft of the grant to the company, of Vancouver's Island, the above work contains accounts of the country, the boundary settlement with the U. S., and reports of Explorations as prepared by Sir George Simpson, James Douglas and Peter Skene Ogden.

1212 [HUDSON'S BAY COMPANY.] (Vancouver's Island). Return to the Address by the Honourable House of Commons, dated 17 June, 1862:—For return made since 1849 by the Hudson's Bay Company to the Secretary of State for the Colonies, in conformity with the Grant of Vancouver's Island to the said Company; of acres of land sold, and the number of colonists settled in the said island, and of all monies which have been received by the said Company for the purchase of said lands, etc. 4 pp. Folio. London, 1852. $22.50

Smith 1492 locates but one copy.

1213 [HUDSON'S BAY COMPANY.] Documents Relating to the Opening Up of the North-West Territories to Settlement and Cultivation. 17 pp., original wrappers. 8vo. Victoria, 1865. $17.50

Relates to the negotiations with the Hudson's Bay Company for the extinction of their territorial claims and the surrender of their claim to the exclusive privilege of trade in the country east of the Rocky Mountains.

1214 [HUDSON'S BAY COMPANY.] Return to an Address of the Honorable Legislative Assembly, dated March 16th, 1857, requiring copies of any Charter, Leases or other Documents, under which the Honorable Hudson's Bay Co. claims title to the Hudson's Bay Territory, or any Maps relating thereto in the possession of the Government. 8vo. 112 pp. Toronto (1857). $13.50

1215 [HUDSON'S BAY COMPANY.] The Governor and Company of Adventurers of England trading into Hudson's Bay. A Brief History. 30 pp. 8vo, original wrappers. Ottawa, N. d. $4.75

1216 HUESTON, BENJAMIN F. Rice Mills of Port Mystery. 206 pp. 8vo, cloth. Chicago, 1894. $3.50

Smith 1664.

1217 HUGGINS, EDWARD. Map of Nisqually Plains. 28½ by 21 inches, drawn and hand colored. N. d. (c. 1860). $22.50

Shows the location of old Ft. Nisqually and surrounding landmarks. Huggins went to Ft. Nisqually in 1850 as clerk for the Hudson's Bay Co., and later was in charge of that post.

1218 HUGGINS, EDWARD. The Story of "Bill" or "Sclousin." 5 typewritten pages of manuscript. Folio, N. p., N. d. $7.50

Huggins arrived at Ft. Nisqually in 1850 and was in the employment of the Hudson's Bay Company there until the company retired to Victoria.

1219 HUGGINS, EDWARD. The Story of the Seizure of Hudson's Bay Company's Steamer "Beaver" and the Brigantine "Mary Dare" by the Custom House Authorities at Olympia, Washington Territory (then Oregon Territory) in Nov., 1851. Seven typewritten pages copies from the original manuscript. Never published. N. p., N. d. $7.50

1220 HUGGINS, EDWARD. A Trip to "Alki," near Duwamsh Bay with a large War Canoe full of potatoes, sold to Mr. Lowe at $1.00 a bushel, from Ft. Nisqually, Friday, March 12, 1852. This was the first cargo of provisions to reach the Seattle market. Five typewritten pages from the original manuscript Never before published. N. p., N. d. $5.00

1221 HUGHES, KATHERINE. Father Lacombe, the Black-Robe Warrior. 467 pp., front., 14 plates, map. 8vo, cloth. N. Y., 1911. $7.50

Father Lacombe was at Pembina, 1849-50, at Edmonton, 1850-1861. He spent many years among the Plains Indians. This work is of high historical importance.

1222 HUICHLIFF, THOMAS WOODBINE. Over the Sea and Far Beyond, being a Narrative of Wandering Round the World. 416 pp. 8vo, cloth. London, 1876. $4.75

1223 HULBERT, ARCHER BUTLER. Pilots of the Republic; the Romance of the Pioneer Promoter in the Middle West . . . 268 pp., 15 ports., 1 plate. 8vo, cloth. Chicago, 1906. $4.00

Contains a chapter each on "Astor" and "Marcus Whitman," the hero of Oregon.

1224 HULL, CLINTON C. Manual of the Washington Legislative Session, 1907. 203 pp. 8vo, calf. Olympia, 1907. $2.50

1225 HULSWITT, IGNATZ VON. Tagebuch einer Keiser nach den Vereinigten Staaten und der Nordwestkuste von Amerika. 379 pp. 8vo. Munster, 1828. $50.00

Lieut. von Hulswitt was at Nootka in 1820. This work is excessively rare and important. Smith does not report a copy.

1226 HUMBOLDT, ALEXANDER DE. Political Essays on the Kingdom of New Spain, containing Researches relative to the Geography of Mexico, the Extent of its Surface and its Political Aspect of the Country, the Population, the State of Agriculture and Manufacturing and Commercial Industry, the Canals projected between the South Sea and Atlantic Ocean, &c., the Quantity of the Precious Metals which have flowed from Mexico into Europe and Asia, since the Discovery of the New Continent, and the Military Defense of New Spain. Maps and plates. 4 vols., 8vo, calf. London, 1822. $22.50

This important work contains the most complete and accurate picture of the natural riches of the southwest. Complete sets with the maps and plates are now scarce.

1227 HUME, HARRY. Prosperous Washington. 160 pp., illus. Folio. Seattle, 1906. $3.50

Smith 1818.

1228 HUME, H. D. Salmon of the Pacific Coast. 52 pp. 8vo, original wrappers. San Francisco, 1893. $7.50

Smith 1820.

1229 HUMFREVILLE, JACOB LEE. Twenty Years Among our Savage Indians. Illus. 8vo, cloth. N. Y. (1899). $5.00

1230 HUMPHREY, SETH K. The Indian Disposed. 298 pp., illus. 8vo, cloth. N. Y., 1906. $3.75

Smith 1822.

1231 HUMPHREYS, MATY G. Missionary Explorers among the American Indians. 306 pp. 8vo, cloth. N. Y., 1913. $4.75

Smith 1823.

1232 HUNT, HERBERT. Tacoma, its History, its Builders. A Half Century of Activity. 3 vols. 4to, cloth. Chicago, 1916. $12.50

Smith 1825.

1233 HUNT, HERBERT, and KAYLOR, FLOYD. Washington West of the Cascades. Historical and Descriptive. The Indians, the Pioneers, the Modern. 3 vols. 8vo, illus., cloth. Chicago, 1917. $14.50

1234 HUNTER, COL. GEORGE. Reminiscences of an Old Timer. A Recital of the Actual Events, Incidents, Trials, Hardships, Vicissitudes, Adventures, Perils, and Escapes of a Pioneer, Hunter, Miner and Scout of the Pacific Northwest etc. The Several Indian Wars, etc. Illus. 8vo. 454 pp., original cloth. San Francisco, 1887. $10.00

Privately printed previous to copyright. The Battle Creek edition did not appear until 1889. The Hunter family made the trip overland by wagon train in 1852.

1235 HUNTER, MARTIN. Canadian Wilds. 8vo, cloth. Columbus (c. 1907). $4.75

Hudson's Bay Co., northern Indians and their modes of hunting and trapping.

1236 [HUTCHINGS CALIFORNIA MAGAZINE.] Vol. 3, No. 2, August, 1858. 8vo, wrappers. San Francisco, 1858. $4.50

Contains an article on the cities of Puget Sound and views of Port Townsend, city of Whatcom, and a view of Mt. Baker.

1237 HUTCHINSON, ROBERT. Journal of a Voyage from Cherryfield, Maine to California. 45 typewritten pages from the original manuscript. Never before published. N. p., N. d. $12.50

Hutchinson left Maine Nov. 25, 1849. He gives a list of other members of the train, there being 48 names in all besides himself.

1238 HUTTON, MARY ARKWRIGHT. The Coeur D'Alenes; or, A Tale of Modern Inquisition in Idaho. 246 pp., illus. 8vo, cloth. N. p., 1900. $6.00

A history of the "Bull Pen." Not in Smith.

1238a HUYSHE, CAPT. G. L. The Red River Expedition. Maps and Portrait. 8vo, cloth. London & N. Y., 1871. $6.50

Map of the route of the Red River Expeditionary Force from Toronto to Ft. Garry.

1239 HYDE, JOHN, JR. Mormonism, Its Leaders and Designs. 12mo, cloth. N. Y., 1857. $4.75

1240 HYERS, WILLIAM H. Through Wonderland to Alaska. 271 pp. 8vo, original wrappers. Reading, Pa., 1895. $12.50

No copy has ever been reported.

1241 [IDAHO.] Outlines of the Constitution of the U. S., of the State of Idaho and of the History of Idaho. By R. Ross Arnold and Elta M. Arnold. 31 pp. 8vo, original wrappers. Boise (1928). $3.50

1242 [IDAHO.] (Arnold, R. Ross, and Elta, M.). Outline of the Constitution of the United States of the State of Idaho and of the History of Idaho. 31 pp. 8vo, original wrappers. Caldwell, n. d. $2.50

1243 [IDAHO.] (Arnold, R. Ross). Indian Wars of Idaho. Illus. 268 pp. 8vo, cloth. Caldwell, Idaho, 1932. $3.50

1244 [IDAHO.] Reminiscences of Joseph H. Boyd. Recorded and arranged by Wm. S. Lewis. Large 8vo, original printed wrappers. Seattle, 1924. $10.00

Original Edition, one of 100 copies printed. Contains views of Lewiston, Idaho, in 1865; the old mining camp at Warren; Facsimile of the "Golden Age," first newspaper in Idaho, etc. Now very scarce.

1245 [IDAHO.] (Brogan, James M., S.J.). An Historical Landmark. Old Mission Church of the Coeur d'Alene Indians. Built without nails . . . 1846, at Shoot-Loty, near Cataldo, Idaho. 15 ills. 8vo, cloth. N. p., N. d. $7.50

1246 [IDAHO.] History of the State of Idaho. By C. J. Brosnam. 237 pp., illus. 8vo, cloth. N. Y. (1918). $3.75

1247 [IDAHO.] The Bannock Stake. 8vo, cloth. N. p., n. d. $3.00

The Bannock Stake embraces the northern portion of Bingham County, Idaho.

1248 [IDAHO.] Three Heroines of the Nez-Perce's Mission. By F. F. Ellmwood. Missionary Review of the World, March, 1894. 8vo, cloth. 1894. $3.50

1249 [IDAHO.] (Erwin, Richard P.). Indian Rock Writing in Idaho. 79 pp., illus. 8vo, original printed wrappers. Boise, 1930. $4.75

1250 [IDAHO.] Falls City. 16 pp., illus., map. Falls City Commercial Club. 8vo, wrappers. (1905). $4.00

1251 [IDAHO.] (Foote, Mrs. Mary Hallock). Cœur d'Alene. 240 pp. 8vo, cloth. Boston, 1899. $4.50

1252 [IDAHO.] (French, Hiram T.). History of Idaho; Narrative Account of its Historical Progress, its People and its Principal Interests; very numerous illus. and maps. 3 vols. 4to, half morocco. Chicago, 1914. $12.50

1253 [IDAHO.] (Gregg, Herbert). Idaho. 70 pp., illus. 4to, wrappers. St. Paul, 1893. $3.75

1254 [IDAHO.] (Hailey, John). History of Idaho. 395 pp., illus. 8vo, cloth. Boise, 1910. (Autographed copy). $7.50

1255 [IDAHO.] (Hawley, James H.). History of Idaho, the Gem of the Mountains. 3 vols. 8vo, cloth. Chicago, 1920. $12.50

1256 [IDAHO.] Progressive Men of Southern Idaho. 952 pp., illus. 4to, cloth. Chicago, 1904. $7.50

Biographies of many pioneers of Idaho.

1257 [ILLINOIS.] Edwards Papers; being a portion of the Collection of Letters, Papers, and Manuscripts of Ninian Edwards, Chief Justice of the Court of Appeals of Kentucky, first and only Governor of Illinois Territory, one of the first two U. S. Senators from Illinois, third Governor of Illinois, etc. By M. W. Edwards. Portraits, facsimiles. 8vo, cloth. Chicago, 1884. $7.50

1258 [ILLINOIS.] (Faux, M.). Memorable Days in America: Being a Journal of a Tour to the United States, Principally undertaken to ascertain, by positive evidence the Condition and Probable Prospects of British Emigrants; including Accounts of Mr. Birkbeck's Settlement in Illinois: and Intended to Shew Men and Things as they are in America. With frontispiece. 8vo, half calf. London, 1823. $15.00

Paullin 914; Buck 139; Sabin 23933. Original Edition. A fine source book, narrating observations in Illinois, Ohio and Kentucky. The author describes frankly the brutal side of slavery in the Middle-West.

1260 [ILLINOIS.] (Ford, Gov. Thomas). A History of Illinois from its Commencement as a State in 1818 to 1847. Containing a full account of the Black Hawk War, the Rise, Progress and Fall of Mormonism, the Alton and Lovejoy Riots, etc. 447 pp., 12mo, cloth. Chicago, 1854. $9.00

Original Edition. An important and scarce anti-fire imprint, written by one who was active in the affairs of the state from its beginnings.

1261 [ILLINOIS.] (Matson, N.) Memories of Shaubena, with Incidents relatng to the Settlement of the West. 8vo, 269 pp., 13 plates. Chicago, 1878. $8.00

1262 [ILLINOIS.] (Wakefield, John A.) History of the War between the United States and the Sac and Fox Nations of Indians, and Parts of other Disaffected Tribes of Indians, in the Years [1827, 1831, 1841.] 16mo, original boards sheathed in cloth, label, yellow edges (some foxing and light stains). Illus. Port. by Calvin Gounty, 1834. $95.00

The exceedingly rare First Edition of this source book on the Indian Wars of the Period, containing the original Narrative of the Captivity of the Hall girls among the Indians. Abraham Lincoln served in this war.

1263 [ILLINOIS.] Tales of Kankakee Land. By Charles H. Bartlett. 12mo, original cloth, illus. First Ed. New York, 1907. $4.50

Descriptive account of fishermen and hunters paradise in Illinois. This quiet river which meanders down past Momence and Kankakee and on into Indiana is the historic land of the Pottawatamies' Trail and of "the last of the Mohicans," for here is where it is said they finally migrated. It is also the land of snipe and plover and the channel cat.

1264 [INDIANA.] History of Ft. Wayne from the earliest known Accounts of this Point to the Present Period . . . with a sketch of the life of General Anthony Wayne. 8vo, illus., cloth. Ft. Wayne, 1868. $10.00

1265 [INDIANA.] The Wyandotte Cave of Crawford County, Ind. By Jas. Parrish Steele. 8vo, cloth, illus. Cincinnati, 1864. $3.00

1266 [INDIANS.] The Iowa. By Wm. Harvey Miner. 8vo, boards. Cedar Rapids, 1911. $3.00

DICTIONARY-GRAMMAR OF LOWER ALGONQUIN TRIBES

1267 [INDIANS.] (Le Moine, Geo.) Dictionnaire Francais-Montagnais avec un Vocabulaire Montagnais-Anglais, Une Courte Liste de Noms Geographiques et une Grammaire Montagnaise. 8vo, ¾ polished calf. Boston, 1901. $7.50

1268 [INDIANS.] Events in Indian History, beginning with an Account of the Origin of the American Indians . . . with Narratives and Captivities, including the Destruction of Schenectady, Murder of Miss McCrea, Destruction of Wyoming, Battle of the Thames and Tippecanoe, Braddock's Defeat, Gen. Wayne's Victory at Miami, Life of Logan, Massacre of the Indians at Lancaster, etc. Illus. with 8 fine folding engravings. 8vo, half roan. Lancaster, 1843. $4.50

1269 [IOWA]. Early Days at Council Bluffs. By Chas. H. Barrett. 96 pp. illus. 8vo. Washington, 1916. $5.00

1270 [IOWA.] Fulton, A. R. The Red Men of Iowa: Being a History of the various Aboriginal Tribes whose Homes were in Iowa; Sketches of the Chiefs, Traditions, Indian Hostilities, Incidents and Reminiscences; with a general account of the Indians and Indian Wars of the Northwest; also an Appendix relating to the Pontiac War. Port. and Views. 8vo, cloth. Des Moines, 1882. $12.50

Scarce. War with the Miami and Wabash Tribes, Tecumseh's War, Prehistoric Man in Iowa, tribes of the Middle West, Black Hawk War, Massacre of the Lakes, Sketches of Pioneers, Spanish Grants, Indian Treaties, etc.

JOHNSON AND WINTER'S OVERLAND NARRATIVE OF THE GREAT PLAINS MIGRATION OF 1843

1271 JOHNSON, OVERTON, and WINTER, W. H. Route Across the Rocky Mountains, with a Description of Oregon and California, Productions, etc., etc. 152 pp., 8vo, original cloth-backed boards. Lafayette, Ind.: John B. Seamans, Printer, 1846. $500.00

Wagner-Camp 122. Cowan, p. 122: "One of the rarest of the narratives of early Overland Travel." Huntington, No. 469: "A great rarity and of greater historical importance." Mr. Philip Ashton Rollins, the outstanding authority on the Overland calls this the best authentic contemporary work on the great migration of 1843. See the Oregon Historical Society Quarterly, 1906, for an extended descriptive account of this work. This is an unusually good copy, probably one of the best extant of this rare work which ranks with the narratives of Hastings', Zenas Leonard and George Wilkes' as the "big four" of the Overlands.

1272 [KANSAS.] Indian Raids in Lincoln County, Kansas, 1864-1869. By C. Bernhardt. 62 pp., map. 8vo, cloth. Lincoln, 1910. $4.50

1273 [KANSAS.] (Holloway, J.) History of Kansas: From the First Exploration of the Mississippi Valley to its admission into the Union. Embracing a Concise Sketch of Louisiana, with all other items of Interest; Complete, Consecutive and Reliable. 584 pp., 8vo, cloth, illus. Lafayette, Ind., 1868. $7.50

An important and scarce history, written from records and documents long since dispersed. It is the first consecutive history of the territory.

1274 [KENTUCKY.] Narrative of the Suffering and Defeat of the Northwestern Army under General Winchester. By William Atherton. 12mo, original boards, paper label. Frankfort, 1842. $10.00

1275 [KENTUCKY.] The History of Freemasonry in Kentucky. (Has catalogue of membership.) By Rob. Morris. 8vo, 592 pp., cloth. Louisville, 1859. $7.50

1276 LANGWORTHY, FRANKLIN. Scenery of the Plains, Mountains and Mines, or a Diary kept upon the Overland Route to California, by way of the Great Salt Lake; travels in the Cities, Mines and Agricultural Districts . . . in the Years 1850, '51, '52 and '53. 12mo, Orignial Cloth. Ogdensburgh: Published by J. C. Sprague . . . 1855. $45.00

Wagner-Camp 258. Fine copy of the Original Edition. Braislin No. 1121. The author left home April 1, 1850, crossed Iowa to Kanesville, thence across country to the Platte, Ft. Laramie to Salt Lake to Wahsatch, then on via the Humboldt and Carson River to Weaversville.

La ROCHEFOUCAULT LIANCOURT'S TRAVELS IN THE U. S.

1277 La ROCHEFOUCAULT LIANCOURT, FRANÇOIS ALEXANDER, DUC DE. Voyage dans les Etats-Unis d'Amerique, fait en 1795, 1796 et 1797. 3 folding maps and plates. 4 vols., 8vo, contemporary calf; slight stains in some leaves. Paris, lA'n VII [1799]. $22.50

Original edition. With all the half titles, of a book which has been called "an eighteenth century anticipation of Bryce's 'American Commonwealth'. An original source of the first class for American history at the close of the 18th century."—Larned.

1278 [LEWIS AND CLARK.] (Foster, John). Fosteriana, consisting of Thoughts, Reflections and Criticisms . . . 560 pp., 8vo, cloth. London, 1858. $5.00

1279 [LEWIS AND CLARK]. (Fisher, William.) An interesting Account of the Voyages and Travels of Captains Lewis and Clark in the Years 1804 and 1806. Giving a Faithful Description of the River Missouri and its Sources; the various Tribes of Indians through which they passed; Manners and Customs; Soil, Climate, Commerce; Gold and Silver Mines; Animal and Vegetable Production, etc. To which is added a Complete Dictionary of the Indian Tongue. Portraits, 326 pp., 12mo, half morocco. Baltimore, 1812. $20.00

Wagner-Camp, 8 note. Contains, in addition to the narrative of Lewis and Clark, copious extracts from the journals of Dunbar and Hunter. This is the 1812, the original edition of this work, with the portraits.

LINFORTH'S IMPORTANT JOURNAL OF THE OVERLAND

1280. LINFORTH, JAMES. Route from Liverpool to Great Salt Lake Valley, with Views from Sketches made by Frederick Piercy, together with a Geographical and Historical Description; and a Map of the Overland Route from the Missouri River. With a series of thirty full page views of scenes along the trail, and a large folding map. 120 pp., 4to, morocco. Liverpool, 1855. $125.00

Wagner-Camp 259. Fine copy of one of the most important journals of the overland, of which only a few copies are known. The trip was made in 1853 from New Orleans up the Mississippi to St. Louis, thence across Missouri and Nebraska to Wyoming, and over the South Pass into the Great Salt Lake Valley. The views include those of New Orleans, Natchez, Vicksburg, Memphis, St. Louis, Keokuk, Nauvoo, Council Bluffs, Ft. Bridger and Salt Lake City.

EARLIEST ROUTE MAP TO THE WASHINGTON GOLD MINES

1281 [LOWELL, DANIEL W. & CO.] Map of the Nez Perces and Salmon River Gold Mines in Washington Territory, compiled from the Most Recent Surveys. 16mo, original cloth. San Francisco: Printed by Whitton, Waters and Company, Corner of Clay and Sansome Streets. Lithographed by Britton Co., San Francisco, 1862. Map folding to 16mo. $185.00

Wagner-Camp 383. A fine copy of a rare map that is present in only a few private libraries. The map shows routes from the coast districts to the mines. It also contains various mining laws by M. Moore.

1282 McKNIGHT, CHARLES. Our Western Border One Hundred Years ago. Illus. 8vo, full morocco. Phila., 1879. $3.50

1283 MARRYAT, FRED'K. The Travels and Romantic Adventures of Monsieur Violet, among the Snake Indians and Wild Tribes of the Great Western Prairies. Folding Map. 3 vols., 12mo, original cloth. First Ed. London, 1843. $25.00

Fine set of the scarce Original Edition.

1284 [MARYLAND.] The History of Maryland from its first Settlement in 1635 to the Restoration in 1660. 2 vols., 8vo, cloth (worn). 1837. $7.50

1285 [MASSACHUSETTS.] The History of Haverhill, Mass., from its First Settlement, in 1640, to the Year 1860. By Geo. Washington Chase. Illus. 8vo, cloth. Haverhill, 1861. $4.00

1286 [MASSACHUSETTS.] History of Massachusetts for Two Hundred Years: from the Year 1620 to 1820. By Aleden Bradford. 8vo, cloth, paper label. Boston, 1835. $2.50

1287 [MASSACHUSETTS.] (Hutchinson, Thomas). Diary and Letters of Captain General and Governor-in-Chief of his late Majesty's Province of Massachusetts Bay in North America. 2 vols., 8vo, cloth. Boston, 1884-86. $7.50

1288 [MASSACHUSETTS.] Illustrated History of Lowell. By Chas. Cowley. Port., Illus. 8vo, cloth. Boston, 1868. $1.50

1289 [MASSACHUSETTS.] The Town of Roxbury: Its Memorable Persons and Places, its History and Antiquities, with Numerous Illustrations of its Old Landmarks and Noted Personages. By Francis S. Drake. 8vo, cloth. Roxbury, 1878. $3.00

1290 [MEACHAM, ALFRED B.] Life of Alfred B. Meacham; together with the Tragedy of the Lava Beds. By T. A. Bland. Portrait. 8vo. Washington: Bland, 1883. $8.50

Cowan—"These two works were issued together. Col. Meacham was a survivor of the massacre by the Moduc Indians under Capt. Jack . . . Meachan was desperately wounded but after his recovery he traveled extensively delivering his lecture many times. Although a victim of their treachery, Meacham shows the Moducs were suffeirng under great injuries and injustice inflicted upon them by the whites".

THE FOUNDATION OF THE BRITISH CLAIM TO OREGON

1290a MEARES, JOHN. Voyages made in the Years 1788 and 1789, from China to the North West Coast of America. To which are prefixed an introductory Narrative of a Voyage performed in 1786, from Bengal in the ship "Nootka: Observations on the probable existence of a North West Passage, and some Account of the Trade between the North West Coast of America and China. Very fine copy, complete with 3 portraits and all the fine maps and views. 4to, original boards, paper label, uncut (as issued). London. 1790. $80.00

The voyages of Meares are an important link in the chain of American discovery of which he was one of the pioneers. The English claim to Oregon depended mainly on his discoveries.

"A thrilling narrative of this most important voyage. It gives a splendid account of the Indian nations met with on the North West coast of America, their situation, villages, population, manners, customs, languages, together with the intercourse and commerce had with them by members of the expedition. Included is a separate account of the voyage of the "Iphigenia," commanded by Captain Douglas, and the appendix contains Captain Meares' instructions to Douglas; a copy of Robert Duffin's journal kept while exploring the Straits of Juan de Fuca; Meares' Memorial presented to the House of Commons May 13, 1790, containing every particular respecting the capture of vessels by the Spaniards at Nootka Sound, and copies of other important documents on the subject. Most of the plates depict the scenery of the inhabitants of the North West Coast of America."

1291 [METHODIST MISSIONS.] Handbook of Canadian Methodism. 239 pp., 8vo, cloth. Toronto, 1867. $4.00

Relates to the Methodist missions in the far west.

1292 [MEXICO.] (Evans, Col. Albert S.) Our Sister Republic. A Gala Trip through Mexico in 1869-70. 518 pp., illus., cloth. Hartford, 1870. $4.00

1293 MICHAUX, F. A., DR. Travels to the Westward of the Alleghany Mountains, in the States of Ohio, Kentucky, and Tennessee. Fldg. map. 8vo, half calf. London, 1805. $9.00

Tuckerman says: Dr. Michaux . . . gave to his countrymen a correct and impressive idea of the products and promise of the new world, as an arena for botanical investigation and a home for the enterprising and unfortunate.

1294 [MICHIGAN.] Annals of Ft. Mackinac. By Dwight H. Kelton. Illus., advts., 12mo, half mor. (Detroit), 1886. $5.00

1295 [MINNESOTA.] (Bond, J. W.). Minnesota: with Campfire Sketches or Notes of a Trip from St. Paul to Pembina and Selkirk Settlement on the Red River. 12mo, cloth, folding map and colored plates. Chicago, 1856. $3.00

LONG RUN OF THE MISSIONARY HERALD

1296 MISSIONARY HERALD (The). Published at the Expense of the American Board of Commissioners for Foreign Missions, and the profits devoted to the promotion of the Missionary Cause. 26 years in 19 vols., 8vo, half calf. Boston, 1825-1850. $87.50

A complete run of this store house of information, from 1825-1850, for 26 most important years in the building of the west to which so much of this work relates. The set is a mine for the scholar, containing, as it does, letters, maps, and much eye-witness factual information from hundreds of missionaries stationed throughout the various trading posts of the west. There is much on the Indians, Indian wars, manners and customs of the settlers, etc. Such a long run as this is extremely difficult to find.

1297 [MONTANA.] The Battle of the Big Hole. A History of General Gibson's Engagement with the Nez Perces Indians in the Big Hole Valley, Montana, August 9th, 1877. By G. O. Shields (Coquina). Illus. 12mo, cloth, (ex. lib.) Chicago and N. Y., 1889. $7.50

1298 [MONTANA.] (Carrington, Mrs. M. J.). Ab-Sa-Ra-Ka, Home of the Crows; being the Experience of an Officer's Wife on the Plains, and Marking the Vicissitudes of Peril and Pleasure during the Occupation of the New Route to Virginia City, Montana, 1866-67, and the Indian Hostilities thereto: with Outlines of the Natural Features and Resources of the Land, Tables of Distances . . . Map and Illus. 12mo, cloth. Phila., 1868. $17.50

Original edition, fine copy of a scarce factual work of first-hand experience in Montana in the 50's and 60's.

1299 [MONTANA.] (Chenoweth, Fannie E.). Montana Pioneers. 8vo, cloth. N.p., n.d. (1914). $3.50

1300 [MONTANA.] (Edwards, George). Pioneer work of the Presbyterian Church in Montana. 213 pp., illus., 8vo, cloth. Helena: Independent Pub. Co., 1907. $7.50

1301 [MONTANA.] (Fogarty, Kate Hammond). The Story of Montana. 302 pp., illus., 7 maps. 8vo, cloth. N. Y., (1916). $4.75

1302 [MONTANA.] (Freeman, Harry C.). A Brief History of Butte, Montana; the World's Greatest Mining Camp. 123 pp., illus. 8vo, cloth. Chicago, 1900. $10.00

1303 [MONTANA.] (Garver, Frank Harmon). Significance of County Names of Montana. 16 pp., 8vo, original wrappers. Dillon, Mont., n.d. $6.00

A scarce work. Not mentioned by Smith.

1304 [MONTANA.] (Garver, Frank Harmon). Marking Historical Sites in Montana. 36 pp., original wrappers. Dillon, Mont., N. d. $4.75

An interesting and important work on Montana.

1305 [MONTANA.] (Garver, Frank Harmon). Montana as a field for Historical Research. Reprinted from the Mississippi Valley Historical Review. 8vo, original wrappers. N. d., N. p. $2.50

SCARCE CATHOLIC MISSION PRESS WORK

1306 [MONTANA.] Our Friends the Coeur d'Alene Indians. 21 pp., original wrappers. St. Ignatius Print, Missoula, 1886. $22.50

1307 [MONTANA.] Progressive Men of the State of Montana. 8vo, cloth. Chicago: A. W. Bowen (1886). $7.50

Contains many biographies of Pioneers.

1308 [MONTANA.] Reports of Inspection made in the Summer of 1877 by Generals P. H. Sheridan and W. T. Sherman of the Country North of the Union Pacific Railroad. 10 large folding maps, illus., 110 pp., 8vo, original printed wrappers. Washington, 1878. $10.00

An important expedition authorized by the Secretary of War shortly after the conclusion of the Sioux hostilities. Gen. Sheridan went overland as far as Green River Station on the U. P., thence by stage through the Bighorn Mountains and the Valleys of the Bighorn and Yellowstone in Wyoming and Montana. Gen. Sheridan went by steamer from the Upper Yellowstone to the Forks of the Yellowstone where he met Gen. Sheridan. Gen. Sherman's reconnaissance took him through Idaho, Oregon and Washington. Col. Poe, of the Sherman party has kept a day-by-day journal of the expedition. This expedition may be said to be the last great reconnaissance for increasing the strength of the various posts so that the ruinous wars of the previous winter were not renewed on such a scale thereafter. This is an important historical record.

1309 [MONTANA.] Report of the Helena Board of Trade for the Year 1878, Territory of Montana. 32 pp., sewn. Helena, 1879. $15.00

1310 [MORMONS.] (Gregg, Thomas). The Prophet of Palmyra. Mormonism. 552 pp., 8vo, cloth. N. Y., 1890. $3.50

1311 [MORMONS.] Handbook on Mormonism. 12mo, wrappers. Salt Lake City, 1882. $4.00

1311a MORMONS. Handbook on Mormonism. 12mo, wrappers. Salt Lake City, 1882. $2.50

1312 [NEW JERSEY.] (Newark). Historical Discourse relating to the First Presbyterian Church of Newark. By Jonathan F. Stearnes. Notes and illus. 320 pp., 8vo, ¾ turkey morocco, uncut. Newark, 1853. $7.50

Contains much of the history of Newark and Essex County.

1313 [NEW MEXICO.] (Connelly, Wm. E.). War with Mexico, 1846-47. Doniphan's Expedition and the Conquest of New Mexico and California. Maps and Illus. 8vo, cloth. Kansas City, 1907. $15.00

Original Edition, presentation copy from the Author. Includes a reprint of Hughes' Doniphan Expedition.

EARLY ACCOUNT OF SANTA FE, THE RAILROAD AND THE S. W.

1314 [NEW MEXICO-ARIZONA-CALIFORNIA.] With the Invader. Glimpse of the Southwest. 12mo, cloth. San Francisco, 1885. $7.50

Roberts' tour of the southwest, fifty odd years ago, took him along the route of the Santa Fe, of which he gives a crowded account. The little book is quite scarce.

1315 [NORTHERN PACIFIC RAILROAD.] Its Land Grant, Traffic and Tributary Country. Valley Route to the Pacific. [By Jay Cooke.] Folding colored map. Also laid in is a long folded map showing the route of the road and its completion as far as Edwinton, on the Missouri. 52 pp., 8vo, original printed wrappers. Phila., 1873. $5.00

1316 [NEW YORK CANALS.] History of the Rise, Progress and Existing Condition of the Western Canals of the State of New York from Sept. 1788 to the Completion of the Middle Section of the Grand Canal in 1819, etc. By Elkanah Watson. Portrait and Illus. 8vo, original printed boards, entirely uncut. Albany, 1820. $15.00

Pages 25-53 contains "Journal of travel by water from Albany to the Seneca Lake in 1791 by Elkanah Watson." He also writes on the state of "modern agriculture Societies in the Berkshire System from 1807 to the establishment of the board of agriculture in the state of N. Y., Jan. 10, 1930."

1317 [NEW YORK.] History of Cherry Valley from 1740 to 1898. By John Sawyer. 8vo, cloth. Cherry Valley, N. Y.: Gazette Print, 1898. $3.50

1318 [NEW YORK]. History of the Town of Kirkland, New York. By A. D. Gridley. Map, ports. 12mo, cloth. N. Y., 1874. $2.50

1319 [NEW YORK.] Chronicles of Monroe in the Olden Time. Town and Village, Orange County, New York. By Daniel Niles Freeland. Map. 8vo, cloth. N. Y.: De Vinne Press, 1898. $3.50

1320 [NEW YORK.] The Dutch Colonial House, it Origin, Design, Modern Plan and Construction. Illustrated with Photographs of Old Examples and American Adaptions of this Style. By Aymar Embury. Illus. 4to, cloth. N. Y., 1913. $4.75

1321 [NEW YORK.] History of the Town of Marlborough, Ulster County, N. Y., from the first settlement in 1712 by Capt. Wm. Bond, to 1887. By Chas. H. Cochrane. Illus., map. 8vo, cloth. Poughkeepsie, 1887. $4.00

THE BIRTH OF THE ERIE CANAL

1322 NEW YORK. Report of the Commissioners Appointed by Joint Resolution of the Honorable the Senate and Assembly of the State of New-York, of the 13th & 15th March, 1810, to Explore the Route of an Inland Navigation from Hudson's River to Lake Ontario and Lake Erie. 8vo, stitched, entirely uncut. Albany: Printed by S. Southwick, 1811. $20.00

First Edition of the report for the proposed Erie Canal.

1323 [NEW YORK CITY.] Anthology of New Netherland, or Translations from the Early Dutch Poets of New York, with Memoirs of their Lives. By Henry C. Murphy. Roy. 8vo, original wrappers. No. 22 of 125 copies printed by the Bradford Club. N. Y., 1865. $5.00

1324 [NOOTKA SOUND CONTROVERSY.] (Etches, John Cadman.) An Authentic Statement of all the Facts relative to Nootka Sound; its Discovery, History, Settlement, Trade and the Probable Advantages to be derived from it. In an Address to the King. (By Argonaut). 26 pp., 4to. London: Debrett, 1790. $75.00

Smith 1158. Lib. of Cong. F. 1089. Excessively Rare Original Edition.

1325 [NOOTKA SOUND CONTROVERSY.] Extracts from the Treaties between Great Britain and other Kingdoms and States of such Articles as Relate to the Duty and Conduct of the Commanders of His Majesty's Ships of War. 4to, 379 pp., calf. London, 1792. $27.50

Smith 1186 locates one copy, that in the Provincial Library of British Columbia.

1326 [NOOTKA SOUND CONTROVERSY.] Annual Register, or a View of the History, Politics and Literature for the Year 1790. 8vo, calf. London, 1793. $20.00

The above work contains a message from both Houses of Parliament relative to the capture of certain vessels by the Spaniards in Nootka Sound; the address of the House of Lords in consequence of the foregoing; and a memorial presented by Lieut. Meares to the Rt. Hon. W. W. Grenville, etc.

1327 [NORTHWEST.] Cache la Poudre. Romance of a Tenderfoot in the Days of Custer. By Herbert Myrick. Illustrations by Chas. Schreyogel, E. A. Deming and Henry Fangel and many photographs. 202 pp., 4to, cloth, dust wrapper. New York, 1905. $9.00

Scarce first edition. Not only interesting for the illustrations but deals much with cowboys, Indians and the entire northwest.

1328 [NORTHWEST.] Map of Central and Western Washington. (Sectional). 28 by 48 inches folding to 12mo, in cloth cover. Anderson Map Co.: Seattle, 1897. $5.00

1329 [NORTHWEST TERRITORY (NEW).] Bulletins of the Campaign, 1795. 211 pp., 8vo, calf. London, 1795. $27.50

Contains a report from Lieut. Pearce regarding his trip to Nootka Sound. Very scarce. Not in Smith.

1330 [OGDEN, J. C.] A Tour through Upper and Lower Canada. By a Citizen of the United States. Containing a view of the present state of Religion, Learning, Commerce, Agriculture, Customs and Manners among the English, French and Indian Settlements. 4to, cloth. New York, 1917. $7.50

An extremely scarce reprint from the Litchfield edition of 1799, Ogden, graduate of Princeton, was an active and zealous missionary and founded many churches.

1331 [OGDEN, PETER SKENE.] Traits of American Indian Life and Character. By a Fur Trader. 218 pp., 8vo, cloth (worn on backstrip). London, 1851. $30.00

Wagner-Camp 232. Ogden was chief factor of the Hudson's Bay Co., and as such came directly in contact with the American fur traders who also were struggling to exploit the Northwest.

1332 [OHIO.] (Fernow, Berthold). Ohio Valley in Colonial Days. 299 pp., 4to, original boards, uncut. Albany, 1890. $7.50

From the library of Wm. L. Stone with his book-plate and two letters signed by the author inserted.

1333 [OKLAHOMA.] (Horton, Roderic.) The Sooners; a Romance of Early Oklahoma. 8vo, cloth. Los Angeles, (c. 1927). $3.50

ACRE'S FIELD NOTES ON HIS OREGON SURVEY

1334 [OREGON.] (Acres, Robert, Deputy Surveyor). Field Notes of the Survey of the Exterior Boundaries of Township 25, North of Range 2, West of the Willamett Meridian, in the Territory of Oregon. Under Contract No. 1, bearing date the 2nd of January, 1854. Engraved Plate, Engraved Folding Diagram and Large Engraved Folding Map of the survey. 8vo, 56 pp. Contained at Part 2, with separate pagination, in "Instructions to the Surveyors General of Public Lands in the United States, for those surveying Districts Established in and since the year 1850; containing also a Manual of Instructions to Regulate the Field Operations of Deputy Surveyors. Illus. by Diagrams." 8vo, VI and 35 and 56 pp., original calf (worn). Washington: A. O. P. Nicholson, 1855. $22.50

Rare. Acres' Oregon survey was used as the model by all other government surveyors in the far west.

1335 [OREGON.] (Adams, W. L.) Oregon as it is; its Present and Future. By a Resident for Twenty-five Years. 62 pp., and leaf of Errata. 8vo, original wrappers. Portland, 1873. $17.50

Smith 21 locates but two copies. See Braislin No. 20—"Said to be the first guide to the Northwest printed in Oregon."

1336 [OREGON.] Ashland Club, Ashland, Oregon. 32 pp., 8vo. Illus. Ashland, (c. 1905). $4.00

Not in Smith.

1337 [OREGON.] Astoria, Oregon and Clapsop County. 48 pp., illus., map. 8vo, original wrappers. (1905). $4.50

1338 [OREGON.] The Ship Atahualpa. Extracts from a Journal kept on Board the Ship Atahualpa, bound on a Voyage from Boston to the Northwest Coast. 8vo, cloth. Boston, 1801. (Photostat Copy). $7.50

1339 [OREGON.] (Cornelison, J. M.) Weyekin Stories. Titwatit Weyekishnim. 30 pp., 8vo, wrappers. San Francisco, n.d. $4.75

The author was missionary to the Umatillas in northern Oregon for many years.

1340 [OREGON-CIVIL WAR.] Baltz, John D. Hon. Edward D. Baker, U. S. Senator from Oregon . . . Col. Baker's defence in the Battle of Ball's Bluff, fought Oct. 21st, 1861, in Virginia; and slight Biographical Sketches of Colonel Baker and Generals Wistar and Stone. 248 pp., 2 ports., map. 8vo, cloth. Lancaster, Pa.: Inquirer Print Co., 1888. $6.00

Smith 199.

1341 [OREGON BAPTIST ASSOCIATION]. Minutes of the Baptist Convention held at Mt. Pleasant Butte Church, Linn County, Oregon, July 2, 1868 for the Purpose of Organizing a General Association. Eugene, 1868. Together with the Minutes of the Third Annual Session, Walla Walla, 1870; Fourth Annual Session, Walla Walla, 1872; Sixth Annual Session, Walla Walla, 1873; Ninth, Walla, Wala, 1876; Tenth, Walla Walla, 1877; Eleventh, Walla Walla, 1878; Twelfth, Colfax, 1879; Thirteenth, Albany, 1880; Fourteenth, Walla Walla, 1881; Eighteenth, Walla Walla, 1885; Twentieth, Walla Walla, 1887; Twenty-first, Walla Walla, 1888; Twenty-second, Walla Walla, 1889. 8vo. V. p., V. d. $30.00

Very rare collection showing the organization and growth of Baptist affairs in the Northwest.

1342 [OREGON.] The Oregon Treaty and the Hudson's Bay Company. By George Barnston and John Swanston. 15 pp., original printed wrappers. N. p., N. d. (c. 1868). $47.50

Excessively rare. Smith does not seem to locate a copy, nor can we locate copies in libraries of the Northwest. Barnston and Swanston were chief factors of the Hudson's Bay Co. Both claim that under the articles of agreement of the company the fur traders were entitled to four-tenths of the award under the Oregon Treaty. The work is an arraignment of the company for refusing to comply with that agreement.

1343 [OREGON.] Oregon, the Struggle for Possession. By William Barrows. 363 pp., map, 12mo, cloth. Boston, 1885. $3.75

1344 [OREGON.] The Oregon Missions. The Story of how the line was run between Canada and the United States. By James W. Bashford. 311 pp., 8vo, cloth. N. Y., 1918. $3.50

1345 [OREGON.] Sacajawa and Land of Oregon. By R. K. Beecham. 25 pp. 8vo, original printed wrappers. Portland, 1905. $7.50

1346 [OREGON.] The Greater Portland Plan. By Edward H. Bennett. 43 pp., 4to, cloth, illus. Portland, 1912. $2.00

1347 [OREGON.] Speech of Mr. Benton, of Missouri, on the Oregon Question. Delivered in the Senate of the U. S., May 22, 25 and 28, 1846. 39 pp. 8vo, sewn. Washington: Blair, 1846. $12.50

Smith 328. The Original Edition of a most important speech in Oregon.

1348 [OREGON.] Oregon and the Orient. By Alfred D. Bowen. 159 pp., illus. 8vo, cloth. Portland, 1901. $4.50

Smith 386. Gives the resources of the state and some biographical sketches.

1349 [OREGON.] (Brown, J. H.) Political History of Oregon. Portrait, folding map, folding broadside, 462 pp., 8vo, cloth. Portland, 1892. $37.50

Rare and important work of which there are probably not more than twenty copies extant. The entire edition except for a few copies the author sent to a bindery were destroyed by fire. Describes the provisional government, treaties, conventions and diplomatic correspondence, boundary dispute, explorations, Cayuse War, etc.

1350 [OREGON.] Early Okanogan (Oregon) History. With an Account of the White Men of the District and Events leading up to and attending the Establishment of the American Flag at the mouth of the Okanogan River in 1811. By W. Brown. (Portrait of John Jacob Astor, early view of the old fort and the Hudson's Bay Post). 8vo, original wrappers. Okanogan, n.d. $7.50

1351 [OREGON.] (Cardwell, Dr. J. R.) Brief History of Early Horticulture in Oregon. 37 pp., original wrappers. Portland, 1906. $4.00

1352 [OREGON.] (Calhoun, J. C. and Buchanan, James). Oregon: the Claim of the U. S. to Oregon, as stated in the letters of the Hon. J. C. Calhoun and the Hon. J. Buchanan (American Secretaries of State) to the Rt. Hon. R. Packenham, with an Appendix containing the counter statement of Mr. Packenham to the American Secretaries of State. 55 plus 16 pp., folding map [lacks the map.] 8vo, original wrappers. London: Wiley, 1846. $7.50

1353 [OREGON.] Chambers Miscellany of Useful and Entertaining Tracts. 8vo, calf. Edinburgh, 1845. $10.00

Contains an account of an excursion to Oregon in the 40's. The above is a fine copy of this rare little work which numbers but 32 pages.

1354 [OREGON.] Chapman, Charles H.) The Story of Oregon and its People. 176 pp., plates, maps, ports. 8vo, cloth. Chicago (c. 1907). $3.00

1355 [OREGON.] (Cleland, Mable Goodwin). Early Days in the Fir Tree Country. 8vo, cloth. Seattle (1923). $3.50

Narratives of Indians and Pioneers.

1356 [OREGON.] Columbia County. 8 pp., illus., map. 8vo, original wrappers. N.p. (c. 1905). $3.75

1357 [OREGON.] (Colvig, Wm. M.). Early Days in Southern Oregon, Clatsop County. 42 pp. 8vo, original wrappers. Portland, 1908. $10.00

A factual account written by an early pioneer and now extremely scarce. Not in Smith.

1358 [OREGON.] (Cook, Marion). Where Flows Hood River. 91 pp., illus. 8vo, cloth. Portland, 1907. $2.50

1359 [OREGON.] The Yamhills. By J. C. Cooper. With map inside covers and sketches by F. G. Cooper. 12mo, boards McMinnville, Ore., 1904. $7.50

The myths and legends of the Indians of Yamhill County, Oregon.

1360 [OREGON.] (Cooper, J. C.) Walnut Growing in Oregon. 62 pp., illus. 8vo, wrappers. (Portland, 1910). $3.75

1361 [OREGON.] (Cooper, J. C.) Military History of Yamihll County. 122 pp., illus. 8vo, cloth. N. p., N. d. $5.00

1362 [OREGON.] Cottage Grove, Ore. 20pp., wrappers. N.p. (1905). $3.50

1363 [OREGON.] Coos Bay. Nature Gateway, Oregon's Deep Sea Port. 32 pp., illus. 8vo, wrappers. Marshfield, N. d. $4.75

1363a [OREGON.] Corvallis and Benton County. 32 pp., map, illus. 8vo. wrappers. Corvallis (c. 1905). $3.75

1364 [OREGON.] Journal of Medorem Crawford: An Account of his trip across the Plains with the Oregon Pioneers of 1842 . . . 26 pp., wrappers. Eugene: Star Job Office, 1897. $3.75

1365 [OREGON.] (Cummins, Sarah J.) Autobiography and Reminiscences of Sarah J. Cummins. Portrait. 8vo, original printed wrappers. In a red morocco slipcase. La Grande, Ore.: La Grande Printing Co., 1914. $25.00

Original Edition of an important Overland Narrative. The author went part of the way overland with Fremont; she met Whitman in the Sioux Country; gives an account of the Yellowstone Region in 1845 and much other out-of-the-way material of the overland as seen through a woman's eyes.

1366 [OREGON.] (Cushing, Caleb). Lecture on Oregon. Contained in Smith's Weekly, Vol. 1. Phila., 1845, and "Oregon and Our Clear and Unquestioned Title". (Contained in Smith's Weekly, Vol. 2, Phila., 1845.) Together 2 vols., 8vo, calf. Phila., 1845. $10.00

1367 [OREGON.] (Dodge, Orvil). Pioneer History of Coos and Curry Counties. Heroic Deeds and Thrilling Adventures of the early Settlers. Historical Illustrations and Portraits. 571 pp. 8vo, cloth. Salem, 1898. $7.50

1368 [OREGON.] (Estes, George). The Old Cedar School. 44 pp., 8vo, wrappers. Troutdale, Ore., N. d. (1922). $3.75

1369 [OREGON.] Eugene, Oregon. Eugene Commercial Club. 32 pp., illus. 8vo, wrappers. (Eugene). (c. 1905). $4.50

1370 [OREGON.] (Fagan, David D.) History of Benton County. 532 pp., 35 plates. 8vo, cloth. Portland, Ore.: Walling, 1885. $15.00

1371 [OREGON.] (Faris, John T.) Winning the Oregon Country. 241 pp., map, illus. 8vo, cloth. N. Y., 1911. $4.75

1372 [OREGON.] (Farnham, T. J.) History of the Oregon Territory, it being a Demonstration of the Title of these United States of North America to the Same. 80 pp. Map. 8vo, original wrappers. N. Y.: Winchester, 1844. $27.50

Original Edition. The work was written "to convince my countrymen of the insolent selfishness of Great Britain—her grasping injustice; her destitution of political honor and to serve to show the necessity for the people to act for themselves, and to expect from the hands of their government the maintenance of the rights and honor of their country to the Oregon Territory—the whole of it, and nothing else."

1373 [OREGON.] (Finley, William L.) Game and Fish Protection in Oregon. 23 pp., wrappers. N.p. (1923). $1.50

1374 [OREGON.] Sixty Miles of Progress, 1859-1919. Ed. by Martin Edward Fitzgerald. 8vo, cloth. Portland, 1919. $4.50

1375 [OREGON.] Fortieth Anniversary of the Statehood of Oregon, exercises before the Legislative Assembly at Salem, Oregon, Feb. 14, 1899. 60 pp., roy. 8vo, wrappers. Salem: Leeds, 1899. $4.75

Contains addresses by Gov. Wm. P. Lord on the judiciary of Oregon and a Historical Review by Judge George H. Williams.

1376 [OREGON.] (Freemasons). The Bylaws of Steilacoom. Lodge No. 8 of Ancient, Free and Accepted Masons. Adopted June, A.D., 1855. 31 pp., 8vo, original wrappers. Steilacoom, 1855. $10.00

1377 [OREGON (FREEMASONS).] Oregon Grand Lodge. Proceedings of the Grand Lodge of Oregon, A. F. & A. M. Special Communication held in the city of Salem, Oct. 8, A.D. 1873 for the purpose of laying the corner stone of the State Capitol. 47 pp., 8vo, original wrappers. Portland, 1873. $12.50

Smith 1310 locates two copies. The work contains a valuable historical address by S. F. Chadwick.

1378 [OREGON (FREEMASONS).] Oregon Grand Lodge. Constitution, Standing Orders, and Resolutions of the Grand Lodge of Ancient Free and Accepted Masons of the Territory of Oregon, with Code of Bylaws for Subordinate Lodges, etc. Published by Order of the Grand Lodge. 15 pp., 8vo. N. Y., 1857. $12.50

Smith 1306 locates one copy in the Oregon Hist. Soc. Collection.

1379 [OREGON (FREEMASONS).] Willamette Lodge, 1850-1900. 8vo, cloth, 12 full page plates. N. p., N. d. (Portland). $4.75

The history of the Willamette Lodge is practically the history of Masonry in Oregon.

1380 [OREGON.] (Fultz, Hollis B.) An Industrial Survey of Gray's Harbor Country and Tributary Territory. 104 pp., illus., map. 4to, cloth. N. p., N. d. $3.50

1381 [OREGON.] (Grisson, Charles). The Birth of Oregon. Illus. 8vo, original wrappers. McMinnville, N. d. $3.50

1382 [OREGON.] (Gairdner, Dr.) Notes on the Geography of the Columbia River. By the Late Dr. Gairdner, M.D., communicated by his Mother, Mrs. Gairdner, of Edinburgh. 8vo, cloth. Edinburgh, 1841. $7.50

Journal of a trip to the Columbia River in 1835 by Dr. Gairdner, who was stationed in the Oregon Territory for 11 months. This is contained in the Royal Geographical Documents of London, 1841. Not mentioned by Smith.

1383 [OREGON.] (Gantenbein, Calvin U.). Official Record of the Oregon Volunteers in the Spanish War and Philippine Insurrection. 547 pp., 8vo, cloth. Salem, Ore., 1903. $4.00

1384 [OREGON.] (Gaston, Joseph.) The Centennial History of Oregon, 1811-1912. 4 vols., 4to, cloth. Chicago, 1912. $12.50

An important history of Oregon.

1385 [OREGON.] (Gilbert, James Henry). Trade and Currency in Early Oregon; a study in the Commercial and Monetary History of the Pacific Northwest. 26 pp., plates, tab. 8vo, cloth. N. Y., 1907. $5.00

1386 [OREGON.] Gillam County. 32 pp., illus., map. 8vo, wrappers. N.p. 1905. $4.00

1387 [OREGON.] (Grover, Isabel M.). A Soul Victorious. A Little Story of McMinnville College. 8vo, cloth. N.p., n.d. $5.00

Not in Smith.

1388 [OREGON.] (Harris, Lawrence T.) A History of the Judiciary of Oregon. 16 pp., 8vo, sewn. San Francisco, 1918. $7.50

1389 [OREGON.] Hodgkin, Frank E. and Galvin, J. J. Pen Pictures of Representative Men of Oregon. 199 pp., illus. 8vo, original wrappers. Portland: Farmer and Dairyman Publishing Co., 1882. $7.50

1390 [OREGON.] (Horner, John B.) Oregon Literature. 104 pp., port., 9 pl. 8vo, cloth. Corvallis (Ore.), 1899. $7.50

The above is the scarce first edition.

1391 [OREGON.] (Horner, John B.) Oregon Literature. Numerous portraits and illus. 8vo, cloth. Portland, 1902. $3.75

Anthology of Oregon writers, with biographical and historical sketches.

1392 [OREGON.] (Horner, John B.) Oregon, her History and Great Men of her Literature. 408 pp., map. 8vo, cloth. Corvallis (Ore.), 1919. $4.75

Smith 1774.

COPY OF UNRECORDED OVERLAND TO OREGON IN 1853

1393 [OREGON.] Journal from Indiana to Oregon, March 23 to December 27th, 1853. By George Belshaw. 29 pp. Typewritten copy of the original dairy. 8vo, cloth. N. p., N. d. $17.50

Interesting day by day journal of an overland journey by an early Oregon pioneer.

1394 [OREGON.] Journal of the Ethnological Society of London, Vol. 1, 1848. Contains: "Language of the Oregon Territory," by R. G. Latham; and "Indian Tribes Inhabiting the Northwest Coast of America", by John Schuler". 374 pp., 8ov, calf. London, 1848. $10.00

KELLEY STOCK CERTIFICATE TO GO WITH "GENERAL CIRCULAR"

1395 [OREGON.] American Society for the Settlement of. This certifies that ——————— has paid Twenty Five Dollars to the American Society for Encouraging the Settlement of the Oregon Territory, as a Pledge for the Faithful Performance of Obligations to be Stipulated, etc. 8vo. (Boston), N. p., N. d. $7.50

The above is one of Hall J. Kelley's Stock Certificates, a book of which he issued with his "General Circular to All Persons of Good Character" in 1830. The two really go together; either one certificate or a book of certificates to complete the original publication.

1396 [OREGON.] Map of Seattle. 34 by 52 inches. Anderson Map Co.: Seattle, 1898. $2.50

1397 [OREGON.] Map of Yakima County. Anderson Map Co. 24 by 28 inches. N.p., 1909. $2.00

1398 [OREGON.] Official Map of Greater Seattle. Large folding to small 12mo. Anderson Map Co. Seattle, 1909. $2.00

1399 [OREGON.] Proceedings of the Sixteenth Annual Encampment of the Grand Army of the Republic, Independence, Oregon, 1897. 90 pp., 8vo, cloth. Portland, 1897. $3.00

1400 [OREGON.] Story of Marcus Whitman; early Protestant Missions in the Northwest. 211 pp., 8vo, cloth. Phila., 1895. $3.50

1401 [OREGON QUESTION.] (Baker, Luther.) Letter to the Hon. John Quincy Adams on the Oregon Question. 16 pp., 8vo, original wrappers. New Bedford, 1846. $17.50

Original Edition. No other copy located. The author, strongly opposed to war over the question, privately printed the above work.

1402 [OREGON QUESTION.] (Hannegan, of Indiana). Speech delivered in the Senate, Feb. 16, 1846. 8vo, sewn. 12 pp. Washington, 1846. $2.50

Not in Smith.

1403 [OREGON AND WASHINGTON.] A Guide Book and Itinerary for use of Tourists and Travellers. 390 pp., 8vo, cloth. St. Paul, 1888. $3.50

1404 [OREGON TERRITORY.] Correspondence relative to the Negotiation of the Question of disputed right to the Oregon Territory on the Northwest Coast of America; subsequent to the Treaty of Washington of Aug. 9, 1842; presented to both Houses of Parliament, 1846. 71 pp., folio. London: Harrison, 1846. $27.50

Smith 1496.

1405 OWEN-ADAIR (Dr.). A Life Experience: Reminiscences of my Trip to Oregon 47 years ago, and Sketches of other Pioneers of the Early Oregon Emigration. Plates, 537 pp., 8vo, cloth. Portland, N. d. $4.00

Important work. Lists of the early settlers with their memoirs, and historic records not found elsewhere.

1406 OWEN-ADAIR (Dr.) A Souvenir. 64 pp., 8vo, original printed wrappers. Portland, 1922. $3.50

1407 OWEN-ADAIR (Dr.) The Eugenic Marriage Law and Human Sterilization. 12 pp., 8vo, sewn. Salem, Ore., 1922. $5.00

1407a [PACIFIC RAILROAD.] [Britannicus, pseud.—McLeod, Malcolm.] The Pacific Railway. Britannicus' Letters from the Ottawa Citizen. 42 pp., 8vo, original wrappers. Ottawa, 1875. $15.00

Not in Smith.

HIMES' COPY OF PALMER'S JOURNAL

1408 PALMER, JOEL. Journal of Travels over the Rocky Mountains to the Mouth of the Columbia River; made during the years 1845 and 1846; containing minute descriptions of the Valleys of the Williamette, Umpqua, and Clamet; a General Description of the Oregon Territory, etc. 12mo, cloth. Cincinnati, 1847. $90.00

Wagner-Camp 136. Original Edition of one of the best works ever done on the Overland and the Oregon Trail. Thwaites said the book was so full of factual matter that it was used as a "Guide" by following emigrants. The above copy is from the library of George H. Himes, curator of the Oregon Historical Society, with his name on the title-page and his marginal notes in ink. Only a fair copy, with the date corrected on title.

1409 [PARKMAN, FRANCIS.] A Life of, by Chas. Haight Farnham. 394 pp., 8vo, cloth. Boston, 1901. $4.00

1410 PATTIE, JAMES O. The Personal Narrative of James O. Pattie, of Kentucky, during an Expedition from St. Louis through the vast Regions between that place and the Pacific Ocean, and thence back through the City of Mexico to Vera Cruz, during Journeyings of Six Years; during which his father, who accompanied him, suffered unheard of hardships and dangers, had various conflicts with Indians, and were made Captives, in which Captivity his father died; together with a description of the Country and the various nations through which they passed. Edited by Timothy Flint. 5 engravings by Woodruff of Cincinnati. 8vo, original calf (loose hinge). Cincinnati, 1833. $75.00

1411 [PENNSYLVANIA.] Sketches of the Life and Indian Adventures of Captain Samuel Brady, a Native of Cumberland County, born 1758, a few miles above Northumberland, Pa. 8vo, cloth. New York, 1914. $7.50

These sketches were first printed in the Blairsville, Pa. "Record."

1412 PENDLETON, N. G. Military Posts—Council Bluffs to the Pacific Ocean. 27th Cong., 3rd Sess., H. R. Doc. 31. Jan. 4, 1843 Folding map of the United States west of the Rocky Mountains (dated) 1838 78 pp., 8vo, sewn. Washington, 1843. $25.00

Wagner-Camp 100. Contains the reports of Albert, Totten, Towson, Gibson, and Elijah White, with extracts from the Wilkes' and Spalding Journals.

1413 [PENNSYLVANIA.] Fort Duquesne and Port Pitt. Early Names of Pittsburgh Streets. Illus. Small 4to. [Pittsburgh]. 1889. $2.50

LEADER OF THE LUTHERAN CHURCH OF AMERICA

1414 [PENNSYLVANIA.] Life and Letters of W. A. Passavant. By G. H. Gerberding. 8vo, original cloth. Portrait and Illustrations. Greenville, Pa., 1906. $3.50

Of an early Pa. German family, Passavant was educated at Canonsburg, attended the Lutheran Seminary at Gettysburg, went to Baltimore as Asst. Editor of a church paper, then went to Pittsburgh where he was a pastor for many years. Then went to Chicago and Jacksonville, Ill. Was instrumental in establishing Lutheran churches throughout America—Cincinnati, Louisville, etc.

1415 [PENNSYLVANIA.] Early History of the Falls of Schuylkill, Manayunk, Schuylkill and Lehigh Navigation Company, etc. By Chas. V. Hagner. Frontis. 8vo, cloth. Phila., 1869. $3.75

1416 [PENNSYLVANIA.] Logan, the Last of the Race of Skikellemus, Chief of the Cayuga Nation . . . Appendix relating to the Murder of the Logan Family. 4to, loose front wrapper only. Cincinnati, 1868. $3.50

1417 [PENNSYLVANIA.] Captain Jack the Scout; or Indian Wars about old Fort Duquesne. By Charles McKnight. Front., illus. 12mo, cloth. Phila., (1873). $2.50

1418 RAE, JOHN. Narrative of an Expedition to the Shores of the Arctic Sea in 1846-47. Two large Folding Maps, 247 pp., 8vo, original cloth. London, 1850. $50.00

Wagner-Camp 187. Fine uncut copy of the Original Edition. Rae passed over the Fort William-Norway House trail on his northward journey. The work gives a fine account of Indians from whom he derived most of his aid while traveling; of Indian habits, manners, customs, fishing, hunting, etc.

1419 [RAILROADS.] First Annual Report of the Directors of the New-York and Erie Rail Road Company made to the Stockholders, Sept. 29, 1835. 36 pp., tab. newspaper clipping laid in. 8vo, original printed wrappers. N. Y.: John T. Scott Co., 1835. $4.50

1420 [RAILROADS.] New England Association of Railway Superintendents. Report of the Trial of Locomotive Engines, made upon 1st and 2nd of October, 1851. 19 pp., tab. 8vo, original printed wrappers. Lowell, 1852. $2.50

1421 [RAILROADS.] Observations addressed to those Interested in either Rail-Ways or Turnpike-Roads; showing the comparative Expedition, Safety, Convenience, and Public and Private Economy of these two Kinds of Road for Internal Communication. By Alexander Gordon. 31 pp., 8vo, sewn (slight shipping on outer margin first 2 pages). London, 1837. $3.00

FIRST REPORT ON THE PROJECT TO BUILD THE B AND O

1422 [RAILROADS.] (Maryland). Proceedings of Sundry Citizens of Baltimore, convened for the purpose of devising the Most Efficient Means of Improving the Intercourse between the City and the Western States. 8vo, sewn. 38 pp., all edges uncut. Baltimore: Printed by William Woody, 1827. $27.50

Rare in the Original State, as the above. In the early 1800's when canal navigation was heaping trade on Philadelphia and New York, apparently to the detriment of Baltimore, a committee of citizens, including Charles Carroll of Carrollton, Isaac McKim, Thomas Ellicott, and others, met to discuss the situation. Out of their discussion, among others, grew the first germ for the construction of a railroad from Baltimore to the Ohio, namely, the present Baltimore and Ohio Railroad. The committee gives an elaborate report on the per mile cost of the proposed railway, the advantages that would accrue to the state of Ohio, Indiana, Kentucky and Michigan; it also refers optimistically to the Quincy [Mass.] Railroad, a three-mile route which had but recently been built.

1423 [RAILROADS.] American Railway Transportation. By Emory R. Johnson. 12mo, cloth. Illus., map. N. Y., 1908. $2.50

1424 [RAILROADS.] (Clinton, Dewitt). Correspondence on the Importance and Practicability of a Railroad from New York to New Orleans, in which is Embraced a Report on the Subject. 8vo, sewn. N. Y.: Vanderpool and Cole, 1830. $42.50

Excessively rare. Report on the probable cost for a railroad through the Atlantic states to Louisiana, describing the states, topography, &c., through which the road would pass. Brought $150 in 1926.

1425 [RAILROADS.] Sketch of the Geographic Rout of a Great Railway by Which it is Proposed to Connect the Canals and Navigable Waters of the States of New York . . . and the Missouri Territory. [By W. C. Redfield.] Folding Map. 8vo, sewn, uncut. Fine copy. N. Y., 1839. $32.50

Rare. One of the earliest works on Railroads in the Country.

1426 [RAILROADS.] Report upon the Use of Anthracite Coal in Locomotive Engines on the Reading Rail Road, made to the President of the Philadelphia and Reading Rail Road Company by George Whistler, Jr., April 20, 1849. 36 pp. 8vo, original printed wrappers. Baltimore, 1849. $3.00

1427 [RAILROADS.] The Public Railway. Britannicus's Letters from the Ottawa Citizen. 42 pp. 8vo, original printed wrappers. Ottawa, 1875.

Not in Smith.

REDPATH AND HINTON'S KANSAS GUIDE

1428 REDPATH, JAMES, and HINTON, RICHARD J. Hand-Book to Kansas Territory and the Rocky Mountain Gold Region; accompanied by reliable Maps and a Preliminary Treatise on the Pre-emption Laws of the United States. 18mo, original cloth. N. Y., 1859. $22.50

Wagner-Camp 343. The first handbook printed on the Kansas gold regions. This is a fine copy with only 3 leaves of adv. and two blank pages.

1429 REMY, JULES. Voyage au Pays Mormons Relation—Geographic—Histoire Naturelle—Histoire—Theologie—Moeurs et Coutumes. 10 Plates and a Map. 2 vols. 8vo, original cloth. Paris, 1860. $27.50

Wagner-Camp 364. The plates and map are the original French plates with the English translation added. Remy went from San Francisco to Salt Lake via Carson Valley in 1855. He stayed there only about a month, then went to Los Angeles and Las Vegas. There is some account in the above work of Brenchley's (Remy's companion) journey from Missouri to Oregon in 1853.

1430 [RHODE ISLAND.] History of the State of Rhode Island and Providence Plantations. By S. G. Arnold. 2 vols. 8vo, cloth. N. Y., 1859-60. $7.50

SAGE'S "SCENES IN THE ROCKY MOUNTAINS", 1846

1431 SAGE, RUFUS B. Scenes in the Rocky Mountains, and in Oregon, California, New Mexico, Texas, and the Grand Prairies; or, Notes by the Way, During an Excursion of Three Years, with a Description of the Countries Passed through, including their Geography, Geology, Resources, Present Condition, and the Different Nations Inhabiting Them. Complete with the large Folding Map of Oregon, California, New Mexico, Texas and the proposed Territory of Ne-Bras-Ka. 303 pp. 12mo, original cloth. Philadelphia, 1846. $125.00

Wagner-Camp 123. A fine copy of the Original Edition. The volume is one of the important source books of the overland, dealing very interestingly with California. Texas, Wyoming and the old Oregon country. There is also much first-hand material on the Snively Expedition.

1431a SAINT-ANDRE, JEAN BON (On Board the Flagship). A Summary of the Cruise undertaken for the Purpose of protecting the Chesapeak Convoy by the Fleet of the French Republic, commanded by Rear Admiral Villaret; the Journal kept day by day by the Representative of the People, Jean Bon S. Andre, . . . on board the Flagship, Translated from the French by H. P. Nugent. Small 8vo, 32 pp., unbound and uncut as it was issued. Philadelphia: Printed and sold at 112 Market Street, 1794. $27.50

This work gives a first hand account of two engagements between the French and British Fleets on May 19 and May 29, 1794 respectively. In the early part of May a fleet of provision ships was expected to arrive at Brest from America. It was Lord Howe's task to intercept these. For this purpose he cruised with a fleet of twenty-six ships on the parallel of Nahant. To protect the provision ships the French fleet put to sea on May 16, and on the 28th sighted the British fleet.

1431b SCHOOLCRAFT, HENRY. Historical and Statistical Information. Respecting the History, Condition and Prospects of the Indian Tribes of the United States: Collected and prepared under the Direction of the Bureau of Indian Affairs . . . Illus., many in color, by S. Eastman and others. 6 vols., 4to, cloth. Phila., 1851-7. $150.00

Complete sets such as this are scarce. Some are presentation copies from Schoolcraft and Eastman, as follows: V. 2, presentation to Charles Lannman by H. L. Schoolcraft; V. 3, to Charles Lannman by S. Eastman, artist; V. 5, to Charles Lannman, Commissioner of Indian Affairs by Charles Lannman. The wording of the engraved titles differs in the various volumes. The printed title of Vol. 6 reads: "History of the Indian Tribes of the United States; Their Present Condition and Prospects, and a Sketch of their Ancient Status."

"Schoolcraft's work was intended to be a great encyclopaedia of information relating to the American Aborigines. With great earnestness, some fitness for research, and a good degree of experience of Indian life, Mr. Schoolcraft had but little learning and no scientific training . . . Badly arranged, and selected as it is, the work contains a vast mass of really valuable material. It has indeed performed a very important service for Indian history, in collecting and preserving an immense amount of historic data. Vocabularies of Indian languages, grammatical analyses, legends of various tribes, biographies of chiefs and warriors, narratives of captivities, histories of Indian wars, emigrations, and theories of their origin, are all related and blended in an extraordinary and perplexing manner. A very large number of beautiful steel engravings, representative of some phase of Indian life and customs, are contained in the work, but the most valuable of its illustrations are the drawings of weapons, domestic utensils, instruments of gaming and amusement, sorcery and medicine, objects of worship, their sculptures, paints and fortifications, pictograph writing, dwellings, and every form of antiquities, which have been discovered."—Field.

1432 [SEATTLE.] The Argus. Historical Edition. Illus. Folio. Seattle, 1909. $4.00

1433 [SEATTLE.] The Argus. Alaska-Yukon Pacific Edition. Folio. Seattle, 1909. $4.00

1434 [SEATTLE.] Associated Industries of Seattle. Revolution, Wholesale Strikes, Boycotts. Two Years' Attacks on Seattle's Business and Industrial Institutions by a certain Radical Element. 8vo, 16 pp., original wrappers. N. p., N. d. (c. 1920). $5.00

Account of the celebrated general strike during 1919 and following.

1435 [SEATTLE.] Her Faults, her Virtues. By Almira Bailey. 38 pp. Illus. 8vo. Seattle, 1925. $2.50

1436 [SEATTLE.] (Beaton, Welford). City that made Itself: a Literary and Pictorial Record of the Building of Seattle. 275 pp. Plates, map. Folio, cloth. Seattle (1914). $12.50

1437 [SEATTLE.] Pig-Tail Days in Old Seattle. By Sophie Frye Bass. 178 pp., illus. 8vo, cloth. Portland (1937). $2.50

1438 [SEATTLE.] (Buchanan, Laura D.). Souvenir of Chief Seattle and Princess Anegline. Gleanings from Indian Traditions and Historical Records of Puget Sound. 8vo, original wrappers. N. p., N. d. (c. 1909). $5.00

1439 [SEATTLE.] Bards and Company's Classified Business Directory of Olympia, Tacoma, Puyallup, Seattle, Everett, Port Townsend, Fairhaven, New Whatcom and Port Angeles, for the years 1898-1899, containing a Classical List of the Representative Men engaged in Professional and Commercial Pursuits. 157 pp. 8vo, cloth. N. Y., n. d. (1900). $10.00

1440 [SEATTLE.] (Calvert, Eliz. B.). Seattle, the City by the Inland Seas. Illus. 4to. N. p., N. d. (c. 1897). $4.75

1441 [SEATTLE.] (Calvert, Eliz. B.). The Boat-Man's God. 89 pp. 8vo, cloth. Seattle, 1898. $3.50

1442 [SEATTLE.] (Carlson, Frank). Chief Sealth. 35 pp. 8vo, original wrappers. Seattle, 1903. $3.00

Historical sketch of Sealth, after whom Seattle was named.

1443 [SEATTLE.] (Calvert, Frank). The Cartoon Reference Book on Seattle's Successful Men. 306 pp., illus. Folio. N. p., N. d. (1911). $7.50

Smith 576. Has illustrations by the Seattle Cartoonists' Club.

1444 [SEATTLE.] (Chadwick, H. A). Men Behind the Seattle Spirit. 368 pp. 8vo, cloth. Seattle, 1906. $3.75

1445 [SEATTLE.] (Conover, Chas. T.). Thomas Burke, 1849-1925. 173 pp., front. 8vo, cloth. Seattle, 1926. $3.75

Judge Burke was an early pioneer in Seattle and one of its most prominent citizens. The work was privately printed in a small edition.

1446 [SEATTLE.] Emblem Club. Seattle Contrasts; dedicated to the Seattle Ad Club. 24 pp. of Views. 8vo, original wrappers. Bend, Ore., 191-. $4.50

1447 [SEATTLE.] History of Seattle, Washington, with Illustrations and Biographical Sketches of some of its prominent Pioneers. By Frederic James Grant. 526 pp., ports. 8vo, cloth. N. Y., 1891. $22.50

Smith 1467. An exceedingly scarce local history.

1448 [SEATTLE.] (Grant, Howard F.). The Story of Seattle's Early Theatres. 47 pp. 8vo, wrappers. Seattle, 1934. $2.50

1449 [SEATTLE.] Addresses upon the Life and Character of John J. McGilvre. 78 pp., plate, port. 8vo. (Seattle: Lowman, 1904). $7.50

Contains many full page views of early Seattle.

1450 [SEATTLE.] Plan of Seattle; Report of the Municipal Commission. 225 pp., many folding maps. 4to, half morocco. Seattle, 1911. $10.00

1451 [SOUTHWEST.] (Burdick, Arthur J.). The Mystic Mid-Region. The Deserts of the Southwest. 234 pp., illus. 12mo, cloth. N. Y., 1904. $3.75

1452 [TEXAS.] (Crane, Wm. Carey). Life and Selected Literary Remains of Sam Houston, of Texas. 2 vols. in 1. 8vo, cloth. (C. 1884). $6.00

1453 [TEXAS.] (Duval, John C.). The Young Explorers, a continuation of the Adventures of Jack Duval. 238 pp. Original wrappers. N. p. (c. 1892). $7.50

Pioneering in Texas. Duval was a survivor of the Goliad massacre.

1454 [TEXAS.] (Filisola, Vicente). Memorias para la Historia de la Guerre de Tejas. 2 vols. in 1. 8vo, original calf backed boards. Mexico: I. Cumplido, 1849. $20.00

Sabin 24324. Also see Adventures in Americana, pp. 2 and 246. This work has been long esteemed as a valuable contribution to the early history of Texas, and of the Texas Revolution, written from the Mexican point of view.

1455 [TEXAS.] Texas and the Texans; or, Advance of the Anglo-Americans to the South-West; including a History of Leading Events in Mexico, from the Conquest of Fernando Cortes to the Termination of Texan Revolution. By Henry Stuart Foote. 2 vols. 12mo, original cloth. Philadelphia, 1841. **$22.50**

"A work which the author says he was invited to undertake by more than twenty conspicuous actors in the revolution. It contains rare documents, and is a valuable authority, but does not always show judicial fairness toward the Mexicans"—Prof. G. P. Garrison. Vol. 1 deals exclusively with the history of Texas from the Burr expedition down to the Revolution, and in less detail with the earlier history of Texas. Vol. 2 deals with the Revolution.

1456 [TEXAS.] Six Years with the Texas Rangers. By James B. Gillett. Illus. Austin (1921). $2.50

1457 [TEXAS.] (Gillett, James B.). Six Years with the Texas Rangers, 1875 to 1881. 259 pp., illus. 8vo, cloth. New Haven, 1925. $3.75

Gillett was a ranger and this is perhaps the best account of the rangers ever published, a fascinating relation covering an interesting period of the activities of the rangers in their dealings with Indians and outlaws.

1458 [TEXAS.] (Gouge, W. H.). The Fiscal History of Texas, from the commencement of the Revolution in 1834 to 1851-52. 8vo, cloth. Phila., 1852. $6.50

1459 [TEXAS.] (Helm, M. S.). Scraps of Early Texas History. Never before Published. 199 pp. 12mo, original cloth. Austin: Printed for the Author, 1884. $7.50

The personal experiences and first-hand information of a pioneer of 1828. Almost 100 pages are given to a description by E. R. Wightman of the Province of Texas, between the Sabine River and Rio Grande.

1460 [TEXAS.] (McCalla, W. L.). Adventures in Texas, chiefly in the Spring and Summer of 1840, with a Discussion of Comparative Character, Political, Religious, Moral. 199 pp. 16mo, cloth. Phila., 1841. $14.50

Journal of a tour in Texas "alone on an Indian pony." A presbyterian minister, the author sailed from Phila. to Galveston and toured through Texas on behalf of his church. Visited Houston, Austin, San Antonio, Goliad, Victoria, the Brazos Region, &c. The appendix contains a proposed charter of the Galveston University in the Republic of Texas.

1461 [TEXAS.]. The History of the Republic of Texas from the Discovery of the Country to the Present Time; and the Cause of her Separation from the Republic of Mexico. By N. Doran Maillard. [Folding Map.] 8vo, original blue cloth stamped in blind. London, 1842. $27.50

First Edition. The author says "My object is to present to the public an unvarnished account of what Texas and the Texans really are." Says Raines: "The effusions of a distempered Englishman. The chief value of this book is in its numerous official documnts."

1462 [TEXAS.] (Montgomery, Cora.). Eagle Pass; or, Life on the Border. 8vo, cloth. N. Y., 1852. $4.00

1463 [TEXAS.] Reminiscences of a Texas Missionary. By P. F. Parisot. Portrait. 277 pp. and ads. 12mo, cloth. San Antonio, 1899. $7.50

Father Parisot, of the Oblate order, reached Texas in 1852. This is the story of his years of wandering through the new settlements and the Wilderness. One of his colleagues (Father Keralum) was lost in the woods and starved to death. His bones were found ten years later. Parisot was the priest who confronted and denounced the Mexican prophet called Tatita and who was nearly killed for so doing.

1464 [TEXAS AND CALIFORNIA.] Traugott Bromme's Hand-und Reisebuch fur Auswanderer nach dem Vereinigten Staaten von Nord-Amerika. Large colored folding map. 8vo, cloth-backed boards. Bayreuth, 1849. $6.00

1465 THISSELL, G. W. Crossing the Plains in '49. (By O-Team from the Missouri River to the Gold Fields in 1849-50). 176 pp. 12mo, cloth. Oakland, 1903. $15.00

Quite scarce. Thissell's diary in itself is interesting, but, interpolated in it are the adventures of other gold-seekers. He was a member of the Chambers train and his day-by-day record includes many out of the way incidents, such as the first wedding on the plains, captivity of Jackson Reynolds, some new light on the Donner Party, etc.

1466 [THOMSON, DAVID.] (Cochran, Chas. Norris). David Thomson, the Explorer. 173 pp., front. 8vo, cloth. Toronto, 1924. $4.50

The only complete and authentic life of this famous explorer to the Northwest Pacific.

1467 [UNITED STATES ARMY.] Autobiography of an English Soldier in the U. S. Army. 288 pp., front. 8vo, cloth. N. Y., 1853. $5.00

1468 [UTAH.] (Chetlain, Gen. A. L.). Recollections of Seventy Years. 304 pp. 8vo, cloth. Galena, 1899. $7.50

The author, Brigadier and Brevet Major General Augustus L. Chetlain of the U. S. Volunteers, was stationed at Salt Lake City.

1469 [UTAH.] (Ferris, Benjamin G.). Utah and the Mormons. 347 pp. 8vo, cloth. N. Y., 1854. $5.00

1470 [UTAH.] (Franklin J. Benjamin). A Cheap Trip to Salt Lake City. An Annotated Lecture delivered before the President of America and Representatives; the Mayors of Liverpool and Manchester [wrapper title]. 12mo, original printed wrappers. Ipswich (1884). $15.00

The author gives an account of an overland trip by way of Council Bluffs, Fort Laramie, the Sweetwater and South Pass. He was at one time associated with the Deseret News, in which, on Jan. 29, 1857, Brigham Young published the following statement: "There is a little matter of business, that we want to lay before you, in regard to J. B. Franklin who 'went' to California . . . it will be the duty of my brethern to secure this man, if possible, on his way across the mountains, so that his lying tongue shall not reach the Saints in England."

1471 VANCOUVER, GEORGE. A Voyage of Discovery to the North Pacific Ocean, and Round the World; in which the Coast of North-West America has been carefully examined and accurately surveyed. Undertaken by his Majesty's command, principally with a view to ascertain the existence of any navigable communication between the North Pacific and North Atlantic Oceans; and performed in the years 1790-1795, in the Discovery Sloop of War, and armed Tender Chatham. 3 vols., 4to, and folio Atlas. Complete with all the Maps, Charts and Views, original boards, uncut, very fine copy. Partially unopened. London, 1798. $300.00

First Edition. One of the most important works for the history of California, Vancouver Island, British Columbia, Oregon and Washington. A most desirable copy in this original state, as the volume is entirely uncut and partially unopened.

1472 VANCOUVER, GEORGE. Voyage de decouvertes, a l'Ocean Pacifique du nord, et autour du monde; dans lequel la cote Nord-Ouest de l'Amerique a ete soigneusement reconnue et exactement releve . . . execute en 1790, 1791, 1792, 1793, 1794 et 1795; tr. from the English. 3 vols. and folio of Plates and Maps. Par. l'Imprimerie de la Republique. An VII. $125.00

Rare French Edition. The maps and plates in this edition are equally as fine as those in the English issue of 1798. Rarely found with the Atlas.

1473 VANCOUVER, GEORGE. Putshestvie v Sievernuiu chastj Tikhago Okeana i vokrug svieta, sovershennoe v 1791-5 godakh. Kap. G. Vankuverom, 1791-5). 6 vols., 8vo, calf. St. Petersburg, 1827-28. $50.00

Fine set. Wickersham 6288.

1474 VANCOUVER, GEORGE. Reisen nach dem Nordl. Theile der Sudsee, 1790-95. A. d. Engl. von J. F. V. Herbst. 2 bde mit 1 Karte und 2 Kupfern. 8vo, calf. Berlin, 1799-80. Cart $30.00

1475 [WASHINGTON AND OREGON.] Aborigines Protection Society. Canada West and the Hudson's Bay Company: A Political and Humane Question of vital importance to the Honor of Great Britain, to the Prosperity of Canada, and the Existence of Native Tribes. 8vo, 19 pp. London, 1856. $20.00

1476 [WASHINGTON STATE.] Mt. Baker Cartogram. A Pictorial Brochure of the Great Kama Kushan of the Lummis, the Wonderland of the Northwest. 20 pp., illus., folding map. 8vo, wrappers. N. p., N. d. (Bellingham, Wash.).

1477 [WASHINGTON STATE.] Central Point (Wash.). The Central Point Commercial Club. 16 pp., map., illus. 8vo, wrappers. Central Point (c. 1905). $3.75

1478 [WASHINGTON STATE.] (Clark, James E.). Proceedings of the Washington Teachers' Institute at the Fifth Annual Meeting: and Washington School Law. 94 plus 24 pp. 8vo, wrappers. Olympia (Wash.). J. E. Clark at the Courier Printing Office, 1881. $17.50

This with the preceding item is of rare interest in the educational history of the state of Washington.

1479 [WASHINGTON STATE.] (Clark, James E.). Appeal for Teachers' Institutes and Proceedings of the Washington Teachers' Institute and Educational Association. 67 pp. 8vo, wrappers. Olympia (Wash.), at the Courier Book Printing Office, 1880. Smith 698. $17.50

An edition of less than 200 copies were printed by the author for free distribution.

1480 [WASHINGTON STATE.] (Conover, Chas. T.). Proposal to change the name of Mt. Ranier. Decision of the U. S. Geographical Board. 8vo, cloth. Illus. N. p., 1917. $3.00

Contains a great deal of local historical information regarding place names and of the Indian tribes.

1481 [WASHINGTON STATE.] A Report on Washington Territory. By W. H. Ruffner. Illus. and maps. 8vo, cloth. N. Y., 1889. $2.50

1482 [WASHINGTON STATE.] (Crane, Florence B.). Faithful Indians of St. Ignatius. By Redfeather, daughter of White Buffalo. 114 pp., illus. 8vo, cloth. N. p., N. d. (1907). $6.50

Smith 844 reports one copy in the Seattle Public Library.

FIRST MASONIC LODGE IN WASHINGTON

1483 [WASHINGTON STATE.] (Freemasons). Proceedings of the Convention to Organize the M. W. Grand Lodge of Free and Accepted Masons of the Territory of Washington, and of the First Grand Communication of the Grand Lodge; held at Masonic Hall, in the City of Olympia, Dec. 6, 7, 8, 9, A.D. 1865. 16 pp. 8vo, sewn. Olympia, 1865. $15.00

1484 WASHINGTON STATE. (Freemasons). Proceedings of the M. W. Grand Lodge of the Territory of Washington at the Second Annual Communication held at the Masonic Hall in the City of Olympia, commenced on Monday, Sept. 5, A.D., 1859. 75 pp. 8vo, sewn. Olympia, 1859. $10.00

1485 WASHINGTON STATE. (Freemasons). Proceedings of the M. W. Grand Lodge of the Free and Accepted Masons of the Territory of Washington at the Third Annual Communication held at the Masonic Hall, in the City of Olympia, commenced on Monday, Sept. 3, A.D., 1860. 151 pp. 8vo, sewn. San Francisco, 1860. $7.50

1486 WASHINGTON STATE. (Freemasons). Proceedings of the M. W. Grand Lodge of Free and Accepted Masons of the Territory of Washington, at the Fourth Annual Communication held at the Masonic Hall, in the City of Olympia, commenced on Monday, Sept. 2, A.D., 1861. 8vo, sewn. Olympia, 1861. $7.50

1487 —— The same. 5th Communication, Dec. 1, 1862. 8vo, sewn. Olympia, 1862. $7.50

1488 —— the same. 6th Annual Communication, No. 24, 1863. 8vo, sewn. Olympia, 1863. $7.50

1489 —— The same. 7th Annual Communication, No. 29, 1864. 8vo, sewn. Olympia, 1864. $7.50

1490 —— The same. 8th Annual Communication, No. 28th, 1865. 8vo, sewn. 1865. $7.50

1491 [WASHINGTON STATE.] Gonzaga's Silver Jubilee. A Memoir. 280 pp., illus. 8vo, cloth. Spokane (1916). $7.50

Contains an account of early missionary work in Spokane County as well as the history of Gonzaga College. Not in Smith.

1492 [WASHINGTON STATE.] Historic Sketches of Walla Walla, Whitman, Columbia and Garfield Counties, Washington Territory, and Umatilla County, Oregon. 8vo, cloth. Illus. Portland, Ore., 1882. $15.00

1493 [WASHINGTON TERRITORY.] Map of Washington Territory west of the Cascades. Large map in color, size 52 by 64 inches. By G. W. Colton. 1870. $30.00

Very fine and rare map, not listed by Smith.

1494 [WASHINGTON STATE.] An Illustrated History of Spokane County, State of Washington. By Jonathan Edwards. Map and illus. 8vo, cloth. (Spokane), 1900. $7.50

1495 [WASHINGTON STATE.] State of Washington. Barton's Legislative Hand-Book and Manual, 1893-94. 8vo. Olympia, 1893. $3.50

1496 [——.] The same, 1889-90. Olympia, 1890. $3.50

1497 [——.] The same, 1891-92. Olympia, 1892. $3.50

1498 [WASHINGTON TERRITORY.] (Chenoweth, F. A.). Opinion of Hon. F. A. Chenoweth, delivered on 24th May, 1856, on the return of the Marshall to his service of Writs of Habeas Corpus for the bodies of Chief Justice Lander and others, at Steilacoom, W. T. Also a letter to Members of the Bar. 14 pp. 8vo, wrappers. Steilacoom, May 24, 1856. (Photostat copy of this rare and unprocurable work). $8.50

The above work, the original of which is unprocurable, relates to the arrest of Chief Justice Lander of the Territorial Court by military officers under the proclamation of Governor Stevens, who declared Pierce County under martial law.

1499 WURTTEMBERG, PRINCE PAUL WILHELM HERZOG VON. Erste Reise nach dem Nordlichen America in den Jahren 1822 bis 1824, von Paul Wilhelm, Herzog von Wurttemberg. Mit enier Karte von Louisiana. 8vo, original printed front wrapper. 394 pp., with the leaf of errata. Stuttgart und Tubingen, J. G. Gotta . . . 1835. [Sold]

Wagner-Camp 58. Prince Paul arrived at New Orleans from Hamburg in 1822. He gives a considerable account of Louisiana and the trip up the river. After visiting on the Ohio and Wabash he went to the Osage country. Later that year he made a trip up the Missouri from St. Louis, visiting the Pawnees and Otoes of Iowa. On a second trip he went as far as the Yellowstone. As usual, with the German traveler in America, he looked at all things with hopeful interest and discussed them with impartiality.

1500 [WYOMING.] Souvenir of Cheyenne Frontier Show. Illus. 8vo, wrappers. N. p., N. d. (Cheyenne). $2.50

1501 [ZETES.] *Pscudonym.* An Address to the Parliament and People of Great Britain, on the past and present state of Affairs, between Spain and Great Britain, respecting their American Possessions. 49 pp. 8vo, cloth. London: Printed for J. Debrett, 1790. $140.00

Extremely rare. All the Nootka Sound pamphlets printed in 1790 are excessively rare. Smith locates a copy of the above in the Provincial Library of British Columbia.

1502 ZIMMERMAN, H. Reise um die Welt mit Capitain Cook. M. Portratvignette (Silhouette). 8vo, boards, fine, clean copy. 110 pp. Mannheim, 1781. $325.00

Original Edition of an excessively rare work. In 1930 the well-known authority, Judge F. W. Howay, made a world census of this work and was unable to locate more than four copies of this edition.

Zimmermann was a brass-founder who, after travelling through Europe, took part as a sailor in Capt. Cook's third and last voyage to the Pacific Ocean and to the N. W. Coast of America, 1776-80. He was assigned to the crew of the "Discovery," commanded by Capt. Clerke, and though only a simple workman he gives a lively description, in concise form, of all the important events during the voyage. He deals at length with the death of Capt. Cook and the character of the great explorer. This is the first narrative of this great voyage that appeared in print, as the original English edition in three volumes was not issued until 1784. See Howay's "Zimmermann's Captain Cook" for further remarks on this work.

FINE RUN FROM FATHER LEJEUNE'S INDIAN MISSION PRESS INCLUDING A COMPLETE SET OF HIS INDIAN NEWSPAPER "THE KAMLOOPS WA WA"

LE JEUNE, PERE JEAN-MARIE, RAPHAEL. A collection of works relating to Indian Tribes of Oregon and Washington, among which is a complete run, with extra numbers, of the rare "Kamloops Wawa", printed, published and edited by Father Le Jeune. The various items were printed at various places and on various dates and are mostly in the original wrappers as issued.

The collection includes the following works:

1. Practical Chinook Vocabulary comprising all and the only usual words of the wonderful Language arranged in a most advantageous order for the speedily learning of the same, after the plan of Right Rev. Durieu, O.M.I. the most experienced Missionary and Chinook speaker in British Columbia. (In English). 16 pp., Original Wrappers. St. Louis Mission, Kamloops, 1886.

NOTE—As to the authorship of the above see Pilling's Chinookan Language, p. 45. Smith seems to locate but one copy of this original edition.

2. Chinook Vocabulary. Chinook-English. From the Original of Rt. Rev. Bishop Durieu, O.M.I., with the Chinook words in Phonography by J. M. R. Le Jeune, O.M.I. Second Edition. Mimeographed at Kamloops. October, 1892. 16 pp., Original Wrappers.

3. Elements of Short Hand. Part I. Kamloops. 1891. (Cover Title) 32 pp. (4½ by 3¾ inches). (Mimeographed).

4. Chinook Primer; by which the Natives of British Columbia and any other persons speaking the Chinook are taught to read and write Chinook in the space of a few hours. Price: 10 Cents. Mimeographed at St. Louis Mission. Kamloops, B. C., May, 1892. 8 pp., Original Wrappers.

5. Joseph Sold By His Brothers. 20 pp. Mimeographed at the Mission. 1891.

6. The Kamloops Phonographer. Introductory Number. How to teach Shorthand to the Natives. 1. It is Very Simple. First write on the black or blue board, whatever it may be, the following seven signs (characters). Have them repeat over a few times so that they become familiar to the ears of the pupils. They may be divided into groups as follows: N. p., N. d. 16 pp. in mimeograph. Original Wrappers. The Kamloops Phonographer No. 1. Elements of Phonograhy. 1st Lesson. The first lesson comprises five phonographic elements and Exercises (characters). pp. 16. N. d. Original Wrappers. The Kamloops Phonographer, No. 2, August, 1892. Price: 25 Cents. St. Louis Mission, Kamloops, B.C., pp. 17-32. Original Wrappers. (Mimeographed). The Kamloops Phonographer, No. 3. September, 1892. Phonographic Syllables, etc. pp. 34-48. Original Wrappers. (Mimeographed). The Kamloops Phonographer, No. 4. October, 1892. Guide for Beginners. pp. 49-64. Original Wrappers. (Mimeographed).

The Same. No. 5. November, 1892. Original Wrappers (Mimeographed).

The Same. No. 6. Dec., 1892. Original Wrappers. (Mimeographed).

The Same. No. 7. Jan., 1893. Original Wrappers. (Mimeographed).

7. Chinook Vocabulary. N. p., N. d. 32 pp. Mimeographed.

8. Calendar for 1893. pp. 12.

9. Chinook Library. Our Lady of Lourdes, by Rev. Father J. M. J. Le Jeune, O.M.I. 64 pp. St. Louis Mission, Kamloops, 1893. (Mimeographed).

10. (Prayers in Thompson). 32 pp. (Kamloops, 1891). See Pilling's Salishan Languages, pp. 39-40.

11. Prayers in Thompson or Nllakapmah. Morning Prayers. 16 pp. (Kamloops, 1891).

12. First Catechism in Thompson Language. Lesson 1. 32 pp. (Kamloops, 1892).

13. Prayers in Thompson Language. 1st Part. 3rd Edition. 18 pp. Kamloops, April, 1894.

14. Prayers in Ckunagon Language (no title page issued, heading only. See Pilling, pp. 80). Kamloops, 1893.

Morning Prayers, pp. 1-16
Night Prayers, pp. 17-32
Prayers for Communion, pp. 33-48

Pilling omits the following:
History of the Rosary, pp. 49-64
Sin, pp. 65-80.

15. Night Prayers in Nllakapmah or Thompson Language. (No title page, caption heading only, as issued). pp. 17-32.

16. Prayers in Shuswap Morning Prayer. (No title page, caption heading only, as issued. pp. 16. (Kamloops, 1893).

17. First Catechism in Shushwap. (No title page, caption heading only, as issued. pp. 32. (Kamloops, 1893).

18. Prayers in Shushwap. 1st Part. Morning Prayers, Night Prayers, and Prayers for Communion, 2nd Edition. Kamloops, April, 1894. 20 pp. Original Wrappers.

19. The Shushway Vocabulary. No. 184. Jan., 1900. Kamloops Wawa. pp. 96.

20. Skwamish. Morning Prayers. (No title page, caption heading only as issued. 16 pp. N.d.

21. Stalo-Morning Prayers. (No title page, caption head as issued). 16 pp. N. d.

22. Chinook Hymns. 5th Edition. Kamloops, Mar., 1894. pp. 18. Original Wrappers.

23. Chinook Hymns. 6th Edition. Kamloops, 1895. pp. 18. Original Wrappers.

24. Misse Royale. (No title page, caption heading as issued). 8 pp. N. d.

25. Missa de Requiem. (No title page, caption heading as issued). 16 pp. N. d.

26. Benediction of a Church. (No title page, caption head as issued.) 16 pp. N. d.

27. Latin Manual. 1. Mass. (No title page, caption head, as issued). 16 pp. N.d.

28. Elements of Shorthand. A Phonetic or Sullabary after the Duployan System of Phonography. Second Ed. Kamloops, 1894. 18 pp. Original Wrappers.

29. Coldwater. Aug. 24, 1892. (No title page, caption head, as issued). 4 pp.

30. Chinook Hymns. Sixth Edition. Kamloops, 1895. 18 pp. Original Wrappers.

31. (Bible History, by Right Rev. Richard Gilmour, D.D., Bishop of Cleveland. Benzinger Brothers.)

Interleaved with the above, without title page or heading from pp. 1 to 215 are mimeographed phonographic characters. The leaves from the English book have been removed and the mimeographed sheets inserted. Kamloops, N. d.

32. THE KAMLOOPS WAWA

NOTE—This very rare set was secured from Father Le Jeune, who stated that it is a complete file of the Wawa. A casual inspection would seem to indicate that some of the numbers are missing, but closer study reveals that this is not so. In some cases the number was wrongly numbered, or not issued at all. See Pilling, where Father Le Jeune explains this wrong numbering in a letter to a colleague. This set of the Wawa begins with No. 1, May 2, 1891, and continues through No. 212. Numbers 1-119 are mimeographed.

Numbers 172-185 are mimeographed.

Numbers 204-5-6 and 8 are mimeographed.

All others are printed in Stenographic characters.

In addition to the foregoing there is a bound volume of the Wawa, from No. 1 to 31. At the end of this volume are bound in the Sacred History portions commencing with No. 15 and continuing through No. 32. These are usually lacking.

There are 2 numebrs of No. 174, each with different text. Two numbers of 178, each with different text. No. 184 is a double number of 98 pp.

There are two numbers of No. 204.

Number 205 is misnumbered on cover as "206".

Seven lines from the top should read "mystery" not "history."

Number 209 was not issued. At this time the Wawa was issued at intervals of three months. No. 208, Vol. 13, No. 1, March, 1904. No. 209, Vol. 13, No. 1, June, 1904.

33. NOTE—The following works of Father Le Jeune are printed in phonetic characters.

English Manual or Prayers and Catechism in English Typography with the Approbation of Right Rev. Durieu, D.D., O.M.I., Bishop of Westminister. Kamloops, B.C., 1896. pp. 1-19.

Prayers and Catechism in English (Phonography). pp. 20-40. Kamloops, B.C., 1896.

Chinook Manual or Prayers, Hymns and Catechism in Chinook. pp. 46-100. Kamloops, 1896.

Latin Manual or Hymns and Chants in use by the Indians of British Columbia. pp. 113-133. Kamloops, 1896.

Salto Manual or Prayers, Hymns and the Catechism in the Salto or Lower Fraser Language. pp. 30. Kamloops, 1897.

Thompson Manual, or Prayers, Hymns and the Catechism in the Thompson or Nlta Kapmah Language. pp. 31. Kamloops, 1897.

Lillooet Manual, or Prayers, Hymns and the Catechism in the Lillooet or Stlatliemoh Language. pp. 31. Kamloops, 1897.

Okanogan Manual or Prayers and Hymns and Catechism in the Okanogan Language. pp. 32. Kamloops, 1897.

Shushwap Manual, or Prayers, Hymns and the Catechism in Shushwap. pp. 63. Kamloops, 1896.

Skwamish Manual, or Prayers, Hymns and Catechism in the Skwamish. pp. 56. Kamloops, 1896.

Sheshel Manual, or Prayers, Hymns and Catechism in the Sheshel Language, pp. 61-109. Kamloops, 1896.

Slayamen Manual, or Prayers, Hymns and Catechism in the Slayamen Language. pp. 113-153.

NOTE—All of the above are bound in one volume.

34. The Wawa Shorthand Instructor or the Duployan Stenography adapted to English. First Edition. pp. 25. Kamloops, 1896.

35. Chinook Bible History, by the Right Rev. Paul Durieu, O.M.I. pp. 112. Kamloops, 1899.

36. The Old Testament (in Thompson Chinook English). This was issued with caption title only. pp. 16. N. p., N. d.

37. Chinook and Shorthand Rudiments. pp. 16. Kamloops, 1898.

38. Chinook Rudiments. pp. 36. (Kamloops), 1924.

39. Studies in Shushwap. pp. 32. (Kamloops), 1925.

40. Chinook Book of Devotions throughout the Year. 188 pp. Kamloops, 1902.

41. Okanogan Contrition. pp. 64. (Kamloops), 1913.

42. Contrition. pp. 32. (Kamloops). N. d.

43. English Manual or Prayers and Catechism in English Typography. pp. 19. Prayers and Catechism in English Phonography. Kamloops, 1896. pp. 24-20. Chinook Manual or Prayers, Hymns and Catechism in Chinook. pp. 45-100. Kamloops, 1896.

Lation Manual. pp. 105-183. (Kamloops). 1896. Original Wrappers.

PART II

THE GEORGE W. SOLIDAY COLLECTION OF WESTERN AMERICANA

PART II

---

1 ADAMS, EMMA H. Up and Down in Southern California, Oregon, and Washington Territory. With Sketches in Arizona, New Mexico, and British Columbia. 608 pp. 8vo. Illus. Chicago (c. 1888). $4.75

An interesting account of persons and places on the Pacific coast; Oregon Pioneers; Tacoma; expulsion of Chinese; riots. Presentation copy.

2 ADAMS, G. MERCER. Lewis and Clark Exploring Expedition, 1804-06. 189 pp., 12mo, half calf. N. Y., 1904. $3.75

3 ADAMS, W. H. DAVENPORT. The Hunter and the Trapper in North America; or, Romantic Adventures in Field and Forest. 12mo, cloth, illus. London, 1874. $7.50

4 ADAMS, W. L. Oregon as It Is. 8vo, original wrappers. Portland, 1873. $22.50

Said to be the first Guide to the Northwest printed in Oregon.

5 ADAMS, W. L. Lecture on Oregon and the Pacific Coast. 39 pp., 8vo, original printed wrappers. Boston, 1869. $32.50

Adams describes a trip to Oregon from Illinois in 1848. Smith locates but one copy in all the libraries of the Northwest Coast.

6 ADDITION, MRS. LUCIA M. FAXON. Twenty Eventful Years of the Oregon Woman's Christian Temperance Union, 1880-1900; Statistical Historical and Biographical . . . 112 pp., illus., ports. 8vo, clóth. Portland, 1904. $7.50

7 [AERONAUTICS.] The Great Steam Duck; or, A Concise Description of a most Useful and Extraordinary Invention for Aerial Navigation. [Frontis.] By a Member of the L. L. B. B. [Louisville Literary Brass Band], Louisville, 1841. 4to, cloth. N. Y., 1928. $7.50

Earliest published work in the western states on the subject of aviation.

8 [ALASKA.] Klondike; the Chicago Record's' Book for Gold Seekers. 8vo, cloth, illus. Chicago (1897). $7.50

9 [ALASKA.] Ketchikan, First City in Alaska. 64 pp., illus. 8vo, original wrappers. N. p., N. d. $5.00

10 [ALASKA.] (Jackson, Sheldon). Alaska, and missions on the north Pacific coast. 400 pp., illus. 1 port., 1 map. 8vo, cloth. N. Y., [c. 1880.] $7.50

11 [ALASKA.] (Jackson, Sheldon). Report on Introduction of Domestic Reindeer into Alaska. 187 pp., map, illus.. 3rd Annual Report. 8vo, ¾ morocco. Washington, 1894. $3.75

12 [ALASKA.] (Jackson, Sheldon). Report on Introduction of Domestic Reindeer into Alaska. 7th Report. Maps., illus. 8vo, morocco. Washington, 1897. $3.75

13 [ALASKA.] (Jackson, Sheldon). Fourteenth Annual Report, on Introduction of Domestic Reindeer into Alaska. Maps and illus. 1903. 8vo, ¾ morocco. Washington, 1904. $3.75

14 [ALASKA.] (Jackson, Sheldon). Fifteenth Annual Report on Introduction of Domestic Reindeer into Alaska. 1904. Maps and illus. 8vo, ¾ morocco. Washington, 1905. $3.75

15 [ALASKA.] (Jackson, Sheldon). Report on Introduction of Domestic Reindeer into Alaska. 261 pp., maps, illus. 9th Report. ¾ morocco. Washington, 1910. $3.75

16 [ALASKA.] (Jackson, Sheldon). Report on Education in Alaska. 1886. 93 pp., illus., plates, 2 maps. Washington, 1899. $5.00
Smith No. 1914.

17 [ALASKA.] (Jackson, Sheldon). Thirteenth Annual Report on the Introduction of Domestic Reindeer in Alaska with map and illus. 1903. 192 pp., maps, etc. 58th Cong., 2nd Sess., Senate. Doc. No. 210. Washington, 1904. $4.75

17a [ALASKA.] Speech of William H. Seward at Sitka, Aug. 12, 1869. 31 pp., 8vo, unbound. Washington: Philip & Solomons, 1869. $5.00

ALCALA-GALIANO'S VOYAGE TO PUGET SOUND, 1792

17b ALCALA-GALIANO (Don Dionysio). Relacion del Viage hecho por las Goletas y Mexicana en el ano de 1792 para raconocer el Estrecho de Fuca; con una Introduccion en que se da Noticia de la Expeciones executadas anterioramente por los Espanoles en Busca del Paso del Noroeste de la America. De Orden del Rey. Madrid en la Imprenta Real, 1802. Complete with the folding sheet of the missions of California, and accompanied by the folio atlas of 9 maps and 8 curious plates. Small 4to, full polished calf, and Folio. $150.00

One of the most important Voyages to the Northwest Coast of America. The Commander of the expedition, Don. Dionysio Alcala-Galiano, was probably the author of the work. It contains several Indian vocabularies, notably those of the Eslen, Runsien and Nutka. The 9 maps (4 of which are folding ones) delineate the Western Coast of North America from Acapulco to Unalaska; and the coast of Claifornia on a larger scale; with Plans of the harbors of S. Diego, Monte Rey, Cala de los Amigos (Nootka), Mulgrave & Desengano. The plates include portraits of Macuina, chief of Nootka, Tetacus, chief of Juan de Fuca and his wife, a large folding aquatint view of the Cala de los Amigos (the Spanish Establishment on the Bay of Nootka), and a curious folding plate of the Feast celebrating the attainment of marriageable age of the Chief of Nootka's son.

Cowan says this work of great importance is rendered more valuable by the Introduction, which is a masterly resume of Spanish Voyages to the coast, written by Martin Fernandez de Navarette, whose name does not appear in the work.

[NOTE: See item No. 82, Cat. 17, where this item was erroneously dated 1812. The above is the original rare editon of 1802.]

18 ALEXANDER, PHILIP F. The Northwest and North East Passage, 1576-1611. Illus., maps. 8vo, cloth, 211 pp. Cambridge, 1911. $10.00

19 ALGER, HORATIO. The Young Adventurer; or, Tom's Trip Across the Plains. 293 pp., 12mo, cloth (binding showing use). Boston, 1878. $3.50

20 ALLA, OGAL. Blue Eye: A Story of the People of the Plains (Reminiscences of Life and Adventure on the Western Plains in the 60's. 8vo, cloth. Portland, 1905. $4.00

Deals with the Sioux and Cheynnes.

21 ALLEN, A. J. Ten Years in Oregon and Adventures of E. White and Lady, West of the Rocky Mountains. Containing also a brief History of the Missions and Settlement of the Country. The Indians, Incidents witnessed while Traversing and Residing in the Territory, etc. Crude Woodcut Portrait. 399 pp., 8vo, cloth. Ithaca, 1848. $17.50

Wagner-Camp 144. The Rare First Edition and the only one to contain the portrait.

22 ALLEN, A. J. Ten Years in Oregon. Travels and Adventures of E. White and Lady, West of the Rocky Mountains. 8vo, cloth (worn at backstrip). Ithaca, 1848. $2.50

Wagner-Camp 144.

23 —— The Same. 430 pp., 8vo, cloth. With the Fremont extracts appended. $7.50

24 ALLEN, W. A. The Sheep Eaters (Journal of Travel and Observations among the Extinct Mountain Tribe of Indians of Montana and Wyoming. 12mo, cloth. N. Y., 1913. $12.50

Privately printed for the author and now scarce.

25 ALTER, J. CECIL. James Bridger, 1804-1881. Western Trapper, Scout, Frontiersman and Guide. A Historical Narrative. Illus., 8vo. Salt Lake City, (1925). $7.50

Limited and numbered edition. Contains a verbatim reprint of the rare life written by Gen. Dodge.

26 AMBLER, CHAS. H. The Life and Diary of John Floyd, Governor of Virginia and Apostle of Secession and the Father of Oregon. 248 pp., 8vo, cloth. (Richmond, 1918). $7.50

27 [AMERICAN ARMY.] Autobiography of an English Soldier in the United States Aarmy. 288 pp., front., 8vo, cloth. N. Y., 1853. $7.50

27a [AMERICAN REVOLUTION.] The Journal of Lieut. William Feltman, of the first Pennsylvania Regiment, from May 26, 1781 to April 25, 1782, embracing the Siege of Yorktown and the Southern Campaign. Collections Historical Society of Pennsylvania. Vol. I, May, 1853. 8vo, original Printed Wrappers. Phila., 1853. $6.00

One of the most imporatnt journals relating to the siege of Yorktown. Scarce.

27b [AMERICAN REVOLUTION.] Personal Recollections of Capt. Enoch Anderson, an Officer of the Delaware Regiment in the Revolutionary War. Portrait. 8vo, wrappers. Wilmington, 1896. $2.50

SECRET HISTORY OF THE SOUTHERN CAMPAIGN

27c [AMERICAN REVOLUTION.] Correspondence du Lord. G. Germaine avec les Generaux Clinton, Cornwallis & the Generaux dans la station de l'Amerique, avec plusiers lettres interceptees du General Washington, du Marquis de La Fayette & de M. de Barras, Chef d'Escadre. Traduit de l'Anglois sur les Originaux publies Par ordre de la Chambre des Pairs. 304 pp. 2 fldg. documents. 8vo, ¾ polished calf, edges untrimmed. Berne, 1782. $47.50

An excessively rare work, being secret instructions carried on between Lord Germaine and Clinton and Cornwallis and others regarding the Southern Campaign. The work is a veritable store-house of facts relating to the secret history of the revolution, facts nowhere else accessible. Included are letters intercepted from Washington, Lafayette, and others. No copy has appeared at public sale in over 40 years.

27d [AMERICAN REVOLUTION.] Journal of Captain Pausch, Chief of the Hanau Artillery during the Burgoyne Campaign. Trans. and Annotated by Wm .L. Stone. Portrait. No. 16 of Munsell's Historical Series. 4to, orig. cloth. Albany, 1886. $10.00

A scarce work printed in a small edition. Pausch was with Reidesel's Artillery brigade and took an active part in defending Breyman's Redoubt at Freeman's Farm (Saratoga). The work is important in that the author describes the sufferings of the German troops while on their way from the German hinterland to the ports of Hamburg and Bremen.

27e [AMERICAN REVOLUTION.] The Journal of Isaac Senter, Physician and Surgeon to troops detached from the American Army at Cambridge, Mass., on a Secret Expedition against Quebec, under the command of Col. Benedict Arnold, in Sept., 1775. 40 pp., 8vo, original printed wrappers, uncut. Phila., 1846. $10.00

The Original Edition. One of the best narratives of the many on Arnold's March to Quebec by the Surgeon to the Expedition. He was the prototype of the philosophisizing doctor in Roberts' "Rabble in Arms."

27f [AMERICAN REVOLUTION.] A Journal of the Southern Expedition, 1780-1783. By William Seymour, Sergeant-Major of the Delaware Regt. 8vo, original wrappers. Wilmington, 1896. $2.50

27g [AMERICAN REVOLUTION.] The Revolutionary Soldiers of Delaware. By William G. Whiteley. 8vo, wrappers. Wilmington, 1896. $2.50

28 [AMERICAN STATE PAPERS.] Documents, Legislative and Executive of the Congress of the United States, from the First Session of the First to the Second of the Twenty-second Congress, inclusive . . . Selected and edited . . . by Walter Lowrie and Matthew St. Clair Clarke . . . First and Second Series. Together 26 vols. Folio, half calf (bindings showing some wear). Washington, 1832-1862. $100.00

Fine set save volumes 3, 4, 5, 6, and 7 of Military affairs, the binding of which show wear. "This valuable work was printed by order of the U. S. government and distributed through the members of Congress. It contains reprints, not only of all the early occasionally publications of the Congress that could be found, but many important papers from the Archives of the Government never before published."

29 ANDERSON, ADA WOODRUFF. The Heart of the Red Fir. A Story of the Pacific Northwest. Front., plates. 8vo, cloth. Boston, 1908. $3.50

Smith 91.

30 ANDERSON, ADA WOODRUFF. Strain of White. 300 pp., front., illus. 8vo, cloth. Boston, 1909. $3.50

Smith 93.

31 ANDERSON, ADA WOODRUFF. The Rim of the Desert. 402 pp., illus. 8vo, cloth. Boston, 1915. $3.50

Smith 92.

32 ANDREWS, LORRIN. Vocabulary of Words in the Hawaiian Language. 12mo, 32 pp., 8vo, boards. Lahainaluna, 1836. $27.50

Very rare first Hawaiian vocabulary.

33 ATHERTON, GERTRUDE The Splendid Idle Forties. Stories of old California. 8vo, cloth. N. Y., 1902. $3.50

34 ATHERTON, GERTRUDE. Rezanov. 8vo, cloth. N. Y., 1906. $3.50

35 ANTHONY, C. V. Fifty Years of Methodism. History of the Methodist Episcopal Church within the bounds of the California Annual Conference from 1847-1897. 443 pp., 8vo. San Francisco, 1901. $10.00

"In this work which is a complete history, the author, a California clergyman since 1851, has brought together a vast amount of local material."—Cowan.

36 APPLEGATE, JESSE. Pioneer and Builder. By Joseph Schafer. 8vo, original printed wrappers. Portrait of Applegate. Eugene, 1912. $20.00

One of 50 copies privately printed by the author. This is a separate publication.

JESSE APPLEGATE'S "RECOLLECTIONS" OF THE '43 MIGRATION

37 APPLEGATE, JESSE. Recollections. By an Oregon Pioneer of 1843. 99 pp., 8vo, pictorial wrappers. Roseburg: Privately printed, no copyright. 1914. $35.00

The author here recounts the trials and sufferings, experiences and adventures of the great migration of 1843. He describes the Whitman Station at Wailatpui; the Dalles; McLoughlin and Vancouver; first winter in Oregon, &c. Emerson Hough's "Covered Wagon" is said to have been based largely upon this book. It is a much-sought item.

38 APPLEGATE, JESSE. A Day with the Cow Column in 1843. Excerpted from the Overland Monthly, Aug., 1868. $5.00

This is a narrative of the overland emigration to Oregon in 1843.

39 ARGYLE, ARCHIE. Cupid's Album. 12mo, cloth. N. Y., 1866. $15.00

Original edition of this overland narrative begun in the Spring of 1861, with the expedition of Capt. Armath. Dedicated to Gen. and Mrs. Sterling Price.

O'FALLON'S FAMOUS MISSOURI RIVER EXPEDITION, WHICH PACIFIED THE TRIBES FOR ST. LOUIS FUR TRADERS

40 [ARIKARA CAMPAIGN.] General Gaines to the Secretary of War, Headquarters Western Department, Louisville, Ky., July 28, 1823. Document L, attached to the Report of J. C. Calhoun, Nov. 29, 1923. Ex. Doc. No. 1, 18th Cong., 1st Sess. 108 pp., 8vo, sewn. $75.00

Wagner-Camp 22. A fine copy of the Original Edition. The principal point in this work is O'Fallon's letter, of July 8, 1823, from the Upper Missouri, in which he describes the disposition of the Indians. This was most important to the Ashley-Smih trappers who were rapidly exploiting the region following the government expeditions of 1819 and 1820. Included in this work also is Wm. Gordon's letter from the Dakotas reporting the killing of Immel and Jones and comments on the same by Joshua Pilcher; Ashley's letter from the keel-boat "Yellowstone" reporting the celebrated attack on the party who were returning to St. Louis via the Missouri.

41 ATKINSON, REV. G. H. The Northwest Coast, Including Oregon, Washington and Idaho: a Series of Articles upon the N. P. R. R. in its relation to the Basins of the Columbia and of Puget's Sound. Large folding map entitled "Routes from Atlantic Ports to Oregon." 56 pp., 8vo, original printed wrappers. Portland, Oregon: A. H. Walling, 1878. $22.00

Smith 134. Discusses land grants to the Northern Pacific, Central Pacific and California and Oregon railroads; insists that the natural route for a North-Pacific road is down the Valley of the Columbia; tells of the troubles of the road due to the four years of the panic and the failure of Jay Cook and Co., etc.

42 [ATKINSON, REV. GEO. H.] Biography of Rev. G. H. Atkinson, D.D. With Illustrations. Journal of Sea Voyage to Oregon in 1848, and Selected Addresses and Printed Articles, and a Particular Account of His Church Work in the Pacific Northwest. Prepared by Myron Eells. Compiled by Nancy Bates Atkinson. Illus., 8vo, cloth. Portland, 1893. $12.50

43 [ATKINSON, REV. GEO. H.] In Memoriam, Rev. George H. Atkinson, Born May 10, 1819. Died Feb. 25, 1889. 51 pp. Atkinson, 1889. $10.00

Now Scarce.

44 ATWOOD, A. T. The Conquerors. Historical Sketch of the American Settlement of the Oregon Country, embracing Facts in the Life Work of Rev. Jason Lee. 316 pp., front., maps, illus., 12mo, cloth. N. p. (1907). $4.75

Rev. Lee arrived in Oregon via the overland in 1834. Smith 137.

45 AYLMER, FENTON. Cruise in the Pacific from the log of a Naval Officer. 2 vols., 8vo, cloth. London, 1860. $12.50

Item 40, Date should read 1823 instead of 1923.

46 BACK, CAPT. R. N. Narrative of the Arctic Land Expedition to the Mouth of the Great Fish River and along the Shores of the Arctic Ocean in the Years 1833-35. Map and plates, 8vo, cloth. London, 1836. $5.00

Smith 150.

47 BAILLIE-GROHMAN, WM. A. Camps in the Rockies. Plates, folding map, 12mo, cloth. London, 1882. $7.50

48 BALL, JOHN. Remarks upon the Geology and Physical Features of the Country West of the Rocky Mountains. (American Journal of Sciences and Arts, April 1835). 8vo, wrappers. New Haven, 1835. $7.50

Wagner-Camp 53. Ball was the first school teacher at Vancouver Fort. Gives account of his overland trip in 1832, as well as experience among the Blackfeet.

49 BALL, JOHN. Autobiography of John Ball. Compiled by his Daughters. Ports. and plates, 8vo, cloth. Grand Rapids, 1925. $3.00

50 BALLANTYNE, R. M. Hand-Book to the New Gold Fields: A Full Account of the Richness and Extent of the Fraser and Thompson River Gold Mines, with a Geographical and Physical Account of the Country and its Inhabitants, the Routes, Native Tribes; Proclamation of Gov. Douglas, list of prices, table of Distances, etc. 116 pp., large folding map, 12mo, original boards. Edinburgh, 1858. $35.00

Contains a view of Vancouver's Island.

51 BALLANTYNE, R. M. The Buffalo Runners: a Tale of the Red River Plains. Illus. London, N. d. $4.50

52 BALLANTYNE, R. M. Ungavem, a Tale of Esquimo Land. 8vo, cloth. London, 1901. $4.50

53 BALLARD, D. P. Washington Territory and the Far Northwest: Oregon, Idaho and Montana. Facts by an Old Settler, not in the interest of Railroads or Localities. 60 pp., 8vo, original wrappers. Chicago, 1889. $7.50

54 BARNEBY, W. HENRY. Life and Labour in the Far, Far West: Being Notes of a Tour in the Western States, British Columbia, Manitoba, and the Northwest Territory. 432 pp., maps, 8vo, cloth. London, 1884. $8.50

Smith 245.

55 BARNES, WILL C. Western Grazing Grounds and Forest Ranges. A History of the Live-Stock Industry as Conducted on the open Ranges of the Arid West. 390 pp., illus., 8vo. Chicago, 1913. $7.50

56 BARNUM, REV. FRANCIS S. J. Grammatical Fundamentals of the Innuit Language as spoken by the Eskimo of the West Coast of Alaska. 384 pp., 4to, cloth. Boston, (1901). $7.50

Item 52, Should read "Ungaver."

57 BARRETT-LENNARD (Capt. B. C.). Travels in British Columbia, with a Narrative of a Voyage round Vancouver's Island and a Trip to California. Plate. 307 pp., 8vo, original cloth, uncut and unopened. London, 1862. $7.50

The author came from England in 1850 and spent two years on the Northwest Coast and California. The book is one of personal observations and adventures, with chapters on the Indians; speculations on the several overland railroad routes; the mines; pony express; Vigilantes Committee; and travels about the gold diggings.

58 BARROW, WILLIAM. "Oregon." The Struggle for Possession. 363 pp., map, 8vo, cloth. Boston, 1885. $4.50

Smith 266.

59 [BARROW, WILLIAM.] The General; or, Twelve Nights in a Hunter's Camp: A Narrative of Real Life. Plates. 12mo, original pictorial wrappers (lacks back wrapper). Boston, (1869). $10.00

Hidden behind this title are the life memoirs of Gen. Williard Barrows, embracing the personal narrative of his trip across the plains to California in 1850; on to Idaho and Montana, with adventures among the Indians, 1864-5.

60 BARRY, T. A., and PATTEN, B. A. Men and Memories of San Francisco in the Spring of '50. 12mo, cloth. San Francisco, 1873. $7.50

61 [BARTLETT, JOHN.] The Sea, the Ship, and the Sailor. Tales of Adventure from Log Books and Original Narratives. Map of Northwest Coast and another, and 31 plates. Royal 8vo, cloth. Portland: Marine Research Society, 1925. $7.50

Contains first printing of Bartlett's voyages to Canton and the NW Coast of America in 1790-3.

62 BARTLETT, LAURA B. Student's History of the Northwest and State of Washington. Vol. 1 (all published). 232 pp., illus., 8vo, cloth. Tacoma, (1922). $5.00

63 BATES, D. B. Incidents on Land and Water; or, Four Years on the Pacific Coast. 336 pp., illus., 12mo, cloth. Boston, 1858. $7.50

Not in Smith.

64 BATES, RUSSELL S. The Man on the Dump. His Songs and Adventures. 8vo, cloth. Seattle, (1909). $3.00

Material on Alaska.

65 BAUGHMAN, THEODORE. The Oklahoma Scout. Illus., 12mo, cloth. Chicago, N. d. $4.00

BAYLIES' ACCOUNT OF HIS TRIP OVERLAND IN 1826

66 BAYLIES, FRANCIS. Northwest Coast of America, May 15, 1826. Referred . . . Mr. Baylies from the Select Committee . . . made the following report: [Baylies' 2nd Report.] 19th Cong., 1st Sess., H. R. Doc. 213. 22 pp., 8vo, sewn. Washington, 1826. $37.50

Wagner-Camp 31. Account of an Overland Journey from Council Bluffs to the mouth of the Columbia River, via the Platte and Santa Fe.

67 BAYLIES, FRANCIS. Narrative of Major General Wool's Campaign in Mexico in the years 1846-48. 8vo, original wrappers. Albany, 1851. $7.50

68 BEARDSLEY, ARTHUR S. Code Making in Early Oregon. 8vo, wrappers. Seattle, 1936. $4.00

69 [BEAVER, THE.] The Beaver. A Journal of Progress Devoted to the Interests of those who Serve the Hudson's Bay Company. Vol. 1, 1920 to date. $60.00

70 BECKNELL, CAPT. THOMAS. The Journal of Capt. Thomas Becknell from Boone's Lick to Santa Fe and from Santa Cruz to Green River. 8vo, original wrappers. Missouri Historical Review, Jan., 1910. $5.00

71 BEEBE, MRS. IOLA. The True Story of Swiftwater Bill Gates by his Mother-in-Law. 139 pp., ports., illus., 16mo, original wrappers. N. p., (1908): $7.50

72 BEESON, J. A Plea for the Indians; Facts and Features of the late War in Oregon, and Affairs in California. 143 pp., 12mo, cloth. N. Y., 1857. $20.00

Cowan, p. 15. Trip across the Plains from Illinois in 1853 to California and Oregon; Affairs and Adventures in California, Vigilance Committee, etc.; Indian wars; depraved condition of the American Settlers iin Oregon; "political rottenness" of the territory, etc. The author was about one jump ahead of the Vigilantes during his sojourn and barely escaped with his neck.

73 —— The Same. 144 pp., 12mo, original printed wrappers. N. Y., 1858. $15.00

74 BEGG, ALEXANDER. History of the Northwest. 3 vols., 8vo, cloth, illus. Toronto, 1894. $22.50

Smith 314.

75 BELCHER, CAPT. SIR EDWARD. Narrative of a Voyage Round the World, performed in Her Majesty's Ship Sulphur during the Years 1836-42. 2 vols., maps and plates, 8vo, calf. London, 1843. $30.00

Belcher called at various places on the Northwest Coast.

76 BELDEN, ALFRED LORD. The Fur Trade of America and some of the men who made and Maintained it, together with Fur Bearing of other Continents and Countries and Islands of the Sea. 591 pp., illus., ports., 8vo, cloth. N. Y., 1917. $12.50

77 BELL, A. D. Argument in favor of Immigration with an Explanation of the Measure recommended by the Immigrant Union read before the Hon. Members of the Committee on Immigration of the House of Assembly of California, Feb. 1, 1870. 27 pp., 8vo. San Francisco, 1870. $6.00

78 BELL, CHARLES N. Our Northern Waters: A Report presented to the Winnipeg Board of Trade, regarding the Hudson Bay Straits. Two folding plans showing Churchill Harbor and the mouth of the Nelson and Hayes Rivers. 80 pp., original wrappers. Winnipeg, 1884. $7.50

79 BELL, JAMES CHRISTY. Opening the Highway to the Pacific, 1838-1846. 209 pp., illus., 8vo, cloth. N. Y., 1921. $4.50

80 BELL, H. P. British Columbia. Report on an Exploratory Survey for a Line of Railway to connect the Canadian Pacific Railway with Barkersville, Cariboo District. 8vo, cloth. Victoria, 1888. $5.00

Not in Smith.

81 BELL, W. S. Old Fort Benton, What It Was, and What It Came to Be. 31 pp., original wrappers. Helena, 1909. $12.50

Now scarce. The only history of this old trading post. Smith 320.

82 BELTRAMI, J. C. A Pilgrimage in Europe and America leading to the Discovery of the Sources of the Mississippi and Bloody River: With a Description of the Whole Course of the former and the Ohio. Map, two folding plans, ports., and 3 plates. 2 vols., cloth. London, 1828. $17.50

83 BENNETT, EMERSON. Leni Leoti; or, Adventures in the Far West. 8vo, original wrappers. Cincinnati, (1850). $5.00

84 BENNETT, W. P. The First Baby in Camp. A full account of the Scenes and Adventures during the Pioneer Days of '49. 12mo, original wrappers. Salt Lake, 1893. $3.50

85 BENTON, J. A. The California Pilgrim. A Series of Lectures. 261 pp., 6 plates., 8vo, cloth. Sacramento, 1853. $22.50

The author arrived in California in 1849 where he founded and was pastor of the Congregational Church. The six plates are apparently the earliest works of Charles Nahl.

86 BENTON, THOMAS HART. Mr. Benton, from the Committee on Indian Affairs, reported a bill: "For the better Regulation of the Fur Trade, etc." 12 pp., 19th Cong., 1st Sess., Senate No. 58. 8vo, sewn. Washington, 1826. (Sold)

87 BENTON, THOMAS HART. In Senate of the U. S., March 18, 1824, Mr. Benton from the Committee on Indian Affairs communicated the following Documents. 18th Cong., 1st Sess., Sen. Doc. 56. 20 pp., 8vo, sewn. Washington, 1824. [Sold]

Considers the advisability of establishing a military post either at the mouth of the Yellowstone, Falls of the Missouri, or Marias River, etc. Wagner-Camp 26.

88 BENTON, THOMAS HART. In the Senate of the U. S., 1826. Mr. Benton, from the Committee on Indian Affairs, reported a bill "for the better regulation of the Fur Trade, etc." 12 pp., 8vo, sewn. Washington, 1826. [Sold]

89 BENTON, THOMAS HART. Speech of Mr. Benton, of Missouri, on the Oregon Question. Delivered in the Senate of the U. S., May 22, 25 and 28, 1846. 8vo. Washnigton: Blair, 1846. $12.50

Smith 328.

90 BERKELEY, GRANTLEY F. The English Sportsman in the Western Prairies. 431 pp., and 10 plates, 8vo, morocco. London, 1861. $22.50

Wagner-Camp 368. Fine tall copy of the Original Edition.

FIRST BOOK TRANSLATED AND EDITED ON NORTHWEST COAST

90a BERKH, V. N. Puteshestvie po Sievermoi Amerikie k Ledovitomu moriu i Tikhomu Okeanu Sovershennyia g. Ebernom i Miakenziem s Prisovokupl niem Opisaniia, Miekhovoi v Kanadie Proizvodimoi, vsiekh zvierei v Amerikie Obrietaiushchikhsia, nravov i obyknovenien Vnutrennykh Dikikh, s Angl. Na Ostrovie Kadiakie. (Voyage through North America to the Frozen Sea and Pacific Ocean made by Messrs. Hearne and McKenzie with description of the Fur Trade in Canada, etc. Translated from the English at Kadiak Island). Small 4to, half calf, xiv-196 pp., and large folding map. St. Petersburg, 1808. $50.00

91 BERNHARDT, C. Indian Raids in Lincoln Co., Kansas. 62 pp., map, 8vo, wrappers. Lincoln, 1910. $5.00

92 BINGHAM, HIRAM. A Residence of Twenty-one Years in the Sandwich Islands; or, the Civil, Religious and Political History of those Islands. Illus., 8vo, cloth. Hartford, 1848. $5.00

93 BIRD, GEORGE ROBERT. Tenderfoot Days in Territorial Utah. 221 pp., illus., 8vo, cloth. Boston, 1918. $4.50

Bird went to Salt Lake iin 1874.

94 BIRD, ISABELL. A Lady's Life in the Rocky Mountains. Illus., 8vo, cloth. N. Y., 1879. $2.50

95 BIRNEY, HOFFMAN. Vigilantes. A Chronicle of the Rise and Fall of the Plummer Gang of Outlaws in and about Virginia City, Montana in the early 60's. 346 pp., illus., 8vo, cloth. Phila., (1929). $3.50

96 BLAINE, DAVID, and BLAINE, CATHERINE PAINE. Letters written between Sept., 1853 and Feb., 1858 from Seattle to friends in the East. 235 pp., of typescript. Small folio size. Seattle, 1853-1858. $50.00

The Blaines arrived in Seattle in 1853. He was the first resident clergyman and his wife the first schoolteacher. Both were educated people and their letters back east contain much expert comment and valuable historical material. The above is the only available form of these historic letters.

97 BLAIR. JAMES. Notices of the Harbor at the Mouth of the Columbia River. Wilkes' map with Inset of Columbia River. 8vo, sewn, uncut. In half red morocco slipcase. (Lancaster, 1846.) (Sold)

Excessively rare. The pamphlet contains letters from Thomas H. Benton, Wilkes, Knox, Reynolds, Emmons, Sinclair, Ludlow, Case and Blair, all officers of the exploring squadron; all give details of the climate, soundings, appearance and other details concerning the mouth of the Columbia River. The pamphlet was published by Blair in disapproval of Capt. Wilkes' account of the dangers of the entrance to the Mouth of the Columbia and to prove the superior skill of Knox as a navigator of this difficult harbor.

BLANCHET'S REPORT ON OREGON AND THE CALIFORNIAS

98 BLANCHET, F. N. Memoire presente a la Congregation de la Propogande sur le Territoire de L'Oregon: (1) Description and Importance of Oregon; (2) European and American Discoveries; Expeditions; (3) Overland Expeditions; (4) Colonizations made by the British and Americans; (5) Russian Settlements; (6) Missionary Settlements; (7) The Two Californias; (8) Journey of Rev. Demers to Cowlitz, Walla Walla, Okanogan, Colville, Oregon City. Etc.; (9) The Letters of Bolduc and Demers, 1845-46. (In Rapport Sur les Missions du Quebec). 129 pp., 8vo, original wrappers. Quebec, 1847. $37.50

Wagner-Camp 127. An important collection of source material relating to the evangelization of both Oregon and California. The volume is seldom offered.

99 BLANCHET, BISHOP, A.M.A. Mission de Walla Walla. (In: "Rapport sur les Missions du Diocese de Quebec, Avril, 1849. No. 8"). 32 pp., 8vo, original wrappers. Quebec, 1849. $32.50

Wagner-Camp 164. Contains a short account of Bishop Blanchet in 1847 from Westport to Oregon, together with the account of Brouillet and the Whitman Massacre.

100 BLANCHET, BISHOP, A.M.A. Voyage de l'Eveque de Walla Walla. (In: "Rapport sur les Missions du Diocese de Quebec, Mars, 1851, No. 9"). With a Map: "Trace de la Route de Westport, Etat de Missouri, a Walla Walla, Oregon." 8vo, original wrappers. Quebec . . . 1851. $37.50

Wagner-Camp 195. The author left Montreal in April, 1847, and arrived at Walla Walla in Sept., 1847. He went via Pittsburgh to St. Louis, thence by steamer to Kansas Landing. The party left Westport May 8.

101 BLAND, T. A. Life of Alfred B. Meacham, by T. A. Bland, together with his Lecture—The Tragedy of the Lava Beds. 48 pp., 8vo, cloth. Washington, 1893. $7.50

Smith 354.

102 BLANKENSHIP, G. Early History of Thurston County, Wash. Together with Pioneer Days, and the Narratives of some Pioneer Trips across the Plains in the 40's. 398 pp., illus., 8vo, cloth. Olympia, 1916. $12.50

103 BLINDLOSS, HAROLD. The Boy Ranchers of Puget Sound. 12mo, cloth. N. Y., 1912. $3.50

104 [BLOCK PRINT HISTORY OF THE NORTHWEST.] Introduction by Professor Edmond S. Meany, Dept. of History, University of Washington. 20 plates, 8vo, cloth. Seattle, N. d. $3.50

105 BOAM, HENRY J. (Compiler). British Columbia: its History, People, Commerce, Industries and Resources. Edited by Ashley G. Brown, accorded the patronage of the Provincial Government of British Columbia. 495 pp., illus., 4to, cloth. London, 1913. $17.50

106 BOAZ, FRANZ. Chinook Texts. 278 pp., 8vo, original wrappers. Washington, 1894. $4.50

Smith 359.

107 BOGUE, VIRGIL. Plan of Seattle: Report of the Municipal Commission. 225 pp., many folding maps, 4to, half morocco. Seattle, 1911. $8.00

Smith 3556.

108 BOIT, JOHN. Boit's Log of the Columbia. Oregon Historical Society Quarterly, Dec., 1921. 8vo, wrappers. Portland, 1921. $2.00

109 BOLLER, HENRY A. Among the Indians, Eight Years in the Far West, 1858-1866. Embracing Sketches of Montana and Salt Lake. Folding map. 12mo, original cloth. Phila., 1868. $35.00

Rare with the map which is almost invariably missing, as the map was inserted in but few copies.

110 BOND, J. W. Minnesota: With Camp-Fire Sketches; or, Notes of a Trip from St. Paul to Pembina and Selkirk Settlement on the Red River. Folding map. 12mo, cloth. Chicago, 1856. $3.50

111 BONISTEEL, MARY G. Army Boys and Girls. 248 pp., illus., 8vo, cloth. Baltimore, 1895. $6.00

Frontier army stories. One relates to Ft. Benton.

112 BONNEY, B. F. Across the Plains by Prairie Schooner. Personal Narrative of B. F. Bonney of his trip to Sutter's Fort, California, in 1846, and his pioneer experiences in Oregon. Ed. by Fred Lockley. 8vo, wrappers. Eugene, N. d. $1.50

113 BOURKE, J. G. On the Border with Crook; Campaigning against the Indians in Montana, Wyoming, Arizona and New Mexico. Port. and plates. 8vo, cloth. N. Y., 1892. $12.50

114 BOURNE, EDWARD GAYLORD. The Legend of Marcus Whitman. American Historical Review, Jan., 1901. 8vo, separate publication, printed wrappers. 1901. $4.50

This is the article that started the discussion whether Dr. Whitman did or did not save Oregon for the U. S.

115 BOURNE, EDWARD GAYLORD. Essays in Historical Criticism. 304 pp., 8vo, cloth. N. Y., 1901. $4.50

Material on Dr. Whitman. Smith 384.

116 BOWER, B. M. Rim of the World. 349 pp., front., 8vo, cloth. Boston, 1919. $4.00

Story of a ranch and feuds between cattle rustlers in Idaho.

117 BOWEN, A. W. Progressive Men of the State of Montana. 1886 pp., 4to, cloth. Chicago, N. d. $7.50

Contains many biographies of Montana pioneers.

118 BOWLES, SAMUEL. Across the Continent: a Summer's Journey to the Rocky Mountains. The Mormons and the Pacific States. Map, 12mo, cloth. Springfield, 1865. $2.50

119 BOWLES, SAMUEL. Our New West; record of Travel between the Mississippi River and the Pacific Ocean. Illus., 8vo, cloth. Hartford, 1869. $2.50

120 BOYD, JOSEPH H. Reminiscences of. By Wm. S. Lewis. 8vo, illus., original printed wrappers. Seattle, 1924. $10.00

Scarce. Only 100 copies were printed. Views of Lewiston, Idaho in 1865; the old mining camp at Warren; facsimile of "The Golden Age", first newspaper in Idaho, etc.

121 BRACE, CHARLES LORING. The New West; or, California in 1867-1868. 8vo, cloth. N. Y., 1869. $4.00

122 BRACKETT, ALBERT G. History of the U. S. Cavalry from the formation of the Federal Government to the first of June, 1863. 337 pp., 8vo, cloth. N. Y., 1865. $7.50

Describes in detail the overland march of the cavalry, the Oregon difficulties, Indian wars, etc.

123 BRACKETT, LINUS PIERPONT. Our Western Empire; or, The West Beyond the Mississippi. 12 maps, tables, 8vo, cloth. Phila., 1881. $5.00

Smith 472.

124 BRACKENRIDGE, H. M. Views of Louisiana; together with a Journal of a Voyage up the Missouri River in 1811. 304 pp., 8vo, calf. Pittsburgh, 1814. $35.00

Original Edition. One of the most important early sources of western history. The author left St. Charles in company with the noted Manuel Lisa and Charboneau (of the Lewis and Clark Expedition) on April 2, 1811 to join Bradbury, who was with Hunt's party. He gives an interesting narrative of Hunt's expedition, an episode made much by Irving in his "Astoria".

125 BRADLEY, GLENN D. The Story of the Pony Express. 175 pp., illus., 12mo, cloth. Chicago, 1913. $7.50

Original edition. Presentation copy from the author. Smith 409.

126 BRADY, CYRUS TOWNSEND. The West Wind: A Story of the Red Men and White in Old Wyoming. Illus., 8vo, cloth. Chicago, 1912. $5.00

127 BRAMBLE, CHAS. A. Klondike, a Manual for Gold-Seekers. 313 pp., map., 8vo, cloth. N. Y., (1897). $7.50

128 BRIDGES, ROBERT. Rail and Water Facilities. 16 pp., 8vo, original wrappers. N. p., N. d., 1916. $4.00

Smith 426. Smith was for years president of the Seattle Port Commission.

129 BRIGGS, HOWARD R., and McCONNELL, WILLIAM J. Frontier Law; a Story of Vigilante Days. 229 pp., 12mo, cloth. 1924. $4.75

McConnell, one time governor and U. S. Governor from Idaho, gives an account of his overland journey to California, placer mining, homesteading, in Oregon, farming and prospecting in Idaho.

130 BRINISTOOL, E. A. A Trooper with Custer and other Historical Incidents of the Battle of the Little Big Horn. Illus., 8vo, cloth. Columbus, 1925. $5.00

131 [BRITISH COLUMBIA.] Guide Map of the Province of, with Short Geographical Description of the Country. Map, 46 pp., 8vo, cloth. Victoria, N. d. $12.50

Smith 1557.

132 [BRITISH COLUMBIA.] Papers relating to the Commission Appointed to Enquire into the conditions of the Indians in the North-West Coast. 8vo, cloth. Victoria, (1868). (Sold)

133 [BRITISH COLUMBIA.] Its Present Resources and Future Possibilities; a Brief Attempt to Demonstrate the Value of the Province. 109 pp., illus., map, 8vo, original wrappers. Victoria, 1893. $7.50

134 BROMLEY, GEO. Tisdale, The Long Ago and Later on; or, Recollections of Eighty Years. 12mo, cloth. San Francisco, 1904. $7.50

Contains chapters on Calif., the author having reached San Francisco in 1851.

135 BROOKS, ALFRED H. The Geography and Geology of Alaska. A Summary of Existing Knowledge. Illus., map, 8vo, cloth. Washington, 1901. $7.50

136 BROOKS, ALFRED H. Reconnaissance in the Cape Nome North Bay Region, Alaska, 1900. Illus., map, 8vo, cloth. Washington, 1901. $7.50

137 BROOKS, ALFRED H. Mineral Resources of Alaska. Report on Progress of Investigation in 1907. 294 pp., illus, maps, 8vo, half morocco. Washington, 1908. $7.50

138 BROOKS, NOAH. First Across the Continent; the Story of the Exploring Expedition of Lewis and Clark. Front., plates, map, 8vo, cloth. N. Y., 1904. $4.00

Smith 480.

THE EXCESSIVELY RARE OREGON EDITION OF THE "WHITMAN MASSACRE" BY THE CAYUSE INDIANS

138a BROUILLET, J. B. A. An Authentic Account of the Murder of Dr. Whitman and other Missionaries by the Cayuse Indians of Oregon in 1847, and the causes which led to that Horrible Catastrophe. With a journal of the principal events that occurred in the Walla Walla country; a letter of Sir James Douglas, Chief Factor of the Hudson's Bay Co., and an Appendix wherein will be found additional irrefutable evidence beyond the suspicion of partiality. 108 pp., shmo, original printed wrappers. Portland, Ore., 1869. [Sold] $187.50

We are able to trace two copies, one in the Jones library and in the Library Association of Portland. This volume is one of the most important in the whole of early western Annals, depicitng as it does the many historic details of a massacre more important in many and more tragic in all its features than any other that has ever occurred in the west. The work is that of an eye-witness and prominent actor in many of the events narrated. Father Brouilett reaching the fort just after the massacre, while the naked and bloody corpses of the victims were lying about. His work is a defense of the accusations made against himself and the Catholic Church of having instigated the massacre. The Oregon work has added material not included in the New York edition, published a few years earlier.

139 BROWN, COL. W. C. The Sheep-Eater Campaign. 8vo, original wrappers. Boise, 1926. $6.00

140 —— The Same. 12mo, cloth. Boise, 1926. $4.50

141 BROWN, VALENTINE. The Chieftain and Satires. 192 pp., 8vo, cloth. Portland, 1903. $4.00

Smith 499.

142 BROWNE, BELMORE. The Conquest of Mt. McKinley. The Story of the Three Expeditions through Alaska Wilderness to Mt. McKinley, etc. Illus., 8vo, cloth. N. Y., 1915. $6.00

Smith 502.

143 BROWNE, J. ROSS. Crusoe's Island: A Ramble in the Footsteps of Alexander Selkirk. With Sketches of Adventure in California and Washoe. Map and plates, 8vo, cloth. N. Y., 1864. $6.00

Original edition. "One of the most interesting books relating to California life"—Cowan, p. 26.

144 BROWNE, J. ROSS, and TAYLOR, JAMES W. Report upon the Mineral Resources of the U. S. 8vo, cloth. Washington, 1867. $4.50

Smith 508.

145 BROWNE, J. ROSS. Resources of the Pacific Slope, &c. 8vo, cloth. N. Y., 1869. $3.50

146 BROWN, J. C. Calabazas, Amusing Recollections of an Arizona "City." 251 pp., 8vo, original printed wrappers. San Francisco, 1892. [Sold]

147 BROWNE, JAMES S. California Gold: An Authentic History of the First Find. With the names of those interested in the Discovery. Port. 20 pp., 12mo, wrappers. Oakland, 1894. $12.50

An important work, in that, aside from Marshall's, this is the only printed relation by an eye witness.

148 BROWN, JAMES S. Life of a Pioneer. Portrait. 528 pp., plates, 8vo, cloth. Salt Lake City, 1900. $17.50

Original edition. One of the most important of pioneer narratives. The author went overland with the "Mormon Batallion" to California in 1846 and was present when the first piece of gold was discovered.

149 BRUCE, MINER W. Alaska: its History and Resources, Gold Fields, Routes and Scenery. Map, illus., 8vo, cloth. Seattle, 1895. $6.00

Smith 518.

150 BRUSETH, NELS. Indian Stories and Legends of the Stillaguamish and allied Tribes. Illus., 21 pp., 8vo, original printed wrappers. N. p., (1926). $5.00

Privately printed in a small edition.

ONLY COMPLETE COPY REPORTED OF BUACHE'S EXPLANATIONS AND ATLAS OF THE N.W. DISCOVERIES

150a BUACHE, PHILIPPE. Considerations Geographiques Physiques sur les Novelle Decouvertes au Nord de la grand Mer, appelle'e Vulgairement la Mer du Sud. 158 pp. Paris: Imprimierie Ballard, 1753. Together with the Liste de Cartes, 4 pp., of which the last catch-word is "Expose". Together with: Expose des Decouvertes au Nord de la Grand Mer, soit dans le Nord-Est de l'Asie, soit dans le Nord-Ouest de l'Amerique, entre le 160 degrees de Longitude et le 287, depuis le 43 de Latitude Septentrionale, jusqu'au 80. Decouvertes des Russe depuis 20 ans, comparees avec les idees qu'on avoit cidevant du Nord-Est de l'Asie & des Terres Voisines de l'Amerique, comme en etant separees par un Detroit. Decouvertes des Francois, depuis 15 ans, scavoir la Partie plus Occidentale de Nouvelle France ou du Canada, jusqu'au du Lac Superieur. Resultat de Diverses Recherches. Faites par feu Guillaume de Lisle & Philippe Buache, dont l'object est d'un Cote la Mer de l'Ouest au Nord de la Californie & de l'Ouest du Canada, avec sa Prolongation jusqu'ru la Baye d'Hudson & de l'autre Cote, une Grande Presq Isle qui forme un long Detroit entre la Nord-Est de l'Asie & le Nord-Ouest de l'Amerique. Decouvertes de l'Amiral de Fonte, au Nord des Precedentes & avec tout ce que l'on connoit d'allieurs. Presente au Roy, 2 Septembre, 1753. 6 pp. Followed by Twelve engraved and numbered colored plates containing 16 maps and 5 numbered Coast Elevations, each plate containing 5 outlines.
The maps are as follows:

(1) Carte des Nouvelles Decouvertes, entre la Partie Orientale de l'Asie, et l'Occidental de l'Amerique. 1752. (9½x14 inches); (2) Carte des Decou-

---

Item 150a, In 19th line, note should read 2 leaves not 6pp. In the 6 point note on p. 18, 18th line should read 1754, not 1854; line 21 should read "two leaves with text" not "two blank pages."

vertes de l'Amiral de Fonte selon la Carte Angloise d'annee par Ecrivian du Vaisseau la California. 1752. (9½x14 inches); (3) Carte du Geometrique des Decouvertes de l'Amiral de Fonte et de son Capitaine Bernarda, compare avec le systeme de la carte Angloise. 1752. (9½x14 inches); also (b) Extract de la Relacion de l'Amiral de Fonte, fait d'apres un manuscript que M. de l'Isle m'a communique en 1748. (9½x14 inches); (4) Reduction d'une Carte publiee a Nuremberg representant l'une Premieres Idees qu'on s'est forme du Kamchatka et de Environs. (5x9½ inches); also (b) Vue de Glaces au milieu desquelles l'on voit la Peche qui se fait au Nord-Est de l'Asie. 1753. (9x14 inches); (5) Essai d'une Carte qui Mr. Guillame deLisle, avait joint a son Memoire, presente a la cour en 1717 sur la Mer de l'Ouest. 1752. (8x9½ inches); (6) (a) Carte des Terres aux Environ du Japon. (9½x12 inches); (b) Carte des Terres Nouvellement connues au Nord de la Mer du Sud. 1752. (7x12 inches); (7) Carte Marine des Parties Septentrionale de la Grand Mer et de l'Ocean. 1752. (11x21 inches); (8) Carte Physique des Terriens les plus eleves de la Partie Occidentale du Canada. 1754. (9½x15 inches); (9) La Californie d'apres une Tres Grande Carte Espagnole . . . de l'Amerique dressee a Florence en 1604 par Mathieu Neron Peciolen; (b) Carte du Passage par Terre a la Californie, 1754. (9½x15 inches); (10) Carte de l'Isle de Jeso et de ses Environs. 1754. (11½x16 inches); (11) Carte du Royaume et des Isles de Lieou Kieou. 1754. (9x13 inches); (12) Vues des Cotes de la Terre au Isle d'Eso. 1754. (10x21 inches.

All contained in 2 vols., 4to, calf. Paris, 1753-1754. $750.00

The "Expose" together with the "Considerations, and third and last parts, together with the final list of maps, as cited in the above work, is an accumulation of great rarity. The fine colored maps, each with engraved number, and expertly engraved after the greatest map-makers of their day, De Lisle and Buache, were never excelled among the first maps of early discovery. The maps and explanatory text are of the highest importance and of superlative rarity among all Western Americana. We can locate no other complete copy in any of the World libraries.

Explanatory note:—It is quite obvious that the Royal Academy of Sciences (Paris) published at various times the materials that make up this volume. The material was not all published at once, hence when the books were made up the various papers were bound in different form.

Collation of "Considerations": Title page date, 1753. At p. 7, dated Paris, 6 Septembre, 1752, is the certificate of the Academie Royale des Sciences. At p. 24, dated Juillet, 1753, is the certificate of the Academie and de l'Imprimerie de Ballard, Rue S. Jean de Beauvais a Sainte Cecile. (This is the end of first part). At p. 49, dated Sept., 1753, a certificate of the Academie and de l'Imprimerie de Ballard; p. 62, dated Dec., 1753, certificate of the Academie, etc. (end of second part); p. 74, dated Juillet, 1754, certificate of Academie, etc.; p. 148, dated Sept., 1854, certificate of the Academie, etc.; p. 158, de l'Imprimerie de Ballard, Rue S. Jean de Beauvais, 1754. (End of Vol. I, 158 pp. with "Table des Matieres." Collation of Vol. 2. "Expose," as quoted in general text above. Two pages with text and 2 blank pages. Then follows the "Liste des Cartes," 4 pp., with catch-word "Expose." This in turn is followed by "Considerations" again with 62 pp., or the first part duplicated. Followed by the 12 engraved colored plates, with 16 maps and 5 numbered coast elevations, each containing 5 coast elevations.

The above work is not to be confused with the work published by Buache, 15 November., 1781. See Bibliotheque Nationale Cat. No. 5571. See note to item No. 159, Cat. 17, describing the De Lisles. In line 12 of descriptive notes De Lisle is described as "biographer." This should read "ablest Geographer."

Buache was a brother-in-law of the De Lisles.

151 BUEL, J. W. Heroes of the Plains; or, Lives and Wonderful Adventures of Wild Bill, Buffalo Bill, Kit Carson, Capt. Payne, "White Beaver," Capt. Jack, Texas Jack, California Joe, etc. Colored front., other illus., 12mo, cloth. St. Louis, 1884. $7.50

152 [BUFFALO BILL.] Four Years in Europe with Buffalo Bill. A Descriptive Narrative of the Big American Show's Successful Tour in Foreign Lands. Illus. by Chas. Eldridge Griffin. 8vo, original cloth. Albia, Iowa, 1908. $5.00

153 BULFINCH, THOMAS. Oregon and Eldorado. 464 pp., 12mo, cloth. Boston, 1866. $7.50

154 BULFINCH, ELLEN SUSAN. Life and Letters of Thomas Bulfinch. Map, illus. 8vo, cloth. Boston, 1896. $7.50

155 BURNHAM, FREDERICK W. A Missionary Trip to Alaska. Illus., map, 30 pp., 8vo, original printed wrappers. Cincinnati, (1918). $7.50

A scarce privately printed work dealing with the author's experiences in Alaska.

156 BURR, AGNES RUSH. Alaska, our Beautiful Northland of Opportunity. 428 pp., front., plates, map. 8vo, cloth. Boston, 1919. $4.75

157 BURPEE, L. J. Highways of the Fur Trade. 8vo, wrappers. N. p., 1914. $5.00

157 BURPEE, L. J. Highways of the Fur Trade. 8vo, wrappers. N.p. 1914. $5.00

158 BUTLER, JAMES DAVIE. New Found Journal of Charles Floyd, a Sergeant under Captains Lewis and Clark. 30 pp., 8vo. Worcester, 1894. $7.50

Smith 558.

159 BUTLER, SIR WM. F. Great Lone Land: a Narrative of Travel and Adventure in the Northwest of America. Illus., map. 8vo, cloth. London, 1873. $5.00

Smith 559.

160 BUTLER, SIR WILLIAM F. Wild North Land; being the Story of a Winter's Journey with Dogs across Northern North America. Illus., map. 8vo, cloth. Montreal, 1874. $2.50

161 CABRILLO, JUAN RODRIQUES. Relation; or, Diary of the Voyage which Juan Rodriques Cabrillo made with the two ships for the discovery of the passage of the South Sea, at the North from 27th of June, 1542, etc., etc. United States Geographical Suryeys west of the 100th Meridian. 8vo. Washington, 1879. $7.50

162 CAIRNES, DE LORNE DONALDSON. The Yukon: Alaska International Boundary between Porcupine and the Yukon Rivers. 161 pp., front., illus., 2 maps. 8vo, cloth. Ottawa, 1914. $7.50

Smith 568.

163 CAIRD, JAMES. Prairie Farming in America. With notes by the way on Canada and the United States. 12mo, original printed wrappers. N. Y., 1859. $7.50

Red River, Valley of the Saskatchewan, Hudson Bay Territory, Wisconsin and the Mississippi Valley are thoroughly noted in the description.

164 [CALIFORNIA.] Ranch Life in California. By R. M. H. 117 pp., 8vo, cloth. London, 1886. $7.50

164a [CALIFORNIA.] Argument in the Case of the Rancho de los Capitancillos (Fossat vs. the U. S.), before the Supreme Court. By J. S. Black, one of the Counsel for Claimant, 56 pp., 8vo, original printed wrappers. Washington, 1864. $7.50

The famous and protracted case over the title to the New Almaden mine, which had already involved six surveys and no less than nine court decisions. It concerned the original Mexican grants to Larios and Berreyesa, and, by analogy, all land titles in the state.

164b [CALIFORNIA.] A Month in California. By James Cropper. 44 pp., frontispiece, sm. 8vo, Orig. Printed Wrappers. London, 1873. $20.00

Not mentioned by Cowan. Describes the overland journey by rail; Yosemite Valley; San Jose and Napa; the Chinese; Customs and Manners, etc. No other copy reported.

165 [CALIFORNIA AND THE OVERLAND.] Jones Pantascope. Twenty Four Views. Reprint of California Historical Society Pictures of the Overland Trail and California in 1850. The complete. N. p., N. d. $7.50

166 [CALIFORNIA.] The City and County of San Diego. Laberthon and Taylor. 218 pp., illus. 8vo, cloth. San Diego, 1888. $4.50

LAUR'S REPORT ON CALIFORNIA MINES

167 [CALIFORNIA.] De la Production des Metaux Precieux en California. Rapport as exc. M. Le Ministre des travaux publics. Par M. P. Laur. 132 pp. 8vo, cloth backed boards. Paris, 1862. $17.50

Rare. Not in Cowan. Soon after the first shipment of gold from the Calif. mines to Paris, the French Government commissioned M. Laur to visit the Calif. gold fields and to make a report to the French Government. M. Laur not only visited the mines in Calif., but pushed on into Utah where he gave a report on other metals than gold. M. Laur's book is one of the most interesting contemporary books written by a foreigner on the mines.

168 [CALIFORNIA.] California of the South. By Walter Lindley and J. P. Widney. 377 pp., illus., map. 8vo, cloth. N. Y., 1888. $5.00

169 [CALIFORNIA.] A Memorial and Biographical History of Northern California. Illus. 4to, leather. Chicago, 1891. $7.50

170 [CALIFORNIA.] (Meyer, Carl). Nach dem Sacramento Reisbilder eines Heimgekehrten. 364 pp., 12mo, original printed wrappers. Aarau, 1855. $7.50

Original Edition. Although the original edition is often catalogued as the 1857 edition, the actual title page date of the original is 1855. This is the journal of Meyer's trip; life at Monterey, at San Francisco, and in the mines and among the Indians.

170a [CALIFORNIA.] The Wasp. Christmas Souvenir Edition. Numerous full-page plates showing San Francisco before the 1906 fire. Folio, original wrappers. San Francisco, 1898. $4.50

171 [CALIFORNIA AND IDAHO.] [Clark, Austin S.] Reminiscences of Travel, 1852-65. Portrait. 54 pp., 8vo, original boards. Middletown: J. S. Stewart, Printer, N.d. No copyright. $40.00

Not in Cowan. The work was printed "for my two sons, and the few friends who may chance to see it". The narrative is that of a gold-seeker who made a trip to California in 1852. He located at Coloma, spending 13 years at the mines, and gives an interesting account of his life and times at the diggings, and among the Indians. In 1865 he left California for Idaho which he describes in the second half of his book.

172 [CALIFORNIA.] White, W. F. A Picture of Pioneer Times in California, illustrated with Anecdotes and Stories taken from Real Life. By William Grey. 8vo, cloth. San Francisco, 1881. $17.50

Extremely important work by a pioneer of '49. The author was the father of Senator White of Calif.

173 [CALIFORNIA.] Wise, Lieut. H. A. Los Gringos; or, An Inside View of Mexico and California. 453 pp. 12mo, cloth. N. Y., 1849. $4.50

Original Edition. The author who went to California in 1849, witnessed the arrival of the Donner Party, of which he gives an account. He was also at Monterey, San Francisco, San Jose, and elsewhere.

174 CAMP, CHARLES L. Kit Carson in California. With Extracts from His Own Story. Portrait. 8vo, original wrappers. San Francisco, 1922. $3.50

175 CAMPBELL, ALBERT H. Pacific Wagon Roads. Letter from the Secretary of the Interior transmitting a report upon the several wagon roads constructed under the direction of the Interior Department. (Report by Robert H. Campbell, dated Feb. 10, 1859.) 35th Cong., 2nd Sess., House Ex. Doc. 108. 125 pp., 6 maps. 8vo. [Washington, 1859.] $27.50

Wagner-Camp 321. Important not only for the fine field maps, but for the various reports from the supts. under Campbell. The report covers projects from South Pass and the Platte to Texas and New Mexico.

FINE COPY OF THE ORIGINAL EDITION OF J. L. CAMPBELL'S IDAHO GUIDE

176 CAMPBELL, J. L. Idaho. Six Months in the New Gold Regions. The Emigrant's Guide. Map. 8vo, original pictorial wrappers. Chicago: J. R. Walsh, 1864. [Sold] $425.00

Wagner-Camp 398. A fine, almost mint, copy of the Original Edition, with 52pp. of text and 3 leaves of adv. The original title reads: "Idaho; Six Months in the New Gold Diggings. The Emigrant's Guide Overland. Itinerary of the Routes. Features of the Country. Journal of Residence, etc., etc. By J. L. Campbell. New York: Published by J. L. Campbell, 1864."

There is an adv. on verso of cover title, also on the inside back cover. The verso of title has the following: "Entered according to the Act of Congress, in the Year 1864, by J. L. Campbell, in the Clerk's Office of the District Court for the Northern District of Illinois." Below on the lower margin of the outside wrapper appears: "Printed by the Tribune Company, 51 Clark Street, Chicago."

Wagner-Camp describes a copy with 53 plus 16 pages of text. Other copies contain an extra map of Idaho. The above copy has an adv. proclamation that the Idaho map would soon appear. There is a reference to Campbell on page 9 of those copies containing extra pagination. There is no such reference in the above copy.

Campbell was a correspondent for the Chicago Tribune and was sent overland by that newspaper to gather reports for its columns.

177 CAMPBELL, ROBERT. The Discovery and Exploration of the [Yukon] Pelley River. Contributed by the Discoverer. 443 pp., illus. In the "Royal Reader," 5th Book. Nelson, Ont., (1882). $22.50

This is the first printed account of the Pelley or Yukon River by Chief Factor Campbell. The book is scarce because it was printed without the approval of the Canadian Dept. of Education, thus not used.

178 CAMPBELL, ROBERT. A History of the Scotch Presbyterian Church. 801 pp., illus. 8vo, cloth. Montreal, 1887. $17.50

Contains many sketches of members of the church who were prominent in the fur trade in the Northwest, among them being Simon Fraser, McDonald, Alexander Mackenzie, Simon McTavish and many more. This book was published in a small edition and is now quite scarce.

179 CAMPBELL, WILFRED. The Scotsman in Canada. Eastern Canada. The Scotsman in Canada. Western Canada. 2 vols., 8vo, cloth. Toronto and London, N. d. $12.50

A scarce source book containing the biographies of many fur traders.

180 CANNON, ELDER C. Q. Writings from the "Western Standard." 512 pp. 8vo, full diced calf. Liverpool, 1864. $15.00

First Edition in book form. A rare volume that has sold as high as $90 at auction. Mr. Cannon was stationed at San Francisco while printing the first translation of the Mormon Bible into the Hawaiian language, and while there contributed these sketches and controversial monographs to the press. The "Western Standard" lasted some 19 months, when Mr. Cannon was compelled to move to England, where he gathered and printed this material for the first time as a whole. The articles contain many incidents and facts relating to the pioneer west, the plains, Utah, and California, outlawry and depredations of the Carson Valley, the Indians, Overland Railroads, Vigilante Committees, &c.

181 CANNON, M. Waiilatpu: Its Rise and Fall: 1836-1847. A Story of Pioneer Days in the Pacific Northwest: (Incidents of the Trail, Life among the Cayuse Indians, Massacre of Dr. and Mrs. Whitman and twelve others, the taking into captivity of two score women and girls and the treatment accorded them by the Savage Indians.) Ports. and plates, 171 pp. 8vo, original wrappers. Boise: Privately Printed, 1915. $7.50

182 CANSE, JOHN M. Pilgrim and Pioneer in the Northwest. 306 pp., 12mo, cloth, illus. N. Y., 1930. $3.75

183 CAREY, CHARLES HENRY. History of Oregon. 3 vols., 8vo, illus. Chicago, 1922. $10.00

184 CAREY, CHARLES HENRY. The Oregon Constitution and Proceedings and Debates of the Constitutional Convention of 1857. 543 pp., 8vo, cloth. Salem, 1926. $6.00

185 CAREY, CHARLES H Some Early Maps and Myths. 19 pp., 8vo, original wrappers. N. p., (1929). $4.00

Presentation copy.

186 CARHART, EDITH BEEBE. History of Bellingham. 39 pp., 12mo, original printed boards. Bellingham, 1926. $5.00

187 CARR, ROBERT V. Black Hills Ballads. 12mo, cloth. Denver, 1902. $5.00

188 CARREL, FRANK. Canada's West and Farther West. 12mo, illus., cloth. Toronto, 1911. $4.50

189 CARRERE, JOHN F. Spokane Falls—Washington Territory and Its Tributary Country, comprising Eastern Washington and the Idaho Panhandle. 40 pp., illus. 8vo. (Spokane Falls), 1889. $7.50

Very scarce. Smith No. 602 locates but one copy.

190 CARRINGTON, MRS. M. J. Ab-Sa-Ra-Ka, Home of the Crows; being the Experiences of an Officer's Wife on the Plains, and Marking the Vicissitudes of Peril and Pleasure during the Occupation of the New Route to Virginia City, Montana, 1866-67, and the Indian Hostility thereto; with Outlines of the Natural Features and Resources of the Land, Tables of Distances . . . [etc.]. [Map and illus.]. 12mo, cloth. Original edition. Phila., 1868. $15.00

191 CARTERET, J. D. A Fortune Hunter; or, The Old Stone Corral. Narrative of the Santa Fe Trail. 12mo, cloth. Cincinnati, 1888. $2.50

The "Stone Corral" was a refuge for travellers on the trail when it crossed the Cottonwood.

192 CASTERLINE, EDWIN D. Pages from a Young Man's Journal. 215 pp., 8vo, original printed wrappers. San Jose, Cal., 1895. $4.50

193 CASTLEMON, HARRY. Frank on the Prairies. 245 pp., 12mo, half calf. Phila., (1865). $7.50

194 [CATHOLIC MISSIONS.] Mission de la Congregation Des Missionnaires Oblats de Mari Immaculate. 8vo, cloth. Paris, 1867. $7.50

Mission of Mackenzie; Nouvelle Bretagne, etc.

195 [CATHOLIC MISSIONS.] Prayers in the Crow Indian Language composed by the Missionaries of the Society of Jesus. De Smet Mission Print, Idaho, 1891. $12.50

196 [CATHOLIC MISSIONS.] (Missionaries of the Society of Jesus) A. M. D. G. Selecta ex Historia Sacra. De Smet Mission Print. (DeSmet, Idaho, 1891). $12.50

Not mentioned in any bibliography consulted.

197 CHAMBERS, MARGARET WHITE. Reminiscences by Margaret White Chambers. 48 pp., 8vo. N. p., N. d. Written in 1894 and published in 1903. [Sold] $125.00

Excessively rare copy of the Original Edition. Mrs. Chambers crossed the Plains in 1851 with her three brothers (White) and reached Portland the same year, where she was employed by Rev. Lyman. She arrived at Chambers Prairies, Puget Sound, October of 1852. An interesting Overland Narrative, as well as important for Indian wars of 1855-56. Married Andrew J. White Jan. 18, 1854. The only copy Smith, No. 648, locates is in the Oregon Historical Society.

198 CHANDLER, GEORGE. Textbook of Civics for the State of Washington. 418 pp., illus. 12mo, cloth. N. Y., (1910). $3.75

Smith 653.

199 CHANDLER, KATHERINE. The Bird Women of Lewis and Clark Expedition. 109 pp., 12mo, cloth. N. Y., 1905. $3.50

200 CHANDLESS, WM. A Visit to Salt Lake; being a Journey across the Plains and a Residence in the Mormon Settlements at Utah. Folding map. 12mo, cloth. London, 1857. $7.50

Wagner-Camp 287. Relates to Southern California.

201 CHAPMAN, CHAS. E. Catalogue of the Materials in the Archive de Indias for the History of the Pacific Coast and American Southwest. 775 pp., 8vo, cloth. Berkeley, 1919. $6.00

202 CHAPMAN, KATHERINE HOPKINS. The Fusing Forces. An Idaho Idyl. 416 pp., 8vo, cloth. Chicago, 1911. $4.50

203 CHEEVER, HENRY T. Life in the Sandwich Islands; or, The Heart of the Pacific as it was and is. 355 pp., 8vo, cloth. N. Y., 1851. $7.50

204 CHENOWETH, F. A. Opinion of the Hon. F. A. Chenoweth, delivered on 24th May 1865, on the return of the Marshall to his Service of Writs of Habeas Corpus for the Bodies of Chief Justice Lander and others, at Steilacoom, W. T., also a letter to a member of the Bar. 14 pp., sewn. Steilacoom, May 24, 1856. (Sold)

205 CHETLAIN, GEN. A. A. Recollections of Seventy Years. 304 pp., 8vo, cloth. Galena (Ill.), 1899. $3.00

Was stationed at Salt Lake.

205a CHINALE, REV. JOS. (S.J.). The Universal Papal Hymn. Numpiu, or Nez Perce Version. Broadside, 4½x6¼ inches. N.p. (1908). $6.00

A scarce and important contribution to the study of Indian languages.

206 [CHINOOK JARGON.] Gill's Dictionary of the Chinook Jargon. 63 pp., 8vo, cloth. Portland, 1889. $4.50

206a CHINOOK JARGON.] Dictionary of the Chinook Jargon, or Indian Trade Language of the North Pacific Coast. 33 pp., 8vo, unbound. Victoria: Hiben, (1877). $7.50

Not in Smith.

207 CHIROUSE, EUGENE CASIMIR. The Indian Sentinel. Chirouse Number. (By Charles Milton Buchanan and others). Vol 1, No. 7. 48 pp. Washington Bureau of Catholic Indians, 1918. 8vo. Washington, 1918. $7.50

Smith 530 locates only the copy at Washington University. The subject of this work was born in the province of Dauphine, France in 1821 and became a missionary to the Yakima Indians of Washington Territory in 1848. He spent the remainder of his life there until his death in 1892. The work contains much local history of the Indians and localities of western Washington and Idaho.

208 CHITTENDEN, HIRAM M. The American Fur Trade in the Far West. History of the Pioneer Trading Post and Early Fur Companies of the Missouri Valley, the Rocky Mountains and of the Overland Commerce with Santa Fe. Large map and 10 plates. 3 vols., 8vo, cloth. N. Y., 1902. $30.00

Contains the adventures of Jedediah Smith, James Bridger, Ashley and others. Appendix contains list of western forts and locates them; journal of steamboat voyages from St. Louis to Ft. Union, etc.

209 CHITTENDEN, H. S. History of Early Steamboat Navigation on the Missouri River. Life and Adventures of Joseph La Barge, Pioneer, Navigator and Indian Trader for Fifty Years. 16 ills. and plates of Missouri scenes and crafts. 2 vols., 8vo, cloth. N. Y., 1903. $22.50

210 CHITTENDEN, H. M. Yellowstone National Park: Historical, Descriptive, maps, plates, portraits. 12mo, cloth. Cincinnati, 1905. $3.50

211 CHITTENDEN, H. M. Verses by. 83 pp., 16mo, full calf. Seattle, (1916). $7.50

Only a few copies were printed for Mr. Chittenden's friends. The above is a presentation copy.

AN UNRECORDED GUIDE TO BRITISH COLUMBIA AND ALASKA

212 CHITTENDEN, NEWTON H. Travels in British Columbia and Alaska. Circular of the World's Guide for Home, Health and Pleasure Seekers. Containing new and valuable Information concerning this comparatively unknown region, its Physical Features, Climate, Resources and Inhabitants. 8vo, origial printed wrappers. Victoria, 1882. $27.50

Presentation copy from the author. Smith 683 cites but one copy.

213 [CHOCTAW LANGUAGE.] Kiahlik Iksa Nana-Aiymmika I Katikism. 200 pp., 8vo, cloth. Washington, N. d. $5.00

A catechism of the Catholic religion translated into Choctaw.

214 [CHRISTIAN ENDEAVOR.] Twenty-third International Christian Endeavor Convention, Seattle, Wash., Oct. 10-15th, 1907. 8vo, wrappers. Seattle, 1907. $3.00

215 CHRISTOE, ALICE HENSON. Treadwell. An Alaskan Fulfillment. 8vo, original wrappers. N. p., N. d. $2.50

216 [CHURCH MISSIONARY SOCIETY.] Metlakahta and the North Pacific Mission of the Church Missionary Society. 130 pp., 2 maps. 8vo, cloth. London, 1880. $7.50

216a [CIVIL WAR.] Report of the Advocate General on "The Order of American Knights" alias "The Sons of Liberty". A Western Conspiracy in aid of the Southern Rebellion. 16 pp., 8vo, uncut, sewn. Washington: Chronicle Print, 1864. $4.00

216b CLARK, A. B. Travels in Mexico and California: comprising a journal of a tour from Brazos Santiago, through Central Mexico, by way of Monterey, Chihuahua, the country of the Apaches, and the River Gilt, to the mining districts of California. By A. B. Clark. 138 pp., 8vo, original wrappers. Wright & Hasty's Steam Press, Boston, 1852. $47.50

217 CLARK, M. Roadhouse Tales; or, Nome in 1900. 267 pp., map, illus. 12mo, cloth. Gerard, Kans., 1902. $7.50

Not in Smith.

218 CLARK, ROBERT CARLTON. History of the Willamette Valley, Oregon. Illus. 3 vols., small 4to, cloth. Chicago, 1927. $12.50

219 CLARK, W. P. The Indian Sign Language, with brief Explanatory Notes. And a Description of some of the peculiar Laws, Customs, Myths, Superstitions, Ways of Living, Code of Peace and War Signals of our Aborigines. Map. 8vo, cloth. Phila., 1885. $7.50

UNRECORDED GUIDE TO N. W. GOLD MINES

220 CLAUDET, M. The Handbook of British Columbia, and Emigrant's Guide to the Gold Fields. Large folding map with borders in colors, double-page woodcut view of Westminster and another of the Harbor. 82 pp., 12mo, printed yellow wrappers. London, (1862). $75.00

Extremely rare. No copy located in the Union Library List of the Northwest. The discovery of gold on the Fraser River caused great excitement. An exodus of miners from California and elsewhere to those diggings occurred.

221 CLAYSON, EDWARD, SR. Historical Narratives of Puget Sound. Hood's Canal, 1865-1885. The Experience of an only Free Man in a Penal Colony. Portrait. 12mo, wrappers, in cloth case. Seattle, Wash., 1911. (Sold)

222 CLAYTON, W. William Clayton's Journal: A Daily Record of the Journey of the Original Company of "Mormon" Pioneers from Nauvoo, Illinois, to the Valley of the Great Salt Lake, Feb. 8, 1846 to Oct. 21, 1847. (Including details of the first settlement of Salt Lake City, and the return journey Eastward over the Plains to Winter Quarters). Portrait. 376 pp., 12mo, cloth. Salt Lake, 1921. Printed for the Clayton family. $5.00

Clayton was appointed "historian" of the Company, and kept a daily journal of the expedition, recording all events of interest that befell them.

223 CLELAND, MABLE GOODWIN. Early Days in the Fir Tree Country. 221 pp., 8vo, cloth. Seattle, (1923). $3.00

Sories of Indians and pioneers.

224 CLEVELAND, RICHARD J. A Narrative of Voyages and Commercial Enterprises. 2 vols., 12mo, cloth, paper labels. Cambridge, 1842. $37.50

Original Edition. Cowan p. 131. An important source book much used by Bancroft. The author was an adventurer and fur trader of the old school. His voyages include the narrative of his four years' expedition to the Northwest Coast, in the Brig Carolina, 1799-1802, and the voyage of the Leslie Byrd to California in 1803-4.

225 —— The Same. 8vo, cloth-backed boards, frontis. London, 1842. $10.00

226 COCCOLA, NICHOLAS, O.M.I. The Life Work of Father Nicholas Coccola, O.M.I., as described by Himself while a Patient in St. Paul's Hospital, Vancouver, B. C., in Aug., 1924. Typescript of 102 pp., bound in cloth. N. p., N. d. (Vancouver, 1924). $25.00

The only copy. Contains much regarding missions, church work and early history of the Northwest.

227 CODMAN, JOHN. The Mormon Country. A Summer with the Saints. 225 pp., illus., map. 12mo, cloth. N. Y., 1874. $3.75

228 CODY, REV. EDMUND R. History of the Coeur d'Alene Mission of the Sacred Heart. 47 pp., illus., 8vo, original wrappers. (Caldwell, 1930). $5.00

229 CODY, H. A. On Trail and Rapid by Dog Sled and Canoe. 203 pp., illus. 12mo, cloth. London, 1911. $7.50

The story of Bishop Bompas' life among the Indians and Eskimos. The Bishop arrived in the Red River country in 1865.

230 CODY, WILLIAM F. True Tales of the Plains. 259 pp., illus., 8vo, cloth. N. Y., 1908. $3.50

231 COKE, HENRY J. A Ride over the Rocky Mountains to Oregon and California. Portrait. 8vo, 3/4 morocco. Fine. London, 1852. $12.50

Wagner-Camp 211. Journal of an expedition across the plains in 1850.

232 COLLIS, SEPTIMA M. A Woman's Trip to Alaska; being an Account of a Voyage through the Inland Seas of the Sitkan Archipelago in 1890. Illus., some in color; folding map. 8vo, cloth (shaken). N. Y., (1890). $3.75

233 COLTON, WALTER. Three Years in California. Complete with large folding "Declaration of Rights of Califrnia," 6 plates and 6 portraits. 456 pp., 12mo, original cloth. N. Y., 1850. $7.50

The earliest issue of the first edition, issued before the blocks for the "tinted plates" had been properly prepared, which has resulted in some weird and amusing color effects. The author was Alcade of Monterey.

234 —— The Same. Deck and Port; or, Incidents of a Cruise to California, with Sketches of Rio, Honolulu, San Francisco, etc. Map, portrait and tinted plates. N. Y., 1850. $4.50

235 CONARD, HOWARD L. "Uncle Dick" Wootton, the Pioneer Frontiersman of the Rocky Mountain Regin. An Account of the Adventures and Thrilling Experiences of the Most Noted American Hunter, Trapper, Guide, Scout, and Indian Fighter now living. With introduction by Major Kirkland. 40 portraits, plates and illus. Royal 8vo, cloth. Chicago, 1890. $35.00

The original edition and one of the few presentation copies.

236 —— The Same. 8vo, cloth. Unsigned copy. $27.50

237 CONDON, MARY ALICE. Mt. Hood our Indian's Pah-to. 47 pp., illus. 12mo, original wrappers. Portland, (1911). $2.50

238 CONDON, THOMAS. Two Islands and What Came of Them. 211 pp., plates. 12mo, cloth. Portland, 1902. $10.00

Smith 761. This is the rare first edition published by Gill.

239 CONDON, THOMAS. Oregon Geology. A Revision of "The Two Islands." 187 pp., 12mo, cloth. Portland, 1910. $4.75

Smith 760.

240 [CONFEDERACY.] Hunt, Cornelius B. The Shenandoah; or, The Last Confederate Cruiser. 270 pp., 8vo, cloth. N. Y., 1867. $10.00

Gives an interesting account of privateering in the North Pacific and the capture and destruction of a large number of American whaling vessels in Alaskan waters. See Whymper p. 92.

241 CONOVER, C. T. Proposal to Change the Name of Mt. Ranier. Decision of the U. S. Geographical Board. 8vo, original wrappers. N. p. (Seattle), 1917. $4.00

Smith 779. Historic statements and Indian names.

242 CONOVER, C. T. In the Matter of the Proposal to Change the Name of Mount Ranier. 74 pp., 8vo, wrappers. Seattle, N.d. $2.50

243 CONOVER, C. T. Mirrors in Seattle. Reflecting some aged men of Fifty. 279 pp., 8vo, cloth. Seattle, 1923. $5.00

Biographies of certain outstanding citizens of Seattle.

244 COOLIDGE, L. A. Klondike and the Yukon Country. 213 pp., map. 12mo, original wrappers. Phila., 1897. $12.50

245 COOK, DAVID J. Hands Up; or, Twenty Years of Detective Life in the Mountains and on the Plains. Reminiscences by General D. J. Cook, Superintendent of the Rocky Muntain Detective Association. A Condensed Criminal History of the Far West. Portrait and numerous illus. 8vo, cloth. Denver: Republican Pub. Co., 1882. N. Y. $32.50

Original Edition. Cook was Chief of the Rocky Mountain Detective Ass'n and from 1871 to 1879 Sheriff of Araphahoe County.

246 —— The Same. Denver, 1897. $7.50

247 COOK, CAPT. JAMES. Voyage to the Pacific Ocean. 3 vols., 4to, half calf and folio of maps and plates, all uncut. London, 1785. $75.00

Inserted in this copy are fine portraits of Capts. Cook and King by Bartolozzi after Weber, published in 1784, and a portrait of Cook, engraved by Sherwin after Dance, also published in 1784. In addition there is also inserted a description of Pingo's medal executed in memory of Capt. Cook for the Royal Society and engraved by Trotter. The above is a fine set, and with the 3 engravings becomes a most desirable one. This is also the best edition of this work.

248 COOK, JAY. The Northern Pacific Railroad. Its Land Grant, Resources, Traffic and Tributary Country. Valley Route to the Pacific. Folding map, colored. Laid in is a long folding map printed on pink paper, showing the route of the road, and its completion as far as Edwinton on the Missouri. 52 pp., 8vo, original wrappers. Phila., 1873. $7.50

249 COOKE, BELLE W. Tears and Victory, and other Poems. 253 pp., front., 8vo, cloth. Salem, Ore., 1871. $4.50

An autographed copy.

250 COOKE, P. ST. GEORGE. The Conquest of California and New Mexico. An Historical and Personal Narrative. 307 pp., 12mo, cloth. N. Y., 1878. $15.00

A first hand narrative by a participant and leader in the thrilling events of 1846-7. Cooke took command of the Mormon Batallion at Santa Fe, with orders from General Kearney to open a wagon route to the Pacific by the Gila Route. This involved a march of 1,100 miles through the unknown wilderness without road or trail.

251 CORNISH, GEORGE H. Hand-Book of Canadian Methodism. 239 pp., 8vo. Toronto, 1867. $5.00

This relates to the earliest Methodist missions in the far west.

252 COUES, ELLIOTT. Description of the original manuscript journals and Field Note Books of Lewis and Clark, etc. American Philosophical Society, Jan. 20, 1983. 17-33 pp., 8vo. $3.50

253 COXE, WILLIAM. Account of the Russian Discoveries between Asia and America. To which are added the conquest of Siberia and the History of the Transactions and Commerce between Russian and China. Map and plates. 4to, calf. London, 1780. $25.00

Smith 826. Original Edition. Coxe states in his preface that the late discoveries made between Asia and America by the Russians having engaged much attention he had during his stay in St. Petersburg particularly directed his inquiries to that interesting subject. He had also endeavored to collect the respective journals of the several voyages subsequent to the expedition of Bering and Tschirikoff in 1741.

254 COXE, WILLIAM. Account of the Russian Discoveries between Asia and America. To which are added the Conquest of Siberia. Third Edition. 4 folding maps and the large folding plate. 8vo, calf. London, 1787. $12.50

In this is added under separate title, "A Comparative View of the Russian Discoveries with those of Capt. Cooke."

Smith 828.

255 COZZENS, S. W. The Marvellous Country; or, Three Years in Arizona and New Mexico. With upwards of 100 engravings, mostly full-page plates. Map. 8vo, half calf. London, 1874. $10.00

Fine copy of the Original Edition with map.

256 CRADLEBAUGH, J. H. Nyeena Kloshe Illahee. Songs of the Good Country. 67 pp., 8vo, cloth. Salem, Ore., 1913. $3.75

257 CRAIG, LULU ALICE. Glimpses of Sunshine and Shade in the Far North; or, My Travels in the Land of the Midnight Sun. 123 pp., 8vo, cloth. Cincinnati, 1900. $4.50

Smith 840.

258 CRAIGHEAD, JAMES G. Story of Marcus Whitman; Early Protestant Missions in the Northwest. 211 pp., 12mo, cloth. Phila., 1895. $3.50

Smith 841. See item 1400. Cat. 17.

259 CRANE, LEO. Indians of the Enchanted Desert. 364 pp., illus., map. 8vo, cloth. Boston, 1925. $4.50

Crane knew the mysterious rites, subtle psychology and involved folklore of the desert Indians.

260 CRAPO, THOMAS. Strange, but True. Life and Adventures of Captain Capro and Wife. 151 pp., illus., 8vo. New Bedford, 1893. $7.50

Capro was cabin boy on the "Marcie", commanded by Captain Billings, sailing from New Bedford for the North Pacific Ocean, where they arrived in 1858. A scarce privately printed narrative.

261 CREWE, FRED. Poems of the Klondyke's Early Days and Alaska's Long White Trail. Photos of the Klondike Stampede taken in 1897-98. About 150 numbered pages. Oblong, full calf, with many fine full-page plates. Milwaukee, 1921. $7.50

262 CROFUTT, GEORGE A. Crofutt's New Overland Tourist and Pacific Coast Guide. Illus., 12m, cloth. Omaha, 1880. $1.50

263 —— The Same. Omaha, 1884. $1.50

CROSS' MARCH TO OREGON IN 1849

264 CROSS, MAJOR OSBORNE. A Report in the Form of a Journal, of the March of the Regiment of Mounted Riflemen to Oregon, from May 10 to October 5, 1849. Complete with the 36 folding and full-page lithograph plates, including views of the plains, Fort Laramie, Fort Hall, Independence Rock, Devil's Gate, Fort Boise, Grand Ronde, the Cascades, etc., etc. Folding map. 114 pp., 8vo, original calf, leather label. Washington, 1850-1851. $30.00

Wagner-Camp 181. This is not excerpted but is the full report. It is the day by day journey of the overland trip from Ft. Kearney to the Pacific.

265 [CROSS, OSBORNE.] Fillmore, Millard. Message from the President of the U. S. 31st Cong., 2nd Sess., House Ex. Doc. No. 1. 487 pp., cloth. Washington, 1850. $15.00

Contains Major Cross's Journal of his overland trip to Ft. Vancouver, as well as much other material relating to western affairs and Indians.

266 [CRUISE OF REVENUE CUTTER CORWIN.] Cruise of the Revenue Steamer Corwin in Alaska and the North West Arctic Ocean in 1881. 4to, cloth. Washington, 1883. $7.50

Smith 4155.

267 [CRUISE OF THE REVENUE CORWIN.] Report of the Cruise of the Revenue Marine Steamer Corwin in the Arctic Ocean in the Year 1885. 102 pp., maps, illus. 4to, cloth. Washington, 1887. $7.50

268 [CRUISE OF THE REVENUE CUTTER CORWIN.] Report of the Revenue Marine Steamer Corwin in the Arctic Ocean in the Year 1884. 128 pp., illus., 4to, cloth. Washington, 1889. $7.50

269 CULBERTSON, THADDEUS A. Journal of an Expedition to the Mauvaises Terres and the Upper Missouri in 1850. 8vo, original wrappers. Washington, 1850. $27.50

Wagner-Camp 198. "Gives a very interesting account of the forts and Indians on the Missouri River". The narrative is in day-by-day form, covering the period from April 27 to July 6. The author set out from Ft. Pierre May 7, visited the Bad Lands, and afterwards ascended the Missouri to a point several hundred miles above Ft. Union; and thence descended the river to St. Louis.

270 CUMMINS, ELLA STERLING. The Story of the Files. A Review of California Writers and Literature. 460 pp., illus. 8vo, cloth. (San Francisco, 1893). $4.75

271 CUSHING, CALEB. Oregon Territory: Report in relation to the Territory oi the U. S. beyond the Rocky Mountains. 51 pp., 8vo, sewn, uncut. Washington, 1839. $20.00

An important historical document being the claim of the U. S. to the Oregon Territory. It contains much material relating to the Hudson's Bay Co. early NW voyages, treaties, Gray's Log and Bulfinch's Statement.

272 CUSHING, CALEB. Oregon Territory: Supplemental Report, embracing (1) Lee's Memorial, signed by 36 petitioners, praying the protection of the U. S. (2) N. J. Wyeth's Memoir on the Climate, Soil, Trade, Resources. (3) W. J. Slocum's Report on the Indians, Political situation. (4) Hall J. Kelley's Memoir on Oregon and California. 61 pp., 8vo, sewn. Washington, 1839. $20.00

Hall Kelley always referred to this memoir as the best contribution to the history of Oregon.

273 CUSHING, CALEB. Treaty of Washington: its Negotiation, Execution and Discussions relating thereto. 280 pp., 12mo, cloth. N. Y., 1873. $3.00

Smith 873.

274 CUSTER, ELIZABETH B. Tenting on the Plains; or, General Custer in Kansas and Texas. Illus., 8vo, cloth. 1889. $2.75

275 —— The Same. Sheep. N. Y., 1887. Orig. Ed. $3.00

276 CUSTER, ELIABETH B. Following the Guidon. Front., 12mo, cloth. N. Y., 1890. $2.00

277 CUSTER, GEN. G. A. My Life on the Plains; or, Personal Experiences with Indians. 8vo, cloth (binding worn). N. Y., 1876. $3.50

278 CUSTIS, VANDERVEER. The State Tax System of Washington. 142 pp., 8vo, original wrappers. Seattle, 1916. $4.00

279 CURTIS, EDWARD S. Indian Life and Indian Lore. Indian Days of the Long Ago. 221 pp., illus. 12mo, cloth. N. Y., 1915. $3.50

Smith 685.

280 CURTIS, GEORGE-TINCHOR. Life of James Buchanan, Fifteenth President of the U. S. 2 vols., 8vo, cloth. N. Y., 1885. $7.50

Has considerable material relating to the Oregon country.

281 DABNEY, OWEN P. True Story of the Lost Shackle; or, Seven Years with the Indians. Plates. 98 pp., 12mo, original pictorial wrappers. N. p., N. d. (Salem, Oregon: Capital Print, 1897). $10.00

Shea No. 143. Narrative of the captivity of Lillian Ainsley, the overland journey of the Ainsley and Bentley families to the Yellowstone, etc.

282 [DAKOTA.] House Journal of the First Legislative Assembly of the Territory of Dakota; to which is prefixed a list of the Members and Officers of the House, with their Residence, Post Office Address, Occupation, age, etc. 265 pp., 8vo, calf. Yankton, 1862. $17.50

At the time this work was published Dakota Territory included all North and South Dakota, Montana, Idaho, and northern portions of Wyoming.

282a [DAKOTA.] South Dakota okna Niobrara Deanery Omniciye Kin. 3 plates, 8vo, original wrappers. (Sioux Falls), 1891. $6.00

The plates show views of various Indian mission schools

283 [DAKOTA MISSION PRESS.] Blackrobe in the Lands of the Wigwam. Illus., 8vo, cloth. N. p., N. d. St. Francis Mission, South Dakota. $4.50

Relates to the Nex Perce Indians.

284 DALL, W. H., and GIBBS, GEORGE. Tribes of the Extreme Northwest [Dall.] Also Tribes of Western Washington and Northern Oregon [Gibbs]. [Contained in Contributions to North American Ethnology, Vol. 1]. Illus., plates, 2 maps. 8vo, cloth. Washington, 1877. $7.50

285 DALLES [OREGON] METHODIST MISSION CASES. U. S. District Court. District of Oregon. The Dalles Methodist Mission Cases. Opinion of the Court by Matthew P. Deady, District Judge. 22 pp., 8vo, sewn. Portland: Hines, (1879). $47.50

Smith 4076 locates only the copy in the Oregon Historical Society. This is a rare and important work dealing with the establishment of Oregon.

286 DALRYMPLE, ALEXANDER. An Historical Journal of the Expedition by Sea and Land to the North of California, in 1768, 1769 and 1770; when Spanish Establishments were first made at San Diego and Monterey. From a Spanish Translation by William Roveley, Esq., published by Dalrymple. 11 and 76 pp., 2 maps. Royal 8vo. London, 1790. $30.00

Fine photostatic replica of the only known copy in the British Museum.

286a DALRYMPLE, ALEXANDER. Plan for promoting the Fur-Trade, and securing it to this country, by uniting the operations of the East-India and Hudson's Bay Companies. 32 pp., 4to, calf. London, 1789. [Sold]

286b DALRYMPLE, ALEXANDER. Spanish Memorial of 4th June considered. 21 pp., 8vo, sewn. London, 1790. [Sold]

286c DALRYMPLE, ALEXANDER. Spanish pretentions fairly discussed. 19 pp., port., 18 maps. 8vo, sewn. London, 1790. [Sold]

287 DAMON, C. M. Sketches and Incidents; or, Reminiscences of Interest in the life of the Author. 366 pp., 8vo, clth. Chicago, 1900. $7.50

288 DAMPIER, CAPT. WILLIAM. Voyages: A Complete collection of all his Voyages, edited by John Masefield. Handsomely printed in large antique type by Ballantyne with all the rare and curious folded maps and plates carefully reproduced, and photogravure portrait. 2 vols., 8vo, gilt. London, 1906. $37.50

Printed in an edition of 1,000 copies and now long out of print. The volumes contain the complete unabridged account of all Dampier's voyages, including a life of Dampier by Masefield.

289 DANA, CHARLES A. The United States Illustrated. Vol. 1. The West; or, The States of the Mississippi Valley and the Pacific. Vol. 2. The East. 2 vols., 4t, full morocco. N. Y., (1850). $17.50

The first volume contains forty full page engravings of western scenery with descriptive text. These are the first and in many cases the only views of places of historic interest in the west.

290 DANA, RICHARD HENRY. Two Years before the Mast. Personal Experiences of Life at Sea. 12mo, original cloth (repaired backstrip). N. Y., 1840. $40.00

Original Edition. Harpers Family Library No. 106, and with the advertisement notice ending at No. 105 "Travels of Mungo Park".

291 DARBY, WILLIAM. Geographical Description of the State of Louisiana; presenting a view of the Soil, Climate, Animal, Vegetable and Mineral Productions, etc., with an account of the Character and Manners of the Inhabitants, with map. Crown 8vo, half roan. Phila., 1816. $12.50

292 DARBY, WILLIAM. Geographical Description of the State of Louisiana, the Southern part of the State of Mississippi and Territory of Alabama; presenting a view of the Productins, etc., with an account of the character and manners of the inhabitants. Maps. 8vo, original calf. N. Y., 1817. $12.50

293 DARBY, WILLIAM. A Tour from New York to Detroit, in the Michigan Territory; with Observations on the Natural History and Geography of the Regions traversed, and Remarks upon such events and characters as have contributed to give interest to the different places. 3 colored folding maps. 8vo, original boards, uncut. N. Y., 1819. $20.00

Original edition with 3 maps. Braislin 553.

294 DARBY, WILLIAM. Universal Gazeteer; or, a New Geographical Dictionary. 892 pp., maps. 8vo, calf. Phila., 1827. $10.00

295 DARBY, WILLIAM. New Gazetteer of the United States of America. 8vo, calf. Hartford, 1833. $7.50

296 DARLING, ESTHER BIRDSALL. Up in Alaska. 59 pp., 12mo, bound in white cloth (slightly stained). Sacramento (c. 1912). $5.00

Discusses George Davidson.

297 DARLING, ESTHER BIRDSALL. Baldy of Nome. 301 pp., illus. 8vo, cloth. Phila., 1920. $3.50

298 DAVIDSON, GEORGE. Pacific Coast. Coast Pilot of Alaska (first part) from Southern Boundary to Cook's Inlet. 251 pp., colored plates. 8vo. Washington, 1869. $13.50

299 DAVIDSON, GEORGE. An Examination of some of the Early Voyages of Discovery and Exploration on the Northwest Coast of America from 1539 to 1603. U. S. Coast and Geodetic Survey. 4to. Washington, 1887. $7.50

Smith 4079.

300 DAVIDSON, GEORGE. Tracks and Landfall of Bering and Chirikof on the Northwest Coast of America, 1714. 44 pp., 8vo. (San Francisco), 1901. Privately published. *In photostat.* $7.50

301 DAVIDSON, GEORGE. Francis Drake on the Northwest Coast of America, 1579; the Golden Hinde did not anchor in Bay of San Francisco. With Bibliography. 118 pp., 8vo, original wrappers. (San Francisco), Geog. Soc. of Pacific, 1908. $7.50

302 DAVIDSON, GORDON CHAS. The North West Company. 6 folding maps and reproduction. Royal 8vo, cloth. Berkeley: 1918. $10.00

Story of the early struggle for the fur trade.

303 DAVIS, HORACE. Record of the Japanese Vessels driven upon the North-West Coast of America. 8vo, original wrappers, in a cloth case. Worcester, 1872. $12.50

Not in Smith.

304 DAVIS, MARY LEE. Uncle Sam's Attic; the Intimate Story of Alaska. 402 pp., illus., 8vo, cloth. Boston, (1930). $3.00

305 DAVIS, WALTER BICKFORD, and DURRIE, DANIEL S. Illustrated History of Missouri. 639 pp., illus., 8v, cloth. St. Louis, 1875. $8.50

Biographies of the early fur traders and the navigators of the Missouri river.

306 DAVIS, WILLIAM HEATH. Sixty Years in California. A History of Events and Life in California, Personal, Political and Military, under the Mexican Regime, etc. 8vo, cloth. San Francisco, 1889. $22.50

Braislin 564. The author went to California in 1831. He had lived in California 17 years before the discovery of gold at Sutter's Mill, and took part in all the political and material changes in the country. His narrative is interesting and important.

307 DAWSON, JOHN WILLIAM. Canadian Ice Age. 301 pp., illus., 8vo, cloth. Montreal, 1893. $7.50

Smith 919.

308 DAWSON, GEO. M. Preliminary Report on the Physical and Geographical features of that portion of the Rocky Mountains between latitude 49° and 51° 30'. Folding map, 169 pp., 8vo, original wrappers. Montreal, 1886. $7.50

Not in Smith.

309 DAWSON, SIMON JAMES. Report on the Explorations of the country between Lake Superior and the Red River Settlement, and between the latter place and the Assiniboine and Saskatchewan. Printed by order of the Legislative Assembly. 44 pp., 3 maps. 4to, unbound. Toronto, 1859. $12.50

Wagner-Camp 322.

310 DAWSON, S. J. Report on the Line of Route between Lake Superior and the Red River Settlement. Printed by order of the House of Commons. 44 pp., map, 8vo, original wrappers. Ottawa, 1868. $14.50

310a DAVYDOV, G. I. Dawudov's Nachrichten von der Insel Kadjak. In Beit Kemt Russland u seine Geschichte. Two parts in one. 8vo, cloth. Dorpat, 1816-1818. $47.50

Wickersham 6154. An account of Kodiak Islands. This work contains an account of the great fur company, a description of Kodiak and the settlement of Cook's Inlet and Sitka, together with much information concerning the manners and customs of the natives.

311 DEANE, CAPTAIN R. BURTON. Mounted Police Life in Canada; a Record of 31 Years' Service. 4 plates, map. 8vo, cloth. London, 1916. $5.00

312 DEATHERAGE, CHAS. P. Steamboating on the Missouri in the Sixties. 39 pp., illus., 8vo, original wrappers. N. p., 1924. $5.00

313 DE BARTHE, JOE. The Life and Adventures of Frank Grouard, Chief of Scouts, U. S. Many portraits and illus. 545 pp., 8vo, original cloth. St. Joseph, Mo., (1894). $37.50

Huntington 231. "Of the highest importance historically; probably the most thorough and reliable work on scouting on the plains that has ever been written". Nearly the entire edition was lost in the St. Joe flood. Joe Debarthe, after many years' effort, succeeded in obtaining from "The Silent Man of the Plains" the story of his life and adventures. The noted scout tells of his journey to Helena in 1865; his capture by the Sioux and his intercourse with Sitting Bull; his meeting with Custer; account of the massacre; General Crook; California Joe, etc.

314 DE COSMOS, AMOR. Typescript manuscript of 19 pages, dated San Francisco, Dec. 5, 1878, of a conversation of Amor de Cosmos, of Victoria, with H. H. Bancroft, in regard to the early history of Vancouver Island, British Columbia and Victoria. N. p., N. d. San Francisco, 1878. $20.00

The only available copy.

315 DE COURCY, BOLTON W. On the Straits of Juan de Fuca, Puget Sound, and Government Improvements on the Pacific Coast. 8vo, original wrappers. N. p., (1891). $4.75

316 DEFENBACK, BYRON. Red Heroines of the Northwest. Illus., map. 301 pp., 8vo, cloth. Caldwell, Idaho, 1929. $3.50

317 DE FIGUEROA, JOSEPH MARIANO SUAREZ. Notices de Nutka. (Information re Nootka). 63 typescript pages in English. 8vo, bound in half leather. N. p., N. d. $25.00

De Figueroa was commissioned by his Excellency Count de Revilla Gigedo to make a geographical chart and report on conditions from the Strait of Juan de Fuca (Puget Sound) to the Port of San Francisco. Under the command of Capt. Bodega y Quadra, they arrived at Nootka, April 29, 1792, where De Figueroa remained four months. The above work consists of 12 reports of great interest, describing the country, natives, Meares, Vancouver, etc. The work is not available in English.

318 DELANEY, MATHILDA J. SAGER. A Survivor's Recollections of the Whitman Massacre. Portrait and plate. 8vo, original wrappers. Spokane, (1920). $10.00

Probably the only narrative ever written by a survivor. The author was one of Whitman's pupils at the Mission. Her brothers John and Frank were among the victims.

319 DEMERS, L. J. Esquisse Generale du Nord-Ouest du Canada ou Etendu, bois forets, richesses minerales et climatologie des quatres districts provisires d'Assiniboia, Saskatchewan, Alberta et Athabaska. 89 pp., 8vo, original wrappers. Trois-Rivieres, 1886. $7.50

320 [DE MILT, ALONZO.] The Life, Travels and Adventures of; A Truthful Narrative of Events containing his Early Adventures among the Indians, his Life in the Gold Mines of California, with Sketches of his Life, Manners and Customs. By F. Fitch. 12mo, 228 pp., portrait and plates. N. Y., 1883. $10.00

Journal of an expedition across the plains in 1849; the Donner Party, Mormons, Incidents of life among the gold-seekers, 1849-52.

321 DENKSCHRIFTEN DER RUSSISCHEN GEOGRAPHISCHEN GESELLSCHAFT ZU ST. PETERSBURG. Vol. 1 (all published). 4 maps., 8vo, cloth. Weimar, 1849. $37.50

Contains an account of Sagoskin's voyage to the islands of Northwestern America.

322 DENMAN, A. H. The name Mount Tacoma. 93 pp., 8vo, cloth. Tacoma, 1924. $3.00

Original Edition. Privately printed by the author in a few copies, nearly all of which were destroyed in the great Seattle fire of 1889. "This book is deservedly prized as an authoritative source upon the early history of Seattle and Puget Sound; its intrinsic worth, the small number of copies and the fact that it has never been on sale to the public have all combined to make it extremely rare"—Washington Historical Quarterly.

Item 320, Date should be in brackets (1883).

ORIGINAL EDITION OF DENNY'S PIONEER DAYS

323 DENNY, A. A. Pioneer Days on Puget Sound. 83 pp., 12mo, original cloth. Seattle, 1888. $17.50

Original Edition. Privately printed by the author in a few copies, nearly all of which were destroyed in the great Seattle fire of 1889 "This book is deservedly prized as an authoritative source upon the early history of Seattle and Puget Sound; its intrinsic worth, the small number of copies and the fact that it has never been on sale to the public have all combined to make it extremely rare"—Washington Historical Quarterly.

324 DE SMET, PIERRE-JEAN. Western Missions and Missionaries. 532 pp., 2 vols., 12mo, original cloth. N. Y., 1863. $20.00

Signed presentation copy from DeSmet of the Original Edition, and a fine copy.

325 DE SMET, PIERRE-JEAN. Oregon Missions and Travels over the Rocky Mountains in 1845-46. Folding map and 13 tinted plates. 408 pp., original cloth. N. Y., 1847. $25.00

Wagner-Camp 141. The author was superior of the Indian Missions of the Oregon country. Herein he describes a tour through Washington and elsewhere. In 1846 he traveled overland to the Upper Missouri, making his way down the river to St. Louis.

326 DE SMET, PIERRE-JEAN. Letters and Sketches; with a Narrative of a Year's Residence among the Indian Tribes of the Rocky Mountains. Numerus illus. 12mo, original cloth. Phila., 1843. $22.50

Shea 576. Fine copy of an account of Indian Life by a Pioneer Missionary, with the folding plate.

327 DE SMET, P. J. The Life of Father De Smet (1801-1873). By E. Laveille, S. J. 400 pp., illus., 8vo, cloth. N. Y., 1915. $7.50

328 DEVINE, EDWARD J. Across Widest America, Newfoundland to Alaska. 307 pp., 12mo, cloth. Montreal, 1905. $5.00

Smith 951.

329 DEWAR, J. CUMMING. Voyage of the Nyanza, R. N. Y. C.; being the record of a three years' cruise in a schooner yacht in the Atlantic and Pacific, and her subsequent Shipwreck. Illus., plates, maps. 8vo, cloth. Edinburgh, 1892. $7.50

Smith 952.

330 DE WINDT, HARRY. Through the Gold Fields of Alaska to Bering Straits. 312 pp., 2 maps, 2 maps. 8vo, cloth. London, 1898. $7.50

Smith 954.

331 DICKSON, ARTHUR JEROME. Journey across the Plains in the Sixties, and Pioneering Days in the Northwest; from the Journals of Arthur Jerome Dickson. 287 pp., illus., 8vo, cloth. Cleveland, 1929. $8.50

332 DIKE, SIR CHAS. Wetworth. Problems of Great Britain. 738 pp., 8vo, cloth. London, 1890. $4.50

Smith 968. Contains material relating to British Columbia.

FATHER DIOMEDI'S RARE WORK ON THE NORTHWEST

333 DIOMEDI, FATHER A. Sketches of Modern Indian Life. 79 pp., 8vo, original wrappers. N.p., N.d. (1894). [Sold] $75.00

Original and Only Edition of an excessively rare and little known work. Only a few copies of the above work were printed for private use. Father Diomedi went to the Rocky Mountains in the sixties and stayed there the rest of his life, dying at the age of 90. The above account was written in 1879. It relates to the Indians of Montana, Idaho and Washington, their manners and customs, his missionary experiences among them, his tour of the missions, the Coeur d'Alenes, etc., etc. Has much concerning Idaho, Montana and Washington. Father Diomedi founded Lewiston, Idaho, and St. Ignatius mission, as well as Gonzaga College at Tacoma.

334 DIONNE, N. E., M.D. Etats-Units, Manitoba, et Nord-Ouest. Notes de Voyage. 180 pp., 8vo, original printed wrappers. Quebec, 1883. $5.00

335 DIXON, J. K. The Vanishing Race. The last Great Indian Council, and the Indian's Story of the Custer Fight. Illus., 8vo, pictorial cloth. N. Y., 1914. $4.00

336 DIXON, CAPT. GEORGE. A Voyage Round the World, but more particularly to the North-West Coast of America; performed in 1785-88 in the King George and]ueen Charlotte, Captains Portlock and Dixon. Maps and plans, 4to, half calf. London, 1789. $27.50

337 DODGE, GRENVILLE M. Union Pacific Railroad Report of G. M. Dodge, Chief Engineer to the Board of Directors on a Branch Railroad Line from the Union Pacific Railroad to Idaho, Montana, Oregon and Puget's Sound. Fine large scale folding maps in colors "From U. P. R. R. to Portland, Oregon, Puget Sound, Washington, Ty., and Montana." 8vo, original printed wrappers. Washington, 1868. $32.50

Smith 996. Rare. This map accompanying the report is on a larger scale than the survey map in the report of 1865-66, and includes western Dakota and Montana, Oregon, California, with San Francisco, Northern Nevada, Utah and the Northwest. But one copy, that in the Library of the University of Montana is known to Smith.

338 DODGE, GEN. G. M. Short Sketch of the Services of Major Grenville Mellen Dodge. 16 pp., port., 8vo, original wrappers. N. Y., N. d. $6.00

339 DODGE, GRENVILLE M. Biographical Sketch of James Bridger, Mountaineer, Trapper and Guide. Port., plate and view of Bridger's Fort drawn by Dodge. 27 pp., 8vo, original printed wrappers. N. Y., 1905. $17.50

340 DODGE, R. I. The Hunting Grounds of the Great West; a Descriptin of the Plains, Game and Indians of the Great North American Desert, with an Introduction by W. Blackmore. Ports., map and plates. 8vo, cloth. London, 1877. $7.50

Fine copy. This work is the best book upon the old plains country—Theodore Roosevelt in "Outdoor Pastimes of an American Hunter".

Item 333, Last line of note should read "Spokane," not "Tacoma."

341 DODGE, R. I. Our Wild Indians: Thirty-Three Years' Personal Experience among the Red Men of the Great West. With Adventures on the Great Plains and Mountains. Portrait and colored plates. 653 pp., 8vo, half morocco. Hartford, 1882. $3.50

Original Edition. During his early and extended experience among the Indians, especially the plains tribes, General Dodge was enabled to make observations of their character and customs that would not be possible in their present modified condition.

342 DONAN, P. Utah. 90 pp., illus., 8vo, original wrappers. N. p., 1891. $4.00

343 DONNER, P. Last Days of the Republic. 258 pp., illus., 8vo, cloth. San Francisco, 1890. $3.50

344 DORRIS, JONATHAN TRUMAN. The Oregon Trail. Journal of the Illinois State Historical Society, Vol. 10, No. 4. 8vo, wrappers. Springfield, 1918. $2.50

345 DORSEY, JAMES OWEN. The Cegiha Language. (Contribution to North American Ethnology, Vol. 6). 8vo, cloth. Washington, 1890. $5.00

346 DORSEY, JAMES OWEN. Cruise among the Haida and Tlingit Villages about Dixon's Entrance. 15 pp., 8vo, original wrappers. N. p., 1898. $5.00

347 DORSEY, JAMES OWEN. The Geography of the Tsimshian Indians. 7 pp., 8vo, original wrappers. N. p., N. d. $5.00

348 DOSCH, COL. H. E. Vigilante Days at Virginia City. Personal Narrative of Col. Henry E. Dosch, member of Fremont's Body Guard and one-time Pony Express Rider. Edited by Fred Lockley. 19 pp., 8vo, original wrappers. Portland, 1925. $2.50

349 DOUGLAS, R. Nipigon to Winnipeg. A Canoe Voyage through Western Ontario by Edward Umfreville in 1784. 63 pp., 8vo, original wrappers. Ottawa, 1929. $4.00

350 DOUGLAS, WALTER B. Manuel Lisa. (Contained in the Missouri Historical Society Collections. Vol. 3, Nos. 3 and 4. 1911). 8vo, original wrappers. St. Louis, 1911. $5.00

This is by far the best work on Manuel Lisa, the greatest of the fur traders of St. Louis and the Upper Missouri.

351 DOVELL, W. F. "A Scrap of Paper." 19 pp., original wrappers. N. p., N. d. $12.50

Not in Smith. Privately printed in a small edition for friends. The work gives an account of the Nez Perce Indians and the Nez Perce wars by an eyewitness.

352 DOWELL, B. F. (Oregon). B. F. Dowell vs. Jesse Applegate. Brief and Argument of Plaintiff. 59 pp., 8vo, original wrappers. Portland, 1882. $17.50

Litigation between two prominent and early Oregon pioneers. Slight stain on upper blank margin.

353 DOWELL, B. F. (Oregon). Brief and Argument for Payment of Indian War Claims. 64 pp. and errata. 8vo, no wrappers, text on p. 51 and 64 defective. N. p., no publisher, N. d. $12.50

The above is Dowell's own copy with his notations signed by him. Dowell states that this brief is the only true history of the war. Smith 1020 which locates a copy in the Portland Public Library.

354 DOWELL ,B. F. The Petition of B. F. Dowell and Others asking Pay for two companies of Oregon Volunteers and their Expenses, called into service in 1854. Portrait. Small 4to, original printed wrappers, in a cloth slip-case. Jacksonville, Ore., 1869. **$35.00**

Fine copy of the Original Edition in Wrappers. On pp. 9-10 is related in a communication to Joel Palmer the capture of the Ward Family, Aug. 20, 1854, in Northern Oregon.

355 DOWELL, B. F. Brief on Indian Depredations. 20 pp., 8vo, no wrappers. N. p., N. d. (c. 1870). $12.50

The above is Dowell's own copy with his corrections noted.

356 DOWNE, THOMAS. Manitoba and the Northwest Territories. 34 pp., illus., 4to, original wrappers. St. Paul, 1879. $4.75

357 DOWNIE, WILLIAM. Hunting for Gold: Reminiscences of Personal Experiences and Research in the early days of the Pacific Coast from Alaska to Panama. 407 pp., portraits. 8vo, cloth. San Francisco, 1893. $20.00

Smith 1023. The author was the first white man to cross from the coast to the Frazer River. His narrative is of the kind to furnish the novelist with first hand material. It deserves a place among the best of Pacific Coast pioneer works.

358 DRAKE, SAMUEL G. The Aboriginal Races of America. 15th ed. Ed. by Prof. H. L. Williams. 8vo, cloth. N. Y., (1880). $3.50

Smith 1027. Indian lnaguages of the Pacific states and Territories by Albert S. Gatschet.

359 DRANNAN, CAPT. W. F. Chief of Scouts. 407 pp., 8vo, cloth. Chicago, (1910). $3.50

Smith 1028.

360 DRANNAN, CAPT. W. F. Thirty-one Years on the Plains and in the Mountains. 586 pp., illus., 8vo, cloth. Chicago, 1900. $3.75

Smith 1029.

361 DRAPER, LYMAN C. King's Mountain and its Heroes; History of the Battle of King's Mountain, October 7th, 1780, and the Events which led to it. Illus., maps. Thick 8vo, original cloth. Cincinnati, 1881. $17.50

362 DRIGGS, B. W. History of the Teton Valley, Idaho. 227 pp., illus. 8vo, boards. Caldwell, 1924. $3.75

363 DRUMM, STELLA. Down the Santa Fe Trail and into Mexico. Diary of Susan Shelby Magoffin. Illus., map. 8vo, cloth. New Haven, 1926. $3.75

363a DRUMM, STELLA M. Glimpses of the Past. The Old Court House. 41 pp., 8vo, original wrappers. St. Louis, 1940. $1.50

An important and informative account of early days in St. Louis, including accounts of Missouri's part in the Mexican War; the great National Railway Convention in St. Louis in 1849; account of the Dred-Scott Trials at St. Louis; Henry Clay.

364 DRUMHELLER, "UNCLE DAN." "Uncle Dan" Drumheller Tells Thrills of Western Trails in 1854. 131 pp., 8vo, cloth. Spokane, 1925. $7.50

Important privately printed narrative of a pioneer of the West who crossed the plains to California in 1854; Pony Express; Nevada; was under Major Ormsby at Pyramid Lake, 1860; mining camps; placer mining in Idaho; Walla Walla; British Columbia; leading stockman of eastern Washington.

365 DRUMMOND, WILLIAM HENRY. The Voyageur and other Poems. 142 pp., illus. 12mo, cloth. N. Y., 1905. $4.50

366 DRURY, CLIFFORD MERRILL. Pioneer of old Oregon—Henry Harmon Spaulding. 438 pp., illus. 8vo, cloth. Caldwell, 1936. $3.50

367 DUFFERIN AND AVA, HARIOT GEORGIANA. [Hamilton, Marchioness of.] My Canadian Journal, 1872-78; extracts from my letters home while Lord Dufferin was Governor-General. 456 pp., plates, folding map. 8vo, cloth. N. Y., 1891. $5.00

Smith 1035.

368. DUFUR, A. J. Statistics of the State of Oregon, etc. 128 pp., 8vo, cloth. Salem, 1869. $5.00

Smith 1041.

369 DUGAS, GEORGE. Legendes du Nord-Ouest. 142 pp., front. 12mo, cloth. Montreal, 1904. $7.50

370 DUGAS, GEORGE. Les Pionniers de l'Ouest Canadiens Francais. 96 pp., 8vo, cloth. St. Boniface, 1912. $7.50

371 DUMONT, M. Memoires Historique sur la Louisane, &c. Par M. L. M. (l'Abbe le Mercier). 2 vols. in one, 8vo, half calf. Paris, 1753. $45.00

Original Edition. In vol. 2, p. 246 is given the first narrative of Moncuchtabe's journey to the North Pacific, which precedes by five years a similar account given by le Page Du Pratz.

372 DUNBAR, SEYMOUR. History of Travel in America. Illus., 4 vols., 8vo, cloth. Indianapolis, 1915. $12.50

373 DUNIWAY, ABIGAIL J. Captain Gray's Company; or, Crossing the Plains and Living in Oregon. 12mo. Portland: Printed by S. J. McCormick, 1859. $125.00

Fine copy of the Original Edition. This is the first literary production written and printed in Oregon. The author crossed the plains in 1852 and the above is a narrative of her experiences "This work must ever occupy a place among the foundation items of Pacific Coast history."

374 DUNIWAY, ABIGAIL S. Path Breaking; an Autobiographical History of Equal Suffrage Movement in Pacific Coast States. 398 pp., ports., 8vo, cloth. (Portland, 1914). $4.50

Smith 1053.

375 DUNIWAY, ABIGAIL S. From the West to the West. Across the Plains to Oregon. 311 pp., plate. 8vo, cloth. Chicago, 1905. $4.50

376 DUNN, JOHN. Oregon Territory and the British North American Fur Trade; with an Account of the Habits and Customs of the Principal Native Tribes on the Northern Continent. 12mo, cloth. Phila., 1845. $12.50

Smith 1059. Fine copy of the First American Edition

377 DUNN, J. P. Massacres of the Mountains, History of Indian Wars of the Far West. Folding map and illus. 8vo, original cloth. N. Y., 1886. $12.50

378 DUNN, JOHN. History of Oregon Territory and British North-American Fur Trade; with an account of the habits and customs of the principal native tribes in the Northern Continent. By John Dunn, late f Hudson's Bay Company, eight years a Resident of the Country. 359 pp., map. Uncut. 8vo, calf. N. Y., 1844. $37.50

Wagner-Camp 106. Fine tall copy of the Original Edition, entirely uncut.

379 DUNN, ROBERT. The Shameless Diary of an Explorer. With illustrations from photographs by the Author. 297 pp., 8vo, cloth. N. Y., 1907. $5.00

Exposes Dr. Cook's claim to having made the ascent of Mt. McKinley.

380 DURIEU, BISHOP PAUL. Bible History containing the most Remarkable events of the old and new Testament. Translated into Chinook Jargon by the Rev. Paul Durieu of British Columbia. 8vo, cloth. Kamloops, B. C., 1893. $17.50

381 DURIEU, BISHOP PAUL. Chinook Bible History. 112 pp., 8vo, cloth. Kamloops, 1899. $10.00

382 DUTHIE, D. WALLACE. A Bishop in the Rough. 386 pp., illus. 8vo, cloth. N. Y., 1909. $7.50

Life of Rev. John Sheepshanks, early missionary to the Northwest Coast, arriving there in 1860. He remained there many years, later becoming Bishop of Norwich.

383 DUVAL, JOHN C. (Texas). The Young Explorers, a continuation of the Adventures of Jack Duval. 238 pp., original wrappers. N. p. (c. 1892). $7.50

Pioneering in Texas. Duval was a survivor of the Galiod massacre.

384 DYE, EVA EMERY. The Hudson's Bay Company Regime in the Oregon Country. (Bulletin of the University of Oregon, Historical Series, Vol. 1, No. 2, Nov., 1898). 8vo, original wrappers. Eugene, 1898. $4.50

Smith 1069.

385 DYE, EVA EMERY. Stories of Oregon. 203 pp., illus., 8vo, cloth. San Francisco, 1900. $4.50

Smith 1073.

386 DYE, EVA EMERY. McLaughlin and Old Oregon, a Chronicle. Port. 8vo, cloth. Chicago, 1906. $3.50

Smith 1070.

387 DYE, EVA EMERY. McDonald of Oregon, a tale of two Shores. Illus. 8vo, cloth. Chicago, 1906. $3.50

Smith 1071.

388 DYE, EVA EMERY. The Conquest; the True Story of Lewis and Clark. 8vo, cloth. Chicago, 1902. $5.00

Smith 1067.

389 DYE, EVA EMERY. The Soul of America and Oregon. 8vo, cloth. N. Y., 1934. $2.50

390 [EARL, THOMAS.] The Life, Travels and Opinions of Benjamin Lundy, including his Journeys to Texas and Mexico, with a Sketch of Contemporary Events, and a Notice of the Revolution. Portrait and folding colored map of "California, Texas, Mexico and Part of the United States." [Lacks map.] 316 pp., 12mo, calf. Phila., 1847. $7.50

An important source book, embracing: Narrative of a trip to Texas in 1830; journey to New Orleans and Texas, 1833; tours of observation to San Antonio; journey from Brazoria to Austin, and stay, etc.

391 EASTMAN, ELAINE GOODALE. Indian Legends Retold. 161 pp., 8vo, cloth. Boston, 1919. $3.50

392 EDY, J. W. Hunting on the Kenai Peninsula; and Observations on the Increase of Big Game in North America. 90 pp., illus., 8vo, cloth. Seattle, 1924. $4.00

393 EDGAR, WILLIAM C. Judson Moss Memis, Pioneer. 340 pp., illus., 8vo, cloth. Minneapolis, 1926. $4.50

394 EDWARDS, JONATHAN. An Illustrated History of Spokane County, State of Washington. 726 pp., port., plates, map. 4to, cloth. (Spokane), 1900. $7.50

395 EELLS, MYRON. Hand of God in the History of the Pacific Coast. 15 pp., 8vo, wrappers. N. p., N. d. (1888). $3.50

Smith 1089. Commencement address at Whitman College, June 1, 1888.

396 ELLIOTT, HENRY W. A Monograph on the Seal Islands of Alaska. 176 pp. Together with an "Introduction to the Study of Sign Language of the North American Indians," 72 pp. By Garrick Mallery; and a "Study of Mortuary Customs among the North American Indians," 114 pp. Washington, 1880. 8vo, cloth. Washington, 1880. $7.50

The James G. Swan copy.

397 ELLIOTT, HENRY W. Report on the Seal Islands of Alaska. 188 pp., illus., 8vo, cloth. Washington, 1884. $4.75

Smith 1114.

398 ELLIOTT, HENRY W. Our Arctic Province Alaska and the Seal Islands. 473 pp., illus., 5 maps. 8vo, cloth. N. Y., 1906. $3.50

Smith 1114.

ONLY BIOGRAPHY OF PETER SKENE OGDEN

399 ELLIOTT, T. C. Peter Skene Ogden, Fur Trader. 50 pp., original wrappers. Portland, 1910. $10.00

The above is a separate publication in printed wrappers of which only about 50 copies were printed. Smith 1126.

400 ELLISON, W. G. H. The Settlers of Vancouver Island. 154 pp., 2 plates. 8vo, original wrappers. London, N. d. $10.00

Smith No. 1135 who locates only one copy in the Legislative Society at British Columbia.

401 EMMONS, LIEUT. G. T. The Art of the Northwest Coast Indians. 8vo, wrappers. N. p., 1930. $2.00

402 EMORY, WILLIAM H. Report of the United States Mexican Boundary Survey. 2 parts in 1 vol. 34th Cong., 1st Sess., Sen. Ex. Doc. 108. 8v, cloth. Washington, 1857. $7.50

Contains all the maps and beautifully colored plates.

403 ENGEL, SAMUEL. Memoires et Observations Geographiques et des pays Septentrionaux de l'asie et de l'Amerique d'apres les relations les plus recentes. Auquelles on a joint un Essai sur la route aux Indes par le Nord, et sur sun Commerce tres vaste et tres riche a etablir dans le mer du Sud. Complete with the two large folding maps. 4to, calf. Lausanne, 1765. 75.00

Important for the geographical history of Northwest America. The maps are of the northernmost regions of America and Asia, with several smaller maps of California indented in the margin.

404 EUWER, ANTHONY H. Rhymes of Our Valley. 95 pp., front., 8vo, cloth. N. Y., 1916. $3.50

Smith 1772.

405 EUWER, ANTHONY H. By Scarlet Torch and Blade. 152 pp., 8vo, cloth. N. Y., 1923. $2.50

406 [EURYALUS.] Tales of the Sea: a Few Leaves from the Diary of a Midshipman. Colored and plain plates. 8vo, cloth. N. p., 1860. $12.50

A compound of serious and comic narrations, among which a Ball at San Francisco is amusing; which other passages may be divided between the headings "humorous" and "interesting" in the life of a sailor. He stays at the Cape, and goes to China, the South American Coast, Panama, Juan de Fuca, Vancouver Island (where he meets with Flathead Indians), Sandwich Islands, Russian America, and among the Esquimos, Guaymas and Mazatlan, Californis.

407 EVANS, COL. ALBERT S. Our Sister Republic. A Gala Trip through Mexico in 1869-70. 518 pp., illus. Hartford, 1870. $4.00

408 EWING, CHARLES. Circular of the Catholic Commissioner for Indian Missions to the Catholics of the United States. 14 pp., 8vo, boards. Baltimore, 1874. $5.00

409 FAIRBANKS, HAROLD WELLMAN. Western United States; a Geographical Reader. Illus. 12mo, cloth. Boston: Heath, 1904. $4.50

Smith 1188.

410 FANNING, CAPTAIN EDMUND. Voyages and Discoveries in the South Seas, 1792-1832. 335 pp., illus., 8vo. Marine Research Soc., Salem, 1924. $7.50

411 FARMER, E. J. The Resources of the Rocky Mountains; being a Brief Description of the Mineral, Agricultural and Timber Resources of Colorado, Utah, New Mexico, Wyoming, Idaho, Montana and Dakota. 196 pp., illus. Presentation copy. Cleveland, 1883. $10.00

Smith 1196.

412 FARNHAM, CHARLES HAIGHT. Life of Francis Parkman. 8vo, cloth. Boston, 1901. $4.50

Material on the Oregon Trail.

413 FARNHAM, THOMAS J. Travels in the Great Western Prairies, the Anahuac and Rocky Mountains, and in the Oregon Territory. 197 pp., 12mo, clth. Poughkeepsie: Killey & Lossing, 1841. $40.00

Original Edition. Wagner-Camp 85. "Ordinarily this is seen with the date 1843". Farnham, member of the Peoria Party, left that place, May 1, 1839, and Independence May 30, following the Santa Fe Trail to Ft. Bent, where they arrived July 5. Here the company divided, the larger number, 11 in all, proceeding up the Platte River, but Farnham with four others went up the Arkansas to South Park and thence over the Divide to the North Fork of the Platte. From there they proceeded to Brown's Hole. They met Meek on Bear River. They finally arrived at Ft. Hall, Sept. 1 and found Joe Walker in charge. They arrived at Whitman's Mission on Sept. 23.

414 FAUX, W. Memorable Days in America: being a Journal of a Tour to the U. S., principally undertaken to Ascertain, by Positive Evidence, the Condition and Probable Prospects of British Emigrants. Including Accounts of Mr. Birkbeck's Settlement in the Illinois; and Intended to Shew Men and Things as they are in America. Frontis. 8vo, half calf. London, 1823. Scarce. $12.50

Original Edition. Buck 139.

415 FENNER, CLARENCE N. The Origin and Mode of Emplacement of the Great Tuff Deposit of the Valley of Ten Thousand Smokes. 74 pp., 8vo, wrapeprs. Washington, 1923. $3.50

416 FERRIS, BENJAMIN G. Utah and the Mormons. History, Government, Doctrines, Customs and Prospects of the Latter-Day Saints from Personal observations during six months' Residence. 347 pp., illus., 12mo, cloth. N. Y., 1854. $7.50

417 FERRIS, JACOB. The States and Territories of the Great West; Including Ohio, Indiana, Illinois, Missouri, Michigan, Wisconsin, Iowa, Minnesota, Kansas and Nebraska. Illus. 12mo, cloth. N. Y., 1856. $4.00

418 FIELD, HENRY M. Our Western Archipelago. Illus. 8vo, cloth. N. Y., 1895. $2.00

Has chapters dealing with the Pacific Northwest. Smith 1229.

419 FINNERTY, JOHN F. War-Path and Bivouac; or, The Conquest of the Sioux. Illus. 8vo, cloth. Chicago, N. d. (1890). $4.50

420 FISH, HERBERT CLAY. Our State of Washington. 102 pp., illus. 8vo, cloth. N. Y., (1927). $3.50

421 FITZGERALD, JAMES EDWARD. An Examination of the Charter and Proceedings of the Hudson's Bay Company, with References to the Grant of Vancouver's Island. Double-page map in colors. 12mo, original cloth, uncut. London, 1849. [Sold]

Fine copy. Mostly testimony as to the treatment accorded the Indians with whom they traded, by he Hudson's Bay Company.

422 FITZPATRICK, F. J. E. Sergeant 331. Personal Recollections of a member of the Canadian Northwest Mounted Police from 1879-1885. 129 pp., 8vo, cloth. N. Y., 1921. $5.00

423 FITZPATRICK, THOMAS. Letters dated Bent's Fork, Ark's River, September 18, 1847. In Messages to the two Houses of Congress announcing the Conquest and Occupation of California and New Mexico, etc. 16 folding maps. Thick 8vo, calf. Washington, 1847. $22.50

One of the most important source books on the conquest of California. Besides the letter above cited it contains reports of field officers; Col. Mason's correspondence; report of Gen. Kearney's overland expedition; Sterling Price's narrative of the conquest of New Mexico, etc. Wagner-Camp 133.

424 FLINT, TIMOTHY. Recollections of the Last Ten Years, Passed in Occasional Residences and Journeyings in the Valley of the Mississippi from Pittsburgh and the Missouri to the Gulf of Mexico, and from Florida to the Spanish Frontier. 8vo, half morocco. Boston, 1826. $10.00

425 FLINT, TIMOTHY. History and Geography of the Mississippi Valley to which is appended a Condensed Physical Geography of the Atlantic United States and the whole American Continent. 2 vols. in one. 8vo, cloth. Cincinnati, 1832. $10.00

"The peculiar value of Timothy Flint's account of the remarkable region of whose history and aspects he wrote consists in the fact that it is not the result of cursory survey or rapid tour, but years of residence, of intimate contact . . . and patient observations. The record thus prepared is one which will often be consulted by subsequent writers"—Tuckerman.

426 FORCE, PETER. American Archives: Consisting of a Collection of Authentick Records, State Papers . . . and Letters and other Notices of Public Affairs, the whole forming a Documentary History of the Origin and Progress of North American Colonies . . . 4th Series, from March 7, 1774 to the Declaration of Independence. 6 vols., folio. Washington, 1837-46. Fifth Series. 3 vols., folio. Washington, 1848-1853. Together 9 vols., folio (bindings showing wear). Washington, 1837-53. $65.00

427 FORCE, PETER. Tracts and other Papers, relating principally to the Origin, Settlement and Progress of the Colonies in North America, from the Discovery of the Country to 1776. 4 vols., Royal 8vo, half morocco. Washington, 1836-46. $85.00

428 FOSTER, JOHN. Fosteriana, consisting of Thoughts, Reflections and Criticisms . . . Ed. by Henry G. Bohn. 560 pp., 8vo, cloth. London, 1858. $7.50

Gives an account of the Lewis and Clark Expedition. Smith 1283.

429 FORSYTH, GEN. GEO. Thrilling Days. Thrilling Days in Army Life. 199 pp., illus., 12mo, clth. N. Y., 1900. $6.00

430 FOSTER, J. R. Foster's Animals of Hudson's Bay. Willoughby Society Publication. 8vo, cloth. London, 1882. $4.50

431 FOSSETT, FRANK. Colorado: its Gold and Silver Mines. Tourist's Guide to the Rocky Mountains. Folding map. 8vo, cloth. N. Y., 1880. $2.00

432 FOWLER, W. Woman on the American Frontier. An Authentic History of the Heroism, Privations, Captivities among the Indians, Trials, Lives and Deaths of Pioneer Mothers. Plates. 257 pp., 8vo, cloth. Hartford, 1878. $3.50

433 [FRAZIER, ANDREW.] Poems of Oregon and other Verse. 78 pp., 8vo, cloth. Portland, 1914. $3.00

434 FRANKLIN, J. BENJ. A Cheap Trip to Salt Lake City. An Annotated Lecture delivered before the President of America and Representatives; the Mayors of Liverpool & Manchester. (Wrapper title). 12mo, original printed wrappers. Ipswich, (1864). $15.00

Franklin gives an account of his overland trip by way of Council Bluffs, Fort Laramie, the Sweetwater and South Pass. He was one time manager of the Deseret News.

435 FRASER, MRS. HUGH, and FRASER, HUGH C. Seven Years on the Pacific Slope. Illus. 8vo, cloth, d.w. N. Y., 1914. $4.00

Interesting recollections of a settler in northwestern Washington.

436 FRASER, JOHN FOSTER. Canada as it is. 303 pp., illus., 8vo, cloth. London, 1911. $4.50

DE GROOT'S MINERAL RESOURCES OF BRITISH COLUMBIA

437 [FRASER RIVER GOLD RUSH.] (De Groot, Henry). British Columbia: its Condition and Prospects, Soil, Climate and Mineral Resources Considered. 24 pp., 8vo, original printed front wrapper. San Francisco: Alta California Job Office, 1859. $80.00

Smith 928 who locates but one copy in the Seattle Public Library. De Groot joined in the new gold rush of '58 and spent seven months at the mines, at the trading posts and among the Indians of the interior. His narrative, a first hand relation, was used by Bancroft in his "British Columbia."

438 [FRASER RIVER GOLD RUSH.] (Douglas, James). Fraser River Mines Excitement. Copies of Extracts of Correspondence relative to the Discovery of Gold in the Fraser's River District, in British Columbia. 18 pp., folio, sewn. Map. London, 1858. **$32.50**

Not in Smith. Fine copy of the Original Edition with the rare map.

DOWER'S GUIDE TO THE FRASER RIVER MINES, 1859

439 [FRASER RIVER GOLD RUSH.] (Dower, R. John). New Gold Fields. A Guide to British Columbia and Vancouver Islands. Map. 52 pp., 12mo, original printed wrappers. London [1858]. $65.00

Not in Smith. One of the earliest descriptions of the discoveries along the Fraser and Thompson Rivers. Half the work is devoted to an account of the California and Oregon excitement over the northern gold fields.

440 FRASER, SIMON. First Journal of Simon Fraser, from April 12th to July 18th, 1806. Also Letters from the Rocky Mountains from Aug. 1, 1806 to Feb. 10th, 1807 by Simon Fraser. In Dominion of Canada Reports of the Public Archives, 1929. 8vo, cloth. Ottawa, 1930. $7.50

441 FRENCH, BENJAMIN F. Historical Collections of Louisiana, embracing many Rare and Valuable Documents. Folding maps and plates. 5 vols., tall 8vo, original cloth. N. Y., and Phila., 1846-53. [Sold]

All First Edition, fine copies. Contains the most extensive collection of previously unpublished manuscripts and documents ever brought together on the Territory and State of Louisiana up to this time. No collection of western material is complete without these valued recrods.

442 FRENCH, BENJAMIN F. Historical Collections of Louisiana and Florida, including Translations of Original Manuscripts relating to their Discovery and Settlement. 2 vols., royal 8vo, ¾ green morocc, uncut. N. Y., 1869-75. $40.00

A fine and perfect set of the complete series of French's Louisiana and Florida collection of historical documents not otherwise obtainable.

443 FUHRMANN, ERNST. Tlinkit u. Haida Indianerstamme der Westkuste von Nordamerika. Kultische Kunst und Mythen des Kulturkreises. 46 pp., 4to, 61 plates. Dermstadt, 1912. $7.50

444 [FUR TRADE.] Message from the President of the U. S. communicating the letter of Mr. Prevost and other Documents relating to Establishment made at the mouth of the Columbia River. 17th Congress, Second Session, H. Doc. 45. 65 pp., sewn. Washington, 1823. $52.50

Smith No. 4086 and 2542 locates one copy. An extremely valuable document in that it contains the articles of agreement between the Pacific Fur Company and the Northwest Company, dated Oct. 16, 1813 for the transfer of Astoria to the British, together with an inventory of stores. Also contained in the report is Astor's letter to the Secretry of State.

445 GALLOWAY, C. F. J. The Call of the West. Letters from British Columbia. 328 pp., illus. 8vo, cloth. London, (1916). $5.00

Smith 1355.

446 GANNETT, HENRY. Boundaries of the U. S. and of the several States and Territories. 8vo, wrappers. Washington, 1904. $3.50

447 GARRISON, GEORGE PIERCE. Westward Extension, 1841-1850. 366 pp., port., 9 maps. 8vo, cloth. N. Y., 1906. $5.00

Smith 1369.

448 GASS, PATRICK. Journal of the Voyages and Travels of a Corps of Discovery, under the Command f Capt. Lewis and Capt. Clarke, from the Mouth of the River Missouri, through the Interior Parts of North America, to the Pacific Ocean; during 1804-1806. 8vo, original boards (backstrip repaired), uncut. London, 1808. $27.50

449 GASS, PATRICK. Lewis and Clarke's Journal to the Rocky Mountains, in the Years 1804-5-6, as Related by Patrick Gass, one of the Officers of the Expedition. New Edition with Numerous Engravings. 8vo, cloth. Dayton, 1847. $10.00

450 GASS, PATRICK. Gass's Journal of the Lewis and Clarke Expedition. By Sergeant Patrick Gass, one of the Persons employed in the Expedition. Reprinted from the edition of 1811, with facsimiles of the original title-page and the five original illustrations, a reproduction of a rare portrait of Gass, and a map of the Lewis and Clarke Route. 298 pp., half vellum and boards. Chicago, 1904. $12.50

Large paper copy. Only 75 copies of this magnificent volume were printed. About the only edition of Gass that can be easily read.

451 GASTON, JOSEPH. Portland, Oregon. Its History and Builders in connection with the Antecedent Explorations, Discoveries and Movements of the Pioneers that selected the Site for the great City of the Pacific. 4 vols., 4to, cloth, illus. Chicago, 1911. $15.00

Smith 1378.

452 GAYARRE, CHARLES. Histoire de la Louisiana. 2 vols., 8vo, new boards, uncut. Nouvelle Orleans, 1846. $10.00

453 GERSTAECKER, F. Wild Sports in the Far West. 8vo, cloth. Boston, 1861. $4.00

With sketches of Indian migration of the Arkansas and Mississippi, early settlers on the Ohio, Indian adventure.

454 GIFFEN, FANNIE REED. Oo-Mah-Ha-Ta-Wa-Tha. Omaha City, 1854-98. 94 pp., 8vo, cloth. Lincoln, N.d. $4.50

455 GILBERT, KARL GILBERT. Alaska. Glaciers and Glaciation. 231 pp., illus. 8vo, cloth. Washington, 1910. $5.00

This is vol. 3 of the Harriman Alaska Series.

456 GILDER, WM. H. Schwatka's Search Sledging in the Arctic in Quest of the Franklin Records. Illus., map. 316 pp., 8vo, cloth. N. Y., 1881. $5.00

457 GILL, FRANK B. An Unfinished History of Transportation in Oregon and Washington. In the form of Contributed Articles to the "Pacific Semaphore." With some Supplementary Notes. 64 pages in typescript covering the years from 1850 to 1855, plus about 216 printed pages of the articles from the "Semaphore." N.p., N.d. $75.00

The above is Mr. Gill's own collected material of his published and unpublished work. The typescript represents a plan to expand the printed text with subsequent discoveries of other material in obscure newspaper sources covering his subject. There are probably not three sets of the above work in existence and certainly none as complete as the above.

458 GILMAN, ISABEL AMBLER. The Great Northwest. Illus. 8vo, cloth. Olympia, 1909. $5.00

Not in Smith.

459 GILMAN, ISABEL AMBLER. Alaska, the American Northland. 8vo, cloth. N. Y., 1923. $2.50

Smith 1417.

460 GIBSON, ALICE E. Silence. 214 pp. 8vo, cloth. Caldwell, Idaho, 1930. $3.50

Western pioneering.

461 GLAZIER, WILLIARD. Ocean to Ocean on Horse-Back. 544 pp., 8vo, cloth. Phila., 1899. $2.00

462 GODWIN, GEORGE. Vancouver, a Life, 1757-1798. 308 pp., maps, illus. 8vo, cloth. London, 1930. $7.50

463 GOODFELLOW, JOHN C. The Totem Poles in Stanely Park. 44 pp., illus. 8vo, cloth. Vancouver, N.d. $3.50

464 GOODRICH, FREDERICK W. The Oregon Catholic Hymnal. 162 pp., 8vo, cloth. Portland, (1912). $2.50

465 GOODRICH, S. G. History of the Indians of North America. 12mo, cloth. Boston, 1865. $2.50

466 GORDON, CHARLES WILLIAM. The Patrol of the Sun Dance Trail. 363 pp., 8vo, cloth. Westminster, N.d. $4.00

467 GORDON, RALPH, and KING, STODDARD. Pioneer Daze. 8vo, cloth. Seattle, N.d. $2.50

468 GORDON, WILLIAM. History of the Rise, Progress and Establishment of the Independence of the U. S., including an Account of the Late War. 4to, calf. London, 1798. $15.00

469 GOULDER, W. Reminiscences: Incidents in the Life of a Pioneer of Oregon and Idaho. Portrait. 376 pp., 12mo, cloth. N.p., Privately Printed, 1909. $12.50

The author started overland in 1844, went up the Missouri with Benton and Robidoux, joined the Waymire Oregon Train and reached the Boise Valley in '45; here his party were induced to take the "Meek Cut-Off" to the Dalles, and it was only after enduring the greatest hardships that they finally reached Oregon. His work deals with early days in Vancouver, Oregon City, Salem, the mines, and among the pioneers.

470 [GRAND ARMY OF THE REPUBLIC]. Proceedings of the 16th Annual Encampment, Independence, Oregon, 1897. 90 pp., 8vo, original wrappers. Portland, 1897. $4.50

471 GRAVES, J. A. Out of Doors, California and Oregon. 122 pp., 8vo, cloth. Los Angeles, 1912. $2.50

ORIGINAL DOCUMENTS PRESENTING THE CLAIMS OF CAPT. ROBERT GRAY, DISCOVERER OF THE COLUMBIA

(The following rare documents present the claims of Martha Gray and the heirs of Capt. Gray, discoverer of the Columbia River. The claim of Mrs. Gray for a pension and other rights due her on account of her husband's discoveries lagged in Congress for several years. The list of documents cited below is perhaps the fullest and most extensive ever offered in any bookseller's catalogue).

472 [GREY, CAPT. ROBERT.] (Barrell, George). Memorial of the Heirs of the Owners of the Ship "Columbia" and Sloop "Washington," praying the confirmation of their Title to Lands on the Northwest Coast of America purchased in 1791, or compensation for their Explorations and Discoveries in these Regions. 32 pp., 8vo. Washington, 1832. $35.00

See item No. 473, which was Bulfinch's claim. A Mr. S. V. Wilder was joined with Barrel in this claim. All were heirs of Capt. Gray and Capt. John Kendrick, Commander of the Columbia Rediviva. This item is seldom come across.

473 [GRAY, CAPT. ROBERT.] Bulfinch, Charles. Memorial of Charles Bulfinch, et al., praying that their Title to Certain Lands in the Territory of Oregon may be Confirmed. 2 pp., 8vo. Washington, 1838. $35.00

This is the original document relating to Bulfinch's claim to title for certain lands in Oregon. A later and fuller document was issued in 1840.

474 [GRAY, CAPT. ROBERT.] Memorial of Martha Gray of Boston, widow of Capt. Robert Gray. 2 pp., 8vo. March 27, 1846. Washington, 1846. $25.00

This is the original document offered on behalf of Mrs. Gray. The Brodhead document was issued two years later.

475 GRAY, CAPT. ROBERT. Report of the Commission (regarding the claim of Martha Gray, widow of Capt. Robert Gray). 8 pp., 8vo. Washington, 1846. $25.00

See item No. 474, which should accompany this. The Brodhead document relating to the same matter was issued two years later. See item 476.

476 [GRAY, CAPT. ROBERT.] (Brodhead, Richard). Claim of Martha Gray for a Pension on Account of the Services of her husband, on Account of his Discovery of the Columbia River. 10 pp., 8vo. Washington, 1848. $25.00

Contains much information regarding the voyage of Gray to the Columbia.

477 GRAY, CAPT. ROBERT. Report of the Commission (regarding Brodhead's Claim for Martha Gray, widow of Capt. Robert Gray). 10 pp., 8vo. Washington, 1848. $25.00

This should accompany Brodhead's claim. See No. 476

478 [GRAY, CAPT. ROBERT.] Report on the Commission of Martha Gray, widow of Capt. Robert Gray, Jan. 9, 1851. Washington, 1851. $20.00

A further report of the commission examining Mrs. Gray's claims.

479 GRAY, CAPT. ROBERT. Report of the Committee on Foreign Relations on the memorial of the Heirs, etc., of William A. Slocum, deceased. 3 pp., 8vo. Washington, 1850. $20.00

480 [GRAY, CAPT. ROBERT.] Massachusetts Historical Society Proceedings, 1869-1870. (Contains an article on Captain Kendrick and Captain Gray). 8vo, cloth. Boston, 1871. $7.50

481 [GRAY, CAPT. ROBERT.] Massachusetts Historical Society Proceedings, Second Series, Vol. 7, 1891-1892. (Contains material on Captain Gray, discoverer of the Columbia). Boston, 1892. $5.00

482 GRAY, THERESA. Life and Letters of Mrs. Jason Lee, first wife of Rev. Jason Lee of the Oregon Mission. 224 pp., 12mo, cloth. Portland, (1936). $3.50

483 GREELY, GEN. A. W. Handbook of Alaska, its Resources, Products and Attractions. 280 pp., illus., folding map. 8vo, cloth. N. Y., 1909. $5.00

Smith 1526.

484 GREELY, GEN. A. W. Reminiscences of Adventure and Service. A Record of Sixty-five Years. 356 pp., illus. 8vo, cloth. N. Y., 1927. $4.50

485 GRIFFIN, GEO. BUTLER. Documents from the Sutro Collection. Publication of the Southern California Hist. Soc. Coll., Vol. 2, part 1. 214 pp., 8vo. Los Angeles, 1891. $5.00

486 GRINNELL, J. Gold Hunting in Alaska: Dedicated to Disappointed Gold-Hunters. Portrait and plates. 96 pp., 8vo, cloth. Elgin, 1901. $7.50

Smith 1548.

487 GRISSOM, IRENE WELCH. The Superintendent. 288 pp., 8vo, cloth. Seattle, 1910. $4.50

Tale of the Northwest lumber mills. Smith 1550.

488 GRISSOM, IRENE WELCH. Daughter of the Northwest. 225 pp., 8vo, cloth. Boston, (1918). $4.50

Smith 1549.

489 GRISSOM, IRENE WELCH. Verses of the New West. Illus. 8vo, cloth. Caldwell, 1931. $2.50

490 [GROUARD, FRANK.] The Life and Adventures of Frank Grouard, Chief of Scouts, U. S. Illus. 8vo, original decorated cloth. St. Joseph, Mo., N.d. Fine copy. $37.50

491 GRUBBS, FRANCIS HERRON. Memorial Services at the Re-Internment of Rev. Jason Lee, Salem, Oregon, Friday, June 15, 1906. 73 pp., port., plates. 8vo, cloth. N.p., N.d. $7.50

Smith 1555.

492 HALL, MARSHALL. Story of Old Frontier. 302 pp., 8vo, cloth. Phila., (1927). $3.50

493 HAMILTON, BASIL G. Naming of Columbia River and the Province of British Columbia. 16 pp., 8vo, wrappers. Cranbrook Currier Print, (1921). $4.50

494 HANDSACKER, "UNCLE SAM." Pioneer Life: (Journal of an Overland Trip to Oregon in 1853). Portrait. 104 pp., 8vo, cloth. Eugene: Published by the author, 1908. $7.50

Smith 1591.

495 HANNA, CHARLES A. The Wilderness Trail. Maps. 2 vols., 8vo. N. Y., 1911. $20.00

496 HANNA, CHARLES A. The Scotch-Irish. Folding maps. 2 vols., 8vo, cloth. N. Y., 1902. $22.50

497 HANSEN, MARCUS L. Old Ft. Snelling, 1819-1858. 270 pp., 8vo, cloth. Iowa City, 1918. $4.50

498 HANSON, OLE. Americanism versus Bolshevism. 299 pp., 8vo, cloth. N. Y., 1920. $5.00

Now scarce work on the Seattle General Strike of 1919.

499 HARLAN, J. California 1846 to 1888. Portrait. 242 pp., 8vo, cloth. San Francisco, 1888. $17.50

Original Edition. An important and circumstantial narrative of the 1843 plains emigration. Harlan traversed the wilderness as far as Ft. Bridger with the Donner Party, where, by a lucky chance, he decided to go over the Ft. Hall route, leaving the Donner Party to attempt the celebrated "Cut-off", which cost so many lives. He became an active participant in the California Revolution, describes the events of that war, life and advenures on the Coast during the early days, etc.

500 HARGRAVES, SHEBA. Heroine of the Prairies: A Romance of the Oregon Trail. 288 pp., 8vo, cloth. N. Y., 1930. $3.50

501 HARLOW, FRED'K PEASE. The Making of a Sailor; or, Sea Life aboard a Yankee Square-Rigger. 377 pp., 8vo, cloth. Marine Research Society, Salem, 1928. $7.50

502 HARMON, DANIEL WM. A Journal of Voyages and Travels in the Interior of North America, between the 47th and 58th Degrees of North Latitude, extending from Montreal nearly to the Pacific Ocean, a distance of 5,000 miles, including an account of the principal occurrences, during a residence of 19 years in different parts of the country. To which are added a concise Description of the face of the Country, its Inhabitants, their Manners, Customs, Laws, Religions, &c. 432 pp. Portrait of Harmon and map. 8vo, calf. Andover: Printed by Flagg and Gould, 1820. $45.00

Wagner-Camp 17. Fine tall copy of the Original Edition. Harmon was a partner in the Northwest Fur Company and did considerable exploring for that company throughout the Northwest. He spent some time with Dr. McLoughlin at Sturgeon Lake, and, in 1810, went with John Stuart to New Caledonia.

503 HARRIMAN, ALICE. Song o' the Olympics. 69 pp., illus., 8vo. Seattle, 1909. $3.50

504 HARRIS, THADDEUS M. The Journal of a Tour into the Territory Northwest of the Alleghany Mountains, made in the Spring of the Year 1803. With a Geographical and Historical Account of the State of Ohio. Five plates and maps. 8vo, half turkey morocco, all edges uncut. $15.00

505 —— The same. Original boards. $17.50

506 HARVEY, ARTHUR. Statistical Account of British Columbia. 8vo, cloth. Ottawa, 1867. $5.00

Smith 1621 locates but two copies.

507 HASSELL, SUSAN WHITCOMB. A Hundred and Sixty Books by Washington Authors. 40 pp., 8vo. N.p., (1916). $3.00

508 [HAWAII.] Hawaiian Mission Children Society. Voyages to Hawaii before 1860. 107 pp., 8vo, cloth. Honolulu, 1929. $4.00

509 [HAWKEYE HARRY.] Tracy the Outlaw, King of Bandits. 184 pp., 8vo, cloth. Baltimore, (1908). $5.00

A noted Washington bandit.

510 HAWKSWORTH, JOHN. An Account of the Voyages undertaken by the order of his present Majesty for making Discoveries in the Southern Hemisphere, and Successfully Performed by Commodore Byron, Capt. Carteret, Capt. Wallis and Capt. Cook. 4 vols., 8vo, calf. London, 1775. $17.50

Meares dedicated his great work to Hawksworth.

511 HAYES, A. A. New Colorado and the Santa Fe Trail. Map and views. Large 8vo, cloth. N. Y., 1880. $3.50

512 HAZLETINE, F. A. Lost Ships. In South Bend Journal, South Bend, Wash., Friday, Feb. 5, 1932. $2.00

513 HEADLEY, C. P. Life and Military Career of Major-General Philip Henry Sheridan. 358 pp., 8vo, cloth. N. Y., 1865. $2.50

Gen. Sheridan served in the Oregon wars.

514 HEAP, G. H., and BEALE, E. F. Central Route to the Pacific from the Valley of the Mississippi to California: Journal of E. F. Beale and G. H. Heap from the Missouri to California in 1853. 13 full-page colored views. 136 pp., 8vo, cloth. Phila., 1854. $10.00

515 HENRY, HON. FRANCIS. The Old Settler. Dedicated to the Pioneers of Puget Sound. Illus. by Major W. H. Bell. 12 pp., illus., 8vo, wrappers. N.p., N.d. $4.50

516 HENTY, G. A. Redskin and Cow-Boy. A Tale of the Western Plains. 384 pp., 12mo, cloth. London, N.d. $3.75

517 HIGGINS, D. W. The Mystic Spring and Other Tales of Western Life. 407 pp., 8vo, cloth. Toronto, 1904. $12.50

A scarce item, containing historical tales of British Columbia.

518 HIGGINSON, ELLA. The Flowers that Grew in the Sand and other Stories. 256 pp., 8vo, cloth. Seattle, 1896. $4.50

Smith 1896.

519 [HIMMELWRIGHT, A. L. ARTMAN.] (Heclawa, pseud.) In the Heart of the Bitter Root Mountains; the Story of "The Carlin Hunting Party." Sept.-Dec., 1893. Illus., port., map. 8vo, cloth. N. Y., 1895. $7.50

520 HIND, HENRY YOULE. Report on Exploration of Country between Lake Superior and Red River Settlement. 8vo, cloth. Toronto, 1859. $10.00

Contains large folding map of the Red River Valley.

521 HIND, HENRY YOULE. Narrative of the Canadian Red River Expedition of 1857, and of the Assiniboine and Sashkatchewan Exploring Expedition of 1858. 2 vols., complete with all the maps and tinted plates. 8vo, cloth. London, 1860. $22.50

Wagner-Camp 361. During the expedition Hind lived almost continuously among the Crees and Chippeways, whose habits and peculiarities he was able to study. The expedition started from Toronto to ascertain the practability of an emigrant route between Lake Superior and the Selkirk Settlement, and to establish a new colony at Lake Winnipeg, etc.

522 HINES, G. Wild Life in Oregon. 437 pp., plate. 8vo, cloth. N. Y., (1881). $2.50

Smith 1710.

523 HITTELL, JOHN S. Hittell's Hand-Book of Pacific Coast Travel. 2 maps. 8vo, cloth. San Francisco, 1885. $4.50

Smith 1731.

524 HITTLE, THEO. H. George Bancroft and his Service to California. 20 pp., 8vo, original wrappers. San Francisco, 1893. $4.50

525 HODSON, JOHN MILTON, et al. Masonic History of the Northwest, a Graphic Recital of the Organization and Growth of Freemasonry in the Northwest States. 8vo, cloth. San Francisco, (1902). $7.50

Smith 1743.

526 HOLMAN, FRED'K V. Addresses of the Oregon Bar Association. 8vo, wrappers. Portland, 1910. $3.50

Smith 1755.

526a HOPKINS, GERARD T. A Mission to the Indians, from the Indian Committee of Baltimre Yearly Meeting, to Fort Wayne, in 1804, written at the time by Gerard T. Hopkins, with an Appendix compiled in 1862 by Martha E. Tyson. Small 12mo, original wrappers. Phila.: T. Ellwood Zell, 1862. $37.50

Sabin 32917, Thompson 605, Jones 1448. Original Edition. Relates principally to the Indians of Ohio. The appendix, occupying half the book, gives a heretofore unpublished account of a journey to Upper Sandusky, Ohio, in 1799, written by George Ellicott, father of Martha E. Tyson, who edited the book. A letter from the daughter of Mrs. Tyson states that the book was printed for private use only—Thompson

527 HORN, TOM. Life of Tom Horn, Government Scout and Interpreter. Written by Himself. Illus. 12mo, wrappers. Denver, (1904). $4.50

528 HOWAY, F. W. A List of Trading Vessels in Maritime Fur Trade, 1785-1794, 1795-1804, 1804-1814. 8vo, original printed wrappers. Ottawa, 1930. $10.00

529 HOWE, HENRY. Historical Collections of the Great West . . . Sketches of Oregon, New Mexico, Texas, Minnesota, Utah and California . . . 2 vols. in 1. Illus. 8vo, cloth. Cincinnati, (1851). $3.50

Smith 1797.

530 HOWE, HENRY. Adventures and Achievements of Americans. A Series of Narratives. 720 pp., 8vo, cloth. Cincinnati, 1864. $3.50

531 HOWELLS, WM. C. Recollections of Life in Ohio, 1813-1840. 8vo, cloth. Cincinnati, 1895. $5.00

Valuable account of life in southeastern and southwestern Ohio in the period named.

532 HOY, P. R. Journal of an Exploration of Western Missouri in 1854, under the Auspices of the Smithsonian Institute. 438 pp., 8vo. Washington, 1864. $4.75

533 HRDLICKA, DR. A. Remains in Eastern Asia of the Race that Peopled America. Smithsonian Misc. Coll. Vol. 60, No. 16. Washington, 1912. $3.50

534 HUBBARD, BELA. Memorials of a Half Century. 581 pp., 8vo, cloth. N. Y. 1887. $4.50

535 [HUDSON'S BAY.] Aborigines' Protection Society. Canada West and the Hudson's Bay Company: A Political and Humane Question of vital importance to the honor of Great Britain and the existence of the Native Tribes. 19 pp., 8vo, original wrappers. London, 1856. $22.50

A rare work, not in Smith, dealing with the Northwest and the Hudson's Bay Administration.

536 [HUDSON'S BAY.] Exhibition of Ancient Maps and Charts. 20 pp., 8vo, original wrappers. N.p., N.d. $4.00

537 [HUDSON'S BAY COMPANY.] Fur Animals, Fur Skins; their Grade, their Size, their Value, their Habits, and how they should be handled. 18 pp., illus., 8vo, wrappers. N.p., N.d. $3.00

538 [HUDSON'S BAY.] Historical Exhibit Guide. 12 pp., 8vo, wrappers. Winnipeg, N.d. $2.50

538a [HUDSON'S BAY.] The Masters of the Wilderness: a Study of the Hudson's Bay Co., from its Origin to Modern Times, &c. By Chas. B. Reed. Folding map. 8vo, original wrappers. [Chicago], 1909. $2.50

539 HUNT, WILSON P. Voyage de l'Embouchere de la Columbia a Saint Louis, sur le Mississipi, en 1812. Precede d'une Voyage par mer de New-York a l'embouchere de la Columbia; de la relation de ce qui s'est passe au fort Astoria pendant plus an (de 1811 a 1812), et d'un Extraits des journaux tenus par les voyagesus en Anglois. Fine folding map. Nouvelles Annales des Voyages. 2 vols., 8vo, half calf. Paris, 1821. $150.00

An extremely rare work and one of the most important relating to the establishment not only of Astor's trading post on the Columbia, but to the discovery of South Pass.

540 [IDAHO.] State Historical Society of Idaho Publications. Bulletins. Vol. 1, No. 1, April, 1908; V. 1, No. 2, July, 1908; V. 1, No. 3, Oct., 1908; V. 1, No. 4, Jan., 1909. Also the following Biennial Reports: No. 4, 1913-14; No. 5, 1915-16; No. 6, 1917-18; No. 7, 1919-20; No. 8, 1921-2; No. 9, 1923-4; No. 10, 1925-6; No. 11, 1927-8; No. 12, 1929-30; No. 13, 1931-32; No. 14, 1933-4; No. 15, 1935-6; No. 16, 1937-8. 20 vols., 12mo and 8vo, original wrappers. Boise, 1908-1938. $75.00

Such a complete run as the above is rarely come upon. The first numbers are now practically unprocurable.

RARE EARLY LAWS OF MONTANA AND IDAHO

541 [IDAHO AND MONTANA.] Laws of the Territory of Idaho, First Session, Convened the 7th of December, 1863, and adjourned, 4th day of February, 1864, at Lewiston, containing the Territorial Act, Declaration of Independence, etc. 8vo, 686 pp.-xxxiii original wrappers. Lewiston, J. A. Glascock, 1864. $75.00

Excessively rare. One of the Earliest specimens of Printing in Idaho. For a long account of this item see the works of Hailey, McConnell and Bancroft. The Territory then embraced Montana, and hence, the volume is also this Territory's earliest laws, being used, as stated by Bancroft, by Chief Justice Hosmer of Montana.

542 [IDAHO.] Kootenai Catechism. 8vo, sewn. DeSmet, 1892. $10.00

An important rare work from the Indian Boys Press of Idaho, under the supervision of the Turin Province of the Jesuit Fathers.

543 [IDAHO.] Proceedings and Debates of the Constitutional Convention of Idaho, 1889. 2 vols., 2143 pp., 8vo, cloth. Caldwell, Idaho, 1912. $27.50

Edited and annotated by I. W. Hart, Clerk of the Supreme Court of Idaho.

544 [IDAHO.] Scenic Idaho. 4to, cloth. N.p., N.d. (1909). $3.75

544a [ILLINOIS.] Recollections of a Busy Life. By Henry S. Comstock. Portrait. 206 pp., 12mo, cloth. Cambridge, Ill., [1896]. $4.50

A valuable work by an enterprising editor who describes men and events, including Lincoln and the Civil War.

545 IMLAY (GILBERT). A Topographical Description of the Western Territory of North America: containing a succinct Account of its Soil, Climate, Natural History, Population, Agriculture, Manners and Customs. With an ample Description of the Several Divisions into which that country is partitioned. To which are added the Discovery, Settlement and Present State of Kentucky. By John Filson, &c., &c. The third edition, with great additions. Contemporary half calf, complete with the 3 maps and plan. London, 1797. $47.50

The author was a captain in the American Army and Commissioner for laying out land in the back settlements. "In this enlarged shape which the work took in its present and last edition, it comprises a most valuable mass of materials for the early history of the Western Country, embodying the entire works of Filson, Hutchins and various other tracts and original narratives."—Sabin.

546 IMRAY, JAMES F.. Sailing directions for the West Coast of North America between Panama and Queen Charlotte Island. 2nd edition. 380 pp., map. 8vo, boards. Imray, London, 1868. $15.00

547 [INDIANS.] Report of the Commissioner of Indian Affairs. For Year 1864. 507 pp., 8vo, cloth. Washington, 1865. $5.00

548 [INDIANS.] Report of the Commissioner of Indian Affairs for Year 1866. 372 pp., 8vo, cloth. Washington, 1866. $5.00

549 [INDIANS.] Reports of the Indian Commissioner for 1871 (3rd); 1872 (4th); 1874 (6th); 1879 (11th). 4 vols., 8vo. 1871-79. $15.00

550 [INDIANS.] Canadian Government. Copies of the Treaties made May 3 and Aug. 21, 1871 between Her Majesty the Queen and the Chippewa and Cree Indians. 8vo, sewn. Ottawa, 1873. [Sold]

551 [INDIANS.] (Cree). Instructions en Langue Crise sur Toute La Doctrine Catholique par un Missionnaire Oblat De La Saskatchewan. 505-IV pp., 8vo, cloth. St. Boniface, 1875. $20.00

551a [INDIAN JUVENILE.] Oowa Wowapi. Dakota Lapi En. By John P. Williamson. Fine engravings. 12mo, original printed boards. N. Y., 1871. $7.50

552 [INDIAN WAR VETERANS.] Memorial to Congress by the Indian War Veterans of the North Pacific Coast. 15 pp., 8vo, original printed wrappers. Salem, Ore., 1880. $15.00

Not in Smith.

553 [INDIANS.] The Facts respecting the Indian Administration in the Northwest. 74 pp., 8vo, original printed wrappers. Ottawa, (1886). $6.00

553a [INDIANA.] Sketches of Things and People of Indiana. By Aaron Wood. 48 pp. Port. 8vo, original wrappers. Indianapolis, 1883. $12.50

Autographed copy of this scarce work, with notes in author's own hand. A Pioneer preacher in the State, Rev. Woods deals to some extent with the manners and customs and types of peoples settling in the various localities.

554 INGERSOLL, CHARLES JARED. Historical Sketch of the Second War between the United States and Great Britain. 2 vols., Royal 8vo, calf. Phila., 1845-49. Series 2. History of the Second War. 2 vols., Royal 8vo, calf. Phila., 1852. Together 4 vols., calf. [Beautifully bound by Zaensdorf.] Phila., 1845-52. $40.00

555 INGERSOLL, ERNEST. Crest of the Continent. Record of a summer's ramble in the Rocky Mountains and beyond. Map and illus. 8vo, cloth. Chicago, 1885. $2.50

The Santa Fe Valley, the home of Kit Carson, Fremont's Pass, etc.

556 INGERSOLL, ERNEST. Alaskan Bird-Life as Depicted by many Writers. 72 pp., 7 colored plates. Large 8vo, cloth. N. Y., 1914. $12.50

557 INGHAM, G. T. Digging Gold Among the Rockies; or, exciting adventures of wild camp life in Leadville, Black Hills and the Gunnison Country. Illus., 12mo, cloth. Phila., (1882). $4.00

The country known as Black Hills was, in 1876, little better than a howling wilderness. Contains exciting discoveries, thrilling scenes of life among the miners, treachery of the Indians, histories of the various mines, etc.

THE ORIGINAL EDITION OF INMAN'S "SANTA FE TRAIL"

558 INMAN, COL. HENRY. Stories of the Old Santa Fe Trail: (The Babbs Ranch Massacre; Forsyth's Fight on the Arickaree; Race with the Kiowas; the Scout's last Ride; Coronado's March; Wal Henderson, etc., etc.) 12mo, original cloth. Plates. Kansas City, 1881. $27.50

This is Inman's first work printed on thin paper with 291 pages. There was another edition printed the same year on heavy stock paper with 287 pp.

559 INMAN, COL. HENRY, and CODY, COL. WM. F. The Great Salt Lake Trail. Map, portraits and plates. 529 pp., 8vo, cloth. N. Y., 1898. $7.50

Original edition. Col. W. F. Cody's quota has the distinctive merit of being drawn mainly from its narrator's own experience. To the trials of the Mormons during their arduous march and their pioneering adventures Col. Inman devotes some interesting pages. The Salt Lake Trail was also the route followed by the expeditions of Fremont Stansbury and Lander, and by the famous Pony Express, with its lumbering colleague, the overland stage.

560 INMAN, HENRY. The Old Santa Fe Trail; the story of a great highway. Photogravure plates by Frederick Remington; map and other illus. 8vo, cloth. N. Y., 1898. $5.00

FIRST LAWS OF IOWA AND ROCKY MOUNTAIN STATES

561 [IOWA.] The Statute Laws of the Territory of Iowa enacted at the First Session of the Legislative Assembly of said Territory, held at Burlington, 1838-39. 8vo, original boards. DuBuque: Russell and Reeves, 1839. $37.50

Original edition. The famous old "Blue Book" which was adopted by the provisional government of Oregon in 1843 and was for many years the law of all the country west of the Rocky Mountains, between the 42nd and 49th parallels of latitude.

562 [IOWA.] Revised Statutes of the Territory of Iowa Revised and compiled by a joint committee of the Legislative Session, 1842-43. 8vo, original calf. Hughes & Williams, Iowa City, 1843. $60.00

Smith No. 1868. These rare statutes were adopted by the Oregon Territorial Legislature February 1, 1851. Smith locates but one copy.

562a [IOWA.] (Rittenhouse, Rufus). Boyhood Life in Iowa Forty Years Ago. 23 pp., 12mo, original printed wrappers. Dubuque, 1880. $20.00

Bay's "Third Handful of Western Books," p. 43 "A charming privately printed Iowa pamphlet of imporatnce."

563 [IOWA.] History of Western Iowa, First Settlement and Growth. 571 pp., 8vo, cloth. Sioux City, 1882. $15.00

564 [IOWA.] Semi-Centennial of Iowa. A Record of the Commemoration of the Fiftieth Anniversary of the Settlement of Iowa, held at Burlington, June 1, 1883. 104 pp., original printed wrappers. Burlington, 1883. $7.50

565 [IOWA.] Statute Laws of the Territory of Iowa, enacted at the First Session of the Legislative Assembly of said Territory, held at Burlington, A.D., 1838-1839. Dubuque, 1839. Reprinted by the Historical Department of Iowa. 8vo, cloth. Des Moines, 1900. $10.00

566 IRVING, WASHINGTON. The Crayon Miscellany. By the Author of the Sketch Book. No. 1—Containing "A Tour of the Prairie." 12mo, cloth (some wear). Phila., 1835. $7.50

Wagner-Camp 56.

567 IRVING, WASHINGTON. The Rocky Mountains; or, Scenes, Incidents and Adventures in the Far West; Digested from the Journal of Capt. B. L. E. Bonneville, of the Army of the United States and Illustrated from various other sources. 2 vols., 12mo, cloth, maps. Phila., 1837. $30.00

Wagner-Camp 67. Original edition. Contains an account of the Walker Expedition to Calif. in 1833; adventures on the plains; fur hunting; discovery of Great Salt Lake; experiences of Wyeth in Oregon, etc.

568 IRVING, WASHINGTON. Astoria; or, Anecdotes of an Enterprise beyond the Rocky Mountains. Map. 2 vols., 12mo, original cloth. Phila.: Carey, 1836. $25.00

Wagner-Camp 61. Irving had the advantage of the use of the manuscripts relating to Astoria which had been loaned to him by John Jacob Astor. In addition he drew upon the various writers on Oregon up to that time, the result being a work indispensable to the student of early western history. The map shows the route of Hunt and Stuart. Fine clean copy.

569 —— The same. Tacoma edition, with fine plates. 2 vols., 8vo, cloth. N. Y., 1897. Scarce. $10.00

570 IRVING, WASHINGTON. The Adventures of Captain Bonneville . . . in the Rocky Mountains and the Far West. The Pawnee Edition. 2 vols., 8vo, cloth. [Illustrated with many fine plates.] N. Y., 1898. $10.00

571 IRVING, JOHN TREAT. Indian Sketches taken during an Expedition to the Pawnee and other Tribes of American Indians. 2 vols., 8vo, half calf. London, 1835. $15.00

572 IRVING, JOHN TREAT. Hunters of the Prairie; or, the Hawk Chief: a Tale of the Indian Country. 2 vols., 8vo, original boards, uncut. London, 1837. $15.00

573 ISRAEL, JOSEPH BENJAMIN, II. Drei Jahre in Amerika, 1859-1862. Von J. J. Benjamin, II. 1. Theil. Die Ostlichen staaion der Union und San Francisco. In three parts separate pages, and the third part again divided into two parts separately paged. All parts with individual title-pages. 3 vols., 8vo, original wrappers. Hanover, 1862. [Sold]

Wagner-Camp 380. Whereas Wagner-Camp describes all three parts bound in one volume, the above work is in the original three parts with the original wrappers to each part. The author devoted himself to tracing the history of the Jews in North America. After spending some time in the East, he went via Panama to San Francisco in 1850, thence to Vancouver Island and Oregon. He didn't return overland until 1861 via Salt Lake. He gives a long account of the Mormons as well as the habits, customs and manners of various places visited.

573a IVANSHINSTOV, N. Obozrienie Russkikh Krugosvientnyph Puteschestvii . . . (Review of Russian Voyages Round the World). 8vo, calf. St. Petersburg, 1872. $27.50

Wickersham 6328 states that only 25 copies of the Edition of 1850 were printed and they are not for sale. He does not mention the above edition. The review takes in the voyage of Krusenstern and others during the period mentioned.

574 IVINS, VIRGINIA WILCOX Pen Pictures of Early Western Days. 157 pp., illus., 8vo, cloth. N.p., 1905. $37.50

Narrative of an overland journey to California in 1853 by the author and her husband. The work was privately printed in a small edition and is now difficult to procure.

575 JACK, ELLEN E. The Fate of a Fairy; or, Twenty Seven Years in the Far West. 313 pp. Chicago, c. 1910. $7.50

576 JACKSON, ANDREW. Message from the President of the U. S. in answer to a Resolution of the Senate relative to the British Establishment on the Columbia and the state of the Fur Trade, etc. 21st Cong., 2nd Sess., Sen. Doc. 39. Dated Jan. 24, 1831. 8vo, 36 pp., sewn. Washington. 1831. $75.00

Wagner-Camp 46. A most valuable account of transactions in the Rocky Mountains during this period.

577 JACKSON, CHARLES ROSS. Sheriff of Wasco. 318 pp., 4 plates. 8vo, cloth. N. Y., (1907). $5.00

578 JACKSON, HELEN HUNT. Glimpses of Three Coasts. 418 pp., 8vo, cloth. Boston, 1887. $5.00

Part One of this work relates to California and Oregon.

579 JACKSON, HELEN HUNT. A Century of Dishonor: a Sketch of the U. S. Government's dealing with some of the Indian Tribes. 8vo, cloth. N. Y., 1881. $3.50

580 JACKSON, HELEN HUNT. Report of the Mission Indians in 1883. 37 pp., 8vo, cloth. Boston, 1887. $4.75

581 JACKSON, JAMES. Basketry of the Coast and Islands of the Pacific etc. Exhibited April, 1896 at the Portland Library. 31 pp., 8vo. Gill, Portland, (1896). $7.50

Contains an article by H. K. McArthur, Basketry of the Northwest. Smith, 1909, locates one copy in the Portland, Ore., Library.

582 JACKSON, MARY E. The Life of Nellie C. Bailey; or, a Romance of the West. 8vo, cloth. 399 pp. Topeka, 1885. $7.50

583 JACKSON, ORICK. The White Conquest of Arizona: a History of the Pioneers, with Reminiscences of Capt. Joe Walker's Famous Expedition, the Ghastly Pinole Treaty; the Wickenburg Massacre and other Memorable Indian Fights; Desperate Days and Desperate Men. Illus. 12mo, original wrappers. Los Angeles, N.d. $7.50

584 JACOB, J. G. The Life and Times of Patrick Gass, now sole survivor of the Overland Expedition to the Pacific, under Lewis and Clarke, in 1804-5-6; also a Soldier in the War with Great Britain from 1812 to 1815, and a participant in the Battle of Lundy's Lane. Together with Gass' Journal of the Expedition condensed; Sketches of some Events occurring during the last Century in the Upper Ohio country; Biographies, Reminiscences, etc. [Port. and 3 illus.) 12mo, cloth (rebacked). Wellsburg, Va., 1859. $45.00

The rare first edition.

Item 576, Date should read 1832, not 1831.

585 JACOB, JOHN J. Biographical Sketch of Capt. Michael Cresap; also a Journal of Wayne's Campaign against the Northwestern Indians by Lt. Boyer. The two items bound in one volume. 4to, new cloth. Cincinnati, 1866. $10.00

586 JAMES, BUSHROD WASHINGTON. Alaskana; or, Alaska in description and Legendary Poems. 368 pp., illus. 8vo, cloth. Phila., 1892. $6.00

587 JAMES, BUSHROD WASHINGTON. Alaska, its Neglected Past, its Brilliant Future. 444 pp., frontis., 16 maps, 32 plates. 8vo, cloth. Phila., 1897. $7.50

Smith 1917 reports three copies.

588 JAMES, EDWIN, M.D. An Account of An Expedition from Pittsburgh to the Rocky Mountains, Performed in the Years 1819 and '20, by Order of the Hon. J C. Calhoun, Sec'y of War; Under the Command of Major Stephen H. Long. From the Notes of Major Long, Mr. T. Say, and Other Gentlemen of the Exploring Party. 2 vols., 8vo, roan-backed boards, together with the rare atlas containing two folding maps, chart and eight plates (one colored). 4to size, original boards, paper label. Together 3 vols. Phila., 1823-2. $75.00

Wagner Camp 26. A good set of this fine work, containing plates and material not found in the London edition. Six of the views were drawn by Seymour and one by T. R. Peale. Probably no other western American expedition was more systematically arranged than this of Major Long's up the Missouri and Yellowstone to the Rocky Mountains. Each man of the expedition was picked according to specific qualifications and the company moved ahead with the thoroughness of experts. The scientific observations of Dr. Baldwin, and, after his unfortunate death on the Missouri, that of Dr. James, author of the above work, are set down with an earnestness that is always apparent when men are devoted to their work. One can rightfully say that Long's expedition, arranged unsparingly by the government, marks the beginning of the full expansive movement westward of free trapper and hunter and the fur combines. In a few months "Jim" Bridger, Clyman, Rose, Sublette, Fitzpatrick, Jedediah Smith and old Hugh Glass—the pathfinders—were on the forks of the Yellowstone, on the Sweetwater, the Green, the Little Bear; were worming through the South Pass for peltry and a continent.

589 JAMES, EDWIN. Account of an Expedition from Pittsburgh to the Rocky Mountains, performed in the Years 1819, 1820. Compiled from the Notes of Major Long, Mr. T. Say and other Gentlemen of the Party. Folding map and plates. 3 vols., 8vo, calf. Some plates colored. London, 1823. $50.00

590 JAMES, GEORGE WHARTON. Indian Basketry. 8vo, cloth. 238 pp. N. Y., 1901. $7.50

591 JAMES, GEORGE WHARTON. The Indians of the Painted Desert Region. Hopis, Navahoes Wallapaism Tavasupais. 268 pp., illus., 8vo, cloth. Boston, 1907. $3.50

592 JAMES, GEORGE WHARTON. The Wonders of the Colorado Desert. 547 pp., 8vo, cloth. Boston, 1918. $4.00

593 JAMES, THOMAS. Strange and Dangerous Voyage in his intended Discovery of the Northwest Passage into the South Sea in the years 1631-32, etc. 4to, half calf. London, (1633). $37.50

594 JAMES, GENERAL THOMAS. Three Years among the Indians and Mexicans. Illus. 8vo, boards, cloth back, uncut. St. Louis, 1916. $27.50

Wagner-Camp 121 (note). Printed in a limited edition by the Missouri Historical Society the above work is now scarce. The original work by James is one of the rarest items in the entire field of Western Americana. The author gives an account of his experiences on the Upper Missouri, 1809-10, his expedition to Santa Fe in 1821-2; and his adventures on the prairies in 1823-4. Moreover, the work contains much source material on the fur trade. The author came from Monroe County, Illinois and originally published his work at Waterloo, Ill., in 1846. This new edition has been carefully edited by Judge Walter B. Douglas with copious notes which give locations of later printed journals.

595 JAMES, THOMAS HORTON. (Pseud. Rubio). Rambles in the United States and Canada during the year 1845, with a short Account of Oregon. 259 pp., cloth. London, 1846. $7.50

Smith 1927. Behind the protection of a nom de plume our British visitor roasts America and the Americans in an amusing but sarcastic manner.

596 JAMIESON, MATTHEW H. Recollections of Pioneer and Army Life. 263 pp., frontis., 8vo, cloth. Kansas City, N.d. $17.50

Overland trip to Pike's Peak, 1859-1860.

597 JANSON, CHARLES WM. The Stranger in America; Containing Observations made during a long residence in that Country, on the Genius, Manners and Customs of the People of the United States . . . Plates and 2 vignettes. 4to, roan back, uncut. London, 1807. $37.50

The original edition. Scarce with all the plates, which include views of Boston, Hell Gate, Mt. Vernon, several of Philadelphia, the funeral of Washington, etc. Janson appears to have fared none too well during his thirteen years in America and returned to England to sound off his prejudices in this work.

598 JARMAN, W. U. S. A. Uncle Sam's Abscess; or, Hell upon Earth for U. S. 194 pp., 8vo, original wrappers. Exeter, 1884. $10.00

599 JARVIS, JAMES JACKSON. History of the Hawaiian or Sandwich Islands. 407 pp. 24 plates, map. 8vo, cloth. Boston, 1843. $7.50

600 JEBB, MRS. J. G. Life and Adventures of John G. Jebb. Portrait. 8vo, cloth. Boston, 1895. $7.50

Adventures in Colorado, New Mexico, Sacramento, Rocky Mountains, etc.

601 JEFFERSON, H. E. Oklahoma; the beautiful Land. An exciting narrative of the scenes incident to the occupation of Oklahoma. A complete History of the Country and its Wonderous Development. 202 pp., 8vo, original wrappers. Chicago, 1889. $10.00

602 JEFFERSON, THOMAS. The Life of Captain Clark. (Contained in the Portfolio, August, 1814). 8vo, original wrappers. Phila., 1814. $22.50

A rare work, now seldom found.

603 JEFFERYS, THOMAS. Voyages from Asia to America for completing the Discoveries of the North-West Coast of America. To which is prefixed a Summary of the Voyages made by the Russians on the Frozen Sea in search of a North-East Passage. Serving as an Explanation of a Map of the Russian Discoveries, published by the Academy of Sciences at St. Petersburgh. Translated from the High Dutch of S. Muller, of the Royal Academy of St. Petersburgh. 4to, half polished morocco, large copy Complete with the 4 maps. London: T. Jefferys, 1761. $92.50

Original edition. One of he most important works relating to the Discoveries on the North West Coast of America. The Maps are entitled: (1 "A Map of the Discoveries made by the Russians on the North West Coast of America". (2) "A Map of the N. E. Parts of Asia and N. W. parts of America showing their situation with respect to Japan". (3) "A Map of Canada and the North Part of Louisiana, extending to the Pacific Ocean containing the new discoveries made by the Russians and French." (4) "A General Map of the discoveries of Admiral de Fonte and other Navigators, Spanish, English and Russian, in quest of a Passage to the South Sea, by Mr. De l'Isle, Septr. 1752."

605 JEFERYS, THOMAS. The Great Probability of a North West Passage deduced from Observations on the letter of Admiral De Fonte, who sailed from the Callao of Lima on the Discovery of a Communication between the South Sea and the Atlantic Ocean; and to intercept some Navigators from Boston in New England, whom he met with, then in search of a North West Passage. 4to, half morocco, complete with the 3 maps. London: Thomas Jefferys, 1768. $87.50

A most important work for the history of geographical discovery on the North West Coast of America. The Maps are as follows: (1) A copy of an authentic Spanish Map of America published in 1608. (2) The Discoveries made in Hudson's Bay by Capt. Smith in 1746-7. (3) A General Map of the Discoveries of Admiral De Fonte. This work, though usually catalogued under the publisher's name "Jefferys", was in reality written by Theodore Swaine Drage. Sabin, Vol. VIII., No. 24860, says: "The Author, according to Meusel, was Theodore Swindrage but is named by Watte, Dragge." A copy of the work once possessed by us had on the half-title, "Presented me by the author", and at the foot of page (vi), after the printed words "The Author" was written in manuscript, "Theodorus Swaine Drage."

606 JENKINS, JOHN STILWELL. James K. Polk and a History of his Administration . . . frontis. 8vo, cloth. Auburn, c. 1850). $7.50

607 JENKINS, JOHN S[TILWELL). Voyage of the U. S. exploring squad-rn commanded by Captain Charles Wilkes . . . in 1838, 1839, 1840, 1841 and 1842; together with explorations and discoveries made by . . . other navigators and travellers. 517 pp., illus., 8vo, cloth. Auburn, 1852. $5.00

608 JENKINS, JOHN S[TILWELL]. Explorations and adventures in and around the Pacific and Antarctic oceans, being the voyage of the U. S. exploring squadron, commanded by Captain Charles Wilkes of the U. S. navy in 1838, 1839, 1840, 1841 and 1842; together with explorations and discoveries made by Admiral D'Urville, Captain Ross, and other navigators and travelers; and an account of the expedition to the Dead sea, under Lieutenant Lynch. 517 pp., 8vo, cloth. New York: Hurst, n. d. $5.00

First part of chapter 17 contains a description of Oregon.

Item 605, Should read "Jeffreys."

609 JENKINS, W. C. Early Days of the Wells Fargo Company. N. p., illus., 8vo. N.p., N.d. $5.00

610 JENNESS, DIAMOND. Life of the Copper Eskimos. From report of the Canadian Arctic Expedition 1913-18. 217 pp., 8vo, original wrappers. Ottawa, 1922. $6.00

611 JENNESS, DIAMOND. Report of the Canadian Arctic Expedition, 1913-18. (Eskimo Folk-Lore,, Part A, Myths. 8vo, original wrappers. Ottawa, 1924, and Part B, original wrappers, Ottawa, 1924). 2 vols., 8vo, original wrappers. Ottawa, 1924. $7.50

612 JENNESS, DIAMOND. The Indians of Canada. (National Museum of Canada, Bulletin 65, 446 pp., Ottawa, 1932). 8vo, cloth. Ottawa, 1932. $4.00

613 JENSON, ANDREW. The Historical Record: A Monthly Periodical Devoted Exclusively to Historical, Biographical, Chronological and Statistical Matters. 4 vols.: VOL. 5, 1868; VOL. 6, 1887; VOL. 8, 1889; VOL. 9, 1890. 8vo, cloth. Salt Lake City, 1886-90. $27.50

One of the most important western historical works ever published. The publication was started in Salt Lake in 1886 by Jenson, who had previously published four vols. of Scandinavian-Mormon material in Danish, hence the first vol. of the Utah work was called Vol. Five. Complete sets are practically unprocurable as but few copies of the last vol. were published. Every fact connected with the mormons, their Settlement in Missouri, Iowa, Illinois, etc., their adventures, massacres, exploits, overland migration, Indian campaigns, etc., etc., is here exhaustively presented. The Index covers some 70pp., and the whole of the final vol. is given over to the preservation of a day-by-day overland narrative of the trip across the plains in 1847, with interesting sketches of Fort Bridger, Laramie, etc.

614 JEREMIE, NICHOLAS. Relation du Detroit et de la Baie d'Hudon. 12mo, calf. Amsterdam, 1720. $47.50

The rare Original Edition. Jeremie's work is the first narrative of Hudson Bay, with the descriptions of the geography of the country and of the struggle between England and France for the Bay. The author spent 18 years at Ft. Nelson and York Factory.

615 —— Same. Translated from the original edition by R. Douglas and J. N. Wallace. Illus., map, 8vo, cloth. Ottawa, 1926. $7.50

616 [JESUIT RELATIONS.] Relations des Jesuits contenant ce qui s'est de passe de plus remarquable dans les Missions des Peres de la Compagnie de passe de plus Nouvelle France. 3 vols., 8vo, original boards, uncut. Quebec, 1858. $32.50

617 JEWITT, JOHN B. Narrative of the Adventures and Sufferings of John R. Jewitt; only survivor of the Crew of the Ship "Boston", during a Captivity of nearly three years among the Savages of Nootka Sound: with an Account of the Manners, Mode of Living, and Religious Opinions of the Natives. Frontispiece, 12mo, calf. Middletown: Printed by Loomis and Richards, 1815. $17.50

The rare original Edition with this title. Theodore Dwight says that this book was written by his uncle, Richard Alsop, who drew the story from Jewitt It was published by Jewitt in various places nad sold throughout the country. The "Boston" was taken by savages in 1803.

618 —— Another Edition. Frontispiece. 12mo, original printed bards. Middletown: Printed for Seth Richards, 1815. $10.00

619 —— Another Edition. Frontispiece and 10 woodcuts. 12mo, original printed boards. N. Y.: Printed for the Publisher, (1815). $7.50

First New York edition with the date, Nov., 1815 on third page.

620 —— Another Edition. 259 pp., illus. 8vo, cloth. N. Y., 1835. $5.00

621 —— Another Edition. 256 pp., illus., port. 8vo, cloth. London, 1896. $7.50

622 —— Another Edition. 91 pp., illus. 8vo, cloth. Boston, 1931. $15.00

With an introduction and check list of later editions of Jewitt's capture by Norman L. Dodge. Limited to 100 copies.

623 JEWITT, JOHN R. A Narrative of the Adventures and Sufferings of John R. Jewitt, during a captivity of nearly three years among the Savages of Nootka Sound . . . (Excerpted from the Analectic Review, 493-496 pp., Phila., 1815). 8vo. Phila., 1815. $5.00

The first publication of Jewitt's work in a periodical.

624 JEWETT, STANLEY G. Direction for preparing mammals, birds, etc. 20 pp., 8vo, original wrappers. Salem, Ore., 1914. $6.00

625 JOCHELSON, WALDEMAR. Archaelogical Investigations in the Aleutian Islands. 145 pp., illus., map. 8vo, cloth. Washington, 1925. $7.50

626 JOHNSON, CHARLES H. L. Famous Frontiersmen and Heroes of the Border. 356 pp., ills. 8vo, cloth. Boston, 1913. $4.50

Smith 1978.

627 JOHNSON, CLARK. Seven and nine years among the Comanches and Apaches, an autobiography. 309 pp., 8vo, cloth. Jersey City, 1873. $7.50

628 JOHNSON, CLIFTON. Highways and byways of the Pacific coast. 323 pp. 63 pl. 8vo, cloth. New York, 1908. $4.50

629 JOHNSON, EBENEZER. A Short Account of a Northwest Voyage, performed in the Years 1796, 1797, 1798. 15 pp., 8vo. Massachusetts: Printed for the Author, 1798. (A photostat reprduction of the rare original edition). $15.00

630 JOHNSON, EDWIN F. Railroad to the Pacific Northern Route. Its General Character, Relative Merits, etc. Folding maps, and lithographic views. 8vo, original wrappers. N. Y.: Railroad Journal Job Printing Office, 1854. $25.00

The author maintained that the Straits of De Fuca, or the mouth of the Columbia, was the proper terminal point for a railroad to the Pacific. He predicted that the prominent city of the Pacific coast would some day be located here. The work gives a detailed account of the western country; proposed route; character of the country; mountain passes; climate; soil; Upper Missouri country; Saskatchewan nad Clark's River Valley; Whitney's Route; South Pass Route; Colorado Valley; the Sierra; Route from San Francisco to the Walker and Tejon Pass; connection of California with Oregon and Washington; Expedition from San Francisco to meet Capt. Beale; Capt. Walker's Account; Aubrey's exploration from Tejon Pass to Alburquerque, etc.

631 JOHNSON, EMILY PAULINE ("Tekahionwake"). Legends of Vancouver. 136 pp., frntis., illus. 4th ed. N. p., n. d. (1911). $5.00

The author states that the legends were told to her personally by the late Chief Capilano, of Vancouver, and that the latter frequently remarked that they had never been revealed to any other English speaking person.

632 JOHNSON, EMILY PAULINE, ("Tekahionwake'). Flint and Feathers; The complete poems of E. Pauline Johnson ("Tekahionwake"). With introduction by Theodore Watts-Dutton and a biographical sketch of the author. Ills. 3rd ed. 8vo, cloth. Toronto, 1914. $5.00

Contains poems in honor of British Columbia written by the Indian poetess of Vancouver.

633 JOHNSON, JOHN. Childhood Travel, and British Columbia. 349 pp., 30 plates, 5 ports. 8vo, cloth. (Abertillery Raffan, N. d.). $15.00

Smith 1965.

634 JOHNSON, LIONEL A. Oregon at Malabon. 19 pp., 8vo, wrappers. Portland, 1905. $4.75

635 JOHNSON, PHIL. Phil. Johnson's Life on the Plains. 358 pp., illus. 8vo, cloth. Chicago, 1888. $6.00

636 JOHNSON, R. BYRON. Very Far West Indeed; A Few Rough Experiences on the North-West Pacific Coast. 12mo, cloth. London, 1872.

Original Edition. California, Vancouver's Island, etc. $12.50

637 JOHNSON, [GEN.] R. W. A Soldiers Reminiscences in Peace and War. 428 pp., front., 8vo, cloth. Phila., 1886. $15.00

Johnson, was stationed at Ft. Snelling in 1849; Scouting after Indians; off to Texas; Mexican War; Indian wars, etc.

638 JOHNSON, SIDONA V. (compiler). A Short History of Oregon. Early discoveries; the Lewis and Clark Explorations; Settlement; Government; Indian Wars; Progress. 329 pp., 5 portraits, map, facsimiles. 8vo, cloth. Chicago, 1904. $6.00

639 JOHNSON [THEODORE T.]. Sights in the Gold Region and scenes by the Way, Second Edition, with a Folding Map of the Gold Regions, two views of San Francisc (one colored, the other tinted), and five plates, 324 pp. 12mo, cloth. New York, 1850. $15.00

Cowan, p. 122. Superior to the first edition; the work has been rewritten and enlarged with eight new chapters, comprising information on the routes, the latest intelligence from the mines, and an account of Oregon prepared by Hon. S. R. Thurston, of that territory. The illustrations are from original sketches taken in California by J. Prendergast.

640 —— Same. 12mo, cloth. Dublin, 1850. $10.00

641 JOHNSON, W. FLETCHER. Life of Sititng Bull and a History of the Indian War of 1890-91. 587 pp., front. 8vo, cloth (1891). $3.50

642 JOLLY, W. Christian Progress. 151 pp. 8vo, cloth. Salem, 1870. $3.75

643 JONES, CHAS. C., JR. History of Georgia. Engraved portraits and plans. 2 vols., thick 8vo, cloth. Boston, 1833. $10.00

"One of the best State histories. The author is the leading authority upon the subject and has devoted great care to the collection of maerials. The treatmnt is full and in he text will be found many valuable documents. The style is smooth and agreeable. The first volume is devoted mainly to the history of Georgia as a royal province, which leads presently into the Revolution. To the share which Georgia bore therein nearly all of the second volume is devoted. The history closes with the achievement of independence."—Literature of American History.

644 [JONES, COL. CHARLES J.] Buffalo Jones' Forty Years of Adventure . . . compiled by Col. Henry Inman. Illus. 8vo, cloth. London, 1899. $30.00

A scarce work. Jones went west from Kansas in 1871, and the result of his experiences encompassed in this work gives a most complete and detailed account of the buffalo.

645 JONES, LIVINGSTON F. A Study of the Thlingets of Alaska. 261 pp., ills. 8vo, cloth. Chicago, c. 1914. $7.50

646 JONES, DR. N. E. Squirrel Hunters of Ohio; or Glimpses of Pioneer Life. Numerous illustrations of early pioneer life, customs, methods of transport, etc. 12mo, pp. 369, cloth. Cincinnati, 1898. $2.50

An exceedingly interesting volume on life of Old Northwest and only volume of any historical value dealing with this particular group of early pioners. It is interesting in regard to early transportation, railroads, canals, coach, steamboats, and early educational, social and political conditions.

647 JONES, N. W. Indian Bulletin for 1867, No. 1, containing a brief account of the North American Indians and the interpretations of many Indian names. 16 pp., 8vo, original wrappers. Alvard, N. Y., 1867. $7.50

648 JONES, N. W. Indian Bulletin for 1868. No. 2. Containing a Brief Account of Chinese Voyages to the North-West Coast of America, and the Interpretation of 200 Indian Names. 8vo, original wrappers. New York, 1869. $10.00

Contains Indian place names in the New England States, New York, New Jersey, Maryland, and Pennsylvania. Scarce.

649 JONES, HON. S. Speech on the Oregon Question January 15th, 1846. 7 pp., 8vo, sewn. Washington, 1846. $4.50

650 JONES, T. L. From the Gold Mine to the Pulpit; Story of a Backwoods Methodist Preacher in the Pacific Northwest, during the closing years of the Nineteenth Century. 13 ports., 12 plates. 12mo, cloth. Cincinnati (1904). $12.50

651 JONES, WILLIAM A. Report upon the Reconnaissance of North-Western Wyoming including Yellowstone National Park, made in the summer of 1873. 331 pp., maps. 8vo, colth. Washington, 1875. $7.50

652 JORDAN, DAVID STARR. Imperial democracy; a study of the relation of government by the people, equality before the law, and other tenets of democracy, to the demands of a vigorous foreign policy and other demands of imperial dominion. 293 pp. 8vo, cloth. New York, Appleton, 1899. $7.50

Pp. 183-214 contains Colonial lessons in Alaska.

653 JORDAN, DAVID STARR. Matka and Kodik. A Tale of the Mist Islands. 68 pp., lilus. 8vo, cloth. San Francisco, 1897. $7.50

Not in Smith. This work, which depicts the life of the seal, was written on Pribilof Island, Bering Sea, July, 1896.

654 [JOURNAL OF AMERICAN HISTORY.] Vol. I, No. 3, 1917. Contains pictures and views. McLoughlin, Fort Steilacoom, First Protestant Church built North of the Columbia River, First House at Port Townsend, Ship Columbia, ect. $3.00

655 [JOURNAL MILITARY SERVICE INSTITUTION.] For July, August, September, October, 1904. Contained in Vol. 35. 8vo, original wrappers. 1904. $12.50

Contains the important "Vancouver Barracks Past and Present" by Gen. Thomas M. Anderson The above series relating to this subject was all that was ever published. Smith 1985 locates but one set.

656 JUDSON, KATHERINE BERRY. Montana the land of Shining Mountains. 244 pp., map. McClurg, Chicago, 1909. $5.00

657 JUDSON, KATHARINE BERRY. Myths and Legends of Alaska. 149 pp., ills. Chicago, 1911. $5.00

658 JUDSON, KATHERINE BERRY. Myths and Legends of the Great Plains, 205 pp. McClurg: Chicago, 1913. $5.00

659 JUDSON, KATHERINE BERRY. Subject Index to the History of the Pacific Northwest and Alaska as found in the United States Government Documents Congressional Series, in the American State Papers and in other Documents, 1789-1881. 341 pp. 8vo, cloth. Olympia, 1913. $5.00

660 JUDSON, KATHERINE BERRY. Early days in Oregon. 263 pp. McClurg: Chicago, 1916. $5.00

Smith 1991.

661 JUDSON, KATHERINE BERRY. Myths and Legends of British North America. 211 pp. 8vo, cloth. McClurg: Chicago, 1917. $5.00

662 JUDSON, PHOEBE GODELL. A Pioneer's Search for an Ideal Home, by Phoebe Goodell Judson who crossed the Plains in 1853 and became a Resident of Puget Sound before the organization of Washington Territory. A Book of Personal Memoirs published in the author's 59th year. 315 pp., front. 12mo, cloth. Seattle, 1914. $40.00

Rare. Not in Smith.

663 JUNG, A. M. Jesuit Missions among the American Tribes of the Rocky Mountain Indians. 30 pp., ills. 8vo, original printed wrappers. Spokane, 1925. $7.50

An important contribution.

664 KAHLO, DOROTHY MILLER. History of the Police and Fire Departments of the City of Seattle. 292 pp., ills. 8vo, cloth. Seattle, 1907. $7.50

665 KANE, PAUL. Wanderings of an Artist among the Indians of North America from Canada to Vancouver's Island and Oregon through the Hudson's Bay Companys Territory and back again. Folding map and 8 colored plates. 8vo, cloth. London, 1859. $50.00

Fine copy of the scarce first edition. The author traversed almost alone the territories of the Red River Settlement, valley of the Saskatchewan, across the Rocky Mountains, down the Columbia to Puget Sound and Vancouver's Island. The book is a transcript of the daily journal in narrative form. The beautiful plates are copies of the labors of his brush. It is interesting to note that Kane spent some time in 1847 at the Whitman Mission, and warned Dr. Whitman of his danger.

666 [KANSAS.] Six months in Kansas. 231 pp., 8vo, cloth. Boston, 1856. $7.50

667 [KANSAS.] The Kansas Magazine. Volumes 1, 2 and 3. Three volumes. 8vo, cloth. Topeka, 1872-73. $27.50

667a [KANSAS.] House Journals. First session, Shawnee, 1855; second session, Lecompton, 1857; Special session, 1857; third session, Lecompton, 1860 (with the Senate Journal bound in); fourth session, Lawrence, 1861; fifth session, Lawrence, 1864; sixth, Special session. Lawrence, 1864; 7 vols., 8vo, sheep (worn). Shawnee, Lecompton, Lawrence, 1855-1864. $35.00

668 [KANSAS-NEBRASKA.] (Stephen A. Douglas and Others). Nebraska Question, comprising speeches in the United States Senate; together with the history of the Missouri Compromise, Daniel Webster's memorial in regard to it, history of the Annexation of Texas, the organization of Oregon Territory, and the Compromise of 1850. 12mo, original wrappers. N. Y., 1854. $7.50

Smith 1016.

669 KASHEVAROFF, A. P. Descriptive Booklet on the Alaska Historical Museum. 61 pp., illus. 8vo, cloth. Juneau, Alaska, 1922. $5.00

670 KEARNEY, GEN. PHILIP. Letter, dated Ft. Scott, Indian Territory, Sept. 16, 1845. By H. L., Jr. 8vo (removed from a book). (1845). $5.00

The writer was a member of Kearney's summer campaign to the Rocky Mountains which he describes fully in a long letter to the Boston Atlas and here reprinted in the London Athenaeum, Dec. 15, 1855, pp. 1198-99.

671 [KEARNEY, GEN. PHILLIP.] Personal and Military History of Philip Kearney, Major-General U. S. Volunteers. By John Watts DePeyster. Illus. 8vo, cloth. Elizabeth, N. J., 1870. $7.50

672 KEATING [W. H.]. Narrative of an Expedition to the Source of the St. Peter's River, Lake Winnepeek, Lake of the Woods, &c., performed in the year 1823, by order of the Hon. J. C. Calhoun, under the command of Stephen H. Long. 2 vols., 8vo, maps and plates, calf, edges uncut. London, 1825. $17.50

Known as "Long's Second Expedition." It is one of the earliest reports of the Upper Mississippi, and almost a cyclopaedia of material relating to the Indians of that part of the Country.

673 KEATING, WILLIAM H. Narrative of an Expedition to the Source of St. Peter's River, Lake Winnepeek, Lake of the Woods, &c. Performed in the year 1823 by order of the Hon. J. C. Calhoun, Secretary of War, under command of Stephen H. Long, Major in the U. S. T. E. Map and Plates 2 vols., 8vo, half polished calf. Phila., 1824. $22.50

The Scarce Original Edition.

674 KEELER, CHARLES. San Francisco and Thereabouts. 97 pp., illus., map. 8vo, cloth. San Francisco, 1903. $7.50

675 KEELER, N. E. A Trip to Alaska and the Klondike. 115 pp. 8vo, original wrappers. Cincinnati, 1906. $12.50

HALL J. KELLEY'S OWN COPY OF "SKETCH OF OREGON"

676 KELLEY, HALL J. A Geographical Sketch of that Part of North America called Oregon; containing an Account of the Indian Title, Nature of Government, &c. Second Edition enlarged with an Appendix embracing an Account of the Expedition and some Directions for Becoming an Emigrant.. 80 pp., large folding map. ¾ morocco with the original wrappers bound in. (Three leaves in photostat). Boston, 1831. [Sold] $150.00

This was Hall Kelley's own copy and he has signed on front wrapper "Hall J. Kelley, of Three Rivers, Mass." He has made in his own hand 15 marginal notes throughout the text. There are inserted three personal notes and a clipping from the Washington Intelligencer, May, 1848, entitled "Hall J. Kelley," 20 inches long. Signed "Justitia".

The copy was apparently used by Kelley as a corrected Copy for the Printer as there are many corrections and emendations in his own hand.

677 —— The same. Port. and map. Roy. 8vo, cloth. Abbatt. N. Y., 1919. $7.50

KELLEY'S "SKETCH OF OREGON" IN WRAPPERS

678 KELLEY, HALL J. A Geographical Sketch of that Part of North America, Called Oregon: Containing an Account of the Indian Title; the Nature of the Right of Soverignty; the First Discoveries: Climates and seasons; face of the Country and Muntains; Natural Divisions. Physical Appearances and Soil of Each; Forests and Vegetable Productions; Rivers, Bays, &c.; Islands, &c.; Animals; the Description of the Indians and the Number and Situation of their Tribes; Together with an Essay on the Advantages Resulting from a Settlement in the Territory. Folding Map of Oregon Drawn by H. J. Kelley and Lithographed by Pendleton; 8vo, wrappers. Boston, 1830. [Sold]

A splendid copy of this exceedingly rare classic of Oregon history, with the first engraved map of Oregon. Kelley claimed to be the colonizer of Oregon and was the earliest to advertize the advantages of Oregon as a place for settlers.

679 KELLEY, HALL J. A General Circular To All Persons of Good Character, who Wish to Emigrate to the Oregon Territory, Embracing Some Account of the Character and Advantages of the Country; the Right and the Means and Operations by which it is to be Settled; And All Necessary Directions for Becoming An Emigrant. Woodcut Map on last page. 22 pp., 8vo, original printed wrappers. Boston, 1831. $125.00

Osiginal Edition. A Remarkably fine tall copy, uncut. Paulin, No. 2336; "Rarely Found in the Original Printed Wrappers One of the Rarest of the Early Tracts Relating to the Settlement of Oregon." An important and one of the earliest works on the Oregon Territory, discussing the right of settling; the resources of the Country; its advantages; the proposed survey and division of the lands; self government; freedom of religion and education; types of emigrants desired; Indians; route to be taken; rules of the proposed expedition; funds; etc.

680 [KELLEY, HALL J.] Article on his Oregon Expedition. New England Magazine, January-June, 1832. 536 pp. 8vo, original boards. Boston, 1832. $20.00

An important original contribution by Hall J. Kelley, which was immediately attacked by William J. Snelling. Both are rare. See Fred Wilbur Powell's "Hall Jackson Kelley, Prophet of Oregon".

681 KELLEY, HALL J. Memorial of Hall J. Kelley, praying a Grant of Land for the purpose of Establishing a Colony thereon. Dec. 27, 1839. Laid on the table and ordered to be Printed. 26th Con., 1st Sess. Senate. 8vo. Washington, 1839. [Sold]

682 KELLEY, HALL J. Discoveries, Purchase of Land, etc., on the Northwest Coast, being part of an Investigation of American Title to the Oregon Territory. 16 pp., sewn. (Boston, 1838). [Sold]

The rarest of the Kelley items. The above is one of the three or four copies located. Kelley states at p. 16: "The churches of all religious orders in our country were generally informed in the years 1831-2 that the visionary man Hall J. Kelley was determined to respond to the call of Indians living in all parts of Oregon Territory, and raising their voices to Heaven, the "Madman" published, in religious journals of those years, accounts of the peaceable disposition of the Indians and their desire for the word of Life".

683 [KELLEY, HALL J.] This certifies that has paid Twenty Dollars to the American Society for Encouraging the Settlement of the Oregon Territory, and as a Pldege for the faithful performance of obligations, between him and the said Sciety. Broadside 8½ x 7½). N. p. 1831. $15.00

This should accompany all copies of the "General Circular," as the two were issued together.

684 [KELLEY, HALL J.] History of the town of Palmer, early known as the "Elbow Tract," including Records of the Plantation District and Town, 1716-1889. With a genealogical register. By J. H. Temple. Ports. and folding maps, etc. Clo., 5¾ x 9. Palmer, 1889. $15.00

Much in regard to Hall J. Kelley's early life and ancestry.

685 KELLY, HALL J. Hall Jackson Kelley, Prophet of Oregon. By Fred Wilbur Powell. 185 pp., 8vo, original printed wrappers. Portland, 1917. $22.50

Smith 3207. This is one of the rare separate publications of Powell's work on Kelley. Only a few copies were privately printed by the author.

686 KELLEY, JOSEPH. Thirteen Years in the Oregon Penitentiary. 142 pp., 8vo, original wrappers. Portland, 1908. $6.00

Smith 2016.

687 KELLEY, FANNY. Narrative of My Captivity among the Sioux Indians. 8vo, cloth. Cincinnati, 1871. $5.00

688 KELLEY, WILLIAM. An Excursion to California over the Prairie, Rocky Mountains, and great Sierra Nevada, &c. 2 vols., 8vo, cloth. London, 1851. $22.50

689 KELLEY, LUTHER S. "Yellowstone Kelley". The Memoirs of Luther S. Kelley. Edtied by Milo S. Quaife. With a foreword by Gen. Nelson A. Miles. 350 pp., map, illus. 8vo, cloth. New Haven, 190 $5.00

At the close of the Civil War Kelley was sent with his regiment to the Dakota frontier. 1868 he took up the life of a hunter, trapper and explorer on the Upper Missouri and Yellowstone Rivers. His intimate acquaintance with the Indians led to his appointment as Chief of Scouts by Gen. Miles during the Yellowstone River campaigns.

690 KELLEY, WM. D. The New Northwest: an Address on the Northern Pacific Railway. 32 pp., 8vo, wrappers. (Philadelphia, 1871). $4.00

Keley had been a convert and friend of Asa Whitney and had arranged Whitney's first public address at the Chinese Museum, in Philadelphia, on Dec. 23, 1846. He gives much early transcontinental road history, and tells of his own active part in it for 25 years. His predictions regarding the Northern Pacific and the Northwest and of a great metropolis on Puget Sound (which region he had visited and studied) are remarkable.

691 KELLOG, GEORGE ALBETT. A History of Whitby's Island. pp. 108. 8vo, cloth. 1934. $7.50

692 KELLEY, CHAS. Salt Desert Trails. A History of the Hastings Cut-Off and other Early Trails which Crossed the Great Salt Desert seeking a Shorter Road to California. 181 pp., 8vo, cloth. Salt Lake, 1930. $3.75

Valuable contribution to the history of the trail and is essential to both student and Collector. The Smith, Hastings, Bartleson, Fremont, Russell, Harlan and Donner overland parties receive careful factual documentation in this important study.

693 KELLY, WM. A Stroll through the Diggings of California. 240 pp., 12mo, original boards. uncut. London, 1852. $7.50

694 KELLY, FANNY. Narrative of My Captivity among the Sioux Indians. 12mo, cloth. Chicago, 1881. $4.50

695 KELSEY [D.] Pioner Heroes and Their Deeds. The lives and exploits of De Sota, Champlain, Smith, Boone, Kenton, Brady, Crockett, Bowie, Houston, Carson, Harney, Custer, Calif. Joe, Wild Bill, Buffalo Bill, Niles, Crook, and other explorers and frontier fighters. 578 pp. Plates, 8vo, cloth. St. Louis, 1884. $6.00

696 KELSEY, HENRY. Journal of Henry Kelsey (1691-1692). Edited by C. N. Bell. 43 pp., maps. 8vo, cloth. Winnipeg, 1928. $7.50

Now scarce. The work was issued by the Historical and Scientific Society of Manitoba.

697 [KELSEY PAPERS, THE.] With an Introduction by Arthur G. Doughty, Keeper of the Public Records, and Chester Martin, Head of the Department of History, University of Manitoba. Published by the Public Archives of Canada and The Public Record Office of Northern Ireland. 4to, cloth, 128 pp., map. Ottawa, 1929. $27.50

Kelsey left Fort York on June 12, 1690 for an inland trip towards the Sasketchewan River, being the first white man to reach the Canadian prairies. The work was published in a small edition in 1929 and has long been out of print.

698 KEMP, R. H. A Half-Breed Dance and other Far Western Stories; Mining Camp, Indian and Hudson's Bay Tales based on personal experiences of the Author. With illustrations. 135 pp., 8vo, original printed wrappers. Spokane (1909). $15.00

Fine copy in the original wrappers of this extremely scarce work on frontier and Indian life.

699 KENDERDINE, T. S. A California Tramp and Later Footprints; or, Life on the Plains and in the Golden State Thirty Years Ago. Illus. with 39 views, 416 pp., 8vo, cloth. Newtown, Pa., 1888. $12.50

Cowan p. 130. The author enlisted with Russell, Majors and Waddell as an ox-driver and drove train across the plains to Salt Lake, supplying the army during the Mormon Rebellion. From Salt Lake, in company with a party of Mormon freighters, he made the trip to California, going by way of the Great Sandy Desert to San Pedro, thence northward to the settled communities, where he made a considerable stay. This narrative is one of the few which portray in detail the unsavory side of life as a member of one of the great freighting trains en route westward, and of the make-up of such train, the members of which, as Kenderline puts it, were "jailbirds, desperadoes, petty thieves and a few semi-respectable fellows".

700 KENNAN, G. Tent Life in Siberia; with Adventures among the Koraks and other Tribes in Kamtschatka and the Northwest Coast. 12mo, 425 pp. Folding Map. N. Y., 1871. $10.00

701 KENNAN, GEORGE. E. H. Harriman, a Biography. 2 vols., 8vo, cloth. N. Y., 1922. $3.50

Valuable in regard to western railways.

702 KENNEDY, ELIJAH R. The Contest for California in 1861. How Colonel E. D. Baker saved the Pacific States to the Union. 361 pp., 8vo, cloth. N. Y., 1912. $5.00

703 KENNEDY, G. W. The Pioneer Camp-Fire in Four Parts. With the Emigrants on the Great Plains, with the Settlers in the Log Cabin Homes, with the Hunters and Miners. With the Preachers on the Trail, at Camp meetings, and the Log Cabins Anecdotes; Adventures and Reminiscenses by G. W. Kennedy, Pioneer of 1853. 252 pp., 8vo, cloth. Portland, 1913. $10.00

Smith 2023.

704 KENT, ROCKWELL. Wilderness. A Journal of Quiet Adventure in Alaska. 4to, cloth. New York, 1920. $7.50

705 KERCHEVAL [SAMUEL], AND DODDRIDGE, DR. JOSEPH. History of the Valley of Virginia. 486 pp., 12mo, calf. Winchester, 1833. $45.00

Original Edition. An invaluable work on the early history and Indian Wars of the Middle West, with numerous relations of Indian captivities and pioneer hardships. This first edition has material suppressed in later ones, and also contains, under separate ttile page, "Notes on the Settlement and Indian Wars of the Western Parts of Virginia and Pennsylvania-1763-83- by the Rev. Dr. Joseph Doddridge."

706 KERCHEVAL, SAMUEL. A History of the Valley of Virginia. 8vo, contemporary calf. Woodstock, Va., 1850. $12.50

The second edition, which contains a chapter on the Revolution and material on Indian wars that were not in the first edition.

707 KERR, J. B. Biographical Dictionary of Well-Known British Columbians. With a Historical Sketch. 362 pp. 42 ports. Vancouver, 1890. $12.50

Smith 2026, Scarce.

708 KERR, JOHN LEEDS. The Story of a Western Pioneer. The Missouri Pacific, a pioneer railroad in the State of Missouri nearly achieved the distinction of being the first Pacific Railroad, etc. 50 pp., 8vo, cloth. New York, 1928. $7.50

Out of print and scarce.

708a KERR, JOHN. History of Western Railroads. From Railroad and Marine News. Small 4to, 66 pp., unbound. ["Railroad and Marine News," July, 1924-Nov., 1925.] [Seattle, 1924-5.] $12.50

The above is the Author's Clipping, with his commendations and added material which he had prepared for a separate publication in book form.

709 KEYES, GEN. E. D. Fifty Years' Observation of Men and Events, Civil and Military. 515 pp., 12mo, cloth. New York, 1884. $12.50

An important narrative by a 49'er, giving a first-hand account of the early days; the great fire in San Francisco; the Vigilance Committee; Expedition to the San Joaquin Indians; Indian Campaigns on the Coast; Expedition to Fort Vancouver; Steptoe's disaster in Washington Territory; the march to Walla Walla; Coeur d'Alene; Col. Wright's Campaign; California Society of the '50s and '60s—The Parrotts, McAllisters, Thorntons, Lakes, McKinstrys, Gwins, Bowie, Lows, Zanes, and others.

710 KINCAID, HARRISON R. Political and Official History and Register of Oregon. 250 pp., 8vo, calf. N. p., N. d., (1899). $7.50

The author was Secretary of State of Oregon. Gives the lists of various state officials from the earliest time, with brief biographies of mose of them.

711 LIEUT. KING'S NARRATIVE OF THE SIOUX WAR OF 1876. KING, CAPT. CHAS., U. S. A. The Fifth Cavalry in the Sioux War of 1876. Campaigning with Crook. 134 pp., 8vo, original printed wrappers (front wrapper gone). Milwaukee: Sentinel Print, 1880. $55.00

The Original Edition, of which the author says in the preface to the 1890 reprint: "Only enough were printed to reach the few comrades who rode the grim circuit of the 'Bad Lands' in the eventful year, and the edition was long ago exhausted." The Author was first lieutenant of the Fifth Cavalry, and served throughout the Big Horn and Yellowstone Expedition of 1876. The resulting journal is one of the most interesting narratives of Indian warfare in the Wyoming and Dakota country which has ever been written. The company left Laramie on the 22nd of June on an expedition to cut off the Indians on the South Cheyene line. On the 7th of July a courier reached them with the news of the annihilaiton of General Custer and his five favorite companies of the Seventh Cavalry. The Fifth, with nothing but the clothes they wore, and without supply wagons, started in pursuit of the Savages, trailing and fighting them through nearly a thousand miles of country in a period of ten weeks, halting only at the head of Heart River, when the last ration was gone and they were destitute of everything except pluck.

712 KING, CHARLES. Campaigning with Crook. Stories of Army Life. 295 pp., 8vo, cloth, illus. N. Y., 1890. $2.50

713 KING, CLARENCE. Mountaineering in the Sierra Nevada. 308 pp., map. 12mo, cloth. Boston, 1874. $3.00

714 KING, RICHARD. Narrative of a Journey to the Shores of the Atlantic Ocean in 1833-5. Under the Command of Captain Back. 2 vols., contemporary calf, plates. London, 1836. $22.50

The author was surgeon and naturalist to the Expedition. His narrative is filled with details and descriptions of the Chippeway, Cree, Dog Rib, and Esquimaux Indians. Chapter 12 is entirely taken up with an examination and relation of the condition of the Indian Tribes inhabiting the Hudson's Bay Territores. See Field's "Indian Bibliography" for a long note on this most interesting work.

715 KINGSTON, W. Adventures in the Far West. Crossing the Plains to California. 231 pp., 12mo, original wrappers. London, n. d. $4.50

716 KINGSTON, W. H. G. Adventures among the Indians. 252 pp., 8vo, cloth. Chicago, 1889. $4.50

717 KINGSTON, W. H. G. The Frontier Forts. 160 pp., 8vo, cloth. London, n. d. $4.50

718 KINNEAR, GEORGE. Anti-Chinese Riots at Seattle, Washington, February 8th, 1886. 16 pp., 8vo, original wrappers. Seattle, 1911. $12.50

This is the history of the riots by the Captain of the Home Guard on duty at the time. It was privately printed and is now scarce.

719 KINO, FATHER EUSEBIO F., S. J. Historical Memoir of Pimeria Alta. A Contemporary Account of the beginning of California, Sonora and Arizona; by Father Kino, pioner missionary, explorer, cartographer and ranchman, 1683-1711. Translated, edited and annotated by Dr. H. E. Bolton, Professor of American History, University of California. With extensive historical introduction, bibliography, analytical index, plates, facsimiles of rare early maps, plans, etc., and a new carefully prepared colored folding maps. 2 vols., 8vo, cloth. Cleveland, 1919. $50.00

The publication for the first time of Kino's long lost history. This historical memoir is virtually a history of the entire southwest and of the Indian tribes for the period covered. It is the source for practically all that has never been known before of the southwest.

720 KINZIE, MRS. JOHN H. Wau Baun, the Early Day in the North West. Illus. 8vo, cloth. N. Y., 1856. $12.50

Fine tall copy of the original edition

721 KIP, LAWRENCE. Army Life on the Pacific; a Journal of the Expeditin against the Northern Indians, the Tribes of the Coeur d'Alenes, Spokans, and Pelouzes, in the Summer of 1858. 12mo, cloth. N. Y., 1859. $7.50

Life at Forts Dalles, Walla Walla, Taylor, and at the Coeur d'Alene, Spokan, and Pelouze Council. The author took part in the battles of Four Lakes and Spokan Plains.

722 KIP, LAWRENCE. Indian Council at Walla Walla, May and June, 1855; A Journal. 28 pp., 8vo. Eugene, Oregon, 1897. $15.00

Sources of the History of Oregon, V. 1, part 2.

723 KIP, W. I. Early Jesuit Missions in North America, compiled and translated from letters of French Jesuits with annotations and the scarce folded map. First Ed. 12mo, original cloth. N. Y., 1846. $10.00

"An exceedingly valuable collection of early historical documents, which is now scarce. It includes Father Rasles' Wanderings (1689-1714); Catherine, the Iroquois (1656-1715); Montcalm's Expedition, 1757; Marest's Journeys through Illinois and Michigan, 1712; Voyage up the Mississippi, 1727; Mission in Arkansas, 1727; Mission in Illinois, 1750; the Natchez massacre, 1729, etc.

724 KIPPIS, A. A Narrative of the Voyage Round the World performed by Captain James Cook. 424 pp., 8vo, cloth. Phila., N. d. $3.75

725 KIRBY, W. W. A Journey to the Youcan, Russian America. Smithsonian Report. 4to, wrappers. Washington, 1864. $7.50

726 KIRCHOFF, THEODOR. Resiebilder und Skizzen aus Amerika Von Theodor Kirchoff (in San Francisco). 2 vols., original wrappers, 440 and 426 pp. Altoona and New York, 1875-76. [Sold]

Overland in 1867 from Texas to Oregon; Idaho gold rush; California to Oregon in 1865, etc. Mr. Kirchoff was for many years a journalist of San Francisco and one of the best known in the German colony.

727 KIRK, ROBERT C. Twelve Months in the Klondike. 273 pp., illus. 8vo, cloth. London, 1899. $5.00

728 KIRKPATRICK, J. M. The Heroes of Battle Rock: Narrative of the Desperate Encounter of Nine White Men with Three Hundred Indians. Miraculous Escape after Untold Hardships. How a small cannon done its work. The Savages subdued and Rich Gold Mines Discovered. Edited by Orvill Dodge. 8vo, original printed wrappers. N. p., 1904. $5.00

An interesting and valuable historical contribution. Kirkpatrick, a companion of Kit Carson, Joe Meek and other noted plainsmen, here tells the story of the expedition to Port Orford in 1851. Hon. Butler King and Capt. Tichenor of California were the projectors of the enterprise, the details and leadership of which were left to Kirkpatrick. The party was ambushed by the Siwash and Rogue River Indians near Elk River and withstood numerous savage attacks, culminated in a dash for liberty, the details of which are here told.

729 KISER, F. H. Pacific Coast Pictures. 8vo, cloth. Portland, N. d. $4.00

730 KITCHIN, E. A. Distributional Check-List of the Birds of the State of Washington. 28 pp., 8vo, original wrappers. Seattle, 1934. $4.00

731 KITTINGER, CHAS. M. (publisher). Seattle. Plates. 8vo, cloth. Seattle: Kittinger, N. d. $4.50

732 KITTO, F. H. The Peace River District of Canada. Its Resources and Opportuniites. 52 pp., folding map. 8vo, original wrappers. 1920. $4.50

733 [KLONDYKE GOLD.] Miners' New Publishing Company. All about the Klondyke Gold Mines. "Millions in Them". The complete story to date told by those who have been there. How to reach the Mines, etc. 59 pp., 8vo, original wrappers. New York, (1897). $12.50

734 KLOTZ, OTTO. History of the Forty-Ninth Parallel Survey west of the Rocky Mountains. Reprinted from the Geographical Review, V. 3, No. 5, May, 1917. 8vo, wrappers. 1917. $7.50

Smith 2058 locates one copy.

735 KNOWER, DANIEL. The Adventures of a Forty-Niner. An Historic Description of California, with Events and Ideas of San Francisco and its People in those Early Days. Portrait and Plates. 200 pp., 12mo, cloth. Albany, 1894. $10.00

The author was a porminent '49er and went to California with Judge Terry. His memoirs form an essential contribution to the literature of the period.

736 KOHL, JOHANN GEORG. Asia and America; an historical disquisition concerning the ideas which former geographers had about the geographical relation and connection of the old world and the new. 57 pp., illus., maps. Vol. 1, new series, part 2, Procedings of the American Antiquarian Society, Oct., 1911. 8vo, cloth. 1911. $15.00

737 KOLB, E. L. Through the Grand Canyon from Wyoming to Mexico. With a foreword by Owen Wister, with 72 plates from photographs by the author and his brother. 8vo, cloth. N. Y., 1914. $4.75

738 KOTZEBUE, OTTO VON. A Voyage of Discovery into the South Sea and Bering's Straits, for the purpose of Exploring a North East Passage, undertaken in 1815-18, at the expense of His Highness the Chancellor of the Empire, Count Romanzoff, in the ship Rurick, under the command of the Lieutenant in the Russian Imperial Navy. 3 vols., 8vo, original boards, uncut. London, 1821. $65.00

Fine set. This extremely scarce work on the history of the North West Coast of America, including Russian America, contains a long preface by Krusenstern, and is deservedly recognised as one of the most important contributions to this subject. The author has much to say about California. The colored plates are in aquatints.

739 KOTZEBUE, OTTO VON. Entdeckungs-Reise in die Sud See und der Bering's Strasse zur erforschung einer nord-ostlichen Durchfahrt. Undernommen in den yahren 1815-18, euf dem schiffe Rurick. 3 vols. in one, complete with twenty plates (mostly beautifully colored) and 6 maps. Fine copy, 4to, original boards, uncut. Weimar: 1821. $55.00

The Original Edition, which is in many ways superior to the English translation. The third volume is particularly interesting for the notices in natural history, and also for the comparative vocabulary of the native languages by Dr. Adelbert Von Chamisso. The colored plates of butterflies were not printed in the English edition. Kotzebue was one of Krusenstern's former officers. He was sent out in the ship Rurik for the purpose of exploring the supposed Northeast Passage. Among those accompanying him was Chamisso, Eschscholtz and the artist Choris.

740 KOTZEBUE, OTTO VON. New Voyage round the World in the Years 1823, 24, 25 and 26. 2 vols., port., plate, 3 maps. 8vo, calf. London, 1830. $17.50

741 KOTZEBUE, OTTO VON. Neue Reise um die Welt, in den Jahren 1823-26. 2 vols. in one. Maps and plates. Royal 8vo, original cloth, uncut. Weimar, 1830. $17.50

During the voyage Kotzebue visited Brazil, Chili, Kamtschatka, the new Russian settlement at Ross, the Sandwich Islands and the Philippines, Tahiti, etc. It contains interesting accounts of these places and their inhabitants.

742 [KRASHENINIKOV, STEPHEN] and STELLER (GEORGE W.). The History of Kamtschatka and the Kurilski Islands. Translated by Dr. James Grieve. 2 large folding maps by Thos. Jefferys and 4 plates. 4to, sprinkled calf. Glocester, 1764. $17.50

Rare. Chapter 4 "Of America," Steller, the naturalist of Behring's Expedition in devoted to the natives, soil, production, etc., of Alaska. An early source book of our Northwest possessions.

743 KRACHENINNIKOV, STEPHEN PETROVICH. Histoire et Description du Kamtchatka Contenant les Moeurs, la Geographie du Kamtchatka, les Avantages et les desavantage du Kamtchatka, la reduction du Kamtchatka. 2 folding maps and 7 plates. 2 vols., 12mo, calf. Lyons, 1767. $17.50

Not in Smith. See his No. 2074. This work relates to Russian America, unabridged, translated from the original, which also was the source of Grieve's Kamtchatka, an acknowledged abridgement from the Russian.

744 KRAUSE, AUREL. Tlinkit-Indianer; ergebnisse einer reise nach der Nordwestkuste von Amerika und der Beringstrasse. augefuhrt im auftrage der Bremer geographischen gesellschaft in den jahr 1880-1881 durch die Doctoren Arthur and Aurel Krause; geschildert von Dr. Aurel Krause. 420 pp., illus., map. 8vo, cloth. Jena, 1885. $17.50

745 KRESS, BRIG. GEN. JOHN ALEXANDER. Memoirs. 51 pp., frontis. 8vo, original printed wrappers. N.p., N.d. $15.00

Scarce, privately printed work. Contains much on the early local history and Indian wars of Washington. Gen. Kress was stationed at Fort Vancouver in 1871.

746 KRMPOTIC, MSGR. M.D. Life and Works of the Reverend Ferdinand Konscak, S. J., 1703-1759. An early missionary in California. Maps and plates. 12mo, cloth. Boston, 1923. $7.50

Fine source book, the contents of which include not only Father Konscak's diary, but an account of his exploration from Loretto up along the Colorado River.

KRUSENSTERN'S VOYAGE IN ORIGINAL RUSSIAN, WITH THE ATLAS

747 KRUSENSTERN, ADAM JOHAN VON. Puteschestvie Vokrug Svieta v. 1803-6 . . . (Title in Russian). Voyage Round the World, 1803-1806, in the "Nadeshda' and "Neva." 3 vols., 4to, calf. Atlas, 1 volume folio, containing 105 plates and maps. St. Petersburg, 1809-12. $500.00

The famous expedition under the command of Capt. Krusenstern, by order of his Imperial Russian Majesty, Alexander I, sailed from Kronstadt on the 7th of August, 1803, and after touching at Falmouth, the Canaries and Brazil, and rounding Terra del Fuego, reached the Washington Islands, whence on May 18th, 1804, they set sail for Kamtschatka. It afterwards visited Japan, explored the Japanese Sea, returned to Kamtschatka, explored the coast of Sachalin and returned to Russia via China and the Straits of Sunda.

748 KRUSENSTERN, ADAM JOHANN VON. Reise um die Welt in den Jahren 1803-4-5 and 6 auf befehl seiner Kaiserl Majestat Alexanders des Erstein auf den Schiffen Nodeshda und Newa. 16mo, 2 vols. in 3, original wrappers, plates and folding map. Berlin: Haude, 1811, 1812. $30.00

749 KRUSENSTERN, CAPT. A. J. VON. A Voyage Round the World in the Years 1803-1806, by the order of his Imperial Majesty, Alexander the First, on board the ships "Nadeshda" and "Neva." 404 pp., maps and colored plates. 4to, contemporary calf. London, 1813. $75.00

750 KRUSENSTERN. Voyage autour du monde de 1803 a 1806 sur la Nadiejeda et la Neva. Translated par J. B. B. Eyries. 2 vols. and folio Atlas with 9 maps and 21 plates (size 12 by 18 inches). Calf. Paris, 1821. $62.50

An exceptionally fine copy of this rare work from the library of Empress Marie Louise of France, with her Royal insignia stamped on the bindings.

751 KRUSENSTERN, ADAM J. VON. Beytrage zur hydrographic der grossern ozeane als erlauterungen zu einer charte des ganzen erdkreises nach Mercator's Projection, von J. von Krusenstern. 4to, full morocco, large folding map. Leipzig, 1819. $52.50

Wickersham 1759. Fine copy from the Czar's Library.

Item 749, Should read, 2 vols in one. 314, 404 pp.

752 KRUSENSTERN, ADAM J. VON. (Memoirs Hydrographic for Services and Analysis and Explanation of Krusenstern's Atlas of the Pacific Ocean). Title and Text in Russian. Two large 4to vols. and a Supplement to the two vols. in original wrappers. 3 vols., 4to. St. Petersburg, 1823 and 1826. $125.00

Wickersham does not describe this work.

753 LADUE, JOSEPH. Klondyke Facts; being a complete Guide Book to the Great Gold Regions of the Northwest Territories. 205 pp., 4 maps, 3 plates. 8vo, original wrappers. N. Y.: American Technical Book Co., (1897). $12.50

Ladue was a pioneer in Alaska and the founder of Dawson.

754 LADUE, JOSEPH. Klondyke Nuggets. 97 pp., 8vo, original wrappers. N. Y., (1897). $7.50

755 LA FLECHE, RICHER. Lettre de M. Richer Lafleche, Missionaire a un e ses amis. (In "Rapport sur les Missions du Diocese de (Quebec,1853), No. 10. 8vo, original wrappers. Quebec, 1853. $17.50

Wagner-Camp 234.

756 LAGUNA, FREDERICA DE. The Archaeology of Cook Inlet, Alaska. 263 pp., 72 plates. 8vo, cloth. Phila., 1934. $10.00

757 LAJACQ, J. M. J. Missions du Pacifique. Part 1. Missionaires Oblat de Mari Immaculate. Part 1 and Part 2. 8vo, cloth. Paris, 1867-1870. $12.50

758 LA MADELENE, HENDY DE. Le Comte Gaston de Raousset Boulbon, sa vie et ses Aventures. 161 pp., 8vo, half morocco. Alencon, 1856. $37.50

Original edition. Presentation copy from the author. Relates the adventures of Count Gaston de Raousset in California and Sonora during the Gold-rush days.

759 LAMB, JOHN. The Seattle Municipal Water Plant. Historical, Descriptive, Statistical. 316 pp., maps, illus. (Seattle), 1914. $7.50

Smith 3558.

760 LAMBOURNE, A. The Pioneer Trail: (Scenes and Incidents of the Westward March of the Mormons from the Boarders of Civilization to the Great American Desert. By one who crossed the plains in '46). Portrait, early views, "Start from Missouri,' "Camp at Scott's Bluff," "Laramie Peak," "Green River Ford," the "Valley," etc. 78 pp., 8vo, cloth. Salt Lake: Privately Printed, 1913. $7.50

761 LAMBOURNE, ALFRED. The Old Journey. Reminiscences of Pioneer Days. 53 pp., 18 plates. 12mo, cloth. Salt Lake, 1897. $10.00

Thomas No. 171. Scenes and incidents of the westward march of the Mormons to the Great American Desert. Printed for presentation to a few surviving pioneers in celebration of the anniversary of their famous overland trek.

762 LAMSON, J. Round Cape Horn. Voyage of the Passenger Ship James W. Paige, from Maine to California in the Year 1852. 12mo, half cloth and boards. 156 pp. Bangor, 1878. $7.50

763 LANCASTER, SAMUEL CHRISTOPHER. The Columbia, America's great Highway through the Cascade Mountains to the Sea. 140 pp., frontis., colored plates, map. 8vo, cloth. Portland, 1915. $7.50

764 LANDES, HENRY. Preliminary Report on the Underground Waters of Washington. 96 pp., 8vo, cloth. Washington, 1905. $5.00

765 LANDMAN, COLONEL. Adventures and Recollections. 2 vols., 12mo, new cloth. London, 1852. $37.50

Col. Landman, of the Royal Engineers, was in Montreal in 1797, and mentions meeting Alexander Mackenzie, William McGillevry, Mr. McTavish, Mr. Frobisher, etc., of the Northwest Fur Co. The author gives an intimate picture of social conditions, the drinking bouts of the partners in the fur company, etc. Not in Smith.

766 LANE, JOSEPH. Remarks of Hon. Jos. Lane of Oregon on Indian War in Oregon. 8vo. Washington, 1856. $7.50

767 LANE, JOSEPH. Speech of Hon. Joseph Lane of Oregon on the Suppression of Indian Hostilities in Oregon. 8 pp., 8vo. Washington, 1856. $7.50

Not in Smith.

768 LANE, JOSEPH. The Admission of Oregon. The Serenades—The Response. 16 pp., 8vo. N.p., N.d. (Portland, 1859). $15.00

Not in Smith. "The admission of another state into the Union caused much enthusiasm on Saturday evening; and when the event became known throughout the city, it was determined to celebrate."

769 LANE, JOSEPH. Remarks of Joseph Lane in the Senate of the U. S., Dec. 19, 1859. 8 pp., 8vo. (Washington, 1859). $4.00

770 LANG, HERBERT O. (ed.). History of the Willamette Valley; being a description of the Valley and its Resources, with an account of its discovery and settlement by white men and its subsequent history; together with personal reminiscences of its early pioneers. Ports, plate, facsms., tab. 8 vo, cloth. Portland: Himes, 1885. $17.50

771 LANGELIER, J. C. Etude sur les Territoires du Nord-Ouest du Canada. 69 pp., 8vo, sewn. Montreal, 1873. $7.50

Early explorations, geography, forests, rivers and navigation, etc.

772 LANGELIER, J. C. Le Bassin Meridional de la Baie D'Hudson. 104 pp. and table of contents. Royal 8vo, original printed wrappers. Quebec, 1887. $7.50

Langelier's monograph is a careful discussion of the great tributary basin; of its character; its future immense economic possibilities; and the necessity for an adequate transportation system.

773 LANGEVIN, L'HON. H. L. Colombie Britannique Rapport. 244 pp., 8vo, cloth. Ottawa, 1872. $15.00

Smith 2100.

774 LANGEVIN, H. L. British Columbia; Report of the Hon. H. L. Lengevin, Minister of Public Works. 246 pp., 8vo, cloth. Ottawa, 1872. $20.00

Smith 2100 locates 2 copies. Pages 61-82 contain a Dictionary of the Chinook Jargon.

775 LANGFORD, NATHANIEL PITT. Vigilante Days and Ways, the Pioneers of the Rockies, the Makers and Making of Montana, Idaho, Oregon, Washington and Wyoming. 2 vols. Portraits, plates, 426, 485 pp., 12mo, cloth. Boston, 1890. $20.00

Original edition. Contains much valuable frontier history of places and singular characters that made them.

776 LANGFORD, NATHANIEL PITT. Diary of the Washburn Expedition to the Yellowstone and Freehole rivers in the year 1870. 122 pp., illus. |N.p., N.d. (Privately printed). $15.00

Transcript of the original journal of this adventurous expedition through the unexplored regions of Montana.

777 LANGSDORFF, G. H. VON. Bemerkungen auf einer Reise um die Welt in den Jahren, 1803-07. 2 vols., 4to, half calf, complete with the portraits of Langsdorff and Krusenstern, and 43 plates. Frankfort, 1812. $67.50

The rare original edition. Smith 2105. The author was naturalist to Krusenstern's expedition, which was sent out by Czar Alexander I, and which reached Alaska on May 18, 1804. Bancroft states that Langsdorff's account is more reliable than that of Krusenstern.

As a naturalist, Langsdorff's account is of importance for its scientific discoveries relating to the Aleutian Islands. It also contains much information concerning the fur trade, Russian voyages, and most particularly the Russian-American company. The work also gives a full account of Sitka and the settlement of San Francisco.

778 LANGSDORFF, G. H. VON. Voyages and Travels in Various Parts of the World during the years 1803-7. 2 vols. in one. Portrait, map and plates. 4to, ¾ morocco. Fine copy. London, 1813-14. $75.00

First English translation.

779 LANGWORTHY, FRANKLIN. Scenery of the Plains, Mountains and Mines; or, A Diary kept upon the Overland Route to California, by way of the Great Salt Lake; Travels in the Cities, Mines and Agricultural Districts —Embracing the Return by the Pacific Ocean and Central America, in the years 1850-51-52 and 53. 12mo, cloth. Ogdensburg, 1855. $47.50

Wagner-Camp 358, Braislin 1121. Left home April 1, 1850, crossed Iowa to Kanesville; left the Missouri May 15, and travelled via the Platte, Ft. Laramie, Salt Lake. After a short stay there, left Aug. 29, via the Humboldt and Carson Valley, near Weaverville. Diary occupies pages 7-180. Balance of book is devoted to a description of California and life there, and the return trip.

780 LANMAN, CHAS. Haw-Ho-Noo; records of a tourist. 8vo, new cloth, uncut. Phila., 1850. $15.00

781 LANMAN, JAMES H. History of Michigan; complete with the folding map. 8vo, cloth. N. Y., 1839. $12.50

Presentation copy from the author.

782 LARPENTEUR, CHARLES. Forty Years a Fur Trader on the Upper Missouri: the Personal Narrative of Charles Larpenteur, 1833-1872. Edited with many critical notes by Elliott Coues. 2 vols., maps, ports. and plates. Cloth, uncut. N. Y., 1899. $17.50

Much of the great rival fur companies at various ports on the upper Missouri and Yellowstone, as well as much of absorbing interest about the Sioux, Crows, Blackfeet, Assiniboines, Araphoes, and other tribes.

RARE OFFICIAL EDITION WITH FOLIO ATLAS

783 LA PEROUSE, J. F. D. DE. Voyage de La Perouse autour du Monde: Publie conformement au decret du 22 Avril, 1791 et redige par M. L. A. Milet-Mureau. 4 vols. and folio Atlas. 4to and folio, full calf. Paris, (1797). $125.00

Original Edition complete with all the 69 plates, 30 of which are folding maps. (San Blas, San Diego, Monterey, San Francisco, Nootka, etc.).

The narrative of this enterprising but ill-fated expedition is full of absorbing interest. La Perouse siailed from France in 1785 to the Pacific and Northwest coast of America. The present account of the voyage was transmitted by Perouse from Botany Bay, after leaving which place he was never heard of again. His fate, and that of the vessels and their crews, has never to this day been satisfactorily cleared up. The work is of prime importance for the history of geographical discovery on the N.W. coast, Perouse having sailed from Alaska as far down as Monterey. Especially valuable are his descriptions of the peculiarities he observed in the natives in that part of the American continent. Such a fine complete set as the above is seldom offered, as nearly all copies found lack chart No. 1 or are otherwise imperfect.

784 LA PEROUSE, J. F. G. DE. A Voyage Round the World in the Years 1785-8. 3 vols., 8vo, ¾ calf and folio Atlas, original boards. London, 1799. $50.00

The Atlas to the above is the only complete one in English as it contains all the original plates that are in the original French edition.

785 LA PEROUSE, J. F. G. DE. Relation du Voyage a la Recherche de la Perouse fait par ordre de l'Assemblee Constituante pendant les annees 1791, 1792, etc. 2 vols., 4to, original wrappers (worn) and folio Atlas in half leather. With 44 plates and maps. Paris, Jansen, An VIII (1800). $65.00

Original edition of this important voyage by Labillardiere.

785a LA PEROUSE, J. F. G. DE. Viaggio de la Perouse intoro al Mondo Tradotto. 4 vols., 12mo, colored plates. Milano, 1815. $22.50

786 LAPHAM, MACY H. Soil Survey of Franklin County, Washington. 101 pp., plates, maps. 8vo, half morocco. Washington, 1917. $4.00

787 LAROCQUE, F. Journal of Rarocque from the Assiniboine to the Yellowstone, 1805. (Day-by-day Journal and Personal Narrative, with Observations on the Indians, etc.). Edited, with notes, by L. J. Burpee. 82 pp., 8vo, ¾ calf. Ottawa, 1910. $22.50

An important source which ranks among the classics of the fur trade. The work is especially valuable in that it describes the first visit by white men to the Crow Indians. See Wagner-Camp 7.

Item 783, The initials sould read J. F. G. de la Perouse.

788 LATHAM, ROBERT G. The Ethnography of Russian America. From the Journal of the Ethnological Society of London. Vol. 1, pp. 182-191. 8vo. London, 1848. $7.50

See Smith 2120.

789 LATHAM, ROBERT G. The Languages of the Oregon Territory. (Contained in the Journal of the Ethnological Society of London, Vol. 1, pp. 154-166). 8vo. London, 1856. $7.50

790 LATHAM, ROBERT G. Opuscula; Essays chiefly Philological and Ethnographical. 418 pp., 8vo, cloth. London, 1860. $12.50

On the languages of the Oregon Territory by one of the ablest British scholars. Contains a comparative vocabulary of the Shoshonie with other languages, among them the Chinook and Cathlascon, etc.

791 LATOUR, MAJOR A. LACARRIERE. Historical Memoir of the War in West Florida and Louisiana in 1814-1815. Fine portrait of Andrew Jackson and Atlas with 8 maps and charts. 2 vols., 8vo, half calf. Phila., 1816. $50.00

792 LATROBE, CHAS. The Rambler in North America: 1832-1833. Map. 2 vols., 8vo, cloth. London, 1835. $17.50

Wagner-Camp 57. Fine copy of the original edition. Scarce with the map. Latrobe crossed the prairies with Washington Irving. "A much fuller and more entertaining account of this trip with Ellsworth in 1832 than Irving's." Col. Chouteau, Ellsworth, Irving and Count Portales comprised the party. After returning from his trip to the Canadien, Latrobe went down the Arkansas in a canoe and arrived at Little Rock Dec. 9, where he took a steamboat. In 1832 he made an overland journey to Prarie du Chien, thence to St. Peters, Ft. Snelling and back by river to St. Louis.

793 LATTA, R. Reminiscences of Pioneer Life. Portrait and plates. 186 pp., 12mo, cloth. Kansas City, 1912. $10.00

The author trailed up and down the canyons and gulches of the Rockies for more than twenty years, prospecting, working at times for a "grubstake," teaming, lumbering, homesteading, living in cabins, tents and covered wagons. His relation covers the period from 1848 onwards. They tell of early Iowa, of the days of '49, of a trip across the plains, of pioneering sufferings; the Mormons; gold-rush, etc.

794 LAURE, AUGUSTINE (Le Pere). Le Pere Augustine Laure de la Compaginie de Jesus, Missionaire aux Montagnes Rocheuses. 48 pp., original wrappers. Bruxelles, 1895. $20.00

Father Laure joined Father Cataldo in mission work among the Indians of Montana, Idaho and Washington, and this is an account of his work, which was largely devoted to Washington and the various missions there. We can locate no other copy.

795 LAURIDSEN, PETER. Russian Explorations, 1725-1743. Vitus Bering: the Discoverer of Bering Strait. Illus. 12mo, cloth. Chicago, 1889. $12.50

796 LAURIE, THOMAS. Dr. Whitman's Services to Oregon. (Contained in the Missionary Herald, Feb., 1885 and Sept., 1885). 2 vols., 8vo, original printed wrappers. Boston, 1885. $7.50

797 LAUT, AGNES C. Lords of the North. 8vo, cloth. N. Y., 1900. $7.50

798 LAUT, AGNES C. Heralds of Empire; being the story of one Ransom Stanhope, Lieutenant to Pierre Raddison in the Fur Trade. 8vo, cloth. N. Y., 1902. $7.50

799 LAUT, AGNES C. Pathfinders of the West. 380 pp., illus., maps. 8vo, cloth. N. Y., 1904. $5.00

800 LAUT, AGNES C. Vikings of the Pacific, the Adventures of the Explorers who came from the West, eastward. Bering, the Dane; the outlaw hunters of Russia; Benyowsky, the Polish Pirate; Cook and Vancouver, the English Navigators; Gray, of Boston, the discoverer of the Columbia; Drake, Ledyard, and other soldeirs of fortune on the west coast of America. 8vo, illus., maps. N. Y., 1905. $7.50

801 LAUT, AGNES C. Story of the Trapper. 8vo, cloth. N. Y., 1906. $5.00
Valuable work in connection with the N.W. fur trade.

802 LAUT, AGNES C. The Conquest of the Great Northwest; being the Story of the Adventurers of England. 2 vols., 8vo, cloth. N. Y., 1908. $12.50

803 LAUT, AGNES C. The Freebooters of the Wilderness. 8vo, cloth. N. Y., 1910. $7.50

804 LAUT, AGNES C. The "Adventurers of England" on Hudson Bay. A Chronicle of the Fur Trade in the North. 133 pp., 8vo, illus., maps. Toronto, 1914. $6.00

805 LAUT, AGNES C. Pioneers of the Pacific Coast. A Chronicle of Sea Rovers and Fur Hunters. 8vo, illus., maps. Toronto, 1915. $7.50

806 LAUT, AGNES C. A Chronicle of the Gold-Fields of British Columbia. Illus., maps. 8vo, cloth. Toronto, 1916. $7.50

807 LAUT, AGNES C. The Fur Traders of America. Illus. 8vo, cloth. N. Y., 1921. $7.50

808 LAUT, AGNES. The Blazed Trail of the Old Frontier; being the Log of the Upper Missouri Historical Expedition under the auspices of the Governors and Historical Association of Minnesota, North and South Dakota and Montana for 1925. 8vo, cloth. Maps, illus. N. Y., 1926. $7.50

809 LAUT, AGNES C. The Romance of the Rails. 2 vols., 8vo, cloth. N. Y., 1929. $10.00

810 LAUT, AGNES C. The Cariboo Trail. A Chronicle of the Gold-Fields of British Columbia. 116 pp., illus., map. 8vo, cloth. Toronto, 1916. $6.00

811 LA VERENDRYE, PIERRE GAULTIER DE VARENNES, SIEUR DE. Journal of North-West Explorations, 1738-39. (Contained in Report of the Canadian Archives, 1889). 8vo, original printed wrappers. Ottawa, 1889. **$12.50**

Contains this important journal of La Verendrye in French with the English translation on the opposite page.

812 LEA, ST. ALBERT M. Notes on Wisconsin Territory. Map. 16mo, cloth. Phila., 1836. $90.00

One of the rarest items relating to western history.

813 LEACH, A. J. Early Day Stories. The Overland Trail, Animals and Birds that lived there, Hunting Stories, Looking Backward. Illus. 12mo, cloth. N.p., N.d. $5.00

The stories were drawn from personal experiences of the author, during a trip across Nebraska and westward over the mountains to the Pacific in the year 1852, and from a long residence in Nebraska, since May, 1867.

814 (LEAKE, ROBERT M. P.). Piece Work in the Overtime of a Business Man. Printed for Private Circulation. 446 pp., 12mo, cloth. Manchester, 1893. $7.50

A belated suggestion for Britain to fight for the American Northwest.

815 LECLERCQ, FATHER CHRISTIAN. The First Establishment of the Faith in New France. Now first translated with notes by John Gilmary Shea. Illus. and map. 2 vols., 8vo, original wrappers, uncut. N. Y., 1881. $42.50

816 LECOMPTE, LE P. EDOUARD. Les Jesuites du Canada au XIXe Siecle. 1842-1872. 333 pp., 8vo, original wrappers. Montreal, 1920. $6.00

817 LECOMPTE, R. P. Les Missions Modernes de la Compagnie de Jesus au Canada, 1842-1924. 76 pp., illus., 8vo, original printed wrappers. Montreal, 1925. $5.00

818 LEDYARD, JOHN. A Journal of a Voyage to the Pacific Ocean, and in quest of a North-West Passage between Asia and America: Performed in the years 1776-1779; Faithfully Narrated from the Original Manuscript of Mr. John Ledyard. Folding map in photostat. 208 pp., 8vo, calf. Hartford, 1783. $100.00

Braislin 1138. Exceedingly rare. But few copies are known in any condition and most of these lacking a map. Ledyard accompanied Capt. Cook in his last voyage and gives a detailed account of the death of Cook. Historically, the knowledge gained by Ledyard during this voyage on the Northwest Coast and among the Indians at Nootka, etc., showed him the amazing importance of the region, and led to many interviews with Jefferson regarding the country, the necessity of its exploration, prospects of trade and final acquisition by the U. S. Jefferson was so impressed that he agreed with Ledyard's scheme for exploring the great Northwest country. Unfortunately, Ledyard died and twenty years later the explorations were made by Lewis and Clark under Jefferson's auspices. Sabin says of this work: **"The author's narrative is distinguished** by its simplicity and evident authenticity."

819 LEDYARD, JOHN. The Life of John Ledyard, the American Traveller, comprising Selections from his Journals and Correspondence. By Jared Sparks. 8vo, original boards, entirely uncut. Cambridge, 1828. $15.00

820 LEE, CHARLES A. Aleutian Indian and English Dictionary. Common words as spoken by the Oogashik, Egegik, Anangashuk and Misremie Tribes. 23 pp., 12mo, original wrappers. Oogashik, (Seattle), 1896. $7.50

821 LEE, CHARLES H. A Collection of Historical Anecdotes of Early Days in the Valley of the Red River of the North. 76 pp., 8vo, original printed wrappers. Walhalla, N. D., 1899. $42.50

A rare and valuable work, giving an account of the Pembina Country, Selkirk Settlement, etc. The author also gives an account of the arrival at Walhalla, in June, 1853, of Alonzo Barnard, D. B. Spencer and John Smith, all missionaries from Ohio. There is also much local history from that time on. Through an error of the printer page 40 in this work is a blank.

822 LEE, DANIEL, and FROST, J. H. Ten Years in Oregon. 344 pp., map. 8vo, calf. N. Y., 1844. $12.50

823 LEE, JOHN D. Mormonism Unveiled; or, the Life and Confessions of the late Mormon Bishop John D. Lee; Embracing a History of the Horrible Butchery known as the Mountain Meadows Massacre. Portrait and plates. 406 pp., 8vo, cloth (shaken and worn). St. Louis, 1877. $6.50

Original edition. While purporting to have been written by Lee, this work was apparently written by W. W. Bishop while Lee was in prison condemned to death. The work is a simple and honest story of Lee's life, to which has been added an account of the Mountain Meadows Massacre, and of the arrest, trial and execution of Lee.

824 LEEDS, W. H. Manual of the Military Code of the State of Oregon. 269 pp., 8vo, cloth. Salem (Ore.), 1901. $4.75

825 LEEHEY, M. D. Leehey's Mining Code for the use of Miners and Prospectors in Washington and Alaska. With Notes and Annotations. 103 pp., 8vo, original printed wrappers. Seattle, 1900. $10.00

826 LEEPER, DANIEL R. The Argonauts of Forty-Nine: Recollections of the Plains and Diggings. Plates. 8vo, cloth. South Bend, 1894. $27.50

827 LEES, J. A., and CLUTTERBUCK, W. J. B.C. 1887: A Ramble in British Columbia. 387 pp., 18 plates, illus., map. 8vo, cloth. London, 1892. $4.50

828 LEIGHTON, MRS. CAROLINE C. Life at Puget Sound, with sketches of travel in Washington Territory, British Columbia, Oregon and California, 1865-1881. 258 pp., 8vo, cloth. Boston, 1884. $5.00

829 LENOX, E. H. Overland to Oregon: History of the First Emigration to Oregon in 1843. Portrait, maps and plates. 69 pp., 8vo cloth. Oakland: Privately Printed, 1904. $10.00

An important journal bearing autograph of the author. Lenox crossed the plains with Burnett, Whitman, Applegate and others. The appendix gives a complete list of the members of this, the first emigration party to the Columbia River, Nov. 1, 1843.

830 LEONARD, D. L. Metlakahtla, a Marvel Mission. (Contained in Missionary Review of the World, Nov., 1893 and Dec., 1893). 8vo, wrappers. 1893. $4.00

831 LEONARD, JOHN W. The Gold Fields of the Klondike. Fortune Seekers' Guide to the Yukon Region of Alaska and British Columbia. The story as told by Ladue, Berry, Phiscator, and other gold finders. 216 pp., front., illus., folding map. 8vo, cloth. London, (1897). $10.00

Smith 2160 locates one copy.

832 LEONARD, ZENAS. Adventures of Zenas Leonard, Fur Trader and Trapper, 1831-1836. Reprinted from the rare original of 1839. Edited by W. F. Wagner. 317 pp., 8vo, cloth. Cleveland, 1904. $12.50

Personal narrative of adventures and experiences as a member of the Gant and Blackwell Party of 1831, as independent trapper, and as a member of Walker's California Expedition. Leonard's work is one of the most interesting and important records of the early fur trade and overland that has come down to us.

833 LENG, JOHN. America in 1876. Pencillings during a Tour in the Centennial Year, with a chapter on the Aspects of American Life. 8vo, cloth. Dundee, 1877. $12.50

Gives an account of Oregon, British Columbia and the northern section of the U. S.

834 LE PAGE DU PRATZ. Histoire de la Louisane, Contenant la Decouverte de ce vaste Pays; sa Description geographique; un voyage dans les Terres; Histoire Naturelle; les Moeurs, Costumes and Religion des Naturels, avec leurs Origines, etc. 2 maps. Plan of New Orleans and 36 plates. 3 vols., 12mo, calf-backed boards (hinges brken). Paris, 1758. $22.50

835 LESSEPS, M. DE. Travels in Kamtschatka in 1787-88. Maps. 2 vols., 8vo, half calf. London, 1790. $30.00

Not in Smith. The author was interpreter to the Comte de la Perouse and sailed with his ill-fated expedition. Fortunately for him, he left the expedition at St. Peter and St. Paul for the purpose of carrying the Count's despatches to the French government overland through Siberia and Russia. Otherwise he would, in all probability, have shared the same fate as his commander.

836 LEUPP, FRANCIS E. In Red Man's Land; a Study of the American Indian. 161 pp., illus., 8vo, cloth. Chicago, (1914). $3.75

837 LEVER, W. H. Illustrated History of Whitman County, State of Washington. 4to, half calf. 75 portraits, 11 plates. N.p., 1901. $20.00

Smith 2165 located but one copy. This work contains much local history nowhere else available.

838 LEWIS, ALBERT BUELL. Tribes of the Columbia Valley and the Coast of Washington and Oregon. (Contained in Memoirs of the American Anthropological Association, Vol. 1, part 2, pp. 149-209). 8vo, original wrappers. Lancaster, Pa., 1906. $7.50

839 LEWIS, HOWARD T. The Basic Industries of the Pacific Northwest. 174 pp., 8vo, original wrappers. Seattle, (1923). **$4.50**

840 LEWIS, HOWARD T., and MILLER, STEPHEN I. The Economic Resources of the Pacific Northwest. 523 pp., 8vo, cloth. Seattle, 1923. $7.50

841 LEWIS, WILLIAM. Early Days in the Big Bend Country. 35 pp., illus., 8vo, original wrappers. Spokane, 1926. $7.50

Autographed by the author. Only 100 copies were printed.

842 LEWIS, WILLIAM STANLEY. Early Days in the Big Bend Country. 35 pp., illus. No. 17 of 100 copies. Spokane, 1926. $6.50

Autographed by the author.

843 [LEWIS AND CLARK.] Travels into the interior parts of America; communicating Discoveries made in exploiting the Missouri, Red River and Washita. With a Statitstical Account of the Countries adjacent. 8vo, boards. London, 1807. $22.50

Sabin 40826. First English Edition. The book also contains a letter dated April 17, 1805, from Capt. Merriwether Lewis, at Ft Mandan, to Jefferson, reporting the progress of the expedition.

844 [LEWIS AND CLARK.] Travels of Captains Lewis and Clark by order of the Government of the U. S., performed in the years 1804, 1805 and 1806, being upwards of three thousand miles from St. Louis by way of the Missouri and Columbia Rivers to the Pacific Ocean, etc. Folding map and five Indian portraits. 12mo, ¾ calf. Phila.: Hubbard Lester, 1809. $25.00

Braislin 1161, Wagner-Camp 8.

845 [LEWIS AND CLARK.] Travels to the Source of the Missouri River and across the American Continent to the Pacific Ocean. Made by order of the Government of the U. S. in the years 1804-6 by Captains Lewis and Clark. 4to, boards. London: Longmans, 1814. $47.50

Fine copy of the rare First English Edition, and perhaps the most beautiful in typography and mechanical execution of all the editions of Lewis and Clark. It has large margins, clear impressions and otherwise a quite worthy appearance.

846 [LEWIS AND CLARK.] Travels to the scource of the Missouri River and across the American continent to the Pacific Ocean . . . 1804, 1805, 1806 . . . published from the official report. 6 maps. 3 vols., 8vo, ¾ calf. Fine set. London, 1815. $47.50

847 [LEWIS AND CLARK.] Travels to the Scource of the Missouri River, and across the American Continent to the Pacific Ocean. Performed by order of the Government of the U. S. in the years 1804, 1805, and 1806. Published from the Official Report, and Illustrated by a map of the Route and other maps. 3 vols., calf-backed boards. London: Longmans, 1817. $30.00

848 [LEWIS AND CLARK.] History of the Expedition under the command of Lewis and Clark, etc. A New Edition with Copious Critical Commentary, Prepared upon examination of Unpublished Official Archives, the Original Manuscript Journals and Field Notebooks of the Explorers, etc., etc. Edited by Elliott Coues. With new maps, bibliography and complete index. 4 vols., 4to, original vellum-backed boards in original jackets and boxes. N. Y., 1893. $60.00

849 [LEWIS AND CLARK.] In Memoriam: Sergeant Charles Floyd. Report of the Floyd Memorial Association prepared on behalf of the Committee on Publication. By Elliott Coues. Map and facs. 8vo, original wrappers. In a slip-case. Sioux City, 1897. $12.50

850 [LEWIS AND CLARK.] History of the Expedition under the command of Captains Lewis and Clark, to the Sources of the Missouri, thence across the Rocky Mountains and down the River Columbia to the Pacific Ocean; performed during the years 1804, 1805, 1806. 2 vols., 8vo, cloth, folding map. N. Y., Fowle, 1900. $7.50

851 [LEWIS AND CLARK.] Meriwether Lewis and William Clark. 159 pp., 2 portraits, tables. 8vo, cloth. Boston, 1901. $4.75

852 [LEWIS AND CLARK.] History of the Expedition of Captains Lewis and Clark, 1804-5-6; reprinted from the edition of 1814; with introduction and index by James K. Hosmer. 2 portraits, 6 maps and facsimiles. 2 vols., 8vo, boards. Chicago: A. C. McClurg, 1902. $15.00

853 [LEWIS AND CLARK.] History of the Expedition under the Command of Captains Lewis and Clark to the Sources of the Missouri, across the Rocky Mountains, down the Columbia River to the Pacific, 1804-6 . . . 2 portraits, 5 maps, tables. 3 vols., 8vo, cloth. N. Y., New Amsterdam Book Co., 1902. $7.50

854 [LEWIS AND CLARK.] Description of the Original Manuscript Journals and Field Note-Books of Lewis and Clark on which was based Biddle's History of the Expedition of 1804-6, and which are now in possession of the American Philosophical Society in Philadelphia. 8vo, printed wrappers, in a cloth case. Phila., 1893. (Sold)

This is No. 140, Proc. Amer. Philos. Soc., as described by Paltsits in "Bibliographical Data" of L. & C. Exp. in Vol. 1 of "Original Journals," N. Y., Dodd, Mead, 1904.

855 [LEWIS AND CLARK.] Original Journals of, 1804-1806: Printed from the original manuscript in the Library of the American Philosophical Society, with manuscript material from other sources, including notebooks, letters, maps, etc., and the Journals of Chas. Floyd and Jos. Whitehouse, etc. Edited by Dr. Reuben G. Thwaites. With finely executed portraits, views, maps, plans and facsimiles. 8 vols., including the Atlas. 8vo, cloth. N. Y., 1904. $100.00

856 [LEWIS AND CLARK.] Original Journals, 1804-1806, printed from the original Manuscript in the Library of the American Philosophical Society, with Manuscript material from other sources, including notebooks, letters, maps, etc., and journals of Chas. Floyd and Jos. Whitehouse; now for the first time published in full and exactly as written; edited with introduction, notes and index, by Dr. Thwaites. Illus, portraits, views, maps, plans and facsimiles. 15 vols., 4to, original cloth, including the Atlas of maps. N. Y., 1904-5. $150.00

857 [LEWIS AND CLARK.] Laird and Lee. A Glimpse of the Lewis and Clark Exposition. 8vo. Chicago, 1905. $3.75

858 LIENHARD, H. Californien unmittelbar vor und nach der Entdeckung des Goldes. Bilder aus den Leben des Heinrich Lienhard von Bitten, Kanton Glarus in Naurov, Nordamerika. 8v,o cloth. Zurich, 1898. $17.50

The author went to California in 1846 and was employed by Capt. Sutter. He gives a vivid description of California before the discovery of gold. First news of the discovery is described at length, as the author was present when the first gold was brought to Sutter's farm. Especially interesting are the characteristics of Capt. Sutter and his sons. The book was published from a manuscript in the hands of a friend of Lienhard.

859 LINDERMAN, FRANK B. Indian Why Stories. Sparks from War Eagle's Lodge. Illus., 12mo, cloth. N. Y., 1915. $4.50

Myths of the Blackfeet, Chippewa and Cree Tribes.

860 LINDERMAN, FRANK B. Indian Old-Man Stories. More Sparks from War Eagle's Lodge-Fire. Illus., 12mo, cloth. N. Y., 1920. $4.50

861 LINDERMAN, FRANK B. Lige Mounts, Free Trapper. 8vo, cloth. N. Y., 1922. $5.00

Fur trade and trapping on the headwaters of the Missouri.

862 LINDERMAN, FRANK B. The Life Story of a Great Indian. Plenty-Coups of the Crows. 8vo, cloth. N. Y., (1930). $3.50

863 LINDSAY, BATTERMAN. Derelicts of Destiny. 12mo, cloth. N. Y., 1910. $5.00

Smith 2213. An account of the Indians of Puget Sound.

864 LINDSEY, A. L. Sketches of an Excursion to Southern Alaska. 73 pp., original wrappers. N.p. (Portland), N.d. (1880). $15.00

The author made the journey to Alaska in 1879, and his account is replete with information in regard to the natives and the missions. Smith 2216 locates but two copies.

865 LINDSEY, CHARLES. An Investigation of the Unsettled Boundaries of Ontario. 250 pp., 3 folding maps. 8vo, cloth. Toronto, 1873. $17.50

Contains much on the history and geography of the Pacific Northwest, the Hudson's Bay Co., Northwest Company, fur trade, etc.

866 LINDQUIST, G. E. E. The Red Man in the United States. An intimate study of the Social, Economic and Religious Life of the American Indian. Illus. 8vo, cloth. N. Y., (1923). $5.00

This authoritative and exhaustive work is based upon careful surveys of 161 reservations and of numerous scattered bands of Indians.

LINFORTH'S IMPORTANT JOURNAL OF THE OVERLAND

867 LINFORTH, JAMES. Route from Liverpool to Great Salt Lake Valley, with Views from Sketches made by Frederick Piercy, together with a Geographical and Historical Description; and a Map of the Overland Route from the Missouri River. With a series of thirty full-page views of scenes along the trail, and large folding map. 120 pp., 4to, morocco. Liverpool, 1855. $125.00

Wagner-Camp 259. Fine copy of one of the most important journals of the overland, of which only a few copies are known. The trip was made in 1853 from New Orleans up the Mississippi to St. Louis, thence across Missouri and Nebraska to Wyoming, and over the South Pass into the Great Salt Lake Valley. The views include those of New Orleans, Natchez, Vicksburg, Memphis, St. Louis, Keokuk, Nauvoo, Council Bluffs, Ft. Bridger and Salt Lake City.

868 LINN, MRS. ELIZABETH A. (Relfe) and NATHAN SARGENT. Life and Public Services of Dr. Lewis F. Linn. 441 pp., portrait and plate. 8vo, cloth. N. Y., Appleton, 1857. $22.50

Presentation copy from Mrs. Linn. Linn was the first member (1838) to introduce a bill in Congress authorizing the occupation of the Oregon country by the U. S., and providing for the establishment of an "Oregon Territory."

LINN'S FAMOUS REPORT ON OREGON WITH THE TWO RARE FOLDING MAPS

869 LINN, LEWIS F. Report of the Select Committee on the Occupation of Oregon Territory. 23 pp., sewn, with two rare folding maps. Washington, 1838. $50.00

This is Linn's famous Report presented to the Senate, June 6, 1838, wherein the rights of the U. S. to the Oregon Territory are set forth and the Senate urged to occupy the country. Linn assembled his factual report out of a mass of material obtained from the War Department and every other available source. He gives a history of the several treaties with Great Britain affecting the title, taking the American view of he question, that the line between them could not fall below the 49th parallel. He pointed out that the occupation by the U. of the Columbia would give this country access to the valuable fur trade, the fisheries, trade with the Far East and California, etc. Linn also includes part of the log of the ship "Columbia" in this work.

870 LIONNET, JEAN. Chez les Francais du Canada, les emigrants, Quebec, Montreal, Ottawa, le Grand Ouest, Vancouver. 284 pp., 8vo, original wrappers. Paris, 1908. $7.50

871 [LISHER, J. J.] The Decline and Fall of Samuel Sawbones, M.D., on the Klondike, by his Next Best Friend. 197 pp., 8vo, cloth. N. Y., (1900). $4.00

ORIGINAL RUSSIAN EDITION OF LISIANSKY'S ACCOUNT OF KRUSENSTERN VOYAGE ROUND THE WORLD

872 LISIANSKY, UREY. Puteshestvie vokrug svieta v 1803-6 godakh na korablie Nevie pod nachaljstvom Iuriia Lisianskago. (Voyage Round the World, 1803-6 in the Ship "Neva," under the command of I. Lisisnskii). 2 vols., 4to and one Atlas of 14 large maps and 3 plates. Original wrappers. St. Petersburg, 1812. $200.00

Fine set of the Excessively Rare Original Russian Edition of the above work.

Smith 2255. Most important work dealing with discoveries on the N.W. coast of America. The author was a captain in the Russian navy and commander of the "Neva." He visited Kodiak and Sitka, wintering at the former island, and his long stay there gave him ample time and scope for a study of the native inhabitants and their habits and customs. The long chart shows the track of the voyage, and there are charts of the Washington Islands, Cadiack, and the Harbor of St. Paul, the coast from Bering's Bay to Sea Otter Bay, Sitka or Norfolk Sound, etc.; with colored views of the Harbor of St. Paul in the Island of Cadiack, and New Archangel in Norfolk Sound. There are also plates of Indian implements, etc. The work is important also as the principal source for the Sitka Massacre.

873 LISIANSKY, UREY. A Voyage Round the World in the Years 1803-06; performed by Order of his Imperial Majesty, Alexander First, Emperor of Russia, in the Ship "Neva." Portrait, colored plates and charts. 4to, half contemporary calf. London, 1814. $85.00

A fine copy of the rare English Edition.

874 LITTLE, JAMES A. From Kirkland to Salt Lake City. (Events on the Overland Trail from 1846 to 1852). Illus. with interesting early views. 8vo, cloth. Salt Lake City, 1890. $7.50

A pioneer overland work of first importance.

875 LITTLEFIELD, L. O. Reminiscences of Latter-Day Saints: Giving an Account of much Individual Suffering endured for Religious Conscience. 208 pp., 12mo, cloth. Logan: Journal Print, 1888. $15.00

Not only contains the personal experiences of the author, but contains unpublished journals and statements of the early-day Saints. There is much source material relating to David Osborn, victim of Missouri mobs; Hammer's narrative of the Haun's Mill Massacre; the author's removal from Far West to Liberty, Mo.; Governor Boggs' infamous course of action; legalization of the mobs; betrayal of Joseph Smith and others—their trial and murder; removal to Illinois; founding of Nauvoo; expulsion from Illinois; the exodus across the plains to Utah, etc., etc.

876 LLOYD, B. E. Lights and Shades in San Francisco. Restaurant Life; Barbary Coast; the Elite; Saloons; Gambling; Chinatown; Blackmailing and Confidence Games; the Turf; early Reminiscences, etc. Plates. 523 pp., 8vo, cloth. San Francisco, 1876. $7.50

877 LLOYD, J. P. The Message of an Indian Relic. 21 pp., illus. 8vo, original wrappers. Seattle, 1909. $3.50

878 LOCKLEY, FRED. Vigilante Days at Virginia City. Personal Narrative of Col. E. Dosch, Member of Fremont's Body-Guard, and one time Pony Express Rider. 19 pp., original wrappers. Portland, (1924). $2.50

879 LOCKLEY, FRED. Oregon Yesterdays. 350 pp., 8vo, cloth. N. Y., 1928. $3.00

880 LOCKLEY, FRED. Oregon Folks. 220 pp., 8vo, cloth. N. Y., 1927. $3.00

Historical sketches of Oregon pioneers.

881 LOCKLEY, FRED. Oregon Trail Blazers. 369 pp., 8vo, cloth. N. Y., 1929. $3.00

882 LOCKLEY, FRED. Across the Plains by Prairie Schooner. Personal Narrative of B. F. Bonney of his trip to Sutter's Fort, California, in 1846, and of his pioneering experience in Oregon during the days of Oregon's Provisional Government. 20 pp., 8vo, original wrappers. Eugene, Ore., N.d. $2.50

883 LOCKLEY, FRED. To Oregon by Ox-Team in '47. The Story of the coming of the Hunt Family to the Oregon country and the experiences of G. W. Hunt in the Gold Diggins of California. 8vo, original wrappers. Portland, N.d. $2.50

884 LOCKLEY, FRED. A Talk with Edwin Markham. 8vo, wrappers. N.p., N.d. $2.00

885 LOMAX, JOHN A. Cowboy Songs and other Frontier Ballads. 325 pp., 8vo, cloth. N. Y., 1910. $6.00

886 LONDON, JACK. Burning Daylight. 361 pp., 12mo, cloth. N. Y., 1915. $3.00

887 LONDON, JACK. Call of the Wild. 231 pp., illus., 12mo, cloth. N. Y., 1903. $5.00

888 LONDON, JACK. The Faith of Men. 286 pp., 12mo, cloth. N. Y., (1904). $2.00

889 LONDON, JACK. Love of Life. 265 pp., 12mo, cloth. N. Y., 1906. $2.00

890 LONDON, JACK. Smoke Bellew. 385 pp., 12mo, cloth. N. Y., 1912). $2.00

891 LONDON, JACK. Son of the Wolf; Tales of the Far North. 251 pp., 12mo, cloth. Boston, 1904. $4.00

892 LONDON, JACK. White Fang. 327 pp., illus., 12mo, cloth. N. Y., 1906. $3.00

893 LONG, FREDERICK J. Dictionary of the Chinook Jargon. English-Chinook. 41 pp., 8vo, cloth. Seattle, 1909. $4.00

894 LONGSWORTH, B. N. Over the Oregon Trail: Diary of Basil Nelson Longsworth, March 15, 1853, to Jan 22, 1854, covering the period of his Migration from Ohio to Oregon. 43 pp., original wrappers. Denver: Privately Printed, 1927. $10.00

Day-by-day diary of a trip across the plains, giving accounts of trails, forts, Indians, incidents of the route, character of the country; deaths, murders, drownings, etc.

895 LOOMIS, LEANDER V. A Journey of the Birmingham Emigration Company. The Records of a trip from Birmingham, Iowa to Sacramento, California, in 1850. 198 pp., illus., map. 8vo, cloth. Salt Lake 1928. $12.50

895a [LOPEZ, RAFAEL.] Utah's Greatest Man Hunt. The True Story of the Hunt for Lopez by an Eye Witness. 142 pp., original printed wrappers. Salt Lake City, N.d. $4.00

896 LORD, MRS. ELIZABETH. Reminiscences of Eastern Oregon. Illus. 8vo, cloth. Portland, 1903. $25.00

Privately printed narrative with a minute account of an overland trip by ox team in 1850 on the Oregon Trail, and adventures and conditions in the Territory in 1859. With extracts from a diary kept by W. C. Laughlin, 1856-62, also family records including the Laughlin, Yeargain, Woodford, Buckner and Madison families.

897 LORD, JOHN KEAST. Naturalist in Vancouver Island and British Columbia. 2 vols., plates. 8vo, cloth. London, 1866. $20.00

The author of this scarce and valuable work was naturalist to the British North American Boundary Commission. He has not confined himself merely to dry details of natural history, but in addition to his personal observations on that subject he gives an interesting account of the country and its Indian inhabitants. Small library stamp on title.

898 LORD, JOHN KEAST. At Home in the Wilderness, What to do there and How to do it; a Hand-Book for Travellers and Emigrants. 323 pp., illus., portrait. 8vo, cloth. London, 1867. $10.00

Relates many interesting incidents in Vancouver and British Columbia.

899 LORD, WILLIAM ROGERS. A First Book upon the Birds of Oregon and Washington. A Pocket Guide and Pupil's Assistance in the study of most of the land Birds and a few of the water Birds of these states. 195 pp., index. 12mo, cloth. Portland, Ore., 1901. $12.50

Smith 2251.

900 LORD, WILLIAM ROGERS. First Book upon the Birds of Oregon and Washington. 304 pp., illus., plates. 12mo, cloth. Portland, Ore.: Gill, 1902. $6.50

Smith 2251.

901 LORID, EMILY S. Fort Bridger. (From Overland Monthly, p. 251, Sept., 1890). 8vo. San Francisco, 1890. $2.50

902 LORING, W. C. Memoir of the Hon. William Sturgis. Detailing his Voyage to the Northwest Coast in 1798. Prepared agreeably to the Resolution of the Massachusetts Historical Society. 64 pp., 8vo. Boston, 1864. $12.50

Voyage to the N.W. coast in 1798 under Capt. Rowan; trade with the Indians; mutiny on the coast; manners and customs of the natives; account of the country; Oregon boundary troubles, etc.

903 LORNE, MARQUIS. Canadian Life and Scenery with Hints to Intending Emigrants and Settlers. 191 pp., illus., 8vo, cloth. London, 1886. $6.00

904 LOSSING, BENSON J. History of the United States. Small 4to, half calf. N. Y., 1857. $5.00

At page 528 Lossing mentions the Indian attack on Seattle, which is said to be the first mention of that city in any historical work.

905 LOSSING, BENSON J. Pictorial Field-Book of the War of 1812 . . . with several hundred engravings on wood. Royal 8vo, half calf. N. Y., 1869. $10.00

906 LOTHROP, THORNTON KIRKLAND. William Henry Seward. 423 pp., 8vo, cloth, illus., port. Boston, (1890). $3.00

907 [LOUISIANA PURCHASE.] State Papers and Correspondence bearing upon the purchase of the Territory of Louisiana. 299 pp., 8vo, cloth. Washington, 1903. $4.50

908 LOVE, GEORGE. Court of Claims Indian Depredations, No. 280. George M. Love, Administrator vs. Rogue River and Umpqua Tribes of Indians and the United States. Evidence for Claimants. 44 pp., 8vo. N.p., N.d. $22.50

Not in Smith. Gives the full history of the massacre of Mrs. Harris, Oct. 9th, 1855, together with 16 affidavits of early pioneers relating to the same, including the affidavit of C. C. Beekman, pioneer banker of Oregon. This copy was from the library of B. F. Dowell, prominent lawyer of the Northwest, with annotations in his handwriting.

909 LOVE, ROBERTUS. The Lewis and Clark Fair. (From World's Work, pp. 645, Aug., 1905). 8vo. N. Y., 1905. $3.50

910 LOVE, ROBERTUS. The Rise and Fall of Jesse James. 446 pp., 8vo, cloth. N. Y., 1926. $4.50

911 LOW, CHARLES RATHBONE. Captain Cook's Three Voyages Round the World, with a Sketch of his Life. 472 pp., 8vo, cloth. London, N.d. $3.50

Smith 2256.

912 LOWE, MARTHA. The Story of Chief Joseph. Ports. and plates. 40 pp., 12mo, cloth. Boston, (1881). $7.50

Chief Joseph's narrative as given by Bishop Hare of Niobara, recast in poetic form.

913 LOWE, P. Five Years a Dragoon: Adventures on the Plains from 1849 to 1854. Portraits, early views. 12mo, cloth. Kansas City, 1906. $5.00

Daily journal kept by the author narrating an expedition across the Plains, 3,000 miles on one horse in seven months; adventures among the Cheyenne and Snake Indians; Santa Fe Expedition and New Mexico campaigns; Colorado in the 50's, etc.

914 LUDINGTON, FLORA BELL. The Newspapers of Oregon, 1846-1870. 34 pp., 8vo. Eugene, N.d. $7.50

Thesis submitted in partial fulfillment of the Degree of Master of Arts at Mills College, 1925.

915 LUDLOW, FITZHUGH. Heart of the Continent: a record of travel across the Plains to Oregon, with an Examination of the Mormon Principle. 8vo, cloth. N. Y., 1870. $5.00

916 LUDLOW, WILLIAM. Report of a Reconnaissance of the Black Hills of Dakota. 121 pp., 2 maps. 4to, cloth. Washington. 1875. $5.00

917 LUGRIN, N. DE BERTRAND. The Pioneer Women of Vancouver Island, 1843-1866. 311 pp., illus., 8vo, cloth. Victoria, 1928. $7.50

918 LUIGI, DUKE OF THE ABRUZZI. The Ascent of Mt. St. Elias (Alaska) by H. R. H. Prince Luigi Amedeo di Savoia. Duke of the Abruzzi, narrated by Filippo de Filippi, illustrated by Vittorio Sella and translated by Signora Linda Villari, with the author's supervision. 240 pp., illus., portrait, 37 plates, 2 maps. 4to, cloth. N. Y.: Stokes, (1899). $17.50

Fine large copy of this scarce work.

CZAR'S COPY OF THE ONLY COMPLETE SET EVER REPORTED OF LUKE'S "VOYAGES" IN ORIGINAL RUSSIAN, WITH THE ATLASES AND BEAUTIFUL PLATES OF NORTHWEST AMERICA

918a LUTKE, FEODOR PETROVITCH. Puteschestvie vokrug Svieta Sovershennoe po Poveliebiiu Imp. Nikolai I. Otdielnie Istoricheskoe . . . (Journey Round the Wrld, undertaken by Order of the Emperor Nicholas I, in the Sloop of War Seniavin, by Capt. F. Lutke, 1826-9. Historical Section, Vol. 1, 294 pp., folding plate; Vol. 2, 282 pp., 5 plates (3 folding); Vol. 3, 270 pp., with 25 views. Together, 3 vols., 4to, ¾ morocco. St. Petersburg, 1834 1835, 1836. Together with other voyages made by Lutke in 1823-4-5-6, comprising 200 pp., folding plate and 3 folding maps. (Title in Russian). 8vo, original wrappers bound in. St. Petersburg, 1828. [All the above comprising the text of the celebrated Lutke Voyages are four books bound in 2 vols., ¾ morocco.] Accompanying the above is the celebrated "Partie Historique Atlas"—["Voyage autour du Monde fait par Order de sa Majeste l'Emperor Nicholas I'er su le Corvette le Seniavine, pendant les Annees 1826, 1827, 1828 & 1829, soues le Commandement de Frederic Lutke. Lithographie d'apres les dessins originaux d'Alexandre Postels . . . ed du Baron Kittlitz. Lithographee de Engelmann et Compagnie.] Folio, ¾ morocco. 38 pp., 3 maps and 51 plates. This copy contains the plates in two states—51 plates in black and white and 51 plates beautifully hand-colored apparently in oil. Size of plate 17x22 in. The legends on each plate are in both Russian and French.

Also accompanying the above: The renowned Atlas, with the title in Russian, comprising 34 double-paged maps (26x34 in.). with legends in both Russian and French. Imperial folio, bound in full morocco, with the Russian Imperial Insignia stamped in gold on the outside cover.
Also accompanying the above is the rare "Partie Nautique Atlas," with the Original Russian Title and Text. This Atlas contains 10 maps and plans, a large folding map of Alaska, and 32 views of the Northwest Coast of America. 4to, half calf. St. Petersburg, 1835
Together 7 vols. bound in 5. 8vo, 4to and Imperial folio, morocco and calf. St. Petersburg, 1828-36. $1250.00

One of the superlative rarities of Western Americana No complete set of the Original Russian Edition, as cited above, can be located in any of the world libraries. The above is not to be confused with the later French Edition which is in itself very rare, but is dated later and not complete. The set offered above is from the library of Czar Nicholas I of Russia, and bears his Royal Insignia in gold on the covers. Following Kotzebue's voyage, the Imperial government sent out a corps of skilled scientists to chart in the details of the explored lands, to survey the regions, and above all to give the world a graphic pictorial account of the exciting lands. Capt. Lutke was chosen for this task. Kittlitz, Postels and Mertens headed the scientific corps. The expedition reached Sitka in June, 1827, beginning at once the exploration and survey of the Northwestern coast, naming various points, visiting Unalaska and discovering St. Mathew Island. In 1829 important explorations were made in Bering Sea, where important place names were given to coast-line points, and the Caroline Islands were discovered. Among the beautiful plates, all superbly engraved by Englemann from the original drawings by Kittlitz, and pronounced by Sabin as "The most interesting representations ever made", are: "Etablissement de Novo-Arkhangelsk"; Vue de Bai de Sitka"; "Interieur d'un Cabane de Caloches'; "Vue du Port de St. Pierre et St. Paul"; "Habitans avec luer Canots"; "Habitans a Ounalachka"; "Vue de Bai d'Avutcha", etc. The fifty-odd folding maps are all superbly executed. In their execution these plates far exceed those by Prince Max. von Wied.

ORIGINAL RUSSIAN ACCOUNT OF LUTKE'S SCIENTIFIC VOYAGE TO NORTHWEST AMERICA

919 LUTKE, FEODOR PETROVITCH. Chetyrekratnoe puteshestvie v sievernyi Ledovityi Okean, sovershennoe po povelieniiu Imp. Aleksandra I—ago na voennom brigie Novaia Zemlia, v 1821-24 godakh, flota Kap. Lieut. F. Lutke. (Four voyages to the Arctic Ocean undertaken in the Brig of War Nova Zembia in 1821-24 by Capt. Lieut. Lutke, at Command of Emperor Alexander I). 2 vols. in one, with all the 23 maps and 14 plates. 4to, calf. St. Petersburg, 1828. $100.00

920 LUTTIG, JOHN C. Journal of a Fur-Trading Expedition on the Upper Missouri, 1812-1813. Edited by Stella M. Drumm. Illus. 8vo, boards. St. Louis, 1920. $12.50

One of 365 copies. The author was clerk of the Missouri Fur Co. and tells of expeditions among the Indians, of competition with the British Northwest Co., Indian wars; and, at page 106, Luttig records the death of "Sakakawea," who was with Lewis and Clark.

LYMAN'S JOURNEY TO CALIFORNIA

921 LYMAN, A. Journal of a Voyage to California and Life in the Gold Diggings. By Albert Lyman, a member of the Connecticut Mining and Trading Company, which sailed from New York, Feb. 22, 1849. Full-page and other plates. 192 pp., 12mo, cloth. Hartford, 1852. $47.50

Braislin 1202, Cowan p. 145: "A very rare and curious book." Neither the work of a tourist, nor the scientific explorer, but simply the every-day records of facts, observations and events, by a candid though minute observer. The work was done for the author's family and relatives.

922 LYMAN, CHESTER S. Around the Horn to the Sandwich Islands and California, 1845-1850, being a personal Record kept by Chester S. Lyman. 328 pp., 8vo, cloth. New Haven, 1924. $5.00

923 LYMAN, HORACE S. Mile Posts in the Development of Oregon, and Characteristics of Oregon as an American Commonwealth. 22 pp., map. 8vo. Eugene, 1896. $4.00

924 LYMAN, HORACE S. History of Oregon. Maps, numerous plates, facsimiles, etc. 4 vols., 8vo, cloth. N. Y., 1903. $22.50

Smith 2267. Said to be the best illustrated history of Oregon.

925 LYMAN, WILLIAM D. Lake Chelan. (From the Overland Magazine, March, 1899). 8vo. San Francisco, 1899. $2.50

926 LYMAN, WILLIAM D. Illustrated History of Walla Walla County, State of Washington. 510 pp., 40 portraits, 7 plates. 4to, cloth. N.p., Lever, 1901. $17.50

Smith 2272.

927 LYMAN, WILLIAM D. The Columbia River: its History, its Myths, its Scenery, its Commerce. 400 pp., illus., map. 8vo, cloth. N. Y., 1909. $4.75

928 LYMAN, WILLIAM D. Indian Myths of the Northwest. 23 pp., 8vo, original wrappers. Worcester, 1915. $4.00

929 LYMAN, R. Beecher Island Memorial. (Narratives of the desperate stand of Capt. Forsyth and his little band of forty worn scouts in the bloody combat against the Cheyenne, Arapahoe and Sioux, twelve hundred strong, under Chief Roman Nose, at the Battle of the Arickaree, September, 1868). With the Personal Narratives, Accounts and Reminiscences of Survivors. Portraits and plates. 28 pp., 8vo, original printed wrappers. Wray, Colo., 1904. $7.50

930 LYMAN, R. The Beecher Island Memorial. With Accounts and Reminiscences of the Survivors. Map, portraits and plates. 32 pp., 8vo, original printed wrappers. Wray, Colo., 1905. $7.50

931 LYNCH, JEREMIAH. Three Years in the Klondike. 280 pp., illus., maps. 8vo, cloth. London, 1904. $7.50

Smith 2274.

932 LYNCH, JEREMIAH. A Senator of the Fifties, David C. Broderick of California. 246 pp., illus., 8vo, cloth. San Francisco, 1911. $5.00

933 [McAFEE, R. B.] History of the late War in the Western Country, comprising a full Account of all the transactions in that quarter, from the commencement of hostilities at Tippecanoe, to the termination of the contest at New Orleans. 534 pp., 8vo, original calf, with "extra" leaf at end denouncing the work, and the blank leaf following. Lexington, 1816. $60.00

Original Edition. One of the most important sources for the war in the west, the author being one of the first to join the Northwest Army.

934 McARTHUR, HARRIET NESMITH. Recollections of the Rickreall. 24 pp., front. and illus. 8vo, original printed wrappers. Portland, Ore.: Privately Printed, 1930. $22.50

Alhough printed only eleven years ago in a small edition for friends and relatives, the above work has already become exceedingly scarce. The author's father, James W. Nesmith, reached Walla Walla in the autumn of 1843, and was later U. S. Senator from Oregon. The work also includes an interesting sketch of pioneer days in Oregon.

935 McARTHUR, LEWIS. Oregon Geographic Names. Maps and illus. 450 pp., 8vo, cloth. Portland, Ore., 1928. $7.50

936 McBETH, KATE. The Nez Perces since Lewis and Clark. Portraits and plates. 272 pp., uncut. 8vo, cloth. N. Y., (1908). $10.00

The author was a teacher and missionary among the Nex Perces for 27 years, coming to the Lapwai Mission in 1873, following the death of Rev. H. H. Spalding, who had founded the settlement in 1836.

937 MACBETH, R. G. The Romance of Western Canada. 309 pp., illus. Toronto, 1918. $6.00

938 MACBETH, R. G. Policing the Plains, being the Real Life Record of the famous Royal Northwest Mounted Police. 320 pp., illus., 8vo, cloth. London, 1921. $7.50

939 McCAIN, CHARLES W. History of the SS. "Beaver." Being a Graphic and Vivid Sketch of this Noted Pioneer Steamer and her Romantic Cruise for over Half a Century on the Placid Island-Dotted Waters of the North Pacific. Also Containing a Description of the Hudson's Bay Company from its formation in 1670, down to the present time. Biography of Captain McNeill. The Narrative of a Fraser River Prospector of 1859. Historical Mementoes of the Beaver's Copper Remains. The sad ending of the author's last trip in search of old-time Naval Relics. Important Developments in Steam since its introduction in 1769. Illus. Sq. 12mo, cloth. Vancouver, B. C., 1894. $30.00

Smith 2281. The above copy contains a gold-plated medal made of copper taken from the "Beaver" and a certificate from McCain to that effect. The Braislin copy brought $37.50.

940 McCALL, GEORGA A. Letters from the Frontiers. Written during a period of thirty years' service in the Army of the United States. 8vo, cloth. Phila., 1868. $10.00

Overland across the plains to New Mexico in '49; Texas; hunting on the plains; Fort Scott and the Cherokee Country, etc. "An exceedingly interesting and truthful narrative of the astonishing endurance of the United States troops, and the fortitude and courage of he Indians opposed to them."—Field.

941 McCARTER, MARGARET HILL. The Peace of the Solman Valley. 91 pp., 8vo, original printed wrappers. Chicago, 1911. $6.00

Not in Smith.

942 McCLELLAN, R. GUY. Golden State; a history of the region west of the Rocky Mountains, embracing California, Oregon, Nevada, Utah, Arizona, Idaho, Washington Territory, British Columbia and Alaska . . . with a history of Mormonism and the Mormons. Illus. and maps. 8vo, cloth. Phila., 1872). $7.50

943 [McCLELLAND, THOMAS.] The inauguration of Thomas McClelland, of Forest Grove, Oregon, as President of Tulatin Academy and Pacific University, June 15, 1892. 32 pp., original printed wrappers. Forest Grove, Ore., 1892. $5.00

944 McCLINTOCK, CAPT. The Voyage of the "Fox" in the Arctic Seas; Narrative of the Discovery of the Fate of Sir John Franklin and his Comparrions. Maps and plates. 8vo, cloth. Boston, 1860. $7.50

Capt. McClintock, engaged by Lady Franklin for the final expedition to search for her husband, was the first to bring home authentic intelligence of the death of Sir John Franklin.

945 McCLINTOCK, WALTER. The Old North Trail; or, Life, Legends and Religion of the Blackfeet Indians. Illus., some in color. 8vo, cloth. London, 1910. $7.50

946 McCONNELL, M. The Early History of Idaho, by W. J. McConnell, who was present and cognizant of the events narrated. 420 pp., portrait. 8vo, cloth. Caldwell, 1913. $7.50

947 McCORMACK, ELLEN CONDON. Thomas Condon, Pioneer Geologist of Oregon. 355 pp., front., 8vo, cloth. Eugene, Ore., 1928. $5.00

948 McCORMICK, S. J. Almanac . . . 1862, 1868, 1879, 1881. 5 vols., 8vo, original printed wrappers. Portland, Ore.: McClintock, 1862-1881. $20.00

Smith 2302. Contains useful material relating to Oregon, Washington, Idaho and Montana.

ORIGINAL EDITION OF McCOY'S "CATTLE TRADE"

949 McCOY, JOSEPH. Historic Sketches of the Cattle Trade of the West and Southwest. Portrait and illus. 472 pp. and 24 pp. of advertisements at the end. 8vo, cloth. Kansas City, 1874. $40.00

Very fine presentation copy, signed by the author, and complete with all the illustrations including the rare view facing p. 416. The author was one of the pioneer cattle men of the West. He gives biographical sketches of early ranchmen, famous cowboys, drovers, cattle fanciers of the trade and the personnel of the stock-yards. He also describes cowboy dances, wintering the herds, brnading and other features of the trade.

950 MACDONALD, ALEXANDER. In Search of Eldorado. A Wanderer's Experience. 291 pp., illus., 8vo, cloth. London, N.d. (c. 1880). $7.50

RARE SOURCE WORK RELATING TO HUDSON'S BAY

951 McDONALD, ARCHIBALD (Chief Factor). Peace River: A Canoe Voyage from Hudson's Bay to the Pacific by the Late George Simpson (Governor Hon. Hudsons Bay Company) in 1828—Journal of the late Chief Factor, Archibald McDonald Hon. Hudson's Bay Company), who accompanied him, with notes by Malcolm McLeod. Map. 119 pp., cloth. Ottawa, 1872. $125.00

Smith 2311 cites only the copy at Victoria, B. C. Presentation copy by the author to the Canadian Minister of Agriculture. An important journal, the notes to which are by the son of Chief Factor, John McLeod. Each of the great Empire Builders mentioned in the journal appear to have been known to the editor, and he gives many personal reminiscences of each.

952 MACDONALD, DUNCAN GEO. FORBES. Lecture on British Columbia and Vancouver's Island delivered at the Royal United Service Institution, on March 27, 1863. 12mo, ¾ calf. Fine. London: Longmans, 1863. $20.00

Smith 2311 locates only the copy at Victoria. Contains much descriptive and historical material.

953 MACDONALD, C. D. F. British Columbia and Vancouver's Island, comprising a Description of those Dependencies; their Physical Character, Climate, Capabilities and future Prospects. Also an Account of the Manners and Customs of the Native Indians. Folding map. 8vo, original cloth. London, 1862. $15.00

954 McDONALD, JOSEPH LANE. Hidden Treasures; or, Fisheries Around the North-West Coast. In one volume. By J. L. McDonald, of Washington Territory. 8vo, 110 pp., index and five leaves of Washington Territory business advertisements, sewn, as issued. Proctor Brothers, Printers, Advertiser Office, Gloucester, Mass., 1871. $100.00

Smith 2312. Excessively rare. Probably not more than four copies known: one noted by Bancroft, one in the Library Association of Portland, one in the Huntington Collection, and the above. Although printed at Gloucester, Mass., and the author's postscript dated at Gloucester, Nov. 3, 1871, this work was undoubtedly published in Washington Territory, probably at Olympia, as all the advertisements but one, at the end, are of West Coast business men located in Olympia, Tumwater, Seattle, Teekalet, San Francisco, Port Townsend, etc. Although the title should indicate that the work relates to the fisheries only, the author writes of the acquisition of California, Coast Islands, Indians, Traders, Pioneers, Milling and Mining towns, Railroad Explorations, etc.

955 [MAC DONALD, RANALD.] Lewis, William S., and Naojiro Murakami. Ranald MacDonald. The Narrative of his early life on the Columbia under the Hudson's Bay Co. Regime. 333 pp., illus., 8vo, cloth. 1923. $6.50

See Philip Ashton Rollin's "Discovery of the Oregon Trail" for an account of this work.

956 McELROY, ROBERT McNUTT. The Winning of the Far West. History of the regaining of Texas, the Mexican War, and the Oregon Question; and of the successive additions to the Territory of the U. S., within the Continent of America, 1829-1867. 384 pp., maps., 8vo, cloth. N. Y., 1914. $6.50

Smith 2317.

957 McELWAINE, E. The Truth about Alaska. 445 pp., plates. 8vo, cloth. Published by the Author, N.p. 1901. $7.50

958 MACFIE, MATTHEW. Vancouver Island and British Columbia. Their History, Resources and Prospects. Folding maps and illus. 574 pp., 8vo, cloth. London, 1865. $12.50

The author maintains that an early settlement of British Columbia and the country west of the Rocky Mountains hinges on the opening of an emigrant route via wagon road, coupled with the opening of a telegraph route. With the bookplate of Charles William Roe.

959 McGHEE, MICAJAH. Rough Times in Rough Places. (From the Century Magazine, March, 1891). 8vo. N. Y., 1891. Northwest history. $2.00

960 McGIBBON, ELMA. Leaves of Knowledge. 237 pp., port. 12mo, cloth. (Spokane, 1904). $7.50

Smith 2323. Sketches of travel in the U. S., mainly in the West.

961 [McGILLIVRAY, DUNCAN.] The Journal of Duncan M'Gillivray of the North West Company at Fort George on the Saskatchewan, 1794-5. With Introduction, Notes and Appendix by Arthur S. Morton. 8vo, cloth. Toronto, 1929. $15.00

An important work on the Fur Trade of which only 350 copies were printed.

962 [McGILLIVRAY, SIMON.] Narrative of Occurrences in the Indian Countries of North America since the connexion of the Right Hon. the Earl of Selkirk with the Hudson's Bay Company, and his Attempt to Establish a Colony on the Red River, with a Detailed Account of his Lordship's Military Expedition to, and Subsequent Proceedings at Ft. William in Upper Canada. 8vo, 152 pp.; Appendix 87 pp., half sprinkled calf. London: B. McMillan, Bow St., 1817. $110.00

Sabin 20703. A rare and important work in defence of the action of the Northwest Co. issued by the representatives of that company in London, of which Edward Ellice was the head. Sabin attributes the work to Thomas Douglas, but this can hardly be correct because Douglas was the author of works in favor of Lord Selkirk. Others attribute it to the above author who had the work ghost-written by Samuel Hull Wilcocke, who came to Montreal in 1818 as a paid writer for the N.W. Co.

963 McILHANY, EDWARD W. Recollections of a '49er. A Quaint and Thrilling Narrative of a Trip Across the Plains, and Life in the California Gold Fields during the Stirring Days following the Discovery of Gold in the Far West. Portraits. 212 pp., 12mo, cloth. Kansas City, 1908. $12.50

Privately published from the author's original manuscript memoirs. The author was an early plainsman and California pioneer. His company left Jefferson County, Va., on March 3rd, 1849.

964 McINTIRE, JIM. Early Days in Texas and New Mexico. Ranch Life, Buffalo Hunting with the Rangers, Life and Adventures in New Mexico, etc. Portrait. 229 pp., 12mo, cloth (edge of binding stained). Kansas City, 1902. $8.50

965 MACKAY, ALEXANDER. The Western World; or, Travels in the U. S. in 1846-47, including a chapter on California. Maps of the U. S., and California. 3 vols., 8vo, original cloth. London, 1850. $7.50

Contains a long and interesting description of New York City. The Astor House is referred to as "this enormous granite pile." Slavery is treated at length, and interesting descriptions are given of numerous cities in various parts of the country.

966 McKEEBY, LEMUEL CLARK. The Memoirs of. 75 pp., 8vo, original printed wrappers. San Francisco, 1924. $6.00

Day-by-day journal of an Overland Journey to California in 1850.

967 McKEEVOR, THOMAS. A Voyage to Hudsons Bay, during the Summer of 1812. Also a Description of the Esquimaux and North American Indians, their manners, customs, dress, languages, etc. Plates. 8vo, boards. London, 1819. $15.00

At the end is a vocabulary in the Chippeway language.

968 McKENNEY, THOMAS L. Memoirs, Official and Personal; with Sketches of Travel among the Northern and Southern Indians; Embracing a War Excursion, and Description of Scenes along the Western Borders. Portrait, colored and lithographed views. 436 pp., 8vo, ¾ morocco. N. Y., 1846. $7.50

969 McKENZIE, N. M. J. The Men of Hudson's Bay Company. 214 pp., 12mo, original wrappers. Fort William, 1921. $7.50

970 MACKENZIE, SIR ALEXANDER. Voyages from Montreal, on the River St. Lawrence, through the continent of North America to the Frozen Pacific Oceans . . . 412 pp., portrait, 3 maps, table. 4to, calf. London: Cadell, 1801. $30.00

Original Edition. Wagner-Camp No. 1. The above is an interesting copy in that it formerly belonged to Caroline E. Norton, noted English novelist of the 19th century. She has inserted a note which states: "Bought this book that I might describe with accuracy the dangers and toils of my hero 'Sinclair Davidson,' but had not had time to read it through before Mr. Washington Irving's 'Astoria' came out, making my intention useless, a great disappointment, as I fancied I had so original a subject."

971 —— The same. 2 vols. Portrait, 2 maps. 8vo, cloth. N. Y., 1902. $5.00

972 McKINSTRY, C. Thrilling and Tragic Narrative! Journal kept by a Suffering Emigrant on the California Mountains, on his way Overland to California, with a party of Emigrants (the last three who died were eaten by the survivors), who were finally rescued by Lieut. Woodworth, U.S.A., and brought to Capt. Sutter's Fort, on the Sacramento in the year 1847. Long, narrow red paper broadside, folded. West Hoboken: C. Reining, Printer, N.d. $15.00

Only 65 copies published from the original in St. Louis newspapers in 1847.

973 McKNIGHT, CHAS. Our Western Border in early Pioneer Days. Illus. Large 8vo. (Phila., 1876). $6.00

974 McKNIGHT, THOMAS. Thirty Years of Foreign Policy; a History of the Secretaryships of the Earl of Aberdeen and Viscount Palmerston . . . 440 pp., 8vo, cloth. London, 1855. $7.50

Includes the treaty of Washington and the Oregon Question.

975 M'KONOCHIE, CAPTAIN A. Summary View of the Statistical and Existing Commerce of the Principal Shores of the Pacific Ocean, with a Sketch of the Advantages, Political and Commercial, which would result from the establishment of a central Free Port within its limits. 8vo, calf. London, 1818. $20.00

Smith 2333. Valuable for accounts of the soil, climate, vegetable and mineral productions, population, commerce, means of communication, etc., of the Northwest Coast of America.

976 McLAIN, JOHN SCUDDER. Alaska and the Klondike. 324 pp., illus., map. 8vo, cloth. N. Y.: McClure, 1905. $5.00

Smith 2334.

977 McLAUGHLIN, ANDREW C. Lewis Cass. 363 pp., 8vo, cloth. Boston, N.d. $3.50

978 McLAUGHLIN, JAMES. My Friend, the Indian. By James McLaughlin. 417 pp., illus. N. Y., 1910. $4.50

RARE ORIGINAL ISSUE OF THE TRIAL OF JOHN McLOUGHLIN AND OTHERS FOR THE MURDER OF GOVERNOR SEMPLE AND OTHERS OF THE ILL-FATED RED RIVER SETTLEMENT

979 [McLAUGHLIN, JOHN.] Report of the Proceedings connected with the Dispute between the Earl of Selkirk and the North-West Company, at the Assize held at York, in Upper Canada, October, 1818. From Minutes taken in Court. PP. XXIII-300-218-55-4-XLVII. 8vo, original boards, uncut. Montreal, 1818. $100.00

Excessively rare Original Issue. The most complete and authentic account of the controversy between the Hudson's Bay Company and the Northwest Co. in their rivalry for the monopoly of the Fur Trade. In this work is the complete testimony of eyewitness and participants on both sides of the celebrated controversy between the two rival fur companies, which finally led to the murder of Governor Semple and his party at Lord Selkirk's colony on the Red River. The volume comprises the trial of Paul Brown and Francois Firminboucher; the trial of John Silveright, Alexander Mackenzie, Hugh McGillis, John McDonald, John McLaughlin and Simon Fraser. The above fine copy of this important work is probably the only copy that has been offered for sale in many years.

980 [McLAUGHLIN, JOHN.] Report of the Trials of Charles de Reinhard, and Archibald M'Lellan for Murder, at the Court of Oyer and Terminer, held at Quebec, May, 1818. Pp. XXIV-652-52-159. 8vo, original boards, uncut. Montreal: Printed by James Lane and Nhum Mower, 1818. $100.00

Excessively rare companion volume for item No. 979. McLellan and de Reinhard, partner and clerk, respectively, in the North-West Company of Montreal, were tried for the murder of one of the Selkirk Colony at Red River. Owing to the high state of excitement and prejudice prevailing at Montreal the prisoners were transferred to Quebec and the trial held there. McLellan was acquitted and de Reinhard was found guilty and executed.

Item 979, First line of headting McLoughlin should read McLaughlin. Date should read 1819, not 1818. The fourth line of title should read XLVIII, not XLVII.

THE RARE MR. MACLAURIES NARRATIVE

981 MACLAURIES, MR. A Narrative; or, Journal of Voyages and Travels through the Northwest Continent of Amercia; in the Years 1789 and 1793. 91 pp., 12mo, ¾ calf. London: Printed for J. Lee, No. 12 King St., Covent Garden. J. Smeton, Printer, 148 St. Martin's Lane, Charing Cross, 1802. $300.00

Wagner-Camp No. 2. A good copy of this rare work with the plate and half-title.

982 M'LEAN, JOHN. Notes of Twenty-Five Years' Service in the Hudson's Bay Territory. 2 vols., 8vo, original cloth, uncut. Fine copy. London, 1849. $50.00

Wagner-Camp 169. Incidents of travel among the Indians of Hudson's Bay Territory; descriptions of life, character, habits of the various tribes and of the Fur Traders. The second volume terminates with a vocabulary of Indian dialects. Smith 2339.

983 MACLEOD, XAVIER DONALD. History of the Devotion to the Blessed Virgin Mary in North America . . . with a memoir of the author by the most Rev. John B. Purcell, D.D., Archbishop of Cincinnati. 8vo, cloth. N. Y., 1866. $12.50

Smith 2342 cites one copy. There is a hymn to the Blessed Mary in Chinook Jargon at p. 255. The work includes material on Oregon and the Rocky Mountains.

984 McLEOD, MALCOLM. Oregon Indemnity: a claim of Chief Factors and Chief Traders of the Hudson's Bay Company, thereto, as partners under the Treaty of 1846. 57 pp., 8vo, original printed wrappers. N.p., 1892. $17.50

Smith 2341. Annotated by the author. Contains much new material on the dealings of the company.

985 McLUNG, JOHN A. Sketches of Western Adventure: Containing an Account of the most interesting incidents connected with the settlement of the West from 1755 to 1794. 360 pp., 12mo, original calf. Maysville, Ky., 1832. $40.00

Original Edition. Thomson, p. 214: "The most complete collection of captivities and early adventures ever published in one volume." Daniel Boone had been a resident of Maysville only a few years before the author settled there. Others dealt with in this work are Simon Kenton, William Kennan, James Ward, Charles Ward, Major Hugh McGary, Thomas Marshall, and other frontier heroes.

986 McLUNG, J. A. Sketches of Western Adventure. containing account of the most Interesting Incidents connected with the Settlement of the West, 1755 to 1794; with Appendix. Woodcut plates. 12mo, cloth. Louisville, 1879. $7.50

987 McLUNG, J. W. Minnesota as it is in 1870. 299 pp., 12mo, cloth. 1870. $7.50

988 McMURRAY, CHARLES A. Pioneers of the Rocky Mountains of the West. 248 pp., illus., maps. N. Y., 1912. $4.50

Smith 2345.

989 McMURTIE, DOGULAS C. The First Printing in British Columbia. 22 pp., 8vo. Chicago, 1929. $7.50

Limited to 250 copies.

990 McNAUGHTON, M. Overland to Cariboo: An Eventful Journey of Canadian Pioneers to the Gold Fields of British Columbia in 1862. 176 pp., plates. 12mo, cloth. Toronto, 1896. $15.00

Original Edition. Narrative of the first trans-continental migration, crossing overland from Canada to British Columbia, written directly from the original diaries of several of the pioneers. Departure from Ft. Garry; crossing the Assiniboine; deserted by the guide; final arrival at Ft. Pitt; Ft. Edmonton; Leatherhead Pass; crossing the Athabasca; facing starvation; pushing on to the Fraser River; division of the party; shooting the rapids; the Symington Overland party; the Thompson River Expedition; biographical sketches of pioneers, etc.

991 McNEMEE, A. J. "Brother Mack," the Frontier Preacher. A Brief Record of the Difficulties and Hardships of a Pioneer Itinerant. 79 pp., 12mo, original wrappers. Portland, Ore., N.d. $12.50

Privately printed. Narrates the Overland Expedition of the Waymire Train of 1845. The author was the nephew of Fred Waymire. This was the expedition of which Meek, the guide, lost his way and led the emigrants into the wilderness. The author recounts incidents of early life in Oregon, McNemee's part in the developmtnt of Portland; his claim for 64 acrs of the town site; his legal fight therefor; Indian War of 1856; experiences in the Fraser River country, etc.

992 MACOMB, CAPT. J. N. Report of the Exploring Expedition from Santa Fe, New Mexico, to the Junction of the Grand and Green Rivers of the Great Colorado of the West, in 1859, under the Command of Capt. J. N. Macomb, with Geological Report by J. S. Newberry. Maps and plates, some colored. 4to, cloth. Washington, 1876. $12.50

993 MAC RAE, DONALD. Chief Joseph's Story. 31 pp., original wrappers. Illus. N.p., N.d. $4.50

994 McREYNOLDS, R. Thirty Years on the Frontier: Personal Experiences and Events as a Cowboy, Miner and Pioneer. 256 pp., portrait and plates. 8vo, cloth. Colorado Springs, 1906. $10.00

Interesting narrative of the early days in the Black Hills, across the desert to California. New Mexico Indian campaign, Indian fighting in Colorado, the Custer massacre, wild horse hunting, etc.

995 MACTAGGART, JOHN. Three Years in Canada: the Actual State of the Country in 1826-28, its Resources, Productions, Improvements, Capabilities, Emigrants, &c. Folding colored map. 2 vols., 8vo, cloth. London, 1829. $15.00

Much on Hudson's Bay.

996 McWHORTER, L. V. The Crime Against the Yakimas. Plates. 56 pp., 8vo, original printed wrappers. North Yakima: Republic Print, 1913. $7.50

The author lived for years among the Yakimas in Washington Territory and was adopted into the Tribe. His work is an exposure of the attempts made by the Reclamation Service and the Indian Dept. to break the Walla Walla Treaty of 1855, and take over the Yakima lands.

AUTOGRAPHED COPY OF McWILLIAMS' "RECOLLECTIONS"

997 McWILLIAMS, JOHN. Recollections of John McWilliams. His Youth, Experiences in California, and the Civil War. Portrait. 8vo, original cloth, uncut. N.p., N.d. $20.00

Rare privately printed life of a California pioneer, who crossed the plains in '49. Describes many of the early mining camps on Trinity River, Olney Creek, Scotch River, Sailors' Diggins, Shasta River, etc. Also relates considerable early pioneer life in Tazewell County, Illinois, near Bloomington and Peoria, where the author was reared.

998 MACOUN, J. Manitoba and the Great Northwest. Its Early History, Settlement, etc. Maps and plates. 8vo, cloth. Guelph, 1882. $5.00

998a MADDREN, A. G. The Innokp Gold-Placer District, Alaska, with Accounts of the Central Kushkowin Valley and the Ruby Creek and Gold Hill Placers. 87 pp., folding maps. 8v, ¾ morocco. Washington, 1910. $6.00

999 MAGNUM, A. W. Reconnoissance Soil Survey of the Western Part of the Puget Sound Basin, Washington. 116 pp., illus., 4 large folding maps. 8vo, half morocco. Washington, 1912. $5.00

1000 MAGNUM, A. W. Reconnoissance Survey of Southwestern Washington. 136 pp., charts. 8vo, half morocco. Washington, 1913. $5.00

1001 MAGUIRE, AMY JANE. Indian Girl who lead them, Sacajawa. 87 pp., 8vo, original printed wrappers. Portland, Ore.: Gill, 1905. $5.00

1002 MAGUIRE, W. H. Samuel T. Hauser, an Early Governor of Montana. (From the Magazine of Western History, P. 587, March, 1891, Vol. 13, No. 5). 8vo. 1891. $4.00

1003 MAIR, CHARLES. Through the Mackenzie Basin. A Narrative of the Athabasca Expedition of 1899. 149 pp., map, illus. 8vo, original printed wrappers. Toronto: Briggs, 1908. $9.50

Not in Smith.

1004 MAJORS, ALEXANDER. Seventy Years on the Frontier. Memoirs of a Lifetime on the Border. With a Preface by Buffalo Bill. Edited by Col. Prentiss Ingraham. Portraits and plates. 12mo, cloth. Chicago, 1893. $16.50

Original Edition. An authentic account of varied experiences on the Plains and in the Rockies by the man who inaugurated the famous Pony Express. A much sought after work.

1005 MALASPINA, D. ALEJANDRO. Viaje Politico-Cientifico alrededor Mundo por las corbetas Descubierta y Atrevida, al mando de los Capitaines de Navio, D. Alejandro Malaspina y Don Jose de Bustemente y Guerra, desde 1789-1794. Map, portrait of Malaspina and plates. Large 4to, ¾ calf. Madrid, 1885. $37.50

Smith 2353. An important exploration covering the N.W. Coast. Malaspina left Cadiz on July 29, 1789, and visited the western coast of South America from Cape Horn to Panama, afterwards sailing along the western coast of North America as far as 60 degrees north latitude. He then retraced his route as far as Acapulco, and again reached South America, after visiting the Philippine Islands and Australia. He then returned to Cadiz via Cape Horn, reaching home in Sept., 1794. During this long voyage he visited Nootka Sound, North West Coast of America, and narrates the events which took place there during his stay. He also gives an account of his visit to Monterey and his explorations of the coast of California. In addition to the diary of the voyage, this important work contains a description of the North West Coast of America; Maldonado's relation of the discovery of the Straits of Anian; accounts of the principal Spanish expeditions to the North Pacific between 1774 and 1791; description of the country and customs of California; and a long historical introduction on the voyage by Don Pedro de Novo y Colson.

1006 MALDONADO, LORENSO FERRER. Viaggio del Mare Atlantico al Pacifico per la Via del Nord-Ouest fatto del Capitano Lorenzo Ferrer Maldonado l'Anno 1588. Tradotto da un Manoscritto Spagnuollo inedit de Carlo Amoretti. Maps. Folio, morocco. Milano, 1811. $47.50

Smith 1224.

1007 MALDONADO, LAURENT FERRER. Voyage de la Mer Atlantique a l'Ocean Pacifique par le Nord-Ouest dans la Mer Glaciale l'An 1588. Traduit d'un Manuscrit Espanol et Suivi dun discours qui en demontre l'authenticite et la veracite par Charles Amoretti. Maps. 4to, contemporary calf (lacks backstrip, but otherwise a good copy). Plaisance, 1812. $47.50

Important and scarce work for the history of geographical discovery on the Northwest coast of America. Only 600 copies of the work were printed. Smith 1226 cites one copy.

1008 MALLANDAINE, EDWARD. First Victoria Directory, Second Issue, and British Columbia Guide. 82 pp., cloth. Victoria, 1868. $20.00

Smith 2355.

1009 MALLINSON, FLORENCE LEE. My Travels and Adventures in Alaska. 200 pp., 8vo, original wrappers. Seattle, 1914. $7.50

Smith 2360 reports one copy. The author was for nine years a resident of Alaska.

1010 [MALTE-BRUN.] Neuestes Gemalde von Amerika und seinen Bewolnern. Aus dem Franzosischen ubers, und mit Zusatzen vermehrt von E. W. von Greipel. 4to, unbound (title-page slightly soiled). Leipzig, 1819. $15.00

30 pages are devoted to a description of the Northwest Coast of America, and there is also a chapter on California.

1011 [MALTE-BRUN.] Universal Geography; or, a Description of all parts of the world. . . . Vol. 4, containing the description of America. 615 pp., 8vo, calf. Boston, 1826. $8.50

1012 [MANITOBA.] Statutes of Manitoba, Second Session of Second Parliament. 134 pp., 8vo, original wrappers. Winnipeg, 1876. $7.50

1013 MANLY, WM. L. Death Valley in '49, Important Chapter of California Pioneer History. Illus. 8vo, cloth. San Jose, Cal., 1894. $14.50

Original Edition. Nearly the entire work is devoted to the author's experiences during twelve months' crossing the Plains, and to the desperate experience of his party in Death Valley, where they narrowly escaped a fate less tragic than that of the Donner Party.

1014 MANNERHEIM, GRAF. C. G. Dritter Nachtrag zur Kaefer-Fauna der Nord-Amerikanischen Laender des Russischen Reiches von Graf C. G. Mannerheim. 181 pp., folding map, original wrappers. Moacau, 1853. $37.50

Very rare. The above is probably the earliest work on the fauna of Alaska. Can locate no other copy.

1015 MANNING, WILLIAM. The Nootka Controversy. From the Annual Report of the American Historical Association for the Year 1904. 8vo, cloth. Washington, 1905. $7.50

Smith 2361. The Justin Winsor Prize Essay. The best account of the controversy, containing an important bibliography.

1016 MANRING, B. F. The Conquest of the Coeur d'Alenes, Spokanes and Palouses: The Expeditions of Col. E. J. Steptoe and George Wright against the Northern Indians in 1858. Large folding map, portraits and plates. 280 pp., 8vo, cloth. Spokane: Privately Printed, N.d. (1912). $7.50

An important historical work based on original sources and personal knowledge of actors in the events recorded, the result of years of research. It also has an important bibliography.

1017 MANYPENNY, GEO. W. Our Indian Wards. 436 pp., 8vo, cloth. Cincinnati: Robert Clarke and Co., 1889. $7.50

Pays particular attention to the Chivington campaign: destruction of Fetterman's command; attempt to exterminate the New Mexico and Arizona Indiana; massacre of the Apaches at Camp Grant; the Custer Defeat and Sioux War; miiltary operations in Montana, 1869-70; and other campaigns.

1018 MARBOIS, BARBE. The History of Louisiana, particularly of the cession of that Colony of the U. S. of America. 8vo, half calf. Phila., 1830. $12.50

1019 MARCEL, GABRIEL. Reproductions de cartes et de Globes relatifs a la Decouverts de l'Amerique du xvie au xviiie seicle, avec texte explicatif. 146 pp., 2 vols., folio (Text and Atlas with 40 Sheets). Original wrappers. Paris, 1893. $37.50

Notable for its very fine reproductions of rare maps. Smith locates only the copy at Victoria.

1020 MARCHAND, ETIENNE. Voyage autour du Monde, pendant les annees 1790-92. Precede d'une introduction Historique; auquel on a joint Recherches sur les Terres Australes de Drake, et un Examen Critique du Voyage de Roggeween. Par C. P. Claret Fleurieu. 4 vols., 4to. Fine clean sound set with all the maps. Paris, 1798-1800. $65.00

The original and best edition. Smith 1261. Marchand's expedition sailed round the Horn, turned northward, and after touching at the Marquesas Islands, visited Norfolk Sound, Queen Charlotte Islands, Nootka Sound, and other parts of the Northwest Coast of America. He gives interesting descriptions of those places and of the island inhabitants. The work is also valuable for its scientific observations and the learned researches of the author on the early navigators.

1021 MARCHAND, ETIENNE. Die Neueste Reise um die Welt in den Jahren 1790-92. 2 vols., maps and plates. Leipzig, 1802. $17.50

See Smith 1261 and 1262.

1022 MARCY, CAPT. R. B. Prairie Traveler: A Hand-Book for Overland Expeditions. With maps, illustrations and itineraries of the Principal Routes between the Mississippi and the Pacific. 340 pp. N. Y., 1859. $7.50

Wagner-Camp 335. "Very few had a better knowledge of the western plains than Capt. Marcy, and his experience is here reduced to a compendium of prairie life."

1023 MARCY, CAPTAIN R. B. Thirty Years of Army Life on the Border, comprising descriptions of Indian Nomads of the Plains; explorations of new Territory; a trip across the Rocky Mountains in the winter; descriptions of the habits of different Animals found in the west, and the methods of Hunting them; with incidents in the life of different frontier men. 442 pp., illus., 8vo, cloth, uncut. N. Y., 1866. $7.50

1024 MARCY, CAPT. R. B. Border Reminiscences. 396 pp., 8vo, cloth, illus. N. Y., 1872. $5.00

1025 MARGRY, PIERRE. Memoires et Documents pour servir a l'Histoire des Origines Francaise des Pays outre-mer: Decouvertes et Etablissment des Francaise dans L'Ouest et dans le Sud, de Amerique Septentrionale (1614-1698). Portraits, maps, facsimiles. 6 vols., original printed wrappers. Paris, 1879. $50.00

Vol. 6 contains: Exploration des affluents du Mississippi et decouverts de Montagnes Roucheues (1679-1754). Smith 2372.

1026 [MARINE RESEARCH SOCIETY.] The Sea, the Ship, the Sailor. Tales of Adventure from Log Books and Original Narratives. 253 pp., illus. 8vo, cloth. Salem, 1925. $15.00

Contains narratives of the adventures of Capt. Barnard, of New York, during a voyage round the world in 1812-1816; adventures of John Nichol, who was with Portlock on the N.W. Coast; journal of the Brig "Spy"; remarkable transactions at Tompa Island; narrative of John Bartlett, of Boston, in 1790-1793 during voyages to Canton, the N.W. Coast, etc. The latter has never been before published.

1027 MARKHAM, MRS. ELIZABETH. Poems of Mrs. Elizabeth Markham, an Oregon Pioneer of 1847-1857. 8vo, cloth. Portland: Gill, 1921. $4.00

1027a MARKHOV, ALEKSANDR. Russkie na Vostochnom Okeanie. Vostochmaia Sibirj. Rossiiskiia Vladieniia v Amerikie. Rvt Dikarei. Kaliforniia. Proekt Krugosvietnoi Torgovoi Ekspeditsii. (The Russians on the Pacific Ocean. Eastern Siberia. Russian Possessions in America. Condition of the Natives. California. Plan for a Trading Expedition round the World) 8vo, calf. Moscow, 1849. $37.50

Wickersham, 5801.

1028 MARRYAT, FRANK. Mountains and Molehills; or, Recollections of a Burnt Journal. Fine colored plates. 8vo, calf. London, 1855. $17.50

Relates to San Francisco and early California history, including the mines at Weaversville, etc.

1029 MARRYAT, CAPTAIN FREDERICK. Narratives of the Travels and Adventures of Monseiur Violet in California, Sonora and Western Texas. Folding map. 3 vols., 8vo, original decorated crimson cloth. London, 1843. $17.50

Wagner-Camp 97. Original Edition. Violet's travels carried him east of the Pacific coast as far as the Snake River, north to the Oregon country, and south to Santa Fe. Gregg, in his "Commerce of the Prairies," accuses Marryat of lifting whole episodes from his contributions to the newspapers, but Wagner points out that the narrative is based on the crude geographical knowledge of the thirties.

1030 MARSH, E. L. Where the Buffalo Roamed: The Story of Western Canada. Illus. 12mo, cloth. Toronto, 1908. $3.75

1031 MARSH, SIDNEY H. An Inaugural Discourse by the President of Pacific University, Oregon. 20 pp., 8vo. Burlington, Iowa, 1856. $4.75

1032 MARSHALL, EDWARD WINSLOW. The Life and Public Services of Schuyler Colfax. 512 pp., 8vo, cloth. Bancroft: San Francisco, 1868. $7.50

1033 MARSHALL, ORSAMUS H. The Historical Writings of. Relating to the Early History of the West. Maps and plates. 4to, cloth. Albany, 1887. $7.50

Deals mainly with the Great Lakes and Niagara frontier, with accounts of the expeditions of Champlain, Nonville, La Salle, etc.

1034 MARSHALL, R. B. Profile Surveys of the Snoqualmie, Sultan and Skykomish Rivers, Washington. 7 pp., 12 profile folding maps. 8vo. Washington, 1914. $4.50

1035 MARSHALL, W. I. Acquisition of Oregon and the Long Suppressed Evidence about Marcus Whitman. Portrait. 818 pp., 2 vols., 8vo, cloth. Seattle, 1911. $27.50

A monumental work of which only 200 copies were printed. The author is considered the best authority upon the subject and spent 25 years gathering materials for his work. The book is essential to any complete library bearing upon the history of Oregon, Washington, Wyoming, Idaho and Montana.

1036 MARSHALL, W. I. History vs. the Whitman Saved Oregon Story. Three Essays towards a true History of the Acquisition of the old Oregon Territory (being nearly one-twelfth of all our domain on this continent), which was the longest, most remarkable—and when truly told—the most interesting struggle we have ever made for Territory. 92 plus 16 pp., 8vo, cloth. Chicago, 1904. $7.50

Smith 2382.

1037 MARSHALL, W. I. (The) Hudson's Bay Company's Archives furnish no Support to the Whitman Saved Oregon Story. 36 pp., 8vo, original wrappers. Chicago, 1905. $4.50

1038 MARSHALL, W. P. Afloat on the Pacific; or, Notes of Three Years' Life at Sea. Comprising Sketches of People, Places and Things Along the Pacific Coast (California) and among the Islands of Polynesia, Visited during several Voyages. Plates. 12mo, cloth. Zanesville, Ohio, 1876. $12.50

Privately printed. An apparently unrecorded volume on early California and the Northwest Coast and California.

1039 MARTIN, CHESTER. Red River Settlement. Papers in the Canadian Archives relating to Pioneers. 27 pp., 8vo, original wrappers. 1910. $4.75

Item 1031, Should read Burlington, Vermont, not Iowa.

1040 MARTIN, HORACE T. Castorologia; or, the History and Traditions of the Canadian Beaver: an Exhaustive Monograph popularly written, numerous full-page illustrations from nature and facsimiles from old authors. 8vo, pictorial cloth. Montreal, 1892. $17.50

Scarce. Probably the most important work on the beaver. It not only records all known scientific facts, habits of life, modes of capture, uses of the animal, but also the legendary lore and fallacies of writers concerning the beaver.

1041 MARTIN, R. M. The Hudson's Bay Territories and Vancouver's Island, with an Exposition of the Chartered Rights, Conduct and Policy of the Hon. Hudson's Bay Corporation. Folding map. 175 pp., 8vo, half calf. London, 1849. $12.50

A scarce and extensive work with detailed information of the climate, physical aspect, geography and territory of the Hudson's Bay holdings, and also with much data concerning the Indian tribes.

1042 MARTINDALE, THOMAS. Hunting in the Upper Yukon. 320 pp., front., 23 plates and a map. 8vo, cloth. Phila., 1913. $5.00

Smith 2391.

1043 MARTYN, WM. FREDERICK. The Geographical Magazine; or, New System of Geography with Beautiful and Correct Views and Maps. 2 vols., 8vo, calf (bindings broken). London, 1793. $15.00

1044 MARTZ, HENRY. The Alaska-Yukon-Pacific Exposition, 1909. 112 pp., illus., 8vo, cloth. Seattle, 1909. $4.00

FIRST REPORT ON THE PROJECT TO BUILD THE B. AND O.

1044a MARYLAND. Proceedings of Sundry Citizens of Baltimore, convened for the purpose of devising the Most Efficient Means of Improving the Intercourse between the City and the Western States. 8vo, sewn, 38 pp., all dges uncut. Baltimore: Printed by William Woody, 1827. $27.50

Rare in the Original State, as the above. In the early 1800's when canal navigation was heaping trade on Philadelphia and New York, apparently to the detriment of Baltimore, a committee of citizens, including Charles Carroll of Carrollton, Isaac McKim, Thomas Ellicott, and others, met to discuss the situation Out of their discussion, among others, grew the first germ for the construction of a railroad from Baltimore to the Ohio; namely, the present Baltimore and Ohio Railroad.

1045 MASON, GEORGE. Lo, the Poor Indian. 8vo, cloth. Victoria, 1875. $7.50

Not in Smith.

1046 MASON, GEORGE. Ode on the Loss of the Steamship "Pacific," November 4th, 1875. 8vo. Nanaimo, B. C., 1875. $7.50

Not in Smith.

1047 MASON, OTIS TUFTON. Aboriginal American Basketry Studies in Textile Art without Machinery. Smithsonian Institute Report, 1902. 784 pp., 8vo, cloth. Washington, 1904. $7.50

1048 [MASSACHUSETTS.] History of the Town of Medford, from its Settlement in 1630 to 1855. By Charles Brooks. 8vo, sheep. Boston, 1855. $7.50

1049 MASSETT, S. C. "Drifting About"; or, what "Jeems Pipes of Pipesville" saw-and-did. Comic illustrations. 371 pp., 12mo, cloth. N. Y., 1863. $5.00

Humorous incidents about California, Oregon, the South Sea, etc.

MASSON'S ACCOUNT OF THE NORTHWEST FUR COMPANY

1050 MASSON, L. R. Les Bourgeois de la Compagnie du Nord-Ouest, recite de voyages, lettres et rapports inedits relatifs au Nord-Ouest Canadien, publies avec esquisse historiques et des annotations. Folding map. Series 1, 2 vols., original wrappers, 154 plus 499 pp. Quebec Cote, 1889. Together with Series 2, 499 pp., one map. Original wrappers. Quebec Cote, 1890. 3 vols., original wrappers. Quebec Cote, 1889-1890. $50.00

Smith 2395 and 2396. An important publication on the Canadian Northwest, dealing with the North West Company; reminiscences of Roderic McKenzie; W. F. Wentzell letters to Mackenzie, 1807-1824; Simon Fraser's Journal from the Rocky Mts. to the Pacific Coast, 1808; extract from the journal of John McDonnell; some account of the Red River about 1797; the Missouri Goal of F. A. Larocque; Charles Mackenzie's journal; John M. Donald of Garth, Notes, 1791-1816; Copies of George Keith's Letters to R. McKenzie; John Johnston's account of Lake Superior, 1792-1807; Duncan Cameron; Peter Grant, etc., etc.

1051 MATHEWS, PERCY W. Notes on the Diseases among the Indians frequenting York Factory, Hudson's Bay. 20 pp., 8vo, original wrappers. Montreal, 1885. $7.50

1052 MATHEWS, WASHINGTON. Ethnology and Philogy of the Hidatsa Indians. By F. V. Hayden. 8vo, cloth. Washington, 1877. $7.50

1053 MATTOON, CHAS. HIRAM. Baptist Annals of Oregon. 464 pp., illus., portraits. 8vo, cloth. McKinnville, Ore.: Press of the Telephone Register Pub. Co., (1905). $10.00

Smith 2397. Smith cites only the copy at Portland.

1054 MAUDE, JOHN. Visit to the Falls of Niagara in 1800. Engraved title and views of the Genesee, Niagara, Horse Shoe and Montmorenci Falls, with others on the Hudson. Royal 8vo, original cloth. London, 1826. $22.50

The author not only describes Niagara, but his journey throughout, and an interesting feature is his mention by name of a large number of gentlemen whom he visited or met during his tour, many of them well known in American society, or locally prominent. As the author says: "A faithful copy of a gentleman's journal."

1055 MAURELLE, FRANCISCO ANTONIO. Voyages Around the World, performed in the Years 1785, 1786, 1787, 1788, by M. de La Peyrouse. To which are added a Voyage from Manilla to California by Don Antonio Maurelle, and an Abstract of the Voyage and Discoveries of the late Capt. George Vancouver. 12mo, calf. Boston, 1801. $12.50

1056 MAURY, MRS. SARAH MYTTON (Hughes). Statesmen of America in 1846. 8vo, cloth (worn). Phila., 1847. $4.50

An English woman's views on Oregon, etc.

1057 MAYER, BRANTZ. Mexico, Astec, Spanish and Republican. A Historical, Geographical and Social Account of that country from the period of the Invasion by the Spaniards to the Present Time . . . Historical Sketch of the Late War and Notices of New Mexico and California. 2 vols. in 1, 8vo, cloth. Hartford, 1852. $7.50

1058 MAYER, FRANK B. With Pen and Pencil on the Frontier in 1851. The Diary and Sketches of Frank Blackwell Mayer. Edited with Introduction and Notes by Bertha L. Heilbron, &c. 214 pp., illus., 8vo, cloth. St. Paul, 1932. $4.50

1059 MAYNARD, DAVID S., and MAYNARD, CATHERINE T. Biographies of two of the Oregon Immigrants of 1850. Containing the Narrative of their Journey across the Continent; participation in the Beginnings of Washington Territory; trip to California in 1851; founding and naming of "Seattle"; war with the Indians; life among the Savages. 83 pp., 8vo, original wrappers. Seattle, 1906. $20.00

Rare in the state as above noted. The Overland Journal is in day-by-day form. "The immigrants tired of themselves and of each other. Stretching out these conditions for a period of five months drove some of the participants into suicide, others into insanity, and left many a physical wreck for whom there was no possibility of recovery."—Preface.

1060 MAYNE, R. C. Four Years in British Columbia and Vancouver Island. An Account of their Forests, Rivers, Coasts, Gold Fields and Resources for Colonization. Map and illus. 468 pp., 8vo, original cloth. London, 1862. $10.00

Smith 2401. Gives an account of San Francisco and the Vigilantes.

1061 MAXIMILLIEN DE WIED-NEUWIED, PRINCE. Reise in das Innere Nord-Amerika in den Jahren 1832 bis 1834. 2 vols., 4to, cloth. Coblenz, 1839-1841. Together with large Folio Atlas containing 81 colored plates, each with the Bodmer embossed stamp. Folio, half russia, with the legends in French, German and English, and with the title-page illuminated in many colors and designs, suggesting Indian beadwork. Together with the large folding map. London: Ackerman, 1844. 3 vols., folio and 4to. Coblenz and London, 1839-1844. (Sold)

Wagner-Camp 76 with the complete German text, and perhaps one of the most magnificent sets of this valuable work to be offered in many years.

1062 MAXWELL, WM. A. Crossing the Plains: Days of '57, &c. 12mo, original wrappers. (San Francisco, 1915). $3.50

1063 MAY, COL. JOHN. Journal and Letters relative to two Journeys to the Ohio Country, 1788-1789; with Biographical Sketch of Edes and Notes by Darlington. Large 8vo, cloth. 160 pp. Cincinnati, 1873. $27.50

Scarce. The author, a Revolutionary officer, left Boston in April, 1788, proceeding overland on horseback via Philadelphia, Baltimore, and the Laurel Hills to Pittsburgh, there taking a flatboat for Marietta, where he had landed interests. A year later he made a second trip to the Ohio country, this time on a trading venture, going as far as Maysville, Ky. The volume, now very scarce, furnishes an interesting picture of frontier manners and customs of the times.

1064 [MAZAMA.] A Record of Mountaineering in the Pacific Northwest. Illus., maps. Vol. 1, No. 1 to Vol. 6, No. 4. Complete Eighteen Numbers. (Vol. 3, No. 1 is called Annual Number, dated March, 1907; no other numbers of No. 3 were ever printed). 8vo, wrappers. Portland, Ore.: Manzama, 1896-1919. $47.50

Smith 2404 locates no complete set.

1065 [MAZAMA.] Oregon Out of Doors. Mount Hood. Vol. 1, No. 1, Dec., 1920. 8vo, wrappers. Portland: Mazama, 1920. $5.00

1066 [M. E. J.] Day Spring in the Far West Sketches of Mission Work in North West America. 213 pp., 8vo, cloth. London, 1875. $7.50

Smith No. 1900.

1067 MEACHAM, A. B. Wigwam and Warpath; or, The Royal Chief in Chains . . . 700 pp., portraits, plates. 12mo, cloth. Boston, 1875. $6.00

Smith 2405. Cowan, pp. 151-2. The author was superintendent of Indian Affairs in Oregon, and had some thirty years' experience among the Indian tribes of the Northwest.

1068 MEACHAM, A. B. Wi-ne-ma (the Woman Chief) and Her People. 168 pp., illus., 12mo, cloth. Hartford, 1876. $6.00

Adventures among the Modocs by an eye-witness and participant in many of the adventures narrated. Smith 2406.

1069 MEANY, EDMOND S. Art Work of the State of Washington. 122 plates. Folio. Oshkosh, Wis., 1900. $15.00

Mainly composed of full-page plates, but a few pages of text are scattered through the work.

1070 MEANY, EDMOND S. Vancouver's Discovery of Puget Sound: Portraits and Biographies of the Men Honored in the naming of Geographic Features of Northwestern America. 244 pp., portraits, 4 maps. 8vo, cloth. N. Y., 1907. $10.00

A splendid work by one of the foremost scholars of the N.W., now out of print and quite scarce.

1071 MEANY, EDMOND S. Indian Names of Washington. 20 pp., illus., 8vo, original wrappers. Seattle, (1908). $7.50

Item 1066, 215pp., not 213.

1072 MEANY, EDMOND S. History of Washington. The Lewis and Clark Wyeth & Wilkes Expeditions; Hudson's Bay Co., the Joint Occupancy; the Territorial Days; the Indian Wars; Discoveries of Gold, etc. Maps and plates. 406 pp., 8vo, cloth. N. Y., 1909. $5.00

An important historical contribution.

1073 MEANY, EDMOND. Two Studies in the History of the Pacific Northwest. (a) The towns of the Pacific Northwest were not founded on the fur-trade; (b) Morton Matthew McCarver, frontier city builder. 8vo, wrappers. Washington, 1911. $5.00

1074 MEANY, EDMOND S. A New Vancouver's Journal on the Discovery of Puget Sound. 43 pp., 8vo. Seattle, 1915. $4.50

1075 MEANY, EDMOND S. Governors of Washington, Territorial and State. 114 pp., illus., 8vo, cloth. Seattle, 1915. **$6.00**

Limited edition signed by Prof. Meany.

1076 MEANY, EDMOND S. Mount Ranier, a Record of Exploration. Illus. 8vo, cloth. N. Y., 1916. $5.00

1077 MEANY, EDMOND S., and CONDON, JOHN. Washington's First Constitution, 1878, and Proceedings of the Convention. 104 pp., 8vo. Olympia, 1919. $4.00

1078 MEANY, EDMOND S. Origin of Washington, Geographic Names. 357 pp., 8vo, cloth. Seattle, 1923. $20.00

A very valuable work printed in a small edition.

1079 MEANY, EDMOND S. Diary of Wilkes in the Northwest. 8vo, original wrappers. 99 pp. Seattle, 1926. $7.50

THE EARLIEST LOCALLY PRINTED HISTORY OF WASHINGTON TERRITORY, 1870

1080 MEEKER, EZRA. Washington Territory West of the Cascade Mountains, containing a Description of Puget Sound, and Rivers emptying into it. The Lower Columbia, Shoalwater Bay, Gray's Harbor, Timber, Lands, Climate, Fisheries, Ship Building, Coal Mines, Market Reports, Trade, Labor, Population, Wealth and Resources. 52 pp., and six leaves of advertisements. 8vo, original printed wrappers. Olympia, W. T.: Printed at the Transcript Office, 1870. $60.00

Braislin 1292. The rare original edition. The first book on the Territory to be printed within its confines. It is also the first literary production of "Ox-Team Meeker" of Oregon Trail fame. Jay Cook sent for Meeker and bought up the entire edition, not desiring any "competition" in his Northwest publicity campaign.

1081 MEEKER, EZRA. Hop Culture in the United States, being a practical Treatise on Hop Growing in Washington Territory, from the cutting to the bale. By Ezra Meeker, with Fifteen Years' Experience of the Author, etc. 170 pp., front., illus., 8vo, cloth. Privately Printed: Puyallup, Wash., (1883). $20.00

Next to the History this is Meeker's rarest work. Smith 2429.

1082 MEEKER, EZRA. Pioneer Reminiscences of Puget Sound, the Tragedy of Leschi. An Account of the coming of the first Americans and the Establishment of their Institutions; their encounters with the Native Race; the first Treaties with the Indians and the War that followed; Seven Years of the Life of I. I. Stevens in Washington Territory; Cruise of the Author on Puget Sound 50 Years ago; Nisqually House and the Hudson Bay Co. . . . 554 pp., illus., portraits. 8vo, cloth. Seattle, 1905. $8.00

Smith 2434.

1083 MEEKER, EZRA. The Ox Team; or, the Old Oregon Trail, 1852-1906. 248 pp., illus., 8vo, cloth. Omaha, (1906). $3.75

1084 MEEKER, EZRA. Personal Experiences on the Oregon Trail Sixty Years ago. 150 pp., 8vo, original wrappers. Seattle: Meeker, 1912. $5.00

Smith 2433.

1085 MEEKER, EZRA. Story of the Lost. 31 pp., 8vo, original wrappers. N.p., 1915. $3.75

1086 MEEKER, EZRA. The Busy Life of Eighty-Five Years of Ezra Meeker. Ventures and Adventures; Sixty Three Years of Pioneer Life in the old Oregon Country; an Account of the Author's Trip across the Plains with an Ox Team, 1852, etc. 399 pp., illus., 8vo, cloth. (Seattle), 1916. $5.00

1087 MEEKER, EZRA, and DRIGGS, HOWARD R. Ox Team Days on the Oregon Trail. 225 pp., 8vo, cloth. N. Y., 1922. $3.00

1088 MEEKER, EZRA. Kate Mulhall; a Romance of the Oregon Trail. 287 pp., 8vo, cloth. N. Y., 1926. $3.50

1089 MEEKER, EZRA. Uncle Ezra's Short Stories for Children. 100 pp., 8vo, original wrappers. Tacoma, N.d. $4.00

Smith 2437. Pioneer stories by an old pioneer.

1090 MEEKER, EZRA. Story of the Lost Trail to Oregon. 31 pp., 8vo, original wrappers. Seattle, N.d. $3.75

1091 MELINE, JAMES F. Two Thousand Miles on Horseback. Santa Fe and back. A Summer Tour through Kansas, Nebraska, Colorado and New Mexico, in the year 1866. Folding map. 317 pp., 12mo, cloth. N. Y., 1867. $4.00

1092 MELISH, JOHN. A Geographical Description of the United States with the contiguous British and Spanish Possessions, intended as an Accompaniment to Melish's Map of those Countries. 179 pp., 4 maps., 4to, calf. Phila., 1816. $20.00

1093 [MEMOIRS FOR THE CURIOUS] from Jan., 1707 to December, 1708. Containing an Abstract of the most Valuable Things that have been Published at Home and Abroad. 2 vols. in one. 4to, calf. London, 1710. $35.00

A periodical monthly work published by the celebrated James Pettiver in sixpenny quarto numbers throughout the years 1707 and 1708. The work contains a Voyage to the Islands of Jamaica; a Relation of West India Animals; a letter from Admiral Bartholomew de Fonte, Admiral of New Spain and Peru, etc. Relates to the Northwest Coast.

1094 MENDERHALL, WALTER C. Geology of the Central Copper Region, Alaska. 133 pp., maps. 4to, cloth. Washington, 1905. $5.00

1095 MENEFEE, C. Historical and Descriptive Sketch Book of Napa, Sonoma Lake and Mendocino: Comprising Sketches of their Topography, History, etc. 8vo, plates, cloth. Napa City, 1873. $7.50

1096 MENGARINI, GREGORY. A Selish or Flat-Head Grammar. 8vo, cloth. Cramoisy: New York, 1861. $20.00

Rare. Not in Smith. The above copy is a presentation copy from Father De Smet to Dr. F. V. Hayden.

1097 MERCER, A. S. Powder River Invasion. War on Rustlers in 1892. 12mo, cloth. N.p. (1923). $7.50

1098 MERIETH, WILL J. In Love of Nature. 50 pp., 8vo. Seattle, 1900.

Originally published at Cheyenne in 1894 as "The Banditti of the Plains; or, the Cattlemen's Invasion of Wyoming."

$4.50

Smith 2460. Poetry of Puget Sound.

1099 MERIWETHER, LEE. The Tramp at Home. 296 pp., 8vo, cloth. N. Y., 1889. $7.50

Chapters 12-15 deals with Washsington, Idaho and Nevada, and California.

1100 MERK, FREDERICK. Fur Trade and Empire. George Simpson's Journal. Remarks connected with the Fur Trade, &c. 370 pp., 8vo, cloth. Cambridge, 1931. $7.50

1100a MERKUSHEV, M. Centenary of the Russian Church in America, 1794-1894. Sketch of the History of the American Russian Orthodox Religious Mission, Kadiak Mission, 1794-1837. (Text in Russian). 292 pp., 3 plates. 8vo, original wrappers. St. Petersburg, 1894. $20.00

Wickersham, 5761.

1101 MERRIAM, H. G. Northwest Verse. An Anthology. 355pp., 8vo, cloth. Caldwell, Idaho, 1931. $3.75

1102 MERRICK, GEORGE BYRON. Old Times on the Upper Mississippi, The Recollections of a Steamboat Pilot from 1854 to 1863. Illus. 8vo, cloth. Cleveland, 1909. $17.50

1103 MERRITT, H. CLAY. The Shadow of the Gun. 450pp., illus., 8vo, cloth. Chicago, 1904. $12.50

Original Edition. Privately printed and now quite scarce. Hunting for the market in the early days of the old West.

1104 MERWIN, HENRY CHILDS. The Life of Bret Harte, with some Account of the California Pioneers. 362 pp., 8vo, cloth (ex. lib.). Boston, 1911. $5.00

1105 [METHODIST EPISCOPAL CHURCH.] Official Journal of the Oregon Annual Conference, 48th Session, 1900. 8vo, original wrappers. Ashland, Ore., 1900. $3.00

1106 [METHODIST EPISCOPAL CHURCH] Official Journal of the Oregon Annual Conference, 55th Session, 1907. 114pp., 8vo, original wrappers. Portland, 1907. $2.50

1107 METIN, ALBERT. La Mise envaleur de la Colombie Britanique: Etude de Colonization. These pour le Doctorat des Lettres presentee a la Faculte des Lettres de l'Universite de Paris. 431pp., plates, map. 8vo, wrappers. Paris, 1907. $15.00

Smith 2474.

1108 MEYER, CARL. Nach Dem Sacramento, Reisebilder eines Heimgekehrten. 12mo, original wrappers. Aarau, 1855. $7.50

The cover shows an attractive lithograph of Sutter's Fort, Indians, mining scenes, etc.

1108a [MICHIGAN.] Lake Superior Railroad. Letter to the Hon. Lewis Cass, by Morgan L. Drake, Esq. 12 pp., folding map. Small 8vo, original printed wrappers. Pontiac, Mich., 1852. $12.50

1109 MIGHELS, HENRY R. Sage Brush Leaves. Port. 335pp., 12mo, morocco. San Francisco, 1879. $10.00

With autographed photograph of the author, together with a sketch of his life and character, by Geo. C. Gorham. The author was born in Norway, Maine, 1830. He was editor of various California newspapers.

1110 MILES, GEN. NELSON A. Annual Report, Division of the Pacific. 74-22pp., 8vo, sewn. San Francisco, 1889. $7.50

Relates to fortifications on Puget Sound and the Pacific Coast.

1111 MILES, NELSON A. Personal Recollections and Observations; or, From New England to the Golden Gate. 591pp., illus. Chicago, 1896. $7.50

History of Oregon, Washington , Alaska; Sioux War; Terry and Cook Expeditions; Custer Fight; Cheyenne campaign; Lame Deer Expedition; Nez Perce campaign; Bannock campaign.

1112 MILES, NELSON A. Serving the Public. Memoirs of the Civil and Military Life of Nelson A. Miles, Lieut. Gen. United States Army. 339pp., illus., 8vo, cloth. N. Y., 1911. $4.75

General Miles devotes the larger part of this book to the Indian Wars subsequent to the Civil War in which he won fame as an Indian fighter.

1113 [MILITARY POSTS TO THE PACIFIC.] N. G. Pendleton. Military Posts from Council Bluffs to Pacific Ocean. Title of the U. S.; French Title; Spanish Title; British Discoveries; American Discoveries, etc., etc. 64pp., map, 8vo. Washington, 1842. $25.00

1114 [MILITARY POSTS TO THE PACIFIC.] N. G. Pendleton. Military Posts: Council Bluffs to the Pacific Ocean. Report of the Committee. Large folding map "United States Territory of Oregon West of the Rocky Mountains, compiled by W. Hood." 78 pp., 8vo, sewn. Washington, 1843. $22.50

Wagner-Camp 100. Contains the reports of Albert, Totten, Towson, Gibson, Elijah White; extracts from Capt Spaulding's Journal; Hudson's Bay Co.; trading and whaling; extracts from Wilkes Journal, etc.

1115 [MILITARY POSTS TO THE PACIFIC.] Military Posts on the Route to Oregon. 29th Cong., 1st Sess. H. R., No. 13. 5pp., 8vo, sewn. Washington, 1845. $10.00

1116 MILLER, CINCINNATUS HEINE. Life among the Modocs; Unwritten History. 400pp., 8vo, ¾ calf. London, 1873. $12.50

Snith 2484. Fine copy of the Original Edition .

1117 MILLER, CINCINNATUS HEINE. Unwritten History; life amongst the Modocs. 445pp., illus., 8vo, cloth. Hartford, 1874. $7.50

Snith 2485.

1118 MILLER, CINCINNATUS HEINE. Songs of the Sierras. 8vo, cloth. Boston, 1875. $2.50

1119 MILLER, CINCINNATUS HEINE. The Ship in the Desert. 205pp., 8vo, cloth. Boston, 1875. $5.00

1120 MILLER, CINCINNATUS HEINE. First Families of the Sierras. 258pp., 8vo, cloth. Chicago, 1876. $7.50

1121 MILLER, GEORGE MELVIN. The Alaska-British Boundary: How to Settle the whole matter without Friction. 8pp., map, 16mo, original wrappers. Skagway, 1902. $15.00

Can locate no other copy. The author was the brother of Joaquin Miller.

1122 MILLER, JOAQUIN. An Illustrated History of the State of Montana. Containing a History of the State of Montana from the Earliest Period of its Discovery to the Present Time, together with Biographical Mention of many of its Pioneers and Prominent Citizens of Today. Ports. Thick 4to, morocco. Chicago, 1894. $27.50

A fine copy of this scarce Montana history.

1123 MILLER, JOAQUIN. The Gold-Seekers of the Sierras. 8vo, cloth. N. Y., (1884). **$5.00**

1124 MILLER, OLIVE THORNE. A Bird Lover in the West. 278pp., 8vo, cloth. N. Y., 1894. $4.75

1125 MILLICAN, ADA B. The Heart of Oregon. Legend of the Wascos. Illus. 8vo, original wrappers. Bend, Ore., (1914). $7.50

Smith 2496. Privately printed in a small edition and now scarce.

1126 MILLS, GEN. ANSON. My Story. Portraits, maps and plates. 412 pp., 12mo, wrappers. Washington, 1918. $10.00

Original Edition. Autographed presentation copy. Gen. Mills gives an intimate detailed account of his adventures on the western borders from 1865 to and through the Indian campaign of 1876. His commands included Fort Fetterman, Wyoming, 1867; Fort Sedgwick, Colo., 1868; Arizona, 1869; Fort McPherson, Neb., 1872; Camp Sheridan and Fort D.A. Russell, 1875. He acted as escort to Gen Dodge on the Reconnaissance to find a route from Salt Lake via the Snake River to Oregon in 1867; occupied a similar position with Lord Dunraven on the latter's hunting expedition on the Loup River in 1873. In 1874 he held back the gold rush into the Black Hills Country; captured Gordon and his armed band, etc., etc.

1127 MILLS, DAVID. A Report on the Boundaries of the Province of Ontario. 418 pp., 10 folding maps. 8vo, cloth. Toronto, 1873. $20.00

An important work written by one of the Special Commissioners to enquire into the location of the northwest boundaries of Ontario. The appendix, pp. 147-418 contain copies of many documents relating to the history and rights of the Hudson's Bay Co.

1128 MILLS, DAVID. Canadian View of the Alaska Boundary Dispute . . . in an Interview with the Correspondent of the Chicago Tribune on the 4th of August, 1899. 23 pp., 8vo, original wrappers. Ottawa, 1899. $15.00

Smith 2498 locates on copy.

1129 MILLS, D. O. Our Fur Seal Fisheries. North American Review, September, 1890. 300 pp. N. Y., 1890. $2.50

1130 MILTON, LEUTE, ET LE DR. CHEALDE. Voyage de l'Amerique au Pacific. 312 pp., map. 12mo, ¾ calf. Paris, 1879. $7.50

1131 MILTON, WM. WENTWORTH FITZWILLIAM, VISCOUNT. History of the San Juan Water Boundary Question, as affecting the Division of Territory between Great Britain and the United States. 446 pp., 2 maps. 8vo, cloth. London, 1869. $27.50

Smith 2501. The Expedition went through Hudson's Bay Territory, and explored much of the unknown country in the neighborhood of the sources of the North Branch of the Thompson River.

1132 MILTON, VISCOUNT and CHEADLE, W. B. The North-West Passage by Land, Being the Narrative of an Expedition from the Atlantic to the Pacific, undertaken with the view of exploring a Route across the Continent to British Columbia through British Territory, by one of the Northern Passes in the Rocky Mountains. Maps and plates. 8vo, cloth (one hinge cracking). London, (1865). $17.50

1133 MINER, W. H. The American Indian North of Mexico. 169 pp., 8vo, cloth. Cambridge, 1917. $5.00

1133a [MINNESOTA.] Minnesota in Three Centuries, 1655-1908. L. F. Hubbard, W. P. Murray, J. H. Baker, and W. Upham (Ed.). 4 vols., 8vo, cloth. Mankato, Minn., 1908. $12.50

1134 MINOR, THOMAS TAYLOR. Early Settlers of Seattle. From Magazine of Western History, May, 1890. Vol. 12, No. 1. 8vo, wrappers. $3.50

"SHAYS' REBELLION"—UNCUT COPY OF THE FIRST EDITION IN THE ORIGINAL WRAPPERS, AS ISSUED

1134a MINOT, GEORGE RICHARDS. The History of the Insurrections in Massachusetts in the Year 1786, and the Rebellion Consequent Thereon. Pp. (2), 111-IV, 5-192. 8vo, original wrappers, totally uncut, as issued. Printed at Worcester, Massachusetts, by Isaiah Thomas, 1788. $100.00

Very rare, especially in the above state. Sabin 49324; Evans 21259; Nichols "Bibliography of Worcester", 142. Minot's work is the principal contemporary authority on the outbreak of discontented soldiers and farmers in western Massachusetts. The rebellion is commemorated in a contemporary ballad beginning:

"My name is Shay; in former days
In Pelham, did I dwell, Sirs .. ."

1135 MINTO, JOHN A. (Pioneer of 1844). Rhymes of Early Life in Oregon and Historical Biographical Facts. Portrait. 32 pp., 8vo, original printed wrappers. Salem, Ore., (1897). $10.00

Privately issued in a few copies. The author, a pioneer of the 1844 emigration, was prominent in the early annals of the territory and here gives interesting sidelights on the contest between the Americans and the Hudson's Bay Co. for the occupation of the disputed territory. He was a partner of Williamson, and discusses at length the quarrel with McLoughlin and the Hudson's Bay Co., and the final break-down of British power in Oregon.

1136 [MISSOURI.] Daily News. History of Buchanan County and St. Joseph, Missouri, from the time of the Platte Purchase to the end of the Year 1898, &c. 567 pp., illus. 8vo, cloth. St. Joseph, (1898). $7.50

1136a [MISSOURI.] Report of the Sec'y of War, transmitting in compliance with a Resolution of the Senate, Documents in relation to the difficulties which took place at the payment of the Sac and Fox annuities last Fall, Aug. 9, 1848. 70 pp., 8vo, unbound. [Washington, 1848.] $3.50

1137 [MISSOURI GAZETTE.] Tuesday, July 26, 1808. St. Louis, Louisiana Territory. 4 pp. Slightly worn at the folds, but sound copy of this rare imprint. $30.00

This is the earliest issue of this publication that has been found, and appears to be the first item published in Missouri of which there is a record.

1137a [MISSOURI AND IOWA BORDER WAR.] Message from the President of the United States communicating Information in relation to the Disputed Boundary Line between the State of Missouri and the Territory of Iowa, Jan. 3, 1840. 20 pp., 8vo, entirely uncut. (Washington: Blair and Reeves, 1840). $12.50

In 1839 Missouri and Iowa Territory were on the verge of hostilities because of a dispute over Missouri's insistence upon taxing certain properties along the disputed borders between the two states. The item above is the official document covering the entire controversy..

1138 [MISSOURI RIVER EXPEDITION.] Letter from the Secretary of War transmitting Information requested by a Resolution of the House of Representatives of the 1st Inst. Reporting the Movements of the Expedition which lately Ascended the Missouri River. 16 pp., H. R. Doc. 117. 8vo, sewn. Washington, 1826. $25.00

1139 MITCHELL, HON. JOHN H. Lewis and Clark Centennial Exposition: Speech of Hon. John H. Mitchell, of Oregon, in the Senate of the U. S., June 27, 1902. 40 pp., 8vo. Washington, 1902. $7.50

Snith 2517.

1140 MOBERLY, HENRY JOHN. When Fur was King. 237 pp., illus., map. 8vo, cloth. London and Toronto, 1929. $7.50

Moberly, a factor of the Hudson's Bay Co., arrived at Norway House in June, 1854. In this work he gives an account of the Plains Indians, Fort Edmonton, Jasper House, Cariboo Gold Rush, the Saskatchewan Brigade, British Columbia, and a vivid account of the fifties and sixties.

1141 MOBERLY, WALTER. The Rocks and Rivers of British Columbia. 102 pp., illus., map. 8vo, cloth. London, 1885. $7.50

Smith 2532.

1142 MOBERLY, WALTER, and ROBINSON, NOEL. Blazing the Trail through the Rockies. The Story of Walter Moberly. Portraits and old historical views. 117 pp., 8vo, original printed wrappers. Vancouver: News-Advertiser Print, N.d. $12.50

Life story of a noted explorer and trail-blazer of the western wilderness. c.1880.

1143 MOCK, F. G. Blue Eye, Story of the People of the Plains. 245 pp., 8vo, cloth. Portland, Ore., 1905. $7.50

1144 MOCK, L. BOYD. The Seattle Spirit. 136 pp., 2 folding maps. 8vo, original wrappers. Seattle, 1911. $7.50

1145 MOLLHAUSEN, BALDWIN. Diary of a Journal from the Mississippi to the Coasts of the Pacific with a United States Government Exploring Expedition. With an Introduction by Alex. von Humboldt. 2 vols., 8vo, half calf. Map and tinted plates. London, 1858. $25.00

Wagner Camp 305. The expedition started from Fort Smith in Arkansas and traversed Indian Territory and New Mexico, arriving on the Pacific Coast at the Seaport of San Pedro, to the north of the California mission of San Diego. Mollhausen was topographical draughtsman and naturalist to the expedition. It is said to be a more intering account of the Whipple Expedition than the official journal.

1146 MOLLHAUSEN, BALDWIN. Reisen in die Felsengebirge Nord-A Amerikas bis zum Hoch-Plateau von Neu-Mexico, unternommen als Mitglied der im Auftrage der Reigerung der Vereinigten Staaten ausgesandten Colorado Expedition, etc. Twelve plates in color and a folding map. 2 vols., 8vo, cloth. Leipzig, 1861. $17.50

See Wagner-Camp 297. This work contains an account of the Ives-Newberry Expedition of 1857 and 1858, and has never been translated.

1147 MONETTE, DR. J. W. History of the Discovery and Settlement of the Valley of the Mississippi, by Spain, France and Great Britain, and the subsequent Occupation, Settlement and Extension of Civil Government by U. S. to 1846. Folding colored maps. 2 vols., 8vo, full calf. N. Y., 1848. $17.50

1148 MONTAGUE, PHIL. S. Ready Reference and Hand Book of the Klondike and Alaskan Gold Fields, containing Maps of both Routes. 58 pp., map. 8vo, original wrappers. San Francisco, (1897). $7.50

Not in Smith.

1149 [MONTANA.] Joset, R. P., and Fouillot, R. P. Letters from Mission de Saint Ignace (Kalispels—Flatheads) Feb., 1847. (In "Rapport de Propagation de la Foi, pp. 153-158. Annales, 1849). 8vo, lacks wrappers. Montreal, 1849. $7.50

1150 [MONTANA.] A Year in Montana. (Excerpted from the Atlantic Monthly, Aug., 1866, pp. 236-250). 8vo. (Boston, 1866). $2.50

1151 [MONTANA.] Montana for the Farmer. 62 pp., illus., wrappers. N.p., 1924. $2.50

1152 [MONTANA.] Contributions to the Historical Society of Montana. Vols. 1 to 8 (First Editions). 1876-1917. Portraits. 8 vols., 8vo, original cloth. Helena, 1876-1917. $57.50

With many valuable historical contributions on the Indians, pioneer days, expeditions, etc. The contents of some of the earlier volumes are cited by Wagner.

1153 MONTGOMERY, RICHARD G. The White-Headed Eagle. John McLaughlin, Builder of an Empire. 358 pp., illus., 8vo, cloth. N. Y., 1934. $5.00

1154 MOONEY, JAMES. The Siouan Tribes of the East. 10 pp., map. 8vo, original wrappers. Washington, 1894. $5.00

1155 MOONEY, JAMES. Indian Missions North of Mexico. 909 pp., 8vo, original wrappers. Washington, 1907. $7.50

1156 MOORE, CHARLES. The Northwest under Three Flags, 1635-1796. Maps and illus. 8vo, cloth. N. Y., 1900. $12.50

The early French occupation of the Northwest, Cadillac founds Detroit, the English in the Ohio Country, Pontiac War, the English victory and conquest of 1760. Quebec Act and the Revolution, Revolution in the Northwest, and later campaigns against the Indians down to the campaigns of General Wayne.

1157 MOORE, O. M. Washington Illustrated, including Views of the Puget Sound Country and Seattle, the Gateway of the Orient, with Glimpses of Alaska. 113 pp., illus. Seattle, (1901). $7.50

Smith 2558. An album of views alternating with descriptive text.

1158 MOORE, PHILIP D. Catalogue of the Washington State Library. 329 pp., 8vo, cloth. Olympia, 1891. $7.50

1159 MOORES, CHAS. B. Oregon Pioneer Wa-Wa. A Compilation of Addresses of Charles B. Moores relating to Oregon Pioneer History. 141 pp., original wrappers. N.p., N.d. (1923). $12.50

Scarce. Not in Smith. The work comprises 15 different historical addresses delivered at various times and places from 1880. The work was privately printed by the author for his friends.

NARRATIVE OF JOSIAH MOOSO, AMERICAN FUR COMPANY TRAPPER

1160 MOOSO, JOSIAH. The Life and Travels of Josiah Mooso. A Life on the Frontier among the Indians and Spaniards not seeing the Face of a White Woman for Fifteen Years. Portrait. 400 pp., 12mo, original cloth. Winfield, Kansas: Telegram Print, 1888. $25.00

Privately issued by the author at the age of 85 years. From about 1828 he was a Mississippi flatboat-man; trapper for the American Fur Co. on the Yellowstone and Columbia; Hunter, Indian captive, California pioneer of 1843; and wanderer through all the west. It is one of the most interesting narratives .ever written by a pioneer frontiersman and trapper.

1161 MCRESBY, ADMIRAL JOHN. Two Admirals, Sir Fairfax Moresby and John Moresby, a Record of a Hundred Years. 343 pp., 12mo, cloth. London, 1913. $7.50

Sir John Moresby arrived at Vancouver Island, May 24, 1852 as Gunnery Lieut, of which he gives a graphic account. He gives a very interesting account of an expedition he made under the command of Governor Douglas to apprehand and capture two natives charged with the murder of a Scot near Fort Vancouver.

1162 MORICE, A. G. Carrier Sociology and Mvthology. (From Transactions of the Royal Society of Canada, Sept. 2, 1892. Pp. 109-126). 8vo. Ottawa, 1892. $6.00

1163 MORICE, A. G. Carrier Prayer-Book, containing, together with unusual Formularies, a Complete Collection of Hymns, Catechisms, Directions Relative to Various Points of Catholic Life. 328 pp., 16mo, morocco. Stuart's Lake Mission, 1901. $15.00

A very rare work in phonetic characters of which we have been unable to locte another copy.

1164 MORICE, A. G. A First Collection of Minor Essays, Mostly Anthropological. 74 pp., original wrappers. Quesnel, B. C., 1902. $37.50

Smith 2557. Father Morice, for many years Missionary to the western Denes, is considered the best authority on the Indians of western Canada. The work contains a plea for the poor "Digger Indians"; a description of the Atnas and Carriers; their language, manners and customs; the Dene Syllabary and its advantages. This little work was printed by the Mission Press, and anly one copy has been located, that in the Legislative Library at Victoria.

1165 MORICE, A. G. The Nah-ane and their Language. 8vo, original wrappers. Toronto, 1903. $5.00

Not in Smith.

1166 MORICE, A G. History of the Northern Interior of British Columbia, formerly New Caledonia (1660 to 1880). Illus., map. 8vo, cloth. London, 1906. $7.50

1167 MORICE, A. G. Aux Sources de l'Histoire Manitobaine. 120 pp., 8vo, original wrappers. Quebec, 1908 $7.50

Not in Smith.

1168 MORICE, A. G. Dictionnaire Historique des Canadiens et des Metis Francais de l'Ouest. 329 pp., original wrappers. Quebec, 1908. $17.50

Smith 2565 locates only the copy at the University of Washington. This work contains much valuable material in early fur traders.

1169 MORICE, A. G. Aux Sources de l'Histoire Manitobaine. 121 pp., 8vo, original wrappers. One of 200 copies. Quebeck, 1908. $10 00

1170 MORICE, A. G. History of the Catholic Church from Lake Superior to the Pacific. 1659-1895. 776 pp., large folding map and plates 2 vols., 8vo, cloth. Toronto, 1910. $17.50

Smith 2569 Fur trade; Red River Settlement; life among the Blackfeet, 1839-43; Red River Insurrection; Saskatchewan Rebellion; etc. An important historical work.

1171 MORICE, A. G. Histoire de l'Eglise Catholique dans l'Ouest Canadien du Lac Superieur au Pacifique, (1659-1905). Plates, portrait, facsimiles. 3 vols., 8vo, cloth. Winnipeg, 1912. $17.50

Smith 2568.

1172 MORICE, A. G. Disparus et Survivants Etudes Ethnographique sur les Indiens de l'Amerique du Nord. 371 pp., front. 8vo, cloth. Winnipeg, 1928. $12.50

No. 34 of a small edition.

1173 MORICE, A. G. Fifty Years in Western Canada, being the Abridged Memoirs of A. G. Morice. 257 pp., illus., 8vo, cloth. Toronto, 1930. $7.50

1174 MORICE, A. G. The Carrier Language. 2 vols., large 8vo, cloth. Weiner, Austria, 1932. $27.50

Not in Smith.

1175 MORICE, R. P. Zoilus Redivivus ou un Critique Critique. Lettre a A.M.A. H. de Tremaudan. 24 pp., 8vo, original wrappers. N.p., N.d. $7.50

1176 MORISON, SAMUEL ELIOT. The Maritime History of Massachusetts, 1783-1860. 401 pp., illus. Large 8vo, cloth. Boston, (1922). $10.00

Early New England traders on the Northwest Coast.

1177 [MORMONS.] The Book of the Mormon. Translated by Joseph Smith. Third Ed., carefully revised by the Translator. Plates. 16mo, calf. Nauvoo, 1840. $10.00

1178 [MORMONS.] Handbook of Mormonism. 12mo, wrappers. Salt Lake City, 1882. $4.50

1179 [MORMONS.] A Hand-Book of Reference to the History, Chronology, Religion and Country of the Latter-Day Saints. 157 pp., 12mo, cloth. Salt Lake, 1884. $10.00

Scarce and important work.

1180 MORRELL, ABBY JANE. Narrative of a Voyage to the Ethiopic and South Atlantic Ocean, Indian Ocean, Chinese Sea, North and South Pacific Ocean in the Years 1829-31. 230 pp., 8vo, cloth. N. Y., 1833. $7.50

1181 MORRELL, BENJAMIN. Narrative of four voyages to the South Sea, North and South Pacific Ocean, Chinese Sea, Ethiopic, from the Years 1822 to 31 . . . to which is prefaced a brief Sketch of the Author's early life. 429 pp., prtrait. N. Y., 1832. $22.50

Original Edition. Smith 2579 locates two copies.

The second of these voyages was to California. Morrell, in the "Tartar", reached San Diego in April, 1825. He spent some two weeks in the southern port and then joined a "hunting party" on an expedition into the interior. They traveled eastward until they came upon the "Apacherians", who attacked and drove them back to the coast. Returning to San Diego, Morrell sailed to Monterey and San Francisco, thence to Oregon and the Sandwich Islands. He describes the country and inhabitants; the missions; Indians; manners and customs; the routes; inland regions; the fur trade; Russian encroachments in the Northwest, and warns of the need of planting a colony in the Oregon country "under the protection of the National Banner lest our claim to the country be laughed at."

1182 MORRIS, ALEXANDER. Hudson's Bay and Pacific Territories. 57 pp., 8vo, original wrappers (restored). Montreal: Lovell, 1859. $20.00

Cannot locate another copy.

1183 MORRIS, MRS. JAMES EDWIN. The Travels of a Barnacle. 103 pp., front. 8vo, cloth. N. Y., (1901). $3.50

Deals with Alaska.

1184 MORRIS, MRS. JAMES EDWIN. A Pacific Coast Vacation. 255 pp., illus. 8vo, cloth (cover spotted). N. Y., (1901). $2.75

Alaska, Washington, Oregon, Calif., Yellowstone, etc.

1185 MORRIS, LUCY LEAVENWORTH WILDER. Old Rail Fence Corners. The A.B.C.'s of Minnesota History. 326 pp., illus., 8vo, cloth. [Austin, Minn.], 1914. $7.50

An interesting collection of Minnesota pioneer narratives dealing with the settlement and the Indian wars there.

1186 MORRIS, MAURICE O'CONNOR. Rambles in the Rocky Mountains with a Visit to the Gold Fields of Colorado. 8vo, cloth. London, 1864. $7.50

Wagner-Camp 329.

1187 MORROW, HONORE WILLSIE. We Must March. A Novel of the Winning of Oregon. 427 pp., 8vo, cloth. N. Y., 1925. $3.50

1188 MORROW, HONORE WILLSIE. On to Oregon. The Story of a Pioneer Boy. 247 pp., 8vo, cloth. N. Y., 1926. $3.75

1189 MORROW, WILLIAM G. The Spoilers. (From the California Law Review, Jan., 1916, Vol. 4, No. 2). 8vo. San Francisco, 1916. $3.00

Contains an important Alaska item.

1190 MORSE, JEDEDIAH. Report of the Secretary of War of the U. S., on Indian Affairs, comprising a Narrative of a Tour performed in the Summer of 1820 . . . for . . . ascertaining . . . the actual state of the Indians in our country. 400 pp., map, plates. 8vo, ¾ morocco, edges uncut. New Haven, 1822. $10.00

Wagner-Camp 25. A beautiful handbound copy with untrimmed edges. "The most complete and exhaustive report on the condition, numbers, names, territory, and general affairs of the Indians ever made"—Field.

1191 MORSE, MARY GAY. Lore of the Olympic-Land. 157 pp., cloth. N.p., N.d. (1924). $5.00

Siwash Legends.

1191a MOSER, JEFFERSON F. Alaska, Hydrographic Notes, Sailing Directions, and Charts of Surveys relating to the Vicinity of Prince William's Sound, Cook's Inlet, Kadiak Islands, etc. 121-142 pp., with 6 large folding maps. 4to, original wrappers. Washington, 1899. $7.50

MORTIMER'S VOYAGE TO THE NORTHWEST COAST IN THE FUR TRADE

1192 MORTIMER, LIEUT. GEORGE. Observations and Remarks made during a Voyage to the Sandwich Islands, the Fox Islands and the Northwest Coast of America, &c. Folio, 72 pp., maps and plate. London, 1791. $150.00

Smith locates but one copy of this work. The author was Lieut. of Marines aboard the Brig "Mercury" in which the trip was made. He dedicates the work to the Commander of the Expedition, John Henry Cox, "who excited by a laudable curiousity to explore remote regions, and a desire to add to the science of geography and nautical knowledge, undertook a difficult and perilous voyage to the Northwest Coast." In the introduction, however, Mortimer somewhat qualifies the valiant Cox's altruism and admits that "through the voyage was chiefly undertaken from motives of curiousity, the Fur Trade on the Northwest Coast of America was the ultimate object."

1193 MORVILLO, FATHER ANTHONY, S. J. Dictionary of the Numpi or Nez Perce Language, by a Missionary of the Society of Jesus in the Rocky Mountains. English-Nez Perce. 242 pp., 8vo, original wrappers. St. Ignatius Mission Press, Montana, 1895. $37.50

This was attributed to Father Cataldo and others. But we have been informed by Father Neate and others that Father Morvillo is the author. Very few copies of this work were printed at the mission press and only a few copies have been located.

1194 MOSELEY, H. N. Oregon: Its Resources, Climate, People, and Productions. Folding map. 16mo, cloth. London, 1878. $7.50

1195 MOSER, CHARLES. Reminiscences of the West Coast of Vancouver Island. 191 pp., illus., 8vo, cloth. Kakawis, B. C. $7.50

1196 MOSER, JEFFERSON F. Salmon and Salmon Fisheries of Alaska, 1898. 178 pp., illus. 8vo, cloth. Washington, 1899. $5.00

Smith 2592.

1197 [MOUNT VERNON (Wash.) HERALD.] Skagit County, Washington. 96 pp., illus. Mount Vernon, 1921. $7.50

1198 MOUNTAIN, ARMINE W. A Memoir of George Jehoshaphat Mountain, D.D.D.C.L., Late Bishop of Quebec. 477 pp., 8vo, cloth. Montreal, 1866. $10.00

1199 [MOUNTAIN, GEORGE JEHOSHAPHAT.] Journal of the Bishop of Montreal, during a visit to the Church Missionary Society's Northwest Ameirca Mission . . . 166 pp., 4 plates, map. 8vo, cloth. London, 1845. $20.00

Original Edition. Smith 2594. Gives an account of a journey from La Chine to the Red River and a description of the Indians of the Fur Country, their condition, superstitions, mode of life, etc.

1200 [MOUNTAIN, GEORGE JEHOSHAPHAT.] Songs of the Wilderness; being a collection of poems written in some different parts of the territory of the Hudson's Bay Company and in the Wilds of Canada, on the route to that territory in the Spring and Summer of 1844 . . . 153 pp., 4 plates. 8vo, cloth. London, 1846. $17.50

Smith 2595.

1201 MOWERY, WILLIAM. Territorial Growth of the United States. Our Title to Oregon. Magazine of American History. Vol. 16, p. 333. 4to, original wrappers. N. Y., 1886. $3.50

1202 MOWRY, WILLIAM AUGUSTUS. Marcus Whitman and the Early Days of Oregon. 341 pp., plates, maps. 8vo, cloth. N. Y., [1901.] $5.00

Smith 2599.

1203 MOWRY, WILLIAM AUGUSTUS. American Heroes and Heroism. 223 pp., Illus. 8vo, cloth. N. Y., (1903). $5.00

Contains a chapter on the work of Father Eells and Whitman College.

1204 MOWRY, WILLIAM AUGUSTUS. American Pioneers. 363 pp., illus. 8vo, cloth. N. Y., (1905). $5.00

Contains some of the history of Oregon in the account of the lives of J. A. Sutter, A. L. Lovejoy, and P. H. Burnett.

1205 MUIR, JOHN. Our National Parks. Illus. 8vo, cloth. N. Y., 1901. $7.50

Smith 2605.

1206 MUIR, JOHN. Stickeen. 74 pp., 12mo, cloth. N. Y., 1909. $5.00

Not in Smith.

1207 MUIR. JOHN. The Story of my Boyhood and Youth. 294 pp., 8vo, cloth. N. Y., 1913. $4.50

1208 MUIR, JOHN. Sheep Trails. 391 pp., illus. 8vo, cloth. Boston, 1918. $5.00

Smith 2608.

1209 MULFORD, ISAAC S. Civil and Political History of New Jersey. 8vo, cloth, map. Camden, 1848. $6.00

1210 MULLAN, CAPT. JOHN. Report on the Construction of a Military Road from Fort Walla Walla to Fort Benton. Four large folding maps, 10 plates 363 pp., leaf errata. 8vo, cloth. Washington, 1863. $13.50

Wagner-Camp 393. Contains Mullan's report with itinerary, the engineer's reports, meterological data, etc. The work covers the period from March 1858 to September, 1862.

1211 MULLAN, CAPT. JOHN. Miners' and Travelers Guide to Oregon, Washington, Idaho, Montana, Wyoming and Colorado. Via the Missouri and Columbia Rivers. Accompanied by a General Map of the Mineral Region of the Northern Sections of the Rocky Mountains. Large folding map in colors. Small 153 pp., 8vo. original cloth. N. Y.: Published by William M. Franklin for the Author, 1865. $12.50

Wagner-Camp 418. Privately issued. Mullan was Superintendent of the Northern Pacific Military Wagon Road and a Commissioner of the Northern Pacific Railroad. His guide gives accounts of the first discoveries of gold in Idaho and Montana, and the map (showing from Lake Superior to the Pacific) is particularly valuable and important.

1211a MULLER, GERHARD FREDERICK. Nachrichten von Seereisen und zur See Germachten Entdeckungen, die von Russland aus langs den Kusten des Eimeeres und dem Ostlichen Weltmeere gegen Japan und Amerika Gescheben sind zur Erlauterung einer bei der Academie der Wissenschaften vertertigten Lankart. 8vo, calf. St. Petersburg, 1758. $87.50

Wickersham, 5947-6331. The above is the most important contemporary account of Bering's voyage. Muller was one of the scientists attached to Bering's second voyage. See Golder's "Bibliography of Bering's Voyages", v. 1, p. 359. There was a later edition in 1759.

1211b MULLER, GERHARD FREDERICK. Voyage et Decouvertes faites par les Russes le long des Cotes de la Mer Glaciale & sur l'Ocean Oriental, tant vers le Japon que vers l'Amerique: on y a Joint l'Histoire du Fleuve Amur, dresse sur des Memoires Authentique, publiee par l'Academie des Sciences de St. Petersbourg & Corrigee en dernier lieu; ouvrages traduits de l'Allemand—par C. G. F. Dumas. 2 vols. in one, pp. 388 and 277, one large folding map. 12mo, calf. Amsterdam, 1766. $72.50

Wickersham, 6333.

Item 1211b, Next to last line of title should read 207pp., not 277.

1212 MULLER, HERMAN GERHARD. Oregon and seine Zukunst. Ein Beitrag des fernen Westens. 42 pp., small 8vo, original printed wrappers, uncut. Leipzig, 1872. **$12.50**

Letters on Oregon written from San Francisco.

1213 MUMEY, NOLIE. The Life of Jim Baker, 1818-1898. Trapper, Scout, Guide and Indian Fighter. 237 pp., large folding map, illus. 8vo, cloth back boards. Denver, 1931. $12.50

One of a limited edition of 250 signed copies.

1214 MUNRO, WILFRED HAROLD. Tales of an old Sea Port. 292 pp., 8vo, cloth. Princeton, 1917. $7.50

Has some account of "Norwest John" D'wolf. Now out of print and scarce.

1215 MULVANEY, CHAS. PELHAM. The History of the Northwest Rebellion of 1885, including a history of the Indian Tribes of Northwestern Canada. Engravings, maps, portraits, etc. 8vo, cloth. Toronto, 1885. $7.50

1216 MUNSON, JUDGE LYMAN E. Pioneer Life on American Frontier; Experience of a Federal Justice on the Trail of a Prairie Schooner, carrying Law into the Western Wilderness. Montana in 1865. 97 pp. Vol. 1, No. 1 of the Journal of American History, 1907. $7.50

1217 MURCHISON, R. I. Address to the Royal Geographical Society, 27th May, 1844. 92 pp., 8vo, sewn. London, 1844.

Relates in part to North America, Dease and Simpson, Cree Language, and communications between the Atlantic and Pacific in the U. S.

1218 [MURIETA, JOAQUIN.] Life and Adventures of the Celebrated Bandit. His Exploits in the State of California. Translated from the Spanish by Frances F. Belle. 8vo, cloth. Chicago, 1925. $4.50

FIRST HISTORY AND DIRECTORY OF THE PUGET SOUND COUNTRY, 1872

1219 MURPHY, J. M., and HARNED. Puget Sound Business Directory, and Guide to Washington Territory, Comprising a correct history of the Territory, an Account of her Agricultural, Commercial and Manufacturing Interests, Climatology, Mineralogy, Inhabitants, Natural Advantages and Industries, together with a Complete and thorough Directory of Olympia, Steilacoom, Seattle, Port Madison, Gamble, Ludlow and Townsend, and Every Town and Hamlet on Puget Sound. 72-116 pp., 8vo, original printed boards. Olympia: Randall H. Hewitt's Job Print, 1872. $75.00

The work is divided in two parts with separate titles; the first being historical and descriptive, the second the actual directory. This pioneer history was published by Randall H. Hewitt, whose published narrative is recorded by Wagner-Camp 391, and is known in but one copy.

1220 MURPHY, JOHN M. Sporting Adventures in the Far West. 12mo, cloth. N. Y., 1880. **$10.00**

Grizzly bears, wolves, buffalo, moose, elk, etc.

1221 MURPHY, THOMAS DOWLER. Oregon the Picturesque, etc. 317 pp., front., 39 plates, map. 8vo, cloth. Boston, 1917. $5.00

1222 [MURRAY, ALEXANDER HUNTER.] Journal of the Yukon, 1847-48. Edited with notes by L. J. Burpee. Map and iilus. 8vo, wrappers. Ottawa, 1910. $13.50

Smith 2630.

1223 MURRAY, CHARLES AUGUSTUS. Travels in North America during the years 1834-36, including a Summer Residence with the Pawnee Tribe of Indians in the remote Prairies of the Missouri. Tinted plates. 2 vols., 8vo, calf, uncut. London, 1839. $10.00

Wagner-Camp 77. Original London Edition in fine uncut condition, the best edition with the plates. A most interesting work by an intelligent observer of the peculiarities of the Pawnees before they had been modified by contact with the Whites.

1224 MURRAY, CHARLES AUGUSTUS. The Prairie Bird. 3 vols., 12mo, original cloth. London, 1844. $30.00

Wagner-Camp 112. Romance of adventures on the prairies among the Osage, Delaware, Sioux and Crow Indians.

1225 MURRAY, CHARLES AUGUSTUS. The Prairie Bird. 12mo, cloth. London, N.d. $1.00

1226 MURRAY, HUGH. Historical and Descriptive Account of British America . . . 3 vols., illus., plates, maps. 8vo, cloth. Edinburgh, 1844. $12.50

1227 [MURRELET, THE.] Volume 1, No. 1, May, 1920 through Vol. 13, No. 2, May, 1932. 8vo, original wrappers. Seattle, 1920-32. $65.00

A magazine devoted to the ornithology of the Northwest Coast, published at Seattle in small limited issues. The above is the office file and is probably the only complete file known.

MYERS' RARE ACCOUNT OF THE NORTHWEST FUR TRADE

1228 MYERS, CAPT. JOHN. Life, Voyages and Travels of, detailing his Adventures during Four Years round the World; his various Enterprises on the Coast of South America, and exhibiting a most Instructive Description of the North-West Trade. 8vo, half calf, neat. London, 1817. $47.50

"I have entered very largely into a description of what is called the North-West Trade"—Preface. An important work which rarely appears in booksellers catalogues.

1229 MYERS, HARRIET WILLIAMS. The Bird's Convention. 81 pp., 8vo, cloth. Los Angeles, (1913). $3.75

1229a [NEBRASKA.] Historical Sketch of the Omaha Tribe of Indians. Nebraska. By Alice C. Fletcher. Plates, folding map. 12 pp., 8vo, original printed wrappers. Washington: Detweiler, 1889 $3.50

1229b [NEW MEXICO.] Illustrated New Mexico. Historical and Industrial. By Wm. G. Ritch. 243 pp., numerous full-page illus., some folding, folding map. Fifth Ed., revised and enlarged. 8vo, original wrappers. Santa Fe, 1885. $7.50

1230 [NOOTKA SOUND.] Bulletin of the Campaign, 1795. 211 pp., small 12mo, calf. London, 1795. $27.50

An excessively rare work containing a first hand report from Lieut. Pearce of his trip to Nootka and conditions there. Not in Smith.

1231 [NOOTKA SOUND CONTROVERSY.] Annual Register; or, a View of the History, Politics and Literature for the Year 1790. 8vo, half calf. London. 1793. $27.50

Smith 103. Cantains state papers relating to the Nootka Sound Controversy; also a message from his Majesty relative to the capture of certain Spanish vessels; also a memorial from Capt. Meares.

1231a NOUVELLES ANNALES DES VOYAGES, de la Geographie et de l'Histoire, &c. First and Second Series. 20 vols., 8vo, half calf. Maps, plates. Published par Mm. J. B. Eyries et Malte-Brun. Paris, 1819-1831. $350.00

A mine of information on Travels in the Western Hemisphere. A complete set is rarely offered

1231b [OKLAHOMA.] Northern and Western Boundary Line of the Creek Country Letter from the Sec'y of War transmitting Capts. Sitgreaves and Woodruff of the Survey of the Creek Boundary Line. 32 pp., flding map (large), unbound. [Washington, 1850.] $7.50

RARE "OREGON REPORT" WITH THE RARE MAP

1232 [OREGON] Report on the Territory of Oregon, by a Committee Appointed at a Meeting of the Citizens of Columbus. to collect information in Relation thereto. 21 pp., 8vo, sewn. With the map. 8vo, old wrappers. Columbus, Ohio: Printed at the Office of the Ohio Statesman, 1843. $825.00 [Sold]

This rare work is not mentioned by Wagner. Present is the rare map intitled "Map of the Territory". The type is small, affording much information on the early history of Oregon. The report is a compilation of all information at the time, information for emigrants, climate, routes of travel, Indians, &c. Among the matters not before published are letters from Caleb Williams, dated at Columbia River, O. T., March 20, 1842 from Titian Peale, son of the artist who spent some time in Oregon as a member of Wilkes' Exploring Expedition; a long letter from Philip Legget Edwards (see Wagner-Camp 48 and 89, wherein is described the only known copy of Edwards' Emigrant Guide). The Braislin copy, No. 1416, brought $510 without the map. Also see item No. 1079 "Americana Collection of Herschel V. Jones".

1232a [OREGON.] Constitutions of Oregon. The Preamble, Constitution, and Schedule adopted by the People of the Territory of Oregon, preparatory to admission into the Union of the States. 23 pp., unbound. 8vo. [Washington, 1858.] **$12.50**

1233 [OREGON.] Excursion to Oregon (1845). Chambers Miscellany of Useful and Entertaining Tracts. 32 pp., 8vo. Edinburgh, 1845. $7.50

Fine copy of this rare work.

1234 [OREGON.] Speech of Mr. Dix, of New York, on the Resolution giving the twelve months' notice for the termination of the joint occupancy of the Oregon Territory, delivered in the Senate of the U. S., Feb. 18 and 19, 1846. 16 pp., 8vo, sewn. N.p. (Washington), 1846. $3.50

Smith 974.

1235 [OREGON TERRITORY.] Ethnological Society of London. Journal of. Vol. 1, 1848. 374 pp., 8vo, cloth. London, 1848. $22.50

Smith 1160 reports only one copy. Contains an article on the language of the Oregon Territory by R. G. Latham, another on the various tribes inhabiting the NW by John Schuler, and other material concerning the territory.

1236 [OREGON.] Methodist Episcopal Church (Portland) Manual. 76 pp., 8vo, cloth. Portland, 1884. $5.00

1237 [OREGON BAPTIST ASSOCIATION.] Minutes of the Baptist Convention held at Mt. Pleasant Butte Church, Linn County, Oregon, July 2, 1868 for the Purpose of Organizing a General Association. Eugene, 1868. Together with the Minutes of the Third Annual Session, Walla Walla, 1870; Fourth Annual Session, Walla Walla, 1871; Fifth Annual Session, Walla Walla, 1872; Sixth Annual Session, Walla Walla, 1873; Ninth, Walla Walla, 1876; Tenth, Walla Walla, 1877; Eleventh, Walla Walla, 1878; Twelfth, Colfax, 1879; Thirteenth, Albany, 1880; Fourteenth, Walla Walla, 1881; Eighteenth, Walla Walla, 1885; Twentieth, Walla Walla, 1887; Twenty-first, Walla Walla, 1888; Twenty-second, Walla Walla, 1889. 8vo. V.p., V.d. $30.00

The very rare collection showing the organization and growth of Baptist affairs in the Northwest.

1238 [OREGON.] Board of Trustees of the Labor Exchange Association of Portland. (Relates to immigration into the N. W.). 8 pp., original wrappers. Portland, 1870. $7.50

1239 [OREGON.] Lane County, Ore. 32 pp., map. 8vo, original wrappers. Eugene, Ore., 1888. $6.00

Not in Smith.

1240 [OREGON.] John Day Valley, Oregon. 32 pp., illus., map. 8vo, original wrappers. N.p., 1905. $4.75

1241 [OREGON.] Albany, Ore. 48 pp., illus. 8vo, original wrappers. (Albany, 1905). $7.50

1242 [OREGON.] Klubo, Eldoinis Partlanda. Oregono Lando de Promeso. 24 pp., 8vo, original wrappers. Portland, 1910. $3.75

1243 [OREGON.] True Account of the Whitman murder by the Rev. J. B. A. Brouillet. 40 pp., 8vo. Ferndale, 1912. $25.00

This excessively rare reprint was issued from the small Mission Press in a limited edition. Smith does not locate a copy.

1244 [OREGON.] Ladd and Bush Quarterly. Vol. 1 to No. 2, Vol. 3, July 12, 1912 to Jan. 16, 1916. $10.00

These volumes contain much on Oregon hitherto unpublished and now almost unprocurable.

1245 [OREGON.] Ladd and Tilton Bank. Oldest in the Northwest. 15 pp., original wrappers. Portland, N.d. $3.50

1246 [OREGON.] (Deady, Mathew P.). Oration. Portland, July 4th, 1885. 33 pp., portrait. 8vo, original wrappers. 1885. $7.50

Judge Deady was a prominent Oregon pioneer. Not in Smith.

1247 [OREGON.] (Deady, Mathew P.). Oration delivered at Roseburg by Mathew L. Deady, LL.D., United States District Judge of Oregon, July 4th, 1877. 8vo. Himes. Portland, 1877. $7.50

Not in Smith.

1248 [OREGON.] (Dell, Sidney). Astoria and Flavel, the chief Seaport of the Columbia River Watershed. 32 pp., illus., 8vo, original wrappers. N.p., N.d. (1893). $7.50

Only one library reports a copy in Smith's check list.

1249 [OREGON.] Dell, Sidney. A Book of Clatsop County. 49 pp., 8vo, original wrappers. Astoria, 1899. $7.50

1250 [OREGON.] (Denman, A. H.). The Name of Tacoma. 93 pp., 8vo. Tacoma, 1924. $2.50

An attempt to justify the name Mount Tacomo.

1251 [OREGON.] (Denny). Genealogy of the Denny Family in Europe and America. Descendants of John Denny of Combs, Suffolk, Eng. 265 illus., 8vo, cloth. Leicester, 1886. $12.50

The Dennys was the first family in Seattle.

RUSSIAN EXPEDITION TO THE NORTHWEST

1252 [PACIFIC NORTHWEST.] (Sagoskin, Lieut.). Denkschriften der Russischen Geographischen Gesellschaft zu St. Petersburg. Four folding maps. 8vo. Weimar, 1849. $40.00

Not in Smith. No other copy has been located. (The above is Vol. 1 only, all that was published). Contains chapters taken from the diary of Lieut. Sagoskin and others on their expedition from St. Petersburg into the interior of Northwestern America.

1253 [PACIFIC RAILWAY.] The Central Pacific Railway of California. The Character of the work, its Progress, Resources, Earnings and Future Prospects, and the advantage of its First Mortgage Bonds. 35 pp., map. 8vo, wrappers. N. Y., 1867. $7.50

1254 PENDLETON, N. G. Military Posts from Council Bluffs to the Pacific Ocean. Folding map. 78 pp., 8vo, sewn. Washington, 1843. $22.50

Wagner-Camp 100. Contains the reports of Abert, Totten, Gibson and Elijah White, with extracts from the Wilkes and Spaulding journals.

1254a [PENNSYLVANIA.] The Keelboat Age on Western Waters. By Leland D. Baldurn. Illus. 8vo, cloth. Pittsburgh, 1941. $3.00

1254b [PENNSYLVANIA.] Council Fires of the Upper Ohio. Narrative of Indian Affairs in the Upper Ohio Valley until 1795. By Randolph C. Downes. Illus. 8vo, cloth. Pittsburgh, 1940. $3.00

1254c [PENNSYLVANIA.] Early Western Pennsylvania Politics. By Russell J. Ferguson. Port. 8vo, cloth. Pittsburgh. 1938. $4 00

1254d [PENNSYLVANIA.] Pioneer Life in Western Pennsylvania. By J. E. Wright and Doris S. Corbett. Illus. 8vo, cloth. Pittsburgh, 1940. $2.50

THE RARE LYON EDITION OF PERRIN DU LAC IN WRAPPERS

1255 PERRIN DU LAC, FRANCOIS MARIE. Voyage dans les deux Louisanes, et chez les nations sauvages du Missouri, par les Etats-Unis, L'Ohio et les provinces qui le bordent, en 1801-1802 et 1803: avec un apercu des moeurs, des usages, de caractere et des coutumes religieuses et civiles des peuples de ces diverses contrees. Par M. Perrin du Lac. Map and illus. 479 pp., 8vo, wrappers. A Lyon, chez Bruysset aine et Buynand, 1805. $60.00 [Sold]

Wagner-Camp 3. The Lyon edition of this work is very rare. Wagner-Camp describes an issue with both the Paris and Lyon imprint. The issue bearing the Lyon imprint is considered to be the first issue. The collation is as follows: Title; half title; leaf of Ded.; 10pp. Preface; 479 pp.; Map and Plate of Mammoth.

1256 PIKE, ZEBULON M. Account of Expeditions to the Source of the Mississippi and through the Western Parts of Louisiana . . . 277-65-53-87 pp. Portrait, map, table. 8vo, original boards, entirely uncut. Phila., 1810. $57.50

COMPLETE RUN OF THE RARE "MONTREAL RAPPORTS"

1257 [RAPPORT DE L'ASSOCIATION DE LA PROPAGATION DE LA FOI.] Complete set of 46 numbers, No. 1, Mai, 1839 to No. 46, Dec., 1846. Etablie a Montreal. 12mo, original printed wrappers. Montreal, 1839-46. $400.00

The Excessively Rare Montreal Reports, which are not to be confused with the Quebec Reports. A complete set, such as the above, is of great historical value with much material pertaining to the greater part of the western plains and the Rocky Mountains during its most important years of development. The letters, journals and reports contained herein received from missionaries throughout the vast region in no way duplicate the material contained in the Quebec Reports.

ROBERTSON'S "OREGON" IN ORIGINAL WRAPPERS

1258 ROBERTSON. (Wyndham, of Virginia). Oregon, our Right and Title, containing Account of Condition of Oregon Territory, its Soil, Climate, and Geographical Position; together with a Statement of the Claims of Russia, Spain, Great Britain, and the United States. Complete with the folding map and appendix. 227 pp., 8vo, original printed wrappers. Washington, 1846. [Sold]

Fine copy of the Original Edition. Only known copy in the Original Wrappers.

1259 ROBINSON, JACOB S. Sketches of the Great West. A Journal of the Santa Fe Expedition kept by Jacob S. Robinson. 8vo, original printed wrappers. Portsmouth: Published by Wm. B. Lowd. 1848. [Sold]

We have given the cover title of the above work. The regular title is: "Sketches of the Great West. A Journal of the Santa Fe Expedition, under Col. Doniphan, which left St. Louis in June, 1846. Kept by Jacob S. Robinson of Portsmouth, N. H., a Member of the Expedition. Portsmouth Journal Press, 1848."

1260 RUSSELL, C. B. Tide Lands: their Story. Illus. 8vo, original wrappers. Seattle, N.d. $3.50

1261 [SANTA FE PRISONERS.] Message from the President of the U. S., transmitting in compliance with a Resolution of the House of Representatives of the 10th Inst., information relative to the Arrest and Imprisonment of certain American Citizens at Santa Fe by the Government of Spain, April 15, 1818. 23 pp., sewn. Washington, 1819. $75.00

Relates to the capture of Mcknight, Baird, Chouteau and others in 1811. Wagner-Camp 13.

1261a SAGOSKIN, L. A. Pesechodnaja opis Tschasti Russkich Bladwienij v Amerike v 1842-44. Parts in one vol. with large folding map. 8vo, half calf. St. Petersburg, 1847-48. $37.50

Wickersham 5904. Account of a pedestrian journey in the Russian possessions in America, which includes a journey into the interior of Alaska. The Russians were now studying the interior of their vast possessions.

1261b SAGOSKIN, L. A. Nuszug aus dem Tagebuche des Hernn Lieutenants Sagoskin uber fein Expedition auf dem Feften Land des Nordwestlichen Americas. In Dentfchriften der Russischen Gefellfchaft. Folding map, 307, 374 pp. 8vo, cloth. Weimar, 1849. $20.00

Wickersham 6313. One of the best of the later Alaska expeditions.

1261c SARYCHEV, GAVRILLA A. Puteschestvie Flota Kapitana Sarycheva po Siev-Vostovhnoi Chasti Sibri, Ledivitom Moriu i Vostoch, 1785-95. (Voyage to Siberia, the Arctic and Pacific Oceans on an Eight-Year Expedition under Captain Billings). 2 vols., 4to, xii. 7, 187, and 3 pp., and 3,192 pp., and folding table. Atlas, 4to, 52 plates and maps, size 17x21 in. Together 3 vols., 4to, original calf. St. Petersburg, 1802. $250.00

Wickersham 6128 An excessively rare work, particularly in its relation to the surveys of Unalaska Island, of which they were the first. This was the famous Billings Expedition, a secret expedition sent out by the Russians in 1785 under command of Capt. Joseph Billings, who had served with Capt. Cook. Martin Sauer was the historian of the expedition.

1261d SARYCHEV, GAVRILLA. Account of a Voyage of Discvery to the North-East of Siberia, the Frozen Ocean and the North-East, by Gavrilla Sarychev, Russian Imperial Major-General to the Expedition. Translated from the Russian and embellished with Engravings. 2 vols. in one. ¾ morocco. 70 pp., 80 pp. London, 1806-1807. $35.00

Most important for the Northwest Coast. Sarychev was an officer with Commodore Billings. Some of the engravings are in color.

1261e SAUER, MARTIN. Reise nach den Nordlichen Gegenden von Russichen Asien und America unter dem Commodor J. Billings, 1785-94. A.d. Engl. von M. C. Sprengel. Mit 1 Karte. 8vo, calf. Weimar: H. Leder, 1803. $25.00

Wickersham, 6137. Sauer was the historian on the celebrated Billings Expedition sent out by the Russians in 1785 to explore the coasts of their American possessions

ORIGINAL RUSSIAN EDITION OF THE "VOYAGE" OF SHELEKHOV, WHO FOUNDED RUSSIA'S FIRST COLONY IN AMERICA, 1791

1261f SHELEKHOV, GRIGORII IVANOVICH. Россійскаго купца Григорья Шелехова странствованіе въ 1783 году Изъ Охотска по Восточному Океяну къ Американскимъ берегамъ, съ обстоятельнымъ увѣдомленіемъ объ открытіи новообрѣтенныхъ имъ острововъ Кыктака и Афагнака, и съ пріобщеніемъ описанія образа жизни, нравовъ, обрядовъ, жилищъ и одеждъ тамошнихъ народовъ, покорившихся подъ Россійскую Державу: также Климатъ, годовыя перемѣны, звѣри, домашнія животныя, рыбы, птицы, земныя произрастѣнія и многіе другіе любопытные предмѣты тамъ находящіеся, что все вѣрно и точно описано имъ самимъ. Съ чертежемъ и со изображеніемъ самаго мореходца, и найденныхъ имъ дикихъ людей. Въ Санктпетербургѣ 1791 года. Иждивеніемъ В. С.

Translation: The voyage of Grigorii Shelekhov, a Russian merchant, in the year 1783, from Okhotsk over the Eastern Ocean to the American shores; with a circumstantial account of the discovery of the islands of Kyktak and Afagnak newly found by him; to which is added a description of the manner of life, the customs, the observances, the habitations, and the dress of the peoples, who have submitted themselves to the Russian dominion; also of the Climate, of the yearly changes, of the beasts, domestic animals, fishes, birds, plants, and of many other curious objects found therein, all of which is faithfully and accurately described by himself. With a map and a representation of the traveler himself and of the savages found by him. In St. Petersburg, the year 1791. At the cost of V. S. 76 pp., frontispiece, folding map, and the rare half title. 12mo, calf. St. Petersburg, 1791. [Sold] $425 00

"On August 27 (new style), 1783, Grigorii Ivanovich Shelekhov (Shelikhov, Shelikof, Schelechof), a Siberian merchant, sailed from Okhotsk for the coast of Alaska in command of three galiots. Fully a year elapsed before he reached the island of Kytak (Kodiak). Here he planted the first Russian settlement in America, returning to Siberia in 1787. The following year Izmailov and Bocharov acting under orders of Shelekhov's agent, Delarov, made a similar trading and exploring voyage to Alaskan waters. The account of these two expeditions occupies a place of some importance among early Northwest Americana. Bancroft characterizes the work as "One of the chief authorities for this period (1783-87) of Alaskan history."—Abraham Yarmolinsky, N. Y. P. L. Bulletin, March, 1832.

Shelekhov, in this celebrated voyage, secured for himself and his company a monopoly of the trade in the Russian-American region. Engaging Baranov, later founder of Sitka, as his manager, he laid the foundation for the Russian-American Company.

The narrative of the two voyages first appeared in two separate works published in 1791 and 1792. Sopikov's Bibliography ("Opyt Rossukoi Bibliografii, 1813-21"), item 11566, lists Shelekhov's "Voyage" and the "Sequel", or the book in the two parts as the first edition Cataloguers have followed this error ever since. However, a comparison of the volume listed above with copies in the New York Public Library and the Library of Congress nullifies this theory. As both volumes were published by the same bookseller, it is quite obvious that he changed the tile-page of the 1791 edition when he brought out the Izmailov-Bocharov "Sequel" in 1792, combined the two voyages together in one volume and placed the map at the end. The original Russian Title, which we have listed above, clearly indicates a map in the 1791 "Voyage". Moreover, only one date appears in the text of the title to the 1791 edition, i.e., 1783. Whereas in the later edition which is always found with the 1792 "Sequel" the date "1788" ha been added, apparently to make the first work conform with the "Sequel".

In the opinion of Mr. Yarmolinsky, who examined the above work, the item listed above is the original edition of Shelekhov's "Voyage" and that it was undoubtedly printed separately and sold separately, as no copies with the above listed title can be found bound with the 1792 "Sequal". In any event, the Shelekhov "Voyage" is a book in itself written by Shelekhov, who had nothing to do with the second voyage, except for his financial interest in it The work is a rude enough instrument, but vigorous and effective. Written in the first person, it is in substance a travel diary, reflecting the personality of the rough-and-ready empire-builder.

1261g SCHELEKHOF, GREGORI. Gregori Schelekhof Erste und Zweyte Reise von Ochotsk in Sibirien durch den ostlichen Ocean nach den Kusten von Amerika in den Jahren 1783 bis 1789. Nebst umstandlicher Beschreibung der vom ihm neuent-deckten Insel Kuktak, Afagnak und mehrerer andrer, etc. Aus dem Russischen ubersetzt. Von J. Z. Logan. In two parts. 84 pp., original wrappers. Pt. 1, 1783-1787, part 2, 1788-1789. St. Petersburgh, 1793. $150.00

The first translation of Shelekhov's "Voyage". See Jones 639; Sabin 77539; John Carter Brown Cat. 3, 3624; Adventures in Americana 2, 191.

1261h SHELEKHOF (GREGORY). Journal of the Voyages of Gregory Shelekhof, a Russian merchant from Okhotsk on the Eastern Ocean, to the Coast of America in 1783-87. With a description of the way of life, manners, habitations and dress of the people of the two new islands (Kuktak and Aphagnakk) discovered by him. From Shelekof's manuscript journal (being pages 1-42 of Vol. 2 of Varities of Literature, a complete copy of which is here offered). 2 vols., 8vo, half calf. London, 1795. $125.00

The first appearance in English of this most important voyage.

1261 i SHEMELIN, FEODOR. Zhurnal Pervago Puteschestiviia Rossiian vokrug Zenago Shara . . . (Journal of the First Voyage of the Russians Around the Globe, compiled by Imperial Command, by the Chief Commissioner of the Russian-American Company. F. Shemelin). 2 vols. in one. 111 pp. and 168 pp. and 426 pp. 4to, half calf. St. Petersburg, 1816-18. $50.00

Wickersham 6341.

1261j SOKOLOV, A. P. Sievernaia Ekspeditsiia, 1733-43. . . . (Northern Expedition, 1733-43). 271 pp., 5 maps. 8vo, cloth. St. Petersburg, 1851. $37.50

Wickersham 6116. Contains a full account of the voyages of Bering and Chirikov to the Northwest American Coast.

1261k STELLER, GEORG. V. Beschriebung von dem Lande Kamtschatka dessen Einwhonern deren Sitten, Nahmen, Lebensart und Verschiedenen Gewohnheiten. With 12 folding plates and two maps. 8vo, half calf. Frankfurt and Leipzig, 1774. $47.50

See Golder's "Bering's Voyages", V. 1, p. 359.

Steller, a German physician residing at Novgorod, was appointed naturalist to Bering's Second Expedition He went overland to Siberia in 1739 where he met Muller and Gmelin, other scientists of the expedition. As Golder states, Steller seemed to have been better equipped than the others, as he was a strong man and willing to live and do as the natives. Moreover, he was highly spirited and consequently covered more territory and examined more of the objects about him than any of the scientists on the expedition. "Steller was an interesting man and a great scientist. His discoveries in America and Bering Island assure him eternal fame."

SCHMOLDER'S OREGON AND CALIFORNIA OVERLAND GUIDE AND HISTORY, WITH THE 3 RARE MAPS AND PLATES

1262 SCHMOLDER, CAPT. B. Neuer Praktischer Wegweiser fur Auswanderer nach Nord-Amerika, in drei Abtheilungen mit Karten, Planen and Anischen. Erste Abtheilung enthalt: Oregon und Californien und Allgemeines uber das Mississippi und Missouri Thal; . . . der vortheilhaftesten Reise-Routen zu Wasser and zu Land nach allen neuen Statten und Gebeiten bis an die West-Kuste . . . (2) Die Mittleron Staaten der Union . . . Beschreibung der Staaten von Missouri, Iowa, Wiskonsin, Illinois, Michigan, Indiana, Ohio, Arkansas und Texas . . . (3) Die Beschreibung des Staats-Oder Congress-Landes in Iowa, mit genauester Schilderung Jeder Section, &c., &c. A complete set of all three parts, with the three rare maps and plates. Portrait of Captain Sutter, plan of Sutterville, engraved view of St. Louis in facsimile, of San Francisco, Sutter's Fort, Buffalo Hunting on the Platte. 120-154-106 pp., 8vo, original cloth. Mainz: Published by the Author, 1849. $450.00 [Sold]

Wagner-Camp 155. Schmolder's work is one of the rarest on the west, not only because of its factual information but because of its vast bibliographic appeal inasmuch as it relates to most all the states lying south of the Missouri and west of the Mississippi. Buck No. 442 fails to locate a complete copy, citing the title from Sabin and stating that "The Library of Congress has the first part, and the 'Anhang' to the second part." The Biblioteca Geographia, Leipzig, 1857, gives 1849 as the date of the First Edition. This copy has been carefully collated with copies in two of the largest private collections in America, from which the conclusion must be drawn that the three maps and plates (including the St. Louis view) must appear in any complete copy. Sabin refers to an 1848 edition, but none has ever been found and, moreover, the citation above from Biblioteca Geographia (published only 8 years after Schmolder's book appeared) would seem to refute Sabin.

Schmolder went overhand to California in 1845, where he joined with Sutter and formed a partnership for the colonization of the region. He remained two years in the territory, returning to Germany in 1847. At page 131, part 2, of the above work there is a dated document "Feb. 27, 1848". The work describes the journey to California and Oregon, the route, the prospective trading tation at San Francisco, and the establishment of a communal settlement at Sacramento.

1263 [SEATTLE.] Memoirs and Genealogy of Representative Citizens of the City of Seattle and County of King, Washington, including biographies of many of those who have passed away. 773 pp., many portraits. 4to, calf. N. Y., 1903. $10.00

1264 [SEATTLE.] Forest Club Annual. 71 pp., illus. 8vo, wrappers. Seattle, 1916. $3.00

1265 [SEATTLE.] General Strike Committee. An Account of what happened in Seattle especially the Seattle Labor Movement during the General Strik Feb. 6 to 11, 1919. 8vo, wrappers. (Seattle, 1919). $7.50

Smith 1387.

1266 SMITH, JEDEDIAH. Excursion a l'ouest des Monts Rocky Extrait d'une lettre de M Jedediah Smith. employe de la Compagnie des Pelleteries-Saint Louis, October 11th, 1827. (Contained in Nouvelles Annales des Voyages. Paris, 1828, Second Series, Vol. 37, pp. 208-12). 8vo, half calf. Paris, 1828. [Sold]

Wagner Camp 35. Describes Smith's route from Salt Lake past Little Salt Lake and apparently to the junction of the Virgin with the Colorado, then parallel to the Colorado to the Mohave, and by that river over the mountains to Los Angeles. Wagner gives a long account of this work.

1267 [SOUTHWEST.] Message from President Taylor. With Reports on conditions in New Mexico, by Col. J. W. Washington; in Texas, by Gen. Brooke Lieut. Viele, Col. Harney and Capt. Hardee; and in California by Gen Riley. Also contains Lieut. Whiting's report of a new route from San Antonio to El Paso. 8vo, half roan. 31st Cong., 1st session, House Ex. Doc. 5. Washington, 1849. $22.50

FIRST SPORTING ADVENTURE TO THE ROCKY MTS.

1268 [STEWART, WILLIAM DRUMMOND.] Altowan; or, Incidents of Life and Adventure in the Rocky Mountains. By an Amateur Traveller. Edited by J. Watson Webb. 2 vols., 12mo, original cloth. N. Y., 1846. $25.00

Wagner-Camp 125. Original Edition of what may be termed the first sporting adventure to the Rocky Mountains.

1268a SUMNER, CHAS. Speech of . . . on the Cession of Russian America to the U. S. ([Large tinted folding map]. 8vo, original printed wrappers. 48 pp. Washington, 1867. $7.50

Smith 3894. With signature of "George Gibbs" on outside wrapper.

RARE TEBIENKOV ATLAS, FIRST ATLAS ENGRAVED ON NORTHWEST COAST

1268b TEBIENKOV, CAPT. M. D. Atlas Siev. Zapadnykh Beregov Ameriki. (Atlas of the Northwest Shores of America from Bering Strait to Cape Corrientes and the Aleutian Islands, together with some Places on the Northeast Shore of Asia). 3 pp., 39 maps and plates. 4to, original wrappers. St. Petersburg, 1852. Together with Gidrograficheskiia Zanechaniis k Atlasu Siev-Zapadnykh Beregor Ameriki (Hydrographic Notes to the Atlas of the Northwest Shores of America . . .). 2 pl., 7, 148, 17, (2) pp., 4to, original wrappers. St. Petersburg, 1852. $350.00

Wickersham 5921-5922. An excessively rare work on the Northwet Coast, especially with the Hydrographic Note. The atlas plates were engraved on metal at New Archangel by the native Creole Kozina Terentiev

1268c [TEXAS AND ARKANSAS.] Proceedings of the Second Annual Meeting of the Stockholders of the Cairo and Fulton R. R. Co., held in Little Rock, Ark., May 7th, 1855. With an appendix. 32 pp., maps., 8vo, original printed wrappers. Little Rock, 1855. $8.50

Rare and important. The Report gives a comprehensive survey of the country between Little Rock and Fulton, in S. W. Ark., and also discusses the line running through Texas, via El Paso and the Gila, to the Pacific. There is considerable discussion of he lands, immigration and the economic possibilities of the two states.

1268d TIKHMENEV, P. Materialy dlia Istorii Russikh Zaselenii po Beregam Vostochaago Okeana. (Materials for the History of the Russian Settlements on the Shores of the Pacific Ocean). Four parts in 1 vol. (1) Official reports and correspndence from Irkutsh and Okhotsk (2) Observations of Golovnin on Kamchatka and Russian America (3) Khliebnkov's Journal to America. (4) Extracts from travels and voyages of Russians and Foreigners to the Russian Colonies. 8vo, calf. St. Petersburg, 1861. $37.50

1268e TIKHMENEV, P. Istoricheskoe Obozrenie Obrazonvaniia Ross-Amer. Kompanii i Dieistvii eia do Nastoiashch vremeni . . . (Historical Review of the Organization of the Russian-American Company, and its Operation down to the Present Time). 2 vols., 4to, unbound, uncut. Pp. v, 386, 66 and 388, 1, 79, 292, x, 4 plates. 4 large folding maps. St. Petersburg, 1861-1863. $75.00

1268f TIKHON, BISHOP. Sviatoe Evaneglie ot Luki, na Aleutsko-lisjevakom nariechii. (Holy Gospel from Luke, in the Aleutian-Fox dialect). 124 pp., 8vo, original wrappers. New York, 1903. $10.00

Wickersham 5862.

1268g TSCHITSGHAGOW, HERRN V. Hernn v. Tschitschagow Russich: Kayserlichen Admirals Reise nach dem Eismeer. 8vo, half morocco, gilt top, other edges uncut. St. Petersburg, 1793. $67.50

Very rare. This work is divided into three parts. (1) Introduction in which references are made to the various works on the voyages of the Russians to the American Coast, i e., Engel, Robert, de Vaugondy, Buache, etc. (2) Schiffarten in Eismeer, May, 1764-Jan., 1766. (3) Zwente Reise in Eismeer, 19th May, 1766.

SIGNED PRESENTATION COPY OF TIXIER'S JOURNAL

1269 TIXIER, VICTOR. Voyage aux Prairies Osages, Louisiane et Missouri, 1839-40. Par Victor Tixier. 260 pp., 8vo, original printed wrappers. 5 plates. Clermont-Ferrand, Chez Perol, Libraire-Edieur, etc. . . . Paris, 1844. $125.00

Wagner-Camp 114. Signed presentation copy of this rare journey made by Tixier in 1840. He left France in November, 1839 and arrived at New Orleans in January, 1840. He hunted Buffalo in what is now Arkansas, Oklahoma and Missouri; was in St. Louis in May, 1840, then went on to Independence, then to Papin's Post on the Arkansas. He accompanied the Osages as far as the Grand Saline.

1269a [UTAH.] Letter of the Delegate of the Territory of Utah in Congress, enclosing the Memorial of Delegates of the Convention which assembled in Great Salt Lake City, and adopted a Constitution with a view to the admission of Utah into the Union . . . 10 pp. (list of delegates), unbound. [Washington, 1858.] $7.50

1270 [VANCOUVER.] The Emigrant Soldiers' Gazette and Cape Horn Chronicle. Published originally on manuscript forms, kindly furnished by Capt. W. D. Marsh, R.E., during the Voyage from Gravesend to Vancouver Island, of the Detachment of Royal Engineers selected for Service in British Columbia, between the 10th of Oct., 1858 and 12th April, 1859. Edited by Corp. C. Sinnet, R.E., assisted by Lieut. Col. B. Wofenden, I.S.C. V.d. Illus. 4to, cloth. Victoria, 1907. $12.50

A very rare and little known work with fine illustrations and beautifully printed.

1270a VENIAMINOV, I. Zapiski ob Ostrovakh Unalashkinska go Otdiela. (Notes on the Islands of the Unalaska District). Three vols. in two. 8vo, half calf. St. Petersburg, 1840. $47.50

Wickersham, 5828.

1270b VENIAMINOV, I. Zamiechaniia o Koloshernskom i Kadjiakskom Iazykakh. (Remarks on the Kolosh and Kadiak Languages and other Languages of Russia-America, with Russian-Kolosh Vocabulary). 82 pp., 8vo, original wrappers bound in. St. Petersburg, 1846. $35.00

Wickersham, 5869.

1270c VENIAMINOV, I. Opyt Grammatiki Aleutsko-Lisjevskago Iaszyka. (Essay towards a Grammar and Dictionary of the Aleutian-Fox Languages.) St. Petersburg, 1846. $35.00

Wickersham, 5870.

1270d VENIAMINOV, I. Innokenti, Metropolit Moskovskii i Kolomenskii po ego Sochineneim Pisjmam i Rozskazam Sovremennikov. (Innocent, Metropolitan of Moscow and Koloma, in his Writings, Letters and Reports of his Contemporaries). By F. P. Barsukov. Large 8vo, 769 pp., half calf. Moscow, 1883. $20.00

1271 VILLARD, HENRY. The Past and Present of the Pike's Peak Gold Regions, with Maps and Illustrations by Henry Villard. Special Correspondent of the Cincinnati Daily Commercial. 112 pp., 4 leaves of advertisements, front., 2 maps. 8vo, original printed wrappers. Sutherland & McElroy, Publishers: St. Louis, 1860. [Sold]

1272 [WASHINGTON STATE.] King County (Seattle). Pamphlet descriptive of King County, Washington Territory, showing its wonderful Natural Resources and Commercial Advantages, with a Short Sketch of Seattle, the Largest and Most Flourishing City in the Territory—its present and future Prospects. 10 pp., 8vo, cloth. Seattle, W. T., 1884. $17.50

1273 [WASHINGTON STATE.] Barton's Legislative Hand-Book and Manual of the State of Washington, 1889-90. 8vo, cloth. Olympia, 1890. $2.50

1274 —— Same. 1891-2. 8vo, cloth. Olympia, 1891. $2.50

1275 —— Same. 1893-4. 8vo, cloth. Olympia, 1893. $2.50

1276 —— Same. 1895-6. 8vo, cloth. Seattle, 1896. $2.50

1277 —— Political and Legislative Manual of the State of Washington, 1899. 8vo, cloth. Olympia, 1899. $2.50

1278 —— Souvenir of the Third Legislative Assembly of Washington, 1893. 8vo, cloth. Olympia, 1893. $2.50

1279 [WASHINGTON STATE.] Illustrated History of Klickitat, Yakima and Kittitas Counties, with an Outline of the early History of the State of Washington. 941 pp., frontis., 127 portraits, 22 plates. 4to, cloth. N.p., Interstate Publishing Co., 1904. $15.00

1280 [WASHINGTON STATE.] An Illustrated History of Skagit and Snohomish Counties. 1117 pp. The Interstate Publishing Company. 4to, cloth. N.p., 1906. $15 00

Contains many full-page portraits and other plates included in the paging. Smith 1839.

1281 [WASHINGTON STATE.] Kitsap County, Washington. Plat Book of Kitsap County, Washington, containing maps of Villages, Cities and Townships of the County, including map of the State of Washington, compiled from actual surveys and the County Records. 86 pp., illus., 67 colored maps. 8vo, cloth. Seattle, 1909. $15.00

1282 [WASHINGTON STATE.] Is Lese Majeste a Crime? In America Shall men be Jailed for Free Speech? For making these speeches advocating the Imprisonment of Federal Judge C. H. Hanford the Speakers were arrested. 32 pp., 8vo. Seattle, (1911). $5.00

1283 [WASHINGTON STATE.] Justice to the Rocky Mountain Committee. Brief submitted to the U. S. Geographical Board urging the official removal frm America's most sublime mountain of the name Ranier, and the perpetuation by official adoption of the original Indian name therefor, in its most appropriate, euphonious and generally accepted form—Tacoma. May 2, 1917. 77 pp. Tacoma, 1917. With which is bound Proceedings of the Tacoma Academy of Science, Feb. 8, 1893: Paper by Hon. James Wickersham, "Is it Mt. Tacoma or 'Ranier?' What do History and Tradition Say?" 24 pp., 8vo. Tacoma: Allen, Reprint, 1912. $7.50

Smith 2000.

1284 [WASHINGTON STATE.] King County Commissioners. History and Progress of King County, Washington. 53 pp., illus. 8vo, cloth. Seattle, 1916. $7.50

Smith 2033.

1285 [WASHINGTON STATE.] Klahhane Club. Annual, January, 1918. 88 pp., illus. 8vo, original wrappers. Port Angelus, 1918. $4.50

Olympic mountaineering.

1286 [WASHINGTON STATE.] Land of Opportunity Now. The Great Pacific Northwest. 39 pp., 8vo. N.p., 1924. $2.50

1287 [WASHINGTON STATE.] Bards and Company's Classified Business Directory of Olympia, Puyallup, Everett, Port Townsend, Fairhaven, New Whatcom and Port Angeles for the Years 1898-99, containing a classified list of the Representative Men engaged in Professional and Commercial Pursuits. 157 pp., 8vo, cloth. N. Y., N.d. $7.50

1288 [WASHINGTON STATE.] Mt. Baker Cartogram. A Pictorial Brochure of the Great Kama Kushan of the Lummis, the Wonderland of the Northwest. Illus., folding map. 40 pp., 8vo, wrappers. (Bellingham), N.d. $4.00

1289 [WESTERN BOUNDARY.] Correspondence between this Government and that of Great Britain on the Claims of the two governments to the Territory west of the Rocky Mountains. U. S. Cong., 1st Sess., Doc. 199. 77 pp., 8vo, sewn. Washington, March 15, 1928. [Sold]

WHITE'S "CONCISE VIEW OF OREGON" IN PRINTED WRAPPERS

1290 WHITE, ELIJAH. A Concise View of Oregon Territory, its Colonial and Indian Relations; compiled from Official Letters and Reports, together with the Laws of the Colony. By Elijah White, late Sub-Indian Agent of Oregon. 72 pp., 8vo, original printed wrappers. Washington, 1846. [Sold]

Fine copy of the first issue of the first Edition in the original printed wrappers. On p. 39 the last word is "honored". In later issues "honored" is hyphenated. Has an extra leaf dated Aug. 3, which was two months after date issue, in which White asks for an increase in salary. One of three known copies in the original printed wrappers.

1291 [WHITMAN MASSACRE.] Waiileptu (Waiilatpu). The Whitman Massacre. Contained in The Ladies Repository. 8vo, calf. Phila., 1868. $7.50

1292 WILKES, GEORGE. An Account and History of the Oregon Territory; together with a Journal of an Emigrating Party across the Western Prairies of America, and to the Mouth of the Columbia River. (Doctored and republished in London). 16 mo, original printed wrappers. Printed and Published by William Lott. London, 1846. (Sold)

Smith 7, where date is misprinted 1816. This work contains 160 (viii) pages; p. 160 numbered 169. One of three or four copies known in the above state.

THE ORIGINAL AUTHORITY ON THE OVERLAND MIGRATION OF 1843

1293 WILKES, GEORGE, and BURNETT, P. H. The History of Oregon, Geography and Political. Embracing an Analysis of the Old Spanish Claims, the British Pretensions, the United States Title: an Account of the present Condition and Character of the Country, and a thorough Examination of a Project of a National Railroad, from the Atlantic to the Pacific Ocean. To which is added: A Journal of the Events of the Celebrated Emigrating Expedition of 1843; containing an Account of the Route from Missouri to Astoria, a Table of Distances, and the Physical Description of the Territory, and its Settlements, by a Member of the recently organized Oregon Legislature. With a folding map. 8vo, full blue levant. N. Y.: William H. Coyler, 1845. $300.00

Wagner-Camp No 119. Original Edition of this exceedingly rare narrative of which only a few copies are known. The account of the famous migration of 1832, as contained in Part 2 of this book, is Burnett's narrative of the journey and is entitled "Travels across the Great Western Priaries, with a Description of the line of Route, and the Distances between the intermediate points from Missouri to the Pacific Ocean." Fortunately Wilkes includes this in its entirety in conjunction with his own relation, as the story of this man, later the first Civil Governor of California, is of peculiar interest. Wagner-Camp 119 gives an extended description of this book, and the "Quarterly of the Washington Historical Society" for October, 1906 describes it as "one of the rarest and least known books". Ranking with the Hastings, Leonard, Johnson and Winters, it will always remain one of the corner-stones of pioneer western narratives.

1293a WOODS, JOHN. Two Years' Residence in the Settlements on the English Prairie, in the Illinois Country, United States, etc. 3 maps. 8vo, ¾ polished calf. London, 1822. $55.00

Original Edition with the 3 maps. Copies with all three maps are extremely rare. Braislin 1931.

1294 WOODCOCK, E. N. Fifty Years a Hunter and Trapper. Experiences of E. D. Woodcock, the noted Hunter and Trapper as written by Himself. 12mo, clth. Columbus, (1913). $2.50

WYETH'S "OREGON EXPEDITION" IN ORIGINAL WRAPPERS

1294a WYETH, JOHN B. Oregon; or, a Short History of a long Journey from the Atlantic Ocean to the Region of the Pacific by Land. Drawn up from the Notes and Oral Information of Joseph B. Wyeth, one of the party who left Nathaniel J. Wyeth, four days' march beyond the Rocky Mountains, and the only one who has Returned to New England. 87 pp., half title. 12mo, original printed wrappers, uncut. Cambridge, 1833. $300.00

Fine crisp copy of the Original Edition, about as fine a copy a any collector could hope for. See Wagner-Camp, 47, wherein it is stated that this work was actually written by Dr Benjamin Waterhouse.

1294b [WYOMING.] Resources of. 1889. . . . The Vacant Public Lands and how to obtain them. Plates. 77 pp., map. 8vo, original front wrapper. Cheyenne, 1880. $5.00

CARTOGRAPHY

1295 [ALASKA.] Map of Russian America; or, Alaska Territory compiled from Russian Charts and Surveys of the Western Union Telegraph Co. Col. C. S. Bulkley, Engineer-in-Chief. By J. F. Lewis, Chief Draughtsman, M. Cadin, Asst. Lithographed by Britton and Rey. San Francisco, 1867. Map 4 ft. 2 in. x 5 ft. 9 in. $75.00

This excessively rare map is the largest and finest map ever made of the Alaskan Territory.

1295a —— The same (in photostat, 8 sections). $12.50

Item 1293, Second line from bottom of the note should read "Ranking with the Works of the Hastings" . . .

1296 [ALASKA.] Map of Alaska. Rand, McNally and Co. 48½x30 in., folding. (c. 1890). $7.50

1297 [ALASKA.] Dodds' Map of the Iditarod Placer Fields, Alaska. By C. B. Dodds. 15x18 in., folded in 12mo original wrappers. N.p., 1910. $5.00

1298 ALBERT, COL. J. J. Map of the United States Territory west of the Rocky Mountains, exhibiting the various Trading Posts or Forts occupied by the British Hudson's Bay Company, connected with the Western and Northwestern Fur Trade. 1838. $12.50

One of the most important early Fur Trade and Post Route maps.

1299 ARROWSMITH, A. Map of America, by A. Arrowsmith, in four parts, each measuring 33x31 in., Jan. 1, 1795 additions to 1802. London, 1802. $55.00

One of the earliest of the great maps, with colored boundaries. Vancouver Island has Wabash Nation printed across it; the Northwest Coast is crowded with names and information. The Hudson's Bay Posts such as Osnabury House, Gloucester House, Henley House, Cumberland House, &c., are plainly shown, and the Indian Tribes such as Assiniboines, Blackfeet, Crees, Nathaways, Chippeways, Beavers, Coppers, Strongbows, Hares, and Esquimaux are especially shown.

1300 ARROWSMITH, A. Map exhibiting all the New Discoveries in the Interior Parts of North America, size 48x57 in., on three sheets with colored outlines, Jan. 1, 1795 with additions to June, 1814. London, 1814. $50.00

This is the fourth rare issue of the map, comprehending all the discoveries of Lewis and Clark. It takes in the discoveries of Mackenzie and Hearne in the far north, and reaches south to the Arkansas and Colorado rivers, thence west along the coast of California. It is inscribed to the Hon. Governor and Company of Adventuerers trading into Hudson's Bay, in testimony of their liberal communications.

1301 ARROWSMITH, A. Map of America (North and South). Four large folding sheets, colored, size 31x39 in. London, 1822. $45.00

Detailed information of Hudson's Bay Co., discoveries on the Columbia River and the Upper Missouri Regions.

1302 ARROWSMITH, J. British North America, by permission dedicated to the Hon. Hudson's Bay Company, containing the Latest Information which their documents furnish. Map 18½x23½ in., colored. London, 1834. $15.00

Shows the progress of the Hudson's Bay Company's discoveries.

1303 ARROWSMITH, J. Map of North America: Dedicated to the Hon. Hudson's Bay Cmpany. Containing all the latest information which the Documents furnish. (Exhibiting the territory of the U. S. and Canada from the Atlantic to the Pacific, and the Western Country from Monterey, California northward to Bering Strait.) London, 1837. $15.00

1304 BELLIN, JACQUES NICOLAS. Partie Orientale de la Nouvelle France ou du Canada. 17x21 in. Nuremburg, 1755. $7.50

1305 BELLIN, JACQUES NICOLAS. Partie Occidentale de la Nouvelle France ou du Canada. 17x21 in. Nuremburg, 1755. $7.50

1306 BLAEU, WILLEM JANZOON, and BLAEU, JOHANNES. China Veribus Sinarum Regio Nunc Incolis Dicta. 16x19½ in., engraved surface, beautifully hand-colored, with wide margins. Amsterdam, 1635. $15.00

1307 BLAEU, WILLEM JANZOON, and BLAEU, JOHANNES. India qu Orientalis dicitur et Insulae Adiacentes. Map 16x19½ in., engraved surface, beautifully colored and with wide margins. Amsterdam, 1635. $15.00

1308 BLAEU, WILLEM JANZOON, and BLAEU, JOHANNES. Tartaria Sive Magi Chami Imperium. 16x19½ in., engraved surface, wide margins and beautifully hand-colored. Amsterdam, 1635. $15.00

1309 BLAEU, WILLEM JANZONN. Americae Nova Tabula. Map 16x 21½ in., beautifully hand-colored. Amsterdam, 1635. $65.00

The design of this beautiful map follows Speed, but the coloring is that which makes all Blaeu's maps distinctive and beautiful. This is from Blaeu's Atlas of 1635. See Holman's "Old maps and their makers", p. 36.

1310 BLAEU, WILLEM JANZOON. Asia Noviter Delineata. 16x21½ in., beautifully hand-colored. Amsterdam, [c. 1635]. $37.50

This is from Blaeu's Atlas, with a description. This map shows a small portion of North America. "C(ape) de Fortuna" and C(ape) Medocino".

1311 BLAEU, WILLEM JANZOON. Nova Totius Terrarum Orbis Geographica ac Hydrographia Tabula. 16x21½ in., beautifully hand-colored, with descriptin from Blaeu's Atlas. Amsterdam, (1646). $37.50

1312 BLAEU, JOHANNES. Nova et Accuratissima Totius Terrarum Orbis Tabula. 16x21 in. [Amsterdam, 1664-5]. $27.50

1313 BLAEU, J. Nova et Accuratissima Totius Terrarum Orbis Tabula. 16x21 in. [Amsterdam, 1664-5]. $15.00

1314 BOWEN, EMANUEL. A New and Accurate Map of Mexico and New Spain together with California and New Mexico, &c. Drawn from the best Maps and Charts. 14x16½ in., colored. London, [c. 1755]. $20.00

Contains a note on Father Kino's Journey Overland.

1315 BOWEN, EMANUEL. An Accurate Map of North America describing and distinguishing British and Spanish Dominions on this Great Continent; according to the Definitive Treaty concluded at Paris, 10th Feby., 1763. Also the West Indies. 2 sheets, 19½x22½ in., colored. Insets (a) The Passage by Land to California discovered by Fr. Eusebius Kino, a Jesuit, etc.; (b) Map of Baffin and Hudson's Bay. London [c. 1765]. $40.00

1316 BRADFORD, T. G. Map of the United States. 14x32 in., colored. 1838. $12.50

Fine map by one of America's best map-makers.

1317 BURG, M. (Delin.). A New Map of North-America, Shewing its Principal Divisions, Chief Cities, Towns, Rivers, Mountains, etc. Dedicated to his Highness, William Duke of Gloucester. 14½x19 in. London, (1690). $12.50

1318 [CADELL, T., Jr.] Map of America with the Latest Discoveries. 7¾x9 in. London, 1797. $7.50

1319 (CANFIELD, THOMAS N.). Map of the Country west of Dakota to the Pacific Ocean, from the latest Explorations and Surveys, to accompany the Report of Thomas H. Canfield's Secret Report to the Board of Directors of the Northern Pacific Railroad. 18x50 in. N. Y.: Colton, 1870. $12.50

1320 CLUNY, CAPT. THOMAS. Partie de Carte de Capitaine Cluny, Auteur d'un ouvrage Anglois intitule American Traveller publie a Londres en 1769. [M. de Vaugondy, Paris, 1769]. $12.50

1321 COLLINS, P. McD. Map showing Collins' Proposed Telegraph via Behring's Strait and Asiatic Russia to Europe, under Russian and British Grants. 22½x32 in. (in photostat). N. Y.: Colton, 1864. $7.50

1322 [COLORADO.] Map of Colorado. By J. A. Baker. 14x20 in., colored and folding to 16mo. Denver, 1880. $4.00

1323 COLTON, G. & W. and C. B. Colton's Map of Montana, Idaho and Wyoming. 16x24 in. N. Y., 1876. $5.00

1324 COLTON, G. & W. and C. B. Colton's Map of Oregon, Washington and Idaho. 17x25 in., colored. N. Y., 1876. $5.00

1325 CORONELLI, MARCO V. Mer del Sud, delto Altrimenu Mare Pacifico. 18x24 in. Venetia, 1695. $20.00

1326 COVENS, J., and MORTIER, C. Carte Generale de l'Empire du Russie . . . 19½x38 in., colored. Amsterdam, [c. 1700]. $20.00

Shows the Empire from Europe to the Isle de Laurence on the Pacific. A fine map.

NOTE:—The following comprise a fine list of the excessively rare and important Dalrymple maps and charts relating to the Pacifix Coast line.

1327 DALRYMPLE, ALEXANDER. Plan of Snug Harbor Cove in Prince William Sound. 8½x11½ in. Dalrymple, London, March 24, 1789. $40.00

See item 684, Cat. 17 in this series

1327a DALRYMPLE, ALEXANDER. Milbank's Sound. By Charles Duncan, Master of the Royal Navy, 1788. 6½x11 in. Dalrymple, London, Dec. 24, 1789. $40.00

See item 683, Cat. 17 in this series.

1328 DALRYMPLE, ALEXANDER. (a) Plan of St. Patrick's Bay. By Capt. James Hanna, 1786. (b) Chart of part of Northwest Coast. By Capt. James Hanna, in "Snow Otter," 1786. (c) Track of the Snow Experiment in company with the Capt. Cook. By S. Wedhbrough. All on one sheet (11¼x12½ in.). Dalrymple, London, March 19, 1789. $65.00

See item 681, Cat. 17 in this series.

1329 DALRYMPLE, ALEXANDER. Plan of the Inlet of Bucareli, Latitude 55, 19′ N. Longitude 27, 9′ West from Cape San Lucar. Discovered in 1775 with the Sonora, by Don Juan Franco de la Quadra and Don Franco Anto Mourelle, and minutely examined in the expedition of 1789 by the same and other Officers. From a Spanish manuscript communicated by John Henry Knox, Esq., to whom this Plate is inscribed by his most obliged Dalrymple. 12x12 in. Dalrymple, London, Jan. 17, 1789. $50.00

Refer to item 680, Cat. 17 in this series.

1330 DALRYMPLE, ALEXANDER. Plan of Calamity Harbour. By James Johnstone, a Master in the Royal Navy, 1787. 9½x20 in. Dalrymple, London, Oct. 30, 1789. $35.00

Refer to item 679, Cat. 17 in this series.

1331 DALRYMPLE, ALEXANDER. Sketch of Ahouset. By Capt. Duncan, Master in the Royal Navy, 1788. Dalrymple, London, Dec. 17, 1789. $40.00

1332 DALRYMPLE, ALEXANDER. Plan of Port of San Francisco, on the Northwest coast of California. From a Spanish Manuscript communicated by John Henry Knox, Esq., to whom this plate is inscribed by his most obliged Dalrymple. 11½x18 in. Dalrymple, London, Jan. 17, 1789. $100.00

Refer to item 677, Cat. 17 in this series.

1333 DALRYMPLE, ALEXANDER. (a) Plan of Port San Diego, on the west coast of California, 1782. These plans were taken from Spanish Manuscripts by John Henry Knox, Esq., to whom this plate is inscribed by his most obliged Dalrymple, 1786. (b) Plan of Monterey in California by Don Josef Tobar y Tamariz. 7th Dec. 1786. By a Spanish Manuscript received from Dr. Robertson. The north is misplaced in this plan. (c) Plan of the Road Principe in the Channel of Santa Barbara. By Josef Tobar y Tamariz, 1786. Three plans on one plate. 8½x11½ in. Dalrymple, London, Jan. 7, 1789. $125.00

The above maps or plans were the first published in relation to the various places mentioned and are of the greatest rarity. See item 676, Cat. 17 in this series.

DALRYMPLE'S MAP OF PUGET SOUND

1334 DALRYMPLE, ALEXANDER. Sketch of the Entrance of the Strait of Juan de Fuca. By Charles Duncan, Master of the Royal Navy, Aug. 15, 1788. Plate showing entrance, with a map. 11¾x12 in. Dalrymple, London, Jan. 14, 1790. $125.00

See item 682, Cat. 17 in this series.

1335 DANET, GUILLAUME. L'Amerique Meridionale et Septentrionale dressee sur les Nouvelles et Dernier Relations des Meilleurs Navigateurs dece temps Conformes aux Observations Astronomiqus. 19x27 in., with 18 miniature engravings of famous explorers from Columbus to La Salle. Paris, 1731. $17.50

1336 DE LETH, HENDRICK. Carte de la Mer du Sud, colored. 23x36 in. Paris, [c. 1760]. $50.00

This is a fine colored map with many interesting insets, showing both north and South America and covering the earth from the European and African coasts to the Asiatic coast line.

1337 DE LETH, HENDRICK. Le Nouveau Continent ou l'Amerique. 19x20 in., colored. Paris, [c. 1760]. $17.50

1338 DE LISLE, G. L'Amerique Septentrionale Dressee sur le Observations de Messeiurs de l'Academie Royale des Sciences, & quelque autres, & les Memoirs les plus recens. Par G. De Lisle, Prem. Geographe du Roy. 18x24 in., with colored outlines. Paris, 1700. $27.50

1339 DE LISLE, G. Mappemonde a l'usage du Roy. Par Guillaume De Lisle, Premier Geographe de Sa Majeste. 18x27 in., colored outlines. Paris, [c. 1720]. $7.50

1340 DE LISLE, G. Carte d'Amerique dressee De Lisle . . . 19x24 in., colored outlines. Paris, 1722. $27.50

1341 DE LISLE, G. Hemisphere Occidental dressee en 1720 pour l'usage Particulier du Roy, &c. 20x20 in., colored. Paris, 1724. $20.00

1342 DE LISLE, G. L'Amerique Septentrionale dressee sur les Observations de Messieurs de L'Academie Royale des Sciences. 19x22½ in., colored. Paris, [c. 1730]. $20.00

1343 DE LISLE, G. Carte des Nouvelles Decouvertes au Nord de la Mer de Sud, tant a l'est de la Siberie et du Kamtschatka, qu a l'ouest de la Nouvelle France, &c. 18x25 in. Published, 8 Avril 1750. A Paris. $35.00

1344 DE LISLE, GUILLAUME. Carte d' Amerique, dressee pour l'usage du Roi par Guil. De Lisle et Phil. Buache, etc. Par Dezauche, Geographe, Successor des Srs. De Lisle et Phil. Buache. 18½x24 in., colored. Paris, 1785. $12.50

1345 DUNN, SAMUEL. America, North and South and the West Indies, with the Atlantic, Aethopic and Pacific Oceans. 12x17 in., colored in outline. London, 1786. $8.00

1346 DUNN, SAMUEL. Scientia Terrarum et Coelorum. 42x48 in. London, 1772. $15.00

1347 FADEN, WILLIAM. Eastern Hemisphere, Western Hemisphere. 14x28 in., colored. London, 1773. $15.00

1348 FADEN, WILLIAM. A Chart of the World upon the Mercator's Projection, describing the Tracks of Capt. Cook in the Years 1768-69-70-71 and in 1772-3-4-5, with the Discoveries. London, 1775. $12.50

1349 FER, NICOLAS DE. Carte Generale du Globe Terrestre et Aqutiques ou Mappemonde en Deux Plans—Hemisphere. Par N. de Fer, Geographe de Mon. de Dauphin. 8x11 in. Paris, 1705. $7.50

1350 FINLEY, A. Map of the United States constructed from latest Authorities. 17x21 in., colored, folding. 1825. $12.50

1351 FRANK, THEODORE. Map of the United States and Territories, showing the extent of Public Surveys and other Details, the Routes of Travel and Exploration, the location of Indian Tribes and Military and Wagon Roads; proposed Railroad Routes; the Mineral and Oil Deposits; Boundaries, etc. Drawn by Theo. Frank. Large double folio, folding into 8vo cloth covers, colored. Washington, 1866. $20.00

An important map minutely detailed and splendidly engraved.

1352 FREMONT, JOHN C. Map of Oregon and Upper California. 19½x 24½ in. Washington, 1848. $3.50

FIRST MAP OF JUAN DE FUCA STRAITS; THE ENTRANCE TO PUGET SOUND

1353 [GALIANO-VALDEZ MAP.] (Juan de Fuca Straits.) Carta Esferica de los Reconocimientos en la Costa No. de America desde la Parte en que Empiezan a Angoftar Los Canales de la Entrada de Juan de Fuca hafta la Salida de Las Goletas Sutil y Mexicana. Ano de 1795. 38½x26½ in., with two engraved coast line elevations:—"Vista de la Entrada de Nutka" and "Vista del Cabo Frondoso," etc. $150.00

One of the most important and rarest maps relating to Northwest discoveries. See Henry R. Wagner's "Spanish Explorations in Juan de Fuca Straits," wherein a great part of the book is devoted to the Galiano-Valdez expedition. At p. 228, Mr. Wagner reproduces this map on a much smaller scale. He refers to it as "No. 1." The above is the original edition of this rare map and should not be confused with the reproduction of 1802, which Mr. Wagner states is "superior to the one published in 1802."

Spanish explorations to the Northwest boast had been going on methodically during the 18th Century, but without the usual world fanfare. But in the later years of the century the Spanish were sharply awakened by the world propaganda behind Vancouver and his "Voyage of Discovery." Galiano and Valdez, already on the N.W. coast, began exploring the waters round Vancouver Island, and into Puget Sound. There was a race as to which nation would get their maps before the world first. The map above was executed by Galiano and Valdez on one of the schooners (Sutil and Mexicana).

The map, with Wagner's "No. 2," listed below, was engraved in Madrid in 1795, thus antedating Vancouver's maps. The map begins in 40° 35", about midway on Texado Island and shows the British Columbia coast, and, beginning at about Johnstone's Strait, the N.E. coast of Vancouver Island. From there on the Vancouver coast is seen back round the west side to Nootka. Both maps (see item below) are of great rarity and probably will never be offered again in this generation.

1354 [GALIANO-VALDEZ MAP.] (Juan de Fuca Straits). Carta Esferica de los Reconocimie hechos en 1792 en la Costa No. de America para Examinar la Entrada de Juan de Fuca, y la Internacion de sus Canales Navigables. Levantada de Orden del Rey Neustro Senor abordo de las Goletas Sutil y Mexicana, por D. Dionisio Galiano y D. Cayetano Valdez, Capitaines de Navio dela Rl. Armada. Ano de 1795. 28½x26 in., with view of the coast line showing elevations at the entrance of the Strait, looking east; Canal de la Salida de las Goletas, Vista Este, etc. [Madrid], 1795. $150.00

This is Wagner's "No. 2" map. See item above. This map is on a smaller scale than No. 1 because it includes more territory, as it covers the entire region from 47° to 51° 15". Like the map listed above, this is a beautiful map of great rarity, almost unprocurable. See Wagner's "Spanish Voyages in the Juan de Fuca Straits."

1355 [GALLIANO-VALDEZ MAP.] (Juan de Fuca Straits). Carta Esferica de los Reconocimientos hecos en la costa n.o. de America en 1791 y 92 por las goletas Sutil y Mexicana. (This is a reproduction of the Galino map contained in his "Relacion del viage en el Ano de 1792. Madrid, 1802). 12½x17 in. $5.00

1356 GARDINER, C. K. Map of Oregon Territory west of the Cascade Mountains. Folding, 12x18 in. 1855. $12.50

Not in Phillips.

1357 EPNER, GUST. Map of the Gold Regions in British Columbia compiled from Sketches and Information by His Excellency James Douglas, C.B., Governor of British Columbia and Vancouver's Island, and from data obtained from the most Intelligent and Reliable Miners by Gust Epner. Map 16x20 in., mounted on linen. Lithographed by Britton and Co., San Francisco (1862). $50.00

An excessively rare and accurate map used by the first miners in the Fraser River Gold Rush.

1358 HOMANN, JEAN BAPTISTE. Mississippi Seu Provinciae Ludovicians 19x23 in. Nuremburg, [c. 1700]. $20.00

A beautifully colored map showing the United States from "Pays des Apaches" to the Atlantic Coast and the entire Mississippi Valley. Inset of Niagara Falls.

1359 HOMANN, JEAN BAPTISTE. Virginia, Marylandia et Carolina, in Americae Septentrionale. 19x23 in. Colored Nuremburg, [c. 1700]. $20.00

1360 HOMANN, JOHANNES B. Planiglobii Terrestris cum Utroq Hemispheric Caelesti, &c. 19x22 in., colored. Hamburg, [c. 1730]. $17.50

1361 HOMANN, JEAN BAPTISTE. America Septentrionalis. A Domino d'Anville in Gallis edita nunc in Anglia. Coloniis in Interiorem Virginiam deductis nec non Fluvii Ohio Cursu, etc. 18x20 in., colored. Nuremburg, 1756. $30.00

1362 HOMANN, JOHANNES B. Totium Americae Septentrionalis. 19x22½ in., colored. Nuremburg, [c. 1780]. $15.00

1363 [IOWA.] A Township Map of the State of Iowa, compiled from the U. S. Survey, Official Information and Personal Reconnaissance, showing the Streams, Roads, Towns, Post Offices, County Seats, Works of Internal Improvement, etc. By Henry Williams. Map 22x34 in., colored, folding to 16mo, cloth covers. Fairfield, Iowa, 1855. $22.50

A very early and accurate map of Iowa, now rarely found.

1364 [IOWA]. Chapman's Sectional Map of the State of Iowa, compiled from the United States Surveys and other authentic sources. Map 20x36 in., colored, folding into 16mo, cloth covers. By Silas Chapman. Milwaukee, 1856. $17.50

1365 JAILLOT, CHAS. HUBERT ALEXIS. Amerique Septentrionale Dursee en ses Principales Parties. Presente a Monseigneur le duc de Bourgoyne. 19x22 in., colored. Paris, (1694). $20.00

1366 RAMM, I. DE. Novissima et Accuratissima Totino Americae Descriptio. 17x22 in. Amsterdam, (1695). $15.00

1367 JAILLOT, CHAS. HUBERT ALEXIS. L'Asie divisee en ses Prinsipales Regions. 22x34 in. Paris, (1696). $20.00

Shows the Philippines, N.W. coast.

1368 [JEFFERYS, THOMAS]. A chart of North and South America, including the Atlantic and Pacific oceans, with the nearest coasts of Europe, Africa and Asia. In 3 sheets, each 18x44 in. London, 1776. From Jeffreys' "The American Atlas". $32.50

1369 KELLET, CAPTAIN R. N. America, West Coast. Juan de Fuca Strait. 22x33 in. London: Admiralty, 1858. $5.00

1370 [LAURIE, R. and WHITTLE, J.]. A new map of the Whole Continent of America, divided into North and South and West Indies. 2 sheets, each 20x46 in., colored. London, 1794. $27.50

1371 [LE ROUGE, G. L.]. L'Amerique Suivant le R. P. Charlevoix . . . et plusiers autres Nouvelles Observations. 19½x25 in., colored outline. Paris, 1746. $12.50

Shows the "River de L'Ouest."

1372 LOON, J., VAN. Orbis Terrarum Nova et Accuratissima Tabula. 17x21½. Amsterdam, (c. 1680). $12.50

THE ORIGINAL EDITION OF MELISH'S RARE MAP OF THE WESTERN COUNTRY

1373 MELISH, J. Map of the United States, with the Contiguous British and Spanish Possession. Engraved by J. Vallance. Quadruple elephant folio, colored, size 50x56½ in., printed in 50 sections, mounted on linen. Phila., 1820. $55.00

One of the most important of all maps of the western regions. Several of the secondary treaties and other international questions of the early days depend on this rare map. It is particularly important in that the route across the Rocky Mountains, through South Pass, is here for the first time laid down.

1374 [MITCHELL, JOHN]. L'Amerique Septentrionale avec les Routes, Distances en Miles, Villages et Establishments Francois et Anglois. Par le Docteur Mitchel traduit de L'Anglois. 8 parts, 18½x26 in., total 52x74 in. Paris, 1756. $27.50

Mitchell's map, London, 1755 measured 52x57 in. This map lacks Nos. 3 and 4 (New England and East Canada).

1375 MITCHELL, S. A. A New Map of Texas and Oregon and California with the regions Adjoining. 20½x22 in., with accompaniment. Folio. Phila.: Mitchell, 1846. $27.50

This interesting map marks the emigrant route to Oregon and shows the extreme limits of the Oregon Territory. Scarce.

1376 MITCHELL, S. A. Mitchell's Traveller's Guide through the United States containing the principal Cities, Towns, &c., alphabetically arranged, together with the Railroad, Stage and Canal Routes with the Distances in miles from place to place. Large Folding Map, colored. 12mo, cloth. Phila., 1852. $10.00

1377 MITCHELL, S. A. Manual of Geography embracing the Key of Mitchell's Series of Outline Maps. Six colored plates, 178 pp., 12mo, half calf. Hartford, 1854. $7.50

1378 MOLL, HERMANN. Map of South America. 22x36 in. (5-band). London, (c. 1720). $12.50

1379 MORTIER, PIETER. Carte Generale de Toutes les Costes du Monde et les Pays Nouvellement Decouvert. 22½x36 in. Amsterdam, 1703. $20.00

1380 NOLIN, JEAN BAPTISTE. L'Amerique ou le Nouveau Continent dressee sur les Memoires les plus Nouveaux et sur les Relations les plus, recentes, rectifies sur les dernieres Observations, &c. 17x23 in., colored. Paris, 1742. $22.50

Shows "Mer de L'Ouest," and is probably of an earlier date as the numerals are blurred.

1381 [NEW MEXICO.] Cram's Railroad and Township Map of New Mexico. By George T. Cram. 17x22 in., colored, folding to 16mo in Original Wrappers. Chicago, 1880. $12.50

Fine early map of New Mexico.

1382 OGILVIUM, JOHANEM. Novissima et Accuratissma Totius Americae Descriptio per 17x21 in., beautifully hand colored. Amsterdam, (c. 1671). $37.50

This is the first issue of this fine map.

1383 [OHIO.]. Railroad and Township Map of the State of Ohio. Map, 20x27 in., colored, folding to 16mo, in cloth case. New York: (Colton), 1851. $7.50

1384 [OHIO.]. Township Map of the State of Ohio, showing the County and Township Boundaries, the Location of the Towns, Villages, Railway Stations, Railways, Turnpikes, Common Roads and Canals. Map 19x22 in., colored, folding into 16mo, cloth covers. By E. Memdenhall. Cincinnati, 1865. $6.00

1385 [ORTELIUS (ORTEL, ABRAHAM).] Americae sive Novi Orbis Nova Descriptio. 14x19 in. Antwerpiae, 1570. $50.00

1386 [ORTELIUS, (ORTEL, ABRAHAM).] Tartariae sive Magi Chami Regni. Map 18½x14 in., finely colored by hand. Antwerpiae, (1579). $50.00

1387 [ORTELIUS, (ORTEL, ABRAHAM).] Typhus Orbis Terrarum. Map 14x19 in. Antwerpiae, 1587. $40.00

1388 [ORTELIUS, (ORTEL, ABRAHAM).] Maris Pacifici, (quod vulgo Mar del Zur), cum Regionibus Circumincent ibus Insulisque in eodem Passim, Novissima Descriptio. May 19x13½ in., finely colored by hand. 1589. $50.00

1389 PHELPS, M. World at One View. Map 21x28 in., colored. New York, 1847. $15.00

Shows the outline of a trans-continental railroad from New York to the Columbia River, one of the earliest of the proposed overland routes shown on a map.

1390 PTOLEMY. Novae Insulae-Nova Tabula. (America). Map 13½x10 in., hand colored. Basel (1540). $50.00

South and Central America are recognizable, but North America is a rather fanciful conception. See Holman's "Old Maps and their Makers" for an illustration of this map.

1391 PTOLEMEO. La Geografia, con Alcuni Comenti et aggiunte da Sebastiano Munstero, con le Tavole et Moderne Aggiuntevi di J. Gastaldo, ridotta in volgare Italiano da P. A. Mattiolo. 8vo, vellum, with 60 double-paged engraved maps. In Venetia: G. B. Pedregano, 1548. $125.00

This is one of the indispensable editions of Ptolemy, representing in its maps a great advance upon all anterior efforts to illustrate the best geographical knowledge of the time. Gastaldo may be said to have created a new era, by his addition of five special maps of America to the two world-maps which he designed for this edition. It was the first time that anything of the kind had been done: all preceding editions having confined themselves to a single general map so far as the new world was concerned.

1392 RICHARDS, CAPT. G. H. North America—West Coast. Haro and Rosario Straits. 22x33 in. London: Admiralty, 1858-9. $5.00

1393 ROBERT DE VAUGONDY, G. L'Amerique Septentrionale et Meridionale divisee en ses Principales Parties par Sr. Sanson, Geographe Ordinaire de Roy; rectifee suivant les Nuvelles Decouverts Astronomiqus . . . par Sr. Robert, Geographe de Roy, etc. 19½x20 in., colored outline. Paris, 1749. $20.00

1394 ROBERT DE VAUGONDY. Carte Generale des Decouvertes de l'Amiral de Fonte representant la grande Probabilite d'un Passage au Nord]uest. 11½x14. Paris, 1772. $12.50

1395 ROBERTS, LIEUT. HENRY. Chart of the Northwest Coast of America and the Northwest Coast of Asia, explored in the year 1778-79. Prepared by Lieut. Roberts under the Immediate Inspection of Capt. Cook. 15½x28 in., colored additions to first ed., second ed. London, [1794]. $15.00

1395a —— Same. With additions to 1808. $15.00

1396 [RUSSIAN AMERICA]. Carte Generale de l'Empire de Russie dursee en Quarante en un Gouvermens Redyce en 1800. 28x58 in., colored and mounted on linen. Paris, 1800. $22.50

1397 SAYER, ROBERT. The Russian Discoveries from the Map, published by the Imperial Academy of St. Petersburg. 18x24 in., colored outlines. London, 1775. $20.00

1398 SAYER, ROBERT. A General Map of America divided into North and South America and West Indies, with the newest discoveries. 20x21 in., colored. Londn, 1772. $12 50

1399 SAYER, ROBERT. A New and Correct Map of North America, with the West India Islands divided to the last Treaty of Peace concluded at Paris, 10th Feby., 1763. 19½x22½ in., colored. [One sheet.] London, 1777. $20.00

1400 SAYER, ROBERT. A New Map of the Whole Continent of North America . . . Compiled from Mr. D'Anville's Maps of that Continent and Corrected. 1777. Two sheets, each 20½x46 in., colored in outline. London, 1777. $27.50

1401 SAYER, ROBERT. A Chart of North and South America, including the Atlantic and Pacific Oceans, with the nearest coast of Europe, Africa and Asia. 20x44 in., with colored outline. London, 1775. $30.00

This section, complete in itself, includes the northern coast of Canada from the Atlantic to the Pacific, as well as the N.E. coast of Asia. Alaska is shown as an island.

1402 SAYER, ROBERT. Chart containing the Coasts of California, New Albin, and the Russian Discoveries to the North, with the Peninsula of Kamtschatka opposite thereto. London, 1783. $12.50

1403 SAYER, ROBERT. A Chart of North and South America. 18x20 in. London, 1783. $7.50

Shows the Coastline between Asia and North America.

1404 SCHOYER, SOLOMON. Map of the United States from the most Approved Surveys. 16x20 in., colored, folding. 1826. $15.00

1405 SEALE, R. W. A Map of North America with the European Settlements and whatever else is Remarkable in Ye West Indies from the Latest and Best Observations. 14½x18 in. London, [c. 1745]. $7.50

1406 SEUTTER, MATTHEW. Accurata Delineato Celeberrimae regionio Ludoviciannae vel Gallice of Canadae et Floridie adpellatione in Septemptrionali America descriptae quae hodie nomine fluminis Mississippi vel St. Louis per Colonias et Navigatiomes Gallorum. 19½x22 in., colored. Augsburg, [1734?]. $47.50

1407 SOLINUS, C. J. Rerum Toto Orbe Memorabilium Thesauraus Locupletissimus. Huic ob argumenti similitudinem Pomponii Melae de situ orbes libros tres adiunximus. Folio, half vellum, with 98 maps in the text and two large folding maps, wood-engraved. Basileae, 1538. $70.00

Americanum unknown to Harisse. The large folding map of Asia shows a portion of the American West Coast, bearing the inscription: "Terra Incognita". Nordenskljold. This map is of interest on account of the delineation of the Pacific with a portion of the Western Coast of America.

1408 SPEED, JOHN. America, with those known parts of the world—both People and Manner of Building described and enlarged by J. S. Anno, 1626. [Engraved by Abraham Goos.] 20x15½ in., beautifully hand colored. London, 1626. $30.00

1409 THOMSON, J. Chart of the Northern Passage between Asia and America. 18x23 in., with colored outline. London, 1816. $12.50

One of the first accurate maps of the Bering Straits. Scarce.

1410 TILTON, JAMES. Map of a Part of the Territory of Washington to Accompany a Report of the Surveyor-General. (Worn at fold). N. Y., 1855. $25.00

1411 TILTON, JAMES. Map of Part of Washington Territory to accompany the Report of the Surveyor General 1860-61. 22x27 in. New York, (1861). $7.50

1412 VALK, GERARD, and SCHENK, PIETER. America Septentrio Nalis. Map, 18x21 in., engraved surface, hand-colored, wide margins. Amsterdam, [1680]. $27.50

Shows California as an island as far north as Cape Blanco.

1413 VALK, G. and SCHENK, P. Virginae et Floridae. 14½x19 in., colored. [Probably after Hondius map of 1639]. [c. 1680]. $27.50

1414 [VALK, G. and SCHENK, P.] Nova Virginiae tabula . . . ,14½x19 in., colored; with inset of Powatan and Capt. John Smith. [Probably after the H. Hondius map of 1639]. Amsterdam, [c. 1680]. $27.50

1415 VALK, G. and SCHENK, P. America Septentrionalis. 18x21 in., colored. [c. 1680]. $17.50

1416 VANCOUVER, GEORGE. A Chart showing part of the Coasts of Northwest America with the Tracks of His Majesty's Sloop Discovery, etc. 21x28 in. 1798. (Reproduction). $5.00

1417 VISSCHER, NICOLAS. Nova Tabula Geographia complectens Borealiorum Americae; in qua Exacte Delinaetae Sunt; Canada sive Nova Francia, Nova Scotia, Nova Anglia, Novum Belgium, Pennsylvania, Virginia, Carolina, et Terra Nova, etc. 18x23 in., colored. Amsterdam, [c. 1650]. $20.00

1418 VISSCHER, NICOLAO. Carte Nouvelle contenant la plus Septentrionale ou sout Exactement Decrites les Provences . . . Canada, our Nouvelle France, le Nouvelle Ecosse, la Nouvelle Angleterre, les Nouveaux Pais ba la Pennsylvanie, la Virginie, la Caroline, etc. Two sheets, 18½x23 in., each, beautifully hand-colored. Paris, [c. 1650]. $20.00

1419 VISSCHER, NICOLAO. Insulae Americanae in Oceano Septentrionale ac Regiones Adiacentas. 18x22 in., beautifully colored. Amsterdam, [1690?]. $37.50

1420 [WASHINGTON STATE]. Colored Manuscript Map of Fort Nisqually. 18x23 in., skilfully drawn by a British Officer stationed at the Post. (Ft. Nisqually, 1840). $20.00

1421 [WASHINGTON STATE.] Map of the Harbors of Puget Sound and Cowlitz Valleys, Washington Territory, from the U. S. Land Surveys. 15½x58 in., colored lines. N. Y., 1870. $20.00

Not in Phillips. This is an excessively rare map prepared by Canfield for his secret report to the Directors of the Northern Pacific Railroad.

1422 [WASHINGTON STATE.] Map of Washington Territory West of the Cascade Mountains. Compiled from the Govt. Surveys by Chas. A. White. 63x51 in., colored. N. Y.: Colton, 1870. Copyright by Hazard Stevens. $35.00

Phillips "List of Maps of America," p. 997. This is a very rare map of Washington Territory and is seldom offered.

1423 [WASHINGTON STATE.] Map of Southeastern Washington Territory, compiled frm Official Surveys, by John Hansan. 24x36 in., colored, folded in 12mo cloth. Seattle, 1878. $22.50

A fine rare map of Washington Territory.

1424 [WASHINGTON STATE.] Pocket Map of Tacoma, Puget Sound. By E. L. Terriff. 13x18 in., folded in 16mo, cloth cover. N.p., 1889. $7.50

1425 [WASHINGTON STATE.] New Sectional Township and County Map of Washington. Apprx. 70x54 in., folded into cloth covers. J. K. Gill and Co. Portland, Ore., 1889. $12.50

1426 [WASHINGTON STATE.] Map of Chebalis County, Washington. By C. H. Fenner. Small folding. (Seattle, N.d., 1890). $6.00

1427 [WASHINGTON STATE.] Proposed Plan of Improvement of Salmon Bat Harbor. By Stewart K. Smith. Map, 20x39 in. (Seattle), 1892. $5.00

1428 [WASHINGTON STATE.] Map of Snohomish County, Washington. 20x30 in., folding. N.p., 1893. $6.00

1429 [WASHINGTON STATE.] Anderson's 1896 Street and Guide Map of the City of Seattle, Washington. By C. P. Anderson. 35x52 in., colored, folded in 12mo, cloth cover. Seattle, 1896. $6.00

1430 [WASHINGTON STATE.] Anderson's new Map of Snohmish County, Washington. By C. P. Anderson. 20x39 in. ,folding. (Seattle), 1897. $5.00

1431 [WASHINGTON STATE.] Anderson's Sectional Map of Western and Central Washington, U. S. A. By C. P. Anderson. 28x48 in., colored, folded in cloth, 12mo, cover. Seattle, 1897. $12.50

The above item, one of the best of the regional maps, is now difficult to procure.

1432 [WASHINGTON STATE]. Pierce County Emigration Association. Map of Pierce County, Washington. Map, 34x23 in., folding. Tacoma, 1897. $5.00

1433 [WASHINGTON STATE.] Latest Atlin Map showing Three Routes and Exact Distances of each, Showing Thirty New Creeks Discovered to January 1, 1899. By Brandt and Johnson. 20x28 in., colored ,folded in 16mo with the Original Wrappers. N.p., (1899). $5.00

1434 WASHINGTON STATE. Sectional Map of Washington. Rand, McNally. Map,, 40x56 in., folding. Chicago, 1900. $6.00

1435 [WASHINGTON STATE.] Railroad Commissioner's Map of Washington. Map, 34x48 in., folding in 8vo, cloth covers. N.p., 1907. $4.75

1436 [WASHINGTON STATE.] Map of the Puget Sound Country. By D. H. White. Large Folding. Tacoma (1908). $4.50

1437 WASHINGTON STATE. Anderson's Map of Yakima. By C. P. Anderson. Map, 30x26 ins. (Seattle), July, 1909. $5.00

1438 [WASHINGTON TERRITORY.] New Map of the Western Territories. (Watson's). Large folding. N.p. 1869. $7.50

1439 [WASHINGTON TERRITORY.] Map of Puget Sound and Surroundings. Washington Territory compiled from Official Surveys and Published by Eastwick, Mooris and Co., Civil and Mining Engineers, Seattle, Wash. Terr., 1877. Territory drawn by John Hanson, with Eastwick Mooris and Co. Folding map, 28x21 in. Seattle, 1877. $15.00

1440 [WISCONSIN.] Chapman's Sectional Map of Wisconsin with the most recent Surveys. Map, 22x33 in., colored and folding in 16mo, cloth covers (slight wear in one fold). Milwaukee, 1856. $17.50

1441 [WISCONSIN.] Sectional Pocket Map. The State of Wisconsin compiled from the latest Authorities and Published by P. A. Latham. Map, 32x48 ins., colored, folding into 12mo, cloth covers. Milwaukee, 1850. $10.00

1442 WIT, FREDERICK DE. Accuratissima Totius Tabula Recent Emendata Per . . . 16x19 in., engraved surface, wide margins, beautifully hand colored. Amsterdam, [1688]. $12.50

1443 WIT, FREDERICK DE. America. Novissima et Accuratissima Septentrionales ac Medridionalis Americae. 19x22½ in. Amsterdam, (1690?). $17.50

1444 WYLD, JAMES. Map of North America, exhibiting the recent Discoveries, Geographical and Nautical. 14x18½ in., colored. (1843). $12.50

1444a —— Same. 20½x15, in., colored. 1843. $15.00

1445 WYLD, JAMES. Map of the United States and the Relative Position of Oregon and Texas. Map, approx. 55x37 in. London: Wyld, N.d. $15.00

Smith 4483, cites two copies.

1446 ZATTA, ANTONIO. Nuove Scoperte de Russi al Nord del Sud si nell Asia, che nell America. 12x15 in., colored. Venezia, 1776. $10.00

1447 CAN DOREN, CARL. Secret History of the Revolution. By Carl Van Doren. 576pp., illus., 8vo, cloth. New York, 1941. $3.75

This should be the final source book on the Arnold-Andre Conspiracy; although students will continue to write about it 1000 years hence. The great bin of source material is contained in the British Headquarters Papers, purchased in 1925 by the late William L. Clements. After all, Sir Henry Clinton was on the other end of the receiving line in the Conspiracy. Sir Henry had to keep some of the records relating to this incident to justify himself. His Adjutant, pro tem, Major John Andre, was hung on a little hill in back of Mabie's Tavern at Tappan. He apparently had no papers other than those he stupidly carried upon his person when captured. So Sir Henry's secret codes, letters, maps, ledgers, etc. were to be opened and finally elucidated before the gossip about the Conspiracy could finally be authenticated.

Hitherto historians had enough from word-of-mouth to implicate many "staunch" Patriots, other than Arnold. But, lacking documents, they could only hint. For instance what could Madame Elizabeth Ferguson tell, if she were to sit again at Papa Graeme's house on Chestnut St., Philadelphia? Did lovely Mrs. Ferguson make the first contact? Maybe Mr. Van Doren has answered that. It is just as well if he has not done so. Surely the delver into the Historic Dust Bin will have to have something other than chaff to work upon 500 years from now. Sparks stated Arnold received 6315 pounds for his services. You will find that documented correctly in "Secret History." And how about old Joshua Hett Smith? Was he just a plain fool?

As for pretty "Peggy," daughter of the Downright Shippens, there have been two schools of thought about her—the sentimental and realist. Young Alexander Hamilton heads the sentimentalists. He actually weeped over her acting at the Robinson House that mild September day. Historians have wept along that line ever since. Then, there is the monstrous Burr who despite the hush-hush of certain Philadelphians, came out with the yarn about what Peggy told Mrs. Prevost (Burr's fiancee) that bright afternoon at Paramus, N. J., when Aide Franks was removing her to Philadelphia from the Robinson House. Always circumspect, and a Tammany politician, Burr had to wait 50 years before he told it. Was Peggy guilty? I think so [see Decker's "Arnold," 1932 advt.].

But Mr. Van Doren, thank Heaven, has finally got down to the bottom of the bin. He has served papers on the little lady. All in all, this is the final authoritative work on the Conspiracy, the final culmination of the splendid efforts of those who had to guess regarding many points of the Conspiracy—we refer to Sparks, Isaac Arnold, the late William Abbatt, and others. And finally, we should mention Dr. Randolph G. Adams, Curator of the British Headquarters Papers at the William L. Clements Library, who, as much as anyone, has spaded and hoed so that the facts contained in the "British Headquarters Papers" could be made available for Mr. Van Doren and all other accredited scholars. This is a must book for scholars and collectors.

1448 —— Same. Limited Edition. $15.00

As a biographical source book for the above work, in order to get a complete picture of Arnold's early life and his later life in England and New Brunswick, Canada, we recommend—

1449 DECKER, MALCOLM. Benedict Arnold: Son of the Havens. Colored Frontis., 79 illus. 534pp. Map. One of 269 copies. Tarrytown, 1932. $7.50

1450 SERLE AMBROSE. The American Journal of Ambrose Serle, Secretary to Lord Howe, 1776-78. Edited by Edward H. Tatum, Jr. 369pp., 7 maps. 8vo, cloth. San Marino, 1941. $4.50

This work is valuable for the description of New York under British occupation. The author, Secretary of Lord Howe, Commander of the British Fleet, was in a most favorable position to report on events. He gives detailed accounts of military actions, particularly the Battle of Long Island. As the above this is a must book for collectors and libraries.

PART III

3

THE GEORGE W. SOLIDAY COLLECTION OF WESTERN AMERICANA

PART III

---

1 ADAMS, HENRY. History of the United States of America, 1801-1817. 9 vols., 12mo, cloth. N. Y., 1890-91 $22.50

First Edition. "The most valuable history of this important period; remarkable alike for its research, its penetrating analysis of character and political tendencies, and for the flood of light which is thrown upon every phase of the foreign relations of the country . . . Adams stands aloof from both parties . . ."—Prof. Edward G. Bourne.

2 ADAMS, JOHN. The Works . . . With a Life of the Author, Notes and Illustrations, by his Grandson, Charles Francis Adams. 10 vols., 8vo, cloth. Boston, 1850-6. $17.50

"The famous son of John Adams was well fitted to collect and order the vast mass of documents . . . His cool, judicial portrayal shows no trace of a tendency to exaggerate the merits of his subject . . . the character of John Adams is revealed by these letters and the diary in the most attractive light . . ."—Jas. K. Hosmer.

THE MEMOIRS OF J. Q. ADAMS

3 ADAMS, JOHN QUINCY. Memoirs . . . Comprising Portions of His Diary from 1795 to 1848. Edited by Charles Francis Adams. Portrait. 12 vols., 8vo, cloth. Phila., 1874-77. $100.00

The greatest American diary, by general agreement. It covers an almost continuous period of 65 years. Its accuracy was once attested to by the willingness of Calhoun, fellow member with Adams in Monroe's cabinet, to rely upon the Diary to establish a disputed point. It is doubtful whether a work of this kind has ever been more completely executed by a public figure. The editorial work of Charles Francis Adams consists of an introduction, numerous notes, and the excision of passages not of general interest.

4 ADAMS, JOHN QUINCY. Writings. Edited by W. C. Ford. 6 vols., 8vo, cloth. N. Y., 1913. $22.50

5 ADAMS, JOHN QUINCY. The Jubilee of the Constitution. A Discourse delivered at the request of the New York Historical Society . . . the 30th of April, 1839, being the 50th Anniversary of the Inaugural of G. Washington . . . 128 pp., plate. 8vo. N. Y., 1839. $3.50

6 ADAMS, JOHN QUINCY. An Oration pronounced July 4th, 1793, at the Request of the Inhabitants of the Town of Boston, in Commemoration of the Anniversary of American Independence. 16 pp., 8vo, unbound. Boston, 1793. $5.00

7 [ALABAMA.] (Pickett, A. J.). History of Alabama, and incidentally of Georgia and Mississippi, from the Earliest Period. Plates. 2 vols., 12mo, cloth. Charleston, 1851 $12.50

7a [ALASKA.] Alaska-Yukon Gazeteer and Business Directory, 1905-1906. 620 pp., 8vo, cloth. Seattle, Wash.: R. L. Polk and Co. (1905). $12.50
7b ——. The Same. 656 pp. Seattle: Polk, 1903. $12.50

8 [ALASKA.] (Jackson, Sheldon). A Statement of Facts Concerning the difficulties at Sitka, in 1885. 33 pp., 8vo, original printed wrappers. Washington, 1886. $4.50

Not mentioned by Smith.

9 [ALASKA.] (1) The Alaska and Northwest Quarterly. Vol. 1, No. 1 Ed. by C. Jackson. 83 pp., illus., port. Seattle, 1899. (Contains Sumner's celebrated speech on Alaska, articles by T. W. Prosch and others. (2) The Alaska-Canadian Frontier By Thos. Willing Balch. Phila., 1902. (3) Boundary Disputes with our Northern Neighbors, Settled and Unsettled. By Judge C. H. Hanford. 1899. (4) The Gold Fields of Alaska and Yukon Territory. 140 pp. (5) Report on the Salmon Fisheries of Alaska. By Howard M. Kutchin. 1903. (6) Annual Report of the Alaskan Agricultural Experiment Station for 1902. 8vo, half morocco. V.p., v.d., 1899-1902. $15.00

10 [ALASKA.] Our Northern Domain. Alaska, Picturesque, Historic and Commercial. 237 pp., 8vo, cloth. Boston, c. 1910. $2.75

10a [ALASKA.] (Pierce, W. H.) Thirteen Years of Travel and Exploration in Alaska . . . 223 illus. Lawrence: Kansas Journal Pub. Co., 1890. $7.50

This is a scarce and very desirable narrative relating to Alaska.

11 [ALASKA.] The Coast Indians of Southern Alaska and Northern British Columbia. By Albert P. Niblack. Maps and plate. 8vo, cloth. (Washington, 1888). $4.75

Smith 2662. Presentation copy from the author to James G. Swan.

12 [ALASKA.] New York Legislature. Committee to the Alaska-Yukon Pacific Exposition, 1909. Transmitted to the Legislature Jan. 25, 1910. 197 pp., 11 plates, 23 portraits. 4to, original wrappers. Albany, 1910. $4.50

Can locate only two copies in Northwest libraries. The work was done by the state at considerable expense.

13 [ALASKA.] Lecture on the Yukon Gold Fields. Delivered at Victoria, B. C., by Mr. William Ogilvie . . . 32 pp., 8vo, original printed wrappers. Victoria, 1897. $15.00

This rare pamphlet by the author of one of the best guides to the Alaskan gold fields is seldom come across. Ogilvie was the Dominion Surveyor.

14 [ALASKA.] Information Respecting the Yukon District from Reports of William Ogilvie, Dominion Land Surveyor, and from Other Sources. 65 pp., 5 maps, illus. 8vo, original wrappers. Ottawa, 1897. $12.50

Attached to the above are two clippings from the Ottawa Free Press, dated Dec. 4, 1897, and Jan. 4, 1898. They contain a long letter from Bishop Pascal, of Prince Albert, who passed 24 years in the N.W. Pascal discusses the various routes to the gold fields, and finally recommends the one via Regina, Prince Albert, Green Lake, Isle la Crosse, Portage la Losche, Clearwater River and McMurray. Can locate only one copy, that in the Washington State Library.

15 [ALASKA.] Early Days in the Yukon, the Story of the Gold Fields. 306 pp., 8vo, cloth. London, 1913. $4.50

16 [ALASKA.] Alaska Official Reports. 4 Reports. 8vo. V.p., V.d. $7.50

17 [ALASKA.] Twenty Five Years in Alaska. By Ivan Petroff. (Contained in the North American Review, May, 1892. 628 pp.). 8vo, original wrappers. 1892. $2.50

This is an excellent and little known account of manners and customs in old Alaska by a Russian, who came over to the Colony after it had been sold to the U. S.

18 [ALASKA.] (Pierrepont, Edward). Fifth Avenue to Alaska . . . With Maps by Leonard Forbes Beckwith. 339 pp., 4 maps. 8vo, cloth. N. Y., 1884. $3.75

Smith 3071. Original Edition.

19 [ALASKA.] Trailing and Camping in Alaska. By Addison Monroe Powell. 379 pp., frontis., port., plates. 8vo, cloth. N. Y., 1909. $5.00

20 [ALASKA.] From Euston to Klondike; the Narrative of a Journey through British Columbia and the Northwest Territory in the Summer of 1898. With map and illustrations from sketches by the Author. By Julius Mendes Price. 301 pp., 12mo, cloth. London, 1898. $7.50

Smith 3217.

21 [ALASKA.] (Pringle, L. M.). The Yukon-Tanana Region, Alaska. Illus., map. 233 pp. Washington, 1905. Also bound in "Geology and Mineral Resources of the Controller Bay Region, Alaska." 141 pp., illus., map. Washington, 1908. 8vo, half morocco. Washington, 1905-1908. $6.00

22 [ALASKA.] The Soul of Alaska. A Comment and a Description. 6 fine engravings of Alaskan Indians. 96 pp., 8vo, original wrappers. N. Y.: The Gorham Co., 1905. $3.50

23 [ACQUISITION OF ALASKA.] (1) Russian America. Message of the President, 1848. 40th Cong., 2nd Sess., H. R. Doc., No. 177. 361 pp. (2) Russian America. Message of the President, 1868. Map. 40th Cong., 2nd Sess., H. R. Ex. Doc. No. 177. Part 2. (3) Letter from the Sec'y of War Suffering Soldiers in Alaska. 40th Cong., 2nd Sess., H. R. Ex. Doc. 177. (4) Message from the President in relation to the Transfer of Territory from Russia to the U. S. Jan., 1868. 40th Cong., 2nd Sess., H. R. Ex. Doc. No. 125. 8vo, half morocco. Washington, 1868. $17.50

Collected and bound by Mr. Thomas Wickham Prosch.

24 ALVORD, CLARENCE W. Publications of the Illinois State Historical Society. 148 pp., 8vo, original wrappers. Springfield, 1907. $4.50

25 AMBLER, CHARLES. History of Transportation in the Ohio Valley, with special reference to its Waterways, Trade and Commerce from the Earliest Period to the Present Time. Maps, plates. 465 pp., 8vo, cloth. Glendale, 1932. $6.00

Limited edition. Primitive transportation on the Ohio, keelboats, early steam navigation, etc.

26 [AMERICAN COLONIES.] The Colonial Period of American History. By Charles M. Andrews. 8vo, cloth. New Haven (1935). $4.00

27 [AMERICAN COLONIES.] (Dickerson, Oliver M.). American Colonial Government, 1696-1765; a study of the British Board of Trade in its relation to the American Colonies, Political, Industrial and Administrative. With Bibliography, Analytical Index and facsimiles of manuscripts. Large 8vo. Cleveland, 1912. $17.50

Now out of print and scarce.

28 [AMERICAN COLONIES.] The Middle Colonies. By J. A. Doyle. 564 pp., 8vo, cloth. London, 1907. $7.50

Settlement and Colonial History of N. Y., N. J., Pa.

29 [AMERICAN COLONIES.] The Colonies under the House of Hanover. By J. A. Doyle. Folding colored map. 630 pp., 8vo, cloth. London, 1907. $7.50

Original and best edition. Colonial history, 1688-1763; administrative developments; religion; Indian and Negro; French Wars; literary and intellectual development.

30 [AMERICAN COLONIES.] The English in America—Virginia, Maryland and the Carolinas. By J. A. Doyle. Map. 556 pp., 8vo, cloth. London, 1882. $7.50

31 [AMERICAN COLONIES.] The Beginners of a Nation. History ot the Source and Rise of the Earliest English Settlements in America with Special Reference to the Life and Character of the People. By Edward Eggleston. Maps. 8vo, cloth. N. Y., 1900. $4.00

32 [AMERICAN COLONIES.] The Puritans as a Colonist and Reformer. [Frontis.] By Ezra Hoyt Byington. 8vo, cloth. Boston, 1899. $4.00

33 [AMERICAN COLONIES.] The Story of the Pilgrim Fathers, 1606-1623, as told by Themselves, their Friends, and their Enemies. Map and portrait. 644 pp., 8vo, cloth. London, 1897. $4.00

34 [AMERICAN COLONIES.] Sir Walter Raleigh, a Biography. By Wm. Stebbing. 8vo, cloth. Oxford, 1899. $4.50

35 [AMERICAN COLONIES.] Sir Walter Raleigh, Last of the Elizabethans. By Edward Thompson. Frontis. 8vo, cloth. New Haven, 1936. $4.00

36 [AMERICAN COLONIES.] The Puritan Age and Rule in the Colony of the Massachusetts Bay, 1629-1685. 8vo, cloth. Boston, 1888. $4.75

37 [AMERICAN EMIGRANT.] The Gentleman Emigrant: His Daily Life, Sports and Pastimes in Canada, Australia and the United States. By W. Stamer. 2 vols., 8vo, cloth. London, 1874. $4.50

38 [AMERICAN HISTORY.] (Bancroft, Geo.) History of the U. S. A. 6 vols., 8vo, cloth. N. Y., 1895. $12.50

The best edition of Bancroft's work, as it was his last printed version.

38a [AMERICAN HISTORY.] (Poussin, G. T.) The United States, its Power and Progress. Trans. from the French by E. I. DuBarry, Surgeon U. S. Navy. 8vo, cloth. 1851. $7.50

Discovery and exploration; early settling; New England; Plantations of New France; Louisiana and Florida; Oregon Terr.; etc.

39 [AMERICAN HISTORY.] (Hildreth, Richard). The History of the U. S. A. 3 vols. (first series), 3 vols. (second series). 6 vols., 8vo, cloth. N. Y., 1851-56. $14.50

40 [AMERICAN HISTORY.] (McMaster, John Bach.) History of the People of the U. S., from the Revolution to the Civil War. Maps. 8 vols., 8vo, cloth. N. Y., 1886-1913. $20.00

Fine set of the original and best edition of the best history of the period covered.

41 [AMERICAN HISTORY.] (Rhodes, James Ford). History of the U. S. from the Compromise of 1850. 8 vols., 8vo, cloth. N. Y., 1904. $17.50

42 [AMERICAN HISTORY.] (Schouler, James). History of the United States of America, under the Constitution. 8 vols., 8vo, cloth. N. Y. (1880-1913). $15.00

43 [AMERICAN HISTORY.] The History of North America. By Various Authorities. Edited by Guy Carleton Lee and Francis N. Thorpe. 21 vols., 8vo, cloth. Printed for Subscribers only: Phila., 1903-07. $30.00

44 [AMERICAN HISTORY.] (Von Holst, Dr. H.). The Constitutional and Political History of the U. S. Translated from the German by John J. Lalor and Alfred B. Mason. 8 vols., 8vo, cloth. Chicago, 1889-92. $15.00

The period covered is from 1750 to 1833 in the first volume and down to Lincoln's first inauguration in the second to the seventh volume; the eighth volume is a general index.

45 [AMERICAN HISTORY.] (Wilson, Woodrow). History of the American People: Folding colored maps, portraits, plates, etc. 5 vols., 8vo, cloth. N. Y., 1906. $7.50

Good clean set of the best edition.

46 [AMERICAN LOYALISTS.] Biographical Sketches of Loyalists of the American Revolution, with an Historical Essay. By Lorenzo Sabine. 8vo, cloth. Boston, 1847. $7.50

The original edition.

47 [AMERICAN LOYALISTS.] (Stark, James H.). The Loyalists of Massachusetts and the other side of the American Revolution. Illus., folding map. 8vo, cloth. Boston, 1910. $3.00

48 [AMERICAN MANNERS AND CUSTOMS.] Sketches of Public Characters . . . By Ignatius Loyola Robertson. 8vo, roan, backed boards. N. Y., 1830. $4.50

A fine account of the Jackson era by a well-known traveling Jesuit; much of Washington and the leading men of the time—Webster, Calhoun, Everett, Randolph, Jackson—; New York, Boston, etc., etc.

49 [AMERICAN PIONEER.] A Monthly Periodical devoted to Objects of the Logan Historical Society; numerous plans and engravings. 2 vols. (all published), large 8vo, half morocco. Cincinnati, 1843-4. $37.50

A valuable work containing original contributions relating mainly to the Ohio Valley, Contains journals of campaigns against the Indians, captivities, incidents of border warfare, etc. It ranks favorably with "Olden Time" for usefulness and authority.

50 [AMERICAN REVOLUTION.] Western Lands and the American Revolution. By Thomas Perkins Abernathy. 8vo, cloth. N. Y., 1937. $4.00

50a [AMERICAN REVOLUTION.] The Journal of Lieut. William Feltman, of the First Pennsylvania Regiment, from May 26, 1781 to April 25, 1782, embracing the Siege of Yorktown and the Southern Campaign. Historical Society of Pennsylvania Collections. Vol. 1, No. 5. 8vo, original printed wrappers. 1853. $4.50

One of the best day-by-day factual accounts of the Southern campaigns by a soldier who participated in them.

51 [AMERICAN REVOLUTION.] (Murdock, Harold). The 19th of April, 1775. Map and illus. Small 4to, cloth. Boston, 1923. $4.50

575 copies printed.

52 [AMERICAN REVOLUTION.] (Henry, John J.). Accurate and Interesting Account of the Hardships and Sufferings of that Band of Heroes who traversed the Wilderness in the Campaign against Quebec in 1775. 12mo, calf. Lancaster, 1812. $12.50

53 [AMERICAN REVOLUTION.] (Stone, Wm. L.). Life of Joseph Brant —Thayendanegea: Including the Border Wars of the American Revolution, and Sketches of the Indian Campaigns of Generals Harmar, St. Clair and Wayne . . . Map and illus. 2 vols., 8vo, engraved title, original cloth. N. Y., 1838. $10.00

54 [AMERICAN REVOLUTION.] Some New Light on the Last Resting Place of Benedict Arnold and of his wife, Margaret Shippen. By J. G. Taylor. Maps, tables, illus. 4to, cloth. London, 1931. $6.00

One of the few modern books concerning Arnold which contains original material. Dr. Taylor, the author, was the first to discover Arnold's burial place—in 1926.

55 [AMERICAN REVOLUTION.] The Delaware Continentals, 1776-1783. By Christopher L. Ward. Thick 8vo, cloth. Illus. Wilmington, 1941. $3.75

56 [AMERICAN TELEGRAPH.] Ocean Telegraphing. Adaption of New Principles for the Successful Working of Submarine Cables, etc. Frontis., map. 41 pp., small 4to, original wrappers. Cambridge, 1865. $7.50

Also contains an article on a proposed telegraphic route, via Alaska and Siberia, to Asia and Europe. Inserted is a broadside "Ocean Telegraphing."

57 [AMERICAN VESPUCIUS.] His Life and Voyages, and Discovery of the New World. By C. Edwards Lester and A. Foster. Plates. 432 pp., 8vo, cloth. New Haven, 1858. $6.00

Includes for the first time in English the original writings of Vespucius.

58 APPLETONS CYCLOPAEDIA OF AMERICAN BIOGRAPHY. Edited by James Grant Wilson and John Fiske. Ports. and woodcuts. 6 vols., 4to, cloth. N. Y., 1888-9. $20.00

59 [ARCTIC.] Under the Northern Lights. By J. A. MacGahan. Frontis., numerous other illus. 8vo, cloth. London, 1876. $2.50

69 [ARCTIC—HAYES EXPEDITION.] The Open Polar Sea. Narrative of a Voyage of Discovery Towards the North Pole in the Schooner "United States." By Dr. I. I. Hayes. Portrait, colored maps, plates. 454 pp., 8vo, half polished calf; fine. N. Y., 1867. $4.00

61 [ARIZONA.] The Pima Indians Relate their Story of their Wrongs. An Appeal for Justice. (By Antonito Azul, Chief of the Pimas, Pima Reservation, Sacatom, Arizona). 8 pp., 8vo, sewn. Washington, N.d. $5.00

Not in Munk.

61a [ARIZONA.] Box, Capt. M. J. Adventures and Explorations, being the record of Nen Years Travel. 344 pp., 8vo, cloth. N. Y., 1869. $12.50

Munk p. 36. One of the best descriptive narratives of the southwestern country.

62 [ARKANSAS.] Early Days in Arkansas; being for the most part Personal Recollections of an Old Settler. By Judge Wm. P. Pope. Illus. 330 pp., 12mo, half morocco. Little Rock, 1895. $7.50

63 ARNOLD, SAMUEL GREEN. History of the State of Rhode Island and Providence Plantations. 2 vols., 8vo, cloth. N. Y., 1874. $7.50

64 BAILEY, KENNETH P. The Ohio Company of Virginia and the Westward Movement, 1748-1792; a Chapter in the History of the Colonial Frontier. Five maps, four folding. 374 pp., 8vo, cloth. Glendale, 1939. $6.00

65 [BARBE-MARBOIS, FRANCOIS.] The Man Who Sold Louisiana. The Career of Francois Barbe-Marbois. Portraits, maps, illus. By E. Wilson Lyon. 8vo, cloth. Norman, Okla., 1942. $2.75

66 BARBER, JOHN W., and HOWE, HENRY. Historical Collections of New York; containing a general collection of the Most Interesting Facts, Traditions, Biographical Sketches, Anecdotes, etc., relating to its History and Antiquities, etc. Folding map and illus. 8vo, calf. N. Y., 1841. $3.00

67 BARTRAM, JOHN. Observations on the Inhabitants, Climate, Soil, Rivers, Production, Animals and other matters worthy of Notice, made to John Bartram in his Travels from Pennsylvania to Onondaga, Oswego, and Lake Ontario, in Canada. To which is annexed a curious account of the Cataracts at Niagara by Peter Kalm, a Swedish Gentleman who travelled there. 8vo, boards. No. 101 of 300 copies printed. Rochester, 1895. $5.00

68 BEGGS, S. R. Pages from the Early History of the West and Northwest; embracing Reminiscences and Incidents of Settlement and Growth, and Sketches of the Material and Religious Progress of the States of Ohio, Indiana, Illinois, and Missouri, with especial reference to the History of Methodism. 12mo, cloth (slightly worn). Cincinnati, 1868. $4.50

Early history of Chicago, Black Hawk War, biographical notes, etc.

69 BELNAP, JEREMY. The History of New Hampshire. With the rare map. 3 vols., 8vo, half morocco, g.t., all other edges uncut. Phila. and Boston, 1784-1792. $30.00

This set has the rare first edition of Vol. 1. The author was one of the most refined and scholarly men of his time, and his work always held the highest rank among the older state histories.

70 BENNETT, EMERSON. Wild Scenes on the Frontiers; or Heroes of the West. Engravings. 8vo, original cloth (worn and soiled). Phila., 1859. $5.00

71 BENTON, THOMAS H. Letter from, to the People of Missouri. Central National Highway from the Mississippi River to the Pacific. Citizens: The time has come when the long disputed question of a railroad to the Pacific ocean is assuming a practical form, and is about to receive its solution in the authoritative examination of the country, and the selection of the route, etc. (Caption title). 8vo, 24 pp. (Wash., March 4, 1853). $7.50

Wagner-Camp 163.

72 [BIEBER, RALPH R.] Diary of a Journey to the Pike's Peak Gold Mines in 1859. 8vo, original wrappers. [Cleveland], 1927. $3.50

A separate reprint from the Mississippi Valley Historical Review.

73 BILLION, FRED L. Annals of St. Louis in its Territorial Days, 1804-1821. With portrait and plates. Large 8vo, cloth. St. Louis, 1886. $5.00

A collection of scarce material relating to the early history of St. Louis. There was a sequel to this work published in 1888.

74 ["BILLY THE KID."] Notorious New Mexico Outlaw. The only Truthful and Accurate Account of the killing of this Young Desperado. By John W. Poe. (A member of the Sheriff's posse). 15 pp., 8vo, original wrappers. Los Angeles (1919). No. 62 of 250 copies privately printed. $4.00

75 [BLACK HAWK.] Autobiography of: Dictated by himself to Antoine Le Clair, Interpreter. Edited by J. B. Patterson. 3 ports. 208 pp., 8vo, cloth. Oquawka, Ill., 1882. $5.00

76 BLAIR, CAPT. WALTER A. A Raft Pilot's Log; a History of the great Rafting Industry on the Upper Mississippi, 1840-1915. 10 portraits and 31 plates of early views. 8vo, cloth. Cleveland, 1930. $6.00

ORIGINAL COPY OF "BOSTON PORT BILL"

77 [BOSTON PORT BILL.] Anno Regni Georgii III . . .An Act to discontinue, in such Manner, and for such Time as therein mentioned, the landing and discharging, lading and shiping, of Goods, Wares, and Merchandise, at the Town and within the Harbour, of Boston, in the Province of Massachusett's Bay, in North America. Small folio. London: Printed by Charles Eyre and William Strahan, 1774. $45.00

The extremely rare original "Boston Port Bill."

78 [BOUQUET'S EXPEDITION.] (William Smith). An Historical Account of the Expedition against the Ohio Indians, in the Year 1764, under the Command of Henry Bouquet, including the Transactions with the Indians, relative to the Delivery of their Prisoners, and the Preliminaries of Peace. With an Introductory Account of the preceding Campaign and Battle of Bushy Run, . . . with a large folding map of the country on the Ohio and Muskingum, with 2 inset views of Indian encampments by Thos. Hutchins, folding plan of the Battle of Bushy Run, and folding plate. 4to, half morocco. Phila.: William Bradford, 1765. $275.00

The rare Original Edition with the large folding map. Very few copies appear with the correct map showing the inset views.

78a ——. The Same. Map. 134 pp., 8vo, cloth. Cincinnati, 1907. $4.50

79 BOYER, MARY C. Arizona in Literature; a Collection of the best writings of Arizona Authors from early Spanish Days to the Present Time. Colored frontis., other illus. 574 pp., 8vo, cloth. Glendale, 1934. $5.00

80 BRAINERD, REV. DAVID. Memoirs: Missionary to the Indians on the Borders of New York, New Jersey and Pennsylvania chiefly from his own Diary, by Rev. Jonathan Edwards, including his Journal now for the first time incorporated by S. E. Dwight. 8vo, calf. New Haven, 1822. $2.50

Foxed as usual and lacks flyleaf.

80a ——. The Same. 8vo, cloth. Phila., 1865. $1.00

81 [BREMER, F.] Homes of the New World: Impressions of America (in letters from Chicago, Galena, St. Louis, Cincinnati, New Orleans, Savannah, Macon, Augusta, Charleston.) 2 vols., 8vo, cloth. N. Y., 1853. $4.00

82 [BRETE HARTE.] The Life of. By T. Edgar Pemberton. 358 pp., 8vo, cloth. N. Y., 1903. $4.50

83 [BRITISH COLUMBIA.] Facts and Figures relating to Vancouver and British Columbia. By J. Despard Pemberton. 4 maps, tables. 171 pp., 8vo, cloth. London, 1860. $7.50

Gives an account of gold fields in British Columbia, Vancouver Island and Queen Charlotte's Island; also a journal of a tour across Vancouver's Island from Nimkish River to Nootka Sound, by H. Moffat.

84 [BRITISH COLUMBIA.] Fort Langley, 1827-1927. A Century of Settlement in the Valley of the Lower Fraser River. By Denys Nelson. Illus. 31 pp., 8vo, original wrappers. Fort Langley, 1927. $4.50

85 [BRITISH COLUMBIA.] Native Sons of British Columbia. Romance of Vancouver. Illus. 60 pp., folio, original wrappers. Vancouver, 1896. $6.00

86 [BRITISH COLUMBIA.] The Mineral Resources of British Columbia. Practical hints for Capitalists and Intending Settlers, with an Appendix containing the Mineral Laws of the Province and Dominion of Canada. By D. Oppenheimer. 50 pp., 8vo, original wrappers. Vancouver, 1889. $5.00

Smith 2773.

87 [BRITISH COLUMBIA.] Provincial Museum of Natural History, Victoria, B. C. A Preliminary Catalogue of the Flora of Vancouver and Queen Charlotte Islands. 86 pp., large 8vo, cloth. Victoria, 1921. $4.75

88 [BRITISH COLUMBIA.] Peace River Country. Illus. 47 pp., 12mo, original printed wrappers. Ottawa, 1916. $2.50

89 BURNABY, ANDREW. Travels through the Middle Settlements in North America in the Years 1759 and 1760, with observations upon the state of the Colonies. Reprint Edition by Rufus Rockwell Wilson. 8vo, cloth. N. Y., 1904. $3.50

90 BURNETT, FINN. Frontiersman; the Life and Adventures of an Indian Fighter, Mail-Coach Driver, Miner, Pioneer Cattleman, Participant in the Powder River Expedition, Survivor of the Hayfield Fight, associate of Jim Bridger, and Chief Washakie. By Robert B. David. Portrait, plans. 406 pp., 8vo, cloth. Glendale, 1937. $6.00

91 BUTTERFIELD, CONSUL W. Historical Account of the Expedition against Sandusky under Col. William Crawford, 1782 . . . Portrait. 404 pp., 8vo, cloth. Cincinnati, 1873. $12.50

92 BUTTERFIELD, CONSUL W. Washington-Irvine Correspondence; Official Letters between George Washington and Brig. Gen. Wm. Irvine, concerning Military Affairs in the West, 1781-1783 . . . Map and portraits. 436 pp., 8vo, cloth. Madison, Wis., 1882. $12.50

93 BUTTERFIELD, CONSUL W. History of Brule's Discoveries and Explorations, 1610-1626. Portraits, maps and plates, index. 200 pp., 8vo, cloth. Cleveland, 1898. $9.00

Narrative of his discoveries of Lakes Huron, Ontario and Superior; first explorations of Pennsylvania, western New York and the Province of Ontario.

94 CALHOUN, JOHN C. The Works of. Six Volumes, 8vo, cloth. Charleston, 1851. $30.00

95 [CALIFORNIA.] Ueber die Russische Colonie Ross in Neu-Californien. 416 pp. Also: Einige Bemerkungen uber die Russischen und Spanischen Niederlassungen in Neu-Californien. Von A. Erman. 436 pp. Also: Beitrage zur Klimatologie des Russischen Reiche (Kamtschatka). 441 pp. Also: Ueber die Reise und Entdeckkungen des Lieutenant L. Sagoskin in Russischen Amerika. 499 pp. (Contained in Archiv fur Wissenschaftliche Kunde von Russland, vi Band, 3tes helft). 2 vols., 8vo, original wrappers. Berlin, 1847-1848. $20.00

Included in the above is a large map, 12 x 13 inches showing the coast line and the stations on both sides of Bering's Strait, all of Alaska and the territory as far south as 55. The map is entitled: "Carte des Granzdistricts in den Besitzungen der Aleutischen und der Hudson's Bay Compagnie."

96 [CALIFORNIA.] Land of Sunshine (Los Angeles). Edited by Charles F. Lummis from June, 1894 through July, 1915 (being volumes 1-42); profusely illustrated. 4to and 8vo, original printed wrappers and in mint condition throughout. Los Angeles, 1894-1915. $100.00

Such a complete run as this is excessively rare. The work in its entirety is valuable for its extensive illustrations of old views and landmarks, now obliterated. It includes the reports of the Southwest Society of the Archaeological Institute, the English translation of many important early Spanish documents, and many scholarly contributions by David Starr Jordan, Joaquin Miller, Hittell, Stoddard, Cheney, Coolbrith, Matthews, Winship, Hodge, Markham, etc.

97 [CALIFORNIA.] California and New Mexico. Message from the President of the U. S. transmitting Information on the Subject and New Mexico. Large folding maps. 8vo, half roan. Washington, 1850. $12.50

Cowan p. 40: "This important volume contains the official correspondence and documents relating to California, 1847-49, and is the most extensive source of authorities covering that period. The Mexican War; the Provisional Govt. of Calif.; Statehood, etc.

98 [CALIFORNIA.] Message from the President of the U. S. Folding maps, plans. 30th Cong., 2nd Sess., H. R. Doc. No. 1. 8vo, sewn. Washington, 1848. $12.50

This is President Polk's message relating to California and the Far West; the gold diggings, Mormons, etc.

99 [CALIFORNIA.] (Newmark, Harris). Sixty Years in Southern California. 688 pp., 8vo, cloth. N. Y., 1916. $17.50

The scarce original edition. Although published but 25 years ago the book is already quite scarce. This copy is autographed by both the editors, Maurice H. and Marco R. Newmark. Chas. F. Lummis says of this work: "A chronicle indispensable to every public library, every reference library, the shelf of every individual concerned with California."

100 [CALIFORNIA.] Peninsular California. By Charles Nordhoff. 130 pp., 8vo, cloth. N. Y., 1888. $2.00

101 [CALIFORNIA.] (Norman, Lucia). A Youth's History of California from the Earliest Period of its Discovery to Present Time. 187 pp., 12mo, cloth. San Francisco, 1867. $8.50

See Cowan p. 163.

102 [CALIFORNIA.] A Chapter of California History. By James O'Mera. (Overland Monthly, Vol. 14, No. 84, Dec., 1889). 8vo, original wrappers. San Francisco, 1894. $2.50

103 [CALIFORNIA.] (Palou, Fray Francisco). Historical Memoirs of New California. Edited by Dr. H. E. Bolton. Maps, plates, facsimiles. 4 vols., 8vo, cloth. Berkeley, 1926. $25.00

These annals, here for the first time translated into English, and generally known as Palou's "Noticias", are contemporary records of the earliest statements on the Pacific Coast. They describe in detail the first inland explorations in California, the first overland expeditions into the region, the establishment of the first missions and pueblos, and the diplomacy, hardships and dangers which these achievements entailed. The work includes a vast amount of hitherto unpublished material relating to the period including the correspondence of Palou, Crespi, Galves, Fages, and others.

104 [CALIFORNIA.] Adventuring in California Yesterday, Today, and Day before Yesterday. By Jessie Heaton Parkinson. Illus. 120 pp., 8vo, cloth. San Francisco (1921). $3.00

105 [CALIFORNIA.] The Wild Flowers of California. By Mary Elizabeth Parsons. Illus. 410 pp., 12mo, cloth. San Francisco, 1900. $3.75

PERON'S VOYAGE TO CALIFORNIA AND THE NORTHWEST COAST, 1796

106 [CALIFORNIA.] (Peron, Capt. M.). Memoires du Capitaine Peron sur ses Voyages aux Cotes Nord-Ouest de l'Amerique aux Iles Sandwich, etc. Six folding maps and plates. 328 pp. and 359 pp., 2 vols., 8vo, half calf. Paris, 1824. $75.00

The only account of this work which can be located is in an article prepared by H. R. Wagner and published in the California Historical Society Quarterly, Vol. 1, No. 2. Mr. Wagner describes the narrative as but "little known". It contains a full account of the "Otter's" trading expedition on the Northwest Coast and her visit to Monterey. Of this latter event, which marked the first entry of an American Ship into California waters (Oct. 29th, 1796). Mr. Wagner states: "Peron's account seems to be entirely unknown."

Peron was Chief Officer of the "Otter", under Capt. E. Dorr. He joined the brig at Sydney to engage in a fur trading voyage to the Northwest Coast. The cruise extended northward as far as Nootka and southward to California, upwards of seven months being spent on the coast. Peron's narrative is a day-by-day form and records with fidelity the events of the long cruize and its many adventures, together with observations on the regions, the settlements, Indians and their manners and customs.

107 [CALIFORNIA.] (Peters, Charles). The Autobiography of. In 1915 the Oldest Pioneer Living in California. Also Historical Happenings, Interesting Incidents and Illustrations of the Old Mining Towns in the Good Luck Era, the Placer Mining Days of the 50s. Illus. 231 pp., 12mo, original wrappers. Sacramento, N.d. (c. 1915). $7.50

Although printed as late as 1915 this little item is now quite scarce.

108 [CALIFORNIA.] The Missions of California, their Establishment, Progress, and Decay. By Laura Bride Powers. 105 pp., 8vo, cloth. San Francisco, 1897. $3.50

109 [CALIFORNIA.] Schreiben eines Russen aus Californien. Californische Goldgruben, Fluss Juba . . . etc. (Seven letters written by A. Rottschew. (Contained in Archiv fur Wissenschaftliche Kunde von Russland, 11 Band 4tes helft). 8vo, original wrappers. Berlin, 1852. $12.50

Long letters by a German of the Russian American Company who visited California during the gold rush. Not in Cowan.

110 [CALIFORNIA.] (San Diego). History of San Diego, 1542-1908. An Account of the Rise and Progress of the Pioneer Settlement on the Pacific Coast of the U. S. Illus. By Wm. E. Smythe. 2 vols. in 1, 8vo, cloth. San Diego, 1908. $12.50

111 CAMPBELL, WILLIAM W. The Border Warfare of New York during the Revolution; or Annals of Tryon County. 396 pp., 12mo, cloth. N. Y., 1849. $7.50

Field 238.

112 [CANADA.] Notes sur le Canada. Map. 121 pp., 12mo, original wrappers. Paris, 1878. $4.75

113 [CANADA.] History of Prince Edward Island. By Duncan Campbell. vii, 224 pp., 12mo, cloth. Charlottetown, 1875. $5.00

114 [CANADA.] Ten Years of Upper Canada in Peace and War, 1805-1815; being the Ridout Letters with Annotations by Matilda Edgar. Also an Appendix of the Narrative of the Captivity among the Shawanese Indians in 1788 of Thos. Ridout, afterwards Surveyor-General of Upper Canada; and a Vocabulary, Compiled by him, of the Shawanese Language. [Map and illus.] 8vo, cloth. London, 1890. $17.50

115 [CANADA.] History of Canada from the time of its Discovery till the Union Year (1840-41). Translated from the l'Histoire Du Canada" of F. X. Garneau and Accompanied with Illustrative Notes, etc. Large folding map. 3 vols., 8vo, cloth. Montreal, 1860. $10.00

116 [CANADA.] (Williams, Capt. Griffith). An Account of the Island of Newfoundland, with the Nature of its Trade and method of Carying on the Fishery. With reasons for the great decrease of that most valuable branch of Trade. By Capt. Griffith Williams who resided in the Island Fourteen Years . . . To which is annexed a Plan to exclude the French from that Trade, proposed to the Administration in 1761 by Capt. Cole. 35 pp., 12mo, wrappers. London, 1765. $15.00

117 [CANADA.] The Makers of Canada. Illus. 20 vols., plus 1 vol. of New Series. 8vo, cloth. Toronto, 1906-8 and 1923. $35.00

Parkman Edition. The biographies by various authors include: Champlain, Laval, Frontenac, Wolfe, Montcalm, Haldeman, Simcoe, Alex. Mackenzie, Selkirk, Egerton Ryerson, MacDonald, Douglas, and the pioneers of Ontario.

118 [CANADA.] Newfoundland, Its History, Its Present Condition, and Its Prospects in the Future. By Joseph Hatton and M. Harvey. Map, illus. 8vo, cloth. Boston, 1883. $3.50

119 [CANADA.] The History of Acadia, from its First Discovery to its Surrender to England by the Treaty of Paris. By James Hannay. 8vo, cloth. St. John, N. B., 1879. $5.00

120 [CANADA.] History of Newfoundland from the Earliest Time to 1860. By Chas. Pedley. Map. 550 pp., 8vo, cloth. London, 1863. $10.00

121 [CANADA.] The Conquest of Canada. By the Author of "Hochelaga." (George L. Warburton). [Frontis.] 2 vols., 8vo, cloth. London, 1849. $7.50

122 [CANADA.] Selections from the Public Documents of the Province of Nova Scotia. 8vo, cloth. Halifax, 1869. $7.50

123 CARSTARPHEN, J. E. My Trip to California in '49. Portrait. 8 numbered pages. 8vo, original printed wrappers. N.p., 1914. $10.00

Barber 145.

124 CARTIER, JACQUES. The Voyages of Jacques Cartier. Published from the Originals, with translations and notes and appendices by H. P. Biggar. Published by authority of the Secy. of State under the direction of the Dominion Archivist. Colored frontis., 16 plates and maps (many folding). 8vo, original printed wrappers. Ottawa, 1924. $5.00

125 [CATHOLIC ENCYCLOPAEDIA.] An International Work of Reference on the Constitution, Doctrine, Discipline, and History of the Catholic Church. Edited by Charles G. Herbermann and others. 16 vols., including index. 4to, ¾ morocco. N. Y., 1913. $45.00

Original and best edition. Contains much biographical and testimonial material relating to our western missions and missionaries, material nowwhere else to be found.

126 [CATHOLIC MISSIONS.] The Catholic Church in the Niagara Peninsula, 1626-1895. By Dean Harris. Portrait, illus. 352 pp., 8vo, cloth. 1885. $5.00

127 [CATHOLIC MISSIONS.] Catholic Missionary Activities in the Northwest, 1818-1864. By Sister Mary Aquinas Norton. 154 pp., original wrappers. Washington, 1930. $7.50

The above work was submitted to Catholic University in fulfillment of the requirements for the degree of Doctor of Philosophy.

128 [CATHOLIC MISSIONS.] Missionary Records of the Oblats of Mary Immaculate. Vol. 1, Nos. 2 and 6; Vol. 2, lacks No. 4; Vol. 3, lacks 5, 7, 8, 9, 12; Vol. 4, lacks No. 4; Vol. 5, lacks 1 and 10; Vol. 6, lacks 1, 6, 7, 8, 9, 11, 12; Vol. 7, complete; Vol. 8, lacks 1, 2, 3, 4, 5, 6, 7, 10, 12; Vol. 9, lacks No. 5; Vol. 10, complete; Vol. 11, lacks 1, 2, 5, 8; Vol. 12, complete. 8vo, original wrappers. [Montreal, 1891.] $12.50

129 [CATHOLIC MISSIONS.] Mission de la Congregation de Missionaries Oblat de Mari Immaculate. No. 4, December, 1867 to No. 4, December, 1869. Together 9 Nos., 8vo, original wrappers. Paris, 1867-69. $27.50

Contains much valuable material relating to the Northwest; Indians, missions, pioneers, etc.

130 [CATHOLIC MISSIONS.] Pioneer Catholic History of Oregon. By E. O'Hara. Plates and long bibliography. 235 pp., 12mo, cloth. Portland, 1911. $5.00

Smith 2752. Original Edition.

131 CHAPMAN, J. T. The French in the Alleghany Valley. 209 pp., 12mo, cloth. Cleveland (1887). $4.00

132 CHARLEVOIX, P. F. X., DE. History and General Description of New France. Translated from the Original Edition and Edited, with Notes, by Dr. John Gilmary Shea. With a new Memoir and Bibliography of the Translator by Noah Farnham Morrison. [Maps and ports.] 6 vols., cloth. N. Y., 1900. $32.50

The best edition in English and now scarce. As new.

133 CHASTELLUX, MARQUIS DE. Voyage en Amerique. 408 and 251 pp., 2 vols., 8vo, boards. Paris, 1788-91. $15.00

134 CHATEAUBRIAND, VISCOUNT. Travels in America and Italy. 2 vols., 8vo, original boards. London, 1828. $10.00

135 CLARK, J. V. H. Lights and Lines of Indian Character, and Scenes of Pioneer Life. Port. 12mo, cloth. Syracuse, 1854. $9.50

136 CLAY, HENRY. The Works of. Comprising His Life, Correspondence and Speeches. Edited by Calvin Colton. [Illus.] 10 vols., 8vo, cloth. N. Y., 1904. $60.00

No. 534 of the Federal Edition published by Putnam and limited to 1,000 sets.

137 CLUBB, STEPHEN. A Journal, Containing an Account of the Wrongs, Sufferings, and Neglect, experienced by Americans in France. By Stephen Clubb, late a Prisoner of that Empire. 60 pp., 8vo, sewn. Boston, 1809. $7.50

138 COLE, HENRY ELLSWORTH. Stagecoach and Tavern Tales of the Old Northwest. Edited by Louise Phelps Kellogg. Colored folding map showing stage routes, plates. 376 pp., 8vo, cloth. Glendale, 1930. $6.00

139 [COLORADO.] Progressive Men of Western Colorado. Illus. 4to, morocco. Chicago, 1905. $3.50

140 [COLORADO.] A Parson's Adventures. By G. W. McPherson. Port., illus. 12mo, cloth. Yonkers, N. Y., 1925. $3.00

Early days in Leadville, Denver, the mines, etc.

141 [COLORADO.] Reminiscent Ramblings. By Alonzo Merritt Wells. Illus. 459 pp., 8vo, cloth. Denver, 1905. $10.00

Author's Presentation Copy. Scarce, privately printed work, detailing much of the early history of Colorado. The author went to California via Panama; but was finally attracted by the mines to Colorado, arriving in Denver in 1876. He spent the remainder of his life prospecting in Colorado, Arizona, New Mexico, and elsewhere. His style is racy and extremely informative.

142 [COLUMBUS.] The Life of Columbus, Discoverer of America. By Arthur Helps. 8vo, cloth. London, 1869. $3.00

143 [COLUMBUS.] Christopher Columbus and How he Received and Imparted his Spirit of Discovery. By Justin Winsor. Maps and illus. 8vo, cloth. Boston, 1892. $4.50

"Contains not only a detailed account of Columbus' achievements, but also much bibliographical and cartographical detail of great volume"—Larned.

144 [COLUMBUS.] Columbus and the New World of His Discovery (1451-1506): by Filson Young, with a Note on Columbus' First Voyage, by the Earl of Dunraven, K.P., Comprising the most interesting events of his Youth and training, a complete account of the four voyages, giving the details of the Journey and Description of life on Board and of their Adventures in the West Indies. [Colored frontis., 16 full-page plates and folding maps.] 2 vols., 8vo, cloth. London: E. Grant Richards, 1906. $7.50

145 [CONNECTICUT.] The Norwich Jubilee. Report of the Celebration at Norwich, Conn., on the 200th Anniversary of the Settlement of the Town . . . Historical Documents of Local Interest. By John W. Stedman. Colored plates, other illus. 8vo, original printed wrappers. Norwich, 1859. $3.00

146 [CONNECTICUT.] (Trumbull, Benj.). A Complete History of Connecticut, Civil and Ecclesiastical, from the Emigration of its First Planters, from England, in the Year 1630, to the Year 1764; and to the close of the Indian Wars. Portrait. 2 vols., 8vo, calf. New Haven, 1818. $15.00

147 CONNECTICUT HISTORICAL SOCIETY COLLECTIONS. Complete Set. 20 vols., 8vo, cloth. Hartford, 1860-1923. $65.00

French and Indian War rolls, lists and returns, law papers, Hartford land distributions, 1639, Louisburg Campaign, Ticonderoga Expedition, Deane Papers, Talcott Papers, Orderly Books, Journals, Hartford Town Records, etc.

148 [COOK, CAPTAIN JAMES.] Life of Sir Charles Vinicombe Penrose and Capt. James Trevenen. By John Penrose. 2 ports. 301 pp., 8vo, cloth. London: Murray, 1850. $13.50

Capt. Trevenen on board the Resolution and Discovery with Capt. Cook on his last voyage was a witness to the death of the latter. "A volume which claims a distinguished place in the annals of the British Navy." Trevenen later joined the Russian Navy where he enjoyed a distinguished career, dying in action at the age of thirty. Said Sir Sidney Smith of him: "Trevenen was the very soul of the Russian fleet." Smith 3033 locates one copy.

149 CRAWFORD, LUCY. The History of the White Mountains, from the First Settlement of Upper Coos and Pequaket. By Lucy, wife of Ethan Allen Crawford, Esq. 16mo, cloth. White Hills, 1846. $17.50

A fine copy of a good little source book that's scarce in any condition.

150 CRESAP, CAPT. MICHAEL. Biographical Sketch. By John J. Jacob; also Boyer (Lt.), Journal of Wayne's Campaign against the Northwestern Indians. The two items bound in one volume, 4to, original wrappers. 158 and 23 pp. Cincinnati, 1866. $10.00

Contains many important documents relating to the Colonial period of discontent and revolution, among them the documents of Geo. Rogers Clark, Benj. Tomlinson, etc.

151 CROOKS, GEORGE R. Life and Letters of the Rev. John M'Clintock, Late President of Drew Theological Seminary. [Frontis.] 12mo, cloth. N. Y., 1876. $3.50

152 [CUSTER FIGHT.] (Newson, T. M.). Thrilling Scenes among the Indians. With a graphic description of Custer's Last Fight with Sitting Bull. 241 pp., 12mo, cloth. Chicago, 1884. $5.00

The Original Edition.

153 [DAKOTA.] (Haggarty, Frank H.). 1889—The Territory of Dakota, The State of North Dakota. The State of South Dakota. An Official, Statistical, Historical and Political Abstract. 190-90-102 pp., 8vo, cloth. Aberdeen, 1889. $7.50

154 [DAKOTA.] (Poole, Capt. D. C.). Among the Sioux of Dakota: Eighteen Months Experiences as an Indian Agent. 235 pp., 12mo, cloth. N. Y., 1881. $4.50

Experiences among the Sioux in the '60's.

154a DALRYMPLE (ALEXANDER). The Spanish Pretensions Fairly Discussed by A. Dalrymple. 8vo, full mottled calf. London, 1790. $90.00

An extremely rare work in which the author refutes the Spanish claims to the exclusive navigation of the South Seas. A valuable pamphlet on the British and Spanish claims to the whole of the North West Coast of America, which culminated in the seizure of British ships by a Spanish man-of-war at Nootka and their eventual surrender to Capt. Vancouver.

155 DARBY, WILLIAM. View of the United States, Historical, Geographical, and Statistical. Hand colored folding maps. 666 pp., 12mo, calf. Phila., 1828. $10.00

156 DARNELL, ELIAS. Journal containing Account of the Hardships, Sufferings, Battles, Defeat and Captivity of Kentucky Volunteers and Regulars commanded by Gen. Winchester, 1812-13; also two narratives by men that were wounded in the battle on the River Raisin and taken captive by the Indians. 100 pp., 12mo, fine copy in original printed boards. Phila., 1854. $15.00

157 DAVIS, JOHN. Travels of Four Years and a Half in the United States of America during 1798, 1799, 1800, and 1802. With an Introduction and Notes by A. J. Morrison. xi, 429 pp., 8vo, boards. N. Y., 1909. $4.75

157a De L'ISLE, Guillaume. Explication de la Carte des Nouvelles Decouvertes au Nord de la Mer du Sud; par M. de L'Isle, de l'Academie Royale des Sciences, & Professeur de Mathematiques au College Royale. 18 pp., 4to, half mor. A Paris: chez de Saint et Saillant, 1752.

Carte des Nouvelles Decouvertes au Nord de la Mer du Sud, Tant a l'Est de la Siberie et du Kamtchatka du'a l'Ouest de la Nouvelle France. Dressee sur les Memoires de Mr. de L'Isle, Professeur Royale et d el'Academie des Sciences. Par Philip Buache et presentee a l'Academie 8 Avril, 1750, par Mr. de L'Isle. Se vend a Paris de l'Horologe du Palais evec les Cartes de Guill. de L'Isle et de Phil. Buache. (1752). Colored. Size 25¼ x 17½ in. The map and Explication together $200.00

Original Edition of both the map and explanation. They are very rarely found together. They form one of the most important works on the early history of discovery on the Northwest Coast of America. The map which was based on his manuscript map of 1731 was introduced by de L'Isle to the Paris Academy in 1750. It shows the tracks of all the voyages, then known, from the Atlantic Coast to the Northwest Coast of America, and also the discoveries of Admiral de Fonte. The pamphlet describes these voyages in chronological order with the author's comments. It gives one of the earliest accounts of Bering's Voyage, although the information was wilfully distorted and called forth a burst of indignation from the Russian government. In the following year G. F. Muller, who was the historian during Bering's Voyage very politely corrected de L'Isle's erroneous information in a pamphlet which is better known in the English edition "A Letter from a Russian Sea Officer."

158 [DEMERS, MONSEIGNEUR MODESTE.] Fragments de l'Histoire Religieuse et Civil de la Paroisse de Saint Nicholas. By Etienne Theodore Paquet. 398 pp., 12mo. cloth. Levis, 1894. $10.00

Relates to Monseigneur Demers and the Demers family. Demers, one of the early Northwest Coast missionaries, went overland from Vancouver Island to St. Paul in 1846.

159 DE MEZIERES. (Althanese) and the Louisiana-Texas Frontier, 1768-1780. Documents in the Mexican and Spanish Archives, translated, with notes, by Prof. H. E. Bolton and published here for the first time. Folding map and 8 facsimiles. 2 vols., large 8vo. Cleveland, 1914. $16.50

De Meziers, the central figure of these documents, was for years the principal Indian agent and diplomat of Spain in the remote frontier of what is now Texas, Western La., Ark. and Okla. His papers, letters and reports constitute the most important single group of documents in existence on that period and region; they are practically a history of Indian policies and affairs during the French and Spanish regimes from 1768 to 1780.

160 [DE SMET, PIERRE JEAN.] Pictures of Missionary Life in the Nineteenth Century; the Western World. Frontis. 216 pp., 8vo, cloth. London: Burns, 1858. $7.50

Smith 3065. Contains an account of Father De Smet and the Flathead Indians.

161 DIXON, J. M. The Valley of the Shadow; comprising the Experiences of a Blind Ex-Editor. A Literary Biography, Humorous Autobiographical Sketches. A chapter on Iowa Journalism, and Sketches of the West and Western Men. 336 pp., 12mo, cloth. N. Y., 1868. $7.50

162 DODDRIDGE, JOSEPH. Notes on the Settlement and Indian Wars of the Western Parts of Virginia and Pennsylvania, 1763 to 1783, together with a view of the State of Society and Manners of the First Settlers of the Western Country. The rare first edition, with the 3 parts complete. 316 pp., small 8vo, original tree calf. Wellsburgh, Va., 1824. $45.00

A good sound copy of the Rare Original Edition. The facts were drawn from original sources, mostly from personal observations, or from participants in the border war depicted. The work contains accounts of the Indian captivity of Mrs. Brown, Adam, Poe and others. No one except Withers has approached Doddridge in fidelity or exactness.

163 DOUGLASS, WILLIAM. Summary, Historical and Political, of First Planting, Progressive Improvements and Present State of British Settlements in North America. Large folding map. 2 vols., 8vo, 3/4 morocco, fine. Boston, 1749-51. $37.50

Accounts of Scotch settlements at Panama, Spanish settlements in Florida, Pensacola, etc., French Mississippi Bubble, French in Canada and Louisiana, Hudson-Bay Company, history of the provinces and the colonies of New Hampshire, R. I., Conn., N. Y., N. J., Pa., and Maryland. Early voyages of Frobisher, Gilbert, Davis, Hudson, Middletown, Dobbs, etc., and early attempts to discover the Nortwest Passage.

164 DRAKE, BENJAMIN. Life of Tecumseh and his brother, the Prophet, with Sketches of the Shawanoe Indians. 235 pp., 12mo, cloth. Cincinnati, 1841. $6.00

165 DRAKE, SAMUEL G. Indian Biography, containing lives of over 200 Indian Chiefs . . . Plates. 4th edition. 12mo, cloth. Boston, 1835. $2.50

165a DRIGGS, HOWARD. Westward America. With reproductions of Forty Water Color Paintings by William H. Jackson. 4to, original cloth. Signed copy of the Collectors Edition. N. Y., American Pioneer Trails Association, 1942. $10.00

One of the best modern illustrated books on the growth of the West. The fine reproduction in color of the water colors of Mr. Jackson is a tribute to this venerable artist's fine work. Although now 99 years of age, some of his best work was completed only last year.

166 EDWARDS, COL. PHILIP L. California in 1837. Diary of Col. Philip L. Edwards. Containing an account of a trip to the Pacific Coast. Published in "Thamis" by Authority of the Board of State Library Trustees of the State of California. 47 pp., 16mo. Sacramento, 1890. $20.00

167 EELLS, MYRON. The Works of. 10 items. 8vo, half morocco. V.p., V.d. $15.00

168 [EMIGRANTS.] Norwegian Immigrant Contributions to America's Making. By Harry Sundby-Hansen (ed.). 170 pp., 8vo, original wrappers. N. Y., 1921. $1.50

169 [EMIGRANT'S FRIEND, THE.] By Major Jones. Folding maps, tables. 8vo, cloth. London, 1881. $2.50

Information concerning homestead lands in Neb., Mont., New Mexico, Nevada, Oregon, Wash. Steamship routes, rates, customs, etc. The author was a British Consul in the U. S.

170 EVANS, JOSHUA. A Journal of the Life, Travels, Religious Exercises and Labours in the Work of the Ministry. 212 pp., 12mo, calf. Bybery, 1837. $5.00

Evans was born in western New Jersey, 1731. His travels covered the entire 13 Colonies from Maine to the Carolinas and Tennessee.

170a [FIELD, STEPHEN J.] Some account of the work of Stephen J. Field, as a Legislator, as a Judge, and Justice of the Supreme Court of the U. S. By J. Norton Pomeroy. 522 pp., 8vo, cloth. $12.50

Signed presentation copy from Justice Field. Much on California and the West.

171 FINLEY, REV. JAS. B. Autobiography of; or Pioneer Life in the West. 3 ports., 5 plates. 455 pp., 12mo. Cincinnati, 1872. $2.00

Exploits of Kenton, Massie, Cassady, McArthur, McDonald, and other frontier heroes of Ky. and Ohio.

172 FISKE, JOHN. American Revolution. Maps and ports. 2 vols., 12mo, cloth. Boston, 1891. (2) Beginning of New England. Maps. 12mo, cloth. Boston, 1889. (3) Discovery of America, with Some Account of Ancient America and the Spanish Conquest. Maps and port. 2 vols., 12mo, cloth. Boston, 1892. (4) Dutch and Quaker Colonies in America. Maps. 2 vols., 12mo, cloth. Boston, 1899. (5) New France and New England. Maps. 12mo, cloth. Boston, 1902. (6) Old Virginia and Her Neighbors. Maps. 2 vols., 12mo, cloth. Boston, 1897. Together 11 vols., all First Editions. Boston, 1889-1902. $27.50

173 FITZPATRICK, THOMAS. Letter by, dated Bent's Fort, Arkansas River, Sept. 18, 1847. 30th Cong., 1st Sess., Sen. Ex. Doc. 1; Appendix to the Report of the Commissioner of Indian Affairs. Pp. 238-249. Contained in Polk's Message to Congress, etc. 8vo, half calf. Washington, 1847. $25.00

174 FLINT, TIMOTHY. Indian Wars of the West, containing Sketches of those Pioneers who headed the Western Settlers in repelling the Savages. 240 pp., 12mo, calf. Cincinnati, 1833. $10.00

175 FOOTE, WM. HENRY. Sketches of Virginia, Historical and Biographical. 8vo, cloth (slight wear). Phila., 1850. $15.00

The first Series, the second appearing six years later. "A vast collection of historic material relating to the Presbyterian Church in Virginia . . . mingled . . . are stories of Indian Wars and the experiences of white captives."

176 FORCE, PETER. The Declaration of Independence, on Lord Mahon's History of the American Declaration of Independence. 66 pp., 8vo, original printed wrappers. London, 1855. $7.50

Lord Mahon's History was the first British "Now it can be Told" story of the American dissidence. Southey was asked to do it, but didn't. Peter Force answered it in this work. The British published it. One should state that Lord Mahon's History was about the only one a capable and truthful researcher had to rely on in the early days; inaccurate and biased as it was. But it did tell the British side. The late Prof. Van Tyne, who passed away before he could conclude his great work, was the first foremost, diligent and accurate, and I might say, readable, historian to present the other side.

177 FORD, WORTHINGTON C. Cycle of Adams Letters, 1861-1865. First Edition with numerous portraits and plates. 2 vols., 8vo, cloth. London, 1921. $7.50

178 FORDHAM, ELIAS P. Personal Narrative of Travels in Va., Md., Pa., Ohio, Ind., and Ky.; and of a Residence in the Illinois Territory, 1817-18; edited with notes by Frederic A. Ogg. 248 pp., 8vo, cloth. Cleveland, 1906. $7.50

179 FORREST, EARLE R. Missions and Pueblos of the Old Southwest; their Myths, Legends, Fiestas, and Ceremonies, with some Accounts of the Indian Tribes and their Dances; and of the Penitentes. 32 plates from original photos. 8vo, cloth. Cleveland, 1929. $6.00

180 FRANKLIN, B. Works . . . Including the Private as Well as the Official and Scientific Correspondence. Together with . . . Correct Version of the Autobiography. Compiled and edited by John Bigelow. 12 vols., 8vo, cloth. N. Y., 1904. $55.00

No. 84 of the 600 copies of Putnam's fine Collectors' Federal Edition. The best set.

181 [FRANKLIN, SIR JOHN.] The Grinnell Expedition in Search of Sir John Franklin. A Personal Narrative. By Elisha Kent Kane. [Beautiful tinted full-page views by Sartain.] Folding map. 8vo, original cloth. N. Y., 1854. $3.50

182 [FRANKLIN, SIR JOHN.] Journal d'un Voyage aux Mers Polaires, execute a la Recherche de Sir John Franklin, en 1851 et 1852. By J. R. Bellot. Folding map, port. 8vo, half morocco. Paris, 1854. $4.75

183 [FRENCH AND INDIAN WARS.] The Levis Documents. Collection des Manuscripts du Marechal de Levis. Publie sous le direction de l'Abbe H. R. Casgrain. 12 vols., small 4to, original printed wrappers. Quebec and Montreal, 1889-1905. $55.00

The original issue of documentary source material of the utmost importance in the understanding of the historic phases of the French and Indian Wars. Vol. 2 contains the Journal of M. de Levis; v. 2, letters of de Levis; v. 3, letters of de Levis, Montcalm, de Versailles, Baron de Dieskau, etc.; v. 4, military letters; v. 5, Letters of M. de Bourlamque; 6, Letters of Montcalm; v. 7, Journal of Montcalm; v. 8, Letters of Marquis de Vaudreuil; v. 9, Letters of the Intendant Bigot; v. 10, Levis letters; v. 11, Journals of different war expeditions; v. 12, Index vol.

184 [FRENCH AND INDIAN WARS.] The Journal of Lord Jeffrey Amherst in America from 1758 to 1763. Edited with introduction and notes by J. Clarence Webster. Illus. 8vo, cloth. Chicago (1931). $7.50

185 FROST, JOHN. Thrilling Adventures among the Indians: Comprising the Most Remarkable Personal Narratives of Events in the Early Indian Wars, as well as of Incidents in the Recent Indian Hostilities in Mexico and Texas. Illus. 8vo, cloth. Phila., 1861. $3.50

186 [FUR TRADE.] The Auneau Collection, 1734-45. Edited by the Rev. Arthur E. Jones, S.J. 160 pp., 8vo, original wrappers. Montreal, 1893. $7.50

Father Jean Pierre Auneau accompanied La Verendrye in exploring the vast territory of western Canada, a great fur-bearing region which for a time was diverted from the English. Father Auneau was killed, along with Verendrye's son, while returning to Michillimackinac, (Mackinaw Island).

187 [FUR SEALING.] The Fur Seals and Other Life of the Pribilof Islands, Alaska, in 1914. By Wilfred H. Osgood, et al. Illus., maps. 172 pp., 4to, half morocco. Washington, 1915. $4.50

188 [FUR TRADE.] (Pilcher's Report). Message from the President of the United States in compliance with a Resolution of the Senate concerning the Fur Trade, and Inland Trade to Mexico. 86 pp. Washington, Feb. 8th, 1832. 22nd Cong., 1st Sess., Sen. Ex. Doc. 90. 8vo, sewn. $75.00

Wagner-Camp 46. An excessively rare pamphlet containing a letter from William Clark and Joshua Pilcher's report, dated St. Louis, Dec. 1, 1831, on the rise and present condition of the fur trade; communications from Andrew S. Hughes, and William Gordon, of Oct. 31, 1831, with an account of the Immel-Jones massacre; Alphonso Wetmore on the Santa Fe trade, Oct. 11, 1831, with extracts of his diary on the Santa Fe trail to New Mexico, beginning May 28, 1828; Schoolcraft's Report, Oct. 24, 1831; John Dougherty's statement; B. Riley's report on travelers killed on the Santa Fe Trail; T. Forsyth's letter of Oct. 24, 1831, with a history of the Fur Trade from 1800.

189 GALLATIN, ALBERT. The Life of. By Henry Adams. Ports. Large 8vo, cloth. Phila., 1880. $27.50

An important original source of history, particularly as it relates to our constitutional foundations and the politics of the Jefferson and Madison administrations.

190 GALT, JOHN. The Autobiography of. 420 pp., 2 vols. in 1, 12mo, half roan (weak at spine). Phila., 1833. $3.50

Galt was one of the first to found British settlements on the north shore of Lake Huron. About half of the above work relates the trials and tribulations of his work in America.

191 GEORGE, HENRY. Works. Ports. 10 vols., 8vo, cloth. N. Y., 1898. $20.00

A set of the best and only complete edition of Henry George's works.

192 [GEORGIA.] (Stevens, Wm. Bacon). History of Georgia from its first discovery to the adoption of the present Constitution in 1708. xiii, 503 and xvi, 524 pp., 2 vols., 8vo, cloth. N. Y., 1847-59. $15.00

193 [GEORGIA.] The History of Georgia. By Chas. C. Jones, Jr. Maps and illus. 2 vols., xv, 556 pp. and xv, 540 pp., 2 vols., 8vo, cloth. Boston, 1883. $12.50

Vol. 1 contains aboriginal and colonial episodes. Vol. 2 Revolutionary epoch. Fine copy.

194 GODDARD, FREDERICK B. Where to Emigrate and Why. Homes and Fortunes in the Boundless West and Sunny South . . . With a Complete History and Description of the Pacific Railroad. Illus. with numerous maps and engravings. 8vo, cloth. Phila., 1869. $10.00

195 [GREAT LAKES.] Algoma West, its Mines, Scenery and Industrial Resources. By Walpole Roland. Colored folding map, illus, advts. 217 pp., 8vo, cloth. Toronto, 1887. $4.00

196 GRIFFITH, JOHN. A Journal of the Life, Travels, and Labours in the Work of the Ministry of John Griffith. 427 pp., 8vo, full calf. London, 1779. $7.50

Brinley 3523. The author arrived in America for the first time in 1726, which he describes. He later returned to America in 1765. Name cut from top of title; hinges weak.

197 HANNA, C. A. Wilderness Trail; Ventures and Adventures of Pennsylvania Traders on the Alleghany Path, with New Annals of the West and Records of some strong men and some bad ones; with 80 maps, plates and other illus. 2 vols., 8vo, cloth. N. Y., 1911. $17.50

198 [HAKLUYT'S VOYAGES.] The Principal Navigations, Traffiques & Discoveries of the English Nation, made by Sea and Over-Land to the Remote and Farthest Distant Quarters of the Earth at any time within the Compasse of these 1600 yeares. Folding maps and plates. 12 vols., 8vo, cloth. Glasgow, 1903-1905. $75.00

The best modern edition. Sabin says: "It is difficult to overrate the importance and value of this extraordinary collection of voyages. Mr. Bancroft characterizes Richard Hakluyt as the enlightened friend and able documentary historian of these commercial enterprises, a man whose fame should be vindicated and asserted in the land which he helped to colonize."—Dictionary of Books Relating to America.

199 [HAMILTON, ALEXANDER.] The Works of. Edited by Henry Cabot Lodge. [Illus.] 12 vols., 8vo, cloth. N. Y., 1904. $55.00

199a ——. The Same. 12 vols., 8vo, cloth. N. Y., 1904. $65.00

Putnam's Collectors Federal Edition of 600 copies.

200 HARIOT, THOMAS. Narrative of the First English Plantation of Virginia. First printed at London in 1588, now reproduced after De Bry's Illustrated edition printed at Frankfort in 1590, the illustrations having been designed in Virginia in 1585 by John White. Illus. 46 pp., small 4to. London: Quaritch, 1893. $5.00

201 HARNEY, GEN. WM. SELBY. The General Harney Correspondence, 1857-1860. Affairs in Oregon. Letter from the Secretary of War communicating the Correspondence relating to the Affairs in the Department of Oregon, April 12, 1860. 269 pp. 36th Cong., 1st Sess., H. R. Doc. No. 65. 8vo, half morocco. Washington, 1860. $7.50

202 HARRIS, T. M. Journal of a Tour into Territory Northwest of the Allegheny Mountains, 1803. Complete set of engraved maps, plates and plans. 280 pp., large 8vo, original boards (weak hinges). Boston, 1805. $20.00

An unusually choice and uncut copy, which is rare in this state. A valuable record of early western travel, containing descriptions of frontier towns and settlements, Indian tribes, wars, treaties.

203 HAYWARD, JOHN. The Civil and Political History of the State of Tennessee, from its earliest Settlement up to the Year 1796; including the boundaries of the State. 8vo, calf. Knoxville, Tenn.: Printed for the Author, 1823. $40.00

Original edition of the earliest history of Tennessee, with the rare "Copy Right Secured" leaf preceding the title-page. The work gives an account of the founding of the State of Franklin, and a large portion is devoted to the Indian troubles in that section.

204 HAYWARD, JOHN. The Civil and Political History of the State of Tennessee from its earliest Settlement up to the Year 1796 . . . With a biographical sketch of Judge John Hayward, by Col. A. S. Colyar. 8vo, cloth. Nashville, 1891. $7.50

205 HAYWARD, JOHN. The Natural and Aboriginal History of Tennessee, up to the first Settlements therein by the White People, in 1768. 8vo, calf, foxed. Nashville: George Wilson, 1823. $125.00

The rare Original Edition of one of the most valuable works relating to Tennessee History. With the leaf of Errata.

206 HENNEPIN, FATHER LOUIS. New Discovery of a Vast Country in America. Edited, with notes, by R. G. Thwaites. Maps and illus. 2 vols., 8vo, cloth. Chicago, 1903. $9.50

Reprinted from the London Edition of 1698.

207 HINSDALE, B. A. The Old Northwest, with a View of the Thirteen Colonies as Constituted by Royal Charter. 11 colored maps. 8vo, cloth. N. Y., 1888. $6.00

208 HUBBARD, WM. Narrative of the Indian Wars in New England, from the First Planting thereof, in the year 1607, to the year 1677. 274 pp., 8vo. Danbury, 1803. $7.50

209 [HUDSON'S BAY COMPANY.] Journal of Occurrences at Nisqually House, First Settlement on Puget Sound, commenced May 30, 1833 and ending March, 1859. Together with the Journal of the Puget Sound Agricultural Company, from April 22, 1858 to March, 1859, all available or known records pertaining to. 753 photostatic records of this historic post. $200.00

These historically important records, many of them widely dispersed, were tracked down, collated and finally preserved in photostatic facsimiles at considerable expense by a celebrated historian and pioneer of the Northwest. The records are roughly as follows, in chronological sequence:

May 30, 1833 to April 25, 1835, 155pp. on 79 sheets; Sept. 1, 1836 to Oct. 1837, 69pp., on 36 sheets; Jan. 20, 1845 to April 30, 1847, 86pp., on 45 sheets; July 30, 1847 to Nov. 25, 1848, 88pp., on 46 sheets; March 10, 1849 to Aug. 6, 1850, 86pp., on 45 sheets; Aug. 7, 1850 to Aug. 31, 1851, 87pp., on 46 sheets; Sept. 1, 1851 to Oct. 3, 1852, 94pp., on 50 sheets; Oct. 4, 1852 to May 28, 1854, 166pp., on 86 sheets; May 29, 1854 to Aug. 15, 1856, 166pp., on 90 sheets; Sept. 26, 1857 to Sept. 27, 1859, 66pp., on 34 sheets. Journal of Puget Sound Agricultural Co., April 22, 1858 to March, 1859, 90pp., on 48 sheets.

Nisqually Post, aside from the Headquarters Post at Vancouver, was the most interesting and important of all the Hudson Bay Posts on the Northwest Coast, particularly as it relates to the local history of Washington. Situated on the shores of Puget Sound, not far from the mouth of the river which bears it name, Fort Nisqually was founded on May 30, 1833 by Archibald McDonald, one of the most noted traders and factors in the Hudson's Bay Company. There was at the time a large Indian population in the vicinity and communication with Forts Langley, Simpson and other forts was safe and easy. McDonald, former clerk and agent for Lord Selkirk, had been sent to the coast in 1823 to take possession of the Northwest Company for the Hudson's Bay Company. The journals, therefore, are of the greatest importance for the history of the Northwest Coast, being a complete record of the happenings and occurrences, including Indian troubles, trade, arrival of emigrants, visitors to the post, fur accounts, arrival and departure of the Steamer "Beaver", etc., etc. The Journals have never been published, with the exception of a few short excerpts.

210 [HUDSON'S BAY.] Report on an Exploration of the East Coast of Hudson's Bay, 1877. By Robert Bell. 37 pp., plates, folding map. 8vo, unbound. Montreal, 1879. $4.50

211 [HUDSON'S BAY.] Report on the Country between Lake Winnipeg and Hudson's Bay, 1878. By Robert Bell. 31 pp., 8vo, unbound. Montreal, 1879. $3.50

212 [HUDSON'S BAY.] Report on Hudson's Bay and some of the Lakes and Rivers lying to the West of it. By Robert Bell. Plates, tables. 113 pp., 8vo, unbound. Montreal, 1881. $4.50

213 [HUDSON'S BAY.] The Canadian North West, its Early Development and Legislative Records, Minutes of the Council of the Red River Settlement and the Northern Department of Rupert's Land. By E. H. Oliver. 6 maps. 2 vols., 4to, original wrappers. Ottawa, 1914. $10.00

Contains material and records of the Hudson's Bay Company in Oregon and the Northwest.

214 [HUDSON RIVER.] Summer Excursion Routes. Day Line Steamers on the Hudson River, 1886. Maps and numerous illus. 88 pp. 8vo, original printed wrappers, with all the old advts. N. Y., 1886. $1.50

215 HUTCHINS, THOMAS. Topographical Description of Virginia, Pennsylvania, Maryland, and North Carolina; reprinted from the exceedingly rare original edition of 1778, and edited . . . by Frederick C. Hicks of Columbia University Library. Maps and facsimiles. Royal 8vo, cloth. Cleveland, 1904. $10.00

Only 245 copies of this beautifully executed edition were printed. It contains much valuable information regarding early forts, Indian expeditions, Benj. Franklin, early river navigation, Kaskaskia, Ill., Lake Michigan and Huron, Ft. Mackinac, Missouri River, Ft. Pitt, Public Lands, Southern Michigan, Missouri, Ohio, Vincennes. It also reproduced the rare Hutchings Map.

216 HUTCHINSON, THOMAS. The Diary and Letters of His Excellency Thomas Hutchinson. Compiled from the Original Documents . . . Peter Orlando Hutchinson. Illus. 2 vols., 8vo. London, 1884. $7.50

Covers the period of Hutchinson's service as a Member and Speaker of the House of Representatives and his term in office as Governor of the Colony during the Pre-Revolutionary period.

217 [IDAHO.] A Historical, Descriptive and Commercial Directory of Owyhee County, Idaho. Jan., 1898. 140pp., frontis., illus. 8vo, cloth. Silver City: Idaho Owyhee Avalanche, 1898. $12.50

Smith 1721 locates but two copies.

218 [IDAHO.] Illustrated History of North Idaho. By Averill, Henderson and Shiach. Illus. 4to, morocco. Chicago, 1903. $12.50

Exhaustive history of the Counties of Idaho, Kootenai, Latah, Nez Perce and Shoshone.

219 [IDAHO.] Poor-Man Gold and Silver Mining Co., of Idaho. Colored map (14x22 in.) plates. 23pp., 8vo, sewn. N. Y., 1867. $17.50

Can locate no other copy.

220 [IDAHO.] Progressive Men of Bannock, Bear Lake, Bingham, Fremont and Onieda Counties, Idaho. 664pp., 4to, mor. Chicago, 1904. $7.50

Smith3222.

221 [ILLINOIS.] (Birkbeck, Morris). Notes on a Journey in America from the Coast of Virginia to the Territory of Illinois. Fourth Edition. Map. Half roan. London, 1818. $5.00

222 [ILLINOIS.] (Birkbeck, Morris). History of the English Settlement in Edwards County, Ill., founded in 1817 and 1818. By Morris Birkbeck and George Flower. With preface and footnotes by E. B. Washburne. 402pp. Chicago Historical Society Collection, No. 1. 8vo, cloth. Chicago, 1882. $5.00

223 [ILLINOIS.] Letters from Illinois. By Morris Birkbeck. 8vo, half calf. London, 1818. $8.50

The author, an English Utopian, bought 16,000 acres on English Prairie, Ill., in 1817 and founded the town of New Albion, which was settled by English emigrants. The letters were written to people in England in reply to questions relating to the economic and social conditions in the West.

224 [ILLINOIS.] (Blanchard, Rufus). Discovery and Conquest of the Northwest, with the early history of Chicago, Saint Louis, Detroit, Vincennes, Marietta, Cincinnati, Fort Wayne and Cleveland. 128pp., 8vo, original printed boards. Wheaton, Ill., 1879. $15.00

Fine copy of the Original Edition. On back cover is an illustration of "The costumes, arms, and habitations of early inhabitants."

225 [ILLINOIS.] (Blanchard, Rufus). Discovery and Conquest of the Northwest, with the History of Chicago. Maps, illus. 768pp., 8vo, half morocco. Chicago, 1881. $6.00

Signed presentation copy by the author.

226 [ILLINOIS.] (Brown, Henry). The History of Illinois from its Discovery and Settlement to the Present Time. 8vo, cloth. N. Y., 1844. $4.50

227 [ILLINOIS.] (Carter, Clarence E.). Great Britain and the Illinois country, 1763-1774. 234pp., 8vo, cloth. Washington, 1910. $7.50

Awarded the Justin Winsor Prize in American history, 1908. Legal and political relation between Great Britain and the Illinois Colony, economic importance of the west to the empire, attempts to colonize, struggle for civil government, etc., largely from hitherto unused manuscript material.

228 [ILLINOIS.] Fifty Years in the Church of Rome. By Father Chiniquy, the Apostle of Temperance of Canada. Frontis. 183pp., 8vo, cloth. Chicago, 1885. $6.50

Chiniquy was a client of Lincoln and the author has much to say in approving the able and satisfactory way in which Lincoln conducted his trial. Hinges have been reinforced in this copy.

229 [ILLINOIS.] Lettre du Pere Chiniquy. By A. M. Brassard. 23pp., 12mo, original wrappers. Montreal, 1857. $6.50

230 [ILLINOIS.] (Chiniguy, Father C.). Persecutions aux de l'Abbe Chiniquy, l'Apotre de la Temperance au Canada. 36pp., 16mo, original wrappers. Montreal (1857). $6.50

231 [ILLINOIS.] (Cook County). History of, from the Earliest Period to the Present time. By H. T. Andreas. Maps, illus. 855pp., 4to, half forocco. Chicago, 1884. $4.50

Also gives separate histories of Evanston, Niles Center, Oak Park, Palatine and other suburban towns.

232 [ILLINOIS.] (Davidson, Alexander, and Stuve). Complete History of Illinois, 1673-1873; early Explorations, Aboriginal Inhabitants, French and British Occupation, Conquest of Virginia, Territoial Condition and subsequent Civil, Militay and Political Events. 944pp., thick 8vo, cloth. Springfield, 1874. $17.50

233 [ILLINOIS.] History of Illinois from 1778 to 1833, and the Life and Times of Ninian Edwards. By his son, N. W. Edwards. Portraits. 8vo, cloth. Springfield, 1870. $4.00

234 [ILLINOIS.] (Faux, W.). Memorable Days in America: being a Journal of a Tour to the U. S., principally undertaken to Ascertain, by Positive Evidence, the Condition and Probable Prospects of British Emigrants. Including Accounts of Mr. Birkbeck's Settlement in Illinois; and Intended to Shew Men and Things as they are in America. Frontis. 8vo, calf. London, 1823. Scarce. $12.50

Original Edition. Buck, 139. Fine copy. Source book on Ill., Ohio, Ky., and Ind.

235 [ILLINOIS.] (Fearon, Henry Bradshaw). Sketches of America. A Narrative of a Journey of Five Thousand Miles through the Eastern and Western States of America . . . with Remarks on Mr. Brikbeck's "Notes and Letters." 8vo, calf. London, 1818. $7.50

Thomson p. 118: Buck 98. Original Edition. One of the most important source books on Illinois prior to statehood, and on conditions in America just after the war of 1812. Fearon was the advance agent for 39 English families who were contemplating moving to America. This original edition is scarce.

236 [ILLINOIS.] History of, 1814-1847. By Gov. Thomas Ford. 8vo, cloth. Chicago, 1854. $10.00

Original edition of the standard authority on early state politics, Black Hawk War, Alton Riots, Mormon troubles, etc.

237 [ILLINOIS.] History of Fulton County, Ill.; together with Sketches of its Cities, Villages and Townships. Maps, illus. 190pp., 8vo, half calf. Peoria, 1879. $7.50

238 [ILLINOIS.] Illinois State Historical Society Collections. Volumes 1-12 inclusive. Folding maps, plans, illus. 12 vols., 8vo, cloth. Springfield, 1903-1915. $30.00

Vol. 1, voyages and discoveries down the Miss., edited by H. W. Beckwith; v. 2, Virginia series, Chokia Records, edited by C. W. Alvord; v. 3, Lincoln series; v. 4, Executive series, 1818-34; v. 5, Kaskaskia Records, edited by Alvord; v. 6, Newspapers and Periodicals; v. 7, Governor's Letter-Book, 1840-53; v. 8, George Rogers Clark Papers; v. 9, Travels and Descriptions, ed. by S. J. Buck; v. 10, Critical Period; v. 11, The New Regime; v. 12, County Archives of Illinois.

239 [ILLINOIS.] Journal of the Illinois State Historical Society. Volumes 1 through 9 inclusive. 8vo, original printed wrappers. Springfield, Ill., 1908-1916. $35.00

Fine set of the early numbers of this publication. All were printed at Springfield with the exception of Vol. 1. Each volume averages about 225 pages, with illustrations.

240 [ILLINOIS.] The Illinois Historical Society. Report of the Board of Trustees of the Investigation made by C. M. Thompson in an attempt to locate the "Lincoln Way." 22pp., 8vo, original wrappers. Springfield, 1913. $4.00

241 [ILLINOIS.] State Historical Society Transactions. Numbers 1 to 21 inclusive. Together 21 vols., original cloth. Springfield, Ill., 1899-1915. $45.00

Fine long run, all out of print and many practically impossible to procure. Several of these volumes contain valuable bibliographies. Vol. 1 contains a bibliographical of newspapers published in Illinois prior to 1860.

242 [ILLINOIS.] (Joutel, Henri). Journal Historique du dernier Voyage que feu M. de la Sale fit dans le Golfe de Mexique, pour brouver l'Embouchere, & le cours de la Riviere de Mississippi, nommee a present la Riviere de Saint Louis, etc. With the large folding map. 8vo, calf. Paris, 1713. $80.00

Fine copy of the original edition from the Library of the Earl of Loudon, Governor of Virginia, with his bookplate. The work was written in answer to Tonti's "Dernieres Decouvertes", Paris, 1697. Joutel accompanied La Salle on his last voyage and after the latter's assassination, he and his companions traveled 800 leagues across the interior of North America to Canada. The map, which contains an inset of Buffalo and a View of Niagara Falls, is one of the earliest accurate delineations of the Mississippi River.

243 [ILLINOIS.] (Kinzie, Mrs. J. H.). Wau-Bun; the Early Days in the Northwest. Plates. Large 8vo, original cloth. N. Y., 1856. $15.00

Detailed account of the Chicago of 1831, with a description of the 1812 massacre as related by survivors. Also contains interesting memories of the author's girlhood days among the French and Indian half-breeds at Ft. Winnebago Agency.

244 [ILLINOIS.] Memoir of the Rev. Elijah P. Lovejoy, who was Murdered in Defense of the Liberty of the Press at Alton, Ill., Nov. 7, 1837. By Jos. C. and Owen Lovejoy. With an Introduction by John Qunicy Adams. 12mo, cloth. N. Y., 1838. $4.00

245 [ILLINOIS.] (Lusk, D. W.). Eighty Years of Illinois. Politics and Politicians, Anecdotes and Incidents; a Succinct History of the State, 1809-1889. By D. W. Lusk. Third Edition, revised and enlarged with engraved steel portraits. 8vo, cloth. Springfield, 1889. $3.50

246 [ILLINOIS.] Autobiography of Gurdon S. Hubbard. Edited by E. McIlvaine from the original diary. Port. 12mo, cloth. (Lakeside), 1911. $4.50

The best personal narrative of the early fur trade in northern Illinois.

247 [ILLINOIS.] (Moses, John). Illinois, Historical and Statistical; Essential Facts of its planting and growth as a Province, County, Territory, and State. Numerous ports., maps, facsimiles. 2 vols., large 8vo, cloth. Chicago: Fergus, 1889-1892. $17.50

The scarce original edition. Hinges are cracked in v. 2.

248 [ILLINOIS.] History of Chicago. By John Moses and Joseph Kirkland. Illus., 785, 777 pp., 4to, half leather. Chicago, 1895. $6.00

249 [ILLINOIS.] (Ogle County). History of. Illus., 858pp. Royal 8vo. Chicago (Kett), 1878. $5.00

Practically a history of the Rock River Valley and N. W. Illinois, with an account of the Prairie Bandits.

250 [ILLINOIS.] (Parrish, Randall). Historic Illinois. The Romance of the Earlier Days. Illus., map, 479pp., 8vo, cloth. Chicago, 1905. $3.50

251 [ILLINOIS.] (Pirtle, Henry). George Rogers Clark. Sketch of his Campaign in the Illinois, 1778-79. Introduction by Hon. Henry Pirtle, containing Major Bowman's Journal of the taking of Post St. Vincents. Port. 102pp., 8vo, cloth. Cincinnati, 1907. $6.00

252 [ILLINOIS.] (Sangamon County). History of the Early Settlers of. By John C. Powers. 797pp., 8vo, cloth. Springfield, 1876. $7.50

Includes much on the Lincoln family as well as a long account of the tragic overland expedition of the Donner Party as related by one of the survivors. The Donner Party started from Sangamon County.

253 [ILLINOIS.] (Quaife, M. M.). Chicago and the Old Northwest, 1673-1835. 488pp., map and plates. 8vo, cloth. Chicago, 1913. $7.50

254 [ILLINOIS.] (Quaife, M. M.). Pictures of Illinois One Hundred Years Ago. 12mo, cloth. Chicago, 1918. $5.00

255 [ILLINOIS.] (Stevens, Frank E.). The Black Hawk War, including Black Hawk's Life. Illustrated with upward of Three Hundred Rare and Interesting Portraits and Views. 323pp., 8vo, cloth. Chicago, 1903. $8.00

Fine copy. With an account in the appendix of Abraham Lincoln's and Jefferson Davis's participation in the War.

256 [ILLINOIS.] (Wakefield, John A.). Wakefield's History of the Black Hawk War. A reprint of the First Edition . . . from the Press of Calvin Goudy, Jacksonville, Ill., 1834. With 13 photogravure illustrations and Preface and Notes by Frank Everett Stevens. Colored frontis. 8vo, boards, unopened. Chicago, 1908. $12.50

200 copies printed for the Caxton club.

257 [ILLINOIS.] (Wallace, Joseph). History of Illinois and Louisiana under the French Rule. Embracing a general view of the French Dominion of North America. 432pp., 8vo, cloth. Cincinnati, 1893. $12.50

Scarce. An interesting historical account of the French in the Mississippi Valley and other parts of the Continent. It is really a compendious history of the French Dominions in North America.

258 [INDIANA.] Aboriginal History. Indian Abstract of Title of Bartholomew County (Indiana). 9pp., 8vo, sewn. (Columbus, Ind., 1895). $4.00

259 [INDIANA.] Reminiscences of a Journey to Indianapolis in the Year 1836. By Judge C. P. Ferguson. Vol. 2, No. 9. Indiana Historical Society Publications. 25pp., 8vo, original wrappers. Indianapolis, 1893. $3.00

260 [INDIANA.] (Brice, W. A.). History of Ft. Wayne. Ports. and plates. 374pp., 8vo, cloth. Fort Wayne, 1868. $17.50

Contains much on the original tribes of the Northwest, especially the Miamies, relations of the NW from the latter part of the 17th century to the struggles of 1812-14; sketch of the life of Wayne, manufacturing and early railroads, etc.

261 INGERSOLL, ROBERT G. Works. Illustrations. 12 vols., 8vo, cloth, paper labels, uncut. Dresden Edition. N. Y., 1903. $27.50

Nice set of this large type library edition with an extensive index.

262 [IOWA.] Institutional Beginnings in a Western State. 38pp., 8vo, original wrappers. Baltimore, 1884. $4.75

263 [IOWA.] The Iowa Band. 184pp., 8vo, cloth. Boston, 1870. $5.00

The "Band" arrived in Iowa in 1843.

264 [IOWA.] Message from the President . . . in relation to the disputed Boundary Line between the State of Missouri and the Territory of Iowa, Jan. 3, 1840. 26th Cong., 1st Sen. 35. 20pp., 8vo, sewn. [Washington, 1840.] $12.50

A scarce document containing a long letter from Robert Lucas, at Burlington, the Sheriff (H. Heffleman) at Keosonqua, and others relative to alleged depredations committed on the border of Iowa Terr. by Missourians.

265 [IOWA.] Northern Iowa. Containing Hints and Information of Value to Emigrants by a Pioneer. Frontis., 39pp., 8vo, original wrappers. Burlington, 1858. $6.00

266 [IOWA.] (Parker, N. H.). Iowa as It Is in 1856; a Gazeteer. Illus. 8vo, cloth. N. Y., 1856. $1.00

267 [IOWA.] (N. H. Parker). Iowa as it Is. Gazeteer for Citizens and a Handbook for Emigrants. 8vo, cloth. Chicago, 1855. $1.00

268 [INDIANS.] The Expedition against the Sauk and Fox Indians, 1832. By an Officer who served in General Atkinson's Brigade. Reprinted from the Military and Naval Magazine. 19pp., 8vo, original wrappers. N. Y., 1914. $3.50

269 [INDIANS.] Indian Rights and Our Duties. An Address delivered at Amherst, Hartford, etc., Dec., 1829 by Herman Humphrey, D.D., President of Amherst College. 24pp., 12mo, original wrappers. Amherst, 1830. $4.75

270 [INDIANS.] The Ponca Chiefs. An Indian's Attempt to Appeal from the Tomahawk to the Courts. With some Suggestions towards a Solution of the Indian Question. By Zylyff. 146pp., frontis. 8vo, original wrappers. Boston, 1880. $4.50

271 [INDIANS.] (Newell, Cicero). Indian Stories. 191pp., 8vo, cloth. N. Y. (1912). $3.50

272 [INDIAN CAPTIVITY.] Indian Atrocities; Narratives of the Perils and Sufferings among the Indians . . . with memoirs of Col. Crawford and John Slover, and letter from H. Brekinridge on Rights of Indians. 72pp., o ginal wrappers. Cincinnati, 1867. $10.00

273 JACKSON, SHELDON. Alaska, and Missions on the North Pacific Coast. Illus., folding map. 400pp., 12mo, cloth. N. Y. [N. d.]. $6.50

The original edition, according to Smith 1910, was published with 327pp., of which the Seattle Public apparently has the only known Copy. This, as noted, has added chapters noting population in 1880, and the schools and missions of 1883.

274 JEFFERSON, THOMAS. The Works of. Collected and edited by Paul Leicester Ford. [Illus.] 12 vols., 8vo, cloth. N. Y., 1904. $55.00

Putnam's Federal Edition of this great work.

275 ——. The Same. 10 vols., 8vo, morocco. N. Y., 1892-99. $75.00

Putnam's rare Letter-Press Edition.

276 JONES, DANIEL W. Forty Years Among the Indians. True Yet Thrilling Narrative of the Author's Experiences among the Natives. 8vo, cloth. Salt Lake City, 1890. $6.50

Original Edition. Privately published by the author before copyright. He was one of the most prominent figures in Mormon history, and roamed the whole West during the pioneer period.

277 [KANSAS.] Autobiography of Mary Stile Adams. Port. 288pp., 8vo, cloth. Los Angeles, 1893. $4.50

Born in Macon County, Mo., in 1839, the author narrates the exciting events of "Bleeding Kansas" where both she and her husband were migratory church workers.

278 [KANSAS.] The Western Missionary Priest. By Rev. John Begley. Port., 205pp., 8vo, cloth. (Wichita, 1894). $6.00

Has chapters on the Cowboy, Dodge City, etc.

279 [KANSAS.] Transactions of the Kansas State Historical Society, 1881-1913. 13 vols. in 12, 8vo, calf. 1881-1915. $27.50

279a [KANSAS.] Kansas Miscellanies. By Noble L. Prentiss. 199pp., 12mo, cloth. Topeka, 1889. $2.50

280 KALER, JAMES OTIS. Antoine of Oregon. A Story of the Oregon Trail. Illus., map., 147pp., 8vo, cloth. N. Y. (1912). $3.00

281 KALER, JAMES OTIS. Seth of Colorado. A Story of the Settlement of Denver. Frontis., map, illus., 146pp., 8vo, cloth. N. Y., c. 1912. $3.00

281a KENDALL, GEORGE W. Narrative of the Texan Santa Fe Expedition. Comprising a Description of a Tour through Texas, &c. Map and illus. 2 vols., 8vo, cloth. N. Y., 1844. $17.50

A signed Presentation Copy.

281b ——. The Same. 2 vols., 8vo, cloth. N. Y., 1844. $15.00

282 [KENTUCKY.] Iron Hills Railway Company of Kentucky; Report upon the Value of the Company's Iron Lands, located in Carter County, Ky. By Henry F. Q. D'Aligny. 53pp., 8vo, original wrappers. N. Y., 1870. $4.75

283 [KENTUCKY.] The Pioneer and the First Commodore on Three Principal Rivers of the West. Caput Mortum. By Robert McAfee. 194pp., 12mo, original wrappers. N.p., N.d. $7.50

Robert McAfee with his brothers, James and George, and James McCoun and Sam Adams reached the mouth of Limestone (now Maysville) on June 22, 1773. The above work contains a sketch of the life and genealogy of the McAfee's.

284 [KENTUCKY.] (McElroy, R. McN). Kentucky in the Nation's History. Maps and ports. 590pp., 8vo, cloth, uncut. 1909. As new. $7.50

285 [KENTUCKY.] History of Lexington; its early Annals and Recent Progress, including Biographical Sketches and Reminiscences of Pioneer Settlers, etc. By G. W. Ranck. 428pp., 8vo, cloth. Cincinnati, 1872. $25.00

286 [KENTUCKY.] History of the Bloody Recounters, Street Fights, Battles, etc., extending through a number of Years, in which many Persons were killed . . . Known as the "Hill and Evans Feud" in Garrard Co. By Lieut. J. J. Thompson. 152pp., 8vo, wrappers. Cincinnati, (c. 1860). $3.50

The original feud began between the families of two country doctors.

287 [KENTUCKY.] History of Jessamine County from its Earliest Settlement to 1898. By Bennett H. Young. Illus., 286pp., 8vo, cloth. Louisville, 1898. $7.50

288 KERCHEVAL, SAMUEL. History of the Valley of Virginia. 12mo, original calf, leather label. Winchester: Samuel H. Davis, 1833. Second Edition, revised and extended by the Author. 8vo, sheep. Woodstock, Va., 1850. $8.50

289 KIMBALL, M. B. A Soldier-Doctor of our Army. Port., Plates and folding plate of Ft. Buford, 1868. 192pp., 12mo, original cloth. N. Y., 1917. $7.50

Printed primarily for the author's immediate family this narrative furnishes an intimate chronicle of 30 years' adventures on the western plains, in California, Texas and New Mexico . He went by stage to Carson City in '65; across the plains to Dakota in '67; Indian Campaigning in the "Bad Lands"; Yellowstone Expedition of '73; Battle of the Big Horn; Ute Wars, etc., etc.

290 LAHONTAN, BARON DE. New Voyages to North America. Edited by R. G. Thwaites, reprinted from the English Edition of 1703; with facsimiles of original title-page, maps and other illustrations. 2 vols., 4to, half vellum, edges entirely uncut. Chicago, 1905. $17.50

The most beautiful edition of this important work which is especially valuable because of the fine annotations by Dr. Thwaites. It also has an extensive bibliography and index.

291 LALOR, JOHN J. Cyclopaedia of Political Science, Political Economy and of the Political History of the U. S. 3 large volumes, 8vo, half morocco. N. Y., 1893. $27.50

One of the most valuable works of reference on everything pertaining to political science and political history of the U. S. Alphabetically arranged by subjects and the articles on each subject written and signed by an authority thereon.

292 [LANE, JOSEPH.] National Democratic Executive Committee, Breckinridge and Lane Campaign. Document No. 8, Biographical Sketches of Hon. John G. Breckinridge, Democratic Nominee for President and General Joseph Lane, Democratic Nominee for Vice President. Illus., 32pp., 8vo, original wrappers. Washington, 1860. $7.50

See Wagner-Camp 216. Lane went overland by the Gila Route in the winter of 1848-49, arriving in Oregon in March with only 6 of the original 22 men. Lane was also Governor of Oregon Territory. Pp. 1-19 gives life of Breckinridge and pp. 23-32 the life of Lane.

292a LANG, JOHN D, and SAMUEL TAYLOR. Report of a visit to some of the Tribes of Indians, located west of the Mississippi. 34pp., 8vo, original printed wrappers. N. Y.: Press of M. May & Co., 1843 $12.50

Wagner-Camp 96. They visited the Indians of Kansas, Iowa, Missouri, Arkansas, and Nebraska in 1842.

293 LAPHAUR, I. A. A Documentary History of the Milwaukee and Rock River Canal, Compiled and published by order of the Board of Directors . . . 151pp. and index. 8vo, sewn. Milwaukee: Printed at the Office of the Advertiser, 1840. $35.00

The first publication on uniting the waters of Lake Michigan with those of Rock River, which was started the first year after the settlement of Milwaukee. Of great rarity. This is one of the few perfect copies ever reported of this work.

294 LECLERCQ, FATHER CHRISTIAN. The First Establishment of the Faith in New France. Now first translated from notes by John G. Shea. Illus. and map. 2 vols., 8vo, original wrappers, uncut. N. Y., 1881. $45.00

Rare in the above state.

295 [LEWIS AND CLARK.] Official Catalogue of the Lewis and Clark Centennial Exposition. 160pp., 8vo, original wrappers. Portland (1905). $2.50

Smith 3162.

296 [LINCOLN.] The Writings of Abraham Lincoln. Edited by Arthur Brooks Lapsley. Illus. 8vo, half morocco. N. Y., 1905. $30.00

Putnam's fine Constitutional Edition.

297 [LINCOLN.] (Nicolay, John G., and Hay, John). Abraham Lincoln, a History. Illus. 10 vols., large 8vo, cloth. N. Y., 1890. $25.00

Original Edition.

298 LODGE, HENRY CABOT. Short History of the English Colonies in America. 8vo, half calf. N. Y., 1881. $3.00

299 [LOUISIANA.] An Account of Louisiana, being an Abstract of Documents in the Office of Departments of State and of the Treasury. 50pp., 8vo, sewn. Phila.: Duane, 1803. $22.50

Contains a general description of Upper Louisiana boundaries, St. Bernardo, Baton Rouge, Red River and its settlements, with a good account of the various Indian tribes, sugar cultivation, etc.

300 [LOUISIANA.] (Fortier, Alice). History of Louisiana, 1512-1903. Early Explorers and French Domination; Spanish Domination and Secession to U. S., and American Domination. Also the scarce Atlas of Portraits and Plates, in one volume. Together 5 vols., Imperial 8vo, and Atlas in 4to. Beautifully printed in large type by Goupil of Paris, on Rives hand-made deckle-edged paper, and extensively illustrated with beautifully executed portraits, plates and maps, and bound in ¾ white vellum. Paris, 1904. $50.00

Fine set, almost as new of the large paper edition of this valuable work.

301 [LOUISIANA.] (Martin, Francis X.). History of Louisiana, from the Earliest Period. 2 vols., original sheep. New Orleans, 1827-29. $50.00

Describes the early inhabitants of the Territory, hostilities between France, Spain and England with their treaties, ealy Colonial settlemens, land grants, Wilkinson's Expediton, first steamboat on the Mississippi, etc.

302 LOWERY, WOODBURY. The Spanish Settlements within the Limits of the U. S., 1513-1561. Maps., illus. 515pp., 8vo, cloth. N. Y., 1901. $7.50

303 LYELL, SIR CHAS. Second Visit to the U. S. of North America. 2 vols., 12mo, half morocco. N. Y., 1849. $3.00

McAFEE'S "HISTORY OF THE LATE WAR," 1816

304 M'AFEE, R. B. History of the Late War in the Western Country, Comprising a Full Account of all the transactions in that quarter, from the Commencement of Hostilities at Tippecanoe to the Termination of the Contest at New Orleans. 534pp., with the "extra" printed leaf at end, the blank leaf following title. 8vo, original calf. Lexington, 1816. $52.50

Original Edition. Paullin 1937; Field 1413. The author was one of the first Kentuckians to join the Northwest army, where he sought and obtained a large amount of material regarding the Indian wars on the western frontier from the actors engaged in them. His narrative is of great historical value and contains much material which later histories either do not possess, or only copy from his pages. This copy has a map inserted.

305 McCALEB, WALTER F. The Aaron Burr Conspiracy. A History largely from Original and Hitherto Unused Sources. Folding map. 8vo, cloth. N. Y., 1903. $7.50

306 McKENNY, THOMAS L. Sketches of a Tour to the Lakes, of the Character and Customs of the Chippeway Indians, and of Incidents Connected with the Treaty of Fon du Lac. Also, a Vocabulary of the Algic, or Chippeway Language. Ports. and plates, some foxing. 8vo, original boards, paper label. Baltimore, 1827. $22.50

Braislin 1223. The hinges are weak and it has offsets.

307 McKNIGHT, CHARLES. Our Western Border in Early Pioneer Days. Illus. Large 8vo, cloth. Phila., 1876. $6.00

Contains an immense amount of original material from authentic sources; strange and thrilling narratives of captivities, daring deeds, desperate conflicts, exciting adventures, personal prowess, etc.

308 MARCHAND, ETIENNE. Voyage autour du Monde, pendant les annees 1790-92. Precede d'une introduction Historique; auquel on a joint des Recherches sur les Terres Australes de Drake, et un Examin Critique du Voyage de Roggeween. Par C. P. Claret Fleurieu. 4 vols., 4to. Fine, clean, sound set with all the maps. Paris, 1796-1800. $65.00

Smith 1261. Large paper copy of the Original Edition. The French Edition is valuable for the two volumes on natural history and the "Recherches sur les terres Australes de Drake et un examin Critique de Roggeween", which are not included in the English translation. Marchand's expedition sailed round the Horn, turned northward, and after touching at the Marquesas Islands, visited Norfolk Sount, Queen Charlotte Islands, Nootka Sound, and other parts of the Northwest Coast of America. He gives interesting descriptions of those places and of the island inhabitants. The work is also valuable for its scientific observations and the learned researches of the author on the early navigators. Refer to No. 1020, Cat. 18.

309 [MAINE.] (Williamson, Wm. D.). The History of the State of Maine. Port. 2 vols., 8vo, sheep. Hollowell, 1839. $10.00

310 MARGRY, PIERRE. Memoires et Documents pour servir a l'Histoire des Origines Francaises des Pays l'Ouest et dans le Sud de l'Amerique Septentrionale, 1614-1754. Beautifully printed on Holland handmade deckle-edged paper, with finely engraved portraits and plates. 6 vols., large 8vo, original wrappers, uncut and top edges unopened. Paris, 1879-1888. $60.00

A complete set including both the first and second series. The second series is scarcer than the first. The above work is a storehouse of documents throwing light on the history of La Salle, d'Ibervill, Juchereau, de St. Denis, La Sueur, Hennepin, Cadillac, Dulhut and other explorers of the 17th and 18th centuries.

311 MARTIN, ISAAC. A Journal of the Life, Travels, Labours and Religious Exercises of Isaac Martin, Late of Rahway, in East Jersey, Deceased. 160pp., 12mo, calf. Phila., 1834. $5.00

The author was born in N. Y. in 1758. He gives a vivid account of his travels through New York, Pennsylvania, New Jersey, Virginia and the Carolinas during the Revolution.

312 MARTINEAU, HARRIET. Retrospects of Western Travel. 3 vols., 12mo, calf. London, 1838. $10.00

313 [MARYLAND.] (Carew, Brampfylde-Moore). An Apology for the Life of Brampfylde-Moore Carew . . . Commonly known throughout the West of England, by the title King of the Beggars; and Dog Merchant General, &c. 151pp., 12mo, calf. London, 1749. $10.00

Carew was banished to Maryland about 1740. He gives an amusing account of the Country and his adventures in Maryland, Va., N. J., N. Y. and Conn., until he embarked at New England for England. His accounts of how he bamboozled and bled Whitfield, Thomas Penn., Governor Thomas, and many others of good repute are amusing, true or not."—Stevens.

314 [MASSACHUSETTS.] The History of Massachusetts, By John S. Barry. 3 vols., 8vo, cloth. Boston, 1855. $4.00

315 [MASSACHUSETTS.] The Boston News Letter. No. 1, from Monday, April 17 to Monday, April 24, 1704. Broadside printed on both sides. Boston, 1704. $12.50

316 [MASSACHUSETTS.] The Development of Freedom of the Press in Massachusetts. By Clyde Augustus Duniway. v-202pp., 8vo, cloth. N. Y., 1906. $2.50

317 [MASSACHUSETTS.] The History of Massachusetts . . . until the Year 1750. The Third Edition, with Additional Notes of Corrections. By Thomas Hutchinson. 2 vols., 8vo, calf. Salem, 1795. $15.00

318 [MASSACHUSETTS.] (Peter Oliver). The Puritan Commonwealth; an Historical Review of the Puritan Government in Massachusetts in its Civil and Ecclesiastical Relations from its rise to the Abrogation of the First Charter. 514pp., 8vo, cloth. Boston, 1856. $4.00

319 [MASSACHUSETTS.] Chronicles of the First Planters of the Colony of Massachusetts Bay, from 1623 to 1636 . . . Edited by Alexander Young. [Map and illus.] 8vo, cloth. Boston, 1846. $10.00

Signed Presentation Copy of the Original Edition. Contains John White's Relation, William Hubbard's Narrative, Original Records of the Governor and Company of Massachusetts Bay, the Company's First Letter of Instructions to Endicott, Higginson's Journal, etc.

320 MASSACHUSETTS HISTORICAL SOCIETY COLLECTIONS. Complete Set. 78 vols., 8vo, cloth and boards. Boston, 1792-1925. $300.00

321 MATHER, COTTON. Magnolia Christi Americana; or, the Ecclesiastical History of New-England, from its First Planting in the Year 1620, until A.D. 1698 . . . 2 vols., 8vo, calf (lacks fly-leaf). Hartford, 1820. $17.50

First American Edition of 1702. The above is the most famous of Cotton Mather's many books, and although a curious work, contains much of great historical value, including an account of Harvard College, Indian Wars, etc.

322 MAYHEW, JONATHAN. Remarks on an Anonymous Tract entitled An Answer to Dr. Mayhew's Observations on the Charter and Conduct of the Society for the Propagation of the Gospel in Foreign Parts, being a Second Defense of said Observation. 36pp., with advt. page, dated Boston, June 20, 1764. Numerous annotations in quill pen. 8vo, unbound. Boston, 1764. $4.50

323 MERENESS, NEWTON D. Travels in the American Colonies. 693pp., 8vo, cloth. N. Y., 1916. $17.50

This work contains 18 hitherto unpublished journals, including: Col. Gen. Chicken's Journal from Charleston to the Cherokee Country, 1726; Capt. Fitch from Charleston to the Creek Country, 1726; Bonnefoy's Captivity among the Cherokees, 1742; Beauchamp, from Mobile to the Choctaws, 1746; Hamburgh Travels in Michigan and Ill., 1746; Capt. Gordon, from Pittsburgh down the Ohio, and Mississippi to New Orleans, Mobile and Pensacola, 1746; David Taitt, through the Creek Country, 1772; and two journeys through Kentucky by Wm. Fleming, 1779-1783.

324 MERRICK, CAPT. G. B. Old Times on the Upper Mississippi; the Recollections of a Steamboat Pilot, 1854-63. Maps, plates. 8vo, cloth. Cleveland, 1909. $17.50

Item 323, First line of note, after "Col." should read, George instead of Gen.

325 MICHAUX, F. A. (M.D.). Voyage a l'Ouest des Monts Alleghanys, dans les etats de l'Ohio, du Kentucky et du Tennessee et Retour a Charleston par les Hautes-Carolines, &c. Folding map. 8vo, cloth-backed boards, entirely uncut with the half-title. Paris, 1804. $25.00

Fine copy of the Original Edition.

325a ——. Another Edition. Folding map. 8vo, roan backed boards. London: Phillips, 1805. $7.50

326 [MICHIGAN.] Journal of Events, Principally on the Detroit and Niagara Frontiers, during the War of 1812. By Capt. W. H. Merritt. 82pp., 8vo, original printed blue wrappers. St. Catharines, C. W., 1863. $50.00

Barber Collection, No. 789. An excessively rare work, apparently the first copy to appear in America. The Journal contains facts relating to the War of 1812, especially the northern border aspects, which are nowhere else available.

327 [MIDDLE WEST.] (Winsor, Justin). Cartier to Frontenac. Geographical Discovery in the Interior of North America in its Historical Relations, 1534-1700 . . . [Maps and illus.] 8vo, cloth. Boston, 1894. $4.50

328 MILLER, JOAQUIN. My Life among the Indians. Frontis., 253pp., 12mo, original illustrated wrappers (slight stain). Chicago, 1892. $4.50

329 MILLER, JOAQUIN. The Danites. Illus., 281pp., 12mo, original illustrated wrappers. Chicago, 1892. $4.50

330 [MINNESOTA.] Collections of the Minnesota Historical Society, 1872-1904. 11 vols. in 13 books. Minneapolis, 1872-1904. $30.00

331 [MINNESOTA.] Collections of the Minnesota Historical Society. Vol. 5. Port. 535pp., 8vo, original cloth. St. Paul, 1885. $6.00

Contains the history of the Objibways by William W. Warren.

332 [MINNESOTA.] The Seat of Empire. By Charles Carleton Coffin. 232pp., plus advts. 6 plates, folding map in pocket. Ex-Lib. stamps. 8vo, cloth. Boston, 1871. $6.00

The author, the celebrated "Carleton" was undoubtedly paid by Jay Cooke to make the trip with the Governor of Minnesota, and others. They went by steamer from La Crosse, Wis., to Minneapolis, thence by foot, horseback, steamer, etc. to the Northwest, Oregon and Washington. The trip was made while Jay Cooke's Northern Pacific was under construction. The folding map, as the author states, is the first complete map ever published between the 36th and 55th parallel. Mr. Cooke, of course, used the best map of the U. S. Topographical Engineers, ie. by Major Gen. Humphreys. The trip was made in 1869. The map is dated 1870.

333 [MINNESOTA.] Its Progress and Capabilities. Being the Second Annual Report of the Commissioner of Statistics, for the Year 1860 and 1861 . . . Map, 126pp., 8vo, original wrappers. St. Paul, 1862. $4.00

334 [MINNESOTA.] (William J. Fletcher). A History of the City of Saint Paul, and of the County of Ramsey. [Illus.] 8vo, half morocco. St. Paul, 1876. $8.50

335 [MINNESOTA.] (Neill, Edward D.). Materials for the Future History of Minnesota; Bting a Report of the Minnesota Historical Society to the Legislative Assembly. Plates, 141pp. 8vo, original printed wrappers. Saint Paul, 1856. $12.50

Important volume containing much historical detail not elsewhere to be found. Included are articles by Williamson, the Dakota Missionary, Governor Ramsey, etc. Special chapters on explorations; early Indian traders; Ft. Snelling; British and American fur trade, etc.

336 [MINNESOTA.] A Tale of Two Cities: Minneapolis and St. Paul Compared. 96pp., 8vo, sewn. Minneapolis, 1885. $3.50

337 [MINNESOTA.] Van Cleve, Charlotte O. Three Score Years and Ten: Lifelong Memories of Fort Snelling and other parts of the West. 176pp., port. 8vo, cloth. (Minneapolis), 1888. $4.50

Privately printed. The author lived in the fort in 1821 before it was completed. Also deals with life at Ft. Howard, etc. The portrait is signed by the author.

338 [MISSISSIPPI.] A Memoir of S. S. Prentiss. Edited by his Brother. 2 vols., 12mo, cloth. N. Y., 1855. $7.50

Scarce. Prentiss was a Northerner who settled in Miss., practiced law, served in Congress, and was unrivalled as an orator.

339 [MISSISSIPPI.] Publications of the Mississippi Historical Society, 1898-1906. 9 vols. in 8, 8vo, cloth. Jackson, V.d. $27.50

340 [MISSISSIPPI VALLEY.] Ancient Pottery of the Mississippi Valley. By William H. Holmes. From the Proceeding of the Davenport Academy of Sciences. Illus., 125-196pp., 8vo, original wrappers. Washington, 1885. $5.00

341 [MISSISSIPPI VALLEY.] Licenses to Trade with the Indians. Letter from the Secretary of War, transmitting an Abstract of Licenses granted to Citizens of the U. S. to trade with the Indians during the year ending on the 1st of September, 1825. 8vo, sewn. Washington, 1826. $7.50

342 [MISSISSIPPI VALLEY.] (Walker, C. B.). Mississippi Valley and Prehistoric Events. Colored plates. 8vo, cloth. Burlington, Iowa, 1880. $2.50

343 [MISSOURI AND NORTHWEST.] A Pilgrimage over the Prairies. By the Author of "The Fortunes of a Colonist." 298pp., 313pp. [wrongly numbered 261.] 6 plates. 12mo, cloth. London, 1863. $17.50

Wagner-Camp 394. Romance of the Prairies and the Blackfeet Indians.

344 [MONTANA.] Historical Sketch of the Flathead Indians from the Year 1813 to 1890. Embracing the History of the Establishment of St. Mary's Indian Mission in the Bitter Root Valley, Mont. With Sketches of the Missionary Life of Father Ravalli and other early Missionaries, Wars of the Blackfeet and Flatheads. By Peter Ronan. 80pp., plates. 8vo, cloth. Helena, Mont. [1890]. $7.50

Scarce original work on the northwest by a former Indian Agent stationed among the Flatheads.

345 [MONTANA.] The Calumet of the Coteau and other Poetical Legends of the Border. Together with a Guide Book of the Yellowstone National Park. By Philetus W. Norris. 275pp., maps. 12mo, cloth. Phila., 1883. $7.50

Contains a glossary of Indian words, and Chinook jargon. See Pilling.

346 [MONTANA.] In Memoriam. By Edwin R. Purple. 12pp., 4to, cloth. N. Y., 1881. (125 copies Privately Printed by the Author). $17.50

347 [MONTANA.] Truth Stranger than Fiction. By Mrs. Alma White. Numerous illus. 305pp., 12mo, cloth. Zarephath, N. J., 1913. $4.00

Graphic account of early days in Beaverhead Valley (Bannock and Dillon, Mont.), where the author arrived in 1879 at the age of 19, from Millersburg, Ky. She resided in Montana many years as a schoolteacher and preacher.

348 [MONTREAL.] Hochelaga Depicta: the Early History and Present State of the City and Island of Montreal. Edited by Newton Bosworth. Maps and plates. 184pp., 12mo, original cloth, uncut. Montreal, 1839. $12.50

A very fine copy. This work contains a first-hand account of the rebellions of 1837-1838.

349 MOORE, CHARLES. The Northwest under Three Flags, 1635-1796. Maps and plates. 8vo, cloth. N. Y., 1900. $7.50

A good account of the early French occupation, the Pontiac War ,British conquest of 1760, the Revolution in the Northwest and Wayne's and other campaigns against the Indians.

350 [MORMONS.] John Brent. By Theodore Winthrop. 12mo, cloth (worn, foxed). Boston, 1862. $3.00

Original Edition. See Fullerton's "Selective Bibliography of American Literature." "Winthrop was among the first, perhaps the first, strong writer to adopt a breezy style. He was a gifted story-teller, and in 'John Brent', an excellent tale of the Western Plains, entered a new field until then almost untouched in fiction."

350a [MORMONS.] The Autobiography of Parley Parker Pratt, one of the Twelve Apostles of the Church of Jesus Christ of Latter-Day Saints, embracing his Life, Ministry and Travels. 8vo, cloth. N. Y., 1874. $7.50

351 [MOUNTAIN CLIMBING.] A Climber's Guide to the Rocky Mountains of Canada. By Howard Palmer and J. Monroe Thorington. Maps. 183pp., 8vo, cloth. N. Y., 1921. $3.75

MULLER'S ORIGINAL ACCOUNT OF BERING'S DISCOVERY OF THE NORTHWEST COAST, 1758

351a MULLER, GERHARD FREDERICH. Sammlung Russicher Geschichte. Des Dritten Bandes Erstes, Zwentes u. drittes Stuck. [Collection of Russian History, third volume, first, second and third parts—This is the general title]. The title of first part in high Dutch—Nachrichten von Seereisn und zur See Gemachten Entdeckungen, die von Russland aus langst den Kuste des Eiszmeeres und auf dem Ostlichen Weltmeere gegen Japon und Amerika geschen sind. [News of Voyages and Discoveries made on the Ocean from Russia along the coasts of the Polar Sea and Eastern Ocean toward Japan and America.] St. Petersburg, 1758. [Then follows the same general title in the original High Dutch for the "Viertes" or fourth part]—Nachricht den dreyen in Gebiete der Stadt Casan, Wohnhaften Heidnischen Volkern den Tscheremissen, Tschuiwaschen und Wotiacken. [News of three Heathen Peoples living in the Territory of Kazan.] St. Petersburgh, 1759. [Then follows the same general title in the original High Dutch to the "Funftes" and "Sechstes" parts (fifth and sixth parts).]—Nachrichten von der Handlung in Sibirien. [News of the Commerce in Siberia.] St. Petersburg, 1860. In all, six parts with half-titles and full titles, pp.304, 305-412, 413-612, with register of Index to all, 43pp. 12mo, calf. St Petersburgh, 1758, 1759, 1760. $250.00

Sabin 51, 285. A complete copy of the original account of Bering's discovery of the mainland of the Northwest Coast of America, one of the foundation books of American history. This work in the original High Dutch with all the parts and half-titles thereto and correct dates as above noted is very rare. Muller was the historian of Bering's Second Voyage. The other scientists included Delisle de la Croyere as astronomer, George Steller, naturalist, and Johann Gmelin, botanist. Chirikov commanded the St. Paul and Bering the St. Peter. The St. Paul was the first to reach the American coast, as she anchored south of Sitka, July 15, 1741. Two days later Bering came in sight of the coast opposite Mt. St. Elias. On the voyage home the St. Peter foundered off Bering's Island, but a remnant of the crew managed to reach the starting point, Petrovpavlovsk, about a year after Chirikov and Delisle de la Croyere.

One of the earliest accounts in English of Bering's voyage is Muller's "A Letter from a Russian Sea-Officer," London, 1754 which was in answer to Delisle's none too accurate account of the expedition. [See item 157a "Explication de Carte des Nouvelles Decouvertes, etc."] This controversy was carried further in Philippe Buache's "Considerations Geographiques Physiques sur les Nouvelle Decouvertes au Nord de la grand Mer . . ." (Vide item 150a, Cat. 18). And now here in the great work cited above we have the competent Muller's full account of the voyage in the original edition and with the 1758 title-page.

Prof. Golder states of this work: "This is the most important account by a contempo rary. Muller was one of the scientists who were members of Bering's second voyage . . . The most important book in this field is, after all, the third volume of Muller's 'Sammlung Russicher Geschichte' published in 1758. Soon after its appearance this work was translated into Russian, English and French. Although since that time much paper and ink have been used in telling this story, yet very little that is new has been added to our knowledge of the subject. Both Russian and non-Russian scholars have preferred to follow Muller's version . . .

"Indispensable for the history of discovery and exploration of the Northern Pacific."—Sabin.

352 NATIONAL CYCLOPAEDIA OF AMERICAN BIOGRAPHY, being the History of the U. S. as Illustrated in the Lives of the Founders, Builders and Defenders of the Republic, and of the Men and Women who are doing the Work, etc., etc. 12 vols., 8vo, cloth. N. Y., 1898. $15.00

353 [NEBRASKA.] Journal of the Council of the Legislative Assembly of the Territory of, &c. 1st Sess., 1855, 2nd Sess., 1856, 3rd Sess., 1857, 4th Sess., 1858, 5th Sess., 1859. Also the 5th Sess. of the House Journal, 1859 and the House Journal for 1875. 8 vols., 8vo, original wrappers. Omaha and Brownsville, 1855-1875. $45.00

354 NEBRASKA STATE HISTORICAL SOCIETY, Transactions and Reports, 1885-1893. 8vo, cloth. Lincoln, 1895-1893. $25.00

355 NEWCOMBE, CHAS. FRANCIS. Petroglyphs in British Columbia. (This is a separate publication from the Victoria Daily Times, Sept. 7th, 1907.) 8vo, original wrappers. Victoria, 1907. $4.00

356 NEWCOMBE, CHAS. FREDERIC. Victoria, B. C. Guide to the Anthropological Collection in the Provincial Museum. 69pp., illus., folding map. 4to, original wrappers. Victoria, 1909. $4.75

357 NEWCOMBE, CHAS. FREDERIC. The McGill Totem Pole. (This is a separate publication from the Ottawa Naturalist, Vol. 22, Dec., 1918.) 8vo, original wrappers. Ottawa, 1919. $4.00

358 NEWCOMBE, CHAS. FRANCIS. Menzies' Journal of Vancouver's Voyage, April to Oct., 1792. 171pp., 8vo, cloth. Victoria, 1923. $10.00

359 NEIDHARDT, JOHN G. The River and I. With 50 plates and topographic views. 325pp., 8vo, cloth. N. Y., 1910. $7.50

Original Edition. Narrative of adventures during a trip to the headwaters of the Missouri in a small boat; with visits to the Yellowstone region; the sites and ruins of the frontier forts; Assiniboine Indians; Bad Lands and other regions of the Northwest.

360 NEIDHARDT, JOHN G. The Song of Three Friends. 126pp., 12mo, cloth. N. Y., 1919. $4.75

The Original Edition of a narrative poem of the Upper Missouri in the early 1820's, during the Fur voyagings.

361 NEIDHARDT, JOHN G. Splendid Wayfaring. The Story of the Exploits and Adventures of Jedediah Smith and his Comrades, the Ashley-Henry Men. 290pp., 8vo, cloth. N. Y., 1920. $3.50

Original Edition of a fine narrative of the first Overland Expedition to California. Neidhart has always had the touch of the western country and of the men who fought and bled in it. His books are relatively cheap, as I write, but they eventually will not be, especially in the original editions. In "The Song of Hugh Glass" (poetry), one can learn as much about this celebrated character as in any comparable prose work.

362 NEIDHARDT, JOHN G. The Song of Hugh Glass. 181pp., 12mo, cloth. N. Y., 1922. $4.50

The great ballad story of Hugh Glass, perhaps one of the most romantic characters of the early pathfinders.

363 NEIDHARDT, JOHN G. The Song of the Indian Wars. Illus. 231pp., 12mo, cloth. N. Y., 1925. $4.75

Original Edition.

364 [NEW ENGLAND.] (Caverly, Robt. B.). Heroism of Hannah Duston, together with the Indians of New England. Illus. 12mo, cloth. Boston, 1874. $1.50

365 [NEW ENGLAND.] (King, Thomas S.). White Hills, their Legends, Landspace and Poetry. [First Edition, with best impression of illus.] 414pp., 8vo, cloth. Boston, 1860. $4.50

Includes the Saco Valley, Connecticut Valley, Androscoggin Valley, etc.

366 [NEW ENGLAND.] Economic and Social History of New England, 1620-1789. By Wm. B. Weeden. 2 vols., 8vo, cloth. Boston, 1891. $10.00

"The best book yet written from which to obtain an idea of the life in Colonial and provincial New England"—Jas. K. Hosmer. Indian trading, land tenure, servants, schools, dress, prisons, finance.

367 [NEW ENGLAND.] (White, Henry). Indian Battles; with Incidents in the Early History of New England. 12mo, cloth. N. Y. (1859). $3.75

368 [NEW ENGLAND CLUB.] Souvenir Edition. With Wellesley, Harvard, Yale and Brown Alumni. Illus. 141pp., 8vo, cloth. Seattle, 1910. $5.00

Contains the names of all active alumni of the above mentioned colleges residing in the Northwest at the time of publication.

369 [NEW ENGLAND-RHODE ISLAND.] Memoir of the Life and Labors of Francis Wayland, Late President of Brown University. 2 vols., 12mo, cloth. N. Y., 1868. $4.50

370 [NEW JERSEY.] (Barber, John W., and Howe, Henry). Historical Collection of the State of New Jersey . . . Frontispiece in color and other illus. 512pp., 8vo, sheep. N. Y., 1846. $5.00

371 [NEW JERSEY.] Historical Collections of the State of New Jersey . . . By John W. Barber and Henry Howe. Stipple engravings (colored) of the Battle of Princeton, and the Victory at Trenton, and over 100 woodcut views. Thick 8vo, cloth. Newark, 1844. $5.00

372 [NEW JERSEY.] Mulford, Isaac S. Civil and Political History of New Jersey. 8vo, cloth. Camden, 1848. $4.50

373 [NEW MEXICO.] (Bourke, John G.). The Urine Dance of the Zuni Indians of New Mexico. 7pp., 8vo, original wrappers. N.p., Privately Printed. [One hundred copies printed strictly for private circulation.] 1920. $3.50

374 [NEW MEXICO.] (Calhoun, James S.) The Official Correspondence of James S. Calhoun, while Indian Agent at Santa Fe and Superintendent of Indian Affairs in New Mexico. Edited by Annie H. Abel. 4 large folding maps. 554pp., 8vo, cloth. Washington, 1915. $7.50

Numerous documents and unpublished material relating to Arizona, New Mexico, and Utah.

375 [NEW MEXICO.] Archbishop Lamy of Santa Fe. By Francis Lavalle. Contained in Catholic Family Annual, 1889. Pp. 69-73. 12mo, original wrappers. N. Y., 1888. $2.00

Bishop Lamy went to New Mexico in 1850.

376 NEWTON, CANON WILLIAM. Twenty Years on the Saskatchewan, Northwest Canada. Illus. 184pp., 8vo, cloth. N.p., 1897. $7.50

A thoroughly interesting work relating to the Settlers and Emigrants in the Northwest; the Riel Rebellion; Indians and Half Breeds, etc. Can locate no copies in the bibliographies.

377 [NEW YORK.] A History of Atego. XII, 152pp., 12mo, cloth. (Cooperstown, 1907). $3.00

378 [NEW YORK.] Albany, Settlement and Early History of. By W. Barnes. 8vo, original wrappers. 1864. $2.00

379 [NEW YORK.] Census of Slaves in 1755. Removed from a book. 8vo, old paper wrappers. N.p., N.d. $1.00

380 [NEW YORK.] Red Jacket, Birthplace of. By Conover. Illus. 22p., 8vo. Waterloo, N. Y., 1884. $5.00

A scarce little work published by the Waterloo Historical Society.

381 [NEW YORK.] Historic New York, being the First Series of Half Moon Papers. By Maud Wilder Goodwin, Alice Carrington Royce, and Ruth Putnam. XIV, 462pp. Illus. 8vo, cloth. N. Y., 1897. $2.00

382 [NEW YORK.] The Story of New Netherland—The Dutch in America. By Wm. Elliott Griffis. 12mo, cloth. N. Y., 1909. $2.50

383 [NEW YORK.] From a Forest to a City. Personal Reminiscences of Syracuse, N. Y. By M. C. Hand. Illus. 12mo, cloth. Syracuse, 1889. $4.50

384 [NEW YORK.] Historical Discourse of the Reformed Church of Fonda, N. Y. . . . By Thos. W. Jones. Dec. 28, 1873. 15pp., 8vo, original wrappers. N. Y., 1874. $3.00

385 [NEW YORK.] A History of New York from the Beginning of the World to the End of the Dutch Dynasty . . . By Diedrich Knickerbocker [Washington Irving]. The whole Embellish'd by Eight Pictures from the Hand of Maxfield Parrish, Esq'r. Large 4to, pictorial boards. N. Y., 1903. $12.50

386 [NEW YORK.] Annals of Newtown, containing a History from its first Settlement, together with many interesting facts concerning the Adjacent Towns; also a particular account of numerous Long Island families now spread over this and various States of the Union. 8vo, boards, uncut. N. Y., 1852. $15.00

387 [NEW YORK.] Documents relating to the Colonial History of New York. Edited by E. B. O'Callaghan. Colored plates, folding maps and plans, numerous ills. 15 vols., including Index. 4to, cloth. Albany, 1856-1887. $32.50

388 [NEW YORK.] Settlement in the West. Sketches of Rochester, with Incidental Notices of Western New York. By Henry O'Reilly. [Map and 44 plates.] 12mo, cloth (bit worn). Rochester, 1838. $12.50

389 [NEW YORK.] The Frontiersman of New York, Showing Customs of the Indians, Vicissitudes of the Pioneer White Settlers, and Border Strife in Two Wars . . . By Jeptha R. Simms. [Illus.] 2 vols., 8vo, full sheep. Albany, 1882. $17.50

390 [NEW YORK.] (Stiles, Henry R.). History of the City of Brooklyn, including the Old Town and Village of Brooklyn, the town of Bushwick and the Village of Williamsburg. 3 vols., large 8vo, coth. Brookyn, 1867-1870. $7.50

391 [NEW YORK.] History of the Province of New York, from the First Discovery to the Year 1732 . . . By William Smith. 8vo, calf (broken). Albany, 1814. $5.00

392 [NEW YORK.] (Orleans County). Pioneer History of. By A. Thomas. 8vo, cloth. 1871. $3.75

393 [NEW YORK.] In Olde New York. Sketches of Old Times and Places in both the State and City. By Chas. Burr Todd. 12mo, cloth. N. Y. (1907). $2.50

394 [NEW YORK.] (Van Schaack, Henry C.). History of Manlius Village in a Course of Lectures read before the Manlius Literary Association. 81pp., 8vo, cloth. Fayetteville, N. Y., 1873. $3.50

395 [NEW YORK.] (Herkimer County). History of. Ed. by Hardin & Willard. 4to, half morocco. 1893. $5.00

396 [NEW YORK HISTORICAL SOCIETY.] Catalogues of Printed Books in the Library of. 8vo, cloth. N. Y., 1859. $3.50

397 NEW YORK HISTORICAL SOCIETY COLLECTIONS, Vols. 1 to 38. 8vo, cloth. N. Y., 1868-1905. $41.50

Publication Fund Series. Includes the Lee Papers, Colden Letter Books, Revolutionary Papers, the Montresor Journals, Kemble Papers, Deane Papers, etc. A fine set.

398 [NEW YORK HISTORICAL SOCIETY COLLECTIONS.] Vol, 1, 1811, 8vo, calf (worn); Vol. 2, 1814, original wrappers; Vol. 3, 1821, half calf; (Second Series): Vol. 1, 1841, original cloth; Vol. 3, Part 1, 1857, original wrappers. (Proceedings): For 1843 (N. Y., 1844), and bound in with same "Inaugural Address of Albert Gallatin. N.p., 1843; Also: "A Memoir of the North Eastern Boundary in Connection with Jay's Map. By Albert Gallatin. 74pp., map. N. Y., 1843. Proceedings for 1844, 8vo. N. Y., 1845. Also bound in: "An Address delivered by John Romyn Broadhead. 107pp. N. Y., 1844. Proceedings for 1845, 8vo. N. Y., 1846. Also bound in: "A Discourse by Alexander W. Bradford, 31pp. N. Y., 1847. Also bound in: "An Address by Henry R. Schoolcraft." 38pp. N. Y., 1847. Together 9 vols., 8vo, original wrappers and calf. N. Y., 1811-1847. $32.50

399 [NEVADA.] Nevada, the Land of Silver. By John J. Powell. Illus. 305pp., 8vo, cloth. San Francisco, 1876. $7.50

Original Edition. Treats of the political aspects of Nevada; also of mining laws, principal silver mines, the Sutro Tunnel, Cities, Schools, etc .

400 NICOL, JOHN. The Life and Adventures of. Port. 215pp., 12mo, half calf. Edinburgh, 1822. $35.00

Nicol embarked under Capt. Portlock in the "King George" on their celebrated voyage round the world. Nicol's work is the best and most entertaining account of the voyage. Pp. 84-95 relate to Nootka Sound.

401 NICOLLET, I. N. Report intended to Illustrate a Map of the Hydrographical Basin of the Upper Mississippi River. 170pp., fine large folding map. 28th Cong., H. R. No. 52. The map is dated 1843. 8vo, sewn. Washington, 1845. $27.50

Wagner-Camp 98. Braislin, 1377. This is apparently the original map in a later issue of this work, as both collate 170pp.

401a NIEDIECK, PAUL. Mes Croisieres dans la mer de Behring, Nouvelles Chasses et Nouveau Voyages, par l'Auteur de mes Chasses les Cinq Parties du Monde . . . Frontis., illus. 396pp., 8vo, original wrappers. Paris: Plon-Nourrit, 1908. $12.50

Smith 2668 locates only the copy at Victoria.

402 [NILES WEEKLY REGISTER.] 72 Volumes bound in 71. Complete to September, 1847. One Index Volume. Bindings half leather but not uniform. 8vo. 1811-1847. $200.00

Rare original source book of American History, especially recounting the early exploring expeditions to the west, contemporary accounts of Indian Fights, border warfare, Outlaws and Bandits, development of early Railroads, etc. An unusual feature of this set is that all supplement and addenda are included. These are generally lacking and are even more important than the regular issues, as they contain special documents too long to go in the regular issue, personal narratives, etc.

403 NIXON, H. C. Possum Trot. Rural Community, South. Illus. 12mo, cloth. Norman, Okla., 1941. $2.50

404 [NOOTKA SOUND.] Zetes [Pseud.] An Address to the Parliament and People of Great Britain on the Past and Present State of Affairs between Spain and Great Britain respecting their American Possessions. 49pp., 8vo, cloth (rebound). London: Debrett, 1790. $120.00

Very rare, as are all pamphlets on the Nootka Sound Controversy printed in 1790. Smith 4501 locates only the copy at Victoria. Refer to item 1501, Cat. 17.

405 [NOOTKA SOUND.] Annual Register or General Repository of History, Politics, and Literature for the Year 1790; to which is prefixed a continuation of the History of Knowledge, Learning and Taste in Great Britain during the Reign of Queen Elizabeth. 604pp., 8vo, half calf. London, 1791. $25.00

Smith 2650 cites one copy. Also see item 1231 Cat. 18. Also Smith 103. This work contains many of the important state papers of Great Britain and Spain relating to the Nootka Controversy.

406 [NOOTKA SOUND.] Extracts from a Journal kept on board the Ship "Atahualpa," bound on a Voyage from Boston to the Northwest Coast and the Sandwich Islands. Monday, Nov. 30, 1801. $4.50

The above is a facsiimle of the original publication.

407 [NOOTKA SOUND.] (Bancroft, Herbert Howe). History of the Northwest Coast. Illus., maps. 8vo, 2 vols., morocco. San Francisco, 1886. $12.50

MAURELLE'S JOURNAL

408 [NOOTKA SOUND.] (Barrington, Daines). Miscellanies: Containing Journal of a Voyage in 1775, to explore the Coast of America, Northward from California, by Don Francisco Maurelle. Map of West Coast from Lower California to Cape St. Elias, another map, 2 portraits and 5 unpaged tables. 4to, calf. London, 1781. $25.00

See item 230 cat. 18. The first appearance in English of Bodgea's Voyage occupying pp. 469-534, the map showing Monterey ,Pla. de la Bodega, Pla. Arenas, Pto. de le Trinidad, Rio de las Tortolas, etc. Fine copy.

409 [NOOTKA SOUND.] (Broughton, Wm. R.). Voyage of Discovery to the North Pacific Ocean in His Majesty's sloop Providence and her tender in 1795-1798; complete with all the folding maps and plates in fine condition. 412pp., 4to, half calf. London: Cadell and Davis, 1804. $150.00

An unusually clean copy of this rare work. One of the most important of the voyages made to the Northwest coast of America. The work was the chief authority put forward by Great Britain in 1846, when making her claims to the Oregon territory. Broughton had previously been on the coast in command of the Chatham under Vancouver, when he surveyed Columbia. In 1793 he returned home across the Isthmus from San Blas to Vera Cruz with Vancouver's dispatches. See item 394, Cat. 17.

410 [NOOTKA SOUND.] Bulletins of the Campaign, 1795. 12mo, calf. London, 1795. $27.50

Contains an extract of a letter from Lieut. Pearce to the Duke of Portland, April 25, 1795, giving an account of his journey to Nootka with Brig.-Gen. Alava to receive from him, on behalf of Spain, the restoration of the Port of Nootka to Great Britain. Refer to item 1230, Cat. 18.

411 [NOOTKA SOUND.] (Burgess, James B.). A Narrative of the Negotiations Occasioned by the Dispute between Great Britain and Spain, in the year 1790. Magnificent copy in original boards. 8vo. [London, 1791]. $250.00

From the Library of Sir James B. Burgess, Under-Secretary of State. Collected by him, printed at the Government Press and not published. This extremely rare book was printed in a small number for official use only. It relates entirely to the Nootka Sound troubles and the titles of England and Spain to the Northwest Coast of America. It contains all the instructions, statements, narratives, etc. relating to the voyages of Meares and Colnett and the seizure of the ships at Nootka; also all the official correspondence between the two countries relative to the troubles and the negotiations leading up to the Convention of Oct. 28, 1790. See iem 424, Cat. 17.

412 [NOOTKA SOUND.] (Burney, Capt. James, R.N.). A Chronological History of the Discoveries in the South Sea or Pacific Ocean. 5 vols., 4to, complete with all the charts and plates, original boards, uncut, complete with labels. London, 1803-1817. $160.00

"The Great Reputation of this work has been consistently sustained for a century. Many of the early voyages to California, and the adjacent coast, would be nearly inaccessible were they not herein collected. Among these are the narratives or reports of Alarcon, Cabrillo, Salvatierra, Vizcaino and numerous others. The author has also included the discussions as to whether California was insular or a part of the mainland; dissertations upon the name of California; and an account of the expedition of the Spaniards to conquer California; all of which have been taken from original sources."—Cowan, Bib. of California. See item 426, Cat. 17.

413 [NOOTKA SOUND.] Colnett, (Capt.) James. A Voyage to the South Atlantic and Round Cape Horn into the Pacific Ocean, for the purpose of extending the Spermaceti Whale Fisheries, and other objects of Commerce, by Ascertaining the Ports, Bays, Harbors and Anchoring Births in Certain Islands and Coasts in those Seas. 3 full-page plates, including one of the whale, and 6 large folding maps. 179pp., 4to, cloth. London, 1798. $75.00

For an extended account of this important work see Bancroft's "Northwest Coast," vol. 1, pp. 210-23. One of the chief results of the voyage was the Nootka Controversy. Colnett arrived at this place in 1789 and represented to the Spanish Commander, Martinez "that he had come under authority of the King of England with orders to take possession of Nootka, construct a fort, establish a factory and plant a colony." The Spaniards resisted, Martinez informing him that he had already taken formal possession of the country for Spain. There followed an interview which waxed so exceedingly hot that both commanders forgot the exigencies of the situation and permitted something of the truth to escape them. The English, being sadly outnumbered, Colnett was arrested, his ship and cargo seized, himself placed in the stocks, his officers imprisoned and his crew put in arms. They were then transported to San Blas, where they were plundered of all they had, several dying of fever and one committing suicide. Colnett alleges he was the victim of the most inhuman treatment—"was carried from ship to ship like a criminal, frequently threatened with death by hanging as a pirate on the yardarm," etc. As may be imagined, the affair developed into a most dangerous situation, and relations between England and Spain were seriously strained. Through the negotiations of powerful diplomats war was narrowly averted, which, had it occurred, would in all probability have involved the United States, since the Americans were suspected of having instigated the seizure: Kendrick and Gray (discoverer of the Columbia River) were known to be on terms of close intimacy with Martinez.

414 [NOOTKA SOUND.] Convention between His Britannick Majesty and the King of Spain, signed at the Escurial, the 29th of Oct., 1790. 4to, half morocco. London, 1790. $35.00

By this Convention it was agreed that all the lands and islands on the N. W. Coast of America should be restored to Great Britain, and a just reparation made to the subjects of both contracting parties for all acts of violence and hostility committed subsequent to the month of April, 1780.

415 [NOOTKA SOUND.] (Dalrymple, Alexander). Historical Collection of Several Voyages and Discoveries in the South Pacific Ocean. Vol. 1 being chiefly a Literal Translation from the Spanish Writers. Vol. 2, containing the Dutch Voyages. Maps and plates. 2 vols. in 1. 4to, half calf. London, 1770-1771. $60.00

This important work gives the literal translation of narratives of voyages, etc., made between South America and New Guinea.

416 [NOOTKA SOUND.] (Dalrymple, Alex.). Voyages dans la Mer du Sud par les Espagnols et les Hollandois. Trad. de l'Anglois par Freville. 3 maps. 502pp., 12mo, calf. Paris, 1774. $25.00

417 [NOOTKA SOUND.] (De Figueroa, Joseph Mariano Suarez). Noticias de Nutka. (Information re Nootka). 63 typescript pages translated into English. 8vo, bound in half leather. N.p., N.d. $25.00

De Figueroa was commissioned by his Excellency Count de Revilla Gigedo to make a geographical chart and report on conditions from the Strait of Juan de Fuca (Puget Sound) to the Port of San Francisco. Under the command of Capt. Bodega y Quadra, they arrived at Nootka, April 29, 1792, where De Figueroa remained four months. The above work consists of 12 reports of great interest, describing the country, natives, Meares, Vancouver, etc. The Spanish manuscript is dated 1793.

418 [NOOTKA SOUND.] (De Figueroa, Joseph Mariano Suarez). Noticias de Nutka. Diccionario de la Lengua de Los Nutkeses descripcion del Volcan de Tuxtla por . . . De Figueroa Precedidos de una Noticia Acerca y de la Expedicion Cientifica del siglo XVIII. Por Alberto M. Carrano. 8vo, original wrappers. One of 100 copies. Mexico City, 1913. $20.00

419 [NOOTKA SOUND.] (Dixon, Capt. George). Voyage round the World, but more Particularly to the Northwest Coast of America, performed in 1785-6, in the King George and Queen Charlotte, Captains Portlock and Dixon. Maps and plates. 4to, calf. London, 1789. $20.00

420 [NOOTKA SOUND.] The Errors of the British Minister in the Negotiation with the Court of Spain. 8vo, half calf. London, 1790. $55.00

Relates almost entirely to the dispute between England and Spain over the claim to the possession of Northwest America.

421 [NOOTKA SOUND.] (Espinosa y Tello, Jose). Account of the Voyage made by the Schooners Sutil and Mexicana in the year 1792 to survey the Strait of San Juan de Fuca; with an Introduction containing a Notice of the Expeditions previously carried out by the Spaniards in search of the North West Passage of America. By Order of the King. Madrid: Royal Printing Office, 1802. [This is a typewritten translation by G. F. Barwick, Oct., 1911]. Small 4to, 167, 185 and 20 pp. on sheets 8½x13½ in., bound in half calf. N.p., 1911. $50.00

This is a complete translation of both the "Account" and the "Memoir" and apparently the only complete translation in English. It is far more preferable than the translation by Cecil Jane of the "A Spanish Voyage to Vancouver, and the Northwest Coast of America, etc." London, 1930. This latter omitted much of the text of the "Voyage" and all of the "Memoir."

422 [NOOTKA SOUND.] (Espinosa y Tello, Jose). A Spanish Voyage to Vancouver and the North West Coast of America, Being the Narrative of the Voyage made in the year 1792 by the Schooners Sutil and Mexicana to explore the Strait of Fuca. Translated from the Spanish with an Introduction by Cecil Jane. Illustrated with a folding map and six illustrations. The Argonaut Press, London, 1930. $7.50

Refer to item 793, Cat. 17.

423 [NOOTKA SOUND.] (Etches, John). An Authentic Statement of all the Facts relative to Nootka Sound; its Discovery, History, Settlement, Trade and the Probable Advantages to be derived from it; in an Address to the King. 26pp., 12mo, 3/4 morocco. London: Printed for J. Debrett, 1790. $80.00

Excessively rare. Smith locates but three copies. Etches was the Supercargo with Meares. See item 794a, Cat. 17.

424 [NOOTKA SOUND.] Extracts from the Treaties between Great Britain and other Kingdoms and States of such Articles as Relate to the Duty and Conduct of the Commanders of His Majesty's Ships of War. 379pp., 4to, calf. London, 1792. $27.50

Smith 1186 locates one copy, that in the Provincial Library of British Columbia. Refer to item 1325, Cat. 17.

425 [NOOTKA SOUND.] Voyages dans le Mer du Sud, par les Espagnols and les Hollandois. Traduit de l'Anglois par Freville. XIV-502pp., 12mo, calf. London: A. Dalrymple. $22.50

426 [NOOTKA SOUND.] (Galiano, Dionisio Alcala). Relacion del Viage hecho por las Goletas Sutil y Mexicana en al ano de 1792 para reconocer el Estrecho de Fuca; con una Introduccion en que se da noticia de las Expediciones executadas anteriormente por los Espanoles en busca del Paso del Noroeste de la America. Folding chart. Atlas containing 4 large folding maps of San Diego, Monterey, Nutka, Mulgrave and Desengano; 2 large folding engravings of scenes in Nutka, and 5 full-page engravings. 2 vols., small 4to, calf, and folio Atlas, half roan. Madrid, 1802. $150.00

One of the most important Voyages to the Northwest Coast of America. The Commander of the expedition, Don. Dionysio Alcala-Galiano, was probably the author of the work. It contains several Indian vocabularies, notably those of the Eslen, Runsien and Nutka. The 9 maps (4 of which are folding ones) delineate the Western Coast of North America from Acapulco to Unalaska; and the Coast of California on a larger scale; with Plans of the harbours of S. Diego, Monte Rey, Cala de los Amigos (Nootka), Mulgrave, & Desengano. The plates include portraits of Macuina, chief of Nootka, Tetacus, chief of Juan de Fuca and his wife, a large folding aquatint view of the Cala de los Amigos (the Spanish Establishment on the Bay of Nootka), and a curious folding plate of the Feast celebrating the attainment of marriagable age of the Chief of Nootka's son.

Cowan says this work of great importance is rendered more valuable by the Introduction, which is a masterly resume of Spanish Voyages to the coast, written by Martin Fernandez de Navarette, whose name does not appear in the work. The work has been sometimes ascribed to Espinosa. See item 82, Cat. 17, and item 17b, Cat. 18.

427 [NOOTKA SOUND.] (Greenhow, Robert). History of Oregon and California and other Territories on the Northwestern Coast . . . Folding map. 8vo, cloth. Boston, 1845. $7.50

428 ——. The Same. 8vo, cloth. 1845. With an interesting A.L.s. from the Author. $12.50

429 [NOOTKA SOUND.] (Howay, F. W.). The Dixon-Mears Controversy. Containing remarks on the Voyage of John Meares by George Dixon, an Answer to Mr. George Dixon by John Meares, and further remarks on the Voyages of John Meares by George Dixon. Illus., maps. 156pp., 8vo, cloth. Toronto (c. 1929). $12.50

No. 76 of a limited edition of 250 copies.

430 [NOOTKA SOUND.] (Ingraham, Capt. Joseph). Journal of the Brigantine "Hope" from Boston to the North-West Coast of America, 1790-1792, by Joseph Ingraham, Captain of the "Hope" and formerly Mate of the "Columbia." 241pp. 11x14 inches in positive photostatic copy of the four original manuscript volumes forming this journal which appear to have been obtained during the discussion of the "Oregon Question." They were used by Mr. Greenhow in the preparation of his "The History of Oregon and California." See pp. 226-228. A valuable, interesting and human document. Ingraham was an officer in the American navy during the Revolutionary War. 241pp. Folio. N.p., N.d. $75.00

The original log books are in the Library of Congress. See item 1159, Cat. 17.

430a [NOOTKA SOUND.] Lansdown (Marquis of). The Substance of a Speech, in the House of Lords, 14 December, 1790, on the Convention with Spain, signed on the 28th of October, 1790. By One Present. 8vo, half mor. London: J. Debrett (1790). $45.00

On the question of the Sovereign Rights of Great Britain and Spain in the North Pacific, arising out of the affair of the Capture by the Spaniards of British Vessels at Nootka Sound, the above is a most important pamphlet and of very great rarity.

431 [NOOTKA SOUND.] Letters lately published in the Diary, on the subject of the present Dispute with Spain. Under the Signature of Verus. 8vo, half calf. London, 1790. $75.00

This extremely rare pamphlet relates almost entirely to the troubles between England and Spain over the claims to the possession of North West America. The letters, 18 in number, have been attributed to J. Bland Burgess, Under Secretary of State.

432 [NOOTKA SOUND.] The Nootka Sound Controversy. By William Ray Manning. (Annual Report American Historical Society, 1904, pp. 279-478). 8vo. Washington, 1904. $5.00

THE FOUNDATION OF THE BRITISH CLAIM TO OREGON

433 [NOOTKA SOUND.] (Meares, John). Voyages made in the Years 1788 and 1789, from China to the North West Coast of America. To which are prefixed an introductory Narrative of a Voyage performed in 1786, from Bengal in the ship "Nootka." Observations on the probable existence of a North West Passage, and some Account of the Trade between the North West Coast of America and China. Very fine copy, complete with 3 portraits and all the fine maps and views. 4to, original boards, paper label, uncut(as issued). London, 1790. $85.00

The voyages of Meares are an important link in the chain of American discovery of which he was one of the pioneers. The English claim to Oregon depended mainly on his discoveries.

"A thrilling narrative of this most important voyage. It gives a splendid account of the Indian nations met with on the North West coast of America, their situation, villages, population, manners, customs, languages, together with the intercourse and commerce had with them by members of the expedition. Included is a separate account of the voyage of the "Iphigenia," commanded by Captain Douglas, and the appendix contains Captain Meares' instructions to Douglas; a copy of Robert Duffin's journal kept while exploring the Straits of Juan de Fuca. Most of the plates depict the scenery of the inhabitants of the North West Coast of America."

434 ——. The Same. Portrait, maps and plates. Bound in with this copy is "Mr. Meares Memorial, dated 30th April (1790), with 4 inclosures. To the Right Hon. William Wyndeham Grenville . . . 4to, half morocco. London, 1790. $175.00

The "Memorial" bound in with the above is much rarer than the "Voyage."

435 [NOOTKA SOUND.] (Meares, John). Mr. Meares Memorial, dated 30th April, 1790, with fourteen enclosures, to the Rt. Hon. William W. Grenville, His Majesty's Secretary of State. 31 and 1 pp., folio, morocco. London [1790]. $100.00

436 [NOOTKA SOUND.] (Meares, John). The Memorial of John Meares, to the House of Commons respecting the Capture of Vessels in Nootka Sound. With an Introduction and Notes by Nellie B. Pipes. XIII, 92pp., 8vo, cloth. Portland, 1933. $3.75

437 [NOOTKA SOUND.] (Morris, Gouverneur). The Diary and Letter . . . Edited by Anne Cary Morris. Ports. 2 vols., 8vo, cloth. N. Y., 1888. $6.00

Sparks says: "The editing in these volumes is most judicious." Relates to the Nootka Controversy.

438 [NOOTKA SOUND.] Official Papers relative to the Dispute between the Courts of Great Britain and Spain on the subject of the Ships captured in Nootka Sound, and the Negotiations that followed thereon; together with the Proceedings in both Houses of Parliament on the King's Message, etc. 8vo, half calf. London: Printed for J. Debrett (1790). $100.00

One of the rarest pieces relating to the dispute between Great Britain and Spain relative to the right of possession to the North West Coast of America. The contention was settled at a convention signed Oct. 28, 1790, whereby it was agreed that all lands and islands should be restored to Great Britain, and a just reparation made by Spain for all acts of violence and hostility made in that part of America.

439 [NOOTKA SOUND.] (Portlock, Capt. Nathaniel). Voyage Round the World, more particularly to the Northwest Coast of America, 1785-1788. Folding maps, ports., plates. 4to, half mor. London: Stockdale, 1789. $35.00

Nice clean complete copy. Portlock visited the various tribes along the N. W. Coast, especially those round Nootka Sound.

440 [NOOTKA SOUND.] A Sketch of the Reign of George the Third, from 1780 to the Close of the Year 1790. Fifth Edition. 8vo, half calf. London, 1791. $25.00

441 [NOOTKA SOUND.] (Vancouver, Capt. George). A Voyage of Discovery to the North Pacific Ocean, and Round the World; in which the Coast of North-West America has been carefully examined and accurately surveyed. Undertaken by his Majesty's command, principally with a view to ascertain the existence of any navigable communication between the North Pacific and North Atlantic Oceans; and performed in the years 1790-1795, in the Discovery Sloop of War, and armed Tender Chatham. 3 vols., 4to, and folio Atlas. Complete with all the maps, charts and views, original boards, uncut. Very fine copy. Partially unopened. London, 1798. $175.00

Vancouver visited the Sandwich Islands, Nootka Sound, San Francisco, Montreey, and completed the survey of Vancouver Island and the North-West Coast. This is one of the most important works for the history of geographical discovery in that part of North America. Complete sets with the folio atlas are rare . See item 1471, Cat. 17.

441a ——. The same. 3 vols., 4to, calf. All the maps bound in. $125.00

442 [NOOTKA SOUND.] (George Vancouver). Reisen nach dem Nordl Theile der Sudsee, 1790-95. A. D. Engl von J. F. Herbst. 2 Bands mit 1 Karte und 2 Kupfern. 8vo, half calf. Berlin, 1799-80. $27.50

443 [NOOTKA SOUND.] (Vancouver, Capt. George). A Voyage of Discovery to the North Pacific Ocean, and Round the World, in which the coast of North West America has been carefully examined and accurately surveyed. Maps and plates. 6 vols., 8vo, calf. London, 1801. $60.00

444 [NOOTKA SOUND.] (Vancouver, Capt. George). Voyage de decouvertes, a l'Ocean Pacifique du nord, et autour du monde; dans lequel la cote Nord-Ouest de l'Amerique a ete soigneusement reconnue et exactement releve . . . execute n 1790, 1791, 1792, 1793, 1794, 1795; tr. from the English. 3 vols. and folio of plates and maps. Par. l'Imprimerie de la Republique. An VII. $100.00

Rare French Edition. The maps and plates in this edition are as fine as those in the original English Edition. However, it is rarely found with the Atlas.

444a ——. The Same. Half calf. With all plates, but lacks Atlas. 3 vols., 4to. Orig. boards, paper labels. Paris, An VII. $47.50

445 [NOOTKA SOUND.] (Vancouver, George). Puteshestive v Sievernuiu chastj Tikhago Okeana i vokrug svieta, sovershennoe v 1791-5 godakh. Kap. G. Vankuverom, S. Angl. 6 vols., 8vo, calf. St. Petersburg, 1827-28. $40.00

Fine set. Wickersham 6288. Refer to item 1473, Cat. 17.

446 [NOOTKA SOUND.] (Zetes. Pseudonym). An Address to the Parliament and People of Great Britain, on the past and present state of Affairs, between Spain and Great Britain, respecting their American Possessions. 49pp., 8vo, cloth. London: Printed for J. Debrett, 1790. $120.00

Extremely rare. All the Nootka Sound pamphlets printed in 1790 are excessively rare. Smith locates a copy of the above in the Provincial Library of British Columbia.

447 NORDHOFF, CHAS. Northern California, Oregon, and the Sandwich Islands. Port., 2 maps. 8vo, cloth. N. Y., 1872. $2.00

448 [NORTH DAKOTA.] Bishop of Niabara. Second Annual Report. 20 and 16 pp., 8vo, original wrappers. N.p., 1874. $7.50

A fine relation of the status of the Indians in the Northwest. There are really two reports in one in this work.

449 [NORTH DAKOTA.] Collections of North Dakota Historical Society. Vol. 1, 1906 to Vol. 7, 1924. 8 vols., 8vo, cloth. Fargo, 1906-1924. $28.00

450 [NORTHEASTERN BOUNDARY.] Statement on the Part of the U. S., of the Case referred, in Pursuance of the Convention of 29th Sept., 1827, between the U. S. and Great Britain, to his Majesty, King of the Netherlands . . . With appendices and First and Second Statements on the Part of Great Britain . . . [With the two Maps.] Folio, half calf. Printed but not published. Washington, 1829. [Sold]

450a [NORTHERN PACIFIC RAILROAD.] Charter of the Organization Proceedings, By-laws and Appendix. 64pp., Maps. 8vo, original wrappers. Boston, 1865. $7.50

451 [NORTHERN PACIFIC RAILROAD.] History of the Pacific Northwest: Oregon and Washington . . . also Biographies of the Earliest Settlers . . . of the Pacific Northwest . . . 2 vols., illus., port. Sq. folio. Portland, 1889. $12.50

Smith 2684.

452 [NORTHERN PACIFIC RAILROAD.] Memorial of the Board of Directors of the Company, with Communications from Lt. Gen. Grant, Brevet Major General Meigs, and Brevet Major General Ingalls, and the Report of the Engineer-in-Chief. 39pp., large folding map. 8vo. Washington, 1868. $12.50

Very fine map.

453 [NORTHERN PACIFIC RAILROAD.] Official Directory and Atlas for use of Shippers and Buyers. 184pp., 18 maps. 4to, original wrappers. St. Paul, 1888-9. $5.00

454 [NORTHERN PACIFIC RAILROAD.] Portland and the Columbia River. 24pp., map. 8vo, original wrappers. N.p., N.d. $4.50

Smith 2701.

455 [NORTHERN PACIFIC RAILROAD.] North Pacific Coast Resorts. 79pp., illus., folding map. 8vo, original wrappers. 1909. $2.75

456 [NORTHERN PACIFIC RAILROAD.] The Wonderland Route to the Pacific Coast. 8vo, original wrappers. St. Paul, 1885. $7.50

Smith 2709. The best edition and a fine copy.

457 [NORTHERN PACIFIC RAILROAD.] (1) Wilkinson's Notes on Puget Sound, 32pp., map (1869); (2) The Charter and Amendments, the General Mortgage on the Railroad, Land Grant, etc., 33pp. (1870); (3) Northern Pacific Railroad Land Grant, 32pp. (1870); (4) Land Grant of the Northern Pacific Railroad, 32 pp. (1870). 4 items. 8vo. V.p. (1869-1870). $20.00

458 [NORTHWEST PLAINS.] Father Lacombe, the Black-Robe Voyageur. By Katherine Hughes. Illus. 8vo, cloth. N. Y., 1911. $6.00

459 [NORTHWEST.] The Winnipeg Country; or Roughing it with an Eclipse Party. By A. Rochester Fellow. 32 illus. and map. 12mo, cloth. Boston, 1886. $5.00

Whereas they went to see a total eclipse, Mr. Fellow, an observing fellow, too, has made a very fine little book. The drawings and photographs of the Canoe-men (Indians and half-breeds) are excellent. The work is both a factual scientific and sporting book.

460 [NORTHWEST.] (Pike, Warburton). Through the Subarctic Forest; a Record of a Canoe Journey from Fort Wrangel to the Pelly Lakes and down the Yukon River to the Behring Sea. [Map and plates.] 8vo, cloth. London, 1896. $22.50

Very scarce. To the sportsman and man of the woods, this book offers the events that happened on a long journey through a good game country, without any attempt to make a big bag or of killing game unwanted. The appendix contain a list of geological specimens collected by Mr. Pike near the head waters of the Pelly River, and on Alaska and the Northwest Territory.

460a [NORTH WEST COAST.] Middleton (Christopher. A Vindication of the Conduct of Christopher Middleton in a late Voyage on H. M.'S Ship "The Furnance," for Discovering a North West Passage to the Western American Ocean. In answer to certain objections and aspersions of Arthur Dobbs, Esq. Wtih an Appendix containing the Captain's Instructions, Reports of the Inferior Officers, Letters between Mr. Dobbs, Capt. Middleton, &c. The whole as lately delivered to the Admiralty. 8vo, calf. London: For the Author, 1743. $37.50

This work is the author's reply to Dobb's accusation of his being in collusion with the Hudson's Bay Co. to prevent the discovery of a Passage to the South Seas during his voyage in the "Furnace." Dobbs' accusations practically amounted to a charge of forgery, and Middleton replies to Dobbs and accuses him of endeavoring to seduce him away from the Company by the promise of a man-of-war and the Royal Grant of any lands he might discover.

RARE VANCOUVER ISLAND FIRST PUBLIC LAWS, 1859-1864

461 NORTHWEST COAST. Vancouver Island Public Laws. 102 printed broadsides of the first laws of Vancouver Island, from the first laws of 1859 through the year 1865. Two volumes, 4to, calf. Victoria, 1859-1865. $125.00

A superb collection of all the early printed proclamations for the years mentioned, save ten minor laws. The whole foundation history of the Island is contained herein, laws regulating all the social, economic, political, juridical and strategical phases of Vancouver Island. Such a complete collection is rarely offered.

462 [NORTHWEST COAST.] Northwest Coast of America, being results of recent Ethnological Researches from the Collections of the Royal Museums at Berlin; published by the Directors of the Ethnological Department; trans. from the German. 12pp., 13 finely colored plates. Folio. N. Y.: Dodd, N.d. $22.50

Smith 2719. Locates but one copy.

463 [NORTHWEST FLORA.] Flora of Southeastern Washington. By Charles Vancouver Piper, and R. Kent Beattie. 296pp. Lancaster, Pa., 1914. $10.00

464 [NORTHWEST FLORA.] Flora of the Northwest Coast. By Charles Vancouver Piper, and R. Kent Beattie. 418pp. 8vo, cloth. Lancaster, Pa., 1915. $5.00

465 [NORTHWEST FLORA.] Flora of the State of Washington. By Chas. Vancouver Piper. 637pp., 19 plate, 3 maps (one folding in pocket). 8vo, cloth. Washington, 1906. $12.50

Smith 3085.

466]NORTHWEST BOUNDARY.] Discussion of the Water Boundary Question; Geographical Memoir of the Islands in Dispute; and History of the Military Occupation of San Juan Island. 2 folding maps., 270pp. 8vo. Washington, 1868. $17.50

Smith 2718.

467 [NORTHWEST FUR CO.] On the Origin and Progress of the North-west Company. 32pp., 12mo. London, 1811. (In photostat). $17.50

468 [NORTHWEST (OLD).] Early Northwest. By Wm. F. Poole. Frontis. 26pp., 8vo, original wrappers. N. Y., 1889. $4.50

An address delivered before the American Historical Society of which only a few copies were printed.

469 [NORTHWEST, OLD.] (St. Clair, Major Gen. Arthur). Narrative of Manner in which the Campaign Against the Indians in 1791 was conducted; Observations on Statements of Secretary of War and Quartermaster General; Report of the Committee appointed to Inquire into the Causes of Failure Thereof. 292pp. 8vo, calf. Phila., 1812. $30.00

470 [NORTHWEST MINING.] Northwest Mines Handbook. A reference work on the Mining Industry of Idaho, Washington, British Columbia, Western Montana and Oregon. By Sidney Norman. 366pp., illus. 4to, cloth. Spokane, 1918. $10.00

Not in Smith.

471 NORTON, HARRY J. Wonder-land Illustrated; or Horseback Rides through the Yellowstone National Park. Folding and numerous plates. 132pp., 12mo, cloth. Virginia, Montana (Printed for the Author, 1873). $27.50

Western Americana 578. A general description of Montana Territory, its valleys, cities and towns; and a brief business directory of the towns of Helena, Virginia, Deer Lodge, and Bozeman, etc.

472 NORTON, COL. L. Life and Adventures of. Written by Himself. Port. 492pp. 8vo, cloth. Oakland, 1887. $12.50

A pioneer narrative of very considerable interest.

473 NOVO Y COLSON, PEDRO DE. Historia de las Exploraciones Articas hechas in busca del Paso del Nordeste. 260pp., illus., map. Folio, original wrappers. Madrid, 1880. $12.50

Smith 2729. Locates one copy.

474 NOVO Y COLSON, PEDRO DE. Sobre los Viajes Apocrifos de Juan de Fuca y de Lorenzo Ferrer Maldonado. Recopilacon y Estudio. Contiene tambien este liho la Disertacion del mismo autor titulada Ultima teoria sobre la Atantide. 223pp., 4to, original wrappers. Madrid, 1881. $12.50

Smith 2730. Locates one copy.

475 NUTTALL, THOMAS. A Popular Handbook of the Birds of the United States and Canada. 431pp., 8vo, cloth. Boston, 1908. $3.75

476 OBERHOLTZ, ELLIS PAXON. Jay Cooke, Financier of the Civil War. 2 vols., 8vo, cloth. Phila.: Jacobs, 1907. $7.50

477 OGDEN, PETER SKENE. Traits of American Indian Life and Character. By a Fur Trader. 218pp., 8vo, cloth (worn at backstrip). London, 1853. $30.00

Original Edition. Wagner-Camp 232. The author was Chief Factor of the HBC, and the narrative relates entirely to Oregon and the Northwest, where he trapped and traded from 1820 onward. The work also recounts Jedediah Smith's travels in Oregon in 1828.

478 OGG, F. A. The Opening of the Mississippi: a Struggle for Supremacy in the American Interior. 8vo, cloth. N. Y., 1904. $7.50

From the time of Monette many worthy attempts have been made to write the complete story of the early Mississippi Valley but none have achieved the scholarly perfection of this outstanding work.

479 O'HANLON, REV. J. Life and Scenery in Missouri (and the west);: Reminiscences of a Missionary Priest Among the Pioneers and Indians, 1843-53. 292pp., 12mo, cloth. Dublin, 1890. $7.50

Besides the author's own memoirs, he includes a fine study of early affairs in Louisiana. Chapters include sketches of Hunters and Trappers; Missouri Fur Co.; Frontier Life and Society of St. Joe; Mormons in Missouri; Col. Hull's Expedition; adventures on the prairie; steam boating on the Upper Missouri; the California Migration, etc.

480 [OHIO.] (Burnet, Jacob). Notes on the Early Settlement of the North-western Territory. 501pp., eng. port. 8vo, cloth. Cincinnati, 1847. $7.50

Signed by the author.

481 ——. The Same. Unsigned. Cincinnati, 1847. $6.00

482 [OHIO.] Life of Rufus Putnam, with Extracts from his Journal and an Account of the First Settlement of Ohio. By Mary Bone. 142pp., sm. 4to, cloth. Cleveland, 1886. $5.00

483 [OHIO.] (Cutler, Ephraim). Life and Times, prepared from his Journals and Correspondence by Julia P. Cutler, with Sketches of Jervis and Wm. P. Cutler. Ports. 360pp., 8vo, cloth. Cincinnati, 1890. $12.50

An important work on the early history of Ohio.

484 [OHIO.] (Dwight, Margaret Van Horn). A Journey to Ohio in 1816, as recorded in the Journal of Margaret Van Horn Dwight. Edited with an introduction by Max Farrand. VI, 64pp., 8vo, boards. New Haven, 1913. $4.50

485 [OHIO.] The Ohio Valley in Colonial Days. By Berthold Fernow. 4to, original boards. 299pp. Albany, 1890. $5.00

486 [OHIO.] Memoir of Rev. William Gurley, late of Milan, Ohio. A local Minister of the Methodist Episcopal Church. Including a Sketch of the Irish Insurrection and Martyrs of 1798. By L. B. Gurley. Port. 12mo, cloth. Cincinnati, 1854. $4.00

Gurley migrated from Ireland to Ohio, purchasing and settling on a farm in the "Fire Lands".

487 [OHIO.] (Henry, Charles). History of Transportation in the Ohio Valley, with special reference to its Waterways, Trade and Commerce from the earliest Period to the Present Time. With Index, colored maps, plates. 465pp., 8vo, cloth. Glendale, Cal., 1932. $6.00

488 [OHIO.] (Hildreth, S. P.). Pioneer History; and Account of the first examinations of the Ohio Valley, and the Early Settlement of the N. W. Territory. 525pp., 3 maps (one folding), 6 eng. plates, including views of four western forts. 8vo, cloth. Cnicinnati, 1848. $15.00

489 ——. The Same. 8vo, cloth. This copy has 7 plates and about half of the large folding map lacking. Cincinnati, 1848. $7.50

490 [OHIO.] (Hildreth, S. P.). Contributions to the early history of the Northwest, including Moravian Missions in Ohio. 240pp., 12mo, cloth. Cincinnati, 1864. $22.50

Deals principally with pioneer life and border warfare.

491 [OHIO.] (Howe, Henry). Historical Collections of Ohio; and Encyclopaedia of the State. Profusely illustrated with about 500 ports., views maps. 3 vols. in 2, 8vo, half sheep. Columbus, 1889. $7.50

492 [OHIO VALLEY.] (Hulbert, Archer B.). Washington and the West, being George Washington's Diary, Sept., 1784, during his journey into the Ohio Basin. 217pp., 8vo, cloth. N. Y., 1905. $3.75

493 [OHIO.] (Dr. N. E. Jones). Squirrel Hunters of Ohio; or Glimpses of Pioneer Life. Illus. 8vo, cloth. Cincinnati, 1898. $2.50

494 [OHIO.] Life of the Right Reverend John Barrett Kerfoot, First Bishop of Pittsburgh. With Selections from his Diaries and Correspondence. 2 vols., 8vo, cloth. N. Y., 1886. $5.00

495 [OHIO.] (MacLean, J. P.). The Mound Builders, being an Account of a Remarkable People that once inhabited the Valley of the Ohio, and the Mississippi, with an Investigation into the Archaelogy of Butler County. Maps and illus. 233pp., 12mo, cloth. Cincinnati, 1904. $4.00

496 [OHIO.] (Marsh, O. C.). Description of an Ancient Sepulchral Mound near Newark, Ohio. 10pp., 8vo, original wrappers. (New Haven), 1866. $4.00

This is a seperate publication from the American Journal of Science and Arts, July, 1866.

497 [OHIO.] (May, Col. John). Journal and Letters relative to the Ohio Country, 1788-1789; with a biographical Sketch of Rev. Richard S. Edes, and Notes by Wm. M. Darlington. 160pp., large 8vo, cloth. Cincinnati, 1873. $25.00

The author, soldier of the Revolution, left Boston, April, 1783, proceeding overland on horseback via Phila., Baltimore, Laurel Hills to Pittsburgh, there taking a flatboat for Marietta, where he held some land. A year later he made a second trip to the Ohio country, this time on a trading venture, going as far as Mayville, Ky. The volume furnishes an interesting picture of frontier conditions.

498 [OHIO.] (Pratt, J. J.). Hesperian Tree, Souvenir of Ohio Valley, 1900. Illus. 8vo, 436pp., original boards. Cincinnati, 1900. $6.50

Contains many valuable historical articles relating to Ohio, Ky. and the old Northwest. There is contained in this work an important article on Lincoln by Murat Halsted; etc.

499 [OHIO.] Brief Recollections of the late Rev. George W. Walker . . . By Maxwell Pierson Gaddis. Frontis., 538pp., 8vo, cloth. Cincinnati, 1857. $7.50

500 [OHIO.] The Ancient Earthworks of Ohio. Delivered by Prof. F. W. Putnam, of Harvard University, before the Western Reserve Historical Society of Cleveland, Ohio, Oct. 25th, 1887. Tract No. 76. 8vo, original wrappers. Cleveland, 1887. $3.50

501 [OHIO.] Memoirs on the Military Resources of the Ohio . . . By John Sanders, 19pp., sewn. Pittsburgh, 1845. $10.00

A later edition was published the same year at Washington, D. C. with additions by James L. Mason. The title of the above continues: "As applicable to Operations on the Common Defense of the United States". This copy has some water stains.

502 (OHIO.] The Autobiography of Elder Mathew Gardner . . . By N. Summerbell. Frontis., 286pp., 8vo, cloth. Dayton, 1875. $10.00

An interesting account of pioneer life. Born in New York in 1790, Gardner, at the age of 10, moved overland with his parents to Pittsburgh, thence by flat-boat to Mayville, Ky., near where the Gardner's located.

503 [OHIO.] (Taylor, James W.). History of the State of Ohio, 1650-1787. 558pp., 8vo, calf (broken hinge). Cincinnati, 1854. $10.00

First and best history of pre-territorial Ohio, its aboriginal history, border wars, treaties, etc. Includes portions of Gist's diary, expedition of Rogers, Bradstreet, Bouquet, etc.

504 [OHIO.] (Thomas, Cyrus). The Problem of the Ohio Mounds. 54pp., illus. 8vo, original wrappers. Washington, 1889. $4.00

This is a separate publication.

505 [OHIO.] The Circular, Square and Octagonal Earthworks of Ohio. By Cyrus Thomas. 33pp., 16 illus., many folding. 8vo, original wrappers. Washington, 1889. $5.00

506 [OHIO.] Ohio Valley Historical Series. Miscellanies. (Comprising): (1) A Tour in Ohio, Kentucky and Indian Territory, in 1805 by Josiah Espy; (2) Two Western Campaigns in the War of 1812 by Sam'l Williams; (3) The Leatherwood God by R. H. Tanneyhill. Sm. 4to, cloth. Cincinnati, 1871. $7.50

507 [OHIO.] (Whittlesey, Charles). A Discourse relating to the Expedition of Lord Dunmore, of Virginia, against the Indian Towns upon the Scioto in 1774, delivered before the Historical and Philosophical Society of Ohio, in the Hall of Representatives, Columbus, January, 1840. 33pp., 8vo, unbound. Cleveland, 1842. $7.50

508 [OHIO.] (Whittlesey, Col. Chas.). Abstract of a Verbal Discourse upon the Mounds and Mound Builders of Ohio. Delivered before the Fire Lands Historical Society, at Monroeville, Huron County, Ohio, March 15th, 1865. 5pp., 8vo, wrappers. Cleveland, 1865. $3.50

509 [OHIO.] (Whittlesey, Col. Chas.). Fugitive Essays upon Interesting and Useful Subjects relating to the Early History of Ohio, its Geology and Agriculture; with a Biography of the first successful constructor of Steamboats. 12mo, original cloth (worn at spine). 397pp. Hudson, Ohio, 1852. $5.00

510 [OHIO.] (Whittlesey, Col. Chas.). Ancient Earth Forts of the Cuyahoga Valley, Ohio. 40-9pp., full-page plates. 8vo, original wrappers. Cleveland, 1871. $7.50

511 [OHIO.] (Whittlesey, Col. Chas.). Ancient Rock Inscriptions in Ohio; an Ancient Burial Ground, Hardin County, Ohio, and a Notice of some Rare Polished Stone Ornaments. 16pp., two large folding plates. 8vo, original wrappers. Cleveland, 1872. $5.00

The above is No. 11 of Tracts of the Western Reserve and Northern Ohio Historical Society.

512 [OHIO.] (Whittlesey, Col. Chas.). Archaeological Frauds. Inscriptions attributed to the Mound Builders. Three Remarkable Forgeries. 4pp., Tract 9, Western Reserve Historical Society. 8vo. Cleveland, 1872. $3.50

513 [OHIO.] (Whittlesey, Col. Chas.). Ancient Earthworks—Northern Ohio. 33-39pp., illus., Tract 41, Western Reserve and Northern Ohio Historical Society. 8vo, unbound. Cleveland, (1877?). $3.00

514 [OHIO.] (Whittlesey, Col. Chas.). Relics of Aboriginal Art and their Ethnological Value. 125-128pp., illus. (From No. 52, May, 1880 Western Reserve and Northern Ohio Historical Society). 125-128pp., 8vo, original wrappers. Cleveland, 1880. $3.00

515 [OHIO ARCHAELOGICAL AND HISTORICAL PUBLICATIONS.] Vols. 1 to 27, Part 3. 13 vols., half mor. cloth. 8vo. Columbus, 1888-1918. $20.00

Contains much valuable material on the early history of the Northwest Territory, early explorations, pioneer days, sketches of early travelers, etc.

516 [OKLAHOMA.] (J. H. DeWolff). Pawnee Bill (Major Gordon Lillie). His Experiences and Adventures on the Western Plains, &c. Ports. and illus. 8vo, original pictorial cloth-covered boards. N.p., 1902. (With a letter-cover showing Pawnee Bill's Ranch at Pawnee, Okla., and a clipping of his obituary). $12.50

517 [OKLAHOMA.] A Guide to the Sooner State. Map, illus. By Grant Foreman. 8vo, cloth. Norman, 1941. $2.50

518 [OKLAHOMA.] A History of Oklahoma. By Grant Foreman. Portrait of Sequoyah, folding mapp. 38pp., 8vo, cloth. Norman, 1942. $3.50

519 [OKLAHOMA.] Illustrated History of. By Marion Tuttle Rock. 278pp., illus. 8vo, cloth. Topeka, 1890. $7.50

520 OLMSTED, FRED'K LAW. Journey Through Texas; or a Saddle Trip on the Southwestern Frontier. Frontis., map. 12mo, cloth. N. Y., 1857. $4.50

RARE NORTHWEST YAKIMA INDIAN PRIMER

521 ONGE, L. N. ST. Alphabet Yakima; Contenant les Prieres les Cantiques et le Catechisme dans le meme langue a l'usage de tribu des Yakimas sous le patronage des R.R.P.P. Jesuites. Par L. N. St. Onge, Pretre Ex-Missionaire des Yakimas. 12mo, 104pp., original glazed wrappers, with photograph of author. Imprime a la Providence, 1872. $25.00

Can locate no other copy.

522 [OREGON.] Affairs in Oregon. Letter from the Secretary of War. House of Representatives, 36th Cong., Ex. Doc. 65, 1st Sess. Serial No. 1051. 269pp., 8vo, sewn. [Washington, 1848.] $9.50

523 [OREGON.] Oregon Board of Agriculture. Resources of the State of Oregon. 203pp., 8vo, original wrappers. Salem, 1899. $3.00

Smith 2779.

524 [OREGON.] Oregon Agricultural College. Dignifying the Industries. 64pp., ill. 8vo, original wrappers. Corvallis, Ore., 1912. $2.50

525 [OREGON.] The Oregon Agricultural College. The Enchantment of Rural Life. 80pp., 8vo, original wrappers. Corvallis, Ore., 1913. $2.50

Smith 2777.

526 [OREGON.] Oregon Agricultural College. The Life Career. 96pp., 8vo, original wrappers. Corvallis, Ore., 1914. $2.50

527 [OREGON.] Astoria. Astoria and Columbia River Railroad. Numerous illus. 30pp., long 12mo, original printed wrappers. N.d. $3.00

528 [OREGON.] Pacific Coast Banker and Investor. Midsummer Number, Aug., 1894. 104pp., 8vo, original wrappers. Portland, 1894. $2.50

History of banking in Portland, together with other important articles on San Francisco, Tacoma, Seattle, and Spokane.

529 [OREGON.] Francis Norbet Blanchet, the Apostle of Oregon. By Edwin V. O'Hara. Catholic Sentinel, 40th Anniversary Number, July, 1910. 8vo. Washington, 1910. $3.00

530 [OREGON.] (Brownson, T. G.). Trials and Triumphs of Fifty Years of Baptist Work in Oregon. 18pp., 8vo, original wrappers. Portland, Ore., Chronicle Pub. Co., 1894. $7.50

Smith 513. Locates 2 copies.

531 [OREGON.] (Butterworth, Hezikiah). The Log School House on the Columbia. A Tale of the Pioneers of the Great Northwest. 250pp., 8vo, cloth. Illus. N. Y., 1890. $7.50

This is really a narrative of the "Boston Tilicum" as the Siwashes called the New England Missionaries. It is the story of the Protestant winning of the Northwest; and one of the best narratives relating thereto.

532 [OREGON.] Pioneer History of Camas Valley. By the Student Body. 20pp., 8vo, original printed wrappers. (Roseburg, Ore, N.d.). $7.50

Contains the local history of the Valley gathered from local sources. The Valley was first settled in 1851.

COLLECTION OF PAMPHLETS RELATING TO THE LOCAL HISTORY OF OREGON

533 [OREGON.] Collection of 60 pamphlets, mostly all in original wrappers, dealing with the local history of all sections of Oregon, all briefly described and uniformly priced at $2.00 each.

1. Baker County, Oregon. The Land of Plenty. 24pp., colored map, illus., 4to, original wrappers. (1905).
2. Baker County. 15pp., map. 12mo, original wrappers. Baker City, Ore. N.d.
3. The Lewis and Clark Centennial. By Henry E. Reed. 96pp., illus. Portland, 1904.
4. Pacific City in Tillamook County Oregon, nearest coast Resort to Portland, the Atlantic City of the West. Fine illus., map. 4to, original wrappers. Portland (1910).
5. Medford—Rogue River Valley—Southern Oregon. Map, fine illus., some in color. 48pp. Large 8vo, Portland, (1911).
6. Grant's Pass and Josephine County. Rogue River Valley, Oregon. 47pp., fine illus., some in color. Large 8vo, original wrappers. Portland, (1911).
7. Oregon, the Land of Opportunity. Finely colored map, many colored illus. Large 8vo, original wrappers. Portland, 1911.
8. Stanfield—The Stirring—Umatilla County, Oregon. 48pp., map, illus. 8vo, original wrappers. (Portland, 1911).
9. Gearhart-by-the-Sea. 15pp., illus. Long 16mo, original wrappers. (Portland, 1890).
10. Toledo, Oregon. 31pp., map, illus. 12mo, original wrappers. (Portland, 1911).
11. Hood River, Oregon, 14pp., illus. 8vo, original wrappers. (Portland, 1909).
12. Medford Bulletin. 34pp., map, illus. 4to, colored wrappers. (Portland, 1911).
13. Oregon—Hood River. 32pp., illus. Sm. 4to, colored wrappers. Hood River, 1910.
14. John Day Valley, Oregon. 32pp., map, ill. 8vo, colored wrappers. (Portland, 1911).
15. Neah-kah-nie Mountain and the Nehalem County. 32pp., maps, illus. 12mo, original colored wrappers. (Portland, 1910).
16. Washington County, Oregon. 63 pp., map, illus. 8vo, original wrappers. Forest Grove, (1911).
17. Umatilla County, Oregon. 64pp., illus., maps. 8vo. Pendleton, (1910).
18. Water is King in the Orchard Kingdom. 48pp., illus. 8vo, colored wrappers. Roseburg, 1909.
19. Washington County, Oregon. 32pp., map, illus. 8vo, colored wrappers. Forest Grove, (1909).
20. Gilliam County, Oregon. 32pp., map, illus. 8vo, colored wrappers. Condon, (1911).
21. Tillamock County, Oregon. 32pp., map, illus. Sm. 4to, N.p.N.d.
22. Medford, Oregon. Rogue River Valley. 64pp., maps, illus. Large 8vo, original colored wrappers. Medford, 1910.
23. Morrow County, Oregon. 32pp., map, illus. 8vo, colored wrappers. (Slight damp stain). Hopper, Ore., (1911).
24. Hood River, Oregon. 64 pp., illus. 8vo, colored wrappers. Portland, N.d.
25. The Timberman. Pacific Logging Congress Edition. 144pp., folio. Portland, 1893.
26. Kane's Illustrated West. Vol. 1, No. 2; Vol. 1, No. 3; Vol. 2, No. 1. Three numbers bound together with the original wrappers. Portland, 1886-87.
27. Roseburg, the Umpqua Valley. Douglas County, Oregon. 64pp., illus. 12mo, original wrappers. Roseburg, 1911.
28. Coos County, Oergon. Its Resources, Industries and Opportunities. 48pp., map, illus. 8vo, original wrappers. North Bend, 1909.
29. Scenic Central, Oregon. 48pp., maps, illus. 12mo, original wrappers. Bend, Ore., 1925.
30. Central Oregon. 48pp., illus. 4to, original wrappers, N.p.n.d.
31. Picturesque and Scenic Beauties of the Columbia River and the Metropolis of the Pacific Northwest. 32pp., illus. 12mo, original wrappers. Grand Rapids, Mich., N.d.

32. Oregon Scenery. 24pp., illus. 8vo, original wrappers. Portland, 1904.
33. Oregon Almanac. Official Pamphlet published by the State of Oregon for Home-seekers, Settlers and Investors. 144pp., maps and charts. 8vo, original wrappers. Salem, Ore., 1912.
34. Third and Fourth Annual Report of the State Fish and Game Protection of the State of Oregon, 1885-1896. 115-14pp., plates of game and fish. 8vo. Salem, 1896.
35. A Paper on Forestry Interests. By Hon. John Minto. 24pp., 8vo, original wrappers. Salem, Ore., 1898.
36. Success in Oregon and Washington. Map, 15pp., colored illus. 8vo, N.p., Nd.
37. The Mining Laws of Oregon. 56pp., 8vo, original wrappers. Grant's Press, 1892.
38. Preliminary Report on Artesian Basins in Southwestern Idaho and Southeastern Oregon. 51pp., plates and maps. 8vo, original wrappers. Washington, 1903. By Israel G. Russell.
39. Oregon Blue Book and Official Directory, 1915-16. 192pp., illus. 8vo, original wrappers. Salem, Ore., 1915.
40. The Minutes of the Synod of Oregon, 21st Session, held in the Mt. Tabor Church, Portland, Oct. 12-16, 1911. 64pp., 8vo, original wrappers. N.p.N.d.
41. Biennial Message to the Legislature, 1885. Gov. Z. F. Moody. 28pp., 8vo, original wrappers. Salem, Ore., 1885.
42. Inaugural Address to the Legislative Assembly by Gov. Sylvester Pennoyer, 1887. 40pp., 8vo, original wrappers. Salem, Ore., 1887.
43. Biennial Message to the Legislative Assembly, 1899. By Gov. Wm. P. Lord. 42pp., 8vo, original wrappers. Salem, Ore., 1899.
44. Biennial Message to the Legislative Assembly, 1901. By Gov. T. T. Greer. 64pp., 8vo, original wrappers. Salem, Ore.. 1901.
45. Biennial Message to the Legislative Assembly, 1902. By Gov. T. T. Greer. 37pp., 8vo, original wrappers. Salem, Ore., 1902.
46. Biennial Message to the Legislative Assembly, 1893. By Governor Sylvester Pennoyer. 22pp., 8 vo, original wrappers. Salem, Ore., 1893.
47. Inaugural Address to the Legislative Assembly, 1895. By Gov. Wm. P. Lord, 1895. 20pp., 8vo, original wrappers. Salem, Ore., 1895.
48. Message to the Legislative Assembly, 1911. By Jay Bowerman, Acting Gov. 22pp., 8vo, original wrappers. Salem, Ore., 1911.
49. Message to the Legislative Assembly of Oregon. By Gov. James Whitcombe. 23pp., 8vo, original wrappers. Salem, Ore., 1919.
50. Oregon Primer. 92 plates and maps. 8vo, original wrappers. Portland, (1911).
51. Salem, Oregon. 14 photogravures. Long 12mo. Salem, Ore., 1904.
52. Outings in Oregon. 62pp., maps, illus. The Oregon Railroad and Navigation Co. 8vo, original wrappers. Portland, (1909).
53. Industrial Club Work of Oregon Boys and Birls. 48pp., illus. 8vo, original wrappers. Salem, Ore., 1916.
54. Along the Columbia to the Sea. (On the Spokane, Portland and Seattle Railway). Map and 37 plates. Long 12mo, original wrappers. N.p.N.d.
55. Daily Oregon Statesman, Salem, Oregon, 1901. New Year Edition. 56pp., illus. 4to. Front cover missing. Salem, 1901.
56. Bridal Veil, Oregon. Bridal Veil Lumber Co. 14pp., 13 full-page plates of the lumber industry from forest to mill. Long 12mo. N.p.N.d.
57. Geological History of Crater Lake, Oregon. By J. S. Diller. 31pp., maps, illus. 8vo, original wrappers. Washington, 1913.
58. Directions for preparing Specimens of Mammals, Birds, Fish and Reptiles. By Stanley G. Jewitt. 20pp., illus. 8vo, original wrappers. Salem, Ore., 1914.
59. Editorial Association Souvenir. The Expedition, June, 1903. 16pp., illus, 4to, Portland, Ore., 1903. (Largely devoted to Clatsop County, with a long article on the burial of SergeantFloyd of the Lewis and Clark Expedition).
60. The Oregonian's Annual Number, 1899. Illus., many of historical interest. Folio.

534 [OREGON.] Facts regarding its Climate, Soil, Mineral and Agricultural Resources, means of Communication, Commerce, Industry, Laws, etc., for the use of Emigrants. 14pp., 8vo, original wrappers. Boston, 1876. $7.50
Smith 2846.

535 [OREGON.] Oregon for the Farmer. 63pp., illus. 8vo, original wrappers. N.p., 1924. $2.00

536 [OREGON.] Annual Report of the Department of Fisheries of the State of Oregon. By T. C. Reed. 83pp., 8vo, cloth. Salem, Ore., 1900. $3.00

537 [OREGON.] Hand-Book of the Pacific Northwest. 631pp., illus., tab. 8vo, cloth. Portland, Ore. (1894). $5.00

538 [OREGON.] Oregon Historical Society. Brief Review of its Works to Sept. 30, 1916. 8vo, original wrappers. N.p., N.d. (1916). $2.50
Smith 2855.

539 [OREGON.] On Horseback into Oregon. (Excerpted from the Atlantic Monthly, July, 1864). 8vo. N.p. (Boston, 1864). $2.50

540 [OREGON.] The Oregon State Horticultural Society. First Biennial Report, 1891. 144pp., 8vo, cloth. Portland, 1891. $4.00
Smith 2902.

541 [OREGON.] Oregon Immigration Commission. Oregon Album. 143pp., 193 ill., map. 8vo, original wrappers. Portland (1893). $5.00
Smith 2804.

542 [OREGON.] Oregon State Immigration Commission. Oregon Almanac, 1915. 320pp., 8vo, original wrappers. Salem, Ore., 1915. $2.00

543 [OREGON.] Independent Order of Odd Fellows. Proceedings of, including the First Annual Communication, 1857, through the 22nd annual convention, 1877. Plus the following Proceedings for separate years: 1879, 1882, 1884, 1885, 1886, 1889, 1896, 1897, 1889, 1900, 1901, 1902, 1903. Thirty-three Separate Numbers. 8vo, original wrappers. Portland, 1857-1903. $45.00

544 [OREGON.] North Pacific Coast Indian War Veterans Memorial to Congress. 16pp., 8vo, original wrappers. Salem, Ore., 1886. $7.50

545 [OREGON.] Oregon Industrial Exposition. 48pp., 8vo, original wrappers. Portland, 1895. $2.50

546 [OREGON.] State Supt. of Public Instruction of the State of Oregon. Arbor Day, April 14, 1893. 15pp., 8vo, original wrappers. Salem, Ore., 1893. $2.50

547 [OREGON.] Oregon Journal. Fifth Anniversary Number, Sept. 8, 1907. 96pp., illus., port., map. Folio, original wrappers. Portland, 1907. $4.50

548 [OREGON.] General Laws Passed by the Legislative Assembly at their Session, begun at Salem, Dec. 1, 1851. 8vo, sheep. Salem, 1852. $37.50

This copy belonged to Governor Wallace, first Governor of Idaho.

549 [OREGON.] The Organic and Other General Laws of Oregon, 1843-1872. 992pp., 8vo, sheep. 1874. $7.50

550 [OREGON.] Journal of the Senate Proceedings of the Legislative Assembly of Sept. 9th-Oct. 23, 1872. 837-47pp., 8vo, cloth. Salem, Ore., 1872. $7.50

551 [OREGON.] General and Special Laws. Ninth Regular Session, 1876. 8vo, sheep. Salem, Ore., 1876. $7.50

552 [OREGON.] Oregon Legislative Assembly. Proceedings of the 50th Anniversary of the Admission of the State of Oregon into the Union. 53pp., 8vo, original wrappers. Salem, Ore.: Duniway, 1909. $3.50

Smith 2809.

553 [OREGON.] Oregon and Washington Magazine Articles. 16 Articles bound in one book, from various publications, from 1856 to 1911, all relating to Oregon. 8vo. V.p., V.d. $12.50

554 [OREGON.] Manual of the Militia Laws of the State of Oregon. 289pp., 12mo, mor. Salem, Ore., 1896. $3.00

555 [OREGON.] Mineral Resources and Mineral Industry of Oregon for 1903, compiled by the Dept. of Chemistry. 112pp., 4 plates, map, tab. 8vo, original wrappers. Eugene, Ore., 1904. $4.50

556 [OREGON.] Oregon Mining Journal, containing Mining Laws of Oregon. 74pp., 4to, original wrappers. Grants Pass, Ore., 1897. $5.00

557 [OREGON.] (Nash, Ogden). Oregon, there and Back in 1877. 285pp., illus., map. 8vo, cloth. London, 1878. $5.00

558 [OREGON.] (Nash, Ogden). Two Years in Oregon. Illus. 8vo, cloth. N. Y., 1882. $3.00

559 [OREGON.] (Nash, Ogden). Settler's Hand-Book to Oregon. Tab., 190pp., 8vo, original wrappers. Portland, Ore.: Gill, 1904. $3.75

560 [OREGON.] (Nash, Wallis). Farm, Ranch and Range in Oregon. 32pp., illus. 8vo, original wrappers. Salem, Ore.: Lewis and Clark Centennial Commission for the State of Oregon, 1904. $3.00

Smith 2637.

Item 557, 558, 559, Should read Wallis Nash.

561 [OREGON.] Native Son and Historical Magazine: Devoted to the History, Industries and Development of the Original Oregon, comprising Oregon, Washington, Idaho, and part of Montana. [An absolutely complete set from its beginning in May, 1899, to its termination March, 1901.] Illustrated with Ports. and Views, etc. 21 numbers bound in 20, as issued, in the original wrappers. 8vo. Portland, 1899-1901. $40.00

Smith 2867-2868. A scarce Oregon magazine. It was issued in a limited number originally and now is quite scarce especially in complete runs. The magazine was the official organ of the Oregon Pioneer Association and contains much historical material not available in any other form.

562 [OREGON.] Oregon Naturalist. Oregon City. Vol. 1, No. 1, Sept., 1894. to Vol. 4, No. 1, Jan., 1897. 4 vols., with 23 numbers. (Lacks numbers 4, 5, 9, 10, 12 in Vol. 3). 4 vols., 8vo, cloth. Oregon City, 1894-97. $17.50

Even though incomplete, as cited, this series of the Oregon Naturalist is very scarce and important.

563 [OREGON.] (Nicolay, C. G.). The Oregon Territory; a Geographical and Physical Account of that Country and its Inhabitants, with Outlines of its History and Discovery. Map and plate. 12mo, cloth. London, 1846. $12.50

Bound in with the above is "The Backwoods of Canada, being Letters from the Wife of an Emigrant Officer." 243pp., illus. London, 1846.

564 [OREGON.] (Nesmith, J. R.). Branch Mint of the U. S. Mineral Resources of Oregon, Washington and Idaho. Speech in the U. S. Senate, April 1, 1864. 16pp., 8vo, original wrappers. Washington (1864). $4.50

Nesmith was an Oregon pioneer.

565 [OREGON.] Newport, Oregon. 32pp., illus., map. 8vo, original wrappers. (Newport, Ore., 1905). $3.00

566 [OREGON.] How Marcus Whitman saved Oregon. By Oliver W. Nixon. Illus., map. 8vo, cloth. Chicago, 1895. $1.00

567 [OREGON.] Whitman's Ride through Savage Lands with Sketches of Indian Life. By Oliver W. Nixon. 186pp., 4 ports., 12 plates. 8vo, cloth. (Chicago): Winona Pub. Co., 1905. $4.00

568 [OREGON.] Notice sur le Territoire et sur la Mission de l'Oregon, suivie de quelques lettres des Soeurs de Notre-Dame etalies a Saint Paul du Wallamette. 180pp., map. 8vo. Bruxelles, Bibliotheque d'Education, 1847.

Smith 2728. $22.50

569 [OREGON.] A Brief History of the Diocese of Baker City. By Father Dominic O'Connor. xi-203pp., illus. 8vo, original wrappers. Baker City, 1930. $7.50

Privately printed only 12 years ago and already quite scarce.

570 [OREGON.] The "Vanishing Swede"; a Tale of Adventure and Pluck in the Pine Forests of Oregon. By Mary Hamilton O'Connor. 200pp., illus. 12mo, cloth. N. Y., 1905. $4.00

571 [OREGON.] (Odell, Mrs. W.). 1834-1884: A Semi-Centennial Offering to the Members and Friends of the Methodist Church, Salem. Ports. and plates. 109pp., 12mo, original wrappers. Portland, 1883. $12.50

Written to preserve the record of the early missionary pioneers of the Northwest. Contains a number of important documents and letters. Discusses the overland trip of Lee, of P. L. Edwards and Cyrus Shepard; early days of the mission; correspondence of Shepard, Lee, Pittman and David Leslie.

572 [OREGON.] Oregon Agricultural College. The Trail Blazers. 76pp., illus. 4to. [Corvallis, Ore., 1915.] $2.50

573 [OREGON.] Oregon Central Railroad Co. Statement of Facts relative to the Incorporation and Organization. 181pp., 8vo, original wrappers. Portland, 1868. $12.50

574 [OREGON.] Oregon Constitutional Convention, 1857. Constitution of the State of Oregon, held at Salem, Commencing August 17, 1857, together with the Constitution adopted by the People, Nov. 9, 1857. 130pp., 8vo. Salem, Ore.: Byars, 1882. $7.50

575 [OREGON.] The Oregonian. Souvenir, 1850-1892. 200pp., illus., maps, tab. Folio. Portland, Ore., 1892. $5.00

576 [OREGON.] Pacific Jewish Annual. Vol. 2, 1897-1898. 176pp., 8vo, cloth. San Francisco, 1898. $2.50

Relates to prominent Jewish residents of Oregon.

577 [OREGON.] The Pacific Northwest, its Wealth and Resources. 128pp., illus. 12mo, original wrappers. Portland (1891). $3.00

Smith 2798.

578 [OREGON.] Pacific University, Forest Grove, Ore. Fifty Years of Pacific University, 1848-1898; Exercises of the Semi-Centenniel Anniversary of Tualatin Academy and Pacific University held at Forest Grove, Oregon, July 9, 1898. 86pp., 12mo. N.p., N.d. $6.00

Smith 2973.

579 [OREGON.] (Parrish, Rob Roy McGregor). Echoes from the Valley. 156pp., 8vo, cloth. Portland: Himes, 1884. $3.00

580 [OREGON.] (Pennoyer, Gov. Sylvester). Biennial Message. 16th Biennial Session. 28pp., 8vo, original wrappers. Salem, Ore., 1891. $2.00

580a [OREGON.] (Pennoyer, Gov. Sylvester). Inaugural Address of. 33pp., 8vo, original wrappers. Salem, Ore., 1887. $2.00

581 [OREGON.] (Pennoyer, Gov. Sylvester). Thanksgiving Day Proclamation fixing Thursday, Nov. 24th, 1892. 2pp., 12mo. Salem, 1892. $4.75

Governor Pennoyer, having had some disagreement with President Cleveland, fixed, by proclamation, a different date than that proclaimed by the President. As a result Oregon observed two thanksgiving days in 1892—one by the Pennoyerites, the other by the Clevelandites.

582 [OREGON.] (Philips, George Norris). Nation and State. A Text Book on Civil Government. (Oregon Edition). 237pp., illu., 8vo, cloth. Phila. (1905). $4.00

583 [OREGON.] (Piggot, C. H.). Pearls at Random Strung. 111pp., 8vo, cloth. Portland, 1908. $3.00

COMPLETE 3 VOLUME SET OF THE OREGON PIONEER ASSOCIATION TRANSACTIONS

584 [OREGON.] The Oregon Pioneer Association Transactions. Vol. 1 (Numbers 1-14, 1875-1887), Vol. 2 (Numbers 15-24, 1888-1896), Vol. 3 (Numbers 25-37, 1897-1909). Complete with General and Alphabetical Index. Three volumes (front wrappers bound in). 8vo. Salem, Ore., 1875-1909. $185.00

Complete set of this rare treasure house of early Oregon history, containing much pioneer material relating to the entire Northwest; migration across the plains; early settlements; Indian wars of Oregon and Washington Territories, etc. Included among a great many other narratives in this 3 volume collection are: Allen's Journal of a Voyage to Vancouver, 1841; Crawford's Across the Rockies, 1842 (Hastings Party); Nesmith's Memoirs of the 1843 Emigration; Curry's Early Oregon; Stephen Staat's Across the Plains in 1846 (with Donner Party); Reminiscences of Fort Vancouver, the H. B. C., Indians and Dr. John McLoughlin in 1832; Geer's Narrative of the Overland Trip to Oregon, 1847; Atkinson's Across the Plains in '48; Boise's Narrative of the Emigration of '44; "A Day with the Cow Column by Jesse Applegate; Nesmith's Recollections of the Rogue River War, 1853; Williams' Narrative of the Battle of the Cascades, 1856; The Oregon Question by L. F. Grover; Deady Reminiscences; Biography of Joe Meek by Mrs. F. F. Victor; Elwood Evans Historical Address on the Pioneer Days, etc. A very fine set.

585 [OREGON.] Pioneer and Historical Society of Oregon. Fifth Annual Report . . . Narrative of the Winter Trip of Dr. Marcus Whitman across the Rocky Mountains in 1842, and other Documents. 8vo. Astoria, 1876. $7.50

586 ——. The Same. Fourth Annual Address. The Proceedings. 27pp., 8vo. Astoria, 1875. $7.50

587 ——. The Same. Fourteenth Annual Meeting. 12pp., 8vo. Astoria, 1884. $7.50

588 [OREGON.] Other People's Savings. By Mable Williams Plowman. 75pp., 16mo, original wrappers. Portland, N.d. $2.00

589 [OREGON.] The Discovery of the Columbia River. By Edward G. Porter. 24pp., 8vo. Boston: Directors of the Old South Work, Leaflet No. 131. Boston [1898]. $3.00

Smith p759.

590 [OREGON.] The Ship Columbia and the Discovery of the Oregon. By Edward G. Porter. [Illus.] 8vo, original wrappers. [New England Magazine, June, 1892.] 8vo, wrappers, in cloth case. Boston, 1892. $4.50

591 [OREGON.] (Portland). Charter of the City of Portland, 291-66pp. 8vo, cloth. Portland, 1872. $7.50

Contains the Charter, Chronological Index of Ordinances, 1854-1872, the City Ordinance, etc.

592 [OREGON.] (Portland). Portland Chamber of Commerce. Circular No. 1—Climatic Conditions, Fishing, Hunting and Outdoor Life in Oregon. 40pp. Circular No. 2—Apple Industry and other Fruits and Nuts. 48pp. (3) The Ten Acre Tract in Oregon, 12pp. (4) What can be done with from $1000 to $5000 in Oregon. 24pp. Together 4 numbers. Illus. 8vo, wrappers. Portland (c. 1890). $4.50

593 [OREGON.] (Portland). Charter for the Consolidation Cities of Portland, East Portland and Albina. 47pp., 8vo, original wrappers. Portland, 1891. $4.50

594 [OREGON.] (Portland). Portland Blue Book. A Residence, Address, Visiting, Club, Theatre, and Shopping Guide. 12mo. Portland, 1893. $3.00

595 [OREGON.] (Portland). Portland Illustrated Annual of Portland's Public Schools. 88pp., illus., 4to, cloth. Portland, 1896. $4.00

596 [OREGON.] (Portland). Lewis and Clark Centennial Exposition, 1905. Committee on Congresses. Program, Organization and Addresses, Lewis and Clark Educational Congress, Aug. 28 to Sept. 2, 1905. 121pp., 8vo, original world. [Portland: Anderson, 1905?.] $2.50

597 [OREGON.] (Portland). Chamber of Commerce. What to See and How to See it; Land Book and Guide, containing Valuable Information about Portland and Vicinity . . . 128pp., illus., folding map. 12mo, original wrappers. Portland, 1905. $3.00

598 [OREGON.] (Portland). Portland Architectural Club, First Annual Exhibit Catalogue. 114pp., illus., 4to, original wrappers. (Portland, 1908). $3.50

Smith 3171.

599 [OREGON.] (Portland). Holiday Season. "Night Off" at the Heilig Theatre. Long 12mo., illus. N.p., N.d. (c. 1910). $4.00

600 [OREGON.] (Portland). Chamber of Commerce Bulletin. Feb., June, Aug., 1908; Jan., April, Aug., Nov., 1909; Feb., 1910; Oct., 1911. Nine numbers. 8vo. Portland, 1908-1911. $4.50

601 [OREGON.] (Portland). Portland Chamber of Commerce. Oregon the Land of Opportunity. vii, 32pp., map. 4to. Portland, 1911. $3.00

Has some beautifully colored plates.

602 [OREGON.] (Portland). Reed College. First Annual Catalogue. 144pp., 12mo, original wrappers. Portland, 1912. $5.00

Contains historical sketches.

603 [OREGON.] (Portland). Oregon-Washington Railroad & Navigation Co. Portland, Oregon, the City of Roses. 48pp., illus., 12mo, original wrappers. Portland (1913). $3.00

604 [OREGON.] (Portland). Portland, the Metropolis and Vicinity. Illus. by over 100 plates. Portfolio. Portland, 1914. (Slight stains). $2.50

605 [OREGON.] (Portland). Pictorial Oregon, the Wonderland. Portland Press Club. 167pp., illus., 8vo, original wrappers. Portland, 1915. $2.50

Smith 3187.

606 [OREGON.] (Portland). Progressive Portland. Numerous illus. Portfolio. N.p., N.d. $3.00

606a [OREGON.] Presbyterian Church, Portland, Ore. Dedication Services, Historical Sketch and List of Members. 40pp., 8vo, original wrappers. N.p., 1899. $2.50

607 [OREGON. Oregon Providence of the Sisters of the Holy Names: Gleanings of 50 Years: A History of the Sisters of the Holy Names of Jesus and Mary in the Northwest, 1859-1909. Numerous ports. and illus. 12mo, 240pp., 8vo, cloth. N.p. (Portland, Ore., 1909). $7.50

608 [OREGON.] Sixteen Years in Oregon. By Will E. Purdy. 126pp., illus., 8vo, original wrappers. Portland, 1912. $6.00

609 [OREGON.] Oregon Railway and Navigation Company. Oregon. Facts regarding its Climate, Soil, Mineral and Agriculture, Resources, Means of Communication, Commerce and Industry. 59pp., folding map. 8vo, original wrappers. Chicago, 1881. $4.50

610 [OREGON.] Oregon Railway and Navigation Co. Summer Saunterings, 1882. 35pp., 6 plates. 8vo, original wrappers. Portland, 1882. $4.50

Smith 2889 locates but one copy.

611 [OREGON.] Resources of the State of Oregon. Folding map, 230pp. 8vo, original wrappers (lacks back). Salem, Ore., 1892. $4.00

612 [OREGON.] Reports of the Decisions of the Supreme Court of Oregon during the Years 1853-4. 54pp., 8vo, unbound. Corvallis, Ore.: Asabel Busch, 1855. $20.00

613 [OREGON.] Report of the Decisions of the Supreme Court of the Territory of Oregon. Rendered at the June and December Terms, 1855, and at the June Term, 1856. 72pp., 8vo, unbound. Salem, Ore.: Asabel Busch, 1856. $20.00

614 [OREGON.] The Columbia River Harbor and the City of Astoria, in Sept., 1890. By H. W. Scott. 4pp., 8vo. N.d. (1890). $2.00

615 [OREGON.] Oregon Spectator. Oregon City, O. Terr., Thursday, Dec. 24, 1846. Vol. 1, No. 24. $12.50

A copy of the *Oregon Spectator*, first newspaper published in Oregon.

616 [OREGON.] Statutes of a General Nature passed by the Legislative Assembly of the Territory of Oregon; at the Second Session, begun and held at Oregon City, Dec. 2, 1850. 301pp., 8vo, sheep. Oregon City: Asabel Busch, 1851. $50.00

Extremely rare. Huntington 75. The above work also contains a copy of the Treaty of 1846, the Act of Congress to create the Office of Surveyor-General, etc.

617 [OREGON.] Women's Christian Temperance Union. Minutes of the 26th Annual Convention, held at Hood's River, Oct. 5-8, 1909. 76pp., 8vo, original wrappers. N.p., 1909. $4.00

See Smith 2912.

618 OREGON HISTORICAL SOCIETY. The Quarterly of. Ports, maps, illus. Complete set from Vol. 1 through Vol. 52 (1900-1941). Vols. 1-15, original wrappers bound in, the rest as issued. 52 vols., 8vo, original wrappers. Portland, Ore., 1900-1941. $100.00

Rare when complete. Contains much historical material relating to Oregon, such as: The Aurora Community, History of Barlow Road, Across the Continent Seventy Years Ago, Glimpses of Early Days in Oregon, the Mercer Immigration, Hall J. Kelley, etc., etc.

619 [OREGON.] The Oregon Question. The United States Magazine and Democratic Review, June, 1845. 8vo, cloth. Washington, 1845. $2.50

620 [OREGON.] The Oregon Question. (Contained in the Quarterly Review, Vol. 77, pp. 564-610. 8vo, half calf. London, 1845. $5.00

621 [OREGON.] Oregon Question. (Contained in the Quarterly Review, Vol. 77, pp. 563-610, March, 1846). 8vo, boards. London, 1846. $4.00

622 [OREGON.] Oregon Question. (Contained in the Congressional Globe, 1846). 4to, half calf. Washington, 1846. $7.50

Contains probably the largest aggregation of material relating to Oregon over brought between two covers. 1184pp.

623 [OREGON.] Question of L'Oregon, 1846. By Guillaume Tell Poussin. 100pp., 8vo, original wrappers. Paris, 1846. $22.50

Smith 3202 locates only the copy in the Seattle Public Library. The work includes an early history of the Territory of Oregon by one of the best French scholars on the historv of the U. S.

624 [OREGON.] Speech of Hon. John A. Dix, of New York, on the Oregon Question, del'd in the Senate . . . Feb. 18 & 19, 1846. 22pp., 8vo, sewn (closely cropped). Washington, 1846. $1.50

625 OREGON HISTORICAL SOCIETY. Proceedings of. Seven volumes (4-5-6-7 combined). 8vo, original wrappers. Salem, Ore., 1900-1906. $17.50

626 OREGON HISTORICAL SOCIETY, Proceedings of the Fiftieth Anniversary of the Admission of the State of Oregon to the Union. 53pp., 8vo, original wrappers. Salem, 1909. $2.50

627 [OREGON AND WASHINGTON.] A Guide for Settlers and Travelers. Oregon and Washington Territory, with Maps and Illus. Folding map and illus., 81pp., 8vo, original wrappers. Portland, 1882. $4.75

628 [OREGON AND WASHINGTON.] Information for Settlers and Others. Oregon and Washington Territory. Folding map. 32pp., 8vo, original printed wrappers. N. Y., 1883. $6.00

629 [OREGON-WASHINGTON.] Oregon-Washington Navigation Company. Land that Lures; summer in the Pacific Northwest. 45pp., frontis., illus., map. 8vo, original wrappers. N.p., N.d. [Portland, c. 1911.] $4.00

Smith 2914.

630 [OREGON-WASH., IDAHO.] Oregon Immigration Board. The New Empire, Oregon, Wash., Idaho. 102pp. Portland, Ore.: Ellis and Sons Print, [1888]. $5.00

631 [OREGON-WASH., IDAHO.] Oregon Immigration Board. The Pacific Northwest, its Wealth and Resources, Oregon, Washington, Idaho, the City of Portland. 158pp., illus. 8vo. Portland, 1891. $4.00

632 [OREGON-WASHINGTON-IDAHO.] Pacific Northwest Immigration Board. The Pacific Northwest, its Wealth and Resources, Oregon, Washington, Idaho. 128pp., illus. 8vo, cloth. Portland, N.d. $3.75

633 [OREGON.] The Oregon Territory: Consisting of a Brief Description of the Country and its Production; and of the Habits and Manners of the Native Tribes. With a Map of the Territory. 78pp., 16mo, half mor. London: M. A. Nattali, 1846. $45.00

Scarce detailed description of the country and of its physical character, people and resources at the period when war threatened for possession of the region. The work is believed to have been written by a returned official or long time employee of the Hudson's Bay Co. It reveals an intimate knowledge derived from personal contact and further reveals the author as a man of high intelligence.

634 [OREGON TRAIL.] Oregon Trail Association. The Old Oregon Trail. The Road that Won an Empire. 32pp., illus., 8vo, original wrappers. Baker City, Ore., 1924. $3.00

635 [OREGON TRAIL.] The Oregon Trail. Hearings before the Committee on Roads, House of Representatives, 68th Cong., 2nd Sess. H. R. 232, H. R. 28, and Senate 2053. 205pp., 8vo, original wrappers. Washington, 1925. $5.00

Contains a number of early Overland Narratives.

636 [OREGON TRAIL.] Wagons West. A Story of the Oregon Trail. 361pp., illus., 8vo, cloth. N. Y. (1930). $3.50

637 [OREGON.] (The Marcus Whitman Controversy). Articles by Edward C. Ross, Rev. Myron Eells and W. H. Gray, in reply to Mrs. F. F. Victor and Elwood Evans, whose Contributions appeared in the Oregonian of Nov. 7th and Dec. 26th, 1884, and Feb. 8th and Dec. 15th, 1885. 70pp., 8vo, original wrappers. Portland, Ore., 1885. $17.50

Smith 3357.

638 OSGOOD, ERNEST STPLES. The Day of the Cattleman. Illus., maps. 8vo, cloth. Minneapolis, 1929. $3.50

639 O'REILLY, HENRY. Settlements in the West. Sketches of Rochester; with Incidental Notices of Western New York. A Collection of Matters designed to Illustrate the Progress of Rochester during the First Quarter Century of its Existence . . . [Map and illus.] 12mo, cloth. Rochester, 1838. $15.00

Complete with the 44 plates and map.

640 OSTRANDER, ALSON B. An Army Boy of the Sixties; a Story of the Plains. Illus. 12mo, cloth. Yonkers, 1924. $2.50

641 OSTRANDER, ALSON B. After Sixty Lears. A Sequel to A Story of the Plains. 120pp., illus., 8vo, cloth. Seattle, 1925. $2.50

Ostrander was an enlisted man serving with the troops in the campaigns against the Northwest Plains Indians.

642 OTTLEY, HENRY. On the Errors and Mischiefs of Modern Diplomacy . . . With particular reference to the Treaty of Washington, 1871. 188pp., 8vo, half calf. London, 1872. $7.50

643 OWEN, MAJOR JOHN. The Journals and Letters of Major Owen, 1850-1871. Transcribed and Edited from the Original Manuscripts in the Montana Historical Society and the Collection of William Robertson Coe, by Seymour Dunbar and with notes by Paul C. Phillips. Maps and plates. 2 vols., 8vo, cloth. N. Y., 1927. $12.50

The letters and journals relate to the founding of Owen's Fort in the Montana Wilderness in 1849; his overland travels and adventures on the plains; his relation with the Indians; government work, etc.

644 [OVERLAND.] Rambling Notes of a Trip to the Pacific. By Mary E. Blake. 231pp., 12mo, cloth. Boston, 1883. $2.00

645 [OVERLAND.] Overland Tales. By Josephine Clifford. 383pp., 8vo, cloth. Phila., 1877. $1.50

Local interest tales of the Pacific Coast.

646 [OVERLAND RAILROAD.] People's Pacific Railroad Company Charter. Organization Address of the President. 24pp., 8vo, original printed wrappers. Boston, 1860. $12.50

647 [OREGON JOURNEY.] Magic River Deschutes. By O. M. Pringle. Illus., 8vo, original wrappers. N.p., N.d. $7.50

Scarce little work which narrates Pringle's experience on the Overland to Oregon, in 1846, with his parents.

648 [OVERLAND JOURNEY.] Autobiography and Reminiscences of a Pioneer. By Polly Jane Purcell. 7pp., 12mo, original wrappers. [Freewater, Ore.], N.d. $5.00

Printed on one side the paper only. The author was born in Andrew Co., Mo., in 1842. She crossed the plains to Oregon in 1846 with a 160-wagon train guided by Joe Meek, arriving in Salem after a six month's trip. Family took land on Beaver Creek. Moved to Ochoco Co., in 1868. She faintly remembered the Whitman Massacre. Her brothers fought Indians. Gives names of early settlers and other details of local history.

649 [OVERLAND JOURNEY.] (Horetzky, Chas.). Canada and the Pacific; being an account of a Journey from Edmonton to the Pacific by the Peace River Valley, and of a Winter Voyage along the Western Coast of the Dominion; with remarks on the Physical Features of the Pacific Railway Route and Notices of the Indian Tribes of British Columbia. 244pp., plates, map. 8vo, cloth. Montreal, 1874. $10.00

The author organized and conducted the Overland Expedition of Mt. Sanford Fleming in 1872. His narrative is both interesting and reliable. The route was from Edmonton to Assiniboine, thence to Lesser Slave Lake Dunvegen, Ft. St. John, Rocky Mt. Portage, Stewart's Lake, Hazelton, Naas, Ft. Simpson, Nanaimo, San Francisco.

This little work, printed by the Dawsons' with their map, is quite scarce.

650 PACIFIC COAST. Pacific Art Company. Men of the Pacific Coast. Containing Portraits and Biographies of the Professional, Financial and Business Men of California, Oregon and Washington, 1902-1903. 634pp., illus., 8vo, mor. San Francisco: Pacific Art Co., 1903. $7.50

Contains many illustrations of men prominent on the coast.

651 PACKARD, MAJOR W., and LARISON, G. Early Emigration to California, 1849-1850. Ports. 23pp., 8vo, original wrappers. Bloomington, 1928. $12.50

Thirty copies only of this narrative were printed. Personal narrative of the Overland trip from St. Joe to Hangtown, and of experiences in California in 1830.

652 PAIRPONT, ALFRED. Rambles in America, Past and Present. Ports. and illus., 252pp., 12mo, cloth. Boston, 1891. $3.00

Relates to New England, Canada. N. Y., Mass. Special chapters on tobacco plantations, police systems, religious sects, Mormons, etc.

653 PALFREY, JOHN GORHAM. History of New England. Maps. 5 vols., 8vo. Boston, 1859-90. $22.50

The most comprehensive history of New England.

654 PALLADINO, L. B. Indian and White in the Northwest; or a History of Catholicity in Montana, with an introduction by the Rt. Rev. John B. Brondel . . . 411pp., illus., map, facs. 8vo, cloth. Baltimore: Murphy, 1894. $12.50

This ranks as one of the best early works for the history of Montana an dthe Northwest country. The author lived among the natives for years, conversed with the first white priests who preceeded the gold-seekers by 22 years, witnessed the founding of settlements, etc.

655 PALLADINO, L. B. Historical Notes of the Flatheads (The Indian Sentinel, Flathead Number, Vol. 1, No. 14). 8vo, original wrappers. Washington, 1919. $5.00

This number contains much historical information on the Flathead Tribe by authorities on the subject. Father Palladino was a missionary among the Flatheads for many years.

656 PALLISER, JOHN. Solitary Rambles and Adventures of a Hunter in the Prairies. Illus., 12mo, cloth. London, 1853. $12.50

Wagner-Camp 228. Original Edition. Palliser left Independence with the Kip Party of the American Fur Co. in Sept., 1847. He crossed the plains to Ft. Pierre, thence on to Ft. Union. After a visit to Ft. Berthold in the spring, he returned to Ft. Union. He hunted the Yellowstone, and, in the fall descended the river to St. Louis.

657 ——. Same. 12mo, cloth. London, 1856. $5.00

658 PALLISER, CAPT. JOHN. "On the Rocky Mountains." Latest Explorations in British North America. (Contained in Proceedings of the Royal Geological Society of London. Vol. 4, 1860). 8vo, cloth. London, 1860. $7.50

Also contains Capt. R. W. Torrens' journey to Ft. Simpson.

659 PALMER, JOEL. Journal of the Travels over the Rocky Mountains, to the Mouth of the Columbia River; made during the Years 1845 and 1846: Containing Minute Descriptions of the Valleys of the Willamette, Umpqua, and Clamet; A General Description of Oregon Territory; its Inhabitants, Climate, Soil, Productions, etc.; a List of Necessary Outfits for Emigrants; and a Table of Distances from Camp to Camp on the Route. Also, a Letter from the Rev. H. H. Spalding, Resident Missionary for the last Ten Years; Among the Nez Perce Tribe of Indians, on the Koos-Koos-Kee River; the Organic Laws of Oregon Territory; Tables of about 300 Words of the Chinook Jargon, and about 200 Words of the Nez Perce Language; a Description of Mount Hood; Incidents of Travel, etc.; IV, (9)-189pp., 12mo, original half calf. Cincinnati, 1847. $400.00

Original Edition. Wagner-Camp 136. First Issue of the Original Edition, with the words "sandy plain" for "grassy plain" (line 7th from bottom, p. 31) and "The company own from six to eight mills above the fort" for "The mills are six and eight miles above the fort' (4th line from bottom, p. 121.) See Braislin 1430.

Thwaites pronouces the above work: "The best account of the Oregon Trial, so full that it should be and was, used as a 'Guide' for the following Emigrants". The journal has added importance as a "Plains Guide" in that the author was an eye-witness and participant in the great plains migration of 1845. The regular issue usually has the date crossed over in ink.

In the Bancroft Library (Berkeley, Cal.) there is a manuscript in which Palmer gives an account of the publication of his Journal. He says when he returned East he contracted with a Cincinnati firm to print the narrative. However, according to the manuscript he waited almost two months and did not receive more than a dozen copies. This was unfortunate as the Journal contains a great amount of Overland material which he expected to have ready for those intending to emigrate. Bancroft (in his History of Oregon, v. 1) states, appropos the above: "This is to be regretted, as it is one of the best of its kind". Palmer was truly a great man of the Overland. A large collection of his letters are now in the library of a private collector.

FIRST BOOK PRINTED AT THE WESTMINSTER PRESS, BRITISH COLUMBIA

660 PALMER, HENRY SPENCER. Report of a Journey of Survey from Victoria to Fort Alexander, via North Bentinck Arm. 30pp., 8vo. New Westminster: Royal Engineer Press, 1863. **$35.00**

Excessively rare and apparently the only copy that can be located outside the one in the Legislative Library at Victoria. The first book printed at the Westminister Press. This fact is vouched for by Col. A. Wolfenden, the first King's Printer of British Columbia, in an autograph signed statement on the verso of the title to the above work: "First book printed at the Government Printing Office by A. Wolfenden."

The Royal Engineers were sent out from England to build roads to Cariboo in connection with the gold discovery. When the corps disbanded Walfenden was appointed King's Printer.

661 PALMER, HENRY SPENCER. British Columbia, Williams Lake and Cariboo. Report on that portion of the Williams Lake and Cariboo Districts, and of the Fraser River, from Fort Alexander to Fort George. 25pp., 3 maps (colored), diagram. 8vo. Printed at the Royal Engineer's Press. New Westminster, B. C., 1863. **$22.50**

A rare work of which the only other copy we can locate is in the Legislative Library at Victoria. Smith 2982.

662 PALMER, HENRY SPENCER. Remarks upon the Geography and Natural Capabilities of British Columbia, and the Condition of its Principal Gold Fields. Map. 171-195pp., 8vo. Geographical Society Journal, 1864. **$15.00**

Smith 2983 locates only the copy at Victoria.

663 PALMER, HENRY SPENCER. In the Klondyke, including an Account of A Winter's Journey to Dawson. x-218pp., illus., 8vo, cloth. N. Y., 1899. **$3.50**

664 PALMER, W. J. Report of Surveys Across the Continent on the 35th and 32nd Parallels for a Route Extending from the Kansas Pacific Railway to the Pacific Ocean at San Francisco and San Diego. Folding maps. 8vo. Phila., 1869. **$20.00**

Narrative of the first white man who traversed the Grand Canyon in 1867, not printed elsewhere. All previous efforts to explore the Grand Canyon had proved disastrous. James White, with three others, set out from Ft. Dodge, 13th April, 1867. The other members of the party perished in the rapids, and the surviving member has been able to record the first authentic account of his trek through the Grand Canyon.

665 PARKMAN, FRANCIS. Prairie and Rocky Mountain Life; or California and Oregon Trail. Illus., 448pp., 8vo, half roan. St. Louis, 1858. **$7.50**

Bound in with the above is "The States and Territories of our Western Empire embracing the History, Statistics and Geography of the Territorial Regions of the U. S. St. Louis, 1858".

666 PARKER, SAMUEL. Journal of an Exploring Tour beyond the Rocky Mountains . . . Performed in the years 1835-37. Plate and map. 12mo, cloth. Ithaca, 1838. **$7.50**

The scarce Original Edition.

667 ——. The Same. 12mo, cloth. Ithaca, 1840. $4.50

668 PARRISH, PHILIP H. Before the Covered Wagon. 292pp., 8vo, cloth. Portland, 1931. $3.00

669 PARRY, CAPT. WILLIAM E. Journal of a Voyage for the Discovery of a North-West Passage from the Atlantic to the Pacific Ocean, 1819-20; Journal of a Second Voyage, 1821-23; Journal of a Third Voyage, 1824-25; Narrative of an Attempt to reach the North Pole, 1828. Folding maps and very numerous fine engraved plates, some folding. 4 vols., 4to, uniformly bound in half mor. London, 1821-1828. $35.00

A choice set of Parry's four voyages.

670 PARRY, CAPT. WILLIAM E. Journal of a Voyage for the Discovery of a North-West Passage from the Atlantic to the Pacific, performed in the Years 1824-25. Folding map. 278pp., 8vo, roan-backed boards. Phila., 1821. $4.00

Bound in with above is The North Georgia Gazette and Winter Chronicle . . . By Capt. Edward Sabine. 78pp.

671 ——. The Same. 8vo, binding scuffed. Phila., 1826. $1.50

672 PARSONS, R. M. General Observations on the Circumstances noticed while proceeding from New Westminster to Lake Hache. 3 finely colored maps. 8pp., 8vo, sewn (as issued). New Westminster: Printed at the Royal Engineers' Press (1862). $35.00

Excessively rare early imprint of the British Columbia Press. Parsons was a Captain of the Royal Engineers. This is his report to Col. R. C. Moody, of the Royal Engineers. Can locate no other copy.

673 PARTON, JAMES. Life of John Jacob Astor, to which is Appended a copy of his Last Will. 121pp., 8vo, original wrappers. N. Y., 1865. $12.50

674 PATTERSON, ARTHUR. The Daughter of the Nez Perces: Strictly founded on Fact. An Account of the Troubles of the Nez Perce Tribe, the Battle of the Big Hole, etc. 381pp., 2 vols., 12mo, portrait of Chief Joseph. N. Y., 1894. $10.00

Original American Edition. Smith 3020. This work is based on incidents in the life of Chief Joseph, and is one of the best historical novels relating to the Northwest.

675 PARKMAN, FRANCIS. Works . . . Ports. and plates. 17 vols., 8vo, cloth. Boston, 1901. $27.50

Comprises: Pioneers of France, 2vols.; Jesuits in North America, 2 vols.; Old Regime in Canada, 2 vols.; Frontenac, 2 vols.; Conspiracy of Pontiac, 3 vols.; Oregon Trail, 2vols.; Lofe of Partoman by C. H. Farnham.

676 PARRISH, RANDALL. Great Plains; Romance of Western American Exploration, Warfare and Settlement, 1527-1870. 399pp., 5 ports., 27 plates. 8vo, cloth. Chicago, 1907. $4.50

Relates to the Northwest fur trade.

Item 674, Eliminate "2vols."

PATTERSON'S VOYAGES TO CALIFORNIA, ALASKA AND NORTHWEST COAST

677 PATTERSON, SAMUEL. Narrative of the Adventures and Sufferings of Samuel Patterson, Experienced in the Pacific Ocean and many other Parts of the World, with an Account of the Feegee, and Sandwich Islands. 144pp., 12mo. From the Press in Palmer, 1817. $25.00

Huntington 697. Contains the narrative of three successive voyages (1802-1808) to California and the Northwest Coast, Alaska and what is now British Columbia. On his first voyage to Nootka, Patterson made the acquaintance of John R. Jewitt and tells of the massacre of his companions by the Indians.

PATTERSON'S MAP AND GUIDE TO N.W. GOLD FIELDS

678 PATTERSON, W. D. Map of the Cariboo and Omineca Gold Fields and the Routes thereto. Compiled from Reliable Authorities by Wm. D. Patterson, C.E., Lithographed by F. W. Green. Large folding map and broadside folding text entitled: "Distance Tables and Miscellaneous Information," giving itineraries and details of the country along the various routes, including the Overland Route; the "Land and River Route," and the routes by way of Douglas, Fort Yale, Skeena and Giscombe Portage. 16mo, original printed boards. Victoria, B. C., 1870. $85.00

Not in Smith. Apparently only two copies located.

679 PAXSON, FREDERIC L. History of the American Frontier, 1763-1893. Maps. 8vo, cloth. Boston, 1924. $4.00

680 PAXSON, FREDERIC L. When the West is Gone. 17pp., 8vo, cloth. N. Y. (1930). $3.50

681 PAXSON, FREDERIC L. Last American Frontier. 342pp., 8vo, cloth. N. Y., 1910. $4.50

682 PEARNE, T. H. Sixty-one Years of Itinerant Life. Port. 506pp., 12mo, cloth. Cincinnati: Printed for the Author, 1899. $7.50

Narrative of the author's trip to California and Oregon in 1851 with reminiscences of 15 years on the coast; hardships and adventures among the Indians; and a stage trip across the plains from california to the Missouri in 1864. Pp. 109-258 are devoted to pioneer life in Oregon.

683 PECK, JOHN M. Father Clark; or the Pioneer Preacher; Sketches and Incidents. Frontis., 8vo, cloth. N. Y., 1855. $8.00

This singular character, after many adventures as a seaman, deserted from the British Navy and taught school in S. C., Ga., and Ky. Shortly after 1800 he moved to Kaskaskia; from 1832 to 1836 he was Indian Missionary at Green Bay; was transferred for a time to Texas, and died at Chicago in 1854. Contains much on frontier life.

684 PELZER, LOUIS. Marches of the Dragoons in the Mississippi Valley. An Account of the Marches of the First Regiment U. S. Dragoons in the Mississippi Valley between the years 1833 and 1850. 282pp., 8vo, cloth. Iowa City, 1917. **$3.00**

685 PENHALLOW, SAMUEL. The History of the Wars of New England with the Eastern Indians; or a Narrative of their continued Perfidy and Cruelty, from the 10th of Aug., 1703 . . . to their submission 15th Dec., 1725. 4to, cloth. Cincinnati, 1859. $7.50

The first edition of Penhallow was published in Boston in 1726. It is the chief authority for Queen Anne's and Lovewell's wars. This is the first issue of the black letter title. With the signature in ink on end-paper "Sam'l G. Drake" and the book-plate of Louis Hotchkiss Brittin, Harvard 1901 pasted on this page.

686 PERKINS, JAMES H. Annals of the West; Embracing a Concise Account of Principal Events which have occurred in the Western States and Territories, from the Discovery of the Mississippi Valley to the year 1850. 8vo, half calf. Cincinnati, 1846. $5.00

687 ——. The Same. 8vo, sheep. St. Louis, 1851. $4.50

THE PERKINS BIOGRAPHY

688 PERKINS, JAMES HANDASYD. The Memoir and Writings of James Handasyd Perkins. Edited by William Henry Channing. Engraved portrait in stipple. Two Volumes, 527 and 502 pp., 12mo, original cloth. Cincinnati, 1851. $25.00

"The important biography of the author of "Annals of the West" is so scarce that it was unknown to Thomson and was not listed in his 'Bibliography of Ohio' ". Perkins went to Ohio in 1832, and these volumes are devoted to his life and activities, and to his historical writings relating to the early French Travelers in the west; English discoveries in the Ohio Valley; the Pioneers of Kentucky; Border wars of the Revolution; settlement of the Northwest Territory; and "Fifty Years of Ohio".

689 PERRIN, DU LAC M. Travels through the Two Louisianas, and Among the Savage Nations of the Missouri; Also, in the United States, along the Ohio and the Adjacent Provinces, in 1801-1803. With a Sketch of the Manners, Customs and Character of the People. 106pp., 8vo, sewn. London, 1807. $15.00

Wagner-Camp 3. The first English translation from the French edition of 1805.

690 PERROT, N. Memoire sur les Moeurs, Costumes et Religion des Sauvages de l'Amerique Septentrionale, par Nicolas Perrot, Publie pour la premiere fois par le R. P. Tailhan de la compaignie de Jesus. 341pp., and index. 8vo, half mor. Paris, 1864. $25.00

Original Edition. The work here presented to the public for the first time had remained in manuscript for more than 150 years; but not unknown. It had served Charlevoix in the preparation of his great history of New France; as it had, long before, its governors La Barre, Denonville, and Frontenac in determining their policy toward the various tribes of Indians, allies and foes it describes. Its author was for twenty years a simple fur trader, visiting and residing for long periods from 1661-1665 with the savages he had made his friends. Subsequently he was for twenty years the official intepreter of the Government. "His facility in acquiring the Indian languages, his natural eloquence, his blending of heroism, and hardiness, and coolness and generosity, acquired for him the confidence and affection of a great many tribes." His work therefore has a different and in some respects a higher value than the relations of the missionary fathers regarding the Indian tribes two centuries ago.

691 PETERS, DEWITT C. Life and Adventures of Kit Carson, the Nestor of the Rocky Mountains . . . 534pp., port. and plates. N. Y.: Clarke, 1859. $4.00

692 PETERS, DEWITT C. Pioneer Life and Frontier Adventures. An Authentic Record of the Romantic Life and Daring Exploits of Kit Carson. . . . 567pp., 8vo, cloth. Boston, 1881. $3.50

Smith 3043.

693 PETO, S. MORTON. The Resources and Prospects of America, ascertained during a Visit to the States in the Autumn of 1865. Illus. 8vo, cloth. London, 1866. $5.00

Relates considerably to California and Oregon, especially to the goldfields. Contains colored views of Chicago in 1831 and San Francisco in 1848. The Original and best edition.

694 PETITOT, L'ABBE. Geographie de l'Athabaskaw-Mackenzie et des Grands Lacs du Bassin Artique. 148pp., folding map. 8vo, half calf. Paris: Martinet, 1875. $20.00

Can locate no other copy of this work in North American libraries. Father Petitot was probably the first resident missionary in the far Northland. He was there for many years and his work has great authenticity and value for any accurate study of the region.

695 PETITOT, EMILE. Vocablaire Francaise-Esquimau Dialecte des Tchiglit des bouches du Mackenzie et de l'Anderson, procede d'une Monagraphie de cette tribu et de Notes Grammaticales. 64-78pp., 4to, original wrappers (backstrip weak). Paris, 1876. $15.00

Smith 3047 locates only one copy at Victoria.

696 PETITOT, EMILE. Traditions Indiennes du Canada Nord-Ouest; textes Originaux et Traduction Litteral. 446pp. Alencon Broise, 1887. $10.00

Smith 3046.

697 PETITOT, EMILE. Les Grands Esquimaux. Map. 307pp., 12mo, original printed wrappers. Paris, 1887. $8.50

Father Petitot was an early missionary to the Indians of Northwest Canada.

698 PETITOT, EMILE. Monographie des Dene-Dindjie. 8vo. Paris (Leroux). 1876. $20.00

Smith 3044. Only copy located is at Victoria.

699 [PENNSYLVANIA.] The Keelboat Age on Western Waters. By Leland D. Baldwin. Map. 8vo, cloth. Pittsburgh, 1941. $3.00

700 [PENNSYLVANIA.] Book of Bucks County, containing Biographical Sketches of Leading Citizens of Bucks County, Penna. 558pp., 4to, calf. Buffalo, 1899. $4.50

701 [PENNSYLVANIA.] History of Bucks County from the Discovery of the Delaware to the Present Time. By W. H. H. Davis. 8vo, cloth. $12.50

702 [PENNSYLVANIA.] Catalogue of the Library of the Historical Society of Pennsylvania. Part I, History, Biography and Manuscripts. 8vo, original wrappers. Phila., 1849. $3.75

703 [PENNSYLVANIA.] An Account of the Gospel Labours and Christian Experiences of a Faithful Minister of Christ, John Churchman, late of Nottingham, Pennsylvania; to which is added a short Memorial of the Life and Death of a fellow Labourer in the Church, our valuable friend Joseph White, late of Bucks County. 12mo, full calf. Phila., 1779. $15.00

Brinley No. 3508. Contains an account of Churchman's journey to western Maryland in 1738; to Shrewsbury, N. J.; Fairfax and Hopewell in Virginia; a trip to New England with Samuel Hopwood in 1742. Chapter 5 gives a brief account of the Indian Treaty at Easton in 1757.

704 [PENNSYLVANIA.] Churches of the Valley; or an Historical Sketch of the Old Presbyterian Congregations of Cumberland and Franklin Counties in Pennsylvania. 338pp., 12mo, cloth. Phila., 1852. $5.00

705 [PENNSYLVANIA.] (Darlington, Mary Carson). Fort Pitt and Letters from the Frontier. Illus., maps. 312pp., 8vo, cloth. Pittsburgh, 1892. $7.50

Limited to 200 copies.

706 [PENNSYLVANIA.] Dauphin County Historical Society Addresses delivered before the Dauphin County Historical Society in the State Capitol, Harrisburg, July 4, 1876. 85pp., 8vo, original wrappers. Harrisburg, 1876. $4.50

707 [PENNSYLVANIA.] An Illustrated History of the Commonwealth of Pennsylvania. By Wm. H. Engle. Small 4to, half calf. Harrisburg, 1876. $7.50

708 [PENNSYLVANIA.] Fort Duquesne and Fort Pitt. Early names of Pittsburgh Streets. Illus. Small 4to, cloth. [Pittsburgh], 1889. $2.75

709 [PENNSYLVANIA.] (Franklin, Benjamin). Historical Review of Constitution and Government of Pennsylvania, from its origin; so far as regards the Several Points of Controversy, which have, from time to time arisen between the Governors and their Several Assemblies. 470pp., old calf (broken, and small piece torn from title). London, 1759. $17.50

Original Edition.

710 [PENNSYLVANIA.] "Pennsylvania Dutch" and other Essays. By Phebe Early Gibbons. 427pp., 12mo, cloth. Phila., 1882. $3.50

711 [PENNSYLVANIA.] Narrative of the Christian Experience, Travel and Labor. By John B. Hudson. 176pp., small 12mo, original printed boards. Rochester, 1838. $6.50

Born in Conn., in 1770, Hudson describes school life during the Revolution in Conn., Northern N. Y., and Pa. His adult life was spent in Delaware County in the Susquehanna, which he describes, as well as Western Penna., where he traveled.

712 [PENNSYLVANIA.] (Linn, John Blair). Annals of Buffalo Valley, Pa., 1755-1855. Chronologically arranged, and invaluable to Genealogists and others tracing Families in Penna. Illus. 8vo, cloth. Harrisburg, 1877. $4.50

713 [PENNSYLVANIA.] The Pennsylvania Magazine of History and Biography. Vol. 1, 1877 to Vol. 35, 1911. 35 vols. Illus. 8vo, cloth. Phila., 1877-1911. $75.00

Fine run of this important periodical published by the Historical Society of Pennsylvania.

714 [PENNSYLVANIA.] History of Hanover Township, including Sugar Notch, Ashley and Nanticoke Boroughs, with Genealogical Tables. By Henry B. Plumb. 8vo, cloth. 1885. $5.00

715 [PENNSYLVANIA.] (Proud, Robert). The History of Pennsylvania, in North America, from the Original Institution and Settlement of that Province, under the first Proprietor and Governor William Penn, in 1681, till after the Year 1742; with an Introduction, Respecting, the Life of W. Penn, Prior to the grant of the Province, and the religious Society of the People called Quakers; with the first rise of the Neighboring Colonies, more particularly of West-New-Jersey and the Settlement of the Dutch and Swedes on the Delaware. To which is added, a brief Description of the said Province, and of the General State, in which it flourished principally between the Years 1760 and 1770 . . . [Port. and map.] 2 vols., 8vo, calf. Phila., 1797-8. $35.00

"A learned and valuable work, but poorly arranged. The appendix contains several important documents and many reprints, among which may be mentioned: certain conditions, or concessions, agreed upon by William Penn', 'The Frame of the Government of the Province of Pa., 1682, 1683, 1696', 'The Charter of the City of Philadelphia, 1791', 'Journals of Christian Frederick Post, from Philadelphia to the Ohio, 1758-59', etc. The author was a native of Yorkshire, England, who settled in Philadelphia in 1759, where he resided till his death in 1813. For many years he was a teacher in a school attended chiefly by members of the Society of Friends"—Sabin.

716 [PENNSYLVANIA.] (Rupp, I. Daniel). Early History of Western Pennsylvania, and of the West, and of Western Expeditions and Campaigns, 1754 to 1833. By a Gentleman of the Bar. With an Appendix . . . [2 maps.] 12mo, cloth. Pittsburgh, 1847. $17.50

The great value of the above work is its reprints of French and Indian War Journals and memoranda of Indian Treaties. Contains the Journals of Croghan, Post, Bouquet, and Washington, and also accounts of the Expeditions of Harmer and St. Clair.

717 [PENNSYLVANIA.] History of Berks and Lebanon Counties, Containing a Brief Account of the Indians who Inhabited this Region of the Country, and the Numerous Murders by Them; Notices of the First Swedish, Welch, French, German, Irish and English Settlers, giving the Names of Nearly Five Hundred of them. . . . I. Daniel Rupp. Illus. 8vo, calf. Lancaster, 1844. $12.50

718 [PENNSYLVANIA.] History of Northampton, Lehigh, Monroe, Barton and Schuylkill Counties. 568pp. By I. Daniel Rupp. 8vo, mor. (weak hinge). Harrisburg, 1845. $10.00

719 [PENNSYLVANIA.] The Captivity and Suffering of Benjamin Gilbert and his Family, 1780-83. By Frank H. Severance. Map., illus. 8vo, cloth. Cleveland, 1904. $4.00

720 [PENNSYLVANIA.] Memoirs of Samuel Shryrock Jamison, Late State Senator of Pennsylvania. 158pp., 12mo, cloth. Phila., 1878. $3.00

721 [PENNSYLVANIA.] Memoirs of Major Robert Stobo of the Virginia Regiment. Folding map of Ft. Duquesne. 92pp., 16mo, cloth. Pittsburgh, 1854. $15.00

A scarce little work dealing with the French encroachments on the Ohio, surrender of Ft. Necessity; Stobo and Van Braum delivered as hostages, etc. This work was the prototype for Gilbert Parker's "Seats of the Mighty".

722 [PENNSYLVANIA.] A Memoir of the Life of James Milnor, late Rector of St. George's Church, New York. By John S. Stone. [Frontis., illus.] 12mo, cloth. N.Y. (c. 1849). $4.50

Milnor, born in Phila., in 1773, was a prominent lawyer of that city and had some correspondence with Washington in his early life.

723 [PENNSYLVANIA.] (Veech, James). Monongahela of Old; or Historical Sketches of Southwestern Pennsylvania to 1800. 244pp., 8vo, cloth. Pittsburgh, 1858-92. $17.50

Shea No. 630. An exceedingly interesting volume on the life of the Old Northwest, and the only volume of any historical value dealing with this group of early pioneers. The work deals most intelligently with early transportation, railroads, canals, coach, steamboats, and the early educational, social and political conditions. The author, Judge Veech actually compiled the above work from notes and rare traditions collected by Freeman Lewis.

724 PFEIFFER, IDA. A Lady's Second Journey Around the World . . . 8vo, cloth. N. Y., 1856. $2.50

Relates partly to California and Oregon.

725 PHILLIPS, WALTER SHELLEY. Totem Tales, as told by the Indians, gathered in the Pacific Northwest. 8vo, cloth. 326pp. Chicago, 1896. $5.00

The original edition of this work is scarce.

726 ——. The Same. 8vo, cloth. Chicago (1896). $2.50

727 PHILLIPS, WALTER SHELLEY. Chinook Book: A Descriptiive Analysis of the Chinook Jargon in plain words, giving instructions for Pronounciation, Construction, Expression and Proper Speaking of Chinook with all the various shaded meanings of the words. 118pp., 8vo, original wrappers. Seattle, 1913. $3.50

728 PHILLIPS, WILLIAM. Crossing the Plains in '46. 32pp., 12mo, original printed wrappers. Oregon City: Oregon Courier Herald, 1900. $30.00

We can locate only one other copy of this work, that in the Library of the University of Washington. Mr. Soliday, who has collected Northwestern and Overland Americana for more than 40 years states: "This is perhaps the rarest of all overland accounts published within the last fifty years. Smith, No. 3057 locates but one copy, and after years of search I secured this copy". The account, by a participant of the overland, covers 32 pages of doggerel verse.

729 PHILLIPS, WOLLEY CLIVE. Trottings of a Tenderfoot: A Visit to the Columbian Fiords . . . 350pp., 8vo, cloth. London, 1884. $5.00

730 PHILLIPS, WOLLEY CLIVE. A Sportsman's Eden. 216pp., 8vo, cloth. London: Bentley, 1888. $6.50

Smith 3059. Relates chiefly to Alaska and British Columbia.

731 [PHUCHER, ITOTHE.] The Puget Sound and Inland Empire Railway. Cascade Tunnel Route. 31pp., frontis., folding map. 8vo, original printed wrappers. Seattle, 1909. $7.50

General Chittenden is said to be the author of the above work.

732 PICKERING, CHAS. The Race of Man and their Geographical Distribution. To which is affixed an Analytical Synopsis of the Natural History of Man. By John Charles Ball, M.D. 445pp., map, 13 illus. London: Bohn, 1851. 8$4.50

733 PICKETT, JOSEPH W. Memoirs of Joseph W. Pickett. 150pp., 12mo, cloth. Burlington, 1880. $7.50

Colorado, Black Hills, Wyoming.

734 PICKETT, MRS. LA SALLE (CORBELL). Pickett and his Men. 313pp., 8vo, cloth. Phila., 1913. $4.00

Smith 3064. Pickett was in command of the U. S. troops during the San Juan Island dispute with Great Britain.

735 PIKE, ALBERT. The Life Story of. By Fred W. Allsopp. 130pp., illus., cloth. Little Rock, 1920. $3.00

Pike made a trip to Santa Fe in 1831.

736 PIKE, JAMES. The Scout and Pauper, being the Personal Adventures of Corporal Pike, of the 4th Ohio Cavalry, as a Texas Ranger in the Indian Wars, etc. 394pp., illus., 8vo, cloth. Cincinnati, 1866. $12.50

737 PIKE, WARBURTON. The Barren Ground of Northern Canada. Map. 8vo, cloth. London, 1892. $17.50

"This then was the sole object of my journey; to try and penetrate this unknown land, to seek the musk-ox, and to find out as much as I could about their habits, and the habits of the Indians who go in pursuit of them. My best chance seemed to follow Hearne's example and trust to the knowledge of the Indians to help me"—the author. He also gives interesting accounts of Winnipeg, York Factory, Yukon, Hudson's Bay Co., Northwest Company, etc.

738 PIKE, ZEBULON M. Expedition to Headwaters of the Mississippi River through Louisiana Territory and in New Spain, 1805-7. Reprinted in full from the Original of 1810, with extensive Annotations, Life of Pike and Analytical Index by Elliott Coues. [Maps and ports.] 3 vols., 8vo, as new. N. Y.: Francis Harper, 1895. $15.00

739 PINART [LOUIS] ALPHONSE. Voyage a la Cote Nord-Ouest d'Amerique, d'Ounalashka a Kadiak (Iles Aleoutiennes et Peninsule d'Aliaska). Map. 24pp., 8vo. Paris, 1874. $15.00

Extrait du Bulletin de la Societe de Geographie, Decembre, 1793.

739a——. The Same. Folio, original wrappers. Paris, 1875. $7.50

740 PINART [LOUIS] ALPHONSE. Le Chasse aux Aninaux Marins et les Pecheries chez les Indigenes de la Cote Nord-Ouest d'Amerique. 4to, original wrappers. Boulogne-sur-Mer, 1875. $10.00

741 PINART [LOUIS] ALPHONSE. La Caverne d'Aknanh Ile d'Ounga (Archipel Shumagin, Alaska). Illus. in color. 4to. Paris, 1875. $17.50

Large paper copy of this very scarce work, with all the handsomely illustrated plates.

742 PINE, GEORGE W. Beyond the Great West; Containing an Account of Two Years' Travel far beyond the Old West, on the Plains, in the Rocky Mts., New Mexico, Arizona, Wyoming, Montana, Idaho, Eastern and Western Oregon, Utah, Nevada and California. . . . Illus. 8vo, cloth. Utica, 1871. $4.50

743 ——. The Same. 8vo, cloth. Utica, 1873. $2.50

744 PITEZEL, JOHN H. Lights and Shades of Missionary Life, Containing Travels, Sketches, Incidents and Missionary Exports during Nine Years spent in the Region of Lake Superior. Illus. 431pp., 12mo, cloth. Cincinnati, 1859. $2.50

Commenced his mission work in the region in 1843.

745 ——. The Same. 12mo, cloth. Cincinnati, 1860. $2.00

PITTMAN'S "EUROPEAN SETTLEMENTS ON THE MISSISSIPPI"

746 PITTMAN, PHILIP. The Present State of the European Settlements on the Mississippi, with a Geographical Description of that River. With 8 engraved plans and maps. 4to, calf. London, 1770. $150.00

Paullin 2516. A rare work. The author resided for several years in the countries he describes, and was employed in surveying and exploring the interior. His work is one of the most interesting books relating to the Mississippi.

747 PITTMAN, CAPT. PHILIP. Present State of European Settlements on the Mississippi, with Geographical Description of the river. An exact reprint of the original edition, London, 1775. Edited with introduction, notes and index by Frank H. Hodder . . . 8vo, cloth. Cleveland, 1906. $10.00

Printed in a limited edition of 500 copies.

748 PLATT, WARD. The Frontier. Large colored folding maps and plates. 290pp., 12mo, original pictorial wrappers. N. Y., 1911. $4.50

Narrative of the westward movement of the frontier. The author traces the effect of the fur trade; Pioneer advance following he Louisiana Purchase; gives an account of the historic trails; California gold; and sketches of overland hardships, etc.

749 PLUMBE, JOHN R. Sketches of Iowa and Wisconsin, Taken during a Residence of Three Years in those Territories. Large folding map (in photostat). 103pp., (title-page in facsimile), leaf of ded. 8vo, original boards. St. Louis: Chambers, Harris & Knapp. 1839. $75.00

The first book printed west of the Ohio in which a National Railroad to the Pacific is considered and discussed. Plumbe crossed the plains to California to satisfy himself of the feasibility of his railroad project. At the Dubuque Convention of 1847, he was formally recognized as "the original projector of the great Oregon railroad". While in California, Plumbe became Register of the Squatter Association, and published the first book printed in Sacramento.

750 [POLK, JAMES K.] The Diary of., during his Presidency, 1845-49 now first printed from the Original Manuscript owned by the Secretary. Edited and Annotated by Milo Milton Quaife. With an Introduction by Andrew Cunningham Mc Laughlin. [Ill.] 4vols., 8vo, boards. Chicago, 1910. $22.50

Chicago Historical Society Collections, Vols. 6-9. 500 copies printed. The diary was written in the days of the war with Mexico, the Settlement of Oregon, acquisition of California and the Southwest, gold discoveres, etc.

751 POOLE, FRANCIS. Queen Charlotte Islands; a Narrative of Discovery and Adventure in the North Pacific. Ed. by John W. Lyndon. Plates, 2 maps, tab. 347pp., 4to. London: Hurst, 1872. $8.00

An interesting narrative giving details of life among the Indians, with accounts of their manners, customs, character, etc. Smith 3113.

752 [PONTIAC'S CONSPIRACY.] Journal of Pontiac's Conspiracy, 1763. Facsimiles. 8vo, cloth. (Detroit, 1912). $5.00

The Journal of Pontiac Mss. has long been considered the most important document regarding the conspiracy. Parkman drew heavily upon it. Each column contains both the original French text and an English translation by R. Clyde Ford, on parallel pages.

753 PORTER, KENNETH W. John Jacob Astor, Business Man. 2 vols., 8vo, cloth. Cambridge, 1931. $5.00

754 POST, C. C. Ten Years a Cowboy. 471pp., 12mo, cloth. Chicago, 1903. $2.00

755 POTTER, T. E. The Autobiography of Theodore Edgar Potter. Ports. 228pp., 8vo, cloth. Concord: Privately Printed, 1913. $15.00

The first half of the work is devoted to the trip across the plains, and records in detail the hardships and adventures of the journey, with sketches of the country traversed, Indian tribes, etc. The second part narrates the author's life and experiences of the diggings; his adventures with the Sonora Grays; lynching and marauding in Southern California; his adventures in Walker's Filibustering Expedition; his return eastward to Minnesota in 1862; and campaign against the Sioux in the Dakota Indian war.

756 POWELL, ADDISON M. Echoes from the Frontier. Illus. 60pp., 12mo, cloth. N. Y., 1909. $3.50

757 POWELL, J. W. Exploration of the Colorado River of the West and its Tributaries explored in 1869, 1870, 1871, 1872 . . . Illus. 292pp., 4to, cloth. Washington, 1875. $10.00

758 POWELL, J. W. Introduction to the Study of Indian Languages. 228pp., 2nd ed. 4to, cloth. Washington, 1880. $2.50

759 POWER, TYRONE. Impressions of America, during the Years 1833-35. 2 vols., 8vo, cloth. Phila., 1836. $3.00

760 POWERS, STEPHEN. Afoot and Alone: A Walk from Sea to Sea by the Southern Route. Adventures and Observations in Southern California, New Mexico, Arizona, Texas, etc. Illus. 12mo, cloth. Hartford, 1872. $9.00

Original Edition. Powers made his journey from Charleston to San Francisco in 1868.

761 [POWERS, STEPHEN.] Aborigines of California. (From Atlantic Monthly, March, 1874). 8vo. Boston, 1874. $2.50

762 PORTLOCK, NATHANIEL. Voyage round the World; but more Particularly to the Northwest Coast of America, 1786-1788, in the King George and Queen Charlotte, Captains Portlock and Dixon . . . 384 & 40 pp., 2 ports., 13 plates, 5 maps, tab. Square 4to, calf. London: Stockdale, 1789. $40.00

This copy has the rare colored bird plates. Capt. Portlock visited the N. W. Coast, and his work deals extensively with the tribes round Nootka.

763 PRATT, ORSON. A Series of Pamphlets: Complete Collections of the Original Numbers; together with Elder Gibson's and Elder Taylor's Discussion, each separately paged. 8vo, half calf. Liverpool, 1851. $12.50

The first issue of Orson Pratt's papers, all dated from Wilton St., Liverpool, 1848-1851.

764 PRATT, ORSON. A Series of Pamphlets on the Doctrines of the Gospel. 314pp., 12mo, cloth. Salt Lake City, 1884. $4.50

765 PRICE, MAJOR SIR ROSS LAMBERT. The Two Americas. An Account of Sport and Travel, with Notes of Men and Manners in North and South America. 368pp., 8vo, cloth. London, 1877. $5.00

766 PRICHARD, JAMES COWLES. Natural History of Man. 4th edition, enlarged. With 50 colored plates and other illus. Thick 8vo, cloth. London, 1855. $6.00

Includes 20 colored plates of American Indians of California, the Sioux, Ogibways, etc.

767 PRIEST, J. American Antiquities and Discoveries in the West; exhibition of evidence that an ancient population of a partially civiized nation peopled America before its discovery by Columbus. 8vo, half mor. Albany, 1835. $7.50

Contains supposed ruins of Roman fort at Marietta, discoveries at Muskingum, ruins of ancient works at Circleville, Ohio, ten lost tribes, animals and rocks of Tenn., mummies found in Ky., etc.

768 PRIEST, JOSEPH. American Antiquities and Discoveries in the West. . . . 5th edition. 400pp., folding map, plate. 8vo, cloth. Albany, 1835. $4.00

Has a chapter entitled "Voyages and Shipping of the Mongol Tartars and Settlement on the Western Coast of America".

769 PRUD'HOMME, L. A. Notes Historiques sur la vie de P. E. de Raddison. 60pp., 12mo, original wrappers. St. Boniface, Man., 1892. $6.00

Narrative of the four expeditions (1654-84) of the noted explorer; his travels and adventures among the Indians west of the Mississippi; his journey to Lake Superior and the N. W.; services under the Hudson's Bay Co., etc.

ORIGINAL TYPESCRIPT OF PROSCH'S UNPUBLISHED HISTORY OF SEATTLE

770 PROSCH, THOMAS W. A Chronological History of Seattle, from 1850-1897. Prepared for publication in 1900 and 1901, but never published. 579 original typescript pages, 4to. [Seattle, 1900-01]. $150.00

The only available typescript of this important unpublished historical work by not only one of the early pioneers of Washington Territory but a leading authority on men who and events which shaped the destiny of the state. Prosch is the author of many works on the history of the Northwest.

PROSCH'S PIONEER REMINISCENCES

771 PROSCH, CHARLES. Reminiscences of Washington Territory. Scenes, Incidents and Reflections of the Pioneer Period on Puget Sound. Portrait. 128pp., 8vo, cloth. Seattle, 1904. $35.00

Original Edition. Prosch arrived at Steilacoom in 1858. His volume (privately issued in a few copies) recounts his experiences on the trip to Puget Sound; the beginnings of his "Puget Sound Herald"; early land speculations; defying the Hudson's Bay Co.; Fraser River gold rush; Rise and fall of Whatcom (Bellingham); the San Juan war; Transcontinental railroad projects; early pioneers; Indian depredations; early steamboating, etc., etc.

772 PROSCH, THOMAS W. Dr. D. Maynard, the Pioneer Physician of Seattle. 8vo. Northwest Medicine, Seattle, 1904. $5.00

773 PROSCH, THOMAS W. McCarver and Tacoma . . . Port. and plates. 198pp., 8vo, cloth. Seattle: Privately Printed, 1906. $10.00

774 PROSCH, THOMAS W. The Conkling-Prosch Family, with some reference to the Dotter, Roe, Reynolds, Brooks, McCarver and other Connections. Plates. 141pp., 8vo, cloth. Seattle, 1909. $17.50

Only 150 copies were printed of this important work, which contains interesting material on Olympia, Steilacoom, Seattle, Puget Sound, etc.

775 PROSCH, THOMAS W. The Insane of Washington Territory. 8pp., 8vo, original wrappers. Seattle, 1914. $3.50

Smith 3230.

776 PURCHAS, SAMUEL. Hakluytus; or Purchas His Pilgrimages: Contayning a History of the World in Sea Voyages and Lande Travells, by Englishmen and others, with numerous folding maps, charts, etc. 20 vols., 8vo, cloth. Glasgow: MacLehose, 1905. $55.00

777 PUTER, STEPHEN A. DOUGLAS, and STEVENS, HORACE. Looters of the Public Domain . . . Embracing a complete exposure of the Fraudulent System of acquiring titles to Public Lands of the U. S. . . . Illus. 495pp., 8vo. Portland, Ore., 1908. $7.50

778 QUAIFE, MILO M. Chicago and Old Northwest, Dearborn. Maps and plates. .488pp., large 8vo, cloth. Chicago [1913.] $12.50

779 QUAIFE, MILO M. The Journals of Capt. Meriwether Lewis and Sergeant John Ordway, kept on the Expedition of Western Exploration, 1803-1806. Illus., 3 maps. 444pp., 8vo, cloth. Madison, Wis., 1916. $7.50

Smith 2194.

780 [QUAKERS.] Life, Travels, and Gospel Labours. By Job Scott. 317pp., 8vo, calf. Mount Pleasant, Ohio, 1820. $5.00

Includes life and travels among Quakers of R. I., Pa., Va., South, etc.

781 QUINCY, JOSIAH. An Oration, pronounced July 4, 1798, at the request of the Inhabitants of the Town of Boston, in Commemoration of the Anniversary of American Independence. 31pp., 8vo, sewn (badly foxed). Boston, 1798. $3.00

781a QUINLAN, JAMES E. Tom Quick, the Indian Slayer: and the Pioneers of Minisink and Wawarsink. 16mo, three-quarter red calf and cloth. Monticello, N. Y.: De Voe and Quinlan, 1851. $32.50

The very scarce Original Edition. A very excellent clean copy save for a repair of slightly chipped outer margins on three or four pages.

782 [RAILROAD SURVEYS.] Pacific Railroad Exploration and Survey. 33rd Cong., 1st Sess., Senate Ex. Doc. No. 29. Copies of all Reports of Engineers and other Persons employed to make Explorations and Surveys to ascertain the most practical Route for a Railroad from the Mississippi River to the Pacific Ocean. 3 large folding maps, 118pp., 8vo, sewn. Washington, 1854. $22.50

One of the scarcest of all the early railroad reports. the first part reviews the Northern Route, the second part, the Central Route, and the third, the Southern Route.

783 [RAILROAD SURVEYS.] Pacific Railroad Explorations and Survey. Report of the Exploration and Survey to Ascertain the most Practicable and Economical Route for a Railroad from the Mississippi River to the Pacific Ocean. Numerous maps and lithographic plates. 13 vols., 4to, cloth. Washington, 1856. $22.50

784 RAMSAY, DAVID. The History of South-Carolina from its First Settlement in 1670 to the Year 1808. Map. 2 vols., calf. Charleston, 1809. $30.00

785 ——. The Same. Lacks map. $17.50

786 REAVIS, L. U. A Change of National Empire; or Arguments in favor of the Removal of the National Capital from Washington City to the Mississippi Valley. Folding maps. 170pp., 8vo, unbound. St. Louis, 1869. $5.00

787 REAVIS, L. U. Facts and Arguments in Favor of the Removal of the National Capital to the Mississippi Valley. 12pp., 8vo, unbound. St. Louis, 1869. $4.50

788 [RECONSTRUCTION.] (McPherson, Edward). Political History of the U. S. during the Period of Reconstruction, 1865-70. 648pp., 8vo, cloth. Washington, 1875. $10.00

Embraces the Johnson Controversy and Impeachment, Military Rule in the Southern States, their Re-admission into the Union, etc.

789 [RECONSTRUCTION.] Reminiscences of a Long Life. By Hiram R. Steele. 47 and 11 pp. 8vo, original wrappers. [New York, 1927.] $5.00

A privately printed work. Judge Steele played an active part in the Reconstruction period in Louisiana following the Civil War. By the free choice of southern citizens he became a judicial officer of law.

790 REVERE, PAUL. The Life of. By Eldridge Henry Goss. Illus. 2 vols., 4to, cloth. Boston, 1891. $15.00

Large paper edition, limited to 100 copies. With many portraits and other illustrations and facsimiles, some hand-colored, of Revere's works.

791 RICKMAN, JOHN. Journal of Capt. Cook's Last Voyage to the Pacific Ocean, 1776-80. 8vo, half calf, 434pp. Folding map, 5 engraved plates. London, 1781. $55.00

A surreptitious version of the 3rd Cook voyage, written, it is believed, by the Second Mate of the "Discovery" and anticipating the Official Edition by 2 years, and the Ledyard, Ellis and others by 2 years. The introduction includes a fine summary of South Sea Voyages and of attempts to discover a Northwest Passage. This ranks with both Zimmerman and Ledyard as the two other surreptitious accounts.

792 [RHODE ISLAND.] History of the State of Rhode Island and Providence Plantations. By S. G. Arnold. 2 vols., 8vo, cloth. N. Y., 1859-60. $7.50

793 RHODE ISLAND HISTORICAL SOCIETY, Collections of. Vols. 1-10, inclusive. 8vo, calf and cloth. Providence, 1827-1902. $40.00

794 RHODE ISLAND HISTORICAL SOCIETY, Publications (including Proceedings). New series. 8 vols., 8vo, half roan. Providence, 1893-1900. $20.00

795 [RHODE ISLAND.] (Potter, Elisha R.). An Address delivered before the Rhode Island Historical Society, on the Evening of Feb. 19th, 1851. 27pp., sewn. 8vo. Providence, 1851. $3.00

796 [RHODE ISLAND.] (Villard, Geo. O.). History of the Providence Stage, 1762-1891, Including Sketches of Many Prominent Actors who have appeared in America. Frontis. 298pp., 8vo, cloth. Providence, 1891. $6.00

797 ROBINSON, S. Me-Won-I-Toc; Frontier Life and Indian Character, exhibiting Traditions, Superstitions and Character of a Race that is passing away. 133pp., 8vo, original wrappers. N. Y., 1867. $7.50

Field 1996. Narrative of life and adventures among the Indians in Michigan and Illinois from 1834 on.

798 [RUSSIAN-AMERICAN CO.] (Boguslaw, H.). Ein Blick auf die Flora der Umgegend von Archangle, 49pp. (Contained in VI Band, Archiv fur Wissenschaftliche Kunde Russland). 8vo, original wrappers. Berlin, 1847. **$15.00**

799 [RUSSIAN-AMERICAN CO.] (Freimann, Herrn). Bemerkungen uber eine Reise von Sitcha durch dis Bisitzungen der Hudson's Bay Company. 227pp. Also: (Erman, Von A.) Ueber P. v. Krusenstern's und A. von Keyserling's Reise an die Petschora und deren Zuflusse. 342pp. (Contained in—Archiv fur Wissenschaftliche Kunde Russland, vi Band). 8vo, original wrappers. Berlin, 1847. $15.00

800 [RUSSIAN-AMERICAN CO.] Einige Geognotische Bemerkungen uber Ost-Siberien zwischen 80 und 105 O. v. Paris. 109pp. Also—Daseggende Waschwerk (budaras' horonoju) bei den Sibirischen Goldseifen 125pp. (Contained in: Archiv fur Wissenschaftliche Kunde von Russland). 8vo, lacks wrappers but is from the Czar's Library and contains his imperial bookplate. Berlin, 1845. $15.00

801 [RUSSIAN-AMERICAN CO.] (Erman, von Adolph). Die Geognotischan auf das Gold-Vorkommen in diesem Erdtheile. Also—(Ehrenberg, C. G.) Nueste Beitrage zur Geognosie von Nord-Asien. Together with a finely colored map (size 21x30 in.). (Contained in Archiv fur Wissenschaftliche von Russland Herausgegehen. Von. A. Erman. 8vo, original wrappers. Berlin, 1842. $15.00

802 [RUSSIAN-AMERICAN CO.] Archiv fur Wissenschaftliche Kunde von Russland. Herausgegeben von A. Erman. 11 vols., 8vo, original wrappers. Berlin, 1842-1858. $50.00

A fine broken run of this storehouse of information relating to Alaska, the Aleutians, fur trade, etc. Except for a few exceptions all the articles are complete in each issue. This set from the Czar's Library.

803 [RUSSIAN-AMERICAN CO.] (Erman, Capt. von A.). Ueber zwei auf Kamtschatke und bei Ochozk gefundene Antiquitaten. Also: Die Ersten Kriegszuge der Russen nach Sibirien. 399, 475 pp. (Contained in Archiv Wissenschaftliche Kunde Russland, IV Band, 3tes heft). 8vo, original wrappers. Berlin, 1845. $15.00

804 [RUSSIAN-AMERICAN CO.] (Kashevarov, Lieut. A. F.). Kaschewarow's Reise in aussersten Noden von Amerika. Also—Uebersicht der Hydrographischen Expeditionen und Messungen in Russischen Meeren. (Mentions Krusenstren, Golovinin, Kotzebue, Lutke, etc.). (Contained in Archiv fur Wissenschaftliche Kunde Russland. 8vo, original wrappers. Berlin, 1846. $15.00

Wick. 5890.

CZAR'S COPY OF REPORTS FROM HIS ALASKA COLONIES

805 RUSSIAN-AMERICAN CO. Otchet, R-American Kompanii. Glavnago Pravlieniia. (Report of the Governor General Russian American Co., 1852, 1853, 1860, 1861). Report for 1852, 8vo, full mor., 25pp., 5 views and a beautifully colored map, 17x21½ in. (Title in Russian). Report for 1853, 8vo, full mor., 33pp., 5 views and tables and beautifully colored map (with insets), 15x17½ in. Report for 1860. 8vo, full mor., 107-2pp., 5 tables and a colored plate (16x22 in., with title in Russian, showing natives in canoes with settlement in the background), also folding map, beautifully colored and with insets, size 15x17½ in. Report for 1861, 8vo, full mor., 46pp., 5 tables and colored plate (17x27 in.) showing Sitka. Together 4 vols., full mor. St. Petersburg, 1853-1854-1861-1862. $115.00

The above finely prepared works are from the Czar's library and bear the royal colors. They are very fine copies and were evidently prepared with the special colored plates and maps for the royal library.

ORIGINAL MANUSCRIPT JOURNAL RELATING TO RUSSIAN SETTLEMENTS IN ALASKA, 1832

806 [RUSSIAN-AMERICAN CO.] (Rumiantev [Romanov], Vladimir). Two Original Manuscripts of 37 pages folio written in Russian, between the years 1832 and 1835. The first part, comprising 19 pages, is a diary of the celebrated Russian traveller Vladimir Rumiantev, or Romanov, as he was better known. The second manuscript of 18 pages is a statement of the commercial conditions of the Russian Settlements in Alaska in 1831, delivered to the Assembly of the shareholders on Aug. 23, 1832. All written legibly in ink. Folio, boards (some water stains). N.p., c. 1832. $125.00

Romanov visited the Russian settlements in 1831, probably at the instigation of the Czar who was a large shareholder. As Romanov was a man of considerable ability his report on the Settlement is of genuine historic importance.

807 [RUSSIAN-AMERICAN CO.] Die Ersten Botanischen Nachrichten uber das Amurla ad von Herrn Ruprecht and Regel (Schluss). (Contained in—Archiv fur Wissenschraftliche Kunde von Russland, VII Band). 8vo, original wrappers. Berlin, 1858. $10.00

808 [RUSSIAN-AMERICAN CO.] Topographische Skizze der Gegend Zwischen der Castries—bei und dem Amur. Map—"Karte der Amur Mundug" (fine map of the Coastline, 11x17 in.). (Contained in Archiv fur Wissenschaftliche Kunde von Russland, 19th Band, Istes heft). 8vo, original wrappers. Berlin, 1859. $10.00

809 [RUSSIAN-AMERICAN CO.] Aus dem Jahrenberichte Russisch-Amerikanischen Handles-Compagnia fur 1856-57. 471pp. Together with: Ueber die Schiflahrt auf dem Amour in Jahre 1857. 484pp., 8vo, original wrappers. (Archiv fur Wissenschaftliche Kunde von Russland, xviii Band). Berlin, 1858. $10.00

810 RUSSIAN-AMERICAN CO.] Statistik der von 1822-33 erfolgten Verbannumgen nach Sibirien. (Contained in—Archiv. fur Wissenschaftliche Kunde von Russland, IV Band, 4estes heft). 8vo, original wrappers. Berlin, 1845. $15.00

811 [RUSSIAN-AMERICAN CO.] (Wrangle, Admiral F.). Ueber des Nord-Asiiatische Eismeer und die Erreichung der Erdpoles auf dem Atlantischen. (Contained in—Archiv fur Wissenschaftliche Kunde von Russland, VII Band). 8vo, original wrappers. Berlin, 1848. $15.00

812 [RUSSIAN-AMERICAN CO.] Die Ersten Botanischen Nachrichten uber das Amurland. (Contained in—Archiv fur Wissenschaftliche Kunde von Hussland, XVII Band). 8vo, original wrappers. Berlin, 1858. $10.00

Relates to the Northwest Coast.

813 [RUSSIAN-AMERICAN CO.] (Veniaminov, Ivan). Veniaminov uber die Aleutischen Insel und deren Bewohner. 459pp. (In: Archiv fur Wissenschaftliche Kunde von Russland, II Band etes heft). 8vo, original wrappers. Berlin, 1842. $15.00

814 [RUSSIAN-AMERICAN CO.] (Veniaminov) or, in German (Wenjaminow). Ueber die Sprachen des Russischen Amerika's nach Wenjaminow, 126pp. Also: Der Fischanfg in Ost-Sibirien. 144pp. (Contained in Archiv fur Wissenschaftliche Kunde von Russland. 8vo, original wrappers. VII Band, ites heft). Berlin, 1848. $15.00

815 ST. CLAIR, MAJOR GEN. ARTHUR. Narrative of the manner in which the Campaign against the Indians, in 1791, was conducted; observations on the Statements of the Secretary of War and Quartermaster General. With the scarce portrait which is often lacking. 292pp., 8vo, calf. Phila., 1812. $22.50

"A narrative of terrible defeat and slaughter of 800 soldiers by Ohio Indians. St. Clair's voluminous defense is rendered futile by the passionate ejaculations of Washington, when Major Benny called him from a dinner party to announce defeat. Overcome with surprise and indignation, Washington cursed (the) beaten general with exceeding fervour, adding 'Did not my last words warn him against a surprise?"

816 [ST. PAUL, MINNEAPOLIS & MANITOBA RAILWAY CO.] Laws Constituting the Charter of. Small 4to, original wrappers. N.p., (1891). $8.00

Original record of the railway's organization.

817 SCHOOLCRAFT, HENRY R. Summary Narrative of an Exploring Expedition to the Sources of the Mississippi River in 1820; resumed and completed by the Discovery of its Origin in Itasca Lake, in 1832 . . . Woodcut. 596pp., 8vo, cloth. Phila., 1855. $7.50

818 SCOTT, JOSEPH. A Geographical Dictionary of the United States of America, containing a General Description of each State, etc. With a succinct account of Indiana and Upper and Lower Louisiana Territories. Map. 8vo, calf. Phila., 1805. $7.50

819 [SEA.] An Apprentice System for the U. S. Merchant Service. Also containing a Bill presented to Congress by the Hon. R. C. Fenton and referred to the Committee of the Whole on the State of the Nation . . . By John W. Goin. 36pp., original wrappers. N. Y., 1855. $4.75

The Goins were ship owners in N. Y., and one of them, Thomas Goin, is often called the Father of the U. S. Naval Academy plan.

820 SEARIGHT, THOMAS B. The Old Pike. History of the National Road, with Incidents, Accidents and Anecdotes thereon. Illus. 384pp., 8vo, cloth. Uniontown, Pa.: Published by the Author, 1894. $20.00

The above work is the leading authority on the life and ways of the folk people along the old road; the old taverns and their keepers; the wagons, stages and stage drivers; pioneer reminiscences, etc.

821 [SEATTLE.] Seattle City Directories, Comprising an Alphabetically arranged list of business firms and private Citizens—a Classified List of all Trades, Professions and Pursuits—a Miscellaneous Directory, City and County Officers, Public and Private Schools, Churches . . . R. L. Polk & Co. Vol. 1, 1889 through the 28th Year, 1914. Together 25 vols., 8vo, cloth. Seattle, 1889-1914. $65.00

Such a complete run would be extremely hard to find outside the stocks of the larger libraries. The earlier years are almost impossible to procure.

822 [SEATTLE.] The City of Seattle. By John W. Pratt. [New England Magazine, May, 1893.] 8vo. Boston, 1893. $2.50

823 [SEATTLE.] The Indian Attack on Seattle, Jan. 26, 1856. By Lieut. T. S. Phelps. Edited by Mrs. Carl Gould. Illus. 57pp., 8vo, original printed wrappers. Seattle, 1932. $3.00

824 [SEATTLE MAP.] Map and View of Seattle. By Commodore T. S. Phelps. Folio broadside. January, 1856. $8.50

825 [SENECA INDIANS.] Report on the Memorials of the Seneca Indians and others accepted, Nov. 21, 1940, in the Council of Massachusetts. 29pp., 8vo, original wrappers. Boston, 1840. $5.00

826 [SENECA INDIANS.] Declaration of the Seneca Indians in General Council Assembled, with Accompanying Documents. Also an Address to the Chiefs and People of that Nation. 8vo, original wrappers. Baltimore, 1845. $10.00

827 [SETTLERS' GUIDE.] Old Settler. The Garden of the World; or the Great West. Its History, Wealth, Natural Advantages and its Future. Also comprises a Complete Guide to Emigrants, with a Full Description of Different Routes Westward. 396pp., 8vo, cloth. Boston, 1856. $9.50

828 SHERRARD, ROBERT A. A Narrative of the Wonderful Escape and Dreadful Sufferings of Colonel James Paul, after the Defeat of Col. Crawford, when that unfortunate Commander, and many of his men, were inhumanly burnt at the Stake. 22pp., 8vo, original printed wrappers, uncut. Cincinnati, 1869. $15.00

Shea No. 568. This is the first publication in book form.

829 SIMMS, WM. GILMORE. History of South Carolina from its First European Discovery to its Election into a Republic . . . to the Present Time. Frontis. and engraved title. 12mo, cloth. N. Y., 1860. $4.50

830 SHEA, JOHN G. Discovery and Exploration of the Mississippi Valley, with original narratives of Marquette, Allouez, Membre, Hennepin and Douay. Portraits and Facsimiles. Small 4to, original boards, uncut. Albany, 1903. $5.00

One of 500 numbered copies.

831 —— Same. 8vo, cloth. N. Y., 1852. $7.50

832 SHEA, JOHN G. Early Voyages Up and Down the Mississippi, by Cavelier S. Cosme, Le Sueur, Gravier, and Guignas. With an Introduction, Notes, and an Index by John Gilmary Shea. 4to. Albany, 1861. $10.00

Contains Cavelier's account of La Salle's voyage to the source of the Mississippi, his landing in Texas, and march to the Mississippi; the voyage down the Mississippi in 1699 by Montigny, St. Cosme, Davion, and Thaumur de la Scource; Le Sueur's voyage up the Mississippi in 1699-1700; Gravier's voyage down and up the Mississippi, 1700; Guignas's voyage up the Mississippi, 1738. With a copious and valuable index. This is No. 132 of the McDonough edition.

833 SMITH, COL. JAMES. An Account of the Remarkable Occurrences in the Life and Travels of Col. James Smith during his Captivity with the Indians, in the Years 1755, '56, '57, '58 and '59. With an Appendix . . . by Wm. Darlington, of Pittsburgh. xi, 192pp., 8vo, cloth. Cincinnati, 1907. As new. $6.00

834 SMITH, WILLIAM C. Indiana Miscellany; Sketches of Indian Life; early Settlement, Customs, Hardships, etc. 304pp., 8vo, cloth. Cincinnati, 1867. $7.50

Privately printed for the author in a limited edition. Pioneer settlements, Quakers, Methodism, early schools, education, Indians, War of 1812, politics, etc.

836 SOUTHERN HISTORICAL SOCIETY PAPERS. Twelve Volumes. January, 1876 through Dec., 1884. 8vo, cloth, fine. Richmond, 1876-1884. $35.00

Fine run of the early numbers of this work.

837 [SOUTHWEST.] The Silver Country of the Great Southwest. A review of the Mineral and other Wealth . . . of New Spain, comprising Mexico and the Mexican cessions to the U. S. in 1848 and 1853. Colored Folding Map. By Alexander D. Anderson. 8vo, cloth. N. Y., 1877. $7.50

Original edition of the first general study of the new territory following its acquisition from Mexico. The map shows lines of railways west of Mississippi Valley, also the Ocean Warm Springs, and new boundaries.

838 [SOUTHWEST.] (Goodwin, C. C.). The Cornstock Club. 314pp., 8vo, cloth. Salt Lake City, 1891. $7.50

Only a small number printed. Relates to California, Argonauts, gold rush, pioneers; Utah, Nevada, Nebraska, Wyoming.

839 [SOUTHWEST.] (Paine, A. B.). Capt. Bill McDonald, Texas Ranger. 448pp., colored plates, 8vo, cloth. N. Y., 1909. $4.75

Interesting account of 20-odd years' Ranger Service against outlaws and Indians from the Mexica Border to Oklahoma.

840 STACEY, NATHANIEL. Memoirs of the Life of Nathaniel Stacey. VI, 523p., frontis., 8vo, cloth. Columbus, Pa., 1850. $12.50

The above work is much more interesting and important than the title indicates. It contains an interesting narrative of pioneer life, not only in New England but in N. Y., and Pennsylvania and on the Muskingum in Ohio. Stacey was born in Hampshire County, Pa., in 1778, the son of a soldier of the Revolution who had fought at Bunker Hill. Gives an account of "working out" at the age of 11; teaching school in Vermont; of preaching in Vermont in 1803; Chaplin of N. Y. regiment during War of 1812; removes to Ohio and later to Michigan; New England Purchase in the Muckingum; the Indian Massacre there; flat-boating on the Ohio, etc. The author also made a tour of Ohio in 1834.

841 STEPHENS, JOHN L. Incidents of Travel in Central America, Chiapas and Yucatan. [Map and Illus.] 2 vols., 8vo, cloth, fine. N. Y., 1841. $7.50

842 STONE, WM. L. Life and Times of Sir William Johnson. 2 vols., 8vo, cloth, illus. Albany, 1865. $7.50

843 [TENNESSEE.] The Annals of Tennessee to the end of the Eighteenth Century. By J. G. M. Ramsay. [Map and plan.]. Thick 8vo, cloth. Charleston, 1853. $12.50

First Edition. Nearly the entire volume is filled with a detailed narration of the Indian wars with the various settlements.

844 [TEXAS.] Glimpses of Texas: Its Divisions, Resources, Developments and Prospects. By Wm. Brady. Colored folding map showing Counties, in colors, 15 x 20 in. Done by E. H. Cushing, Houston, 1871. 12mo, cloth. Houston, 1871. $7.50

845 [TEXAS.] History of South America and Mexico. By John M. Niles. In which is contained "Geographical and Historical View of Texas," by L. T. Pease. 2 vols. in 1, 12mo, calf. Hartford, 1844. $7.50

846 [TEXAS AND NEW MEXICO.] (Pages, Viscount Pierre Marie Francois de). Voyages autour de Monde et vers les Deux Poles, par Terre et par Mer, Pendant les annes 1767-1776. Maps and Plates. 2 vols., 8vo, calf. Paris, 1782. $25.00

The Original Edition. The author was born in Toulouse in 1748 and entered the navy at the age of 18. He at once conceived the idea of a voyage round the world and while on duty at St. Domingo he completed his preparations, and in 1767 set sail from Cape Francais for Louisiana. He passed through New Orleans, ascended the Mississippi to Natchitoches, crossed Texas and Mexico, and reaching Acapulco he embarked there for the Philippines. Failing to enter China he continued his voyage by way of India and arrived at Marseilles in 1771. He fought in the American Revolution and afterwards retired to St. Domingo, where he was murdered during the Slave Insurrection in 1793. The work is important because of the account of Texas and New Mexico, and the Indians there.

One of the maps accompanying this original edition is entitled "Carte d'une Partie de l'Amerique Septentrionale qui contient partie de la Nle Espagne et de la Louisiane pour servir aux Voyages au tour de Monde . . ." On this map is shown the overland route of De Pages from Nachitoches on the Mississippi to Acapulco.

847 [TEXAS.] (Parker, W. B.). Notes taken during the Expedition commanded by Capt. R. B. Marcy, U. S. A. through Unexplored Texas in the Summer and Fall of 1854. 12mo, half mor. Phila., 1856. $15.00

Wagner-Camp 279. Parker was a civilian friend of Marcy and went for the adventure. The object was to locate an Indian Reserve in northwest Texas for the Indians of Texas. Party left Ft. Smith, Ark., June 1, Dr. G. G. Shumard, of Ft. Smith, accompanying them. They proceeded via Ft. Washita to the Little Washita, and the headwaters of the Brazos. Returned to Ft. Smith in Oct.

848 [TEXAS.] Texas. Address of the Hon. Wm. H. Wharton, delivered in New York, on Tuesday, April 30, 1836. Also Address of the Hon. Stephen F. Austin, delivered at Louisville, Ky., on the 7th March, 1836. Together with other Documents Explanatory of the Origin, Principles and Objects of the Contest in which Texas is at present engaged. Published by order of the New York Texas Committee. 56pp., 8vo, entirely uncut and unopened. New York, 1836. $57.50

849 [TEXAS BOUNDARY.] Speech of Mr. [George] Ashmun, of Massachusetts . . . upon the Texas Boundary and the Bill for its Settlement. 15pp., untrimmed. Washington, 1850. $4.50

850 THWAITES, REUBEN G. (Editor). Early Western Travels, 1748-1846. A Series of Annotated Reprints of some of the Best and Rarest Contemporary Volumes of Travel, Descriptive of the Aborigines, and Social and Economic Conditions in the Middle and Far West, during the Period of Early American Settlement. 32 volumes, including the Folio Atlas. 8vo, cloth. Cleveland, 1904-07. $200.00

Comprises: Brackenridge's Voyage, 1811; Bradbury's Travels, 1809-11; Bullock's Journey, 1827; Buttrick's Voyages, 1812-19; Croghan's Tours, 1750-63; Cumming's Tour, 1807-9; DeSmet's Letters, 1840-41; DeSmet's Oregon Missions, 1845-6; Evans's Tour, 1818; Farnham's Travels, 1839; Faux's Tour, 1819-20; Flagg's Far West, 1836-37; Flint's Letters, 1818-20; Flower's Letters, 1819; Flower's Letters, 1820-21; Franchere's Voyage, 1811-14; Gregg's Commence, 1831-39; Harris's Tour, 1803; Hulme's Tour, 1818; James' Expedition, 1819-20; Long's Voyages, 1768-82; Maximilian, 1843; Michaux's Travels, 1795-6; Michaux's Travels, 1802; Morris's Journal, 1764; Nuttall's Travels, 1819; Ogden's Tour, 1821-23; Palmer's Travels, 1845-6; Pattie's Narrative, 1824-27; Post's Tours, 1758-59 Ross's Adventures, 1810-13; Townsend's Journey, 1834; Weiser's Tour, 1748; Welby's Visit, 1819-20; Wood's Residence, 1820-21; Wyeth's Journey, 1832; Analytical and subject index in 2 large volumes.

851 THWAITES, REUBEN GOLD. The Colonies, 1492-1750. 4 maps. 12mo, cloth. N. Y., 1904. $2.50

852 [UTAH.] (Remy, Jules). A Journey to Great Salt Lake . . . with a Sketch and Customs of the Mormons and Introduction on the Religious Movement in the U. S. With 10 steel engravings and a map. 2 vols., 8vo, oariginal cloth. London, 1861. $8.00

Wagner-Camp (Note) 364.

853 VAN CAMPEN, MOSES. (Hubbard, J. N.). Sketches of Border Adventures in the Life of Major Van Campen, a Soldier of the Revoultion. 310pp., 8vo, cloth. Bath, N. Y., 1842. $15.00

854 —— The Same, revised and extended, 337pp., 8vo, cloth. Fillmore, N. Y., 1893. $5.00

855 [VERMONT.] (Thompson, Zadok). History of the State of Vermont. Map. 8vo, old sheep. Burlington, 1842. $5.00

856 [VIRGINIA.] Records of the Virginia Company of London; the Court Book, from the Manuscript in the Library of Congress. Edited . . . by Chas. Deane. Folding map, facsimile. 2 vols., 4to, cloth. Washington, 1906. $10.00

857 [VIRGINIA HISTORICAL SOCIETY.] Collections of, New Series, Vols. 1 to 11. [Ports.] 8vo, cloth and original wrappers. Richmond, 1882-92. $37.50

Includes the Spotswood Letters; Dinwiddie Papers, Virginia Co., 1619-1624; Huguenot Emigration to Virginia, Miscellaneous Papers, 1672-1865; Virginia Convention, 1788, etc.

858 [WAR OF 1812.] (Atherton, Wm.). Narrative of the Suffering and Defeat of the Northwestern Army under General Winchester. Massacre of the Prisoners, Imprisonment with the Indians. 152pp., 12mo, boards. Frankfort, 1842. $7.50

859 [WAR OF 1812.] Memoirs of the Campaign of the North Western Army . . . 1812. In a Series of Letters addessed to the Citizens of the U. S. By William Hull. With an Appendix, Containing a Brief Sketch of the Revolutionary Services of the Author. 8vo, wrappers. Boston, 1824. $12.50

860 [WAR OF 1812.] (Latour, Major A. Lacarriere). Historical Memoir of the War of West Florida and Louisiana, 1814-15, translated by Nugent. A perfect copy complete with the fine stipple portrait of Andrew Jackson, and the 8 large folding engraved colored maps. 2 vols. (including Atlas), 8vo, half calf. Phila., 1816. $45.00

An exceedingly fine and unusually clean copy of a work that seldom comes in the state as above noted. "The history of these events is described is pages that still glow with the freshness of their first writing. The appendix contains a collection of exceedingly interesting official documents relating to the campaign, and the series of maps which are most authentic."—Larned's Bibliography. Theodore Roosevelt said: "Latour, who was General Jackson's Chief Engineer, is the ony trustworthy contemporary American historian of this war."

861 [WAR OF 1812.] (Lucas, C. P.). The War of 1812. 269pp., 8 maps, cloth. Oxford, 1906. $4.00

862 [WAR OF 1812.] (O'Connor, T.). An Impartial and Correct History of the War between the U. S. and Great Britain, with a particular detail of the Naval and Military Operations and a Record of the Events produced during the Contest, and including among other Important Documents President Madison's Message to Congress, June 1, 1812, the Act declaring War, Treaty of Peace of 1783, etc. Colored frontispiece. 12mo, broken at hinge, calf. N. Y., 1815. $12.50

863 WASHINGTON, GEORGE. The Diaries of. Edited by John C. Fitzpatrick. [Frontispieces.] 4 vols., 8vo, cloth. Boston, n.d. (1925). $7.50

Regents' edition, published at $25.00.

864 [WASHINGTON STATE.] Brief History of the Diocese of Baker City. By Father Dominic O'Connor. 203pp., illus. Baker City, 1930.. $5.00

865 WASHINGTON STATE.] Bibliography of Washington. Geology and Geography. 63pp., 8vo, original wrappers. Olympia, 1913. $3.50

866 [WASHINGTON STATE.] Everett and Snohomish City and County Directory, 1893. Vol. I. R. L. Polk and Co. 8vo, cloth. Tacoma, (1893). $7.50

867 [WASHINGTON STATE.] Sketches from the North. [Hutchings' California Magazine, Vol. 3, Aug. 1858.] 8vo, original wrappers. San Francisco, 1858. $4.50

868 [WASHINGTON STATE.] National League for Woman's Service. Washington State Report, 1917-1919. 67pp., 8vo, original wrappers. N.p., n.d. $3.75

869 [WASHINGTON STATE.] Dr. Minor. A Sketch of the Background and Life of Thomas T. Minor, M.D. By T. M. Pelly. 8vo, cloth. Seattle, 1935. $.350

870 [WASHINGTON STATE.] Okanogan Independent. Historical Sketch of Okanagon, (1916). $10.00

Scarce little item, not recorded in the NW bibliographies.

871 [WASHINGTON STATE.] Glimpses of Pioneer Life of Okanogan County, Washington, 143pp., 12mo, original wrappers. Okanogan: Independent, n.d. $7.50

An important collection of narratives by early pioneers of the Okanogan region.

872 [WASHINGTON STATE.] Neah Kah Nie Commercial Club. The Neah-Kah-Nie Mountains. 12mo, original wrappers. 32pp., illus. N.p. (1905). $2.00

873 [WASHINGTON STATE.] The Smugglers. A Story of Puget Sound. By Edith Neville. 265pp., 12mo, n.p., n.d. $7.50

Scarce item published by the author which we are unable to find in any bibliography. It has much of factual interest about Puget Sound and its vicinity.

874 [WASHINGTON STATE.] The Louise Olivereau Case Trial and Speech to the Jury in Federal Court of Seattle, Wash., Nov., 1917. 64pp., 12mo, original wrappers. Seattle: Parkhurst, n.d. $2.50

874A [WASHINGTON STATE.] Olympia City and Thurston County. R. L. Polk and Co. 8vo, cloth, 339pp. Tacoma, 1902. $7.50

875 [WASHINGTON STATE.] Olympia Chamber of Commerce and The Thurston County Pioneer and Historical Society. The Great Myth—"Mount Tacoma." Mount Ranier and the Facts of History. 32pp., 8vo, original wrappers. Olympia, 1924. $2.50

876 [WASHNIGTON STATE.] Pacific Publishing Company. Southwestern Washington; its Topography, Climate, Resources, Productions, Manufacturing Advantages, Wealth and Growth, with Illustrated Reviews of the Principal Cities and Towns and Pen Sketches of their Representative Business Men, also Biographical Sketches of prominent State and Municipal Officials. 210pp., illus., 4to, cloth. Olympia, 1890. $9.00

Compiled by Wallace J. Miller.

877 [WASHINGTON STATE.] (Parker, Frank J.). Washington Territory. The Present and Prospective Future of the Upper Columbia Country, embracing the Counties of Walla Walla, Whitman, Spokane and Stevens. With a Detailed Description of Northern Idaho, etc. 17pp., 8vo, original printed wrappers. Walla Walla, W. T., 1881. $17.50

Smith 2996 locates only the copy in the Oregon Historical Society.

877A [WASHINGTON STATE.] (Raymond Burnette Pease). Real and Reign of Mt. Tah-Ho-Ma. 12mo, original wrappers. N.p., n.d. $2.00

878 [WASHINGTON STATE.] How the West Was Won. By Stephen B. L. Penrose. 55pp., 8vo, original printed wrappers. Walla Walla, 1924. $4.00

879 [WASHINGTON STATE.] Pierce County Pioneer Association. Commemorative Celebration at Sequalitchew Lake, Pierce County, Wash., July 5th, 1906. 101pp., 4 pl., map., 8vo, cloth. [Tacoma, Wash., 1906.] $7.50

Smith 3070.

880 [WASHINGTON STATE.] Auditors Annual Exhibit of Finance of Pierce County, Wash., including a brief sketch of its Resources and Progress during the past Fifty Years. 92pp., 8vo, original printed wrappers. Tacoma: Bell, 1910. $3.75

Local history of Pierce County.

881 [WASHINGTON STATE.] Pierce County Emigration Association. MAP OF PIERCE COUNTY, WASH., 24 x 36 in. 1897. $5.00

882 [WASHINGTON STATE.] Pierce County, Washington. Plate Book. Folio, n.d. $12.50

This is an early plate book of Tacoma and vicinity.

883 [WASHINGTON STATE.] Port Townsend, Its Advantages, Resources and Prospects. 40pp., illus., 4to, original wrappers. Port Townsend, 1890. $6.50

884 [WASHINGTON STATE.] R. L. Polk and Co. Puget Sound Directory, 1887. This is Volume No. 1. 630pp., 8vo, cloth. [Seattle.] Polk, 1887. $10.00

Coupville, Friday Harbor, La Conner, Mt. Vernon, Newcastle, Olympia, Port Angeles, Port Discovery, Port Gamble, Port Ludlow, Port Madison, Port Townsend, Puyallup, Renton, Seattle, Sehome, Shelton, Whatcom, Snohomish, Tacoma, Ketsop, San Juan, Skagit, Thurston, etc.

885 [WASHINGTON STATE.] History of the Puget Sound Country; its Resources, its Commerce and Its People. By Wm. Farrand Prosser. Ports., illus., 2 vols., 4to, cloth. N. Y., 1903. $12.50

886 [WASHINGTON STATE.] Protestant Episcopal Church. Proceedings of the Second Convocation of the Clergy and Laity of the Protestant Episcopal Church of Oregon and Washington Territories. 12mo, original wrappers. Portland, 1854. $8.00

887 [WASHINGTON STATE.] The Puget Sound Catechism. A Convenient Compendium of useful information respecting Washington Territory and its Chief City, Seattle. 32pp., 12mo, original wrappers. Seattle, (1887). $4.50

888 [WASHINGTON STATE.] Filbert Growing in the Puget Sound Country. Presenting a Treatise on the Filbert Nut. By A. A. Quarnberg. 36pp., illus., 8vo, original wrappers. Seattle, 1917. $4.00

This work, printed in a small edition by an authority on the subject, is now unobtainable.

889 [WASHINGTON STATE.] Reminiscences of Seattle, Washington Territory, and the U. S. Sloop-of-War, "Decatur," during the Indian war of 1855-56. By Thomas Stowell Phelps. 48pp., 8vo, original printed wrappers. Seattle: Harriman, 1908. $7.50

890 [WASHINGTON STATE.] (Seattle). National Publishing Co. Seattle of Today. 231pp., illus. Long 8vo, original wrappers. Seattle: Lowman (1909). $3.75

891 [WASHINGTON STATE.] (Seattle). Seattle Children in School and Industry. By Anna Y. Reed. 103pp., 8vo, cloth. Seattle, 1915. $1.50

892 [WASHINGTON STATE.] The First Circum-Navigation of Vancouver Island. Archives of British Columbia, Memoir No. 1. 69pp., 8 maps, 8vo, cloth. Victoria, 1914. $7.50

Smith 2659.

893 [WASHINGTON STATE.] A True Exhibit of Washington Territory in 1880. The Field for Capital. Home for Laborers. 88pp., 12mo, original wrappers. New Tacoma, 1880. $17.50

Not in Smith. Elwood Evans is said to be the author of the above work.

894 WEBSTER, DANIEL. The Writings and Speeches of. Illus. 18 vols., 8vo, cloth. Boston, 1903. $35.00

The definitive national edition, almost as new. Much on Oregon question, anti-expansionist, etc.

895 WADDELL, JOSEPH A. Annals of Augusta County, Va. with Reminiscences illustrating the vicissitudes of its Pioneer Settlers, Biographical Sketches, etc. viipp., 374pp., 8vo, cloth. Richmond, 1886. $10.00

896 WELLES, GIDEON. Diary of. With an Introduction by John T. Morse, Jr. Illus. 3 vols., 8vo, cloth. Boston, 1911. $20.00

897 [WEST VIRGINIA.] The Annals of Harper's Ferry, with Sketches of its Founder and many prominent Characters connected with its History. By Josephus, Junior. 126pp. Portraits. 8vo, original printed wrappers, fine. Printed at the office of the Berkeley Union: Martinsburg, W. Va., 1872. $5.00

898 [WILKES EXPEDITION.] Thulia: A Tale of the Antarctic. By J. C. Palmer, U. S. N. 12 finely engraved plates by A. T. Agate, artist of the Expedition. 72pp., 8vo, cloth. N. Y., 1843. $7.50

The above by one of the officers of the Tender "Sea Gull" is probably the second published work on Wilkes' expedition. The preface is dated Sept. 1, 1842. An appendix gives an account of the "Flying Fish," one of Wilkes' schooners used on the expedition. The work is in long ballad form. Apparently Palmer was the poet of the expedition.

899 WINSOR, JUSTIN. Narrative and Critical History of America. Edited by Justin Winsor. Maps and illus. 8 vols., 4to, original boards and paper labels. Boston, v.d. $35.00

900 —— The Same. Regular edition. Cloth. $22.50

A comprehensive history of North and South America and the Indies by specialists in the various fields. With illustrations on nearly every page after contemporary maps, views, manuscripts, etc.

901 WINTHROP, JOHN. The History of New England from 1630-49 . . . From his original Manuscripts. With Notes . . . by James Savage. Portrait. 2 vols., 8vo, half calf. Boston, 1825. $7.50

"A source of early history . . . equalled only by the similar record of William Bradford . . . James Savage, the best antiquarian of his day, has supplemented the Journal with notes of great value."—James K. Hosmer.

902 [WISCONSIN.] Historical Address delivered before the Old Settlers Society of Racine County, Wisconsin. By Chas. E. Dyer. 84pp., 12mo, original wrapper. Racine, 1871. $5.00

903 [WISCONSIN.] Autobiography of the Life and Times of George Pegler, &c. 532pp., 8vo, cloth. Syracuse, 1879. $5.00

Pegler, born in London in 1799, spent his early years at sea, then took up the ministry in Canada and later in Wisconsin and Minnesota.

904 [WISCONSIN.] Fifteenth Annual Session. Proceedings of the Wisconsin Editorial Association, held at Green Bay, June 20, 1871. 66pp., 8vo. Madison, 1872. $5.00

905 [WISCONSIN.] The Wisconsin Historical Society Collections, 1855-1918. Twenty-Six volumes, 8vo, (vol. 1 and 2 bound together). All in good condition. Madison, 1855-1918. $70.00

A storehouse of information relating to the Middle States and the Northwest.

906 WITHERS, ALEXANDER. Chronicles of Border Warfare, or a History of the Settlement of the Whites of Northwestern Virginia; and of the Indian Wars and Massacres in that section of the State; with Reflections, Anecdotes, etc. 12mo, calf. Clarksburg, Va.; Joseph Israel, 1831. $25.00

A good copy of this scarce work with the separate page of advts.

907 —— The Same. 467pp., 8vo, cloth. Cincinnati, 1908. $3.50

908 [WHITMAN, MARCUS.] Whitman, an Unfinished Story. By Stephen B. L. Penrose. 256pp., illus., 8vo, cloth. Walla Walla, 1935. $3.75

909 [WORLD WAR.] Pictorial Review of the World's War Activities. Spruce Production Division, U. S. Army. Oregon and Washington. 127pp., map, illus. Sm. 4to, cloth. Portland (1918). $7.50

Smith 3209.

910 WORTLEY, LADY EMMELINE STUART. Travels in the U. S. . . . During 1849 and 1850. 8vo, cloth. N. Y., 1851. $1.50

Includes her journey down the Ohio on the Mississippi.

911 WURTTEMBURG, PRINCE PAUL HERZOG VON. First Journey to North America in the Years 1822 to 1824. Stuttgart and Tuebingen, 1835. Translated from the German by Dr. Wm. G. Bek. 8vo, cloth. Pierre, S. D., 1941. $4.00

Wagner-Camp 58. This is the first translation of this important work. See cat. 17, item 1499.

912 [WYOMING.] & Remarks of Hon. Joseph M. Carey, of Wyoming, in the Senate of the U. S., Monday, Oct. 30, 1893. 13pp., 8vo, original wrappers. Washington, 1893. $2.00

He spoke for Montana against the Junior Senator from Minnesota [Mr. Washburn.] and the Junior Senator from Idaho [Mr. Dubois.]

SOLIDAY SPECIAL COLLECTION

[The following miscellaneous items relating to the founding, settlement and growth of Washington Territory, and the adjacent territories of Oregon and Idaho, are included herewith under a separate alphabet. This collection, begun in 1908, has been carefully selected, item by item, painstakingly grouped in separate categories, then bound. We have attempted to list each item in the various bound volumes and have supplied our own alphabetical heading. The list as a whole represents a library in itself, containing hundreds of documents relating to the local history and Indian affairs in the Northwest—Ed.]

913 [ADMISSION OF WASHINGTON STATE.] A Collection of 8 Documents, the Enabling Act and the Constitution of Washington.

(1) Admission of Washington Territory into the Union, March 9, 1882. 47th Cong., 1st Sess., H.R. 690, 5 pp.

(2) Admissions of the State of Tacoma, March 24, 1884. 48th Cong., 1st Sess., Sen. Doc. 462, 7pp.

(3) Report of the Committee on Territories to who was referred the bill to provide for the Admission of the State of Washington. 49th Cong., 1st Sess., Sen. 61. 3pp.

(4) Washington, Idaho and Montana Territories, Jan. 20, 1887. 49th Cong., 2nd Sess., H.R. 689, 10pp.

(5) Report of the Committee on Territories, in regard to the Admission of the State of Washington, March 5, 1889, 50th Cong., 1st Sess., Sen. 585., 41pp.

(6) Admission of Dakota, Montana, Washington, and New Mexico into the Union, March 13, 1888. 50 th Cong., 1st Sess. H.R. 1025, map, 25-145pp.

(7) Memorial to the Citizens of Washington Territory praying Admission of that Territory into the Union . . ., Jan. 22, 1889. 50th Cong., 2nd Sess., Sen. Doc. 48, 3pp.

(8) Constitution, Jan. 28, 1889. 50th Cong., 2nd Sess., Sen. Doc. 55, 30pp.

(9) State of Washington. Enabling Act and Constitution with side notes and Index. Olympia: O. C. White, 1891., 93pp.

Together 8 documents, 8vo, half mor. V.p., V.d. $17.50

914 [ANTI-CHINESE RIOTS, 1885-86.] A Collection of 5 documents relating to, as follows:

(1) Report of the Governor of the Terr. to the Sec'y of Interior, 1885. 17pp.

(2) Report of the Governor to the Sec'y of Interior, 1886. 61pp. Also Report of the Governor for 1887. 85pp.

(3) Martial Law at Seattle, W. T. Vancouver, 1886. An inquiry into the Necessity therefor issued by Gov. Semple. 17pp.

(4) Letter from the Sec'y of War relative to the troubles in Seattle, Feb. 17, 1887. 49th Cong., 2nd Sess., Sen. Ex. Doc., 85. 5pp.

(5) Anti-Chinese Riots at Seattle, Feb. 8, 1886. By Geo. Kinnear, 1911. 16pp.

Together 6 documents, 8vo, half mor. V.p., V.d. $15.00

915 [BEGINNINGS OF WASHINGTON TERRITORY.] A Collection of 4 Works, as follows:

(1) In the Beginning, by Clarence B. Bagley, 90pp., 1905.

(2) The Pioneers of the State . . ., 90pp., 1904.

(3) Semi-Centennial Celebration of the Founding of Seattle, 61pp., 1894.

(4) Washington Pioneers Assn. Transactions, 1883-1889. 154pp., 8vo, half mor., V.p., V.d. $17.50

916 [BRITISH COLUMBIA.] Collection of 11 documents relating to the Exploration, Settlement, and U. S. relations with. As follows:

(1) Reports published by the Journal of the Royal Geographical Society. Remarks on Vancouver Island by Capt. W. C. Grant. Map, 6pp. Also—Report on a Journey in B. C., bordering on the Thompson and Harrison Rivers, by Lieut. Richard C. Mayne, Dec. 12, 1859. (Palmer's report on the Harrison and Lilloet Route, Dec. 12, 1859, and Begbie's Journey into the Interior of British Columbia, and Bownie's Exploration in Jarvis Inlet and Desolation Sound, 47pp.

(2) Journal of the Royal Geographical Society. Papers read March 14, 1864. Forbes—Physical Geography of Vancouver Island, map. (2) Palmer—On Principal Gold Fields of B. C. Map.

(3) Commercial Intercourse between the U. S. and British North America, Doc. 2, March, 1851. 21pp.

(4) Message of the President of the U. S. . . . with regard to . . . marking the Boundary line between the U. S. and British North America, March 2, 1860.

(5) Northwestern Boundary Commission, Jan. 14, 1871, 41st Cong., 3d Sess., H.R. 19. 2 pp.

(6) United States Northern Boundary. Letter from the Sec'y of State addressed to the Chairman of the Committee of foreign affairs, Dec. 12, 1872. 42nd Cong., 3d Sess. H.R. 20 5pp.

(7) Bulletin of the U. S. Geological Survey, No. 174. Washington, 1900. An account of the survey of the boundary line between the U. S. and Canada, from Rocky Mts. to Pacific.

(8) Letter from the Sec'y of Treasury . . . in relation shipwreck of the Sloop Georgiana, Aug. 31, 1852. 16pp.

(9) Message of the President . . . relative to the advances made by Governor Douglas of Vancouver Island to Gov. Stevens of Washington Terr., and recommending the payt. of same. Jan. 29, 1859. 11pp.

(10) Message of the President . . . of the Special Agent of the U. S. recently sent to Vancouver's Island and British Columbia, Jan. 31, 1859. 30pp.

(11) Message of the President . . . in reference to the Island of San Juan and of Gen. Harney, in command of the Dept. of Oregon, Jan. 30, 1860. 75pp.

Together 11 documents, 8vo, half mor. V.p., V.d. $35.00

917 [CLAIM TO SAN JUAN ISLAND.] Collection of 6 Works relating to. As follows:

(1) Memorial of the Legislature of Washington Terr, relative to the condition of American Citizens residing on San Juan Island, Feb. 25, 1868. 40th Cong., 2nd Sess. H.R., Miscl. Doc. 79. 2pp.

(2) Memorial of Marshall F. Moore, Governor of Washington Terr. remonstrating against any recognition of Claims of Great Britain to Haro Archipelago, and to San Juan Island, Jan. 19, 1869. 40th Cong., 3rd Sess., Sen. Doc. 27. 2pp.

(3) Letter of the Sec'y of War relative to the occupancy of San Juan Island, March 25, 1868. 40th Cong., 2nd Sess., H.R. Ex. Doc. 226. 2pp.

(4) Letter of J. Gregory Smith, President of the Northern Pacific Railroad Co., addressed to Hon. Geo. F. Edmunds in relation to the Treaty with Great Britain concerning the Island of San Juan, March 12, 1869. 41st Cong., 1st Sess., Sen. 14. 6pp.

(5) Letter of the Sec'y of War communicating a Report of the Chief of Engineers upon the Military Importance of San Juan Island, March 22, 1869. 41st Cong., 1st Sess., Sen. Ex. Doc. 8. 3pp.

(6) Message of the President . . . in relation to the Occupancy of San Juan, Feb. 22, 1868. 40th Cong., 2nd Sess. Sen. 29. 270pp., Maps.

Together 6 Works, 8vo, half morocco. V.p., V.d. $27.50

918 [INDIAN AND MILITARY AFFAIRS OF WASHINGTON.] A Collection of 5 Documents relating to Indian and Military Affairs in the Northwest, 1855-56. As follows:

(1) Indian Disturbances in Oregon and Washington. Message from the President, March 10, 1856. 34th Cong., 1st Sess., H.R. Ex. Docs. 49, 10pp.

(2) Message from the President Communicating information relative to Indian Hostilities in the Territories of Oregon and Washington, April 17, 1856. 34th Cong., 1st Sess., H.R. Ex. Doc. 93, 144pp.

(3) Report of the Sec'y of War transmitting copies of all letters of the Governor of Washington addressed to him during the present year and copies of all Correspondence relative to the Indian Disturbances in the Territory of Oregon and Washington, May 12, 1856. 34th Cong., 1st Sess. Sen. Ex. Doc. 66. 68pp.

(4) Message from the President relative to Indian Hostilities in Oregon and Washington, July 8, 856. 34th Cong., 1st Sess., H.R. Ex. Doc. 118. 58 pp.

(5) Report of the Sec'y of War. The Dept. of the Pacific. 1856. 56pp.

Together 5 documents, 8vo, half mor. Washington, 1855-56. $25.00

919 [INDIAN WAR CLAIMS, 1855-56.] Collection of 34 Documnets, contained in 3 vols., 8vo, relating to claims of various citizens who fought in the Indian Wars of the Northwest. As follows:

(1) Claims growing out of the Indian hostilities in Oregon and Washington . . . Jan. 18th, 1859. 77pp. [with clippings from newspapers].

(2) Report . . . relative to claims growing out of Indian hostilities in Oregon and Wash., Feb. 10, 1860. 132pp.

(3) Report of the Committee . . . of the Expenses incurred by . . . Oregon and Wash. Terr. (Indian Wars), March 29, 1860. 2pp.

(4) Communication from Sec'y George H. Williams and H. W. Corbett on the Indian War Claims of Oregon . . . March 4, 1868. 11pp.

(5) Oregon Territory—Expense of Indian War. Memorial of the Legislative Assembly of Oregon asking Congress to assume the expenses . . . April 2, 1856. 3pp.

(6) Report of Committee on Military Affairs . . . authorizing the Sec'y of War to pay certain volunteers, Feb. 12, 1857. 1pp.

(7) Extract from Report of John B. Floyd, Sec'y of War, Dec. 5, 1857. 1pp.

(8) Report of Sec'y of War . . . on the War Claims of Oregon and Washington Terr., Jan. 26, 1858. 16pp.

(9) Depredations and Massacres of the Snake River Indians. Letter from the Acting Sec'y of Interior, Jan. 28, 1861. 16pp.

(10) Memorial of the Legislature of Wash. Terr., praying an appropriton to defray expenses of the existing war, March 14, 1856. 2 pp.

(11) Memorial of the Legislative Assembly of Oregon asking Congress to assume the expenses of the existing war, April 2, 1856. 3 pp.

(13) Report of the Committee on Military Affairs. Expenses of the Indian War, June 24, 1856. 1p.

(13) Report of the Committee on Military. Pay of Volunteers in Indian War in Washington Terr., Feb. 12, 1857. 1p.

(14) Report of the Sec'y of War Communicating Report . . . on War Claims of Oregon and Wash. Terr., Jan. 26, 1858. 15pp.

(15) Report . . . of the Claims growing out of the Indian Hostilities in Oregon and Washington, Feb. 10, 1860. 132pp.

(16) Statement of the Oregon and Washington Delegation in regard to the War Claims of the two territories. 66pp.

(17) Depredations and Massacres by the Snake River Indians. Letter from the Sec'y of Interior, Jan. 28, 1861. 16pp.

(18) Report of the Committee on Military Affairs . . . for the payment of expenses in the Indian War, March 29, 1860. 2pp.

(10) Report of the Committee on Military Affairs . . . fixing the time from interest allowed on the awards of the Auditor in payment of the Oregon and Washington War debt, Jan. 24, 1862. 2pp.

(20) Message from the President . . . in relation to the Indian War Claims in Oregon and Washington, May 2, 1862. 12pp.

(21) Indian Spoilation Claims . . . March 3, 1868. 2pp.

(22) Certain Claims. Oregon and Washington Indian War, 1885-56 . . . April 20, 1892. 1p.

(23) Letter from the Sec'y of War . . . relative to expenses incurred by the Territories of Oregon and Washington in the Suppression of Indian hostilities in 1856. 68pp.

(24) Expenses of the Indian Wars in Oregon and Washington Territories . . . Jan. 25, 1858. 16pp.

(25) Expenses of the Indian War . . . June 26, 1856. 1p.

(26) Letter from the Sec'y of the Treasury relative to Claims, Dec. 4, 1871. 6pp.

(27) Report of the Committee on Military Affairs. Indian hostilities in Washington and Oregon, June 22, 1874. 2pp.

(28) Letter from the Sec'y of War . . . relative to expenses incurred by the Territories of Oregon and Washington in the Indian hostilities, Jan. 9, 1873. 68pp.

(29) Message from the President . . . in relation to the cause and probable cost of the late Nez Perces War, Jan. 18, 1878. 10pp.

(30) Citizens Volunteers of Idaho and Washington. Report of Committee, May 21, 1880. 2pp.

(31) Claims of Kansas, Nebraska, Nevada, Oregon, Texas, Idaho and Washington for repelling and suppressing Indian hostilities, Jan. 31, 1882. 6pp.

(32) Indian Depredation Claims . . ., March 16, 1886. 290pp.

(33) Letter from the Sec'y of War . . . relative to services of Volunteers in Nez Perce War, Jan. 22, 1889.

(34) Report of the Committee on Military Affairs . . ., April 14, 1892. 6pp.

Together 34 documents, in 3 vols., 8vo, half mor. V.p., V.d. $80.00

920 [LAKE WASHINGTON CANAL.] A Collection of 7 Documents relat-- ing to. As follows:

(1) Report of the Committee on Commerce in regard to the Lake Washington Canal, May 1, 1884. 48th Cong., 1st Sess., Senate, 494. 6pp.

(2) Canal Connecting Lakes Union, Samamish and Washington, with Puget Sound, Jan. 5, 1892. 52nd Cong., 1st Sess., H.R. Ex. Doc. 40, 33pp.

(3) Speech of Watson C. Squire in support of Amendment providing for the Improvement of the Waterway, June16, 1892. 16pp.

(4) Ship Canal. Feb. 1, 1893. 52nd Cong., 2nd Sess., H.R. 2395. 4pp.

(5) The Lake Washington Canal and the Commerce of the Pacific Chamber of Commerce, 1901. 24pp.

(6) Comparison between the Seattle Canal and the Ballard Canal. By Eugene Semple, 1902. 11pp.

(7) South Canal and Harbor Improvements, 1902. Illus., 72pp.

(8) Letter from the Sec'y of War transmitting Report of the Board of Engineers . . . to determine the feasibility of . . . a Canal between Puget Sound and Lake Washington, Jan. 31, 1903. 57th Cong., 2nd Sess., Sen. 1270. 70pp. and maps.

Together 8 documents, 8vo, half mor. V.p., V.d. $17.50

921 [MILITARY OCCUPATION OF SAN JUAN ISLAND, 1859.] Collection of 7 Documents relating to. As follows:

(1) Message of the President of the U. S. . . . in reference to the Island of San Juan and of Gen. Harney in Command of the Dept. of Ore., Jan. 30, 1860. 36th Cong. 75pp.

(2) Letter of the Sec'y of War . . . relative to the occupancy of the Island of Oregon, April 26, 1860. 36th Cong. 16pp.

(3) Correspondence with Gen. Harney. Letter of the Sec'y of War, June 20, 1860. 38th Cong. 29pp.

(4) Indian Depredations in Oregon. 36th Cong. 90pp.

(5) Gen. Harney's Administration of Ore. 36th Cong. 3pp.

(6) Memorial of the Legislature of Wash. Terr. relative to the Citizens of the U. S. residing on San Juan Island. 40th Cong. 2pp.

(7) San Juan and Secession. A paper read on the controversy . . . by Granville Haller, at a meeting of the Loyal Legion, Jan. 16, 1896. 16pp.

Together 7 documents, 8vo, half mor. V.p., V.d. $27.50

922 [MILITARY ROADS.] Walla Walla to Fort Benton. Report on the Construction of a Military Road from Fort Walla Walla to Fort Benton, by Capt.John Mullan. 10 colored illus., 4 folding maps, 363pp., 8vo, half mor. Washington, 1863. $12.50

923 [MISCELLANEOUS INDIAN OFFICIAL DOCUMENTS.] Collection of 20 Documents relating to the Indians of the Northwest and elsewhere. As follows:

(1) Message of the President of the U. S. . . . in reference to the island of San Juan and of Gen. Harney, in command of the Dept. of Ore., Jan. 30, 1860. 36th Cong. 75pp.

(2) Letter of the Sec'y of War . . . relative to the occupancy of the Island of Oregon, April 26, 1860. 36th Cong. 16pp.

(3) Correspondence with Gen. Harney. Letter of the Sec'y of War, June 20, 1860. 38th Cong. 29pp.

(4) Indian Depredations in Oregon. 36th Cong. 90pp.

(5) Gen. Harney's Administration of Ore. 36th Cong. 3pp.

(6) Memorial of the Legislature of Wash. Terr. relative to the Citizens of the U. S. residing on San Juan Island. 40th Cong. 2pp.

(7) San Juan and Secession. A paper read on the controversy . . . by Granville Haller, at a meeting of the Loyal Legion, Jan. 16, 1896. 16pp.

(1) Message from the President . . . relating to the Indian Disturbances of the Territories of Wash. and Ore., March 11, 1856. 34th Cong. 1st Sess., Sen. Ex. Doc. 46. 10pp.

(2) Resolutions of the Legislature of Wash. Terr. relative to the Report made by Gen. Wool concerning the late Indian War in the Territory, April 7, 1858. 35th Cong., 1st Sess., H.R. 116. 2pp.

(3) Message from the President . . . relating to Indian Affairs in Oregon and Wash., May 10, 1858. 35th Cong., 1st Sess., H.R. 112. 21pp.

(4) Letter from the Sec'y of Interior . . . on the Subject of Indian Affairs in the Territories of Ore., and Wash., Jan. 25, 1858. 35th Cong., 1st Sess. H.R. Ex. Doc. 39. 48pp

(5) Letter from the Sec'y of Treasury . . . for the Indian Service on the Pacific Coast and in remote Territories on either side of the Rocky Mts., March 26, 1858. 35th Cong. H.R. 93. 98pp.

(6) Report of the Sec'y of Interior . . . for the Indian Service in Oregon and Wash. Terr. for the current and ensuing fiscal year, March 2, 1860. 36th Cong. 1st Sen. Ex. 17. 15pp.

(7) Expenses of the Indian Wars in Oregon and Washington Terr. Letter from the Sec'y of Interior, Jan. 25, 1858. 35th Cong. 1st H.R. Ex. Doc. 45. 16pp.

(8) Claims growing out of Indian Hostilities in Oregon and Washington. Jan. 18, 1859. 35 Cong., 2nd H.R. Ex. Doc. 51. 77pp.

(9) Letter from the Sec'y of Interior . . . relative to expenses incurred by the Territories of Oregon and Washington in the suppression of Indian Hostilities in 1856, Jan. 9, 1873. 42nd Cong. 3d Sess., Sem. Ex. Doc. 24. 58pp.

(10) Report of the Committee . . . for the relief of Citizens of Oregon, Idaho and Washington, who served . . . in the war against the Nez Perces, Bannock and Shoshone Indians. 6pp.

(11) Letter from the Sec'y of Interior . . . of treaties . . . with Indians in the Territory of Oregon, under the Act of June 5, 1850, and what treaties were ratified by the Senate, and also as to the occupancy of the lands and what sums were paid to said tribes, May 2, 1902. 57th Cong., 1st Sen. Doc. 340. 12pp.

(12) Claims for Compensation for lands owned by Indians in Oklahoma Terr., April 18, 1902. 57th Cong. 6pp.

(13) Report of the Indian Peace Commissioners, Jan. 14, 1868. 40th Cong. 23pp.

(14) Report of W. A. Richards . . . respecting the opening of Kiowa, Comanche, Apache and Wichita Lands in Oklahoma, May 2, 1902. 15pp.

(15) Letter from the Asst. Sec'y of Treasury . . . for the Construction of a new hospital at Ft. Riley, Kansas, May 5, 1902. 57th Cong. 2pp.

(16) Rights of Mississippi Choctaws in the Choctaw Nation, April 24, 1902. 57th Cong. 4pp.

(17) Petition and Papers relative to certain lower Brule Indians in So. Dakota, April 26, 1902. 57th Cong. 7pp.

(18) Letter from the Assistant Clerk of the Court of Claims relative to findings filed in the cause of the eastern Cherokees against the U. S., March 3, 1883. 57th Cong. 7pp.

(19) Letter from the Acting Sec'y of Interior transmitting letters from W. T. Whitaker, et al, recommending that the Indian Bill pending before Congress be amended so as to appropriate $15,000 for the support . . . at Whitaker Home of 100 destitute orphan children of white persons . . . 57th Cong., 4pp.

(20) Claim of Delaware Indians . . . April 26, 1902. 57th Cong. 4pp.

Together 20 documents, 8vo, half mor. V.p., V.d. $47.50

924 [OFFICIAL PAPERS OF WASHINGTON STATE—OREGON—IDAHO.] Collection of 54 Documents relating to. As follows:

(1) Geological Survey of Oregon and Wash., Jan. 31, 1857. 4pp. 35th Cong.

(2) Report of Geological Survey Committee on Oregon and Wash., May 22, 1858, 3pp. 35th Cong.

(3) Report of Committee on Public Lands in regard to making an Appropriation to Supply a Deficiency in Funds for the Completion of the Geological Survey of Oregon and Wash., April 9, 1860. 36th Cong. 35pp.

(4) Report in regard to a Scientific Survey of Washington Terr., Feb. 22, 1881. 46th Cong. 3pp.

(5) Memorial of the Members of the Legislative Assembly of Wash. Terr. in regard to a Custom House Building at Port Townsend, Wash., Mar. 10, 1862. 37th Cong. 2pp.

(6) Letter from the Sec'y of Treasury in regard to changing the Port of Entry from Port Townsend to Port Angeles, Mar. 20, 1862. 39th Cong. 2pp.

(7) Change of location of Port of Port of Entry for Puget Sound . . . from Port Townsend to Port Angeles, June 16, 1862. 37th Cong. 1p.

(8) Memorial of the Legislative Assembly praying the Congress remove the Custom House from Port Townsend, Jan 30, 1865. 38th Cong. 2pp.

(9) Letter from the Sec'y of Treasury relative to the Collector of Customs at Port Townsend, April 17, 1872. 42nd Cong. 2pp.

(10) Letter from the Sec'y of Treasury defining the limits of the Collection Districts of Puget Sound, Dec. 19, 1872. 42nd Cong. 2pp.

(11) Deputy Collector at Puget Sound, June 2, 1880. 46th Cong. 1p.

(12) A Public building at Port Townsend, March 29, 1882. 47th Cong. 2pp.

(13) Marine Hospital at Port Townsend, May 10, 1882. 47th Cong. 2pp.

(14) Immediate Transportation Privileges, Jan. 31, 1901. 56th Cong. 1p.

(15) Granting certain lands to the City of Port Angeles for Park purposes, Mar. 23, 1904. 58th Cong. 1p.

(16) Steam Revenue Cutter for service on Puget Sound, April 19, 1904. 58th Cong. 3pp.

(17) General Statement of Receipts and Disbursements incidental to Surveying the Public Lands in the District of Oregon for the year ending Sept. 30, 1855. 34th Cong. 12pp.

(18) Annual Report of the Surveyor-General of Washington, 1856. 34th Cong. 10pp.

(19) Memorial of the Legislative body of Minnesota in favor of the Establishment of a Mail Route from St. Cloud, Minn., by way of Fort Abercrombie and Bannock to Fort Walla Walla, March 4, 1864. 38th Cong. 2pp.

(20) Memorial of the Citizens of Minnesota praying the establishment of a Mail Route from St. Paul to . . . the Columbia and Puget Sound, Jan. 12, 1859. 35th Cong. 7pp.

(21) Mail Route on Puget Sound, May 28, 1856. 34th Cong. H. R. 17. 2pp.

(22) Washington National Park, Feb. 24, 1899. 55th Cong. 1p.

(23) Forest Reserves in the States of Washington and Idaho, June 5, 1900. 56th Cong. 6pp.

(24) Improvement of Mt. Ranier National Park, Feb. 15, 1904. 58th Cong. 2pp.

(25) Letter from the Sec'y of Treasury enclosing the estimates of the current expenses of the Legislative Assmbly of Washington Terr., Jan. 8, 1869. 40th Cong. 2pp.

(26) Tide Flats, Budd's Inlet, Washington Terr., March 11, 1874. 43rd Cong. 1p.

(27) Capitol Building at Olympia. Letter from the Sec'y of Interior, Jan. 14, 1875. 43rd Cong. 3pp.

(28) Letter from the Sec'y of War relative to the claim of the Roman Catholic Mission of St. James to the Military Reservation at Ft. Vancouver, Jan. 19, 1875. 1p.

(29) Mission of St. James, March 3, 1876. 44th Cong. 2pp.

(30) Mission of St. James, Feb. 13, 1880. 46th Cong. 2pp .

(31) Boundaries of Oregon and Wash., Feb. 23, 1858. 35th Cong. 1p.

(32) Memorial of the Legislature of Oregon in favor of incorporating the County of Walla Walla, Wash., in the State of Oregon, March 14, 1866. 39th Cong. 1p.

(33) Memorial of the Legislature of Oregon asking a change of the Northern Boundary of . . . Oregon, Jan. 2, 1873. 42nd Cong. 1pp.

(34) Boundaries of the State of Oregon, July 15, 1875. 44th Cong. 4pp.

(35) Memorial of the Legislature of Oregon relative to the State Boundary, Dec. 29, 1876. 44th Cong. 23pp.

(36) Report of the Committee . . . to Annex a portion of Idaho to Washington, Feb. 3, 1886. 49th Cong. 2pp.

(37) Territory of Idaho, March 16, 1888. 50th Cong. 8pp.

(38) Report of the Sec'y of Navy . . . as to the Number and Tonnage of Govt. Vessels in the Pacific, also private vessels employed by the Govt. . . . Feb. 9, 1858. 35th Cong. Ex. doc. 38. 2pp.

(39) Letter from the Sec'y of War . . . for the defense of Puget Sound and the entrances of the Columbia River, Jan. 24, 1859. 35th Cong. 1p.

(40) Letter from the Sec'y of War . . . relative to fortifications upon Puget Sound, May 14, 1888. 50th Cong. 75pp.

(41) Memorial of the Citizens of Port Townsend relative to Coast Defenses, Jan. 18, 1892. 52nd Cong. 5pp.

(42) Memorial from Seattle Chamber of Commerce urging the improvement of Coast Defenses, Jan. 7, 1896. 54th Cong. 2pp.

(43) Letter from the Sec'y of War . . . upon the examination of Stillaguamish, Nooksack and Snohomish Rivers, Wash. Terr., and Sinslaw Bay, Ore., Dec. 1, 1880. 46th Cong. 13pp.

(44) Ship Channel between Port Townsend and Oak Bay, Dec. 13, 1890. 51st Cong. 5pp.

(45) Prelim. Examination from Hood's Canal to North Bay, Jan. 23, 1895. 53rd Cong. 7pp.

(46) Ship Canal to connect Puget Sound with Gray's Harbor, Feb. 1, 1900. 56th Cong. 1p.

(47) Branch Mint at Dallas, Oregon, Jan. 30, 1865. 38th Cong. 2pp.

(48) Fog Signal on Point Wilson, April 11, 1876. 4th, Cong. 3pp.

(49) Fog Bell and Steam Whistle on Foulweather Bluff, Jan 23, 1879. 45th Cong. 2pp.

(50) Claims for Transportation of destitute Citizens of Alaska, Jan. 18, 1901. 56th Cong. 2pp.

(51) Dry Dock, Puget Sound. Estimate for Construction, Dec. 17, 1892. 52nd Cong. 3pp.

(52) Revenue from the Oregon Country. Letter from the Sec'y of Treasury, Dec. 8, 1903. 58th Cong. 5pp.

(53) Experiment on the Coals of the Pacific Coast. Letter from Sec'y of Navy, March 15, 1872. 42nd Cong. 31pp .

(54) Gun factories and steel forgings for high power guns . . . with reference to Oregon and Wash., Jan. 27, 1891. 51st Cong. 144pp.

Together 54 documents, 8vo, half mor. V.p., V.d. $87.50

925 [OREGON QUESTION.] 1845-46. A Collection of Eleven Government Documents and other articles on. As follows:

(1) The Oregon Question . . . a Lecture before the Mercantile Library Association, Jan. 22, 1845, by Wm. Sturgis. 32pp., map. Boston, 1845.

(2) Message of . . . the Governor to the branches of the General Court of N. H., June, 1845. 12pp. Concord, 1845.

(3) The Edinburgh Review, July, 1845. Article on The Oregon Question. 30pp.

(4) The Quarterly Review, March, 1846. The Oregon Question, 45pp.

(5) The United States Magazine and Democratic Review, Nov. 1845. 9pp. Oregon Question.

(6) United States Magazine and Democratic Review, Dec. 1845. Oregon Question. 11pp.

(7) Letters of Albert Gallatin on the Oregon Question, originally published in the National Intelligencer, Jan. 1846. 5 letters, 36pp.

(8) Speech of Mr. Calhoun of S. C. on the Resolution giving notice to Great Britain of the Abrogation of the Convention of Joint Occupancy. Senate, March 16, 1846. 18pp.

(9) Mr. Webster's Vindication of the Treaty of Washington, of 1842. In the Senate, April 6-7, 1846. 64pp.

(10) Military Posts on the Route to Oregon, Dec .21, 1845, 29th Cong., 1st Sess., H. R. 13. 5pp.

(11) Message of the President transmitting a copy of the Treaty entered into between Great Britain and U. S. respecting the Oregon Territory ,Aug. 6, 1846. 29th Cong., 1st Sess., H. R. Ex. Doc. 221, 3pp.

All in one volume, 8vo, half mor. V.p., V.d. $22.50

926 [OREGON QUESTION, SPEECHES ON.]

(1) Speech of Samuel McRoberts of Illinois on the Title of the U. S. to the Territory of Oregon . . . Dec. 30, 1842 and Jan. 9, 1843. 12pp.

(2) Remarks of Mr. Semple of Illinois on the Resolution by him relative to the occupation of Oregon Territory . . . Senate, Jan. 24, 1844, 19pp.

(3) Remarks of Mr. Hannegan of Indiana on the OregonTerritory. Senate, Feb. 23, 1844. 8pp.

(4) Speech of Mr. Buchanan of Pa., on the Oregon Question. Senate, March 12, 1844. 15pp.

(5) Speech of Mr. Breese of Illinois on the Oregon Territory. Senate, Feb. 27, 1844. 23pp.

(6) Last Letter of Mr. Buchanan to Mr. Packenham on the American title to Oregon, Aug. 30, 1845. 16pp.

(7) Speech of Mr. Winthrop of Mass., on the Oregon Question. H. R., Jan. 3, 1846. 15pp.

(8) Speech of Mr. Rockwell of Connecticut on the Oregon Question, H. R., Jan. 16, 1846. 16pp.

(9) Speech of Mr. Cobb of Georgia on the Oregon Question, H. R., Jan. 8, 1846. 8pp.

(10) Speech of Mr. Allen G. Thurman of Ohio on the Oregon Question, H. R., Jan. 28, 1846. 15pp.

(11) Speech of Mr. Speight of Miss., on the Bill providing for the Augmentation of the Navy. Senate, Jan. 29, 1846. 8pp. Oregon).

(12) Speech of Mr. Culver of New York on the Texas and Oregon Questions. H. R., Jan. 30, 1846. 16pp.

(13) Speech of Jos. P. Hoge of Illinois on the Oregon Question. H. R., Jan. 30, 1846. 12pp.

(14) Speech of Mr. Gentry of Tennessee on the Oregon Question. H. R., Feb. 5, 1846. 16pp.

(15) Speech of Robert Smith of Illinois on the Oregon Question. H. R., Feb. 7, 1846. 8pp.

(16) Speech of Geo. Evans of Maine on the Oregon Question. Senate, March 9-10, 1846. 30pp.

(17) Speech of Mr. Calhoun of S. C., on the Resolution giving Notice to Great Britain of the Abrogation of the Convention of Joint Occupancy. Senate, March 16, 1846. 16pp.

(18) Speech of Mr. Lewis Cass of Michigan in reply to Mr. Benton of Missouri with some additions. Senate, April 2, 1846. 8pp.

(19) Speech of Mr. Houston of Texas on the Oregon Question. Senate, April 1848. 8pp.

(20) Speech of Lewis Cass of Michigan on the Bill to Protect the Rights of Settlers in Oregon. Senate, June 1, 1846. 14pp.

(21) The Oregon Question, by Abbert Gallatin. 5 articles with an Appendix. 75pp., 1846.

All contained in one volume, 8vo, red cloth and half mor. 21 Speeches. V.p. V.d. 1842-1846. $30.00

927 [OREGON AND WASHINGTON.] (The Cayuse War). A collection of works relating to the Indian uprisings east of the Cascade Range during the summer of 1848, a wär that was a direct outgrowth of the Whitman Massacre the year previous. Certain religious jealousies and animosities were directly attributed to the massacre. The affair was brought to a head in 1858 when J. Ross Browne published his celebrated pamphlet (Ex. Doc. No. 38, 35th Cong.) in which he published Father Brouillett's "Protestantism in Oregon." This caused a furor among all the Protestant sects, and Henry Spalding answered with his equally celebrated Sen. Ex. Doc. No. 37, 41st Cong., 3rd Sess.). However it is asserted that Spalding's pamphlet, although ordered printed, mysteriously disappeared. 7 items as listed, all bound together, 8vo, ¾ calf. V.p., V.d. $45.00

(1) Message of the President of the United States. Peace Establishment . . . Number of Indians in Oregon, California, New Mexico, Doc. 12pp., 30th Cong. 1st Sess., H. R. Ex. Doc. No. 76. Aug. 2, 1848 (Includes the President's report on the uprising.)

(2) Memorial of the Legislature of Oregon, praying for payment of expense in the Cayuse War. 11pp., 31st Cong., 2nd Sess., Sen. Misc. Doc. No. 29. Feb. 25, 1851.

(3) Report of the Committee . . . providing for the payment of Volunteers in the Cayuse War, March 2, 1905. 58th Cong., 3rd Sess., Senate No. 4387. 7pp.

(4) Mullan, Capt. John. Military Road Expedition. Report of Capt. Mullan from Ft. Walla-Walla, on the Columbia River. Oct. 12, 1860. See Wagner-Camp No. 393, which this letter apparently antedates. Not in Wagner.

(5) Mullan, Capt. John. Military Road from Ft. Benton to Walla-Walla. 171pp. Fldg. Map. 36th Cong., 2nd Sess. H. R. Ex. Doc. No. 44. Not in Wagner-Camp, apparently antedates Wagner-Camp No. 393.

(6) Crawford, Capt. Medorem. Report and Journal of an Expedition organized for the protection of Emigrants to Oregon, etc. under the Command of Medorem Crawford, Captain, Assistant Quartermaster United States Army. 37th Cong. 2nd Sess. Senate Ex. Doc. 17. 14pp. See Wagner-Camp 386.

(7) Fisk, Capt. James Liberty. Expedition from Ft. Abercrombie to Ft. Benton. Letter from the Secretary of War, in answer to Resolution of House of 19th instant, transmitting report of Capt. J. L. Fisk, of the expedition to escort emigrants from Ft. Abercrombie to Ft. Benton . . . March 2, 1863. Ordered Printed. [Washington, 1863.] 37th Cong., 3rd Sess., H. R. Doc. 80, 36pp. 1863.

928 [OREGON AND WASHINGTON.] Magazine Articles relating to. 16 items, dated from 1858 to 1917. 8vo, half mor. V.p., V.d. $7.50

929 [OVERLAND JOURNEYS, 1842-1863.] Collection of Seven Works, being Narratives of Trips across the Plains. As follows:

(1) Journal of Medorem Crawford. From Sources of the History of Oregon. 26pp.

(2) Military Roads in Washington Territory, May 10, 1858. 35th Cong., 1st Sess., H. R. 369. 6p.

(3) Report of the Sec'y of War, communicating the Report of Capt. H. D. Wallin of his Expedition of 1859, from Dalles City to Great Salt Lake and Back, April 12, 1860. 35th Cong. 1st Sess. Senate Ex. Doc. 34. 5pp.

(4) Report of Capt. J. W. Macomb, Typographical Engineer in Charge of the San Juan Expedition, Nov. 1, 1860. 52pp.

(5) Letter from the Sec'y of War . . . of the Report of Capt. Medorem Crawford, commanding the Emigrant Escort to Oregon and Washington in 1862, Jan. 9, 1863. 37th Cong., 3rd Sess.., Sen. Ex. Doc. 17, 14pp.

(6) Letter from the Sec'y of War . . . report of Lt. Mullan ,in charge of the Construction of the Military Road from Ft. Benton to Ft. Walla Walla,, Jan. 25, 1861. 36th Cong., 2nd Sess., H. R. Ex. Doc. 44. Map, 171pp.

(7) Letter from the Sec'y of War . . . report of Capt. J. L. Fisk of the Expedition to escort Emigrants from Ft. Abercromble to Ft. Benton, March 2, 1863. 37th Cong., 3rd Sess., H. R. Ex. Doc. 80. 36pp.

Together 7 documents, 8vo, half mor. N.p., N.d. $50.00

This contains both the Fisk and Mullan Narratives as well as just as scarce other narratives relating to the same general subject. All were compiled by Mr. Thomas W. Prosch for his history.

930 [PACIFIC COAST INDIANS.] A Collection of Seven Ethnological Studies compiled by Thomas W. Prosch. As follows:

(1) The Twana, Chemakum and Klallam Indians of Washington Terr., by Myron Eells. 75pp.

(2) Notes on the Customs of the Dakotahs. By Paul Beckwith.

(3) Anatanas; Natives of Copper River, Alaska. By Lt. Henry T. Allen. 7pp.

(4) Indians of the Quinaielt Agency. W. T. By Willoughby. 16pp.

(5) The Stone Age of Oregon. By Myron Eells. 12pp.

(6) Charm Stones. Notes on the so-called Plummets or Sinkers. By L. G. Yates. 8pp., 3pp. of illus.

(7) Chinook Texts. By Fraz Boaz. 1894. Illus. 278pp.

Together in one volume, 8vo, half mor. V.p., V.d. $12.50

931 [PACIFIC COAST MILITARY AFFAIRS.] A Collection of Four Government Documents relating to Indian and Civil War Claims in the Pacific Coast. As follows:

(1) Letter from the Secretary of War transmitting a Report upon the War Claims of California . . . 51st Cong., 1st Sess., Sen. Ex. Doc. 11, 95pp. (Relates to Civil War and Indian War Claims).

(2) Statement of the Case of the State War Claims of Calif., Ore., and Nevada, Aug. 10, 1888. 50th Cong., 1st Sess., Sen., 145pp.

(3) Report of the Committee on Military Affairs as to the War Claims of the State of Nevada, May 14, 1888. 50th Cong., 1st Sess. Sen. 1286. 153pp.

(4) Letter from the Sec'y of War transmitting report relative to raising Volunteer Troops to guard Overland and other Mails from 1861 to 1866. Dec. 19, 1888. 50th Cong., 2nd Sess., Sen. Ex. Doc. 70, 366pp.

Together 4 documents, 8vo, half mor. V.p., V.d. $12.50

932 [SAN JUAN ARBITRATION, 1871-72.] The Berlin Arbitration. 271pp., maps. 8vo, half mor. Washington, 1872. $12.50

933 [SEATTLE.] Official Reports of the City of, 1883-1893. 8vo, half mor. Seattle, v.d. $15.00

934 [SEATTLE CHAMBER OF COMMERCE.] Full Reports from 1886-1901 incl. 8vo, half mor. Seattle, v.d. $22.50

935 [SEATTLE AND VICINITY.]

(1) Military Wagon Road from Walla Walla to Seattle, Jan. 7, 1874. 43rd Cong., 1st Sess., H. R. Ex. Doc. 33. 2pp.

(2) Tide Flats of Duwamish Bay. April 15, 1874. 43rd Cong., 1st Sess., H. R. No. 416. 1p.

(3) Report of Committee to whom was referred the Bill granting right of way to Seattle and Walla Walla Railroad . . . June 8, 1874. 43rd Cong., 1st Sess., Sen. 420. 3pp.

(4) Letter from the Sec'y of Interior transmitting a Communication from the Governor of W. T. relative to the amount exempted during the Chinese Troubles in Seattle, Feb. 17, 1887. 49th Cong., 2nd Sess. Sen. Ex. Doc. 85. 5pp.

(5) Fog Signal, Puget Sound Jan. 23, 1879. 45th Cong., 3rd Sess., H. R. 71. 2pp.

(6) Memorial from the Seattle Chamber of Commerce relative to the dredging of Salmon Bay, Jan. 3, 1896. 54th Cong., 1st Secc., Senate Doc. 53. 3pp.

(7) Letter from the Ass't Sec'y of War transmitting the report of the Preliminary Examination of the Duwamish and Balck Rivers. 51st Cong., 2nd Sess., H .R. 27. 3pp.

(8) Assay Office, Seattle, April 18, 1898. 55th Cong., 2nd Sess., H. R. 1110. 4pp.

(9) Salaries of Deputy Collectors of Customs at Tacoma and Seattle, Feb. 1, 1900. 58th Cong., 1st Sess., Sen. 231, 1p.

(10) Salaries at Tacoma and Seattle . . . Jan. 7, 1904. 58th Cong., 2nd Sess., Sen. Rep. 179. 1pp.

(11) Extending Certain Privileges to Sub-ports in the Customs District of Puget Sound, April 7, 1904 58th Cong., 2nd Sess., H. R. 2321. 3pp.

(12) Making Seattle and Tacoma Ports of Delivery in the Customs District of Puget Sound, Mar. 6, 1884. 41st Cong., 1st Sess., Sen. Rep. 276. 3pp.

(13) Cities of Tacoma and Seattle Ports of Delivery, April 24, 1884. 48th Cong., 1st Sess., H. R. 1335. 1p.

(14) Ports of Entry at Tacoma and Seattle, July 14, 1888. 50th Cong., 1st Sess., H. R., 2883. 1p.

(15) Public Buildings of Seattle, Feb. 6, 1899. 55th Cong., 2nd Sess., Sen. Rep., 1253. 1p.

(16) Report of the Committee on Public Buildings in regard to Seattle, Feb. 10, 1892. 53rd Con., 1st Sess., Sen. Rep. 208. 5pp.

(17) Public Buildings of Seattle, June 17, 1898. 55th Cong., 2nd Sess., Sen. Rep. 1253. 1p.

(18) Public Buildings at Seattle, Feb. 6, 1899. 55th Cong., 3rd Sess., H.R. 1960. 1pp.

(19) Letter from the Sec'y of the Treasury relating to an addition to the Cost of the Public Building at Seattle, March 5, 1904. 1pp.

(20) Survey of Lakes Union and Washington for Ship Canal to Elliott Bay, June 2, 1880. 46th Cong., 2nd Sess., H. R., 1578. 1p.

(21) Canal between Lakes Union and Washington and Puget Sound, Mar. 1, 1884. 48th Cong., 1st Sess., H. R., 603. 2pp.

(22) Report of the Committee on Commerce in regard to the Lake Washington Canal, May 1, 1884. 48th Cong., 1st. Sess., Sen. Rep., 494. 8pp.

(23) Canal. Letter from the Acting Sec'y of War, Jan. 5, 1892. 52nd Cong.., 1st Sess., H. R. Ex. Doc. 40. 33pp.

(24) Estimates of Cost of Canal, April 21, 1896. 54th Cong., 1st Sess., Sen. Doc. 269. 18jj.

(25) Waterway Connecting Puget Sound and the Lakes, Feb. 1, 1902. 57th Cong, 1st Sess., H. R. Doc. 335, map. 6pp.

(26) Report of the Board of Engineers appointed to determine the possibility of constructing the Canal, Jan. 31, 1903. 57th Cong., 2nd Sess., Sen. Doc. 127. Map. 70pp .

Together 26 items, 8vo, half mor. V.p., V.d. Washington, 1874-1904. $22.50

936 [SEATTLE PUBLIC LIBRARY.] Eleven Reports of., 1903-1913. 8vo, half mor. Seattle, v.d. $5.00

937 [UNIVERSITY OF WASHINGTON.] A Collection of 12 Reports of the Regents. 8vo. Seattle, v.d. $7.50

938 [WASHINGTON INDIAN—MILITARY AFFAIRS, 1853-56.] Collection of Four Works on. As follows:

(1) Journal of Lawrence Kip. Sources of the History of Oregon. 28pp.

(2) Indian Affairs of the Pacific. Message from the President, Feb. 16, 1857. 34th Cong., 3rd Sess., H. R. Ex. Doc. 76. 256pp.

(3) Message of the President relative to Indian disturbances in California, Feb. 21, 1856. 34th Cong., 1st Sess. Sen. Ex. Doc. 26. 68pp. Together with newspaper clippings and notes by Mr. Prosch

(4) Reminiscences of Seattle and the Sloop Decatur during the Indian Wars of 1855-56. By the late T. S. Phelps, U. S. N. 50pp.

Together 4 vols., 8vo, half mor. V.p., V.d. $25.00

939 [WASHINGTON INDIAN—MILITARY AFFAIRS, 1854-60.] Collection of Four Works on. As follows:

(1) Correspondence between the late Sec'y of War and General Wool, March 25, 1858. 35th Cong., 1st Sess. H. R. Ex. Doc. 88, 213pp.

(2) From the Report of the Sec'y of War. Dept. of the Pacific. 1855. 15pp.

(3) Report from the Dept. of the Pacific. 34th Cong., 3rd Sess., Sen. Doc. 51, 1856. 54pp.

(4) Indian Affairs in Oregon and Washington Territories. Message from the President, May 10, 1858. 35th Cong., 1st Sess., H. R. Ex. Doc. 112, 21pp.

Together 4 vols., 8vo, half mor. V.p., V.d. $22.50

940 [WASHINGTON INDIAN AND MILITARY AFFAIRS.] A Collection of Four Documents relating to. As follows:

(1) Topographical Memoir of the Dept. of the Pacific. Letter from the Sec'y of War, with the Memoir and Report of Capt. T. J. Cram, March 3, 1859. 35th Cong., 2nd Sess., H. R. Ex. Doc. 114. 126pp

(2) Report of the Sec'y of War Dept. of the Pacific, 1857. 85pp.

(3) Message of the President relative to Indian Affairs in Oregon and Washington Terr., May 10, 1858. 35th Cong., 1st Sess., H. R. Ex. Doc. 112. 21pp.

(4) Report of the Sec'y of War communicating the . . . Memoir and Map of Col. Wright's late Campaign against the Indians in Ore. and Wash., Feb. 15, 1859. 35th Cong., 2nd Sess., Sen. Ex. Doc. 32. 82pp.

Together 4 Works, 8vo, half mor. V.p., V.d. $27.50

941 [WASHINGTON PRESS ASSOCIATION.] Proceedings of, from the First to the Eleventh Annual Meeting, incl., 1887-1897. 8vo, half mor. Seattle, V.d. $22.50

942 [WASHINGTON PUBLIC SCHOOLS.]

(1) Appeal for Teachers' Institutes, and Proceedings of the Washington Institute and Educational Association, compiled and published by J W. Clark. 67pp. Olympia, 1880. This contains reports of the first, second, third and fourth meetings.

(2) Proceedings of the Fifth Annual Meeting. Olympia, 1881.

(3) Reports of the Supt. of Public Instruction for. 1879, 1883, 1885, 1889.

(4) First Annual Report of the City Supt. (Seattle), 1885, 1885-6, 1889.

(5) Fifth Report of the Board of Education of Seattle, 1883.

Together 10 documents, 8vo, half mor. V.p., V.d. $22.50

943 [WASHINGTON STATE.] East of the Cascade Range.

(1) Report of Committee in regard to the Construction of a Canal and Locks at the Cascades of the Columbia, April 10, 1876. 44th Cong., 1st Sess., Sen. Report 251. 6pp.

(2) Information respecting the Navigable Waters of the Upper Columbia and its Tributaries. Letter from the Sec'y of War, April 24, 1862.

(3) Letter from the Sec'y of War, transmitting report of Capt. Powell upon the Survey of the Columbia, at the Dallas, July 25, 1882. 47th Cong., 1st Sess. Senate Ex. Doc. 184. Maps.

(4) Official Proceedings of the Second Session of the Columbia Waterway Convention held at Vancouver, B. C., Oct. 14, 1886. 30pp.

(5) Proceedings of the 3rd Session held at Portland, Oct. 9, 1888. 2pp.

(6) Proceedings of the 4th Session held at Portland, Oct. 9, 1888. 24pp.

(7) A Geological Reconnaissance across the Cascade Range near the 49th Parallel. By Geo. Otis Smith and Frank C. Calkins. 58th Cong., 2nd Sess., H. R. Doc. 730. 110pp. Illus.

Together 7 items, 8vo, half mor. and green cloth. V.p., V.d. $17.50

944 [WASHINGTON STATE.] The Pioneers of Washington. Transactions from the year 1883-1889 incl. 154pp. The Proceedings, 1903-4. 52pp.; Transactions, 1905-10 incl. 8vo, cloth. V.p., V.d. 1883-1910. $2.50

"In the beginning, a sketch of some early events in Western Washington, whlie it was a part of 'Old Oregon' "—Clarence Bagley.

945 [WASHINGTON STATE.] A Collection of Four Documents relating to. As follows:

(1) Enabling Act and Constitution, with side Notes and Index. Olympia, 1891. 93pp.

(2) State of Washington. Brief History of the Discovery, Settlement and Organization of, etc. 1893. 224pp. Illus.

(3) State of Washington. An Official Report of the Resources of . . . 1894. By J. H. Price. 75pp.

(4) State of Washington, 1901. Its Resources, Natural, Industrial, Commercial. Published by Bureau of Statistics, Agriculture and Immigration. Illus., 260pp.

Together 4 Works, 8vo, half mor. V.p., V.d. $10.00

946 [WASHINGTON STATE HISTORY.] Collection of Works relating to. As follows:

(1) Wonderland, 1900. By Olin D. Wheeler. Illus. Descriptive of the region tributary to the Northern Pacific Railway, and including particularly the story of Lewis and Clark's explorations. 76pp.

(2) Historical Sketch of the State of Washington. Illus. 52pp.

(3) Admission of the State of Washington. Speech of Jos. E. Dolph, of Oregon, in Senate, Mar. 31—April 1, 1880. 37pp.

(4) Proceedings of the House of Rep. during the Consideration of H. R. 2889, providing for the Annexation of North Idaho to Washington Terr. 14pp.

(5) Annual Address before the Washington Pioneers, June 7, 1899, by Judge C. H. Hanford. Illus. 30pp.

(6) Transactions of the Washington Pioneer Association for the Years 1883 to 1899 incl. Portraits and illus. 164pp.

(7) History of Thurston County. By J. C. Rathbun. 131pp. Olympia, 1895.

Together 7 Works, 8vo, half mor. V.p., V.d. $27.50

947 [WASHINGTON TERRITORY.] A Collection of Governors' Messages and Reports to the Sec'y of Interior relating to Washington Territory, 1877-1889. 8vo, half mor. V.p., V.d. $17.50

948 [WASHINGTON TERRITORY.] A Collection of Ten Governors' Messages relating to. 1873-1879. 8vo, half mor. V.p., V.d. $20.00

949 [WHITMAN MASSACRE.] A Collection of Six Important Works relating to the Whitman Controversy, as follows:

(1) The Whitman Myth, by Prof. E. G. Bourne. 13pp.

(2) A Reply . . . by Myron Eells. Walla Walla. 123pp

(3) History vs. the Whitman Saved Oregon Story, by Wm. I. Marshall. 236pp. 1904.

(4) The Whitman Myth, by Wm. I. Marshall. 8pp.

(5) Article in the "Oregonian," by Myron Eells.

(6) Oregon Question. (Marcus Whitman), by Clarence B. Bagley.

Together in 1 volume, 8vo, half mor. V.p., V.d. $17.50

950 [WHITMAN MASSACRE.] A Collection of Works relating to the Indian rising in Oregon and the massacre of Dr. Marcus Whitman and members of his Mission. The Collection includes the following Works:

(1) Message of the President of the U. S., in relation to the Indian Affairs in Oregon. 8pp. 30th Cong., 1st Sess., Sen. Ex. Doc. No. 47. March 29, 1848.

(2) Memorial of the Legislative Assembly of Oregon Territory. 26pp. Aug. 10, 1848, 30th Cong., 1st Sess. H. R. misc. No. 98. [This is the report of the Massacre and important.]

(3) Memorial of the Legislature of Oregon. 6pp. 31st Cong., 2nd Sess. ,Sen. Doc. Misc. No. 5, Jan. 6, 1851.

(4) Memorial of the Legislature of Oregon, praying for payment of expenses incurred by the Provisional Government of Oregon, in the Cayuse War. 11pp. 31st Cong., 2nd Sess. Sen. Miss. Doc. No. 29. Feb. 25, 1851.

(5) Expenses of the Cayuse War. 8pp. Feb. 4, 1851. 33rd Cong., 1st Sess., H. R. Ex. Doc., No. 45.

(6) Expenses of the Cayuse War. 5pp. March 8, 1854. 33rd Con.g, 1st Sess. H. R. No. 122.

(7) Browne, J. Ross. Report of on the late Indian War in Oregon and Washington Territories. 66pp. 35th Cong., 1st Sess., Sen. Ex. Doc. No. 40 Jan. 25, 1858. [This report contains a reprint of Fr. Brouilet's "Protestantism in Oregon."]

(8) Letter from the Secretary of the Interior, in relation to the early labors of the Missionaries of the American Board of Commissioners for Foreign Missions in Oregon, commencing in 1836 81pp. [This contains a long article "History of Missions on the Northwest Coast by Rev. Henry H. Spalding in answer to Brouilet.]

(9) The Hudson Bay Company Archives Furnish no Support to the Whitman Saved Oregon Story. 36pp. By William L. Marshall. Chicago, 1905.

(10) Smith, Charles. A Contribution toward a Bibliography of Marcus Whitman. 62pp. October, 1908.

(11) Provisional Govt. Debt of Oregon, March 16, 1866. 39th Cong., 1st Sess., H. R. 66. 1p.

Together 11 items, bound in one volume, 8vo, calf. V.p., V.d. $40.00

PART IV

4

THE GEORGE W. SOLIDAY COLLECTION OF WESTERN AMERICANA

PART IV

---

1 [ABOLITIONISTS.] Autographs for Freedom. Edited by Julia Griffiths. Portraits. 8vo, cloth. Auburn, 1854. $1.00

2 ADAMS, CHAS. FRANCIS. Lee at Appomattox and other Papers. 387 pp., 8vo, cloth. Boston, 1902. $2.50

3 AIKMAN, DUNCAN. Calamity Jane and the Lady Wildcats. 347 pp., illus., 8vo, cloth. N. Y. (1927). $2.50

4 [ALASKA.] Alaska, its Meaning to the World, its Resources, its Opportunities. 318 pp., illus., 2 maps. 8vo, cloth. Seattle, 1914. $3.75
Smith 4039.

5 [ALASKA.] Compilation of the Acts of Congress and Treaties relating to Alaska from Mar. 30, 1867 to March 3, 1905 . . . By Fred F. Barker. Folio, 3/4 mor. Washington, 1906. $7.50
Wick. 7850.

6 [ALASKA.] Reconnaissance in the Cape Nome and Norton Bay Regions, Alaska, in 1900, by Alfred H. Brooks, George B. Richardson, Arthur J. Collier and Walter C. Mendenhall. Colored maps, plates. 4to, cloth. Washington, 1901. $3.75
Wick. 8233. Contains a reconnaissance of the Cape Nome and adjacent goldfields of the Seward Peninsula in 1900.

7 [ALASKA.] Cession of American Territory; a Pacific Coast Protest against the yielding by the United States of any portion of Alaska to the Dominion of Canada. 8 pp., 8vo, original wrappers. [Seattle: Chamber of Commerce, February, 1899.] $7.50
Smith 3484 cites one copy.

8 [ALASKA.] Memorial of Louis Goldstone, May 20, 1870. Addressed to the Senate and House of Representatives of the United States. 4 pp., 8vo. Washington, 1870. $25.00

A rare work of which the only other copy I can locate is in the library of Mr. Thomas W. Streeter. Louis Goldstone, a citizen of San Francisco, was a fur trader in Alaska for many years prior to its accession. Having received knowledge of the termination of the lease between the HBC and the Russian Company, Goldstone set out early to acquire the lease himself. He made lengthy surveys of Alaska but before he could consummate the deal Secretary Seward stepped in and made overtures to buy the Territory, using Goldstone's map and other information gathered in his survey. Goldstone, in the above Memorial, asks for compensation. Goldstone may be said to have inadvertently prompted Seward to acquire Alaska.

Not in Wickersham.

9 [ALASKA.] Guide to the Yukon Gold Fields. Where they are and how to Reach Them. 85 pp., map, illus. 8vo, original wrappers. Seattle, 1897. $12.50

Wick. 3997.

10 [ALASKA.] Holzworth, John M. The Wild Grizzlies of Alaska. 417 pp., illus. 8vo, cloth. N. Y., 1930. $4.50

11 [ALASKA.] Big Game Shooting in Alaska. By Capt. C. R. E. Radclyffe. 292 pp., illus. 8vo, cloth. London, 1904. $7.50

Smith 3253.

12 [ALASKA.] Among the Indians of Alaska. By Charles Replogle. 182 pp., illus. 12mo, cloth. London: Headley, 1904. $7.50

Wick. 2670.

13 [ALASKA.] Sketch of the Flora of Alaska. By T. J. Rothrock. 40th Cong., 2nd Sess., Sen. Misc. Doc. 86. Washington, 1868. $5.00

This is the annual report of the Board of Regents of the Smithsonian Institute for 1867.

14 [ALASKA.] Alaska Man's Luck. A Romance of Fact. By Hjalmar Rutzebeck. 260 pp., 12mo, cloth. N. Y.: Boni (1920). $3.00

15 [ALASKA.] Typescript copy of a Diary kept by Frederick Sargent at Sitka and Kodiak, from Jan. 1, 1868 to Dec. 17, 1869. 15 pages on 4to size paper. N.p., N.d. (1868-1869). $12.50

16 [ALASKA.] Seal and Salmon Fisheries and General Resources of Alaska. 4 vols., illus., maps, charts. 8vo, cloth. Washington, 1898. $12.50

Smith 4161. Appendix and corrections by David Starr Jordan and George Archibald Clark. This is House Doc. 92, parts 1-4, 55th Cong., 1st Sess.

17 [ALASKA.] Alaska. By Mrs. William Walter Smith. 27 pp., 8vo, original wrappers. Hartford (1910). $5.00

The author was the wife of W. W. Smith, author of "Alaska the Eldorado of the North, etc.," published in Hartford in 3 volumes in 1910.

18 [ALASKA.] The Indians of the Yukon and Tanana Valleys, Alaska. By Mathew Sniffen and Thomas Spees Carrington. 35 pp., illus. 8vo, original wrappers. Phila., 1914. $4.50

LOCAL ALASKAN IMPRINT OF "SOAPY" SMITH TRAGEDY

19 [ALASKA.] The "Soapy" Smith Tragedy. Shea and Patton. 24 pp., illus. 8vo, original wrappers. Skagway, Alaska, 1907. $12.50

Wick. 1606.

20 [ALASKA.] Geology of the Yukon Gold District, Alaska, with an Introductory Chapter on the History and Condition of the District in 1897. By Josiah E. Spurr. Illus., maps. 4to, half mor. Washington, 1897. $4.00

21 [ALASKA.] Stephenson, Wm. B. Land of Tomorrow. 240 pp., 12mo, cloth. N. Y. (1919). $3.50

Smith 3841.

22 [ALASKA.] A Woman who Went to Alaska. By Mary Kellogg Sullivan. 302 pp., port., illus. 12mo, cloth. Boston: Earle (1903). $4.00

Smith 3892.

23 [ALASKA.] The Trail of a Sourdough. By Mary Kellogg Sullivan. 258 pp., illus. 12mo, cloth. Boston: Badger (1910). $4.00

24 [ALASKA.] The Yakutat Bay Region, Alaska. Physiological and Glacial Geology. By Ralph S. Tarr and Bert S. Butler. 193 pp., illus. 8vo, mor. Washington, 1909. $4.50

25 [ALASKA.] Alaskan Glacier Studies of the National Geographic Society in Yakutat Bay, Prince William Sound and Lower Copper River Regions. By Ralph Stockman Tarr and Lawrence Martin. 498 pp., illus. 8vo, half mor Washington, 1914. $7.50

26 [ALASKA.] Trails and Tramps in Alaska and Newfoundland. By William S. Thomas. 330 pp., illus. 8vo, cloth. N. Y., 1913 $3.75

27 [ALASKA.] In the Time that Was; done into English by J. Frederic Thorne (Kitchakakahaech), illustrated by Judson T. Sergeant (To-u-sucka). Being the first volume of a series of Legends of the Tribe of Alaskan Indians known as the Chilkats—of the Klingats. As told by Zachook, the "Bear" to Kitchakahaech, the "Raven". (29) pp., illus. 8vo, original wrappers. Seattle: Pub. by the Raven Press . . . (1909). $7.50

Smith 3890 cites one copy.

28 [ALASKA.] Alaska in 1779. By Rev. Walter Thornton, S.J. (From the United States Catholic Historical Records and Studies, Vol. 12, June, 1918). 8vo. N. Y., 1918. $3.00

29 [ALASKA-YUKON.] Reminiscences of the Yukon. By Stratford Tollemache. 316 pp., illus. 8vo, cloth. London, 1912. $5.00

Smith 3896.

30 [ALASKA.] Alaska, an Empire in the Making. By John J. Underwood. 440 pp., illus. N. Y., 1913. $4.50

Smith 4066.

31 [ALASKA.] Alaska: Land of the Nugget. Why? . . . A Critical Examination of geological and other testimony, showing how and why gold was deposited in polar lands. By Isaac N. Vail. 68 pp., 8vo, original wrappers. Pasadena, Cal.: Printed by the Author, 1897. $5.00

Wick. 3693.

32 [ALASKA.] Orphir's Golden Wedge. A Skyborn Treasure. By Isaac N. Vail. 36 pp., 8vo, original wrappers. Pasadena, 1898. $7.50

33 [ALASKA.] Valaam Monastery. Centenary of the Russian Church in America, 1794-1894. Sketch of the History of the American-Russian Orthodox Religious Mission. Kodiak Mission, 1794-1837. (In Russian). 292 pp., 2 plates. St. Petersburg, 1894. $12.50

Wick. 5761.

34 [ALASKA.] A Dog-Puncher in the Yukon. By Arthur T. Walden. 289 pp., illus. 8vo, cloth. N. Y., 1928. $3.50

35 [ALASKA.] Wardman, George. A Trip to Alaska. A Narrative of what was Seen and Heard during a Summer Cruise in Alaskan Waters. 237 pp., 8vo, cloth. Boston, 1884. $4.50

A scarce work. Wardman was the U. S. Treasury Agent at Seal Island.

36 [ALASKA.] Weimer, M. D. K. True Story of the Alaska Gold Fields. 312 33., illus., 8vo, N.p., N.d. (1903?). $20.00

Can locate no other copy. Neither Wickersham nor Smith cites another copy. The work was clumsily published without a title-page, the place of publication probably somewhere in Iowa in 1903. The author left Iowa Feb. 28, 1898, landed at Skagway March 12, and arrived in Dawson City on June 12th. His Journal is in day-by-day diary form and gives an excellent account of the Gold Fields.

37 [ALASKA.] Whymper, Fred'k. Travel and Adventure in the Territory of Alaska, formerly Russian American, now ceded to the United States, and in various other parts of the North Pacific. Map, illus. 8vo, cloth. London, 1868. $6.00

Smith 4378. This is a standard work on the Indians and the Fur Trade of Russian America. The opening chapters contain some early reminiscences of British Columbia and Vancouver Island, and the concluding pages relate to California.

38 [ALASKA.] Williard, Mrs. Eugene S. Life in Alaska . . . edited by her sister, Mrs. Eva McClintock. 384 pp., illus., port. 12mo, cloth. Phila., (1884). $4.50

39 [ALASKA.] Williard, Mrs. Eugene S. Kin-da-shon's Wife. An Alaska Story. 281 pp., 8vo, cloth. Chicago, 1892. $3.75

40 [ALASKA.] Glimpses of Alaska Klondike and the Gold Fields, containing the only Genuine Views of the Interior of Alaska photographed by Veazie Wilson, the Explorer in 1894 and Copyrighted in 1895. Compiled by Miss Esther Lyons. 12mo, original wrappers. Chicago, 1897. $17.50

See Wick. 3996 and Smith 4432, neither of which are the above. Wilson's works on Alaska are hard to come upon. The above work comprises about 100 photographs taken by Wilson in 1894 from Dyea up through the Chinook Pass, Lake Linderman and Bennet, on down the White Horse Rapids, Lake Belarge, Pelly River, Yukon, etc. They were taken two years before the Gold Rush.

41 [ALASKA.] Woodman, Abby Johnson. A Journal of Tour among the Mountains, Seas and Islands of the Northwest, San Francisco to Sitka. 212 pp., plates, map. 8vo, cloth. Boston, 1890. $4.50

42 [ALASKA.] Wright, Julia McNair. Among the Alaskans. 351 pp., illus., 2 maps. 8vo, cloth. Phila.: Presbyterian Board of Pub. (1883). $4.50

Smith 4475.

43 [ALASKA.] Young, Samuel Hall. Alaska Days with John Muir. 226 pp., illus. 12mo, cloth. Chicago (1915). $4.50

Smith 4496. Wick. 4961. Young went to Alaska as a parson in 1879.

44 [ALASKA.] Young, Samuel Hall. The Klondike Clan. A Tale of the Great Stampede. 393 pp., illus., map. 8vo, cloth. N. Y. (1916). $4.50

Smith 4497. Wick. 4443.

45 [ALASKA.] Young, Samuel Hall. Adventures in Alaska . . . 181 pp., illus. 12mo, cloth. N. Y. (1919). $4.50

Smith 4495. Wick. 1368.

46 [ALASKA.] Yukon Bill. Derby Days in the Yukon and Other Poems of the Northland. 128 pp., 12mo, cloth. N. Y., 1910. $3.00

Wick. 5427.

47 [ALASKA COMMERCIAL CO.] Reply of the Alaska Commercial Company to the Charges of Governor Alfred P. Swineford, of Alaska, against the Company in his Annual Report for the Year 1887. By Louis Sloss. 96 pp., 8vo, original wrappers. (San Francisco, 1887). $17.50

Can locate no other copy in bibliographies consulted. This work was apparently issued in answer to Swineford's first report which is cited in Wickersham.

48 [ALASKA-KLONDIKE.] A Wanderer's Trail; being a Faithful Record of Travel in many Lands. By A. Loton Ridger. 403 pp., illus. 8vo, cloth. London, 1914. $6.00

Smith 3316. Pp. 39-113 relate to Pacific Northwest and a trip down the Yukon to the Klondike.

49 [ALASKA-KLONDIKE.] An English Expert on the Klondike. By A. N. C. Treadgold. 94 pp., 2 maps. 8vo, original wrappers. Toronto, 1899. $7.50

Smith 4018 locates only the copy at Victoria.

50 [ALASKA-KLONDIKE.] Klondyke: Truth and Facts of the New Eldorado. By A. E. Ironmonger Sola. 3 maps and illus., 92pp. 8vo, cloth. London (1897). $7.50

Smith 3748. Wick. 4414. One of the earliest books on the Klondike find. It contains a sketch of William Ogilvie.

51 [ALASKA-SKAGWAY.] Skagway Commercial Club. Illus. 12mo, original wrappers. (Skagway, N.d.). $3.75

52 [ALASKA-YUKON.] Through the Yukon and Alaska. B. T. A. Rickard. 392 pp., illus. 8vo, cloth. San Francisco, 1909. $5.00

Wick. 3966. Smith 3314. A scarce work published by the Mining and Scientific Press.

53 [ALASKA-YUKON GOLD.] Stanford's Map Shewing the Position of the Yukon Goldfields, 1897. Folding map, 21x27 in., mounted on linen. London, 1897. $10.00

This is one of the early maps made after the discovery, and is both interesting and accurate and now quite scarce.

54 [ALASKA-YUKON GOLD.] A Mile of Gold. Strange Adventures in the Yukon. By William M. Stanley. 219 pp., illus. 8vo, cloth. Chicago, 1898. $4.50

55 [ALASKA-YUKON.] Stratemeyer, Edward. To Alaska for Gold; or the Fortune Hunters of the Yukon. 248 pp., 12mo, cloth. Boston (1899). $2.50

Wick. 67.

56 [ALASKA-YUKON.] Voyage on the Yukon and its Tributaries. A Narrative of Summer Travel in the Interior of Alaska. By Hudson Stuck. 397 pp., illus., maps. 8vo, cloth. N. Y., 1917. $3.00

Smith 3886.

57 [ALASKA-YUKON.] A Winter Circuit of our Arctic Coast. A Narrative of a Journey with Dog-Sleds around the entire Arctic Coast of Alaska. 360 pp., illus. 8vo, cloth. N. Y., 1920. $3.00

58 ALLEN, JOSEPH. The Making of a Canadian. Illus. by Elmer Rache. 383 pp., 8vo, cloth. Newark, 1918. $2.50

59 [AMERICAN AGRARIANISM.] The Green Rising. An Historical Survey of Agrarianism, with Special Reference to the Organised Efforts of the Farmers of the U. S. to improve their Economic and Social Status. By W. B. Bizzell. 269 pp., 12mo, cloth. N. Y., 1926. $2.50

60 [AMERICAN AGRICULTURE.] North America, its Agriculture and Climate, containing Observations on the Agriculture and Climate of Canada, the U. S. and the Island of Cuba. By Robert Russell. Folding map, 390 pp. 8vo, cloth. Edinburgh, 1857. $3.00

61 [AMERICAN COLONIES.] A Summer Visit to Three Rhode Islanders to the Massachusetts Bay in 1651 . . . By Henry Melville King. 8vo, cloth. 115 pp. Providence, 1896. $3.00

62 [AMERICAN COOK BOOK.] Web-Foot Cook Book. 218 pp., 12mo, original wrappers. Portland, Ore.: Ayres, 1885. $4.00

63 [AMERICAN EMIGRATION.] Handbook of the United States of America and Guide to Emigration . . . for the Settler, Business Man, Merchant, Farmer, Importer and Professional Man. By L. P. Brockett. 8vo, cloth. N. Y., 1879. $2.25

64 [AMERICAN FICTION.] Horse-Shoe Robinson; a Tale of the Tory Ascendency. By John P. Kennedy. 8vo, original cloth, name on title. N. Y., 1852. $3.50

65 [AMERICAN LABOR.] The Labor Movement; the Problem of Today. The History, Purpose and Possibilities of Labor Organizations in Europe and America, Guilds, Trade Unions and Knights of Labor . . . By Terrence V. Powderly. Illus. Thick 8vo, original cloth. N. Y., 1890. $5.00

66 [AMERICAN MANNERS AND CUSTOMS.] The Federal Judge. A Novel. By Charles K. Lush. 12mo, cloth. Boston: Houghton, Mifflin, 1897. $3.00

67 [AMERICAN MILITARY.] Regulations for the Order and Discipline of the Troops of the United States, to which is added an Appendix containing the U. S. Militia Act, passed in Congress, May, 1792, the Mass. Militia Act, passed June 22, 1793, and the Rules and Articles for governing the Troops, Forts and Garrisons within the Commonwealth of Massachusetts, and the Militia when in actual service. A new edition. Folding plans and charts. 12mo, old calf (broken), (stamp and writing on title). Boston: D. West, 1794. $2.00

68 [AMERICAN SPORT.] Fifty Years a Hunter and Trapper. Experiences and Observations of E. N. Woodstock, the noted Hunter and Trapper. . . . Illus. 12mo, cloth. Columbus (1913). $3.00

69 [AMERICAN REVOLUTION.] Travels in the Interior Parts of America; in a Series of Letters. By an Officer. (Anburey, Thomas). Plates and Maps. 2 vols., 8vo, old calf (rubbed). London, 1789. $17.50

Original edition.

69a [AMERICAN REVOLUTION.] The Case of the Sloop Active, &c. Pp. 27 and blank. [Phila.: Hall and Sellers, 1779.] $60.00

Evans 16220 and Harbeck p. 9. The Original Congress Edition of not only the most celebrated case in the annals of American Admiralty Law but the case which largely caused B. Arnold to "turn color." The above copy, while not signed, was originally bound in with other material relating to the Active Case which were signed by Joseph Reed, Arnold's arch enemy and President of the Supreme Executive Council of Pennsylvania. Perhaps no other case in sea law so typifies Yankee courage and fortitude as this of the Active. It was this case and that of the "Charming Nancy" which caused Arnold's run-in with Joseph Reed and the Supreme Executive Council. Although not ultimately settled until 1809, the Case of the Ship Active immediately became and still remains the glorious story of four Connecticutensians—Gideon Olmstead, Artimas White, Aquila Rumsdale and David Clarke. Just like the captors of Major Andre the four Connecticut hill-toppers were cruising around the Atlantic (as our sub-chasers are today) when they were captured by the British. Taken to Jamaica and forced to join the Sloop Active as ABS they sailed to N. Y. with supplies for that city. The Connecticut boys, who had been sailing to the Sugar Islands since they could walk, were as mad as a Connecticutensian can really be. Off the coast of Delaware Gideon and his three companions clapped the rest of the crew below hatches and took over. There were 14 men in the crew of the Active. But they apparently did it. Gideon and his 3 companions nudged the Active into Little Egg Harbor Bay, Somers Point (this is a New Jersey item, too). She was boarded by the Privateer Convention of Philadelphia and taken to port. B. Arnold stepped in here and paid off his four native Connecticut friends. Reed and the Supreme Executive Council of Pennsylvania pounced upon him. Arnold got nothing. He was accused of Champetry. Apparently Olmstead and his companions and heirs lost their money. Olmstead shouted loud and long, but Pennsylvania ordered the ship sold and the proceeds placed in escrow. Finally, in 1809, the Pennsylvania authorities offered armed resistance to the U. S. Marshall who came to collect the money. The case finally ended by the Marshall collecting $18,000. Whether he paid it finally to Gideon Olmstead and his Connecticut companion, or whether it went elsewhere or to the Posse Comitatus which offered the armed resistance, and who assisted the Marshall, still remains confused, although Olmstead is said to have received $14,175. Anyway, it was a great case, and will always have great significance in American history—because it evoked so much From the library of Joseph Reed, President of the Supreme Executive Council of Pa.

69b [AMERICAN REVOLUTION.] Debates in the Legislature of Pennsylvania, on the Case of Gideon Olmstead. Reported by William and Hugh Hamilton. Printed and Published by William Hamilton, June, 1810. 198 pp., with the original fly-leaves, original boards, with extra calf (back-strip has been reinforced with heavy manila paper. Lancaster, Pa., 1810. $25.00

This is the key volume of the series above noted, as it bears the inscribed signature of Joseph Reed on the title-page and the front flyleaf. Joseph Reed of the Supreme Executive Council was the individual who sent Arnold chasing up toward Gloucester, N. J., and points northward. This volume also is the last word on the case.

69c [AMERICAN REVOLUTION.] The Whole Proceedings in the Case of the Olmsted and Others versus Rittenhouse's Executrices, as contained in Documents on Record in the Courts of the United States and Pennsylvania; together with the Act of the Legislature of the State of Pennsylvania in relation to this important subject. Collected and Arranged by Richard Peters, Jun. 8vo, unbound. Phila.: Wm. P. Farrand and Co., Fry and Kamerer, Printers, 1809. $15.00

The above is the entire proceedings in the case. The preface states: "Should a collision take place between the authority of the U. S. and Pennsylvania, and consequences endangering or fatal to our peace or to the Union Ensue, every man will wish to possess the collection now published."

69d [AMERICAN REVOLUTION.] A Report on the Whole Trial of Gen. Michael Bright, and Others; before Washington & Peters, in the Circuit Court, of the United States, and for the District of Pennsylvania, in the Third Circuit; on an Indictment for Obstructing, Resisting and Opposing the Execution, of the Writ of Arrest issued out of the District Court of Pennsylvania; in the case of Gideon Olmstead and others, against the surviving Executrices of David Rittenhouse, Deceased. By Thomas Lloyd, the Arguments of Counsel, and Charge of the Judge, revised by each respectively. 8vo, unbound, 222 pp. and 2 pp. Contents. 8vo, unbound, no flyleaves. Phila.: Printed for P. Byrne, 1809. $15.00

70 [AMERICAN REVOLUTION.] Letters to a Nobleman, on the Conduct of the War in the Middle Colonies. By (Joseph Galloway). Folding map, colored outline. 102 pp., plus page of Advt. 8vo, unbound. London, 1780. $8.50

71 [AMERICAN REVOLUTION.] Philipse Manor Hall at Yonkers, N. Y. The site of the Building and its Occupants. By Edward H. Hall. Illus. 12mo, cloth. N. Y., 1912. $2.00

72 [AMERICAN REVOLUTION.] Nathan Hale, 1776. Biography and Memorials. By Henry P. Johnston. 296 pp., illus. 8vo, original boards (chipped at bottom of spine). N. Y., 1914. $5.00

Has 2pp. supplement inserted. Limited edition.

73 [AMERICAN REVOLUTION.] Van Tyne, Claude H. The American Revolution, 1776-1783. Ports., colored maps. 8vo, cloth. N. Y., 1905. $3.50

74 [ARIZONA.] Adventures in the Canyons of the Colorado. By Wm. Wallace Bass. Illus., 38 pp. 8vo, printed wrappers. Grand Canyon, Arizona, 1920 (privately printed). $2.00

75 [ARIZONA.] A Concise Statement of the Prominent Facts and Grounds of Claim made by Wm. S. Grant, of Maine, upon the United States, for Properties Destroyed in Arizona by Order of the Military Authorities, and Captured by the Rebels; for which Loss he Claims Indemnity. 8vo., 8 pp., original printed wrappers. (Washington: Privately Printed, 1862). $20.00

Grant went overland to Arizona to supply the troops in the Territory in 1860. He narrates his troubles bringing supplies into the Territory from Texas, the establishment of a depot at Tucson, etc. Grant was the builder of Ft. Breckenridge.

76 [ARIZONA.] Grant, Wm. S. In the Court of Claims. William S. Grant versus The United States. Brief of Counsel for Claimant, J. S. Black and M. H. Dunnell, Counsel. 16 pp., original printed wrappers. (Washington): H. Polkinhor, Printer (1863). $17.50

Gives a narrative of the evacuation of the Territory of Arizona in 1861 and the burning of the stores at Tucson and elsewhere.

77 [ARNOLD, BENEDICT.] The Crisis of the Revolution, Being the Story of Arnold and Andre now for the First Time Collected from All Sources, and Illustrated with Views of Identified with it. By William Abbatt. Illus. from Original Photographs. 4to, cloth. N. Y., 1899. $37.50

No. 157 of 250 copies printed.

78 [ASTOR, JOHN JACOB.] John Jacob Astor. By Arthur D. Smith. 296 pp., 8vo, cloth. Phila., 1929. $3.00

79 ATKINSON, REV. G. H. The Northwest Coast, Including Oregon, Washington and Idaho. A Series of Articles upon the Northern Pacific Railroad in its relation to the Basins of the Columbia and of Puget's Sound. 56 pp., 8vo, original wrappers. Portland, Ore., 1878. $25.00

This work by one of the great Missionaries of Oregon was first published in The Oregonian.

80 AUDUBON, J. J. Life of Audubon, the Naturalist of the New World. His Adventures and Discoveries. By Mrs. Horace St. John. 311 pp., 12mo, cloth. Phila. (1850). $5.00

81 AUDUBON, JOHN J. Delineations of American Scenery and Character. Intro. by Francis Hobart Herrick. Tinted port. 8vo, cloth. N. Y., 1926. $3.50

82 AUDUBON, J. W. Illustrated Notes of an Expedition through Mexico and California. 4to, four colored plates. Tarrytown, 1915. $40.00

Wagner-Camp 208 (note). The first reprinting of this rare work from the copy now in the Huntington Library. Only 55 copies were printed and a copy is seldom offered.

83 AUZIAS-TURENNE, R. Comment naquit le quarante-dieuxieme Etat de la Federation Americaine. L'Etat de Washington et sa Ville Reine, "Seattle". 16 pp., 8vo, original wrappers. Paris, N.d. $7.50

Auzias-Turenne, author of one of the earliest Klondike guide books, was long a resident of the Northwest.

84 BAILLIE-GROHMAN, WM. A. Camps in the Rockies, being a Narrative of Life on the Frontier, and Sport in the Rocky Mountains, with an Account of the Cattle Ranches of the West. 12mo, cloth. N. Y., 1882. $3.00

85 BAKER, REV. J. C. Baptist History of the North Pacific Coast. With Special Reference to Western Washington, British Columbia and Alaska. 472 pp., illus. 8vo, cloth. Phila., 1912. $5.00

86 BALLANTYNE, R. M. and P. F. TYTLER. Discovery and Adventure on the Northern Coasts of America and the Hudson's Bay Territories. Engravings. 12mo, original cloth (soiled). London, 1860. $3.50

86a [BAPTIST CHURCH.] Correspondence of Reverend Ezra Fisher, Pioneer Missionary of the American Baptist Home Mission Society in Indiana, Illinois, Iowa and Oregon. Edited by Sarah Fisher Henderson, Nellie Smith Latourette and Kenneth Scott Latourette. 492 pp., 8vo, buckram. N.p., N.d. $20.00

Rev. Ezra Fisher, of Dedham, Mass., whose five sons answered the call to arms of April 19, 1775, was a foremost Missioner Baptist in America. Converted at Wendell, Mass., he went to Amherst, then to Newton Theological, and then accepted his first call at Cambridge, Vt. He married Miss Lucy Taft, of Clinton, N. Y. Then he was engaged by the Baptist Home Mission after it was first organized (1832). The next year he and his young wife went to Indianapolis, Ind., the Home Mission to "furnish him with an outfit and support him there." In 1836 Rev. Fisher went to Quincy, Ill., thence to Iowa (1839), thenafter to Oregon with the great Migration of 1845. Rev. Fisher was both a Bible-carrier and Culture-bearer from New England westward to Oregon. His is a Preacher Book, but he was a cultured man and this book contains as full and discerning letters from 1832-1857, from the midwest and far west as this recorder has ever read. This work was probably printed in Portland, Ore.

87 BARBER, JOHN W. Historical Collections of the State of New York. Numerous plates, folding map. 8vo, cloth (worn at backstrip, foxed). N. Y., 1851. $1.50

88 BARBER, JOHN W. Connecticut Historical Collections . . . Second Edition. Tinted frontis., colored folding map, other plates. 8vo, sheep (worn and foxed). New Haven, (1836). $2.00

88a BARBER, JOHN W. Connecticut Historical Collections, containing a general collection . . . relating to the History and Antiquities of Every Town in Connecticut. Numerous engravings, folding map. 8vo, calf (worn and some foxing). New Haven (1836). $1.75

89 BARNES, WILL C. Apaches and Longhorns. The Reminiscences of. 210 pp., illus. 8vo, cloth. Los Angeles, 1941. $2.50

He went from Indiana to the Southwest, and elsewhere.

90 BEADLE, J. H. Western Wilds, and the Men who Redeem Them. An Authentic Narrative . . . By J. H. Beadle. Illus, map. Thick 8vo, original half mor. Cincinnati (1879). $2.50

91 [BIBLIOGRAPHY.] Bibliotheca Americana, 1886-1893. Catalogue of a Valuable Collection of Books and Pamphlets relating to America. With a Descriptive List of Robert Clarke & Co.'s Historical Publications. 2 vols. in one, 8vo, ¾ mor. (broken at hinge). N. Y., 1886-1893. $7.50

92 [BIBLIOGRAPHY.] Catalogue of Books and Pamphlets Principally Relating to America. 592 pp., index. (The Boon Library). 8vo, half calf (broken). N. Y., 1870. $4.50

93 [BIBLIOGRAPHY.] Important Livres et Manuscrits relatifs aux Ameriques et a la Guerre d'Independence. Precieux Documents Originaux sur la Decouverte et la Colonization du Canada et de la Louisiane. Manuscrits Autographes de la Perouse, Rochambeau, etc. 130 pp., 4to, original wrappers. Paris, 1934. $3.00

94 BIDWELL, JOHN. A Journey to California. With Observations about the Country, Climate and the Route to this Country . . . A Day-byDay Record of the Journey from May 18, 1841 to Nov. 6, 1841. With an Intro. by Herbert Ingram Priestley . . . Folio, boards. San Francisco: Nash, 1937. $6.50

95 BIDWELL, JOHN. Echoes of the Past. An Account of the First Emigrant to California, Fremont in the Conquest of California, Discovery of Gold and early Reminiscences. Port., illus. Small 4to, 91 pp., original printed wrappers. Chico, Cal., N.d. $4.00

96 BIEBER, RALPH P. The Southwest Historical Series. Illus. 9 vols., 8vo, cloth. Glendale: Clark, 1931-1940. $50.00

Fine set. Comprises: Webb, James Josiah; Adventures in the Santa Fe Trail. (2) Bandel, Eugene; Frontier Life, in the Army, 1854-1861. (3) Gibson, Geo.; Rutledge Journal of a Soldier under Kearny and Doniphan, 1846-47. (4) Johnston, Abraham R.; Marcellus B. Edwards, and Philip G. Ferguson; Marching with the Army of the West. (5) Southern Trails to California in 1849. (6) Garrard, Lewis H.; Wah-to-yah and the Taos Trail. (7) Exploring Southwestern Trails, comprising the Journals of Philip St. George Cooke, Lieut. W. H. C. Whiting, and Francis Xavier Aubry. (8) Overland to the Pike's Peak Gold Mines. (9) McCoy, Jos. G.; Historic Sketches of the Cattle Trade.

97 BOLTON, HERBERT E., and STEVENS, H. MORSE. The Pacific Ocean in History; Papers and Addresses presented at the Panama-Pacific Historical Congress held at San Francisco, Berkeley and Palo Alto, Calif., July 13-23, 1915. 535 pp., 8vo, cloth. N. Y., 1917. $7.50

Smith 2990.

98 [BOOKS ABOUT BOOKS.] Out of Doors Library Hunting. By Archibald Rogers, et al. 372 pp., 8vo, cloth. N. Y., 1897. $5.00

99 BOYNTON, C. B., and MASON, T. B. Journey Through Kansas; with Sketches of Nebraska . . . Folding map, 216 pp., 8vo ,original printed wrappers. Cincinnati, 1855. $12.50

99a [BRITISH COLUMBIA.] Letter by Rev. J. Gammage, dated May 3, 1859; and Letter of Rev. R. Dawson, dated April 4, 1859. Contained in the Mission Field, Aug. 1, 1859. 12mo, boards. (London, 1859). $4.50

100 [BRITISH COLUMBIA.] Pioneer Days in British Columbia. Reminiscences. 32 pp., 12mo, original wrappers. Vancouver, N.d. $7.50

101 [BRITISH COLUMBIA.] St. Ann's Academy. St. Ann's in British Columbia and Alaska, 1858-1914. 116 pp., illus. 8vo, original wrappers. Victoria, B. C., 1924. $4.50

102 [BRITISH COLUMBIA.] British Columbia Emigration and our Colonies considered Practically, Socially and Politically. By W. Parker Snow. 108 pp., 8vo, original wrappers. London: Piper, 1858. $30.00

Smith 3739 locates only the copy at Victoria, B. C.

103 [BRITISH COLUMBIA.] Tales of the British Columbia Frontier. By William Ward Spinks. 134 pp., illus., 8vo, cloth. Toronto (1933). $3.00

104 [BRITISH COLUMBIA.] The Harbour and City of Victoria. The Port of Vancouver's Island, 1916. By Thomas C. Sorby. 54 pp., 8vo, original wrappers. (Victoria, 1917). $2.50

105 [BRITISH COLUMBIA.] Forty Years in Canada. Reminiscences of the Great Northwest . . . By Col. S. B. Steele. 428 pp., illus., 8vo, cloth. Toronto, 1915. $4.50

106 [BRITISH COLUMBIA.] Colonization of Vancouver's Island. 26 pp., map. 8vo, original wrappers (lacks the wrappers). London, 1849. $45.00

Smith 741 reports only the copy in the Legislative Library at Victoria. This is an excessively rare work on the early founding of Vancouver Island.

107 [BRITISH COLUMBIA.] Reply of the Victoria Chamber of Commerce to His Excellency Frederick Seymour, Governor of British Columbia, forwarded to the Secretary of State for the Colonies, Oct. 1, 1866. 47 pp., 8vo, original wrappers. Victoria, 1866. $52.50

Can locate no other copy. This excessively rare and important work gives a complete history of the somewhat acrimonious correspondence between the Governor and the Chamber of Commerce of Victoria in regard to Governor Seymour's proposal to make New Westminster the Port of Entry for British Columbia. Seymour states: "The entrance to Victoria Harbor is shoal, narrow and intricate . . ." To which the Chamber of Commerce replies: "The intricate, narrow and uncertain channel through the sand heads at the mouth of the Fraser is available for ships drawing 16 feet of water at the utmost . . ." The work goes on to give a complete history of harbor facilities and shipping, not only at Victoria but of the Mainland.

108 [BRITISH COLUMBIA.] Romance of Vancouver. 60 pp., folio. N.p., 1926. $2.00

109 [BRITISH COLUMBIA.] Victoria Illustrated. 96 pp., illus., 8vo, original wrappers. Victoria, 1891. $3.50

110 [BRITISH COLUMBIA.] Wade, Mark S. The Thompson Country. Being Notes on the History of Southern British Columbia and particularly of the City of Kamloops, formerly Fort Thompson. Illus., 136 pp. 8vo, original cloth. Kamloops, 1907. $12.50

Smith 4218. Original Edition of a scarce work. The above copy has the errata slip.

111 [BRITISH COLUMBIA.] Dinoflagellates and Protozoa from British Columbia. By G. H. Wailes. 41 pp., illus. 8vo, original wrappers. Vancouver, B. C., 1928. $3.00

112 [BRITISH COLUMBIA.] Walbran, Capt. John T. British Columbia Coast Names, 1592-1906, to which are added a few names in adjacent United States Territory. Their Origin and History. 546 pp., folding map, plates. 8vo, cloth. Ottawa, 1909. $22.50

A scarce work of which only 500 copies were printed.

113 [BRITISH COLUMBIA.] Walken, W. Wymond. Stories of Early British Columbia. 287 pp., illus., 8vo, cloth. Vancouver, 1914. $25.00

Smith 4225. Apparently only 35 copies were printed. The work is very interesting and important, according to John Forsyth, Mr. Soliday and others.

114 [BRITISH COLUMBIA.] Water Powers of British Columbia, including a Review of Water Power Legislation relating thereto and a Discussion of various matters respecting the Utilization and Conservation of Inland Waters. By Arthur V. White. ix-644 pp., illus., maps. 8vo, cloth. Ottawa, 1919. $5.00

115 [BROOK FARM.] Brook Farm, Historic and Personal Memoirs. By John Thomas Codman. Illus. 12mo, cloth. Boston, 1894. $3.00

116 [BROOK FARM.] John Sullivan Dwight, Brook-Farmer, Editor, and Critic of Music. A Biography. By George Willis Cooke. 8vo, port., cloth (bit soiled). Boston, 1898. $2.50

117 [BROWN, JOHN.] The Annals of Harper's Ferry. With Sketches of its Founder, and many Prominent Characters Connected with its History, Anecdotes, etc. Second Edition. 126 pp., ports. 8vo, original wrappers. Martinsburg, W. Va., 1872. $5.00

118 BROWNSON, REV. T. G. Trials and Triumphs of Fifty Years of Baptist Work in Oregon. 18 pp., 8vo, original wrappers. Portland, Ore., 1894. $7.50

Smith 518. Dr. Brownson, an early missioner of Oregon, was President of the McMinnville College, Oregon.

119 BOUCARD, A. Travels of a Naturalist. A Record of Adventures, Discoveries, History and Customs of Americans and Indians, Habits and Descriptions of Animals, Chiefly made in North America, California . . . Port. 8vo, cloth. London, 1894. $6.00

120 [BUFFALO BILL.] Buffalo Bill's Boyhood. By Elmer Sherwood. 121 pp., 12mo, cloth. Racine, N.d. $2.50

121 [BUFFALO BILL.] Buffalo Bill and the Pony Express. By Elmer Sherwood. 124 pp., 12mo, cloth. Racine, N.d. $2.50

122 BURDICK, USHER L. Tales from Buffalo Land. The Story of Fort Buford. 215 pp., illus. 12mo, cloth. Baltimore, 1940. $3.00

123 BURPEE, LAWRENCE J. Pathfinders of the Great Plains. A Chronicle of La Verendrye and his Sons. Colored frontis., other illus. 12mo, limp leather. Toronto, 1915. $2.50

124 BURPEE, LAWRENCE J. On the Old Athabaska Trail. 259 pp., illus. 8vo, cloth. London, N.d. $3.50

125 BURR, AARON. A Dream of Empire; or the House of Blennerhassett. By Wm. Henry Venable. 12mo, cloth. N. Y., 1901. $2.00

126 [CALIFORNIA.] (Baywater, J. W.). Perils, Pastimes, and Pleasures of an Emigrant in Australia, Vancouver's Island and California. 404 pp., 12mo, cloth. London, 1849. $17.50

Author's autographed copy. Cowan, p. 176: "The author came to California while that country was still the lazy land of missions, dashing caballeros and laughing senoritas. Neither gold nor conquest had yet come to mar the picture. His narrative records an extremely interesing view of the country as it was during those last days of the old regime, and as it became following the gold discovery. An appendix of nearly 100 pages is given over to an account cf the mining districts, the character of the diggings, the various routes thither, etc."

127 [CALIFORNIA.] Bell, Major Horace. Reminiscences of a Ranger; or. Early Times in Southern California. 457 pp., 8vo, original cloth. Los Angeles, 1881. $20.00

Original Edition. Braislin 1436. An exceptionally interesting and factual narrative of events and conditions from 1851 on. Bell joined Walker's Filibustering Expedition of which he gives a lucid account. He was one of the band who captured Joaquin Murietta, whose history and career he recounts. He also narrates the exploits of Moreno, as well as those of other desperadoes of the region. He further gives the history of the Los Angeles Vigilance Committee; the fraudulent land grants; an account of Bandini's Revolution; Beckwourth, Sublette; in short, Major Bell seems to draw in all the celebrated pioneer figures, good and bad.

128 [CALIFORNIA.] Berthold, Victor H. The Pioneer Steamer California, 1848-1849. 106 pp., illus., map. 8vo, cloth. Boston and N. Y., 1932. $7.50

129 [CALIFORNIA.] Burnett, Peter H. Recollections and Opinions of an Old Pioneer. 12mo, cloth. N. Y., 1880. $15.00

Burnett made the Overland from Independence to Oregon in 1843. He later went to California in the fall of 1848 to look for gold, and the remainder of his book relates to California, of which he was the first governor.

130 [CALIFORNIA.] Remarks on the death of the late Dr. Philip P. Carpenter, before the California Academy of Sciences, July 2, 1877. By Robert E. C. Stearns. 8vo, original wrappers. N.p., N.d. (San Francisco, 1877). $3.50

131 [CALIFORNIA.] (John Carr). Pioneer Days in California. Historical and Personal Sketches. Portrait. 8vo, original cloth. 452 pp. Eureka, Calif., 1891. $20.00

132 [CALIFORNIA.] Carr, John. A Vulcan Among the Argonauts. Being Vivid Excerpts and those Most Original and Amusing Memoirs of John Carr, Blacksmith. Edited by Robin Lanspon. 8vo, boards., illus. San Francisco, 1936. $3.50

133 [CALIFORNIA.] Coke, Henry J. A Ride Over the Rocky Mountains to Oregon and California. With a Glance at some of the Tropical Islands, including the West Indies and the Sandwich Islands. Port., 388 pp. 8vo, 3/4 mor. London, 1852. $12.50

Wagner-Camp 211.

134 [CALIFORNIA.] Pacific Coast Souvenir.. 46 tinted views of the West with descriptive text. Published by E. S. Dennison. Small 4to, cloth. Oakland, 1888. $1.25

135 [CALIFORNIA.] Flirtation Camp; or, the Rifle, Rod and Gun in California. 299 pp., 12mo, cloth. N. Y., 1881. $4.50

136 [CALIFORNIA.] From Ocean to Ocean, being the Diary of a Three Months Expedition from Liverpool to California and Back, and from the Atlantic to the Pacific by the Overland Route. 108 pp., 8vo, cloth. Printed for Private Circulation. (London), 1871. $17.50

A scarce work.

137 [CALIFORNIA.] Harpending, Asbury. The Great Diamond Hoax and Other Stirring Incidents in the Life of Asbury Harpending. Edited by James H. Wilkins. Illus., 283 pp. 8vo, cloth. Published by the Author. San Francisco, 1913. $3.00

138 [CALIFORNIA.] California, 1847-52. Drawings by William Rich Hutton, reproduced from the originals in the Huntington Library. With an Introduction by Willard O. Waters. Colored frontis. and portrait. Oblong 4to, cloth-backed boards. Limited to 700 copies. Grabhorn Press, San Francisco, 1942. $5.00

139 [CALIFORNIA.] 10.000 Miles by Land and Sea. By Rev. W. W. Lord. 284 pp., 12mo, cloth. Toronto, 1876. $7.50

Account of a Canadian pastor's overland trip to the west in 1874 via the Great Lakes; description of San Francisco, Salt Lake City and the Mormons, Digger Indians, etc.

140 [CALIFORNIA.] Priestley, Herbert Ingram. Historical, Political and Natural Description of California, by Pedro Pages, Soldier of Spain. Newly translated from the Spanish . . . 83 pp., 8vo, cloth. Berkeley, 1937. $3.00

141 [CALIFORNIA.] Around the Golden Deep. A Romance of the Sierras. By A. P. Reeder. 495 pp., 12mo, cloth. San Francisco, 1885. $2.50

142 [CALIFORNIA.] San Francisco News Letters. Diamond Jubilee Edition, Sept., 1925. 8vo, original wrappers. San Francisco, 1925. $4.00

Contains many historical items and early prints.

Item 139, Line two should read Rev. W.W. Ross not Lord.

143 [CALIFORNIA.] San Francisco Vigilance Committee of '56, with some interesting Sketches of Events succeeding 1848. By Frank Meriweather Smith. 8vo, original wrappers. San Francisco, 1883. $4.50

Review of the state of residing in San Francisco in 1846. Accounts of the Committee are given, drawn principally from the Press of the day, the best and only fairly accurate authority.

144 [CALIFORNIA.] Memory of Oscar Lovell Shafter. 25 pp., 8vo, original printed wrappers. San Francisco, 1874. $12.50

An address of the Rev. Dr. Stebbins and L. Hamilton, and a sketch of his life and character by the celebrated John W. Dwinelle before the Supreme Court of California. Shafter, a member of the Supreme Court of California, was born at Athens, Vt., 1812, studied at Harvard, started his career at Wilmington, Vt. and was candidate for Governor of that State by the "Liberty Party." He went to California in 1854 where he had a long and useful juridical career. He died in Florence, Italy, in 1873. Scarce.

145 [CALIFORNIA.] Soulie, Maurice. The Wolf Club. The Great Adventures of Count Gaston de Raousset-Boulbon in California and Sonora, 1850-1854. 281 pp., 8vo, boards. Indianapolis (1927). $2.50

146 [CALIFORNIA.] Stewart, W. Frank. Pleasant Hours in an Eventful Life. 94 pp., 8vo, cloth. San Francisco, 1869. $4.00

147 [CALIFORNIA.] San Francisco's Great Disaster, a Full Account of the Recent Terrible Destruction of Life and Property . . . By Sydney Tyler. 8vo, cloth, illus. Phila. (1906). $1.25

148 [CALIFORNIA.] Millionaire for a Day. An Inside History of the Great Southern California Boom. By Theodore S. Vandyke. 208 pp., 12mo, cloth. N. Y., 1900. $6.00

149 [CALIFORNIA.] Wakeman, Capt. Edgar. The Log of an Ancient Mariner: Life and Adventures of Captain Edgar Wakeman. Port., plates. 8vo, cloth. San Francisco, 1878. $12.50

The author is the authority on the early affairs of the Vigilance Committee, as he was Sheriff in 1852. Wakeman landed in San Francisco early in 1850; was a prime mover in the hanging of Jenkins and Stewart. He describes the life and times of his period together with his own experiences in California and as far eastward as the Wyoming-Colorado line.

150 [CALIFORNIA.] Warner, J., and Hayes, B. A Historical Sketch of Los Angeles County, California. From the Spanish Occupancy in 1771 to the Present Time. 12mo, cloth, 88 pp. Los Angeles: Mirror Print, 1876. $15.00

This work is drawn largely from unrecorded sources and from narratives and personal reminiscences "falling directly from the lips of survivors of older generations, now rapidly passing away." It contains the unpublished Overland Journal of Dr. J. S. Griffin, attached to Kearney's command, in day-by-day form; Stern's letters on the gold discovery, etc.

151 [CALIFORNIA.] Birds of California. xxxviii-577 pp., illus. By Irene Grosvenor Wheelock. 12mo, mor. Chicago: McClurg, 1904. $4.00

152 [CALIFORNIA.] Williams, Rev. Albert. A Pioneer Pastorate and Times. Contemporary Local Transactions and Events. Port. and plates.

225 pp., 8vo, cloth. San Francisco, 1879. $7.50

Founder of the First Presbyterian Church of San Francisco. The author discusses his voyage to California in 1849, Vigilance Days of 1850-51, Oregon travels, land titles, famous pioneer men and events, etc.

153 [CALIFORNIA.] Williams, Mary Floyd. History of the San Francisco Committee of Vigilance of 1851. A Study of Social Control on the California Frontier in the days of the Gold Rush. Illus. 543 pp., 8vo, cloth. Berkeley, 1921. $6.50

154 [CALIFORNIA.] Williams, Mary Floyd. Papers of the San Francisco Committee of Vigilance of 1851. 906 pp., 8vo, cloth. Berkeley (1919). $6.50

155 [CALIFORNIA.] Williard, Chas. Dwight. Herald's History of Los Angeles. 365 pp., 12mo, cloth. Los Angeles (1901). $3.75

156 [CALIFORNIA.] Winthrop, R. C. Admission of California. Speech on the President's Message, transmitting the Constitution of California, delivered May 8, 1850. 28 pp., 8vo, boards. Washington, 1850. $4.50

156a [CALIFORNIA.] Wooley, L. H. California, 1849-1913; or, the Rambling Sketches and Experiences of Sixty-four Years. 48 pp., 8vo, original wrappers. Oakland, 1913. $7.50

Printed, but not for publication. The author joined the first mule train of Turner Allen and Co., leaving Independence in May, 1849. He gives an account of the trip Overland across the plains to California, life at the mines, joining the Vigilance Committee (of which he was a prominent member), etc.

157 [CALIFORNIA.] Woods, James. Recollections of Pioneer Life in California. A Record of Scenes and Events that transpired in California in the Early Times. 260 pp., 12mo, cloth. San Francisco, 1878. $7.50

158 [CALIFORNIA.] Young, John F. Journalism in California. Pacific Coast and Exposition Biographies. 8vo, cloth. San Francisco (1913). $2.00

159 [CALIFORNIA.] Zimmerman. Dr. W. E. A. Californie en de Goud koorts, togten in het Westen van Noord-Amerika. Het Leven in de Zeden der Goudgravers, Mormonen en Indianen, naar het Hoogduitsch. Colored plates. 2 vols., 8vo, original wrappers. Amsterdam, 1864. $10.00

159a [CALIFORNIA.] Zimmerman, von E. A. W. Taschenbuck der Reisen, oder Dartellung der Entdeckungen des 18 Jahrhunderts. Achter Jahrgang fur das Jahr 1805. Mit 9 Kupfer, 1 Karte. 283 pp., 12mo, cloth. Leipzig, 1805. $22.50

Gives some account of California and contains 9 fine engravings, 2 of Monterey, of Native Californians and a map of America.

160 [CALIFORNIA LAND CLAIMS.] Argument of H. S. Foote before the Committee on Private Land Claims in the U. S. Senate in support of brief heretofore filed, in the matter of the Rio de Santa Clara Grant. 11 pp., original printed wrappers. (Washington, 1872). $4.50

Relates to 17,000 acres of government land in the county of Santa Barbara which had been ceded and unlawfully patented to claimants under the Mexican grant of "Santa Clara."

160a CAMPBELL, ALBERT H. Pacific Wagon Roads. Letter from the Secretary of the Interior, transmitting a report upon the Several Wagon Roads Constructed under the direction of the Interior Department. [Report by Albert H. Campbell, dated Feb. 19, 1859.] [Washington, 1859.] 35th Sess. Cong., 2nd Sess., H. Ex. Doc. 108. 8vo, sewn, 6 maps. Maps: (1) Ft. Ridgley to South Pass by Meady; (2) Ft. Kearney, South Pass and Honey Lake to Lander; (3) Ft. Kearney via South Pass and Bishop; (4) El Paso and Ft. Yuma Wagon Rd., by Hutton; (5) Wagon Road from Platte River via Omaha Reservation and Dakota City, and one other. $35.00

Braislin 308.

161 CAMPBELL, J. W. A History of Virginia, from its Discovery till the year 1781. With Biographical Sketches of all the Most Distinguished Characters that occur in the Colonial, Revolutionary, or Subsequent Period of our History. 310 pp., 12mo, full dark green levant, t. e. g., all other edges untrimmed. Petersburg, Va., 1813. $17.50

Beautiful copy in gilt paneled borders.

162 [CANADA.] History of the Canadian Bank of Commerce, with an Account of the other Banks which now form part of its Organization. By Victor Ross. Illus., 516-595 pp. 2 vols., 8vo, cloth. Toronto: Oxford, 1920-1922. $10.00

This beautifully printed work has chapters on the Bank of British Columbia and banking in the Yukon.

163 CAPRON, E. S. History of California, from its Discovery to the Present Time; comprising also a full Description of its Climate, Surface, Soil, Rivers, Towns, Beasts, Birds, State of its Society, Agriculture, Commerce, Mines, Mining, etc., with a Journal of the Voyage from New York, via Nicaragua, to San Francisco and back, via Panama. Large folding colored map. 12mo, original cloth. Boston, 1854. (In a cloth slipcase). $10.00

164 CARSON, KIT. Life of Kit Carson: The Great Western Hunter and Guide . . . By Charles Burdette. Illus. 12mo, original cloth. Phila. (1869). $2.50

165 CARVALHO, S. N. Incidents of Travel and Adventure in the Far West; with Col. Fremont's Last Expedition . . . 380 pp., illus., 12mo, cloth. N. Y., 1857. $4.50

166 CASS, GEN. LEWIS. Outlines of the Life and Character of. 64 pp., 8vo, woodcut port. Sewn, as issued. Albany: Munsell, 1848. $3.50

167 [CATHOLIC MISSIONS.] Une Page d'Histoire Decouverte des restes de Trois Missionares de la Compagnie de Jesus. By C. E. Ruleau. xii-69 pp., 8vo, original wrappers. Quebec, 1898. $4.50

168 [CATHOLIC MISSIONS.] St. Boniface (Manitoba) Societe Historique Bulletin, Volumes 1-4. 4 vols., 8vo. St. Boniface, 1911-1913. $10.00

Contains much valuable historical material on the far West and Northwest.

169 [CATHOLIC MISSIONS.] St. Ann's Academy. St. Ann's in British Columbia and Alaska, 1858-1924. 116 pp., illus. 8vo. N.p. (1924). $4.50

COMPLETE SET OF THE CHAMPLAIN SOCIETY WORKS

170 CHAMPLAIN SOCIETY PUBLICATIONS. A Complete Set of this important Society from its beginning in 1927. Each publication was issued in a strictly limited edition and only applied to the membership. All copies are beautifully printed throughout in large type on hand-made paper, and extensively illustrated with folding colored maps, plates, portraits, etc. In all 35 volumes, large 8vo, in the original red cloth, gilt, uncut and new throughout. Toronto, 1907-1942. [Price on application]

The set comprises: (1) History of New France, v. 1, by Marc Lescarbo; (2) The description and Natural History of the Coast of North America (Acadia) by Nicolas Denyd; (3) Documents relating to the Seignioral Tenure in Canada, 1896-1854, by Prof. W. B. Munro; (4) The Logs of the Conquest of Canada. Ed. by Col. Wm. Wood; (5) New Relation of Gaspesia, by Christian LeClerq; (6) Journey from Prince of Wales Fort, in Hudson's Bay . . . by Samuel Hearne; (7) History of New France, v. 2, by Marc Lescarbo; (8) (9) (10) Historical Journal of the Campaign in North America, 1757-1760, by Capt. John Knox; (11) History of New France, v. 2, by Marc Lescarbo; (12) Narrative of David Thompson. Ed. by J. B. Tyrrell; (13) (14) (15) (17) The Canadian War of 1812, v. 1. Ed. by Wm. Wood; (16) Journals and Letters of La Verendrye and his Sons; (18) Documents relating to the early History of Hudson's Bay, by J. B. Tyrrell; (19) Notes of a Twenty-five Years' Service in the Husdon's Bay Territories, by John McLean; (20) Diereville; Port Royal. Ed. by Dr. J. C. Webster; (21) Journal of Samuel Hearne and Philip Turner between the years 1774 and 1792; (22) Documents relating to the Northwest Company; (23) Travels in the Interior Parts of North America, by Patrick Campbell; (24) Hargrave Correspondence, 1821-43; (25) Sagard's Long Journey to the Country of the Hurons; (26) Journal of Capt. Colnett. Ed. by Judge Howay; plus 6 unnumbered volumes being the Works of Samuel De Champlain, an English trans. with the French text. Plus 3 volumes of the Hudson's Bay Series: (1) Simpson's Athabaska Journal (2) Robertson's Letters, 1817-1822; (3) Minutes of the Council, Northern Dept. of Rupert's Land, 1821-31.

The Champlain Society Publications is one of the most important and valuable publications on North America. Each volume is edited by an historical scholar and with extensive introductions and editorial material. The above is one of the few sets ever offered for public sale. Arrangements may be made for a transfer of subscription along with the sale of the set.

171 CLAYTON, WILLIAM. Index to Clayton's Journal. 12mo, original wrappers. Salt Lake, 1942. $1.50

172 CODMAN, JOHN. The Round Trip by Way of Panama, through California, Oregon, Nevada, Utah, Idaho and Colorado, with Routes of Railroads, Commerce, Agriculture, Mining, Scenery and People. 331 pp., 8vo, cloth. N. Y., 1879. $2.50

173 CODMAN, JOHN. Arnold's Expedition to Quebec. Maps, ports., illus. 4to, cloth. N. Y., 1903. $7.50

This is one of 25 copies printed on large paper. A special edition with added matter and illustrations made by William Abbatt. The original author of this work died before his manuscript went to press.

174 COKE, E. T. A Subaltern's Furlough: Scenes in Various Parts of the United States, Upper and Lower Canada, New Brunswick and Nova Scotia, during the Summer and Autumn of 1832. Large folding map with routes in color, long folding facsimile of the signers of the Declaration and 12 fine lithograph plates. 8vo, original cloth, paper label. London, 1833. $7.50

Braislin 429, Paullin 764. The author traveled upwards of 2,000 miles through most of the New England states and through New York, Pa., and New Jersey as far south as Maryland and Virginia.

175 COLDEN, CADWALLADER. The History of the Five Indian Nations Depending the Province of New York. With an Introduction and Notes by John Gilmary Shea. 8vo, half mor. N. Y., 1866. $6.00

One of 125 copies reprinted exactly from Bradford's rare New York edition of 1727. Paullin 765.

176 [COLLINS, CASPAR.] The Life and Exploits of an Indian Fighter of the Sixties. By Agnes Wright Spring. 187 pp., illus. 8vo, cloth. N. Y., 1927. $3.50

176a [COLONIAL WARS.] A Collection of Four Pamphlets relating to British and American Colonials in the Carribean Area under Admiral Vernon. All collected and bound in one volume, uncut, by Lord George Grenville, with his bookplate. The pamphlets are: An Account of the Expedition to Carthagena, with Explanatory Notes and Observations. 58 pp., half title and full title, uncut. 8vo. London, 1743. (2) A Journal of the Expedition to Carthagena, with Notes. In answer to a late Pamphlet, entitled, An Account of the Expedition to Carthagena. 59 pp., 8vo., half-title and full title, uncut. London, 1744. (3) Original Papers relating to the Expedition to the Island of Cuba. 219 pp., half and full title, uncut. London, 1744. (4) Original Papers relating to the Expedition to Panama. 224 pp., plus errata slip. 8vo. London, 1744. Together 4 items bound in one volume, 8vo, contemporary boards. London, 1743-1744. $30.00

George Washington's brother served under Admiral Vernon in the campaigns observed in the works listed above. Mt. Vernon was named after the Admiral. There was considerable discussion of the Colonial American ground troops used in the campaign, which make the accusations back and forth most interesting. Such a fine set of works dealing with the entire campaign is seldom come upon. Grenville (1712-1770), whose bookplate accompanies this work, was the promoter of the famous Stamp Act and thereby one of the main agents in the genesis of the United States.

177 [COLORADO.] History of Clear Creek and Boulder Valleys. Containing a brief history of the State of Colorado . . . an Account of the Ute Trouble, A History of Gilpin, Clear Creek, Boulder and Jefferson Counties, and Biographical Sketches. Illus. Thick small 4to, ¾ mor. Chicago, 1880. $7.50

From the library of D. C. Collier with his bookplate. Collier was a Colorado pioneer. The work was prepared by Capt. James Burrell, Aaron Frost, Capt. E. L. Berthoud, and Amos Bixby, each doing a history of separate counties.

178 [COLORADO.] Denver Press Club. Who's Who ir the Rockies. Compiled by Joseph Landers. 8vo, cloth. Denver, 1923. $3.50

178a [COLORADO.] South By West; or, Winter in the Rocky Mountains and Spring in Mexico. Edited with a Preface by the Rev. Charles Kingsley. With Illustrations. 8vo, ¾ calf. London: Ibister, 1874. $7.50

A very interesting work narrating experiences and explorations in Colorado, the Pacific Railroad, California.

179 [COLORADO.] Life of the Right Reverend Joseph P. Machebeuf, D.D., Pioneer Priest of Ohio, Pioneer Priest of New Mexico, Pioneer Priest of Colorado, Vice Apostolic of Colorado and Utah, and Bishop of Denver. Front., illus., 419 pp. 8vo, cloth. Printed by the Author. Denver, 1908. $10.00

This energetic priest arrived in N. Y. from France in 1839, went immediately to Ohio, serving at Tiffin and Sandusky in the early 40's; in 1851 he went to New Mexico and Texas—the Gadsden Treaty, Gilpin, Parkman, Ruxton, Santa Fe and Albuquerque; went to Denver in the early 60's and helped build his church at Denver. A very able book of men and events taken chiefly from Father Machebeuf's numerous letters.

180 [COLORADO.] Removal of the Southern Utes. Notes of a Hearing before the Committee on Indian Affairs, U. S. Senate, on the Bill to ratify and confirm an Agreement with the Southern Ute Indians in Colorado and to make the necessary Appropriations for carrying the same into effect. 97 pp., 8vo, caption title. (Washington, 1890). $3.50

Statements of Dr. Childs, Adair Wilson, Otto Mears, F. A. Hammond, C. C. Painter, T. C. Graydon, and others.

181 [COLORADO.] William, Ezekiel. Adventures in Colorado. Missouri Hist. Soc. Coll., Vol. 4, No. 2. 8vo, original wrappers. St. Louis, 1913. $3.50

182 COLTON, J. H. The Western Tourist and Emigrant's Guide, with a Compendious Gazeteer of the State of Ohio, Michigan, Indiana, Illinois and Missouri, and the Territories of Wisconsin and Iowa . . . Also describing all the Principal Stage Routes, Canals, Railroads and the Distances between the Towns . . . Accompanied with a correct Map (large colored folding). By J. Calvin Smith. 12mo, original cloth (dull). N. Y.: Colton, 1840. $7.50

183 COLTON, J. H. Traveler and Tourist's Guide-Book through the U. S. and the Canadas; containing the Routes and Distances on the great Lines of Travel, by Railroads, Canals, Stage-Roads and Steamboats, together with Descriptions of the several States, and of the Towns, Cities and Villages in each. 250 pp., 2 colored maps, one folding. 16mo, original cloth. N. Y., 1850. $4.50

184 COLVOCORESSES, LIEUT. GEO. M. Four Years in the Government Exploring Expedition; commanded by Charles Wilkes . . . 5th ed. Illus., 271 pp. 12mo, cloth. N. Y., 1855. $5.00

185 [CONFEDERACY.] Report of the Judge Advocate General on "The Order of American Knights", also "The Sons of Liberty", a Western Conspiracy in aid of the Southern Rebellion. 16 pp., 8vo, sewn. Washington, 1864. $3.50

186 [CONNECTICUT.] The Pioneer Preacher. Incidents of Interest and Experiences in the Author's Life . . . By Rev. S. Bristol. Illus. 12mo, cloth Chicago and N. Y., 1887. $7.50

Original Edition. Born near New Haven, the author went to Andover, thence to Oberlin College, of which he gives a long account during the 30's and 40's. He went overland with the Van Zandt Train to California in '49.

187 [CONNECTICUT.] Statistical Account of the City of New-Haven. By Timothy Dwight. 60 pp., folding map. 8vo, original printed wrappers. New Haven (1874). $1.00

188 [COWBOYS.] The Honor of a Cowboy. A Comedy in Four Acts. By Charles Ulrick. 12mo, original wrappers (backstrip frayed). Chicago, 1908. $3.75

189 CREMONY, JOHN C. Life Among the Apaches. 322 pp., 12mo, original cloth. San Francisco, 1868. $17.50

190 CREVECOEUR, J. H. ST. T. Letters from an American Farmer; describing certain Provincial Situations, Manners and Customs. Maps. 8vo, half lea. London, 1783. $12.50

191 CROSS, OSBORNE. Message from the President of the U. S. . . . at the Commencement of the Second Session of the 31st Congress, Sen. Ex. Doc. No. 1, folding plates, map, tables, etc. Thick 8vo, boards, roan back. Washington, 1850. $25.00

Wagner-Camp 181. Contains Osborne Cross's "Journey to Oregon" (Pt. 2 pp. 126-244). Report also contains material on Texas, New Mexico and California. This copy contains 36 plates.

192 CUMING, F. Sketches of a Tour to the Western Country, through Ohio, Kentucky, Mississippi and West Florida; with a Notice of an Expedition through Louisiana. 12mo, original calf. Pittsburg, 1810. $27.50

193 [CUSTER, GEN. GEORGE A.] A Complete Life of Gen. George A. Custer. By Frederick Whittaker. 648 pp. 8vo, cloth. N. Y. (1876). $5.00

194 [CUSTER CAMPAIGNS.] Campaigns of General Custer in the North West and the Final Surrender of Sitting Bull. By Judson Elliott Walker. 139 pp., 8vo, original wrappers. N. Y., 1881. $7.50

Signed by the author.

195 CUTTS, JAMES MADISON. The Conquest of California and New Mexico, by the Forces of the United States, in the years 1846 & 1847. Illus. 12mo, original cloth. Phila., 1847. $20.00

196 [DAKOTA.] Dakota Land; or, the Beauty of St. Paul. An Original, Illustrated Historic and Romantic Work of Minnesota and the Great Northwest. By Col. C. Hankins. 2nd edition. Illus. 8vo, cloth (bit worn). N. Y., 1869. $2.00

197 [DAKOTA.] Minutes of the Eighth Session of the North Dakota Baptist Association, held with the First Baptist Church of Jamestown, D. T., June 22, 23, 1888. And also the Dakota and the North Dakota Baptist Sunday School Convention, June 1, 1888 . . . 8vo, original printed wrappers. Mandan, Dakota Territory, 1888. $7.50

The above work is one of the few imprints with the Mandan Dakota Territory Imprint. At the end is a long "Church Statistics" chart stating the pioneer Baptist Churches of North Dakota, of which there were only 24, together with the names of their Pastors, among whom are Pastors W. T. Williams, G. W. Huntley, E. B. Haskell, and J. R. Deckard The clerks, the baptisms, expulsions, church properties, number of edifices, date of buildings finally completed, etc. are given here for the 24 original churches.

198 [DAKOTA.] A Brief History of South Dakota. By Doane Robinson. 224 pp., 12mo, cloth. N. Y. (1905). $2.50

199 [DAKOTA.] Deadwood Gold. A Story of the Black Hills. By George W. Stokes and Howard R. Driggs. 163 pp., illus. N Y., 1926. $3.00

An interesting narrative of the personal experiences of the author in the days of the gold discovery in the Black Hills.

200 [DAKOTA.] Breaking Sod on the Prairies. Story of Early Days in Dakota. By Clarence W. Tabor. 292 pp., illus. 12mo, cloth. N. Y., 1924. $3.00

201 [DAKOTA.] Tom's Experience in Dakota: Why he Went; What he Did There, etc. And all about his Ups and Downs, Successes and Failures. . . . Who Ought to Go, and Who ought Not; etc., with Practical Information for all Classes of People who want Homes in the West. 146 pp., 12mo, cloth. Minneapolis, Minn.: Hale & Co., 1883. $5.00

Some hard-pan facts for western settlers given by one who seemed to have had years of experiences.

202 [DAKOTA.] Civil Government for North Dakota. By A. L. Woods. 278 pp., 12mo, cloth. Grafton, N. D., 1897. $4.50

202a [DAKOTA.] St. Joseph Okolakiciye Ta Olowan. 8vo, cloth. (Bismark, 1919). $5.00

An interesting hymn book in the Sioux language and with a local imprint.

203 [DAKOTA AND UPPER MISSOURI.] Cow-Boys and Colonels. Narrative of a Journey across the Prairie and over the Black Hills of Dakota. By William Conn. Illus. 8vo, cloth. London, 1887. $4.50

204 [DAKOTA TERRITORY.] The Empire Builders of the Great West. By Moses K. Armstrong. Illus., 456 pp., 8vo, cloth. St. Paul, 1901. $3.75

205 DANA, E. Geographical Sketches of the Western Country: Designed for Emigrants and Settlers; Being the result of extensive Researches and Remarks, to which is added a Summary of all the Most Interesting Matters of the Subject, a Particular Description of the Unsold Public Lands, collected from a variety of Authentic Sources; also, a List of Principal Roads. 312 pp., 12mo, calf. Cincinnati, 1819. $15.00

Paullin 826. The author spent 8 years in the west, living most of the time with the Indians and exploring new territory. His work embraces Ohio, Indiana, Ill., Tenn., K., and contains "Sketches of the Country watered by the Columbia River." There are further accounts of Missouri Territory and Louisinaa, etc.

206 DE HASS, WILLS. History of the Early Settlement and Indian Wars of Western Virginia, embracing an Account of various Expeditions in the West, also Biographical Sketches . . . 416 pp., illus. 8vo, calf. Wheeling, 1851. $27.50

Thomson 318.

207 DOMENECH, E. Voyage Dans Le Solitudes Americaines. Le Minnesota. 224 pp., 12mo, original wrappers bound in. Paris, 1858. $10.00

208 [DOUGLAS, SIR JAMES.] Sir James Douglas and British Columbia. By Walter N. Sage. 398 pp., map. 8vo, cloth. Toronto, 1930. $5.00

This is by far the best and fullest life of Douglas, the first governor of British Columbia.

209 DRAKE, SAMUEL ADAMS. The Making of the Ohio Valley States, 1660-1837. Illus. and maps. 12mo, cloth. N. Y., 1916. $2.50

210 DUFLOT DE MOFRAS. Travels on the Pacific Coast. Transl. . . . by Marguerite Eyer Wilbur. 2 vols., 8vo, half mor. Los Angeles, 1937. $10.00

211 DWIGHT, CHAS. P. Life in the Northwest Mounted Police and Other Sketches. 139 pp., 12mo, original wrappers (front wrapper pasted on new boards). Toronto, 1892. $3.50

From Agnes C. Laut's Reference Library.

212 EDWARDS, COL. PHILIP L. California in 1837. Diary of Col. Philip L. Edwards, containing an Account of a Trip to the Pacific Coast. 47 pp., 12mo, cloth. Sacramento, 1890. $15.00

213 ELLET, ELIZABETH F. Pioneer Women of the West. Port. 8vo, cloth. Phila., 1873. $3.00

214 ELLIOTT, T. C. The Coming of the White Woman, 1836, as told in Letters and Journals of Narcissa Prentiss Whitman. 113 pp., 8vo, cloth. Portland, 1937. $3.00

215 EMORY, LIEUT.-COL. W. H. Notes on a Military Reconnaisance from Fort Leavenworth to San Diego, in California, including part of Arkansas, Del Notre, and Gila Rivers. Plates, folding map in pocket. 8vo, original cloth, paper label. Washington, 1848. $6.50

Wagner-Camp 148.

216 ENGLE, FLORA PEARSON. Fifty Years Ago—Fifty Stanzas. 12mo, original wrappers. Coopville, Wash. (1916). $4.00

The author was one of the "Merce Girls."

217 ENSIGN, BRIDGMAN & FANNING MAP. Travellers' Guide through the States of Ohio, Michigan, Indiana, Illinois, Missouri, Iowa and Wisconsin; with Railroad, Canal, Stage and Steamboat Routes; accompanied with a New Map of the Above States. Large colored folding map with engraved inset views of Chicago, Detroit, St. Louis and Cincinnati. By J. M. Atwood. 36 pp., 16mo, original cloth binder. N. Y., 1856. $7.50

218 [ERIE RAILROAD GUIDE.] The Erie Railway and its Branches. With Descriptive Sketches of the Cities, Villages, Stations and of Scenery and Objects of Interest along the Route. By H. F. Walling. 59 pp. and advts., colored maps. 16mo, original wrappers. N. Y.: Taintor Bros., (1872). $1.50

219 FARRAR, VICTOR J. The Annexation of Russian America to the United States. 142 pp., 8vo, cloth. Washington, 1937. $4.00

220 FERRIS, W. A. Life in the Rocky Mountains. A Diary of Wanderings on the Sources of the Rivers Missouri, Columbia and Colorado, from Feb., 1830 to Nov., 1835. Ed. by Paul C. Phillips. 365 pp., front., maps. 8vo, cloth. Denver, 1940. $5.00

221 FITZGERALD, JAMES EDWARD. An Examination of the Charter and Proceedings of the Hudson's Bay Company, with References to the Grant of Vancouver's Island. Colored folding map. 293 pp., 12mo, cloth. London, 1849. $6.00

222 [FLORIDA.] A Bill for the Survey of a Route for a Canal between the Atlantic and the Gulf of Mexico. In the Senate of the U. S., Jan. 19, 1836. 19th Cong., 1st Sess., No. 21. 14 pp., 8vo, unbound. (Washington), 1836. $3.50

223 FOOTE, MARY HALLOCK. Coeur D'Alene. 240 pp., 12mo, cloth. N. Y., 1899. $4.50

Smith 1272.

224 FOREMAN, GRANT. A History of Oklahoma. Illus., maps. 8vo, cloth. Norman, Okla., 1942. $3.50

224a [FOSTER, G. G., Ed.] The Gold Regions of California: Being a succinct description of the Geography, History, Topography, and General Features of California: Including a Carefully Prepared Account of the Gold Regions of that Fortunate Country. . . . Map. 80 pp., 8vo, roan-backed boards. N. Y.: Dewitt & Davenport, 1848. $20.00

Barber Sale 431 (1941). Braislin 755. Both describe this as scarce. This work is one of the earliest accounts of the new gold fields and the vast domains just acquired from Mexico.

225 FOUNTAIN, PAUL. The Eleven Eaglets of the West. 362 pp., 8vo, cloth. London: Murray, 1905. $4.50

California, Oregon, Wash., Idaho, Mont., Wyo., Colo., N. M., Ariz., Utah, Nevada.

226 FOUNTAIN, PAUL. The Great Deserts and Forests of North America. With a preface by W. H. Hudson. By Paul Fountain. 295 pp., 8vo, cloth. N. Y., 1901. $4.50

227 FREMONT, JESSIE BENTON. The Story of the Guard. A Chronicle of the War. 227 pp., 12mo, original cloth. Boston: Tichnor and Fields, 1863. $2.75

Inserted is a letter from Mrs. Fremont to W. D. D'Armand telling him the General wished to see him about a D.A.R. Post. Mrs. Fremont, daughter of Benton and wife of Col. Fremont, here tells the story of Cavalrymen from Missouri, Kentucky and Wisconsin fighting west of the Mississippi during the early years of the Civil War.

228 FREMONT, J. C. Narrative of the Exploring Expedition to the Rocky Mountains in the Year 1842 and to Oregon and North California in the Years 1843-4. 8vo, cloth. N. Y., 1846. $1.25

229 FREMONT, JOHN C. Narrative of the Exploring Expedition to the Rocky Mountains, in the year 1842; and to Oregon and North California, in the years 1842-44. 12mo, sheep. Syracuse, 1846. $3.00

230 FREMONT, JOHN C. Life of. 32 pp., map, port., two plates, early view of San Francisco inserted. 8vo, original printed wrappers. N. Y., 1856. $5.00

231 [FRANKLIN, SIR JOHN.] Arctic Adventure by Sea and Land from the Earliest Date to the last Expeditions in search of Sir John Franklin. By Sir John Sargent. viii-480 pp., map. 8vo, cloth. Boston, 1858. $5.00

232 [FRANKLIN, SIR JOHN.] Arctic Searching Expedition: A Journal of a Boat-Voyage through Rupert's Land and the Arctic Sea, in search of the Discovery Ships under the command of Sir John Franklin. With an Appendix on the Physical Geography of North America. By Sir John Richardson. Map and colored plates. 2 vols., 8vo, original cloth. London, 1851. $17.50

233 [FRASER RIVER MINES.] The Assay Office and the Proposed Mint at New Westminster. A Chapter in the History of the Fraser River Mines. By R. L. Reid. Contained in the Archives of British Columbia. Memoir No. 7. 101 pp., plates. 8vo, cloth. Victoria, 1926. $4.50

234 [FUR TRADE.] The Canadian Northwest; its History and its Troubles, from the early Days of the Fur-Trade to the Era of the Railway and the Settler; with Incidents of Travel in the Region, and the Narrative of Three Insurrections. By G. Mercer Adams. Illus. 12mo, original wrappers (flaking). Toronto, 1885. $4.50

235 [FUR TRADE.] Davidson, Gordon Chas. The Northwest Company. 6 folding maps and reproductions. 8vo, cloth. Berkeley, 1918. $7.50

Story of the early struggle for the fur trade.

236 [FUR TRADE.] Canadian Wilds . . . the Hudson's Bay Company, Northern Indians and their Mode of Hunting, Trapping, etc. By Martin Hunter. 12mo, cloth. Columbus (1907). $3.75

237 [FUR TRADE.] Innis, H. A. Petter Pond, Fur-Trader and Adventurer. 153 pp., map. 8vo, cloth. Toronto, 1930. $5.00

238 [FUR TRADE.] Work, John. Journal of a Chief-Trader of the Hudson's Bay Co., during his Expedition from Vancouver to the Flatheads and Blackfeet of the Pacific Northwest; edited, and with account of the Fur Trade in the Northwest, and Life of Work. By William S. Lewis and Paul C. Phillips. Illus. 8vo, cloth. Cleveland, 1923. $6.00

239 [FUR TRADE.] McKay, Douglas. The Honourable Company. A History of Hudson's Bay Company. 396 pp., illus. 8vo, cloth. First Ed. Indianapolis (1936). $3.50

240 [FUR TRADE.] Wallace, J. N. The Wintering Partners on Peace River. From the Earliest Records to the Union in 1821. Dunvegan Journal, 1806. 139 pp., folding map. Ottawa, 1929. $7.50

241 [FUR TRADE.] [Accounts of the Adventures of the Fur Trade Founders of St. Louis, on the Great Plains and Adjacent Region as related in the Missouri Republican, Missouri Intelligencer, etc. By Albert Watkins.] Publication of the Nebraska State Historical Society, Vol. 20. 8vo, cloth. Lincoln, 1922. $4.00

Beside the fur trade the work deals with the Overland to Oregon and California .

241a [FUR TRADE.] The Fur Trade and Early Western Exploration. By Clarence A. Vandiveer. 316 pp., illus., 8vo, cloth. Cleveland, 1929. $7.50

242 [FUR TRADE.] Willson, Beckles. The Life of Lord Strathcoma and Mount Royal. Illus. 2 vols., 8vo, cloth. Boston, 1915. $7.50

Relates to the Fur Trade, Canadian Pacific Railroad and the Northwest.

243 GALE, GEORGE. Upper Mississippi; or, Historical Sketches of the Mound-Builders, the Indian Tribes, and the Progress of Civilization in the North-West . . . Ports. and views. 12mo, cloth. Chicago, 1867. $10.00

244 GALLATIN, ALBERT. Views of the Public Debt, Receipts and Expenditures of the United States. 60 pp., 8vo, unbound. N. Y., 1800. $7.50

245 GARCILASSO DE LA VEGA (L'INCA). Histoire de la Conquete de la Floride, ou Relation de ce qui s'est passe dans la Decouverte de ce Pays par Ferdinand De Soto. Traduite en Francois par P. Richelet. Two Parts in one volume. 12mo, calf. Paris, 1709. $17.50

The second part has a separate title-page which is dated 1707. It reads as follows: "Histoire de la Floride, ou Relation de la Conquete de ce Pays par Ferdinand De Soto.

246 GARLAND, HAMLIN. Rose of Dutcher's Coolly. 12mo, cloth. Chicago: Stowe & Kimball, 1895. (Lacks front flyleaf). $4.00

247 GARLAND, HAMLIN. Money Magic. Illus. 12mo, cloth. N. Y., 1908. $2.50

248 GARLAND, HAMLIN. Prairie Folks. 8vo, cloth. Chicago: Schulte, 1893. $5.00

249 GARRAGHAN, GILBERT J. Chapters in Frontier History. Research Studies in the Making of the West. Illus. 8vo, cloth. Milwaukee (1934).

249a GARRAGHAN, GILBERT J. Jesuits of the Middle United States. Ports., plates, maps and facs. 3 vols., large 8vo, cloth. N. Y., 1938. $15.00

"A study replete with interest and endeavor . . . of great erudition and thoroughness."—American Hist. Rev. A supplement to the Jesuit Relations and Allied Documents, continuing the work of the Jesuit Missionaries westward into the Old Northwest, trans-Mississippi and Rocky Mountain Region, with an offshoot into California.

250 [GEORGIA.] A History of Georgia, from its First Discovery by Europeans to the Adoption of the Present Constitution in 1798. By Rev. William Bacon Stevens, M.D. Port. and plans. 2 vols., 8vo, original cloth. N. Y., 1847-59. $12.50

The standard history of Georgia. The work is based almost entirely upon original sources, and is a model of excellence.

251 [GEORGIA.] Biographical Sketch of the Hon. Major John Habersham of Georgia. By Chas. C. Jones. 30 pp., port. 8vo, original wrappers. N. Y., Privately Printed, 1886. $2.50

252 GHENT, W. J. The Early Far West. A Narrative Outline, 1540-1850. 411 pp., illus. 8vo, cloth. N. Y., 1936. $3.00

253 GIBBON, JOHN MURRY. The Romantic History of the Canadian Pacific. The Northwest Passage of Today. 423 pp., illus. 8vo, cloth. N. Y., 1937. $2.50

254 GIBBS, JOSIAH F. The Mountain Meadows Massacre. Illus. by Nine full-page and Five half-page engravings from photographs taken on the Grounds. 56 pp., 8vo, original printed wrappers. Salt Lake, 1910. $7.50

255 GILPIN, WILLIAM. The Central Gold Region. The Grain, Pastoral, and Gold Regions of North America. With Some New Views of its Physical Geography, and Observations on the Pacific Railroad. Colored folding maps. 8vo, cloth (worn top spine). Phila., 1860. $7.50

Wagner-Camp 358. Gilpin went overland to Oregon in 1843, and was later Governor of the Colorado Territory.

256 GODDARD, FREDERICK B. Where to Emigrate and Why. Homes and Fortunes in the Boundless West and the Sunny South . . . With a Complete History of the Pacific Railroad. Folding maps, plates. 591 pp., 8vo, cloth. Phila., 1869. Together with the Salesman abridged copy with list of sales penciled on customer's sheet in back. Maps, plates. Together 2 vols., 8vo, cloth. Phila., 1860. $10.00

Early accounts of Idaho, Wyoming, New Mexico. Together with account of Arkansas, Iowa, Ky., Texas, etc.

257 GODDARD, PLINY EARLE. Hupa Texts. University of California Publications, American Archaeology and Ethnology. 8vo, original wrappers. Berkeley, 1904. $2.00

258 GOODELL, WM. The American Slave Code in Theory and Practice: its Distinctive Features shown by its Statutes, Judicial Discussions, and Illustrative Facts. 12mo, cloth. N. Y., 1853. (Slight stain on margin). $2.50

259 GOODNIGHT, CHARLES. Pioneer Days in the Southwest from 1850 to 1879. Thrilling Descriptions of Buffalo Hunting, Indian Fighting and Massacres, Cowboy Life and Home Building. Contributions by Charles Goodnight, Emanuel Dubbs, John Hart, and others. 320 pp., colored frontis. and other views. 12mo, cloth. Guthrie, Okla., 1909. $6.00

260 GORLEY, H. A. Selections from the Numerous Letters and Patriotic Speeches of My Husband, H. A. Gorley. 134 pp., 8vo, cloth. San Francisco, 1876. $10.00

Apparently written by Gorley's wife but the copy is signed by H. A. Gorley. It gives an account of a trip to Northern California and Oregon in 1845. Pages 116-153 gives an account of the Whitman Massacre. This work is scarce.

261 GOTTFREDSON, PETER. History of Indian Depredations in Utah. Illus. 8vo, cloth. (Salt Lake City, 1919). $3.50

262 GOULD, DOROTHY FAY. Beyond the Shining Mountains. 206 pp., illus. Portland, Ore., 1938. $3.75

263 GOULDER, W. A. Reminiscences. Incidents in the Life of a Pioneer in Oregon and Idaho. 376 pp., port. 12mo, cloth. Boise: Regan, 1909. **$10.00**

GRABHORN PRESS PUBLICATIONS

264 BAER, WARREN. The Duke of Sacramento. A Comedy in Four Acts . . . Reprinted from the Rare Edition of 1856. 77 pp., illus. 8vo, boards. San Francisco: Grabhorn, 1934. $5.00

265 BARRINGTON, ALEXANDER. A California Gold Rush Miscellany, Comprising the Original Journal of Alexander Barrington, Nine Unpublished Letters from the Gold Mines, Reproductions of Early Maps . . . 8vo, boards. San Francisco: Grabhorn, 1934. $7.50

266 [STIPP, G. W.] Bradford's History of Kentucky taken from Western Miscellanies compiled by G. W. Stipp and Printed for the Author at Xenia, Ohio, 1827. 8vo, boards. San Francisco: Grabhorn, 1932. $5.00

267 BROWN, JOHN R. Reminiscences and Incidents of "The Early Days" of San Francisco . . . Actual Experiences of an Eye-Witness from 1845 to 1850. San Francisco (1886). Royal 8vo, boards. San Francisco: Grabhorn, 1933. $6.00

268 CONNOR, GEN. PATRICK E. Soldiers of the Overland. Being Some Account of the Services of General Patrick Edward Connor and his Volunteers in the Old West. Illus. Royal 8vo, boards. San Francisco: Grabhorn, 1938. $7.50

269 CORONADO, FRANCISCO VASQUES DE. The Journey of, 1540-1542. Transl. and edited by G. P. Winship. With additional Notes by F. W. Hodge. Illus. 4to, cloth. San Francisco: Grabhorn, 1935. $12.50

270 DELANO, ALONZO. Pen-Knife Sketches or Chips from the Old Block. Reprinted from the Original Edition of 1853. Illus. by Charles Nahl, etc. Frontis. and colored illus. 4to, boards. San Francisco: Grabhorn, 1934. $7.50

271 DARBY, GEORGE H. Phoenixiana. A Collection of Burlesque and Sketches of John Phoenix, alias John P. Squibob, who was in fact Lieut. George H. Derby, U.S.A. Illus. 8vo, boards. San Francisco: Grabhorn, 1937. $3.75

272 DAWSON, NICHOLAS. "Cheyenne." Narrative of. (Overland to California in '41 and '49, and Texas in '52). With an Introduction by Chas. L. Camp, and colored drawings by Arvilla Parker. 8vo, boards. San Francisco: Grabhorn, 1933. $17.50

273 EDWARDS, PHILIP L. California in 1837, Diary of Col. Philip L. Edwards, containing An Account of a Trip to the Pacific Coast. Sacramento, 1890. Colored View of Yerba Buena in 1837. Small 4to, boards. San Francisco: Grabhorn, 1932. $7.50

274 [GARRARD, LEWIS H.] Wah-to-qah. The Taos Trail. Praire Travel and Scalp Dances. Illus. 8vo, boards. San Francisco: Grabhorn, 1936. $7.50

275 [JOHNSON, JOHN EVERETT.] Regulations for Governing the Province of the Californias, approved by His Majesty by Royal Order, dated October 24, 1781. Trans. by John Everett Johnson. 2 vols., boards. San Francisco: Grabhorn, 1929. $15.00

276 LEWIS, OSCAR. California in 1846. Described in Letters from Thomas O. Larkin, "The Farthest West," "E. M. Kern" and "Justice". Notes and Introduction. Port., colored views and facsimile. 4to, boards. San Francisco: Grabhorn, 1934. $7.50

277 MERCER, A. S. The Banditti of the Plains; or, the Cattlemen's Invasion of Wyoming in 1892, the Crowning Infamy of the Ages. Foreword by J. M. Clarke. Illus. by Avrilla Parker. 8vo, boards. San Francisco: Grabhorn, 1935. $7.50

278 [MURIETTA, JOAQUIN.] The Life of, being a Complete History of his Life from the Age of Sixteen to the time of his Capture and Death ot the hands of Capt. Harry Love in 1853. Illus. 4to, boards. San Francisco: Grabhorn, 1932. $5.00

279 [OGDEN, PETER SKENE.] Traits of American Indian Life and Character. By a Fur Trader. Illus. 4to, boards. San Francisco: Grabhorn, 1933. $7.50

280 PARSONS, GEO. F. The Life and Adventures of James W. Marshall, the Discoverer of Gold in California. 144 pp., illus. 8vo, boards. San Francisco: Grabhorn, 1935. $15.00

281 [SHIRLEY LETTERS, THE.] California in 1851, by Shirley. Reprinted from the Pioneer. 2 vols., 4to, boards. San Francisco: Grabhorn. $9.50

282 SUTTER, JOHN A. General Sutter's Diary, "A Relation of Incidents in the Life of a Man held in Respect by Every Californian. Reprinted from the Argonaut, San Francisco, 1878. 4to, boards. San Francisco: Grabhorn, 1939. $10.00

283 STRATTON, R. B. Life Among the Indians; or, the Captivity of the Oatman Girls among the Apache and Mohave Indians. Illus. 8vo, boards. San Francisco: Grabhorn, 1935. $6.50

284 TWAIN, MARK. Letters from the Sandwich Islands, written for the San Francisco Union by Mark Twain. 8vo, boards. San Francisco: Grabhorn, 1937. $10.00

285 WATSON, DOUGLAS S. Spanish Occupation of California. Plan for the Establishment of a Government Junta or Council, held at San Blas, May 16, 1768. Diary of the Expedition made to California. Port. and map. 8vo, boards. San Francisco: Grabhorn, 1934. $7.50

286 WIERZBICKI, F. F. California as It Is, and as it May Be; or, A Guide to the Gold Region. 8vo, boards. San Francisco: Grabhorn. $4.00

287 GREEN, THOMAS MARSHALL. The Spanish Conspiracy. A Review of Early Spanish Movements in the Southwest. Containing proofs of the Intrigues of James Wilkinson and John Brown; of the complicity therewith of Judges Sebastian, Wallace and Innes; the early struggles of Kentucky for autonomy; the Intrigues of Sebastian in 1795-7; and the Legislative Investigation of his Corruption. 8vo, cloth. Cincinnati: Clarke, 1891. $7.50

288 GREEN, THOMAS MARSHALL. Historic Families of Kentucky. With special reference to Stocks immediately derived from the Valley of Virginia; tracing in detail their various genealogical connections and illustrating from Historic Sources their influence upon the Political and Social Development of Kentucky and the States of the South and West. First Series. 8vo, cloth, port. Cincinnati: Clarke, 1889. $9.50

289 [GREENWOOD, CALEB.] Old Greenwood. The Story of Caleb Greenwood, Trapper, Pathfinder and Early Pioneer of the West. 133 pp., 8vo, cloth. Salt Lake City, 1936. $5.00

Now out of print.

290 GREGG, JOSIAH. Commerce of the Prairies; or, the Journal of a Santa Fe Trader, during eight Expeditions across the Great Western Prairies. . . . Folding map and plates. 12mo, original dark cloth. N. Y., 1844. $37.50

A good sound set of this work.

291 GREGG, JOSIAH. Diary and Letters of Josiah Gregg. Southwest Enterprises, 1840-47. Edited by Maurice Garland Fulton. 413 pp., front., map. 8vo, cloth. Norman, Okla., 1941. $3.50

292 GROUARD, FRANK. The Life and Adventures of Frank Grouard, Chief of Scouts, U.S.A. By Joe De Barthe. Illus., 545 pp., 8vo, original cloth. St. Joseph, Mo. (1894). $37.50

Huntington 231. A fine bright copy of the Original Edition of this work which usually comes shabby.

293 GUNNISON, ALMON. Rambles Overland. A Trip across the Continent. 245 pp., 12mo, cloth. Boston: Universalist Pub. Co., 1884. $2.00

The author apparently went over the Rockies in a Stage, 50 miles of which he walked.

294 GUROWSKI, ADAM. Diary from March 4, 1861, to November 12, 1862. 315 pp., 12mo, cloth (worn top of spine). Boston, 1862. $1.50

295 HABERSHAM, A. W. The North Pacific Surveying and Exploring Expedition; or, My Last Cruise . . . 8vo, cloth. Phila., 1858. $7.50

296 HAFEN, LE ROY, and YOUNG, FRANCIS MARION. Fort Laramie and the Pageant of the West, 1834-1890. 429 pp., map, illus. 8vo, cloth. Glendale, 1938. $6.00

297 HALKETT, JOHN. Historical Notes respecting the Indians of North America: With Remarks on the Attempts to Convert and Civilize them. 8vo, original boards, entirely uncut. London, 1825. $12.50

298 [HANCOCK, GEN. WINFIELD SCOTT.] A Summer on the Plains. By Theodore R. Davis. (Contained in pp. 292-307 Harper's New Monthly Magazine, February, 1868). Illus. made on the scene by this well-known Harper's artist. 8vo, original wrappers bound in a card binder. N. Y., 1868. $1.50

From the library of the late Joseph G. Shea. A good account of Hancock's Indian Expedition in Nebraska and Kansas, Colorado, and down into the Santa Fe Trail.

299 HASKINS, C. W. The Argonauts of California. Being the Reminiscences of Scenes and Incidents that Occurred in California in Early Mining Days. By a Pioneer . . . Text and Illustrations drawn from Life by C. W. Haskins. 4to, decorated cloth. 501 pp. N. Y., 1890. $12.50

The above work devotes no less than 142 pages to a "Pioneer Index" which lists upwards of 35,000 Argonauts who had reached California by Dec. 31, 1849.

300 HAYDEN, MARY JANE. Pioneer Days. 49 pp., frontis. 12mo, original wrappers. San Jose, California, 1915. $60.00

Author's autographed copy with some textual corrections made in the author's hand. This is probably the rarest of the recent narratives of the Overland. The author was born in Athens, Maine in 1830 and migrated to Wisconsin in 1847. She started her Overland Journey, March 16, 1850, via the Oregon Trail of which she gives an interesting account, especially a perilous trip down the Columbia. She arrived in Oregon Terr., Oct. 10, 1850 and settled on government land. She gives further an interesting account of the Indian Wars of 1855 and later pioneer life. "Of all the Overland Narratives I've read of recent vintage this is certainly the best. It is the best one I've ever read written by a woman. I've never seen or heard of another copy."—Soliday. The author gives an interesting account of Ft. Vancouver where she resided.

301 HEARNEY, W. S. The Life and Military Services of Gen. W. S. Hearney; a Detailed Narrative of his Expedition to the Yellowstone with Major O'Fallon in 1824; his adventures in the Mexican War, Campaign against the Sioux; Expeditions against the Mormons and proposal to hang Brigham Young; his removal to Oregon, and campaigns against the Northern Indians; the San Juan difficulties, with an explanation of the Hudson's Bay Pretensions, giving a full account of this important affair in our national history . 477 pp., port. and plates. 8vo, cloth. St. Louis, 1878. $7.50

302 HECKEWELDER, JOHN. The Gnadenhuetten Centennial, Sept. 29, 1798. Port., illus. [Separate pub. of the Ohio Archaeological and Historical Publications.] 8vo, original wrappers. N.p., N.d. [Columbus, 1898.] $1.50

303 HIGGINS, BETH BELL. Memory Pictures of Puget Sound Region. 53 pp., 12mo, unbound. N. Y., 1900. $2.00

304 HODGKIN, FRANK E., and J. J. GALVIN. Pen Pictures of Representative Men of Oregon. Copyright applied for. 199 pp. Stiff mounted photographs bound in. 8vo, original printed wrappers. Portland: Farmer and Dairyman Pub. House, 1882. $6.00

305 HOOKER, WILLIAM FRANCIS. The Bullwhacker. Adventures of a Frontier Freighter. Edited by Howard Driggs. . . . Illus. with drawings by Herman Palmer, and with photographs. 8vo, cloth. Yonkers, N. Y., 1924. $3.75

Personal adventures of a freighter in the early days in Wyoming.

306 HOWAY, JUDGE F. W. (Ed.). The Voyage of the Hazard to the Northwest Coast, Hawaii and China, 1810-1813, by Stephen Reynolds, a Member of the Crew. 158 pp., illus. No. 38 of 100 copies printed. 8vo, cloth. Salem, 1938. $7.50

307 [HUDSON'S BAY.] Jean Bourdon et la Baie d'Hudson. 19 pp., 12mo, original wrappers. Levis, 1896. $5.00

308 [HUDSON'S BAY.] Chappell, Lieut. Edward. Narrative of a Voyage to Hudson's Bay in His Majesty's Ship Rosamund, containing some Account of the Northeastern Coast of America and of the Tribes inhabiting that remote Region. Map, 4 plates and vignettes. 8vo, calf. London, 1817. $12.50

Braislin 373. The large folding map shows the Great Nelson River from Lake Winnipeg to Cull Lake with all the portages, falls and rapids. The work also contains a minute description of the Esquimaux, Mountaineer and Micmacs of Labrador and the Red Indians of Newfoundland. There is a Cree vocabulary in the index.

309 [HUDSON'S BAY CO.] Willson, Beckles. The Great Company (1667-1871), being a History of the Honourable Company of Merchants-Adventurers trading into Hudson's Bay. Compiled from the Company's Archives, from Diplomatic Documents and State Papers of France and England; from the Narratives of Factors and Traders; and from many Accounts and Memoirs. Map and ports., folding plates. 2 vols., 8vo, cloth. London, 1900. $15.00

310 [HUDSON RIVER.] Letters about the Hudson River, and the Vicinity, written in 1835-36. By a Citizen of New York [Freeman Hunt]. 16mo, original cloth. N. Y., 1836. $3.50

311 HUGHES, JOHN T. Doniphan's Expedition; Containing an Account of the Conquest of New Mexico; General Kearney's Overland Expedition to California; Doniphan's Campaign against the Navajos; His Unparallel March upon Chihauhau and Durango; and the Operations of General Price at Santa Fe. With a Sketch of the Life of General Doniphan. Illus. with Plans of Battlefields, a map (colored folding) and fine engravings. 407 pp., 8vo, cloth. Cincinnati, 1848. $15.00

A bright copy with both the portraits of Gen. Price and Doniphan and without the list of embellishments on p. xii.

312 [HUMBOLDT, ALEXANDER VON.] The Travels and Researches of Alexander von Humboldt, being a condensed narrative of his Journeys in the Equinoctial Regions of America, and in Asiatic Russia: Together with Analyses of his more important Investigations. By W. Macgillivray. Woodcut illus. and a map. 12mo, original cloth. [Harper's Family Library No. 54.] N. Y., 1836. $2.00

312a HUTCHINS (THOMAS). A Topographical Description of Virginia, Pennsylvania, Maryland and North Carolina, comprehending the Rivers Ohio, Kenhawa, Sioto, Cherokee, Wabash, Illinois, Mississippi, etc. The Climate, Soil and Produce; the Mountains, Creeks, Roads, Distances, etc. With a Plan of the Rapids of the Ohio; a Plan of the several Villages in the Illinois Country; a Table of Distances between Fort Pitt and the Mouth of the Ohio. And an Appendix, containing Patrick Kennedy's Journal up the Illinois River and a correct List of the different Nations and Tribes of Indians, with the number of Fighting Men, etc. 8vo, ¾ calf. London: Printed for the Author, and Sold by J. Almon, 1778. $65.00

Hutchins served with considerable distinction during the period of the French and Indian War, and under Colonel Bouquet at Fort Pitt, the plan of which he laid out. He was later engaged with Captain Harry Gordon in a survey of the country bordering the Ohio and Mississippi from Pittsburg to New Orleans, and there is little doubt, that much of the information given in the above work was gleaned during that adventurous voyage. He afterwards went to England where he got into serious trouble with the British Government for holding a supposed correspondence with Benjamin Franklin, who was then acting as American Ambassador at the Court of France. Returning to America, via France, he joined the Southern Army under General Green, and on the close of the war he was appointed Geographer General to the United States, which position he held until his death which took place at Pittsburgh, April 28, 1789.

313 [ILLINOIS.] Narrative of the Captivity of William Biggs among the Kickapoo Indians in Illinois in 1788. Written by himself. Heartman Historical Series No. 37. 8vo, original boards, paper label. N.p., 1922. $4.50

One of 81 copies printed.

314 [ILLINOIS.] Chapin, Louella. Round About Chicago. 200 pp., colored frontis., other fine illus. 8vo, cloth. Chicago (1907). $2.50

315 [ILLINOIS.] A Glimpse at the Great Western Republic. By Lieut.-Col. Arthur Cunygham. 337 pp., 8vo, cloth. London, 1851. $6.00

Chicago in 1850, hunting prairie chickens, visit to La Salle, down the Illinois, visits with farmers enroute, down the Mississippi to Cairo, thence through the southern states.

316 [ILLINOIS.] The Fort Dearborn Massacre. Written in 1814 by Lieut. Helm, one of the Survivors. With Letters and Narratives of Contemporary Interest. Ed. by Nellie Kinzie Gordon. Illus., 137 pp. 12mo, cloth. Chicago (1912). $3.50

317 [ILLINOIS.] Illinois in 1837; a Sketch Descriptive of the Situation, Boundaries, Face of the Country, Prominent Districts, Prairies, Rivers, Minerals, Animals, Agricultural Productions, Public Lands, Plans of Internal Improvements, Manufactures, &c., of the State of Illinois; Also Suggestions to Emigrants, Sketches of the Counties, Cities and Principal Towns in the State. . . . Folding map, 143 pp., original printed boards (backstrip mended). Phila., 1837. $7.50

317a [ILLINOIS.] From Timber to Town. Down in Egypt. By an Early Settler. 287 pp., 12mo, cloth. Chicago: McClurg, 1891. $1.25

318 [IDAHO.] Idaho Chronology Nomencature Bibliography. By John E. Rees. 125 pp., 8vo, boards. Chicago, 1918. $5.00

319 [IDAHO.] Walgamott, C. S. Reminiscences of Early Days. A Series of Historical Sketches and Happenings in Early Days of Snake River Valley. 128 pp., illus. 8vo, cloth. Twin Falls, Idaho (1927). $7.50

320 [IDAHO TERRITORY.] Letters from Long Ago. By Agnes Just Reid. 118 pp., illus., 8vo, boards. Caldwell, Idaho, 1923. $4.50

Letters from the Idaho Territory in 1870.

321 [INDIANS.] The Iroquois Trail; or, Footprints of the Six Nations, in Customs, Traditions, History. By W. M. Beauchamp. 154 pp., 8vo, original boards. Fayetteville, N. Y., 1892. $6.00

322 [INDIANS.] Folklore and Legends. North American Indians. 192 pp., 12mo, ¾ black levant. Phila., 1891. $3.50

A selection of the best forklore tales illustrating the primitive character and beliefs of the leading tribes, east and west of the Mississippi.

323 [INDIANS.] The Mascoutens; or, Prairie Potawatomi Indians. Social Life and Ceremonies. By Alonzo Skinner. 246 pp., plates. (Bulletin of the Public Museum of Milwaukee, V. 6, No. 10, 1924). 8vo, original wrappers. Milwaukee, 1924. $1.25

324 INGRAHAM, WILLIAM KIP. The Early Jesuit Missions of North America . . . Folding map. 8vo, cloth. N. Y., 1846. $10.00

324a JACKSON, SHELDON. Sheldon Jackson, Pathfinder and Prospector of the Missionary Vanguard in the Rocky Mountains and Alaska. By Robert Laird Stewart. 488 pp., illus. 8vo, cloth. N. Y. (1904). $7.50

Smith 3856. Jackson was a pioneer missionary in Colorado, Wyoming, Montana, Utah, New Mexico, Arizona, and Alaska.

325 JACOBS, ORANGE. The Memoirs of Orange Jacobs. Written by Himself. Containing many Interesting, Amusing and Instructive Incidents of a Life of Eighty Years or more, Fifty-six Years of which were spent in Oregon and Washington. Port. 8vo, cloth. 234 pp. Seattle, 1908. $7.50

Author's inscribed copy. Gives the narrative of an overland trip to Oregon, 1852; events of pioneer life on the Pacific Coast, with accounts of Indians, animals and hunting adventures. The author became Mayor of Seattle.

326 JACOBSEN, JEROME V. Educational Foundations of the Jesuits in the Sixteenth Century New Spain. 291 pp., 8vo, cloth. Berkeley, 1938. $3.00

327 [JAMES, JESSE.] Robber and Hero. The Story of the Raid on the First National Bank at Northfield, Minnesota. By the James-Younger Band of Robbers in 1876. The Tragedy in the Bank; the Battle in the Street; the two-weeks Pursuit. By Geo. Huntington. Port. and illus. 8vo, cloth. Northfield, Minn., 1895. $5.00

328 [JEMISON, JOHN.] A True Incident in the Life of., the Noted Son of De-he-wa-mis, the "White Woman of the Genesee". By Irving W. Coats. 12mo, original printed wrappers. Shortsville, N. Y., 1892. $3.50

329 JOHNSON, THEODORE T. Sights in the Gold Regions and Scenes by the Way. 12mo, original cloth. Dublin, 1850. $9.50

330 JONES, JAMES ATHEARN. Traditions of the North American Indians: Being the Second and Revised Edition of "Tales of An Indian Camp." Illus. 8vo, original boards, paper labels. London, 1839. $17.50

A fine uncut set of the best edition of this work which contains the fine plates. The work is volumes 43, 44, and 45 of The New British Novelists.

331 JONES, POMROY. Annals and Recollections of Oneida County (N. Y.). 893 pp., 8vo, cloth. Rome, N. Y., 1851. Signature of author pasted in. $4.75

332 [KANE, ELISHA KENT.] Biography of. By William Elder. Port. 8vo, ¾ mor. Phila., 1858. $1.25

333 KANE, THOMAS LEIPER. The Private Papers and Diary of, a Friend of the Mormons. 79 pp., front. Small 4to, cloth. San Francisco, 1937. $3.50

334 [KANSAS.] Cook, John R. The Border and the Buffalo. An Untold Story of the Southwest Plains. Port. and plates. 8vo, cloth. Topeka, 1907. $6.00

Braislin 472. Reminiscences of an old plainsman and hunter; fights with Kiowas, Commanches and Staked Plain Apaches in 1877, etc.

335 [KANSAS.] The Gun and the Gospel. Early Kansas and Chaplain Fisher. Relation of Kansas to Freedom, John Brown, Jim Lane . . . Quantrell's Raid, Army Life in the Southwest, Among the Mormons . . . By Rev. H. D. Fisher. Port., illus. 12mo, cloth. Chicago, 1896. $10.00

A scarce work privately printed. Inscribed by the author.

336 KELLEY, HALL J. Memorial of Hall J. Kelley, Praying a Grant of Land for the Purpose of Establishing a Colony Thereon. 8vo, sewn. Washington, 1839. $17.50

337 KELLOGG, GEORGE ALBERT. A History of Whidbey's Island (Whidby Island), State of Washington. 108 pp., front. 8vo, original wrappers. N.p., 1934. $2.50

338 KELTON, DWIGHT H. Annals of Fort Mackinac. Illus., 144 pp., plus advts. ¾ mor. (Detroit), 1886. $3.50

339 [KENTUCKY.] Half a Century. By Jane Grey Swisshelm. 363 pp., 12mo, cloth. Chicago: McClurg, 1880. $3.50

Frontier life in western Pennsylvania, Ohio and Kentucky during the 30's and 40's; Abolitionist movement, War of the Rebellion; Women's Rights; hospitals, etc.

340 [KENTUCKY.] Township Map of the State of Kentucky and Tennessee. Colored folding map with engraved border and inset views of Louisville and Nashville, 18x24 in. 12mo, original cloth binder. N. Y.: Colton, 1853. $3.00

341 KERR, JOHN LEEDS. The Story of a Western Pioneer . . . The Missouri Pacific: An Outline History. Illus., 50 pp., 8vo, original boards. N. Y., 1928. $5.00

Service under Scott in Mexican War, California in 1849-50; Indian campaigns on the Pacific; commands the Puget Sound District under Gen. Wool in the Washington Terr. Indian uprisings of 1855, etc.

342 KERR, JOHN LEEDS. The Story of a Southern Carrier, the Louisville and Nashville: An Outline History. Illus., 67 pp. 8vo, original boards. N. Y.: Caxton, 1933. $5.00

343 KEYES, E. D. Fifty Years Observation of Men and Events, Civil and Military. 515 pp., 12mo, cloth. N. Y., 1884. $7.50

344 KINGSTON, WM. H. G. Adventures in the Far West. Illus., 12mo, cloth. London, N.d. $3.50

Account of a trip overland to California.

345 KOTSEBUE, AUGUSTUS VON. The Most Remarkable Year in the Lifetime of Augustus Von Kotzebue, containing an Account of his Exile into Siberia. Translated from the German by the Rev. Benjamin Beresford. 3 vols., 12mo, half calf. London, 1802. $10.00

346 [LEE, MRS. JASON.] Life and Letters of Mrs. Jason Lee, First Wife of Rev. Jason Lee of the Oregon Mission. By Theressa Gay. 242 pp., illus. 8vo, cloth. Portland (1936). $2.50

347 [LEWIS AND CLARK.] Trail of Lewis and Clark, 1804-1904; a Story of the Great Exploration across the Continent in 1804-06, with a Description of the Old Trail . . . 2 vols., illus., 4 maps. N. Y.: Putnam, 1904. $12.50

Smith 4361. Probably the best work which brings the original trail up to date, besides giving a competent historical retrospect of the original trail blazers.

348 [LEWIS AND CLARK.] Sights and Scenes at the Lewis and Clark Centennial Exposition, Portland. Robert A. Reid (pub.). 94 plates. 12mo, cloth. Portland (1905). $2.50

Smith 3294.

349 [LOUISIANA.] Wilkinson, Soldier and Pioneer. By James Wilkinson. Illus. 8vo, cloth. Autographed by the author. New Orleans, 1935. $2.00

350 LOVE, NAT. The Life and Adventure of Nat Love, better known in the Cattle Country as "Deadwood Dick". By Himself. 162 pp., illus. 8vo, original illus. cloth (bit soiled at backstrip). Los Angeles, 1907. $7.50

351 LYMAN, GEORGE D. (M.D.). John Marsh, Pioneer. The Life Story of a Trail-Blazer on Six Frontiers. 394 pp., illus. 8vo, cloth. N. Y., 1930. $3.50

352 MALONE, JAMES H. The Chickasaw Nation. A Short Sketch of a Noble People. Port., illus., maps, 537 pp. 8vo, cloth. Louisville, 1922. $4.50

353 MARCOU, JULES. Esquisse d'Une Classification des Chaines de Montagnes d'une Partie de l'Amerique du Nord. 24 pp., large colored folding Geological Map of New Mexico. 8vo, original wrappers. Paris, 1855. $12.50

Marcou was the geologist with Whipple's Expedition (Wagner-Camp 265), and was with Wheeler's Party on a surveying expedition to Southern California in 1875. Earlier, in 1848, he accompanied Agassiz to Lake Superior. He was considered the leading geologist of his day, both in France and the U. S.

354 MARCOU, JULES. Notes pour servir a Une Description Geologique des Montagnes Rocheuses. 22 pp., 8vo, wrappers. Geneve, 1858. $10.00

355 MARCOU, JULES. Notes on the Cretaceous and Carboniferous Rocks of Texas. 8vo, original wrappers. Boston: Rand and Avery, 1861. $12.50

Wagner-Camp 302 note. Signed Presentation Copy to Albert Ordway.

356 MARCOU, JULES. Une Ascension dans Les Montagnes Rocheuses. 24 pp., original printed wrappers. Paris, 1867. $12.50

Wagner-Camp 265-266 and 302. Deals with Arizona and New Mexico during the Whipple Expedition. Signed presentation copy to Robert C. Winthrop.

357 MATHEWS, JOHN JOSEPH. The Osage and the White Man's Land. 360 pp., front., illus. 8vo, cloth. Norman, Okla., 1932. $2.50

358 McCURDY, JAMES G. By Juan de Fuca Strait. Pioneering along the Northwest Edge of the Continent. 312 pp., illus. 8vo, cloth. Portland (1937). $2.50

359 McKINSTRY, GEORGE, JR. Thrilling and Tragic Journal written by George McKinstry, Jr., while on a Journey Overland to California, in 1846-47. Including an Account of the Death of many of the Party. The last three who died being eaten by their Survivors. Journal from Oct. 31st, 1846 to March 1st, 1847. Folio Broadside folded to a 12mo, with original printed wrappers. West Hoboken, N. J.: Albert A. Bieber, N.d. (1913). $12.50

Signed by Albert A. Bieber, this is the only copy printed on yellow paper with the blue wrapper. 63 copies were printed in all on pink blotter paper, this one copy on yellow paper and one copy on gold wall paper.

360 MACKENZIE, ALEXANDER. Mackenzie of Canada. Life and Adventures of Alexander Mackenzie, Discoverer. By Mark S. Wade. 332 pp., illus. 8vo, cloth. London, 1927. $5.00

361 MACKENZIE, ALEXANDER. Sir Alexander Mackenzie, Explorer and Fur Trader. By Hume Wrong. 171 pp., front. 8vo, cloth. Toronto, 1927. $2.50

362 [METHODIST CHURCH.] Missions and Missionary Society of the Methodist Episcopal Church. 2 vols., 12mo, original cloth. N. Y. (1879). $12.50

Vol. 1 contains information on the Flathead and Oregon Missions.

363[MICHIGAN.] Tales of Kankakee Land. By Chas. H. Bartlett. Illus. 12mo, cloth. N. Y., 1907. $4.50

Tales of the old Pottowattomie Trail by a pioneer.

364 [MICHIGAN.] Forest Life. (By Caroline M. Kirkland-Mrs. Clavers). 2 vols., 8vo, original cloth, paper labels (rubbed). N. Y., 1842. $5.00

One of the best realistic pictures of early western settlements.

365 [MICHIGAN.] My New Home in Northern Michigan, and Other Tales. By Charles W. Jay. 180 pp., 8vo, cloth. Trenton, 1874. $2.50

366 [MICHIGAN.] Protestantism in Michigan: Being a Special History of the Methodist Episcopal Church and incidentally of other denominations. Notices of their Origin and Growth of the Principal Towns and Cities of the State, Biographical Sketches . . . Illus. By Elijah H. Pilcher. 8vo, cloth. Detroit (1878). $7.50

367 [MINNESOTA.] History of the Great Massacre of the Sioux Indians in Minnesota, including the Personal Narratives of many who escaped. By Chas. S. Bryant and Abel B. Murch. Illus. 12mo, cloth. Cincinnati, 1864. $2.50

368 [MINNESOTA.] In the Ojibway Country. A Story of Early Missions on the Minnesota Frontier. By James Peery Schell. xv-188 pp., map. 8vo, original stamped boards. Walhalla, No. Dakota, 1911. $27.50

Excessively Rare. Can locate no other copy.

369 [MINNESOTA.] White and Red; a Narrative of Life among the Northwest Indians. By Helen C. Weeks. Illus. by A. P. Close. 12mo, 266 pp., cloth. N. Y., 1870. $3.50

370 [MISSISSIPPI VALLEY.] Gleanings by the Way. By John A. Clark. 352 pp., 12mo, ¾ mor. N. Y., 1842. $12.50

Voyage on the Ohio, Kentucky, Illinois, Michigan. The author kept a journal of his tour which began in 1837 and extended through four years. About 12 chapters are devoted to the Mormons.

371 [MISSOURI.] Along the Old Trail. Vol. 1. Pioneer Sketches of Arrow Rock and Vicinity, by T. C. Rainey. 94 pp., illus., 12mo, original wrappers. Marshall, Mo., 1914. $7.50

372 [MISSOURI.] The State of Missouri. By Walter Williams. Colored folding maps, numerous illus. Royal 8vo, cloth. Columbus, Mo., 1904. $4.00

Contains short histories of each county.

373 [MISSOURI AND KANSAS.] Lands and Homes in Southwest Missouri along the complete line of the St. Louis and San Francisco Railway. Colored folding map, 40 pp. 8vo, original printed wrappers. St. Louis (1880). $3.50

374 [IDAHO.] Our Friends the Coeur D'Aleine Indians. 21 pp., sm. 4to, sewn. St. Ignatius Print, Montana, 1886. $10.00

A rare work, in which pp. 13-21 records an attack on the De Smet Mission by certain land-grabbers in Washington Territory.

375 [MONTANA.] A History of Montana. By Helen Fitzgerald Sanders. Illus. 3 vols., 4to, half mor. Chicago, 1913. $21.00

A complete history, including the story of George Ives, road agents and their depredations, Henry Plummer and his band, the capture of Chief Joseph, the development of Montana, etc.

376 [MONTANA.] Society of Montana Pioneers, Constitution, Members and Officers. Edited by James V. Sanders. Vol. 1. Ports, and maps. 8vo, cloth. N.p., 1899. $7.50

Has a reprint of the rare De Lacy "Map of the Territory of Montana," 1865.

377 [MONTANA LEWIS & CLARK.] Memorial Celebration in Honor of Sacajawa, the Bird Woman. 11 pp., 8vo, original wrappers. Armstead, Montana, August 30, 1915. $6.00

377a [MISSOURI RIVER, UPPER.] Report of the Secretary of War, of the Terms on which Contracts have been made for the Transportation of the Troops ordered on the Expedition to the Mandan Villages. 10 pp., 8vo, sewn and uncut. Washington, 1820. $5.00

Contains Quartermaster Thomas S. Jesup's report, as well as those of J. H. Ballard and James McGunnigle.

378 [MONTANA.] The Life of Rev. L. B. Statler. A Story of Life on the old Frontier. Containing Incidents, Anecdotes and Sketches of Methodist History in the West and Northwest. By E. J. Stanley. 356 pp., illus., 12mo, cloth. Nashville, 1916. $7.50

Statler was an early missionary in Missouri and Kansas,, going to Colorado in 1862, thence to Virginia City in 1864. He spent the balance of his life in the Montana Territory and Montana.

379 [MONTANA.] Following Old Trails. By Arthur L. Stone. 304 pp., front., illus. 8vo, cloth. Missoula, Mont., 1913. $12.50

Printed in a small edition this work is already out of print and scarce.

380 [MONTANA.] Stout, Tom. Montana. Its Story and Biography. A History of the Aboriginal and Territorial Montana and Three Decades of Statehood. Illus. 3 vols., 4to, cloth. Chicago, 1921. $17.50

Minor explorations of 1805-07, pathfinders of the mining camps, the fur trade era, first discovery of gold, days of outlaws and vigilantes, etc.

381 [MONTANA.] The Truth about Butte. By George R. Tompkins. 47 pp., illus., 12mo, original wrappers. Butte, 1917. $5.00

Deals with the early development of the mining camps, the organization of the miners, battle throughout the years with the operators, etc.

382 [MONTANA.] Flour and Wheat in the Montana Gold Camps, 1862-1870. A Chapter in Pioneer Experiences and a brief Discussion of the economy of Montana in the Mining Days. By Harrison A. Trexler . . . 40 pp., 8vo, original wrappers. Missoula, 1918. $4.50

Smith 4020.

383 [MONTANA AND IDAHO.] The Mining Advance into the Inland Empire. Comparative Study of the beginning of the Mining Industry in Idaho and Montana, Eastern Washington and Oregon, and the southern interior of British Columbia. By William Trimble. 256 pp., map. (Wis. University Bulletin No. 638, Hist. Series v. 3, No. 2). 8vo, cloth. Madison, 1914. $4.00

Smith 4024.

384 [MONTANA—LEWIS & CLARK.] Sacajawea, the Bird Woman, the Unsung Heroine of Montana, 1805-1806. By Laura Tolman Scott. 17 pp., illus. 12mo, original wrappers. Billion, Mont., 1915. $6.00

385 [MORMONS.] The Book of the Mormon. 12mo, original calf (broken). Kirkland, Ohio. $7.50

Second Edition.

386 [MORMONS.] The Doctrine and Covenants of the Church of Latter-Day Saints, containing the Revelations. 503 pp., 12mo, cloth. Salt Lake, 1883. $3.50

387 [MORMONS.] Jacob Hamlin, a Narrative of his Personal Experiences as a Frontiersman, Missionary to the Indians and Explorer, disclosing interpositions of Providence, Severe Privations, Perilous Situations and Remarkable Escapes . . . By James A. Little. 140 pp., 8vo, cloth (dull). Salt Lake City, 1881. $15.00

388 [MORMONS.] Proceedings at the Dedication of the Joseph Smith Memorial Monument at Sharon, Windsor County, Vermont, Dec. 23, 1905. 88 pp., illus., 8vo, cloth. N.p., N.d. (1905). $5.00

389 [MORMONS.] The Mormon Trials at Salt Lake City. By George Alfred Townsend. 49 pp., 8vo, original wrappers. N. Y., 1871. $4.00

390 [MORMONS.] Woodruff, Wilford. Leaves from My Journal. 96 pp., 12mo, cloth. Salt Lake, 1881. $15.00

The scarce Original Edition. Woodruff, from 1833, followed the Mormon fortunes through Kirkland, Nauvoo and ultimately to Salt Lake as one of the pioneers.

391 [MORMONS.] Wyl, Dr. W. Mormon Portraits; or, the Truth about the Mormon Leaders from 1830 to 1886. Story of the Danite's Wife; Mountain Meadows Massacre Re-Examined; a Thousand Fresh Facts and Documents gathered personally in Utah from Living Witnesses. Illus., 320 pp., 12mo, cloth. Salt Lake City, 1886. $7.50

The second title reads "Volume First, Joseph Smith, the Prophet. His Family and His Friends. . . . "

392 MORTIMER, GEORGE. Observations and Remarks made during a Voyage to the Islands of Teneriffe, Amsterdam, Maria's Islands near Van Diemen's Land; Otaheite, Sandwich Islands, Owhyhee, the Fox Islands on the North West Coast of America, Tinian, and from Thence to Canton, in the Brig Mercury, commanded by John Henry Cox, Esq. 8vo, unbound. Dublin, 1791. $75.00

This Dublin Edition is very scarce as it gives some curious details concerning the Mutiny on the Bounty and also concerning Captain Cook. The Bounty section is included between pages 28 and 52. At page 52 is a reference of particular interest wherein one of the natives mentions Captain Bligh's officer Titreano (undoubtedly Fletcher Christian) had returned in the Bounty about two months after Bligh had sailed, but had stated that Captain Blight had left Tahiti 15 days before Mortimer's arrival, and had carried off several Otaheite families with him to Tahiti.

393 [NEBRASKA.] The Great Valleys and Prairies of Nebraska and the Northwest. By C. B. Wilbur. Map and illus. 8vo, cloth. Omaha, 1881. $4.50

394 [NEVADA.] Reminiscences of Senator William M. Stewart of Nevada. Edited by G. R. Brown. Port. 358 pp., 8vo, cloth. N. Y., 1908. $7.50

A narrative of the gold mines, Indians, Pacific Railroad, etc.

395 [NEW MEXICO.] The Land of the Pueblos. By Susan E. Wallace. 285 pp., illus., 12mo, cloth. N. Y., 1888. $3.00

The author was the wife of the author of Ben Hur.

395a [NEW MEXICO.] History and Government of New Mexico. By John H. Vaughn. 369 pp., illus. 12mo, cloth. State College of New Mexico, 1925. $3.50

396 [NEW YORK.] History of the Town of Marlborough, Ulster County, N. Y., from the First Settlement in 1872 by Capt. Wm. Bond, to 1887. By Charles D. Cochrane. Illus., 8vo, cloth, 202 pp. Poughkeepsie, 1887. $4.00

397 [NORTHERN PACIFIC RAILROAD.] North Pacific Tours. By W. C. Riley. Long 12mo, illus., cloth. St. Paul, N.d. $2.00

398 [NORTHERN PACIFIC RAILROAD.] Windom William. The Northern Pacific Railway; Its Effect upon the Public Credit, the Public Revenues, and the Public Debt. Develop the National Resources and thereby Diminish the National Burdens. 60 pp., 8vo, original wrappers. Washington: Gibson Bros., 1869. $7.50

This is Windom's own edition, privately printed in a few copies.

399 [NORTHERN PACIFIC RAILROAD.] Wonderland; Descriptive of that part of the northwest tributary to the Northern Pacific Railway . . . 1899, 1900, 1903, 1904, 1906. 8vo, original wrappers. St. Paul (1899-1906). $10.00

Smith 2709. The Yellowstone National Park, trip through the Bitter Root Mountains, Columbia River and Puget Sound regions, Queniut Indians of the Northwest Coast; also gives some information about Alaska.

400 [NORTHWEST COAST.] Other Merchants and Sea Captains of Old Boston. 70 pp., illus., 8vo, original wrappers. Boston: State Street Trust Co., 1919. $2.00

An excellent monograph on the old merchants and ship captains who plied from Boston in the China Trade.

401 [NORTHWEST COAST.] Old Shipping Days in Boston. 49 pp., illus. 8vo, original wrappers. Boston: State Street Trust Co., 1918. $2.00

402 [NORTHWEST TERRITORY, OLD.] Notes on the Northwest; or, the Valley of the Upper Mississippi. By Wm. J. A. Bradford. 12mo, original cloth (worn at backstrip). N. Y., 1846. $3.75

403 [NOOTKA SOUND.] Sketch of the Reign of George the Third, from 1780 to the close of the year 1790. 206 pp., 8vo, half mor. London: Debrett, 1791. $25.00

Pp. 152-166 deal with Nootka Sound, containing an accurate account of the troubles with Spain.

404 [NOOTKA SOUND.] Zetes, Pseudonym. An Address to the Parliment and People of Great Britain, on the Past and Present State of Affairs between Spain and Great Britain, respecting their American Possessions. 49 pp., 8vo, cloth. Debrett, London, 1790. $125.00

Smith 4501 locates one copy. This is perhaps the rarest of the 1790 pamphlets on the Nootka Sound controversy.

405 NOTICE SUR LES MISSIONS DE DIOCESE DE QUEBEC . . . Vol. 1, Number 1, January, 1839. 12mo, blue wrappers. Quebec, 1839. $7.50

The rare first number of this great work, which at pp. 1-24 contains one of the earliest accounts of the Red River Mission .

406 [OHIO.] History of the State of Ohio. By James W. Taylor. 557 pp., 8vo, half mor. Cincinnati and Sandusky, 1854. $20.00

The work is devoted mainly to aboriginal history previous to the Territorial period. Early Jesuit Missions, the wars of the Eries and Iroquois, Border Warfare, which was raging for nearly a quarter of a century between the inhabitants of Pennsylvania and the Delawares, Shewanees and Wyandots, are the subjects which nearly fill this book. Thompson stated in 1880 that while it "was intended as a text book . . . it is now quite scarce and each year witnesses an advance in price."

407 [OKLAHOMA.] The Oklahoma Scout. By Theodore Braughman. Illus., 215 pp., 12mo, cloth. Chicago: Conkey, N.d. $2.50

408 [OKLAHOMA.] Remarks in Opposition to the Bill to Organize the Territory of Oklahoma. By Wm. P. Ross. 30 pp., 8vo, original wrappers. Washington, 1874. $7.50

409 OLMSTED, FREDERICK LAW. A Journey in the Back Country. 12mo, cloth. N. Y., 1860. $3.50

410 [OREGON.] An Illustrated History of Baker, Grant, Malheur and Harney Counties, State of Oregon. 788 pp., 8vo, sheep. Western Historical Pub. Co., Spokane, 1902. $12.50

A COMPLETE SET OF THE OREGON AND NORTHWEST MISSION REPORTS, QUEBEC, 1839-74

410a OREGON. Notice sur les Missions du Diocese de Quebec, qui sont secourues par l'Association de la Propagation de la Foi. *With large folding map of the Route from Westport, Missouri, to Walla Walla, Oregon; long folding "Catholic Ladder" instruction for the Oregon Indians, etc.* A Complete Set. 23 vols., 8vo and 12mo, original printed wrappers. Quebec: De l'Imprimerie de Frechette & Cie, 1839-1874. $150.00

Wagner-Camp Nos. 78, 80, 93, 127, 164, 167, 195, 224, and several notes. In 1838 this Association, under a Brief of Pope Greogry XVI, organized the Oregon Mission, sending out Francis Blanchet and Modeste Demers. Blanchet became successively Bishop and Archbishop of Oregon, and Demers, Bishop of Vancouver. The Oregon Mission passed out of the hands of the Association later, but it continued its work among the Indians until 1874. The Reports were published annually until June, 1843, and from then until the last number (No. 21) every second year, with the exception of No. 16, which was issued in March, 1864. They contain a vast amount of information regarding the Oregon Territory and the Northwest Country, the Indian affairs of these regions, events of the Overland and at the posts, etc. An immense body of source material which can be found nowhere else, is here reported in full. See *Western Americans,* Sale No. 1781, The Anderson Galleries, N. Y., Nov., 1923, item 699.

One of the few sets reported containing the two variant numbers, known as Variant One and Variant Four. The set is usually described as containing 21 vols. A complete set really comprises 23 vols., with the variants.

410b OREGON. Annales de la Propagation de la Foi pour la Province de Quebec. A complete set, from No. 1, Feb., 1877, to No. 141, Oct., 1923. In all, 141 volumes, each number containing about 80 pages. 8vo, the entire collection in the original printed wrappers. Montreal, various printers, 1877-1923. $250.00

The "Notice sur les Missions" (see preceding number) came to an abrupt stop (under the name) in 1874, as the result of a controversy between the French and Canadian Church authorities. Refusing to comply with the mandates of the parent organization, they transferred the seat of their activities and printing to Montreal, continuing their field work and historical chronicles under the title of "Annales" here described, issuing volumes at the rate of almost three each year. The first number contained a letter from Gen. O. O. Howard regarding affairs in Oregon, the Indians, native polygamy, the Chinook Jargon and kindred matters; and thenceforth for 65 years the reports regularly contained vast quantities of material unavailable elsewhere and dealing with the American West and Northwest. The letters and journals herein printed relate to life and conditions in Oregon; the Sitting Bull troubles; Minnesota affairs; early success of the Northwest Catholic Missions; Non-success of the Protestant; Indian Legends; Travels, Adventures and work in the Mackenzie River and Lake Athabasca Country; in the Hudson's Bay Country; Historical annals of the Northwest (a series); biographical Sketches; Voyages and Explorations in the Far West and Alaska, and many similar narratives of pioneer work, hardship and adventure. Other journals and narratives relate to affairs and conditions in the Far East, the South Seas, and other parts of the world. In fact, herein is contained a vast source bin for the whole history of the western expansion of America during the years mentioned. The "Annales" are much harder to come upon than the "Quebec Rapports." Only a few sets ever offered for sale. See *Western Americana,* Sale No. 1781, The Anderson Galleries, N. Y., Nov., 1923, item No. 700.

410c [OVERLAND TO THE PACIFIC SERIES.] Comprising the following items, being the full set printed to date and edited by Archie B. Hulbert and Dorothy P. Hulbert: (1) Zebulon Pike. Arkansaw Journal. Illus., 8vo, cloth. Denver, 1932. (2) Southwest on Turquoise Trail. First Diaries on the Road to Santa Fe. Maps, illus., 8vo, cloth. Denver, 1933. (3) Where Rolls the Oregon. Prophet and Pessimist look Northwest. Maps, illus., 8vo, cloth. Denver, 1933. (4) The Call of the Columbia. Men and Saints Take the Oregon Trail. Maps, illus., 8vo, cloth. Denver, 1934. (5) The Oregon Crusade Across Land and Sea to Oregon. Maps and illus., 8vo, cloth. Denver, 1934. (6) Marcus Whitman, Crusader. Map and illus., 8vo, cloth. Denver, 1936. (7) Marcus Whitman, Crusader. Map and illus., 8vo, cloth. Denver, 1938. (8) Marcus Whitman, Crusader. Maps and illus., 8vo, cloth. Denver, 1941. Together 8 vols., as new. Denver, 1932-1941. (Not sold separately). $45.00

BROUILLET'S "WHITMAN MASSACRE & PROTESTANTISM IN OREGON"

411 [OREGON.] Brown, J. Ross. . . . The Late Indian War in Oregon and Washington Territories. [and] Brouillet, J. B. A. Protestantism in Oregon. Account of the Murder of Dr. Whitman and the Ungrateful Calumnies of H. H. Spalding, Protestant Missionary. 66 pp., 8vo, 3/4 crimson polished calf. Washington, 1858. $20.00

One of the most important and interesting documents relating to the history of Oregon. In this report, J. Ross Browne, special agent of the Treasury Dept., and himself a Catholic included Brouillet's celebrated "Protestantism in Oregon" which had already been printed in New York. Spalding claims he could not get this document properly answered through his own influence in Congress. His answer was ordered printed but Spalding claimed it was never widely distributed, at least not to the extent that were Browne's and Father's Brouillet's. The latter was Vicar General of Walla Walla. An Indian killed Dr. Whitman by cleaving his head. But who instigated him to kill his generous and well-beloved benefactor? Some say the HBC and the Church Hierarchy were anxious to start an uprising to drive out the too energetic Americans. Others say Spalding was in love with one of Whitman's household and actually had Dr. Whitman killed himself. Still others believe that Father Brouillet had a dagger under his black robe. All one can say is that a great and good man was slain, and thereby still hangs a still unanswered historical question—Who killed Dr. Whitman?

412 [OREGON.] Early Oregon. Jottings of Personal Recollections of a Pioneer of 1850. By George E. Cole. Port. 95 pp., 12mo, cloth. (Spokane, 1905). $4.50

The above first appeared in the "Sunday Oregonian," 1901.

413 [OREGON.] History of the First Unitarian Church, of Portland, Ore., 1867-1892; together with a Sketch of the Life of Rev. Thomas Lamb Eliot. . . . 95 pp., 2 ports., 3 plates. 12mo, cloth. Portland, Ore., 1893. $4.75

Smith 4387.

414 [OREGON.] Steel Points. By William Gladstone Steel. Vol. 1, Numbers 12, 3, and 4; Vol. 2, No. 2. Complete. 8vo. Portland, Ore.: William Gladstone Steel, Pub., 1906-1907. $10.00

Oregon local history. Scarce.

415 [OREGON.] Message from the President of the U. S. (Polk) in answer to a Resolution of the Senate of the 24th of Jan. relative to Correspondence on the Subject of Oregon, 1846. 10 pp., 8vo, unbound. (Washington, 1846). $2.50

416 [OREGON.] Redmond Commercial Club. Redmond, Oregon. 8vo, original wrappers. Redmond, Ore., N.p. N.d. (1905). $3.00

417 [OREGON.] Oregon, a Story of Progress and Development, together with an Account of the Lewis and Clark Centennial Exposition to be held in Portland, Oregon, from June 1 to Oct. 15, 1905. Compiled by Henry E. Reed. 96 pp., illus., 8vo, original wrappers. Portland, Ore.: Bushong and Co., printers, 1904. $7.50

Smith 3288.

418 ——. The Same. Official Guide to the Lewis and Clark Exposition. 63 pp., map. 8vo, cloth. Portland, 1905. $3.00

419 [OREGON.] Republican League Register. A Record of the Republican Party in the State of Oregon. 286-38 pp., ports. 8vo, cloth. Portland, 1896. $4.00

Smith 2890.

420 [OREGON.] Portland Postoffice, its History and Growth. By Charles W. Roby. 88 pp., illus. Long 12mo, cloth. Portland: Bates, 1889. $7.50

Smith 3336.

421 [OREGON.] Salem Board of Trade. Salem, the Capital City of Oregon. 48 pp., illus. Salem, Ore. (c. 1905). $2.50

422 [OREGON.] The Heroine of '49. A Story of the Pacific Coast. By M. P. Sawtelle. 248 pp., plates. 8vo, cloth. N.p., 1881. $6.50

"Feeling the necessity of a historical sketch giving at least a glimpse of the family life of the first settlers on the Pacific Coast, this work was undertaken."

423 [OREGON.] Astoria. By F. H. Saylor. Contained in the Oregon Teachers' Monthly, Vol. 18, Nos. 1-3, Sept.-Oct., 1913. Three vols., 8vo, original wrappers. Salem, Ore., 1913. $7.50

This contains a history of Astoria by a pioneer.

424 [OREGON.] History of Portland, Oregon. With . . . Biographical Sketches of prominent Citizens and Pioneers. By Harvey W. Scott, Ed. 651 pp., port. 4to, cloth. Syracuse: Mason, 1890. $12.50

Smith 3460.

425 [OREGON.] The Pioneer Character of Oregon Progress. By Harvey W. Scott. 26 pp., 8vo, original wrappers. Portland, 1918. $4.50

Smith 3461.

426 [OREGON.] Sherman County, Oregon. 32 pp., illus., map. 8vo, original wrappers. N.p. (1905). $2.50

427 [OREGON.] Silverton, Oregon. 18 pp., map, illus. 1910. Also, Coos Bay, Ore., 64 pp., map, illus. 8vo, cloth. N.p. (1905). 2 vols. N.p., 1910-1905. $3.50

428 [OREGON.] The Mountains of Oregon. By Will G. Steel. 112 pp., 2 ports., plates. 8vo, cloth. Portland, Ore.: Steel, 1890. $2.50

Smith 3830.

429 [OREGON.] Life and Adventures of an Orphan Boy; or, from the Cradle to the Ministry. By Hervey S. Sturdevant. 127 pp., illus. 12mo, cloth. Cornelius, Ore., N.d. $7.50

A scarce privately printed work. The author was an Elder in the Adventist Church in Oregon.

430 [OREGON.] Toledo, Oregon. 32 pp., illus., map. 8vo. N.p. (1905). $2.00

431 [OREGON.] Memorial Addresses on the Life and Character of Thomas H. Tongue (late a Representative of Oregon), delivered in the House of Representatives and Snate, 57th Cong., 2nd Sss. 96 pp., port. 8vo, cloth. Washington, 1903. $3.00

Smith 4083.

432 [OREGON.] Waggoner, Geo. A. Stories of Old Oregon. 292 pp., 19 plates. 12mo, cloth. Salem, Ore., 1905. $4.00

Smith 4220. Personal narrative of the author's trip across the Plains from Iowa to Oregon in 1852; life and adventures in the mines; campaign against the Snake Indians, etc.

433 [OREGON.] Walling, A. G. Oregon, its Advantages as an Agricultural and Commercial State. 62 pp., 8vo, original wrappers. Portland: Walling, 1870. $7.50

Not in Smith.

434 [OREGON.] Walling, A. G., Publisher. History of Southern Oregon, comprising Jackson, Josephine, Douglas, Curry and Coos Counties, compiled from the most Authentic Sources. 545 pp., 15 ports., 4 maps. 8vo, cloth. Portland, Ore.: Walling, 1884. $12.50

Smith 4230.

435 [OREGON.] Walling, A. G., Publisher. Illustrated History of Lane County, Oregon, compiled from the most Authentic Sources. 508 pp., 2 ports., 48 plates, map. Sq. 4to, cloth. Portland, Ore.: Walling, 1884. $12.50

Smith 4231.

436 [OREGON.] Watters, Dennis Alonzo. The Trail to Boyhood. 80 pp., 12mo, cloth. Cincinnati (1910). $3.50

Watters was a pioneer of Portland, Ore.

437 [OREGON.] Wells, Harry L. Popular History of Oregon from the Discovery of America to the Admission of the State into the Union. 480 pp., illus. Small 4to, cloth. Portland, Ore.: Steel, 1889. $7.50

Smith 4340.

438 [OREGON.] White, Elijah. Message from the President of the U. S. [Tyler]. 8vo, 702 pp., 28th Cong., 2nd Sess., Sen. No. 1. Washington, 1844. $10.00

Contains material relating to Oregon by White, which was later used in his "Concise View" of 1846.

439 [OREGON.] Historical Atlas of Marion and Linn Counties, Oregon. By Edgar Williams. 104 pp., colored sectional maps., illus. Folio, cloth. San Francisco: Williams, 1878. $15.00

Smith 4413.

440 [OREGON.] Letters from Oregon Boys in France. By Mrs. Frank Wilmot. 128 pp., 8vo, original wrappers. Portland, Ore.: Glass (1917). $2.50

Smith 4428.

441 [OREGON.] Oregon Boys in the War, including a Second Series of Oregon Boys in France. By Mrs. Frank Wilmot. 256 pp., illus. Portland, Ore., N.d. $4.00

Smith 4429.

442 [OREGON.] Woodward, Walter Carlton. The Rise and early Progress of Political Parties in Oregon, 1843-1868. 277 pp., 8vo, cloth. Portland, Ore.: Gill, 1913. $6.50

Smith 4469.

443 [OREGON—PORTLAND]. Voices of the City. By Marion Cook Stow. 30 pp., 12mo, original wrappers. Portland, Ore., 1909. $3.00

444 [OREGON TERRITORY.] (A. N. Armstrong). Oregon: comprising a Brief History and Full Description of the Territories of Oregon and Washington, embracing the Cities, Towns, Rivers, Bays, Harbors, Coasts, Mountains, Valleys, Prairies, Plains . . . Incidents of Travel and Adventure. 147 pp., 12mo, cloth. Chicago, 1857. $30.00

445 [OREGON TERRITORY.] A Plea for the Indians; with Facts and Features of the Late War in Oregon. By John Beeson. 8vo, cloth. N. Y., 1857. $20.00

Original edition. Beeson went overland from Illinois in 1853, and spent upwards of 3 years in the Oregon Territory.

446 [OREGON TERRITORY.] Supplemental Report, Feb. 16, 1839 . . . Mr. Cushing, from the Committee on Foreign Affairs . . . to which was referred a Message from the President of the United States, together with a Rsolution of the House, in relation to the Territory of the United States beyond the Rocky Mountains . . . (Caleb Cushing). 8vo, 61 pp., large folding map of the fur country. 25th Cong., 3rd Sess., Report No. 101. H. R. (Washington, 1839). $20.00

Contains a long account of the Hudson's Bay Co. by N. Wyeth; Wm. A. Slacum's report on his trip to the Northwest Coast in 1836-37 on the Brig Loriot, his detailed account of the HBC etc.; Hall Kelley's memoir; Jason Lee's Memorial signed by 36 petitioners, praying for the protection of the U. S. for the first Oregon settlers, etc.

447 [OREGON—W. C. T. U.] Minutes of the First Annual Meeting of the Young Women's Christian Temperance Union of Oregon, held at Portland, June 16, 1883. 38 pp., 8vo, original wrappers. Portland, 1883. $4.50

448 [OREGON—WASHINGTON.] Expenses of the Indian Wars in Washington and Oregon Territories . . . Report of the Commissioners to ascertain the expenses incurred in the Indian Wars in Oregon and Washington Territories. 16 pp., 8vo, unbound. Washington, 1858. $7.50

An important item for expenses incurred during the Indian uprising during which Dr. Whitman was slain. The report is dated at Fort Vancouver, W. T., Oct. 10, 1857 and is signed by A. J. Smith, Rufus Ingalls and Lafayette Grover. There are 7 leaves of abstract expenses.

449 [OREGON—WASHINGTON.] Indian Affairs in the Territories of Oregon and Washington . . . Report of J. Ross Browne, Special Agent, on the subject of Indian affairs in the Territories of Oregon and Washington. 48 pp., 8vo, unbound. 35th Cong., 1st Sess., H.R. Ex. Doc. 39. [Washington, 1858.] $7.50

Browne visited all the important settlements and Indian Agencies in 1857. He gives long detailed accounts of Puyallup, Fort Kitsap, Fort Townsend, Salem, the treaties, complaints of the settlers, some account of their economic status, etc.

450 [OREGON AND WASHINGTON WAR CLAIMS.] Statement of the Oregon and Washington Delegation in relation to the War Claims of Oregon and Washington. 67 pp., 8vo, sewn. N.p., N.d. $12.50

Smith 3826. The citizens of the two states called upon Congress to make immediate provision for the payment of their claims as adjusted by law, for expenses incurred during the Indian uprisings of 1855-56.

451 [OREGON AND WASHINGTON.] Year Book of the Sons of the American Revolution. Oregon and Washington Society. 74 pp., 8vo, cloth. Portland, 1895. $3.50

Smith 3754.

452 [OVERLAND GUIDE.] New Guide to the Pacific Coast, Santa Fe Route. By James V. Steel. 12mo, cloth. Chicago: Rand McNally, 1893. $3.50

APPLEGATE'S "RECOLLECTIONS" OF THE '43 MIGRATION

453 [OVERLAND JOURNEY.] (Applegate, Jesse). Recollections. By an Oregon Pioneer of 1843. 99 pp., 8vo, pictorial wrappers, fine copy. Roseburg: Privately printed ,no copyright. 1914. $30.00

The author here recounts the trials and sufferings, experiences and adventures of the great migration of 1843. He describes the Whitman Station at Waiilatpui; the Dalles; McLoughlin and Vancouver; first winter in Oregon, &c. Emerson Hough's "Covered Wagon" is said to have been based largely upon this book. It is a much-sought item.

454 [OVERLAND JOURNEY.] Journal of a Trip to California. Across the Continent from Weston, Mo., to Weber Creek, Cal., in the summer of 1850 by C. W. Smith. Edited with an Introduction and Notes by R. W. G. Vail . . . 79 pp., 12mo, cloth. N. Y., 1920. $7.50

Printed from the manuscript in an edition of 250 copies. Smith, at the time of the gold discovery in California, was on the staff of the Ontario Messenger which perhaps accounts for the interesting and breezy style of his narrative. He gives a vivid picture of the prairies, of experiences on the overland, of wild life, etc.

455 [OVERLAND MAIL.] Mail Contracts. 30th Cong., 1st Sess., H. R. 818. 44 pp., 8vo, sewn. Washington, 1848. $6.00

456 [OVERLAND RAILROAD.] Union Pacific Railroad. Report of the Chief Engineer, with Accompanying Reports of Division Engineers for 1866. Large colored folding maps, plates of the overland. 123 pp., original printed wrappers. Washington: Philip and Solomons, 1868. $27.50

Braislin 613. The map shows in detail the routes from St. Louis and Omaha to San Francisco. The name "Hon. E. McPherson" inscribed on outside wrapper.

457 [PACIFIC COAST PILOT.] Alaska. Part 1. 243 pp., 8vo, cloth. Washington, 1891. $10.00

458 [PACIFIC ISLANDS.] A Memoir of Daniel Wheeler, with an Account of his Gospel Labours in the Islands of the Pacific. 12mo, cloth. Phila., 1859. $2.50

Sandwich Islands, Australia, New Zealand, South Seas in the 1830's.

459 [PACIFIC TOURIST, THE.] Adams and Bishop's Illustrated Trans-Continental Guide of Travel from the Atlantic to the Pacific Ocean . . . By Frederick E. Shearer. 372 pp., illus. N. Y., 1886. $7.50

Smith 4415.

460 [PACIFIC TOURIST, THE.] Williams, Henry T. Williams Illustrated Trans-Continental Guide to Travel from the Atlantic to the Pacific Ocean . . . 342 pp., illus., 12mo, cloth. N. Y., 1879. $5.00

461 ——. The Same. N. Y., 1886. $5.00

462 ——. The Same. N. Y., 1877. $5.00

463 [PANAMA.] The Canal, the Country, and the People. By Albert Edwards. Port., illus. 8vo, cloth. N. Y., 1911. $2.50

464 [PANAMA, ISTHMUS OF.] Communication Across the Isthmus of Panama. 8vo, 7 pp., unbound. (Washington, 1827). $3.50

A proposal to get better service between U. S. vessels on the NW Coast by establishing a quick schooner route from the Chesepeake to the Isthmus to pick up various communications brought overland.

465 PANCOAST, CHAS. EDWARD. A Quaker Forty-Niner. The Adventures of Charles Edward Pancoast on the American Frontier. Edited by Anna Paschall Hannum. 402 pp., front., 8vo, cloth. Phila., 1930. $4.50

466 PECKHAM, HOWARD H. Guide to the Manuscript Collections in the William L. Clements Library. 8vo, cloth. Ann Arbor, Mich., 1942. $5.00

A volume intended to provide a workable check list of the contents of this great repository of documents relating to American history. Certainly any student doing research in the period of the American Revolution will have to visit this repository of the celebrated British Headquarters Papers; but, aside from the Discovery, Colonial and Revolutionary periods, there is also a great amount of manuscript material on the old Northwest Territory and the Anti-Slavery Movement, Book Collecting, etc.

467 PENDLETON, OREGON.] The Pioneer Ladies Club, Pendleton, Oregon. Reminiscences of Oregon Pioneers. 257 pp., 8vo, cloth. Pendleton, Ore., 1937. $4.50

468 [PERRY EXPEDITION.] A Journal of the Perry Expedition to Japan (1853-1854). By S. Wells Williams, Interpreter of the Expedition. Edited by his son, F. W. Williams. 263 pp., front. (Transactions of the Asiatic Society of Japan, Vol. 37, Pt. 2). 8vo, original wrappers. Yokohoma, 1910. $7.50

469 PITKIN, EDWARD. Statistical View of the Commerce of the U. S. its Connection with Agriculture and Manufactures . . . 445 pp., 8vo, original boards, uncut. N. Y., 1817. $2.00

470 PLAN para la defensa de los Estados invadidos por los Barbaros. 8vo, original printed wrapper. Mexico, 1849. $35.00

The frontier line is divided into three great divisions. 1. The Eastern Coahuila, Nuevo-Leon and Tamaulipas; 2. Chihuahua, including Durango and Zacatecas. 3. The Western, extending to Sonora and Baja California. These divisions to be put in a state of military defence as shown in detail, and summarized in four tables of organization at the end, giving estimates of the necessary troops, munitions, etc.

471 [PENNSYLVANIA.] Sketches of the Life and Adventures of Capt. Samuel Brady, a Native of Cumberland County, born 1758, a few miles above Northumberland, Pa. 24 pp., 8vo, ¾ crimson calf, original printed wrappers bound in. Lancaster, 1891. $7.50

These sketches were originally written for the Blairsville "Record." Only 50 copies were printed.

472 [PENNSYLVANIA.] Historical Collections of the Mahoning Valley: Containing an Account of the two Pioneer Reunions, etc. Folding map. 8vo, cloth. Vol. 1 (all published). Youngstown, 1876. $4.00

473 [PENNSYLVANIA.] Monongahela of Old; or, Sketches of Southwestern Pennsylvania to 1800. Port. and plans, 259 pp., 8vo, cloth. Pittsburgh, 1910. $5.00

French War, early settlements, forts, Braddock's Defeat, boundary troubles, etc.

474 [PENNSYLVANIA.] Wilderness Chronicles of Northern Pennsylvania . . . Edited by Sylvester K. Stevens and Donald H. Kent. 342 pp., maps, plates. 8vo, original wrappers. Harrisburg, 1941. $2.50

475 RADISSON, PIERRE ESPRIT. Relations des Voyages de Pierre Esprit Radisson dans les Annees 1682-1684. 83 pp. Contained in Report on Canadian Archives, 1895. 8vo, half calf. Ottawa, 1896. $5.00

476 RAE, W. F. Westward by Rail; the new Route to the East. Map. 8vo, cloth. N. Y., 1871. $3.50

The Pacific Railroad, Great Salt Lake, California, the "Tigers" in San Francisco, etc.

477 RANCK, GLENN N. Pictures from Northwest History. 38 pp., 8vo, original wrappers. Vancouver, Wash. Independent Print, 1902. $5.00

Smith 3261. Autographed by the author. A series of 11 documented sketches covering various phases of Pacific Northwest history.

478 RANCK, GLENN N. Legends and Traditions of Northwest History. 152 pp., front., 11 plates, port., map. 8vo, cloth. Vancouver, 1914. $4.50

Includes sketches of pioneers of Clarke County, Wash. Smith 3260.

479 RANDALL, HARRY. The Conquest of the Northwest Passage. 16 pp., illus., 8vo, original wrappers. Minneapolis, 1907. $3.00

480 RANKIN, MELINDA. Twenty Years among the Mexicans. A Narrative of Missionary Labor. 214 pp., 12mo, cloth. Cincinnati, 1875. $5.00

481 RATHBURN, J. C. History of Thurston County, Wash. 131 pp., 8vo, ¾ calf. Olympia, Wash., 1895. $12.50

Smith 3263.

482 RATTRAY, ALEXANDER. Vancouver Island and British Columbia. Where they are; what they are; and what they may become; a Sketch of their History, Topography, Climate, Resources, Capabilities and Advantages, especially as Colonies for Settlement. 182 pp., 3 plates, 2 maps. 8vo, cloth. London, 1862. $7.50

Smith 3267.

483 RAWLINGS, THOMAS. The Confederation of the British North American Provinces; their Past History and Future Prospects, including also British Columbia and Hudson's Bay Territory. With a Map and suggestion in reference to the True and only Practicable Route from the Atlantic to the Pacific Ocean. 240 pp., 4 plates, folding map. 8vo, cloth. London: Low, 1865. $7.50

Smith 3270. Early efforts of the explorer, geographer and navigator, Hudson's Bay Co., the fur trade, Red River Settlement, Rocky Mountains, discovery of gold, railroads, etc. Two of the plates give full views of Victoria, B. C.

484 RAYMER, CHARLES D. Raymer's Dictionary of Spokane, an Encyclopaedia-Dictionary of the State of Washington, U. S. A., in general and the city of Spokane in particular. 152 pp., illus., map. Spokane (1906). $3.00

485 ——. The Same. 128 pp., illus., map. 8vo, original wrappers. Seattle (1907). $2.50

486 RAYMOND, ROSSITER W. Camp and Cabin; Sketches of Life and Travel in the West. 243 pp., 12mo, cloth. N. Y.: Ford, 1880. $7.50

A trip through the Yellowstone and eastern Washington in 1871. Scarce.

487 RAYNOLDS, W. F. Report on the Exploration of the Yellowstone River, by Brvt. Gen. W. F. Raynolds, communicated to the Secretary of War . . . Sen. Ex. Doc. 77. Folding map. 8vo, cloth. Washington, 1868. $7.50

488 [RAILROADS.] Laws and Ordinances relating to the Baltimore and Ohio Rail Road Company. 90 pp. and iii pp. index. 8vo, unbound. Baltimore, 1834. $5.00

489 [RAILROADS.] Forty Years a Locomotive Engineer. Thrilling Tales of the Rails. By J. Harvey Reed. 143 pp., 12mo, cloth. Prescott, Washington, 1912. $5.00

490 [RAND-McNALLY GUIDE TO NORTHWEST.] Guide to the Great Northwest . . . Information regarding . . . Montana, Idaho, Washington, Oregon, Minnesota, North Dakota, Alaska; also Western Canada and British Columbia . . . By S. H. Soule. 366 pp., illus., map. 8vo, cloth. Chicago (1903). $4.50

491 [RED RIVER SETTLEMENT.] Etablissement des Soeurs de Charite a la Riviere Rouge. 16 pp., 8vo, original wrappers. N.p., N.d. (1894). $4.50

492 [RED RIVER SETTLEMENT.] The Red River Colony. A Chronicle of the Beginnings of Manitoba. By Louis Aubrey Wood. 152 pp., illus., map. 8vo, cloth. Toronto, 1915. $2.50

493 REMINGTON, FREDERIC. Crooked Trails. 8vo, cloth. 151 pp., illus. N. Y., 1899. $5.00

494 REMINGTON, FREDERIC C. Men with the Bark On. Illus. by the Author. 209 pp., 12mo, cloth. N. Y., 1900. $15.00

Original edition. Fine.

495 REMINGTON, FREDERIC. The Way of an Indian. Written and Illustrated by Frederic Remington. 252 pp., illus., 8vo, cloth. N. Y., 1906. $5.00

496 REMINGTON, FREDERIC. John Ermine of the Yellowstone. 274 pp., illus., 8vo, cloth. N. Y., 1913. $2.00

497 REMY, JULES, and BRENCHLEY, JULIUS. A Journey to Great Salt Lake . . . with a Sketch of the History, Religion and Customs of the Mormons and an Introduction on the Religious Movement in the U. S. With 10 steel engravings and a map. 2 vols., 8vo, original cloth. London, 1861. $8.00

Wagner-Camp (Note) 364.

498 RESANOV, N. P. The Rezanov Voyage to Neuva California in 1806, the Report of Count Nikolai Petrovich Rezanov of his Voyage to that Province of New Espagna from New Archangel; an English translation revised and corrected, with notes, etc., by Thomas C. Russell. Annotated, the Count Rezanov; the Russian American Company; the Krusenstern Expedition; settlements in Alaska—the Donna Concepcion de San Francisco, the historic, tragic and alluring spot by the Golden Gate . . . x11-104 pp., illus. 4to, boards. San Francisco, 1926. $15.00

Wick. 6338a. No. 129 of 260 copies printed. This is an interesting and important and little publicised relation of early California and Russian activity there.

499 REVERE, JOSEPH W. Tour of Duty in California; including a Description of the Gold Region; and an Account of the Voyage around Cape Horn; with notices of Lower California, the Gulf and Pacific Coasts, and the Principal Events attending the Conquest of California. Folding map and plates. 305 pp., 12mo, cloth. N. Y., 1849. $15.00

Original Edition. The author, grandson of Paul Revere, wrote here, according to Cowan "one of the most valuable works of the period."

500 REVERE, JOSEPH W. Keel and Saddle, a Retrospect of Forty Years of Military and Naval Service. 360 pp., 12mo, cloth. Boston, 1872. $5.00

501 RICHARDSON, SIR JOHN, and SWAINSON, W. Fauna Boreali-Americana; or, the Zoology of the Northern Parts of British America; containing descriptions of the Objects of Natural History collected on the late Northern Land Expeditions, under command of Sir John Franklin . . . Part 1, the Quadrapeds; Part 2, the Birds. Plates (those of the birds beautifully colored). 4to, half calf. London, 1829. $65.00

Wagner-Camp 39. Dr. Richardson accompanied the Franklin Expedition as surgeon and naturalist. The specimens brought to England were almost all collected in the country north of the great Canadian Lakes, in fact, in the widely extended territory wherein the scattered trading posts of the Hudson's Bay company furnished the only vestiges of civilization.

The work may, therefore, be termed a contribution to the fauna of the British-American fur countries. After having traveled throught the fur districts east of the Rocky Mountains for seven summers, and after having passed five winters at widely different posts, Dr. Richardson asserted that almost all the quadrupeds which were the objects of chase or interest to the natives, and a very great proportion of the birds, either came within his own scope or were mentioned in the many conversations he had with white and native traders and hunters.

502 RIDDLE, GEORGE D. Early Days in Oregon: Narrative of a Trip Across the Plains from Illinois to Oregon in 1851, and Recollections of the Indians and Indian Wars to 1856. Port. 74 pp., 12mo, original wrappers. N.p., N.d. (1920). $4.50

503 RIDDLE, JEFF C. The Indian History of the Modoc War and the Causes that led to it. Illus., 295 pp., 8vo, cloth. N.p., N.d. (San Francisco: Moses, 1914). $4.50

Smith 3315.

504 RIDEING, W. A Saddle in the Wild West: Among the Mountains, Lava Beds, Sand, Deserts, Adobe Towns, Indians and Ancient Pueblos of Colorado, New Mexico and Arizona. 165 pp., 12mo, cloth. N. Y., 1879. $3.50

A journal of two years' adventures while connected with Lieut. Wheelers's survey.

505 RIDINGS, SAM P. The Chisholm Trail. A History of the World's Greatest Cattle Trail. Illus., 8vo, cloth. Guthrie, Okla., 1936. $3.50

506 RIEGEL, ROBERT E. America Moves West. 593 pp., 8vo, cloth. N. Y. (1930). $3.50

507 RIGGS, REV. STEPHEN R. Mary and I: Forty Years with the Sioux. 437 pp., 12mo, cloth. Boston (1880). $5.00

Early days in, and history of, the Northwest; journey to the Missouri River; the Sioux Massacre; Gen. Sibley's Expedition; captivity among the Indians, etc.

508 ROBBINS, GEORGE COLLIER. The Pioneer Reminiscences of. (Contained in Pacific Monthly, June ,July, Aug. and Sept. numbers, 1911). 8vo, wrappers. San Francisco, 1911. $7.50

Robbins crossed the Plains to California in 1851, and subsequently went to Oregon.

509 ROBERTS, B. H. The Mormon Battalion. Its History and Achievements. Folding map, 96 pp., 12mo, cloth. Salt Lake City, 1919. $3.50

History of the noted Mormon Expedition across the Plains in 1846-7.

510 ROBERTS, EDWARDS. Shoshone and other Western Wonders. With a preface by Charles Francis Adams. 275 pp., plates., 8vo, cloth. N. Y., 1888. $5.00

Smith 3323. Colorado, Utah, Wyoming, Montana, Yellowstone Park.

511 ROBERTS, MILNOR W. Report of a Reconnaissance of the Route for the Northern Pacific Railroad, between Lake Superior and Puget Sound, via the Columbia River, made in 1869. 56 pp., 8vo, original wrappers. Phila. (1869). $10.00

Report of the private Expedition sent by Jay Cooke and Company to examine the Country and make a report on the whole route, based on the explorations of Gov. Smith, Gov. Marshall, Gen. Hancock and others, and Roberts' own observations. The exploration covers the Puget Sound Region; the Cowlitz; the Cascade Mountains; Clark's River; the Blackfoot and Hellgate Rivers; Bozeman Pass; Ft. Benton; and the Yellowstone Country.

512 ROBERTS, MORLEY. Western Avernus; or, Toil and Travel in further North America. 307 pp., map. 12mo, cloth. London, 1887. $4.00

Iowa and Minnesota to Manitoba and the Rockies, through Oregon and south to San Francisco on foot.

513 ROBERTS, MORLEY. The Mate of the Vancouver. 203 pp., 12mo, cloth. N. Y., N.d. $3.75

514 ROBINSON, A. Life in California during a Residence of Several Years in that Territory, comprising a Description of the Country and the Missionary Establishments, with Incidents, Observations, etc., etc. By an American. 8vo, cloth. London, 1851. $12.50

515 ——. The Same. 8vo, original cloth. N. Y., 1846. $30.00

516 ROBINSON, JOHN, and DOW, GEO. FRANCIS. The Sailing Ships of New England. Series 2. 252 pp., illus., 8vo, cloth. Marine Research Society, Salem, 1924. $7.50

517 ROBINSON, JACOB S. A Journal of the Santa Fe Expedition under Colonel Doniphan. Reprinted, with Historical Introduction and Notes, by Carl L. Cannon, from the edition of 1848. 95 pp., illus., 12mo, cloth. Princeton, 1932. $2.00

518 ROBSON, JOSEPH. An Account of Six Years' Residence in Hudson's Bay, from 1733-6 and 1744-7. Containing a variety of facts and Observations tending to show the importance of the Countries about Hudson's Bay on account of the extensive improvements that may be made there in Commerce, particularly in the Furs and in the Whale and Sea Fisheries. And the absolute necessity of laying open the trade and making it the object of national encouragement. Folding maps, 179 pp., 8vo, calf. London, 1752. $37.50

The author was a surveyor in the service of the Hudson's Bay Co. The appendix contains a history of the discovery of Hudson's Bay and the proceedings of the English there since the grant of the company's charter; with remarks upon the papers and evidence produced by the company before the Committee of the House of Commons in 1749. The map includes a draught of Nelson, Hayes and Churchill Rivers and plans of York Fort and Prince of Wales Fort.

519 ROCKWOOD, ELEANOR RUTH. Books on the Pacific Northwest for Small Libraries. 55 pp., 8vo, original wrappers. N. Y., 1923. $1.00

Miss Rockwood is Reference librarian of the Library Association of Portland, Ore.

520 ROE (FRANCES M.). Army Letters from an Officer's Wife, 1871-1888. Port. and 25 plates from contemporary photographs. 387 pp., 12mo, cloth. N. Y., 1909. $5.00

An intimate and valuable narrative of army post life in the far west. Mrs. Roe spent seventeen years at the various frontier posts of Kansas, Indian Territory, Colorado, Utah, Montana and Wyoming, and her "Letters" afford a contemporary and almost day-by-day chronicle of this life and the adventures and thrilling experiences which were so much a part of it. Her preface states: "The letters are truthful accounts of experiences that came into my own life with the army, whether they be about Indians, desperadoes or hunting. All flowery descriptions have been omitted as it seemed that a simple, concise narration of events as they actually occurred, was more in keeping with the life, and that which came into it."

521 ROGERS, JOHN. Sport in Vancouver and Newfoundland. 275 pp., front., illus., maps. 8vo, cloth. Toronto, 1912. $5.00

522 ROGERS, JOHN R. The Irrepressible Conflict; or, an American System of Money. 136 pp., 8vo, original wrappers. Puyallup, Wash., 1892. $3.75

Rogers was one time Governor of Washington.

523 ROGERS, THOMAS H. Nehalem, a Story of the Pacific. 182 pp., port., 2 plates. 8vo, original wrappers. McMinnville (1898). $7.50

524 [ROGERS, WILLIAM.] Memoranda of the Experiences, Labors and Travels of a Universalist Preacher. 400 pp., 12mo, original sheep. Cincinnati, 1845. $25.00

A valuable pioneer narrative dealing with travels in the West, Ky., Tenn., Miss., Ala., Wabash region in Indiana, La., Ohio, Va., N. Y., Pa., Mich., Ill. slavery, Indians, etc.

525 ROLLINS, ALICE WELLINGTON. The Three Tetons; a Story of the Yellowstone. 219 pp., 8vo, cloth. N. Y. (1887). $4.50

526 ROLLINS, PHILIP ASHTON. The Cowboy, an Unconventional History of Civilization on the Old-time Cattle Range. 402 pp., illus., 8vo, cloth. N. Y., 1936. $2.50

527 ROLLINS, PHILIP ASHTON. The Discovery of the Oregon Trail. Robert Stuart's Narratives of his Overland Trip eastward from Astoria in 1812-13. From Original Manuscripts in the Collection of William Robertson Coe. Thick 8vo, cloth. N. Y., 1935. $7.50

528 ROOSEVELT, THEODORE. Hoofs, Claws and Antlers of the Rocky Mountains. By the Camera. Photographic Reproductions of Wild Game from Life, with an Introduction by Theodore Roosevelt. 4to, original publisher's binding of full morocco. Denver, 1894. $17.50

Limited edition.

529 ROOSEVELT, THEODORE. Good Hunting in Pursuit of Big Game in the West. 107 pp., illus., 12mo, cloth. N. Y., 1907. $6.00

530 [ROOSEVELT, THEODORE.] Thomas Hart Benton. 12mo, cloth. Boston, N.d. $2.00

ROQUEVILLE'S VOYAGE TO CALIFORNIA AND N.W. COAST

531 ROQUEFEUIL, CAMILLE DE. Journal d'un Voyage autour du Monde pendant les Annees 1816-1819. 2 large folding maps. 2 vols., 8vo, original boards. Paris, 1823. $35.00

Original Edition. The object of the Expedition was the revival of trade in the North Pacific. Roquefeuil gives a long account of his sojourn in California and his explorations on the Northwest Coast, together with many particulars of the native tribes.

532 ——. The Same. English edition. 8vo, calf. London, 1823. $12.50

533 ROSS (ALEXANDER). Adventures of the First Settlers on the Oregon or Columbia River: Being a Narrative of the Expedition fitted out by John Jacob Astor, to Establish the "Pacific Fur Company"; with an Account of the Indian Tribes on the Coast of the Pacific. Folding map. 352 pp., 12mo, half calf. London, 1849. $37.50

Wagner-Camp 172, note. Original Edition. Ross gives a detailed account of the overland expeditions of Hunt and Stuart. For upwards of fifteen years the author traversed the wastes of the Rocky Mountains. As an Indian Trader pushing his commerce among friendly and even among hostile tribes, he was often the first white man to burst upon their wild fastnesses.

534 ROSS, ALEXANDER. The Fur Hunters of the Far West: A Narrative of Adventures in the Oregon and Rocky Mountains. [Map and frontis.] 12mo, half calf. London, 1855. $47.50

A nice copy of Wagner-Camp 269. "Ross was with the Astor Company but joined the Northwest Co. on the breaking up of the Astor enterprise. Left the Pacific in 1825 and went to Red River Settlement, having received the grant of 100 acres there from Gov. Simpson. Gives a good account of his overland journey."

535 ROSS, ALEXANDER. The Red River Settlement, its Rise, Progress and Present State. With some Account of the Native Races and its General History to the Present Date. Frontis. 8vo, half calf. London, 1856. $25.00

536 ROSS, SIR JOHN. A Voyage of Discovery made . . . for the purpose of Exploring Baffin's Bay, and Inquiring into the Probability of a Northwest Passage. London, 1819. Narrative of a Second Voyage in Search of a Northwest Passage, and a Residence in the Arctic Regions during the years 1829-33 . . . including the Reports of James Clark Ross and the Discovery of the Northern Magnetic Pole. London, 1835. Together with the Appendix to the Second Voyage. London, 1835. Maps and numerous plates, some in color. Together 3 vols., 4to. London, 1819-35. $22.50

537 ROSS, SIR JOHN. Memoir of the celebrated Admiral Adam John de Krusenstern . . . trans. from the German by his daughter, Madame Charlotte Bernhordi . . . 75 pp., port. 8vo, cloth. London, 1856. $12.50

Smith 3358.

538 ROSS, PATRICK H. W. Western Gate. 153 pp., 2 maps. 12mo, cloth. N. Y., 1911. $3.75

Smith 3359. Sub-title: Maritime District of Western Washington and a new American Merchant Marine.

539 ROSSI, LOUIS ABBE. Six Ans en Amerique. Californie et Oregon. 322 pp., 2 maps. 8vo, original wrappers. Paris: Perisse, 1863. $12.50

540 ROSSITER, HARRIET, and HOWARD, E. C. Indian Legends from the Land of Al-ay-ek-sa. 26 pp., illus. 8vo, original wrappers. Ketchikan, Alaska, 1925. $4.00

541 ROUHAUD (H.). Les Regions Nouvelles. Histoire du Commerce et de la Civilisation au Nord de l'Ocean Pacifique. 404 pp., 8vo, original wrappers. Paris, 1868. $20.00

Smith 3362 cites one copy. An interesting work in relation to Oregon, California and Texas, dealing with the early explorations, settlements at Astoria, the Texas Conquest, Indian wars, discovery of gold, pioneers, life and economics of California.

542 ROTHENSTEINER, J. The Flat-Head and Nez Perce Delegation to St. Louis, 1831-39. 15 pp., 8vo, original wrappers. St. Louis: Rothensteiner, N.d. $4.75

543 ROWAN, JAMES. The I. W. W. in the Lumber Industry. 64 pp., 8vo, original wrappers. Seattle, N.d. $3.75

544 ROYAL SOCIETY OF CANADA. Proceedings and Transactions of. Second Series, Vol. 1. 279 pp., 8vo, cloth. Montreal, 1895. $4.50

Much on Vancouver.

545 ROYER, EDGAR. Benaiah Longley Whitman, 1862-1911. Port. 8vo, wrappers. N.p., N.d. (1911?). $5.00

Reprinted from the Northwestern Free Mason, December, 1911. Smith 3364 cites but one copy.

546 [ROYER, EDGAR.] Royer's Financial Record: Issued Five Times a Year, after each call of the Comptroller of the Currency. Volumes 1-12. 4to. Seattle: Royer, 1908-1919. $15.00

Smith 3365. Record of Washington, Oregon, Idaho and Alaska.

547 RUFFNER, WILLIAM H. Report on Washington Territory. 12 plates, 5 maps, tab. 8vo, cloth. N. Y., Seattle, Lake Shore and Eastern Railway, 1889. $3.00

548 RUPP, I. DANIEL. History of Lancaster County, Pa., with a Brief Sketch of the Early History of Pennsylvania; also History of York County. Illus. 2 vols. in one, original calf. Lancaster, 1844-45. $25.00

One of the scarcest of the Rupp histories.

549 RUPP, I. DANIEL. History of Berks and Lebanon Counties, Containing a Brief Account of the Indians who Inhabited this Region of the Country, and the Numerous Murders by Them; Notices of the First Swedish, Welch, French, German, Irish and English Settlers, giving the Names of Nearly Five Hundred of them . . . I. Daniel Rupp. Illus., 8vo, calf. Lancaster, 1844. $12.50

550 RUPP, I. DANIEL. History of Northampton, Lehigh, Monroe, Barton and Schuylkill Counties. By I. Daniel Rupp. 8vo, mor. (weak hinge). Harrisburg, 1845. $5.00

551 RUSH, RICHARD. Memoranda of a Residence at Court of London from 1819 to 1825, including Negotiations on the Oregon Question . . . 640 pp., 8vo, cloth. Phila., 1845. $7.50

552 RUSSELL, FLORENCE. Child Life in Oregon. 193 pp., 12mo, cloth. Boston (1866). $17.50

A little known work dealing with domestic life in Oregon in the early days.

553 RUSSELL, ALEXANDER J. The Red River Country. Hudson's Bay and North-West Territories considered in relation to Canada, with the last report of S. J. Dawson, Esquire, C.E., on the Line of Route between Lake Superior and the Red River Settlement. Folding map, 202 pp., 8vo, half calf. Ottawa, 1869. $12.50

This work was written to place before the Canadian people the reasons why the Dominion wanted the Red River and other Northwest Territories. It is particularly valuable for the description of the Hudson's Bay Territories and Forts from Winnipeg Lake to the Barren Grounds.

554 RUSSELL, CHAS. M. Stories of Western Life. 12 plates. Long 12mo, cloth. Cascade, Mont., 1890. $35.00

555 RUSSELL, CHAS. M. Rawhide Rawlins Stories. 60 pp., long 12mo, cloth. Great Falls, Mont., 1921. $7.50

556 RUSSELL, CHAS. M. Trails Plowed Under. xx-211 pp., 4to, cloth. N. Y., 1927. $7.50

557 RUSSELL, CHAS. M. Studies of Western Life. With Descriptions by Granville Stuart. Illus. 8vo, original wrappers. Spokane, N.d. $7.50

558 RUSSELL, FRANK. Explorations in the Far North. Being the Report of an Expedition under the auspices of the University of Iowa during the Years 1892, '93 and '94. 290 pp., illus., maps. 8vo, original wrappers. N.p., 1898. $7.50

559 RUSSELL, ISAAC K. Hidden Heroes of the Rockies. Maps and plates. 205 pp., 12mo, cloth. Yonkers, 1923. $3.50

The "unknown" include such famous explorers as Robert Stuart, Major Henry, Donald Mackenzie, Jedediah Smith, Peter Skene Ogden, Thomas Fitzpatrick, Jim Bridger and Fremont.

560 RUSSELL, OSBORNE. The Journal of a Trapper; or, Nine Years in the Rocky Mountains, 1834-43. Being a General Description of the Country, Climate, Rivers, Lakes, Mountains, etc., and a View of the Life led by a Hunter in those Regions. 8vo, cloth. N.p. (Boise, Idaho), 1921. $10.00

Item 554, Should read "studies."

561 [RUSSIAN-AMERICA.] Archiv fur Wissenschaftliche Kunde von Russland. 36 vols. Numerous maps and plans. 8vo, original wrappers. Berlin, 1842-1859. $90.00

A long run of one of the best repositories of source material relating to Alaska and the far northwest coast. Most all the material is official and often accompanied by maps. Such a long run of the Archiv fur Wissenschaftliche is seldom come upon.

562 RUTGERS, LISPENARD. On and Off the Saddle. Characteristic Sights and Scenes from the Great Northwest to the Antilles. 201 pp., 8vo, cloth. N. Y., 1894. $4.50

Travels in Wyoming, California, Alaska, British Columbia, hunting, etc.

563 RUXTON, GEORGE F. Life in the Far West. 8vo, cloth. N. Y., 1849. $4.50

564 RUXTON, GEORGE F. Adventures in Mexico and the Rocky Mountains. 8vo, cloth. London, 1847. $4.50

565 RUXTON, GEO. F. In the Old West. As it was in the Days of Kit Carson and the "Mountain Men." 8vo, cloth. N. Y., N.d. (1915). $2.50

566 RYAN, WILLIAM R. Personal Adventures in Upper and Lower California in 1848-49. With the Author's Experiences in the Mines. Numerous illus. 2 vols., 12mo, original cloth. London, 1850. $30.00

"The charming narrative of an Artist and Bohemian who left unrecorded but little that he saw. Like most of the wayfarers from Great Britain, his dignity was rudely disturbed and at such times his excess of feelnig has caused his tone to become terse. His descriptions are among the best of his time."—Cowan—Bib. of California.

567 RYDELL, CAPT. EARL. On Pacific Frontiers. A Story of Life at Sea and in the Outlying Possessions of the United States. 267 pp., illus. 8vo, cloth. N. Y., 1924. $3.00

Relates to the old seal "pirates" and sea-otter hunters who scoured the Pacific.

568 RYUS, W. H. The Second William Penn. A True Account of Incidents that Happened along the old Santa Fe Trail in the Sixties. Illus. 12mo, cloth. Kansas City, N.d. (1913). $4.00

The author began as a mail driver in 1861 over the run from Ft. Larned, Kansas, to Ft. Lyon, Colorado. Some of the chapter headings are: The Nine Mile Ridge Massacre; The Chivington Massacre; Major Carleton orders Col. Willis to go into Southwestern Indian Territory; Lucian Maxwell and Kit Carson take Sheep to California; Kit Carson, My Friend; Col. Moore's Graphic Description of a Fight with the Cheyennes; etc.

569 SABIN, EDWIN L. Kit Carson Days, 1809-1868. 669 pp., 8vo, cloth. Chicago: McClurg, 1914. $3.50

570 SABIN, EDWIN L. General Crook and the Fighting Apaches . . . 302 pp., illus., 12mo, cloth. Phila., 1918. $3.75

571 SABIN, EDWIN L. Wild Men of the West. 363 pp., illus., 8vo, cloth. N. Y. (c. 1929). $3.00

A FINE COPY OF THE RARE FIRST EDITION OF SAGE'S SCENES IN THE ROCKY MOUNTAINS

572 [SAGE, RUFUS B.] Scenes in the Rocky Mountains, And In Oregon, California, New Mexico, Texas, and The Grand Prairies; or, Notes By The Way, During an Excursion of Three Years, With a Description of the Countries Passed Through, Including their Geography, Geology, Resources, Present Condition, and the Different Nations Inhabiting Them. By A New Englander. [Map.] 12mo, cloth. Phila., 1846. $125.00

The very scarce first edition. A fine copy, containing the map which Wagner says is often lacking. The second edition was apparently published without one. The title of the map is: "Map of Oregon, California, New Mexico, N. W. Texas, and the Proposed Territory of Ne-Bras-Ka. By Rufus B. Sage, 1846. F. Michelin's lith., N. Y.

Wagner-Camp 123, has the following note: "Sage arrived in Westport in May, 1841, too late to accompany a party to Oregon, but finally left Sept. 2, with me . . . with one of the return fur trade parties. Returned to Independence July 21, 1842. Started out again in early August for Ft. Lancaster and thence to the Arkansas and while on Fountain Creek was passed by Fitzpatrick and Van Dusen on their way to the States. Stopped at the Pueblo and Taos and made an excursion to Uintah River with Roubideau. After a short stay, continued to Ft. Hall and arrived there Nov. 9th, returned in December by North Park and Middle Park on the Platte River and wintered on the Platte below Cherry Creek.

"He says Captain Warfield, a Texan, came to Ft. Lancaster for recruits for some expedition. Sage found the Texans on the Arkansas River below the old Fort. He finally joined Warfield between the Cimaron and the Arkansas. This was the Snively expedition of which he gives a long account, including the surrender to Cooke. He then returned to the Platte. He met Fremont at Fort Lancaster in July, 1843. On the 17th of March, 1844, he started from Ft. Lancaster for he U. S. via Bent's Fort, thence down to Van Buren, Arkansas, which he reached July 4th."

573 ——. The Same. 363 pp., 12mo, cloth. Boston: Thayer, 1857. $7.50

574 [ST. JOHN, A. B.] North Pacific Ports. A Compilation of Useful Maxims, Exporting and Importing Information for Alaska and the Western Coasts of Canada and the United States. 421 pp., 8vo. Seattle: Terminal Publishing Co., 1915. $7.50

Smith 2966-68.

575 SAINT-AMANT, PIERRE CHARLES DE. Voyages en Californie et dans l'Oregon . . . 651 pp., illus., maps. 8vo, original wrappers. Par Maison, 1854. $14.50

Smith 3388.

576 ST. JOHN MOLYNEUX. Sea of Mountains; an Account of Lord Dufferin's Tour through British Columbia in 1876. Ports., facs. 2 vols., 12mo, cloth. London: Hurst, 1877. $12.50

Smith 3391. The author visited Victoria, Vancouver, Nanaimo, toured the Haro Straits, San Juan Island, Fitzhugh Sound, Entrance to Juan de Fuca Straits and other points in the Puget Sound country.

577 ST. JOHN, MOLYNEUX. The Province of British Columbia, Canada, its Resources, Commercial Position and Climate, and description of the new field opened up by the Canadian Pacific Railroad. With Information for Intending Settlers . . . 56 pp., plate, folding map. 8vo. N.p., N.d. $10.00

Smith 3390.

578 ST. MAUR, MRS. ALGERNON. Impressions of a Tenderfoot during a Journey in search of Sport in the Far West. 279 pp., 6 plates, map. 12mo, cloth. London, 1890. $4.50

579 ST. ONGE, LOUIS N. Alphabet Yakama, contenant les Prieres, les Cantiques et la Catechisme dans la meme Langue a l'usage de Enfants de la Tribu des Yakamas sous le patronage des R. R. P. P. Jesuites. Par L. N. St. Onge, Pretre ex Missionnaire des Yakamas. 104 pp., frontis. Montreal: Providence, 1872. $22.50

Smith 3394, locates only one copy, that in the Washington Historical Society.

580 SAMUEL, L. The Traveler's Guide and Oregon Railroad Gazetteer on Railways, Steamers and Stages through Oregon and Washington Territory. 96 pp., illus. 12mo, original wrappers. Portland: Samuel, 1872. $60.00

A rare work of which the only other copy we can locate is in the Oregon Historical Society Collection. The work contains a great amount of local information as well as a brief history and description of nearly every community in Oregon and Washington Territory. There is a table giving local time tables of trains, boats and stages.

581 SANDERS, HELEN FITZGERALD. Trails through Northern Woods. 311 pp., illus., 8vo, cloth. Seattle: Harriman, 1910. $4.00

582 SANFORD, ADAM CASTLE. My Recollections of Eighty Years of Strenuous Life. 96 pp., 8vo, original wrappers. Published by the Author. Portland, N.d. $12.50

A little known work, privately published in a small edition, describing pioneer events in Oregon and the Northwest.

583 SAUER, MARTIN. An Account of a Geographical and Astronomical Expedition to the Northwestern Parts of Russia for ascertaining the Degrees of Latitude and Longitude of the Mouth of the River Kovina; of the whole Coast of the Tshutski, to East Cape; and of the Islands of the Eastern Ocean, stretching to the American Coast. Performed . . . by Commodore Joseph Billings in the Years 1785-94 . . . 332 pp., 14 plates and folding map. 4to, calf. London, 1802. $25.00

The above fine copy contains all the plates and map. At the end are vocabularies of the languages of Kamchatka, the Aleutian Islands and Kodiac. Wick. 6134.

584 SAUER, MARTIN. Voyage fait par ordre l'Imperatrice de Russie Catherine II, dans le Nord de la Russie Asiatique, et sur les Cotes de l'Amerique, depuis 1785 jusqu' en 1794, par le Commodore Billings; traduit de l'Anglais, avec des Notes, par J. Castera. 14 plates and folding map. 3 vols., 4to, calf. Par Buisson, 1802. $60.00

Smith 3416 cites only one set of this rare French Edition of Sauer's work, which is not to be compared with the English edition as it is much finer in format and is accompanied by a 4to Atlas with plates, some of Alaska. Sauer was the historian on the Billings Expedition sent out by the Russians in 1785 to explore the coasts of its North American possessions.

585 SAUER, MARTIN. Reise nach den Nordlichen Gegenden von Russichen Asien und America unter dem Commodor J. Billings, 1785-94. A.d. Engl. von M. C. Sprengel. Mit 1 Karte. 8vo, calf. Weimar: H. Leder, 1803. $20.00

Wickersham 6137.

586 SAXTON, CHARLES. The Oregonian; or, History of the Oregon Territory: Containing the Laws of Oregon, with a Description of the political condition of the country, as well as its Climate, Resources, Soil, Production, Progress in Education. Map. 14 pp. Washington: Ward, 1846. $35.00

Smith 3420. A photostatic copy of the only known copy. Map wanting in the original.

587 SAYRE, ALEXANDER N. Al-Ki-Puget Sound. A Poem by Alexander Sayre. 32 pp., 8vo, original printed wrappers. Stewart and Ebersold, Seattle, 1883. $25.00

No other copy seems to be reported. Twenty pages of the above are devoted to a description of the Puget Sound Country and the last 12 pages contains a Territoral Directory.

588 SCAMMON, CHARLES MELVILLE. The Marine Animals of the Northwestern Coast of North America, described and illustrated; together with an Account of the Northwestern Whale-Fishery. With numerous full-page plates and text illustrations. 319 pp., plates, folio, half mor. San Francisco: Carmony, 1874. $40.00

An elaborate work of much importance. From 1852 onward, Capt. Scammon made an extended study of the mammals of the northwest coast, especially the whales, a department in which but little definite knowledge existed. He gives a full account of their habits.

589 SCHAEFFER, L. M. Sketches of Travels in South America, Mexico and California. 12mo, cloth. N. Y., 1860. $3.00

The author went to California in 1849 by way of the Horn.

590 SCHAFER, JOSEPH. History of the Pacific Northwest. 312 pp., illus., map. 12mo, cloth. N. Y., 1905. $3.00

591 SCHAFER, JOSEPH. Prince Lucien Campbell. 216 pp., 8vo, cloth. Eugene, Ore., 1929. $3.00

Campbell was one time President of the University of Washington.

592 SCHAFER, JOSEPH. Acquisition of Oregon Territory. Part 1, Discovery and Exploration. 31 pp. University of Oregon Bulletin, New Series, V. 6, No. 3. 8vo, original wrappers. Eugene, Ore., 1908. $3.00

593 SCHAFER, JOSEPH. Jesse Applegate. Pioneer and Builder. 13 pp., port. 8vo, original wrappers. Eugene, Ore., 1912. $17.50

One of 50 copies published by the author.

594 SCHERER, JAMES A. B. The First Forty-Niner and the Story of the Golden Tea-Cady. 127 pp., illus., 12mo, cloth. N. Y., 1925. $2.75

Life of Sutter and the discovery of gold.

595 SCHMOE, F. W. Our Greatest Mountain. A Handbook for Mount Ranier National Park. 366 pp., illus., 12mo, cloth. N. Y., 1925. $4.00

The author was a naturalist in the National Park Service.

595a SCHOFIELD, JOHN M. Forty Years in the Army. 577 pp., 8vo, cloth. N. Y., 1897. $4.50

Gen. Schofield commanded in the Pacific Northwest.

595b SCHOFIELD, ETHELBERT O. S., and GOSNELL, R. E. A History of British Columbia. Part one, being a Survey of Events from the earliest times down to the Union of the Crown Colony of British Columbia with the Dominion of Canada. By E. O. S. Schofield. Part two, being a History, mainly Political and Economic, of the Province since Confederation, up to the Present Time. By R. E. Gosnell. 210, 226 pp., front., 390 ports. 8vo, half calf. British Columbia Historical Association. $25.00

No. 263 of the fine limited edition of 350 copies published and sold at $150.00. In the plates, printing and binding it is perhaps the most magnificent book ever produced in the Pacific Northwest.

596 SCHOLEFIELD, ETHELBERT O. S., and HOWAY, F. W. British Columbia from the Earliest Times to the Present. Frontis., illus., ports., maps. 4 vols., half calf. Vancouver: Clarke, 1914. $17.50

Volumes 1-2 historical, vols. 3-4 biographical, with list of authorities, preface, pp. 15-46.

597 SCHOOLCRAFT, HENRY R. Narrative of an Expedition through the Upper Mississippi to Itasca Lake, the actual source of this River . . . in 1832. Maps. 8vo, cloth. N. Y., 1834. $7.50

598 SCHOOLCRAFT, HENRY R. Algic Researches. Comprising Inquiries Respecting the Mental Characteristics of the North American Indians. First Series, Indian Tales and Legends. 2 vols., 12mo, cloth. N. Y., 1839. $17.50

599 SCHOOLCRAFT, HENRY R. Inquiry respecting the History, Present Condition and Further Prospects of the Indian Tribes of the U. S. 4to, sewn. Phila.: Lippincott, 1851. $4.50

600 SCHOOLCRAFT, HENRY R. Historical and Statistical Information respecting the History, Condition and Prospects of the Indian Tribes of the U. S.; Collected and Prepared under the Direction of the Bureau of Indian Affairs . . . Over 300 plates, many in color, by Capt. S. Eastman and others. 6 vols., 4to, cloth (some slightly faded). Phila., 1853-57. $125.00

An interesting set of this great work, as the various volumes are presentation copies signed by Eastman, Schoolcraft, and Charles Lanman.

601 SCHOOLCRAFT, HENRY R. The Myth of Hiawatha and other Oral Legends, Mythologic and Allegoric, of the North American Indians. 12mo, cloth. Phila., 1856. $7.50

602 SCHOOLING, SIR WILLIAM (K.B.E.) The Governor and Company of Adventurers of England Trading into Hudson's Bay during Two Hundred and Fifty Years, 1670-1920. Colored portrait of Prince Rupert, first Governor, facsimile of the first sheet of the original charter granted by Charles II, and other maps and plates. 4to, original wrappers. London, 1920. $7.50

This work was prepared by the Hudson's Bay Co. for private distribution.

603 SCHOONOVER, T. J. The Life and Times of Gen. John Sutter. Plates. 136 pp., 12mo, cloth. Sacramento, 1895. $5.00

Original Edition. "The most complete biography of this noted Californian."—Cowan p. 572.

604 SCHOULER (DR.) JOHN. Observations on the Indigenous Tribes of the Northwest Coast of America, [Journal of the Royal Geographical Society of London, Vol. 2, pp. 215-251.] 8vo, cloth. London, 1840. $7.50

Smith 3442. Includes vocabulary of a number of tribes living on the Columbia River.

605 SCHOULER (DR.) JOHN. On the Indian Tribes of the Northwest Coast of America. [Journal of the Ethnological Society of London, Vol. 1, pp. 228-252.] 8vo, cloth. London, 1848. $12.50

Dr. Schouler arrived at the Columbia River in the Hudson's Bay Co. Brig "William and Mary," April 7, 1825, accompanied by David Douglas, the eminent botanist.

606 SCHRAEDER, FRANK C., and BROOKS, ALFRED. Preliminary Report on the Cape Nome Gold Region, Alaska. 56 pp., folding maps, illus. 8vo, original wrappers. Sen. Doc. 256, 56th Cong., 1st Sess. Washington, 1900. $3.50

Wick. 18228.

607 SCHULTZ, JAMES WILLIARD. With the Indians in the Rockies. ix-228 pp., 12mo, cloth. N. Y., 1912. $3.00

608 SCHULTZ, JAMES WILLIARD. Sinopah, the Indian Boy. 155 pp., 12mo, cloth. Boston (1913). $3.00

609 SCHULTZ, JAMES WILLIARD. Blackfoot Tales of Glacier National Park. 12mo, cloth. Boston, 1916. $3.00

610 SCHULTZ, JAMES WILLIARD. Bird Woman (Sacajawea), the Guide of Lewis and Clark. Her own Story now given to the World. 235 pp., frontis., 3 plates. 12mo, cloth. Boston, (1918). $3.00

610a [SEATTLE GENERAL STRIKE.] The Colonel and His Friends. A Suppressed Play. By Hulet M. Wells. 32 pp., 8vo, original wrappers. [Seattle, 1919.] $7.50

A scarce work on the economic situation in Seattle during the General Strike, in which Col. Blethen, publisher of the Seattle Times, is severely criticised.

611 SCHULTZ, JAMES WILLIARD. Rising Wolf, the White Blackfoot. Hugh Monroe's Story of his first year on the Plains. 255 pp., 12mo, cloth. N. Y., 1919. $3.00

612 SCHULTZ, JAMES WILLIARD. Friends of my Life as an Indian 229 pp., illus., 12mo, cloth. Boston, 1923. $3.00

In the 1880's the author joined the Piegan Tribe of the Blackfeet Confederacy, studied their language, manners and customs, and fought with them in their wars against the Sioux.

613 SCHURZ, CARL. The Reminiscences of. Illus. 3 vols., 8vo, cloth. N. Y., 1907-8. $10.00

614 SCHWATKA, FREDERICK. Report of a Military Reconnaissance made in Alaska in 1883 . . . With Illustrations and Maps of the route traversed (20 folding maps). 8vo, cloth. Washington, 1885. $3.50

Wick. 7767. The author went from Chilkoot Sound to Ft. Selkirk.

615 SCHWATKA, FREDERICK. Nimrod of the North; or, Hunting and Fishing Adventures in the Arctic Regions. 198 pp., illus. 4to, colored printed boards. Boston, c. 1885. $5.00

Adventures in Alaska and the region north of Hudson's Bay. Smith 3451.

616 SCHWATKA, FREDERICK. Along Alaska's Great River; a popular Account of the Travels of the Alaska Exploring Expedition of 1883, along the great Yukon River, from its source to its mouth, in the British Northwest Territory; and the Territory of Alaska. Illus., maps. 4to, cloth. Chicago, 1898. $2.50

617 SCHWATKA, FREDERICK. Summer in Alaska. A Popular Account of the Travels of an Alaskan Exploring Expedition along the great Yukon River, from its Source to its Mouth, in the British Northwest Territory, and in the Territory of Alaska. 418 pp., illus., 8vo, cloth. St. Louis: Henry, 1892. $2.50

618 SCIDMORE, E. RUHAMAH. Alaska, its Southern Coast and the Sitka Archipelago. 33 pp., illus., map., 12mo, cloth. Boston: Lathrop (1885). $3.75

Ft. Wrangel, Chilkoot, Juneau, missions, etc.

619 SCOTT, LESLIE M. History of the Oregon Country. By Harvey W. Scott, Forty Years Editor of the Morning Oregonian. 6 vols., 8vo, cloth. Cambridge, 1924. $45.00

620 SCULL, E. MARSHALL. Hunting in the Arctic and Alaska. 304 pp., maps and plates. 8vo, cloth. London, 1915. $7.50

Smith 3466.

621 [SEATTLE.] The Alaska-Yukon Pacific Exposition. Report of the Commission of the State of Washington. 157 pp., illus. 8vo, original wrappers. Seattle (1910). $2.50

Smith 3470. Contains many fine illustrations.

622 [SEATTLE.] Gold Horizon. The Life Story of Manson F. Backus, Forty-Five Years a Banker in the Pacific Northwest. 222 pp., front., ports. 8vo, cloth. Seattle, 1937. $4.50

RARE SEATTLE DIRECTORY OF 1882

623 [SEATTLE.] Residence and Business Directory of the City of Seattle for the Year 1882. Comprising a Brief Sketch of the Settlement, Development and Present Business of the City. 88-x pp., 8vo. Elliott and Sweet, (Seattle, 1882). $30.00

The rarest of the early directories of Seattle. Only two copies have been located of the K. C. Ward Directory of 1876, and 3 copies of the Choir's Pioneer Directory of 1878. We can locate no other copy of the Elliott and Sweet Directory of 1882, as noted above. See Smih 555 and 685-6.

624 [SEATTLE.] Seattle Blue Book; a Fashionable Residential Address Directory and Ladies' Visiting and Shopping Guide. 12mo, mor. Seattle, 1907 and 1912. $4.00

Smih 3566-67.

625 [SEATTLE.] Semi-Centennial Celebration of the founding of Seattle, under Auspices of the Chamber of Commerce, July 30, 1903. 61 pp., port., 12mo, original wrappers. Seattle: Lowman (1903). $4.50

Smith 3505.

626 [SEATTLE.] Seattle Chamber of Commerce. Alaska, "Our Frontier Wonderland." 93 pp., illus., folding map. 8vo, original wrappers. Seattle (1913). $3.00

627 [SEATTLE.] Chamber of Commerce Report, 1891. 8vo . Seattle, 1891. $3.00

Smith 3492.

628 [SEATTLE.] Chamber of Commerce. A Few Facts about Seattle. 32 pp., illus. 8vo, original wrappers. Seattle: Jackson, 1898. $2.00

Smith 3487.

629 [SEATTLE.] Chamber of Commerce Publications, 1886-1901. 24 various reports compiled by the late Thomas W. Prosch and bound in one volume. 14 of these publications are earlier than any mentioned in Smith's Checklist. 8vo, half mor. Seattle, 1886-1901. $35.00

630 [SEATTLE.] Freeholder's Charter of the City of Seattle. Adopted Oct. 1, 1890, with Amendments, March 8, 1892. 95-36 pp. 8vo, sheep. Seattle, 1892. $5.00

Smith 3510.

631 [SEATTLE.] Seattle Illustrated. Containing a careful Compilation and Review of the Resources, Terminal Advantages, Climate and General Industries of the "Queen City." . . . 76 pp., front., illus. 4to. Chicago, 1890. $4.50

Smith 3501.

632 [SEATTLE.] Seattle Ladies' Relief Society. The By-Laws. 8 pp., 8vo, original wrappers. (Seattle), 1894. $2.50

633 [SEATTLE.] Seattle Public Library. Annual Reports, as follows: 13th Annual Report, 1903, 19 pp.; 14th annual report, 1904, 31 pp.; 15th annual report, 1905, 31 pp.; 16th annual report, 1906, 31 pp.; 17th annual report, 1907, 32 pp.; 18th annual report, 1908, 34 pp.; 19th annual report, 1909, 45 pp.; 20th annual report, 1910, 45 pp.; 21st annual report, 1911, 35 pp.; 22nd annual report, 1912, 38 pp.; 23rd annual report, 1913, 28 pp. Together with an Account of the opening of the Seattle Library, 1906. 32 pp. All contained in one ovlume 8vo, half mor. Seattle, 1903-1913. $17.50

634 [SEATTLE.] Opening of the Seattle Library Building, Dec. 19, 1906. 12mo, original wrappers. Seattle, 1907. $2.50

635 [SEATTLE.] In Memoriam John Harte McGraw. 84 pp., front. 8vo, original wrappers. Seattle: Chamber of Commerce, 1911. $2.00

Smith 3488.

AN EARLY MAP OF SEATTLE, WASHINGTON TERRITORY

636 [SEATTLE.] City of Seattle, Washington Territory. Published by A. Mackintosh, Searcher of Records in Real Estate. Map, size 9x9½ in. Seattle, N.d. (early). $20.00

Can locate no other copy of this map. The map folds and the creases have been reinforced.

637. [SEATTLE.] Municipal Plans Commission. Plan of Seattle: Report of the Municipal Plan Commission, submitting report of Virgil G. Bogue, Engineer, 1911. 235 pp., illus., 31 plates, 20 maps. Folio. Seattle: Ivy, 1911. $4.50

Smith 3536.

638 [SEATTLE.] Municipal Reports. Seattle Municipal Reports for the Fiscal Year ending Dec. 31, 1891, published by order of the Mapor and City Council. 354 pp., 2 folding maps attached to covers. 8vo, original sheep. Seattle: Koch, 1892. $7.50

Smith 3537.

639 ——. The Same. 454 pp., 13 plates. 8vo, sheep. Seattle: Koch, 1893. $7.50

Smith 3538.

640 [SEATTLE.] Children's Orthopedic Hospital. 4th annual report, Feb., 1911 and 13th annual report, Feb., 1920. 2 vols., 8vo, wrappers. Seattle, 1911-1920. $3.00

Smith 3523.

641 [SEATTLE.] Seattle, the Puget Sound Country, and Western Washington, 1901. 36 pp., illus. 8vo, original wrappers. Seattle (1901). $3.50

Smith 3504.

642 [SEATTLE.] The Queen City of Puget Sound, the Industrial Center of the Pacific Northwest. 133 pp., illus. 12mo, original wrappers. Seattle, N.d. $2.50

EARLY ORDINANCES OF THE CITY OF SEATTLE

643 [SEATTLE.] Ordinances of the City of Seattle, published by Order of the Common Council. Compiled by Hall and Osborne. Pp. 176-vi. 8vo, original printed wrappers. Hanford: Seattle, 1880. $12.50

Smith 3540. This publication of the early laws of the city of Seattle is very rare. Smith cites only the copy at Washington University.

644 [SEATTLE.] Revised Ordinances of the City of Seattle, together with the Freeholders' Charter adopted 1890, amended 1892 . . . compiled by John W. Pratt. 843 pp., 8vo, sheep. Seattle: Sunset Pub. Co., 1893. $6.00

Smith 3545.

645 ——. The Same for 1884. 8vo, sheep. Seattle, 1884. $6.00

646 [SEATTLE.] Seattle, King County, Washington Territory, Statistical and Descriptive Report of the Seattle Chamber of Commerce, to the Governor of Washington Territory. 16 pp., illus., 12mo, original wrappers. Seattle: Hanford, 1884. $7.50

Smith 3500 cites but one copy at Washington University.

647 [SEATTLE.] Seattle and King County, Washington. 40 pp., 8vo, original wrappers. Chamber of Commerce: Seattle (1904). $2.00

Smith 3499.

648 [SEATTLE.] The Seattle Spirit. A Chronological History of Seattle, U. S. A., with Chronological Illustrations. By C. A. Rohrabacher. 404 pp., illus. 4to, mor. Seattle (1907). $15.00

Smith 3344 cites only the copy at Seattle.

649 [SEATTLE.] Seattle Memories. By Edith Sanderson Redfield. 78 pp., illus. 8vo, cloth. Boston (1930). $4.50

THE FIRST BOOK PRINTED IN SEATTLE

650 [SEATTLE.] Seattle and Walla Walla Railroad and Transportation Company. Report of the Chief Engineer to the Trustees and Stockholders, November, 1874. 47 pp., folding map. 8vo, original printed wrappers. Seattle Intelligencer Book and Job Printing Office, Seattle, 1874. $75.00

Smith 3562 locates only the copy at the University of Washington. Aside from its bibliographical interest as undoubtedly the first book printed in Seattle, this work takes the lead in the early propagandising of the "Seattle Spirit" which in time was to make Seattle the great city of the Northwest.

651 [SEATTLE.] The Romance of Second Avenue. By J. Willis Sayre. 16 pp., 8vo, original printed wrappers. N.p., N.d. (Seattle). $3.00

652 [SEATTLE.] The Sunset Library. No. 1, October, 1893. 8vo. Seattle, 1893. $7.50

Scarce. Bisides local history, this work gives an account of the Seattle Fire.

653 [SEATTLE.] Watt, Roberta Frye. The Story of Seattle. 387 pp., illus., 12mo, cloth. Seattle, 1931. $5.00

Privately Printed. The author is a native of Seattle, a grand-daughter of A. A. Denny, one of the founders of the city.

654 [SEATTLE GENERAL STRIKE.] Wilson and the Issues of Today. A Socialistic Revision of George Creel's Famous Book. By Hulet M. Wells. 125 pp., 8vo, original wrappers. Seattle, 1918. $3.00

Contains some account of economic affairs of Seattle.

655 SECRETAN, JAMES H. E. To the Yukon and Back. A Journey down the Yukan from its Source to its Mouth . . . With Hints to Intending Prospectors. xii-260 pp., port., illus. 8vo, cloth. London: Hurst, 1899. $5.00

Wick. 4409. Smith 3594.

656 SECRETAN, JAMES H. E. Out West. 12mo, cloth. Illus. Ottawa, 1910. $5.00

Indians, Homesteaders, Sheriffs and Highwaymen, British Columbia, Mounties, Prospectors, Explorers, Canadian Pacific Railway.

657 SECRETAN, JAMES H. E. Canada's Great Highway: From the First Stake to the Last Spike. 16 illus. 12mo, cloth. London (1924). $5.00

The author was intimately associated wtih the building of the Canadian Pacific **Railway.**

658 SEEMAN, BARTHOLD. Narrative of the voyage of H. M. S. Herald, During the Years 1845-51. Large folding map and colored plates. 2 vols., 8vo, cloth. London, 1853. $17.50

The Herald, of which the author was Naturalist, reached California in September of 1846. Seeman tells of the surprise occasioned the Americans by the entry of the British ship into Yerba Buena Harbor, and of Montgomery's prompt action in notifying them that the Americans had taken possession of the country and were engaged in its defense. He describes the life and conditions in California at this period as viewed by English eyes—a ruinous, dirty country, and about to become the abode of the Mormons; the Missions—slovenly ill-built, and tawdry; the Indians—held in confinement and under lock and key until their spirit was entirely broken. From San Francisco the Herald proceeded to Monterey, thence to San Diego and southward. There the author left the vessel to perform a "journey into the interior of Northwestern Mexico," in the accomplishment of which he penetrated the Sierra Madres, crossed Durango, traversed a good deal of previously unexplored country, finally rejoining his ship at Mazatlan, whence the expedition set out in a northerly direction, exploring the coast as far as Kotzebue Sound and Bering Strait.

659 SEMPLE, ELLEN CHURCHILL. American History and its Geographical Conditions. 466 pp., maps. 12mo, cloth. N. Y. (1903). $3.00

660 SEMPLE, EUGENE. Martial Law at Seattle, Washington Territory. 19 pp., 8vo, original printed wrappers. Vancouver, W. T., March 8, 1886. $15.00

Can locate no other copy. The author was in the Anti-Chinese riots of 1885-86.

661 SENES, JOHN. Universal Geographer; or, Compleat Atlas, containing all the known Countries in the World, laid down from the Latest Observations and Discoveries . . . Folio (London), Sayer, N.d. $12.50

Smith 3597. Contains maps of the Northwest Coast.

662 SERVICE, ROBERT W. Ballads of a Cheechacho, ix-146 pp., illus. 12mo, cloth. Briggs: Toronto, 1909. $4.00

Original edition. Smith 3600.

663 SERVICE, ROBERT W. Trail of '98: A Northland Romance; with illustrations by Maynard Dixon. 514 pp., illus. 12mo, cloth. Briggs: Toronto, 1911. $4.00

Smith 3608.

664 SESSIONS, FRANCIS C. From Yellowstone Park to Alaska. 168 pp., illus. N. Y.: Welsh, Fracker Co., 1890. $4.50

Wick. 6464. Smith 3609. Deals also with Montana, Oregon and Washingotn.

665 SETON-KARR, HEYWOOD W. Bear Hunting in the White Mountains; or, Alaska and British Columbia revisited. 156 pp., illus. 12mo, cloth. London: Chapman, 1891. $5.00

Wick. 4221. Smith 3612.

666 SETON-KARR, H. W. Ten Year's Wild Sports in Foreign Lands, Travels in the Eighties. 333 pp., 8vo, cloth. London, 1889. $7.50

Smith 3614. Deals with Northwest.

667 SETON-KARR, SIR HENRY. My Sporting Holidays. 367 pp., illus. 8vo, cloth. London, 1904. $4.50

The author spent upwards of 30 years traveling, hunting and fishing in the Rocky Mountains and British Columbia. He made his first trip to the Rockies in 1876 and gives a lively account of experiences on the North Platte and in the Bighorn Mountains of Wyoming. He met Buffalo Bill, Texas Jack and other later men of the Plains

668 SEYMOUR, FLORA WARREN. The Story of the Red Man. 421 pp., illus., maps. 8vo, cloth. N. Y., 1929. $2.50

669 [SHAKERS.] Autobiography of a Shaker, and Revelations of the Apocalypse. With an Appendix. By F. W. Evans, Mt. Lebanon, Columbia Co., N. Y. 8vo, cloth. (Mt. Labanon, N. Y.), 1869 $300

670 [SHALER, WILLIAM.] Journal of a Voyage between China and the Northwest Coast of America, made in 1804. Contained ni Vol. 3, pp. 137-175 Annual Register. Phila., 1808. $10.00

This is a scarce periodical. The author claims to be a friend and partner of Capt. Richard Cleveland. He gives an interesting description of the Northwest Coast, the Columbia River, Indian Tribes, etc.; also a description of California and its great value and ease of conquest by the Americans.

671 [SHARON, THOMAS.] Viola; or, Life in the Southwest. By a Western Man. Frontis. 12mo, cloth. 422 pp. Chicago, 1874. $4.50

Gives characteristics of western and Indian life from the author's observations on the Kansas Plains, Texas Ranges, and in California mines.

672 SHARP, DALLA LORE. Where Rolls the Oregon. 251 pp., illus. 12mo, cloth. Boston, 1914. $3.00

Smith 3620.

673 SHAW, D. El Dorado; or, California as seen by a Pioneer, 1865-1900. Port. and plates. 313 pp., 8vo, cloth. Los Angeles, 1900. $5.00

674 SHAW, G. C. The Chinook Jargon and how to use it. A complete and exhaustive Lexicon of the Oldest Trade Language of the American Continent. 66 pp., 8vo, cloth. Seattle, 1909. $2.50

675 SHAW, R. C. Across the Plains in Forty-Nine. Portrait. v-200 pp., 12mo, cloth. Farmland, Ind., 1896. $15.00

Shaw was a member of the "Mount Washington Mining Co." of Boston, numbering 50 men. They set out from Boston on April 17, 1849, and reached Independence 17 days later. After outfitting, the company went via the Platte and the Humboldt Desert, reaching California in September. Braislin 1652. Only 200 copies were printed by the Editor of the Farmland "Enterprise" and by him intended as a premium to new subscribers to his country newspaper. Shaw, at 70, wrote this narrative for the paper.

676 SHAW, WILLIAM T. The China or Denny Pheasant in Oregon, with Notes on the Native Grouse of the Pacific Northwest. 24 pp., 15 plates. Long 12mo, cloth. Phila., 1908. $5.00

Smith 3625.

677 SHAW, WILLIAM. Golden Dreams and Waking Realities; Being the Adventures of a Gold-Seeker in California and the Pacific Islands. 12mo, calf. London, 1851. $17.50

First Edition. Rare. Cowan says: "The keen observations, vividly told by a Britisher, who like most of his class, professed to suffer from his contact with Californian Society. His work is entertaining and his description of the venerable Mission Dolores is particularly edifying, of which he says that 'one wing had a decidedly ecclesiastic appearance . . . the other wing formed a separate establishment, having been converted into a tavern . . .'"

678 SHEA, J. G. Discovery and Exploration of the Mississippi Valley: With the Original Narratives of Marquette, Allouez, Membre, Hennepin, and Anastase Douay. Frontis., map. 8vo, cloth. N. Y., 1852. $4.50

679 SHEA, J. G. Early Voyages Up and Down the Mississippi. Sm. 4to, original boards. Albany, 1861. $6.00

Limited to 500 copies.

680 SHEA, J. G. History of the Catholic Missions among the Indian Tribes of the U. S., 1529-1854. 8vo, cloth. N. Y., 1854. $5.00

681 SHEDD, SOLON. The Clays of the State of Washington. 341 pp., illus., 8vo, cloth. Pullman, Wash., 1910. $4.50

682 SHELDON, CHARLES. The Wilderness of the North Pacific Coast Islands. A Hunter's Experience while searching for Wapiti, Bear, and Caribou on the larger Coast Islands of British Columbia and Alaska. 246 pp., illus., map. 8vo, cloth. N. Y., 1912. $5.00

Smith 3638.

683 SHELDON, CHARLES. The Wilderness of the Upper Yukon: A Hunter's Explorations for Wild Sheep in Sub-Arctic Mountains. 4 maps and many illus. 8vo, cloth. N. Y., 1911. $5.00

Smith 3630.

684 SHELDON, EDMUND P. The Forest Wealth of Oregon. 33 pp., 8vo, original wrappers. Portland, 1904. $3.50

Smith 3632

685 SHELDON, REV. STEWART. Gleanings by the Way, from '36 to '89. In two parts (bound in one and numbered consecutively). 262 pp., 8vo, cloth. Topeka, 1890. $15.00

Part 1 narrates the author's trip to California in 1849 and his adventures and experiences at the diggings and in the settlements. The second half gives a detailed account of Sheldon's pioneer mission life in Colorado, Dakota and Missouri.

686 SHELTON, DON ODELL. Heroes of the Cross in America. 403 pp., illus., 8vo, cloth. N. Y. (1904). $4.50

Smith 3634. Marcus Whitman.

687 SHELVOCKE, CAPT. GEORGE. A Voyage Round the World by way of the Great South Sea; performed in a private Expedition during the War, which broke out with Spain, in the year 1718. 8vo, calf. London, 1757. $25.00

Shelvocke sailed from England along with Clipperton, who, in the Success, was his superior Captain. The two vessels were separated, and widely different account of the expedition is given by William Betagh, a subordinate officer, in his "Voyage Round the World," 1728. Cowan says of this work: "Shelcocke has the fullest accounts of California of any of the old voyagers."

688 SHEPARD, ISABEL S. The Cruise of the U. S. Steamer Rush in Behring Sea. 257 pp., illus., maps. 12mo, cloth. San Francisco: Bancroft, 1889. $6.50

Smith 3636.

689 SHEPHARD, ESTHER. Paul Bunyan. 233 pp., 12mo, cloth. Seattle, 1924. $4.50

690 SHEPHERD, MAJOR W. Prairie Experiences in Handling Cattle and Sheep. Numerous plates made from sketches by the Author. 266 pp., 8vo, cloth. London, 1884. $4.50

691 SHERRARD, ROBERT A. A Narrative of the Wonderful Escape and dreadful Sufferings of Colonel James Paul, after the Defeat of Col. Crawford, when that unfortunate Commander and many of his men were inhumanly burnt at the Stake, and others were Slaughtered by other modes of Torture known only to Savages. 8vo, original wrappers. Cincinnati, 1869. $22.50

Shea 568.

692 SHELTON, WILLIAM. The Story of the Totem Pole. Early Indian Legends as handed down from Generation to Generation are herewith recorded. 80 pp., illus. 8vo, original wrappers. (Everett, Wash.), 1923. $3.50

The author, an Indian, states he has put down legends as told to him by his parents, Uncles and great Uncles. "One of the first things I can remember as a child is the large Potlach House at Skagit Head Bay, built by my uncles."

693 SHELTON, WILLIAM. Indian Totem Legends of the Northwest Coast Country. By one of the Indians. 17 pp., illus. 8vo, original wrappers. N.p., N.d. (Chilocco Indian School, Wash.) $7.50

Smith 3635. The colophon states that this pamphlet was printed in the printing department of the Chilocco Indian School by the students.

694 SHIELDS, GEORGE O. Rustlings in the Rockies: Hunting and Fishing by Mountain and Stream. Illus. 12mo, cloth. Chicago, 1883. $6.50

695 SHIELDS, GEORGE O. The Battle of the Big Hole. A History of General Gibbon's Engagement with Nez Perces Indians in the Big Hole Valley, Montana, August 9, 1877. Port. and plates. 120 pp., 8vo, cloth. Chicago, 1889. $7.50

Contains accounts of all the atrocities perpetrated by Chief Joseph and his followers and of the various treaties entered into, only to be broken off again and again by the hostilities.

696 SHIELDS, GEORGE O. Cruisings in the Cascades. A Narrative of Travel, Exploration, Amateur Photography, Hunting and Fishing, with special chapters on hunting the Grizzly Bear, the Buffalo . . . Illus. 8vo, cloth. Chicago, 1889. $5.00

697 SHIELDS, GEORGE O. The Big Game of North America, its Habits, Habitats, Haunts and Characteristics: How, Where and When to Hunt it. 581 pp., illus. 8vo, half mor., fine. Chicago, 1890. $7.50

698 SHIELDS, GEORGE O. Hunting in the Great West. 306 pp., plates. 12mo, cloth. Chicago, 1890. $5.00

Travels and adventures in Montana and Wyoming.

699 SHIELS, ARCHIE W. Alaska, its early History and what it means to us. An Address delivered . . . at a meeting of the St. Albans Conclave . . . in Seattle, Washington, Nov. 28, 1925. 7 pp., 8vo, original wrappers. N.p. (Bellingham, 1925). $2.00

700 SHIELS, ARCHIE W. Early Voyages to the Pacific. A few Notes on the Days of Iron Men and Wooden Ships. 61 pp., 8vo, cloth. Bellingham, Wash., 1930. $3.50

Limited to 250 copies for private distribution.

701 SHIELS, ARCHIE W. Seward's Ice-Box. A Few Notes on the Development of Alaska, 1867-1932. 413 pp., 8vo, cloth, privately printed. (Bellingham, Wash., 1932). $4.50

702 SHIELS, ARCHIE W. Alaska, its Early History and what it means to Us. 8vo, original wrappers. N.d. $2.50

703 SHINN, CHARLES HOWARD. Mining Camps, a Study in American Frontier Government. xi-316 pp., 8vo, cloth. N. Y., 1885. $7.50

704 SHINN, CHARLES HOWARD. The Story of the Mines as Illustrated by the Great Comstock Lode of Nevada. 272 pp., illus. 12mo, cloth. N. Y., 1896. $7.50

Original Edition of the classic of the great discovery.

705 SHIVELY, J. M. Route and Distances to Oregon and California, with a Description of Watering-Places, Crossings, Dangerous Indians, etc. 8vo, photostatic sheets. Washington: Printed by William Greer, 1846. $10.00

A photostatic facsimile or Wagner-Camp 124.

706 SHUCK, OSCAR TULLY (Editor). Representative and Leading Men of the Pacific, being Original Sketches of their Lives and Characters of the Principal Men of the Pacific States and Territories. 702 pp., 23 ports., plate. 8vo, cloth. San Francisco, 1870. $6.50

Sutter, King,, Edward D. Baker, Stephen J. Field.

707 SHUCK, OSCAR TULLY. California Anthology; or, Striking Thoughts carefully selected from California Writers and Speakers. 471 pp., 8vo, cloth. San Francisco, 1880. $5.00

Supplemental work to the "California Scrap Book."

708 [SIBLEY, HENRY HASTINGS.] The Ancestry, Life and Times of Hon. Henry Hastings Sibley . . . By Nathaniel West. x-596 pp., 8vo, cloth. Saint Paul, 1889. $12.50

Gen. Sibley was born in Detroit in 1811, was employed as a clerk by John Hulbert at Sault Ste. Marie for a few years prior to 1828, then, in 1829, entered the employ of Robert Stuart of the American Fur Co., at Ft. Mackinac. In 1834 he became a partner of the American Fur Co., and was transferred to St. Peters. He became a delegate to Congress from the Territory of Wisconsin in 1849, and was also the first delegate from the Territory of Minnesota, as well as the first Governor of Minnesota. Inserted is a 4-page monograph on Gen. Sibley by Ignatius Donnelly.

709 SILINGSBY, MAURICE. Buckskin Joe; or, the Trapper's Guide. 300 pp., 8vo, original wrappers. N. Y. (1879). $7.50

710 SIMMS, JEPTHA R. The Frontiersmen of New York, showing Customs of the Indians, Vicissitudes of the Pioneer White Settlers, and Border Strife in Two Wars. With a Great Variety of Romantic and Thrilling Stories never before Published. Illus. 2 vols., 8vo, sheep. Albany, 1862-83. $20.00

A valuable collection of facts relating to early settlers and local history of New York, especially the various Indian Wars, the Revolution, War of 1812, etc.

711 SIMPSON, GEORGE. Narrative of a Journey Round the World, during the years 1841-42. Port. and maps. 2 vols., 8vo, original cloth (faded backstrip). London, 1847. $15.00

Wagner-Camp 140. Simpson was the great Governor of HBC., who traveled across Canada from the Atlantic, via the Red River Settlements, Edmonton, Ft. Vancouver, Sitka, thence to California, the Sandwich Islands. His trip was most unique as he practically covered everything, even going home via Siberia, the way of the early Russians.

712 SIMPSON, ALEXANDER. The Life and Travels of Thomas Simpson, the Arctic Discoverer. Map and port. 8vo, original cloth. London, 1845. $10.00

713 SIMPSON, SIR GEORGE. An Overland Journey Round the World during the years 1841-42. 230 pp. Phila., 1847. $4.00

Smith 3656.

714 SIMPSON, THOMAS. Narrative of the Discoveries on the North Coast of America effected by the Officers of the Hudson's Bay Co., during 1836-39. Maps. 8vo, original cloth. London, 1843. $15.00

Simpson traveled from the Red River Colony to Ft. Chipewyan, thence to the Polar Sea.

715 SINCLAIR, BERTRAND W. North of Fifty-Three. 345 pp., 12mo, cloth. Boston, 1914. $2.50

716 SIRINGO, CHAS. A. A Texas Cow Boy; or, Fifteen Years on the Hurricane Deck of a Spanish Pony. Taken from real life. Illus. 12mo, pictorial wrappers. Chicago, N.d. (1886). **$7.50**

717 SIRINGO, CHAS. A. A Cowboy Detective. 519 pp., 8vo, cloth. N. Y., 1912. $3.00

718 SIRINGO, CHAS. A. A Lone Star Cowboy. Being Fifty Years Experience in the Saddle as Cowboy, Detective, and New Mexico Ranger, on every Cow Trail in the Wooly Old West. Also the Doings of some "Bad" Cowboys, such as "Billy the Kid," Wess Harding and "Kid Curry." Illus., 291 pp., 12mo, cloth. Santa Fe, N. M., 1919. $4.00

719 SIRINGO, CHAS. A. History of Billy the Kid. 142 pp., 12mo, original wrappers. Santa Fe, 1920. $4.50

720 [SITKA TIMES, THE.] First Published on September 19, 1868, being written out in longhand by the Editor, as there was no printing press available. Nine photostatic copies of the Original Issues. Sitka, 1868. $7.50

721 SITGREAVES, CAPT. L. Report of an Expedition down the Zuni and Colorado Rivers. 198 pp., plates and maps. 8vo, cloth. Washington, 1853. $6.50

722 SKINNER, CONSTANCE L. Adventurers of Oregon. A Chronicle of the Fur Trade. 290 pp., illus. 8vo, cloth. New Haven, 1920. $2.50

723 SLOAN, WILLIAM NICCOLLS. Spiritual Conquest along the Rockies. viii-242 pp., 8vo, cloth. Denver, 1913. $4.75

724 SMALL, F. B. The Autobiography of a Pioneer; being an Account of the Personal Experiences of the Author on the plains between the Missouri and the Rockies from 1867 onward. Port. and crude plates. 106 pp., 8vo, wrappers. Seattle, 1916. $10.00

A pioneer narrative with all its original flavor intact and un-"edited." The author writes his reminiscences as he lived them. Here and there a word is misspelled and occasionally the grammar is somewhat hazy, but the book is obviously true. Among its contents are: Crossing the Plains; Among the Indians; In Pursuit of Wild Horses; Along the Cattle Trails; Living among Rattlers and Indians on the Cheyenne Plains, etc.,

725 [SMITH, JEDEDIAH.] The Travels of Jedediah Smith. A Documentary Outline, including the Journal of the Great American Pathfinder. Edited by Maurice Sullivan. 195 pp., 8vo, boards. Santa Anna, 1934. $10.00

726 ——. The Same. 8vo, cloth. N. Y., 1936. $3.50

727 SMITH, WALLACE. Oregon Sketches. 247 pp., illus. N. Y., 1925. $3.50

728 SMET, PIERRE JEAN DE. Missions de l'Oregon et Voyages dans les Montagnes Rocheuses en 1845 et 1846: ouvrage traduit de l'Anglais par M. Bourlez. 408 pp., 13 plates. 8vo. Par Poussielque-Rusand, 1848. $17.50

Smith 3691 states this is the second French edition in a different translation of his Oregon Missions. He cites only two copies.

729 SMET, PIERRE J. DE. Collection de Precis Historiques. By E. Terwecoren. 8vo, half calf. Paris, 1853. $15.00

Contains six letters by De Smet to the author while De Smet was on his trip over the Plains with the Dragoons.

730 SMET, PIERRE J. DE. Western Missions and Missionaries. A Series of Letters. Port. 532 pp., 12mo, cloth. N. Y., 1863. $17.50

Original Edition in English, and a Signed Presentation Copy.

731 SMET, PIERRE J. DE. New Indian Sketches (with separately titled catechism). The Short Indian Catechism in use among the Flatheads, Kalispels, Pends d'Oreilles, and other Rocky Mountain Indians. Plates. 175 pp., 12mo, cloth. N. Y., 1870. $6.50

This is an account of De Smet's journey in 1858, as Chaplain with the Dragoons against the Mormons and Indians, and of his later travels in the Montana country. Contains the interesting correspondence between Gen. Harney and De Smet written in 1859.

732 SMET, PIERRE J. DE. New Indian Sketches. 174 pp., 12mo, cloth. N. Y., 1870. $4.50

733 SMET, (PIERRE J. DE). Lettres Choisies du Reverend Pere Pierre Jean De Smet missionnaire aux Etats Unis d'Amerique, 1849-1857. Bruxelles, 1875. Portrait. Lettres Choisies, Second Series, 1855-1861. Bruxelles, 1876. Lettres Choisies, Third Series, 1860-1867. Bruxelles, 1877. Lettres Choisies, Fourth Series, Bruxelles, 1878. 6 vols., 8vo, uniformly bound in half calf extra, g. t. $37.50

These most important volumes describe the author's labors and adventures among the North American Indians; their manners, customs, games, warfare, legends, and traditions, all from his personal observations made during many thousand miles of travel in the far North-West, West, and South-West of the North American continent. Complete sets are scarce.

734 SMYTHE, WILLIAM ELLSWORTH. History of San Diego, 1542-1908. An Account of the Rise and Progress of the Pioneer Settlement on the Pacific Coast of the United States. 736 pp., 8vo, cloth. San Diego, 1908. $10.00

735 SNELLING, W. J. The Last of the Mandans. Contained in the Knickerbocker Magazine, May, 1840. 8vo, cloth. N. Y., 1840. $3.00

736 SOMERSET, H. SOMERS. Land of the Muskeg, with a Preface by A. Hungerforce Pollen. 248 pp., illus., 4 maps. 8vo, cloth. London, 1895. $7.50

Smith 3751.

737 SOULE, FRANK; GIHON, J. H., and NISBET, JAMES. The Annals of San Francisco, containing a Summary of the History . . . and Present Condition of California, and a Complete History of the Important Events Connected with its Great City . . . Maps, plates and illus. 8vo, cloth. N. Y., 1855. $10.00

738 SORENSON, ALFRED. Early History of Omaha; or, Walks and Talks among the Old Settlers. Illus., 226 pp. 8vo, cloth. Omaha, 1876. $5.00

Original Edition. Accounts of the Indians, early pioneers and Mormons, Indian troubles of 1864, steamboating and stage coach, etc.

739 SOUTHESK, EARL OF. Saskatchewan and the Rocky Mountains: a Diary and Narrative of Travel, Sport and Adventure during a Journey through the Hudson's Bay Company's Territories in 1859-1860. Maps and plates. 448 pp., 8vo, cloth, uncut. Edinburgh, 1874. $17.50

This work is commonly cited with the 1875 date. We have been unable to locate another copy bearing the 1874 date as cited above. The author, starting from St. Paul, Minn., went northward along the Red River to Ft. Garry in Manitoba, thence westward to the Rocky Mountains.

740 ——. The Same. Half calf. Edinburgh, 1875. $7.50

741 [SOUTHWEST.] Dunn, J. P., Jr. Massacres of the Mountains. A History of the Indian Wars of the Far West. Illus. 8vo, lcoth. N. Y., 1886. $12.50

Fine bright copy of the Original Edition.

742 [SOUTHWEST.] Indian Stories of the Southwest. By Elizabeth Judson Roberts. 258 pp., illus. 8vo, cloth. San Francisco, 1917. $3.50

743 SPALDING, REV. H. H. Matthewnim Taaiskt. The Gospel according to Mathew. Translated into the Nez Perce by Rev. H. H. Spalding. 130 pp., 12mo, calf. N. Y., 1871. $25.00

The above work compiled by Rev. Spalding, who went overland with Marcus Whitman to Oregon in 1836, is very scarce.

744 SPEARMAN, ARTHUR L. Out of the Northland. The Story of an Eskimo Jesuit. 46 pp., illus. 8vo, original wrappers. Jesuit Mission Press, N. Y., 1931. $2.00

745 [SPEED, JOHN.] A Prospect of the Most Famous Parts of the World. [Twenty maps.] London: Printed by M. F. for William Humble, 1646. Second title: England, Wales, Scotland and Ireland Described. By John Speed. [Sixty-four maps] [London], 1627. Thick oblong 12mo, sheep, hinges split, title-pagt loose, flyleaf and portrait lacking, leaf torn in text of Asia. $20.00

Rare, early volume with descriptive text and map of America. Sabin 89228, note. Second edition. Speed, the famous cartographer, renders a naive account of Americans: "yet nothing almost common to the whole but Barbarisme of manners, Idolatry in Religion, and sottish ignorance, such as hardly distinguisheth them from brutes: . . . yet what God was they knew no more than instinct of nature gave them, only a confused thought they had of some place or other (God knows where) behinde some hill . . . The rest of their Customes are answerable to their Religion, beastly. They goe naked, and are very lustful people without distinction of sexe . . ."

746 SPLAWN, ANDREW JACKSON. Ka-mi-akin. The Last Hero of the Yakimas. Profusely illus. 442 pp., 8vo, cloth. (Portland, 1917). $17.50

Privately printed in a small edition. Reminiscences of McClellan's Expedition through the Yakima Country in 1853; the Council of Walla Walla; the Spokane Campaign; Narrative of the discovery of the Boise Basin Gold Mines; a drive into Montana; Gold Hunting, Cow Punching, etc. The book is the recollections of a lifetime of upwards of sixty years on the border, crowded with out-of-the-way material relating to early Indian affairs and pioneer days in the Northwest.

747 [SPOKANE, WASH.] Spokane and the Spokane Country, Pictorial and Biographical. 2 vols., 8vo (fine plates), half mor. Chicago: Clarke, 1912. $17.50

Smith 3802. The de lux supplement.

748 [SPOKANE, WASH.] Spokane District Directory, comprising a Complete and Accurate Business Guide of 35 Cities and Towns in Eastern Washington and Northern Idaho. . . . Vol. 1, 1890. 8vo, cloth. Spokane Falls, Wash., 1890. $15.00

Smith 3801.

749 [SPOKANE, PORTLAND AND SEATTLE R. R.] Along the Columbia River to the Sea. 42 pp., illus. 8vo, original wrappers. N.p., N.d. (Spokane). $3.00

Smith 3806.

750 [SPOKANE, PORTLAND AND SEATTLE R. R.] Oregon and Washington. 48 pp., illus., map. 8vo, original wrappers. N.p., N.d. $3.00

Smith 3807.

751 SPRAGUE, WILLIAM C. The Boy Pathfinder. A Story of the Oregon Trail. 316 pp., 8vo, cloth. Boston (1905). $2.50

752 SPROAT, GILBERT MALCOLM. Scenes and Studies of Savage Life. Tinted lithos., xii-317 pp., 12mo, cloth. London, 1868. $22.50

The author headed an expedition to the western coast of Vancouver Island in 1860. Smith 3813.

753 SPROAT, GILBERT MALCOLM. British Columbia; Information for Emigrants issued by the Agent-General for the Province. 96 pp., illus., folding map. 8vo, original wrappers. London (Sproat), preface, 1873. $22.50

One of the most authoritative works on the Province by the author of "Scenes and Studies of Savage Life."

754 SPROAT, GILBERT MALCOLM. Description of the Kootenay District, British Columbia. 30 pp., 8vo, original wrappers. Victoria, 1881. $10.00

755 STANLEY (EDWIN J.). Rambles in Wonderland; or, Up the Yellowstone. Containing an Account of the recently explored region; Sketches of Indian Customs; and Incidents of Camp-life in the mountains. With the Narrative of the Capture and Sufferings of a party of tourists who fell into the hands of the Nez Perces in 1877. Folding map and plates. 179 pp., 12mo, cloth. N. Y., 1878. $7.50

Original edition. The author records a captivity. The captives, known as the Radersburg Party, were intercepted by the savages near the Fire Hole River. The men were killed and the women carried into captivity. Stanley's account of the bloody affair includes the personal narratives of the survivors.

756 STACEY, JAMES B. Sage of Waha; the Mountain Gem Humorist on Land and on Sea. By Uncle Jim . . . 205 pp., Appendix. 8vo, original wrappers. Portland, 1902. $4.50

Smith 3819. Western stories.

757 STAEHLIN, J. VON. An Account of the New Northern Archipelago lately discovered by the Russians in the Seas of Kamschatka and Anadir. Map. 8vo, half calf. London, 1774. $25.00

Smith 3820. Wick. 52824. Important for the history of discoveries off the Northwest Coast.

758 STEELE, JAMES W. Frontier Army Sketches. 329 pp., 12mo, cloth. Chicago, 1883. $7.50

759 STENNETT, W. H. The North and West Illustrated. 120 pp., 8vo, sewn. Chicago (1875). $3.75

760 STEVENS, ALEXANDER H. Admission of Oregon: Speech of Hon. Alexander H. Stevens of Georgia, in the House of Representatives, Feb. 12, 1859. 8 pp., 8vo. (Washington, 1859). $3.50

Smith, 3836.

761 (STEPHENS, LOUIS G.). Letters from an Oregon Ranch. By "Katherine." 212 pp., illus. 8vo, cloth. Chicago: McClurg, 1905. $5.00

762 STEPHENS, L. D. Life Sketches of a Jayhawker of '49. The Actual Experience of a Pioneer told by Himself in his own way. 68 pp., 8vo, original wrappers. Privately Printed (San Jose), 1916. $10.00

Smith 3839.

The author was a member of Manly's "Death Valley" party who crossed the plains by the southern route then known as the "Route to Hell." Besides his record of harrowing experiences in Death Valley, the author gives much concerning the life and customs of the pioneers, the Vigilantes, life on the Comstock, trip to Alaska and British Columbia, Fraser River Gold Rush, Indians, etc.

763 STEPHENSON, ROBERT LOUIS. Across the Plains. With Other Memories and Essays. 317 pp., 8vo, cloth. N. Y., 1892. $2.50

764 STEPHENS, HELEN NORTH. Memorial Biography of Adele M. Field. 367 pp., 8vo, cloth. Seattle (1918). $3.75

Smith 3845.

765 STEVENS, GOV. ISAAC INGALLS. Campaign on the Rio Grande and of Mexico, with Notices of the Recent Work of Major Ripley. By Brevet-Major Isaac I. Stevens, U.S.A. 8vo, cloth. N. Y., 1851. $12.50

766 STEVENS, GOV. ISAAC INGALLS. Letter from the Secretary of State to the Chairman of the Committee on Foreign Relations communicating the Report of Governor Stevens, of Washington Territory, to the Department of State, of June 21, 1854, relative to the property of the Hudson's Bay and Puget's Sound Company in that Territory. 33rd Cong., 2nd Sess., Sen. Ex. Doc. 37. 8vo, sewn. Washington, 1855. $12.50

767 [STEVENS, GOV. ISAAC INGALLS.] Proceedings of a Meeting of the Bar, 3rd Judicial District, Washington Territory, on the Arrest of the Hon. Edward Lander, Chief Justice of the District Court, by an Armed Force under Orders of Governor Isaac I. Stevens. Together with the Proceedings of a Mass Meeting of the Citizens of Pierce County, W. T. 8 pp., 8vo, sewn. Steilacoom, May 7, 1856.

A very rare and important local Indian War document. Can locate but one other copy.

767A STEVENS, GOV. ISAAC INGALLS. A Brief Notice of the Present Outrage Committed by Isaac I. Stevens, Governor of Washington Territory. The Suspension of the Writ of Habeas Corpus, the Breaking Up of the Courts, and the Kidnapping of Judges and Clerks. 16 pp., 8vo, sewn. Olympia, May 17, 1856. $125.00

767B [STEVENS, GOV. ISAAC INGALLS.] Statement of the Oregon and Washington Delegation in relation to the Indian War Claims of Oregon and Washington. 67 pp., 8vo, sewn. (Salem, Ore., 1857?). $30.00

Smith 3826.

ONLY REPORTED COPY OF GOVERNOR STEVENS' BROADSIDE PROCLAMATION DECLARING MARTIAL LAW IN WASHINGTON TERR., 1856

768 STEVENS, GOV. ISAAC INGALLS. Proclamation. Whereas, in the Prosecution of the existing Indian War, it becomes necessary for the reason set forth in the Proclamation of the Governor of the Territory, of the 3rd of April, to Proclaim Martial Law in and through Pierce County, in said Territory; and whereas, the same efforts are being made in the County of Thurston by the issuance of the Writ of Habeas Corpus, to take from the purview of the Military Commission, which is ordered to convene on the 20th Instant, certain persons charged with giving aid to the Enemy; and, whereas, an over-ruling public necessity leaves no alternative but to persist in that Trial in order that the Military Operations be not rendered abortive and the lives of the Citizens needlessly sacrificed. Therefore, I, Isaac I. Stevens, Governor of the Territory of Washington, do by these presents proclaim Martial Law in and throughout the County of Thurston, and do call upon all good Citizens to see that Martial Law is enforced. Given under my Hand and Seal, this 13th Day of May, in the Year of Our Lord, 1856, and the Year of Independence, the Eightieth. Printed Broadside on sheet 8½ by 11½ inches. Washington Territory, 1856. $125.00

769 [STEVENS, GOV. ISAAC INGALLS.] A Statement of the Facts pertaining to the Proclamation of Martial Law over Pierce County, Washington Territory, by Governor Isaac I. Stevens and the Proceedings of the Court Martial in the Attempt to try Citizens for Treason, containing the Governor's Vindication and the Trial and Discharge of these Citizens. 16 pp., 8vo, wrappers. Steilacoom, June 24, 1856. $125.00

Con locate but one other copy.

770 STEVENS, GOV. ISAAC INGALLS. Message of the President of the United States, communicating in compliance with a Resolution of the Senate, of the 1st ultimo, copies of the Papers relating to the Proclamation of Martial Law in Washington Territory. 31 pp., 8vo, sewn. 34th Cong., 1st Sess., Sen. Ex. Doc. 98. Washington, 1856. $10.00

770A STEVENS, GOV. ISAAC INGALLS. Governor Stevens Message. 8vo, sewn. Olympia, W. T., 1856. $25.00

A rare Washington Territory imprint.

770B [STEVENS, GOV. ISAAC INGALLS.] Washington Territory. Fourth Session, 1856-57. Martial Law. Mr. Wiley, of the Judiciary, submitted the following Report upon the subject of the Proclamation and Enforcement of Martial Law in the months of April and May, 1856 by His Excellency the Governor of the Territory . . . Read Jan. 27, 1857. Martial Law, Minority Report, etc. 50 pp., 47-8 pp., 8vo, sewn. [Olympia, W. T., 1856.] $25.00

No other copy reported.

771 STEVENS, GOV. ISAAC INGALLS. Message of the Governor of Washington Territory. Also the Correspondence with the Secretary of War, Major General Wool, the Officers of the Regular Army, and of the Volunteer Service of Washington Territory. 406-16 pp., 8vo. Olympia, W. T.: Furste, 1857. $60.00

This excessively rare work, of which no other perfect copy has been reported, is of the highest importance in relation to the history of the early Indian wars of the Northwest and the controversy between Governor Stevens and the Courts of the Territory. In a Territorial Proclamation Governor Stevens placed certain districts under Martial Law, suspended the Courts, and had certain Judges and Clerks arrested by the military.

772 STEVENS, GOV. ISAAC INGALLS. Vindication of Governor Stevens for Proclaiming and Enforcing Martial Law in Pierce County, Washington Territory. Steilacoom, May 10, 1856. 8vo. $7.50

A photostatic copy of this rare pamphlet.

GOVERNOR STEVENS' "ADDRESS ON THE NORTHWEST," 1858

773 STEVENS, GOV. ISAAC INGALLS. Address on the Northwest, before the American Geographical and Statistical Society, delivered in New York, December 2, 1858, by Isaac I. Stevens. 56 pp., 8vo. Washington: G. S. Gideon, 1858. $30.00

Wagner-Camp 310. The work is the result of Stevens' several expeditions (1853-'7) across the continent in behalf of the government Railroad Surveys, and contains the conclusions drawn from them.

STEVENS' AND McMULLIN'S "WASHINGTON TERRITORY," 1858

774 STEVENS, ISAAC I., and McMULLAN, FAYETTE. A Circular to Emigrants Desirous of Locating in Washington Territory. 21 pp., 8vo, original printed wrappers. Washington: G. S. Gideon, 1858. $42.50

Wagner-Camp 311. One of the earliest works relating to Washington Territory, in which is fully set forth the condition of the country, its resources and opportunities, and the various routes across the country from the Missouri River. The description of Washington Territory was written by Governor McMullin, and is dated Olympia, Nov. 17, 1857.

774A STEVENS, GOV. ISAAC INGALLS. Speech of Hon. Isaac I. Stevens, Delegate from Washington Territory, on the Washington and Oregon War Claims. Delivered in the House of Representatives of the U. S., May 31, 1858. 16 pp., 8vo, sewn. Washington, 1858. $3.50

Photostatic Copy.

774B STEVENS, GOV. ISAAC INGALLS. Speech of . . . on the Indian War Expenses of Washington and Oregon delivered in the House of Representatives, Feb. 21, 1859. 16 pp., 8vo, sewn. Washington: Towers, 1859. $10.00

775 STEVENS, GOV. ISAAC INGALLS. Pacific Railroad, Northern Route. Letter from Hon. Isaac I. Stevens, Delegate from Washington Territory, to the Railroad Convention of Washington and Oregon called to meet at Vancouver, W. T., May 20, 1860. 24 pp., 8vo, sewn. Washington, 1860. $17.50

Smith 3848.

776 STEVENS, GOV. ISAAC INGALLS. Minority Report of Mr. Stevens, Delegate from Oregon, showing the growth upon which the Regular Southern Delegation were entitled to seats in the Convention at the Front Street Theatre, Baltimore. 15 pp., 8vo, sewn. Washington, 1860. $7.50

777 [STEVENS, GOV. ISAAC INGALLS.] The Seventy-Ninth Highlanders, New York Volunteers in the War of the Rebellion, 1661-65. By Todd Williams. 513 pp., illus. 8vo, cloth. Albany, 1886. $5.00

Contains material on Isaac I. Stevens, first Governor of Washington.

778 [STEVENS, GOV. ISAAC INGALLS.] A Brief Sketch of the Life of General Hazard Stevens. 17 pp., 8vo, original wrappers. Boston, 1908. $6.50

Smith 4036 reports one copy. Hazard Stevens was the son of the first governor of Washington Territory.

779 [STEVENS, GOV. ISAAC INGALLS.] The Life of Isaac Ingalls Stevens by his son, Hazard Stevens. With folding and other maps and plates. 2 vols., 480 and 530 pp., 8vo, original cloth. Boston and N. Y., 1900. $5.00

Wagner-Camp 262 (Note). Records Stevens career in the Mexican War, as Governor of Washington Territory, Indian negotiator, explorer, railroad surveyor, and one of the principal figures in the settlement and growth of the northwest.

780 STEVENS, JAMES. Paul Bunyan. 245 pp., illus. 12mo, cloth. N. Y., 1925. $4.50

First Edition. Tales of the Lumber Jacks.

781 STILLITOE, VIOLET E. Pioneer Days in British Columbia. Reminiscences by Violet E. Stillitoe. 32 pp., illus. 8vo, original wrappers. Victoria, N.d. $7.50

A scarce local work by the wife of Bishop Stillitoe.

782 STITZEL, MRS. H. V. What Came of it. Portrait. 320 pp., 12mo, cloth. Portland, Ore., 1898. $3.50

783 STINE, THOMAS OSTENSON. Scandinavians on the Pacific, Puget Sound. 208 pp., illus. 4to, cloth. [Seattle: Denny and Coryell], (1900). $12.50

Smith 3857.

784 STINE, THOMAS OSTENSON. Echoes from Dreamland. 100 pp., 12mo, cloth. Seattle, 1903. $3.50

Stine was a Puget Sound poet who wrote "An Evening on Puget Sound" and "At Poulsbo Bay." See Smith 3856.

785 STOCKTON, JOHN. Report of the Secretary of War, of John Stockton, Superintendent of Mineral Lands on Lake Superior. 29 pp. Sen. Special Sess., 28th Cong., March, 1845. 8vo. Washington, 1845. $7.50

786 STOCKTON, ROBERT F. A Sketch of the Life of Com. Robert F. Stockton; with his Correspondence with the Navy Department respecting his Conquest of California; and Extracts from the defense of Col. J. C. Fremont. Port. 8vo, cloth. N. Y., 1856. $5.00

787 STODDARD, MAJOR AMOS. Sketches, Historical and Descriptive, of Louisiana. viii-488 pp., 8vo, half calf. Phila.: Carey, 1812. $25.00

Wagner-Camp 12 (note). The author took formal possession of the Louisiana Territory in March, 1804, as the U. S. Commissioner. His work is one of the earliest relating to the vast region which extended to the Pacific.

788 STODDARD, CHAS. WARREN. In the Footprints of Padres. Illus. 12mo, original boards, 335 pp. San Francisco, 1902. $4.00

789 STODDARD, WILLIAM O. Little Smoke. A Tale of the Sioux. 295 pp., illus. 12mo, cloth. N. Y., 1902. $3.50

790 STONE, WILLIAM L. Life of Joseph Brant-Thayendanegea: Including the Border Wars of the American Revolution, and Sketches of the Indian Campaigns of Generals Harmar, St. Clair and Wayne, and Other Matters Connected with the Indian Relations of the U. S. and Great Britain, from the Peace of 1783 to the Indian Peace of 1795. Maps and plates. 2 vols., 8vo, cloth. N. Y., 1838. $12.50

Original Edition, fine copy.

791 STONE, WILLIAM L. Life and Times of Sir William Johnson, Bart. Port. 2 vols., 8vo, half calf. Albany, 1865. $12.50

The life covers the greater part of the history of the Six Nations and other tribes about the lakes and the New York frontier.

792 STOVALL, DENNIS H. Suzanne of Kerbyville. 209 pp., 5 plates. 12mo, cloth. N. Y.: Editor Pub. Co., 1904. $4.50

Smith 3866.

793 STRAHORN, ROBERT E. The Hand-Book of Wyoming and Guide to the Black Hills and Big Horn Regions. Illus., 8vo, cloth. Cheyenne, 1877. $20.00

Strahorn's work was apparently the first guide published giving a history and description of the region. The work is divided into three main sections. The first deals with the territory's resources, the second with miscellaneous information on the military posts, and the last part with the Big Horn and Black Hills Counry, gold hunting, Indians, routes, pioneers, etc.

794 STRAHORN, ROBERT E. To the Rockies and Beyond; or, a Summer on the Union Pacific Railway and Branches, Travels and Hunts in Wyoming, Colorado, Utah, Montana and Idaho, with Sketches of the Black Hills, Big Horn and San Juan Regions. Large folding map and numerous plates. 8vo, original wrappers, 141 pp. Omaha, 1878. $12.50

Original Edition. Smith 3871. This is usually found with the date 1879.

795 STRANGE, JAMES. Records of Ft. St. George [British Columbia]. James Strange's Journal and Narrative of the Commercial Expedition from Bombay to the North-West Coast of America, together with a Chart Showing the Track of the Expedition. With an Introduction by A. V. Venkatarama Ayyar, N.A., L.T., Curator, Madras Record Office. 63 pp., folding map. 4to, original boards. Madras, 1928. $10.00

A detailed report of Strange's two ships, the "Captain Cook" and the "Experiment," from Bombay in Jan. 1786. The two vessels reached Nootka Sound on June 27, mooring in Friendly Cove, July 7, 1786. Anticipating a second visit, Strange left ashore one John McKay, who became the first resident of British Columbia. The latter was found at Friendly Cove in 1787 by Capt. Barkley of the "Imperial Eagle." See the Canadian Historical Review, June, 1928, for an article on Strange, by Judge Howay.

796 STRATTON, R. B. Captivity of the Oatman Girls: Being an interesting narrative of Life among the Apache and Mohave Indians; containing also an Interesting Account of the Massacre of the Oatman Family by the Apache Indians in 1851; the Narrow Escape of Lorenzo D. Oatman; the Capture of Olive A. and Mary A. Oatman; the death by Starvation of the latter; the Five Years' Suffering and Captivity of Olive A. Oatman; also her singular Recapture in 1856; as given by Lorenzo D. and Olive A. Oatman, the only Surviving Members of the Family, to the Author. Map, port. and plates. 12mo, original cloth, 290 pp. N. Y., 1859. $3.00

Third and best edition, with added material and 3 new plates. Relates the celebrated Oatman Expedition across the plains to California, in 1850, from Missouri.

797 STRONG, FRANK, and SCHAFER, JOSEPH. The Government of the American People. 314 pp., illus., map. 8vo, cloth. Boston, 1901. $4.00

Describes the growth of civil government in Oregon, pp. 245-307.

798 STRONG, JAMES CLARK. Biographical Sketches of. 106 pp., port. 8vo, cloth. Los Gatos Calif., 1910. $20.00

Privately printed in a small edition thirty odd years ago, the above work is already difficult to come upon. The above copy is a presentation copy. The author, after a conversation with Dr. Whitman, went to the Oregon Country in 1850, settling in Cathlamet. He was a member of the first Territorial Legislature and the author of "Wha-kee-nah and her People."

799 STRONG, THOMAS NELSON. Cathlamet on the Columbia; Recollections of the Indian People and Short Stories of Early Pioneer Days in the Valley of the Lower Columbia River. 119 pp., 12mo, cloth. Portland, Ore.: Holly Press, 1906. $8.50

800 [STRYKER.] The American Quarterly Register and Magazine. Conducted by James Stryker. Vols. I-VI [all published]. 6 vols., 8vo, half mor. Phila., 1848; N. Y., 1851. $35.00

A large part of the contents relates to the Indians, the West, the discovery of gold, and the Mormons. Vol. IV contains Maj. Carleton's Overland Route to California and Thurston's Geographical Statistics, both overland narratives which are described by Wagner-Camp 180 and 193. Other papers of special interest are An Overland Journey to the Pacific Ocean Forty Years Ago (.ie. in 1811 from St. Louis), Commerce of the Lakes, papers on the whale fishery, Mexican War, the Iroquois, etc. The constitutions of California, Deseret, New Mexico, and other States are given. Contemporary presidential messages and governmental reports relating to the Oregon country, California, and the Southwest are reprinted.

801 STUART, MRS. A. H. H. Washington Territory: Its Soil, Climate, Productions and General Resources. 64 pp., 8vo, original wrappers. Olympia, Wash.: Standard Print, 1875. $75.00

Extremely Rare. The author, a woman, was Chairman of the Board of Immigration, nearly 65 years ago. See Western Americana-Anderson Galleries, Sale No. 1781.

802 STUART, MRS. A. H. H. Washington Territory. Information concerning its Resources, Population and General Statistics for the Use of Immigrants. 8 pp., 8vo. N.p., N.d. [Olympia, W. T., 1874]. $37.50

Can locate no other copy.

803 STUART, GRANVILLE. Forty Years on the Frontier as seen in the Journals and Reminiscences of Granville Stuart, Gold-Miner, Trader, Merchant, Rancher and Politician. Edited by Paul C. Phillips. Numerous early views by the Author. 272 and 265 pp., 2 vols., 8vo, cloth. Cleveland: Clark, 1925. $12.50

Stuart crossed the plains to California and later went to Montana where he became the first great cattle baron of the Northwest. He was a man far above the average in education and discernment and describes what he saw with clearness and fidelity.

804 STURGIS, WILLIAM. The Northwest Fur Trade and the Indians of the Oregon Country. Old South Leaflets No. 219. Boston (1896?). $2.00

Smith 3888, 2759.

805 STUTFIELD, HUGH E. M., and J. NORMAN COLLIE. Climbs and Explorations in the Canadian Rockies. Maps and illus., 342 pp. 8vo, cloth. London, 1903. $7.50

Contains material on British Columbia. Smith 3889.

806 SUCKLEY, GEORGE, and COOPER, JAMES G., et al. Natural History of Washington Territory and Oregon, with much relating to Minnesota, Nebraska, Kansas, Utah and California, between the 36th and 49th Parallel of Latitude, being those parts of the Final Reports of the Surveys of the Natural History of the Regions Explored, with full Catalogues and Descriptions of the Plants and Animals collected from 1853 to 1859. 339 pp., folding map and colored plates. 4to, cloth. N. Y.: Bailliere Bros., 1859. $35.00

Wagner-Camp 262 (note). The above is probably a unique copy in that it bears the date 1859, whereas all other copies examined are dated 1860. There is a note on cover of this edition stating that the name of Gov. Isaac I. Stevens had been omitted by mistake.

807 SUFFLING, ERNEST R. The Fur Traders of the West; or, Adventures among the Redskins. 320 pp., illus., map. 12mo, cloth. London: Warne, 1896. $6.00

Smith 3891. Has considerable material on southern Oregon.

808 SULLIVAN, MAURICE S. Jedediah Smith, Trader and Trail Breaker. 253 pp., 8vo, cloth. N. Y., 1936. $3.50

809 SULTE, BENJAMIN. Melangs Historique. 148 pp., 8vo, original wrappers. Montreal, 1919. $4.00

Contains much material relating to the West and Northwest.

810 SUMMERHAYES, MARTHA. Vanishing Arizona. Recollections of the Army Life of a New England Woman. 8vo, cloth, plates. Phila., 1908. $12.50

811 ——. The Same. Salem, N.d. $2.00

812 SAWYER, LORENZO. Way Sketches, containing Incidents of Travel across the Plains from St. Joseph to California in 1850. With Letters describing life and conditions in the Gold Region. With Historical Notes compiled from rare books and an Introduction by Edward Eberstadt. Port. Royal 8vo, vellum back, large paper edition. N. Y., 1926. $17.50

Large paper edition limited to 35 copies. Sawyer's narrative first appeared in a series of articles published in an obscure village press—The Family Visitor—Hudson, Ohio, during the winter of 1850-51.

813 SWAN, JAMES G. The Northwest Coast: Journal of a Three Years' Residence in Washington Territory. Folding map and 27 plates. 12mo, cloth. N. Y., 1857. $6.50

Fine copy of the Original Edition. The author was an authority on the Indian tribes of the Northwest, and a Secret Agent for the Northern Pacific Railroad.

814 SWAN, JAMES G. Indians of Cape Flattery, at the entrance of the Strait of Fuca, Washington Territory. 108 pp., illus., 4to, cloth. Phila.: Collins, 1868. $7.50

Smith 3901.

Item 810, Should read Vanished not "Vanishing."

815 SWAN, JAMES G. The Amoor River: The Countries drained by the Amoor River and its Tributaries, and the immense trade now lying dormant in Siberia, Manchuria, Northern China, Corea and Japan, which will be . . . diverted to the American Shore of the North Pacific Ocean by the great Continental Railroads which will have the Outlet of their Commerce through the Straits of Fuca to the great Ocean of the West. 38 pp., original wrappers. Seattle (1885). $30.00

Smith 3898. Can locate only one other copy. The appendix has some account of his scientific expeditions for the Smithsonian Institute, trade in the Northwest, etc.

815A SWAN, JAMES G. Notes on the Fisheries and Fishing Industries of Puget Sound. 4to, original wrappers. Washington, 1894. $7.50

816 SWAN, OLIVER G. Frontier Days. 512 pp., illus. Phila., 1928. $4.00

An interesting collection of early western historical incidents, with good illustrations.

817 SWEETSER, ALBERT RADDIN, and MARY E. KENT. Key and Flora; some of the Common Flowers of Oregon. 151 pp., 12mo, original wrappers. Boston (1908). $5.00

818 SWINEFORD, ALFRED P. Alaska: Its History, Climate and Natural Resources. 256 pp., illus., map. 8vo, cloth. Chicago: Rand-McNally (1899). $4.00

Smith 3897. This work often comes without the map.

819 SWISHER, JAMES. How I Know; or, Sixteen Years' Eventful Experiences. An Authentic Narrative embracing a record of Hazardous Enterprises, Thrilling Adventures and Narrow Escapes on the Western Frontier; among the Mormons, the Miners and the Indians. Portraits nad plates. 384 pp., 8vo, cloth. Cincinnati: Printed by the Author, 1880. $20.00

Swisher's Party was ambushed by the Navajoes in the San Re Nado Pass, New Mexico. With the exception of the author and four of his companions the entire company was wiped out. He details the incidents of the journey across the plains to Utah; the Mountain Meadow Massacre; onward to California; early mining experiences, etc.

820 SYMONS, THOMAS W. Report of an Examination of the Upper Columbia River and the Territory in its Vicinity in Sept. and Oct., 1881 . . . 4to, cloth, numerous maps. Washington, 1882. $3.00

821 TACHE, MGR. ALEXANDER A. Vingt Annees de Missions dans le Nord-Ouest de l'Amerique. 8vo, original stamped boards (some wear). Montreal, 1866. $7.50

Mgr. Tache went to the Northwest in 1845.

822 TACHE, MGR. ALEXANDER A. Esquisse sur le Nord-Ouest de l'Amerique. 146 pp., 8vo, original wrappers. Montreal, 1869. $12.50

823 [TACOMA, WASH.] Tacoma and Vicinity. Illus. Album size, cloth. Tacoma, 1888. $5.00

824 [TACOMA, WASH.]. Tacoma Illustrated. 96 pp., illus., map. 8vo, cloth. Chicago, 1889. $4.50

825 [TACOMA, WASH.] Spike's Illustrated Description of the City of Tacoma, Washington. 12 pp., 16 plates. 8vo, cloth. Tacoma: Spike, 1891. $12.50

Smith 3776.

826 TASSE, JOSEPH. Les Canadiens de l'Ouest. Illus. 2 vols., 8vo, half mor. Montreal, 1878. $20.00

An important book of source material hard to come upon. The author's theme is that French-Canadians were the pioneers of the North American Continent, and his two volumes comprise biographies, many with portraits, of Charles de Langade, J. B. Vadot, Chas. Reaume, Jacques Porlier, Jos. Rolette, Salomon Juneau, Julien Dubuque, Antoine Leclerc, Gabriel Franchere, F. X. Aubry, and many others. Sixteen pages are devoted to the "Relation de voyage de la Californie au Neauveau Mexique," 1852, by F. X. Aubry.

827 TATE, C. M. Chinook as Spoken by the Indians of Washington Territory, British Columbia and Alaska. For the use of Traders, Tourists . . . 47 pp., 12mo, original printed wrappers. Victoria (1889). $12.50

Can locate but one other copy.

828 TAVERNER, P. A. Birds of Western Canada. 380 pp., colored plates. 8vo, cloth. Ottawa, 1926. $7.50

829 TAYLOR, BAYARD. Eldorado; or, Adventures in the Path of Empire: Comprising a Journey to California, Life in San Francisco, Pictures of the Gold Region and Experiences of Mexican Travel. 8 full-page colored views of California. 2 vols., 8vo, cloth. N. Y., 1850. $27.50

830 ——. The Same. 2 vols. in one. 12mo, cloth. N. Y., 1854. $7.50

831 TAYLOR, BAYARD. Colorado: A Summer Trip. 185 pp., 12mo, cloth. N. Y., 1867. $5.00

Narrative of the author's trip across the plains from Topeka to Denver.

832 TAYLOR. CHARLES M. Touring Alaska and the Yellowstone. 308 pp., illus. 12mo, cloth. Phila. (1901). $3.75

833 TAYLOR, JOSEPH H. Twenty Years on the Trap Line. Being a Collection of Revised Camp Notes written at intervals during Twenty Years' Experience in Trapping, Wolfing and Hunting on the Great Western Plains. 12mo. Bismark, N. D., 1891. $27.50

A crude but important work printed and published by the author who was a country printer. He spent upwards of 50 years on the plains, in Wyoming and Montana and the Dakotas.

834 TAYLOR, JOSEPH H. Sketches of Frontier and Indian Life on the Upper Missouri and Great Plains. Embracing the Author's Personal Recollections of Noted Frontier Characters, with Observations of Wild Indian Life, during a continuous residence in the Dakotas and adjoining States and Territories between the years 1863-1899. Corrected up to 1897. Portrait and plates. 12mo, cloth. Washburn, N. D., 1895. $15.00

The above work is the scarcest and most important of Joseph Taylor's few works. The material was gleaned from observations made during a trip on the plains in 1854-5, during a term of soldiering on the border, and a residence in Wyoming and Montana as well as a continuous life in the Dakotas. It was first printed in Pottsville, Pa., in 1889. This edition is probably rarer than the original edition. It has added material.

835 TAYLOR, JOSEPH H. Kaleidoscopic Lives. A Companion Book to "Frontier and Indian Life." 8vo, original printed wrappers. Illus., 113 pp., and advts. Washburn, N. D.: Printed and Published by the Author, 1901. $15.00

As are his other books, this book by Taylor was set up and printed by himself. The text is on paper of various hues.

836 TAYLOR, JOSEPH H. Beavers, Their Ways, and Other Sketches. Illus. 12mo, cloth. Washburn, N. D.: Printed and Published by the Author. 1904. $12.50

837 TAYLOR, JOSEPH M. History and Government of Washington, to which are appended the Constitution of the State of Washington and Constitution of the U. S., and lists of Territorial and State Officers. 368 pp., 8vo, lcoth. St. Louis: Becktold, 1898. $6.50

Smith 3949.

838 TAYLOR, WILLIAM. California Life Illustrated. With 16 woodcut drawings, folding map. London (1867). $5.00

839 TEIT, JAMES. Notes on the Tahltan Indians of British Columbia. 8vo, original wrappers. N. Y., 1906. $7.50

This is a separate publication run off by the author.

840 TEIT, JAMES. Two Tahltan Traditions. Reprinted from the Journal of American Folklore. Vol. 22, July-Sept., 1909. 8vo, original wrappers. 1909. $4.50

841 TEIT, JAMES. Traditions of the Lillouet Indians of British Columbia. Reprinted from the Journal of American Folklore. Vol. 20, Oct.-Dec., 1912. 8vo, original wrappers. 1912. $4.50

842 TEIT, JAMES. European Tales from the Upper Thompson Indians. Reprinted from the Journal of American Folklore. Vol. 29, July-Sept., 1916. 8vo, original wrappers. 1916. $4.50

843 [TENNESSEE.] Campbell, T. J. The Upper Tennessee, comprehending a Desultory Record of River Operations in the Tennessee Valley, covering a Period of 150 Years . . . 144 pp., illus. 8vo, cloth. Chattanooga, 1932. $3.00

Privately printed by the author.

844 [TEXAS.] Life and Times of Henry Smith, the First American Governor of Texas. By John Henry Brown. Portrait. 8vo, cloth, 395 pp. Dallas, 1887. $12.50

845 [TEXAS.] The Old Sergeant's Story. Winning the West from the Indians and Bad Men from 1870-1876. Port., illus. By Capt. Robert G. Carter. 8vo, cloth. N. Y.: Hitchcock, 1926. $7.50

A signed presentation copy by the author. Also laid in is a photograph of Gen. MacKenzie, and a booklet "Army and Navy Legion of Valor" with signature and marginal notes by Capt. Carter.

846 [TEXAS.] Sixty Years in Southwest Oklahoma; or, the Autobiography of George W. Conover. With some Thrilling Incidents of Indian Life in Oklahoma and Texas. Illus., 129 pp., 12mo, cloth. Anadarko, Okla., 1927. $4.50

847 [TEXAS.] Early Times in Texas. By J. G. Duval. 8vo, cloth (shaken). Austin, 1892. $3.00

848 [TEXAS.] Edward, David B. The History of Texas; or, The Emigrant's, Farmer's and Politician's Guide to the Character, Climate, Soil and Productions of that Country. . . . Colored folding map, some foxing. 8vo, original cloth, paper label. Cincinnati, 1836. $17.50

849 [TEXAS.] Coup D'Oeil Historique et Statisque sur les Texas par Henri Founiel. 57 pp., 8vo, original printed wrappers. Paris, 1844. $22.50

850 [TEXAS.] Jack Hayes, the Intrepid Texas Ranger. 63 pp., royal 8vo, original wrappers, crude illus. Bandera, Texas, N.d. (1905?). $2.50

A crudely printed work containing some hitherto unpublished material from Miss Betty Hayes's Scrap Book, from Mrs. Maverick, and others.

851 [TEXAS.] Hill, J. L. The End of the Cattle Trail. Illus., 120 pp. 8vo, original wrappers. Long Beach, Cal., N.d. $4.00

852 [TEXAS.] The Life of Sam Houston. (The only Authentic Memoir of him ever published). Illus. 12mo, cloth. N. Y., 1855. $3.00

853 [TEXAS.] Texas and the Gulf of Mexico; or, Yachting in the New World. By Mrs. Houston. Port. Small 12mo, half calf. Phila., 1845. $4.50

854 [TEXAS.] Captain Jeff; or, Frontier Life in Texas with the Texas Rangers . . . By one of the Nine, a Member of Company "E", Texas Rangers. 204 pp., illus. 8vo, original wrappers. Colorado, Texas, 1906. $5.00

855 [TEXAS.] Speech of Hon. James C. Jones, of Tennessee, in defense of Com. Edwin W. Moore, of the late Navy of Texas, in the U. S. Senate, Aug. 3, 1854, in reply to the Speech of Gen. Sam Houston, July 15, 1854. 16 pp., 8vo, sewn. Washington (1854). $5.00

856 [TEXAS.] McConnell, H. H. Five Years a Cavalryman; or, Sketches of Regular Army Life on the Texas Frontier, Twenty Years Ago. 319 pp., 12mo, original cloth. Jacksboro, Texas, 1889. $7.50

857 [TEXAS.] Wooten, Dudley G. A Complete History of Texas. 498 pp., 8vo, cloth. Dallas (1890). $7.50

858 THANET, OCTAVE. Stories of a Western Town. 243 pp., 8vo, cloth. N. Y., 1897. $3.75

859 THISSELL, G. W. Crossing the Plains in '49. Journal of a Trip to California with an Ox-Team, from the Missouri River to the Gold Fields in 1849-50. (Embracing Thrilling Adventures, hair-breadth Escapes, as well as many Amusing Incidents). Port. and plates. 176 pp., 12mo, cloth. Oakland: Privately Printed, 1913. $17.50

Braislin 1771. An interesting Pioneer Narrative written in day-by-day form and recording much out-of-the-way material. The author crossed the plains with an ox-team in the Chambers train.

860 THOM, ADAM. The Claims to the Oregon Territory considered. 8vo, half calf. 44 pp. London, 1844. $17.50

This is one of the rarer of the claims to Oregon works. The author was Recorder of Rupert's Land.

861 THOMAS (D. K.). Wild Life in the Rocky Mountains: Actual Experiences in the Far West, exciting adventures with wild animals, Indians and Desperadoes, with an account of the Mountain Massacre, the secret of Mormonism, etc. An interesting Narrative of the Trials and Hardships of an early Western Gold Miner. Plates. 221 pp., 12mo, cloth. N.p., 1917. $7.50

Personal narrative of adventurers crossing the plains, and life in the Mines and among the Indians of the Idaho-Montana Country in the early 60's.

862 [THOMPSON, DAVID.] David Thompson, Canada's Greatest Geographer. An Appreciation. By J. B. Tyrrell. 8 pp., 8vo, original wrappers. N.p., Aug., 1922. $4.50

863 [THOMPSON, DAVID.] David Thompson, the Explorer. By Charles Norris Cochrane. 175 pp., 8vo, cloth. Toronto, 1924. $4.75

The only life of this great explorer.

864 THOMPSON, ERNEST SETON. Lives of the Hunted; containing a True Account of the Doings of Quadrapeds and Tree Birds. . . . 360 pp., illus. 12mo, cloth. N. Y., 1901. $6.00

865 THOMPSON, L. OWEN. Adventures of a Day-Dreamer. 100 pp., 12mo, cloth. Long Branch, Cal., 1913. $3.50

Contains stories of Oregon.

866 THOMPSON, ORIGEN. Crossing the Plains. Narrative of the Scenes, Incidents and Adventures attending the Overland Journey of the Decatur and Rush County Emigrant's to "far-off" Oregon in 1852. Printed from a Diary of Daily Events kept by the late Origen Thompson. With an Introductory Chapter by Mrs. Camilla T. Donnell, and a Thrilling Narrative of a Buffalo Hunt and Battle Royal with Mountain Wolves, by Mr. Sutherland McCoy. 12mo, stiff paper wrappers. Greensburg, Indiana, 1896. $57.50

867 THOMPSON, WADDY. Recollections of Mexico. 8vo, 304 pp., new wrappers. N. Y., 1846. $7.50

868 THOMPSON, COL. WILLIAM. Reminiscences of a Pioneer. (Narrative of a Trip across the Plains to the Willamette Valley in 1852; life in the Oregon Country; Among the Indians; The Ben Wright Massacre; Battle of the Lava Beds; the Bannock War; Snake Indian Uprising; and the Reign of Vigilantes). 187 pp., 8vo, cloth. San Francisco: Privately Printed, 1912. $3.00

869 THRALL, HOMER S. A Pictorial History of Texas. 900 pp., map. 8vo, sheep. Thompson, N. Y., 1885. $6.00

870 THWAITE, LEON. Alberta. An Account of its Wealth and Progress. 250 pp., illus. 12mo, original wrappers (spine worn). Toronto: Munson, 1912. $3.50

871 THWAITES, REUBEN GOLD. A Brief History of Rocky Mountain Exploration, with special reference to the Expedition of Lewis and Clark. 276 pp., ports., plates, maps. 12mo, cloth. N. Y., 1904. $3.50

872 THAYER, WILLIAM M. Marvels of the New West; a vivid portrayal of the Stupendous Marvels in the Vast Wonderland west of the Missouri River; Six Books in one volume, comprising Marvels of Nature, Marvels of Race, Marvels of Enterprise, Marvels of Mining, Marvels of Stock Raising and Marvels of Agriculture, Graphically and Truthfully Described. 715 pp., illus., ports., 6 maps. 8vo, cloth. Norwich, 1889. $3.50

873 TILICUM, A. BOSTON. A Monograph on the Puyallup Indians of the State of Washington. Their History, Nativity, Lands and Naturalisation. A Plea for the Puyallups . . . 47 pp., original printed wrappers. Tacoma, 1892. $27.50

Can locate no other copy in bibliographies consulted. Tilicum's work is ably presented, giving a history of the tribe, a list of its members, their rights and alleged wrongs.

874 TIXIER, VICTOR. Tixier's Travels on the Osage Prairies. Edited by John Francis McDermott. Trans. from the French by Albert J. Salvan. 309 pp., illus. 8vo, cloth. Norman, Okla., 1940. $3.00

875 TODD, JOHN. The Sunset Land; or, the Great Pacific Slope. 322 pp. 12mo, cloth. London (1869). $7.50

Smith 3995.

876 TOLMIE, WM. F., and DAWSON, GEO. M. Comparative Vocabularies of the Indian Tribes of British Columbia. (Geological and Natural History Survey of Canada). 131 pp., folding map. 8vo, cloth. Montreal: Dawson, 1884. $7.50

Smith 3999.

877 TOPONCE, ALEXANDER. Reminiscences of Alexander Toponce, Pioneer. Portraits and plates. 248 pp., 12mo, stamped cloth. (Ogden, Utah, 1923). $7.50

Toponce helped install the first overland stage from the Missouri to California in 1855. The language of his book is as homely and direct as his career seems to have been. It included Bull Whacking, the Mormon War, trip to Pike's Peak, Montana gold diggings, early days in Helena, freighting, sheep-raising in Wyoming, adventures in Utah and among the Siox and Blackfeet.

878 TOPPING, E. S. Chronicles of the Yellowstone; an Accurate and Comprehensive History of the Country drained by the Yellowstone River, its Indian Inhabitants, its first Explorers, the early Fur Traders and Trappers, the Coming and the Trails of the Emigrants . . . 245 pp., plates, folding map. 8vo, cloth. St. Paul, 1883. $7.50

879 TORREY, WILLIAM. The Life and Adventures of William Torrey, Embracing the Narrative of a Voyage to the Northwest Coast of America and California in 1837. With a Description of St. Francis Drake's Bay, the Indians, their Manners and Customs, etc. 300 pp., port. and plates. 12mo, cloth. Boston, 1848. $20.00

880 TOWNSEND, JOHN K. Narrative of a Journey Across the Rocky Mountains to the Columbia River, and a Visit to the Sandwich Islands, Chili . . . 8vo, original cloth. Phila., 1839. $15.00

Wagner-Camp 79. The author was a member of Wyeth's Expedition and returned in 1838. Because of his scientific knowledge the work has more than the usual travel value. The appendix contains a catalogue of Oregon quadrupeds.

881 TOWNSEND, JOHN. Extracts from a Private Journal kept by Mr. John Townsend during a Journey across the Rocky Mountains in 1834. (Excerpt, p. 6). 4to. Phila., 1835. $6.00

These "Extracts" cover the period from July 10, to Sept. 10, 1834, the day of his arrival at Ft. Vancouver. A preliminary publication which was followed later by his "Narrative of a Journey," etc.

882 TOZIER, D. F. Arts and Crafts of the Totem Indians, collected by Capt. D. F. Tozier of the U. S. Revenue Cutter Service. 8vo, original wrappers. Tacoma, N.d. $3.50

883 [TRACY, HARRY, NORTHWEST BANDIT.] Tracy, the Bandit; or, the Romance of Life and Crime of a Twentieth Century Bandit. By Clarence E. Ray. 185 pp., 12mo, original wrappers. Chicago, N.d. $4.50

After terrorizing citizens of Oregon and Washington, Tracy was killed by a posse near Creston, Washington.

884 [TRANSPORTATION.] Mr. Hemphill's Speech on the Bill to construct a National Road from Buffalo, passing the Seat of the General Government, to New Orleans. . . . 23 pp., 8vo, sewn (foxed). N.p.: Wm. Greer, Printer (1830). $3.50

885 TRIGGS, J. H. History of Cheyenne and Northern Wyoming, Embracing the Gold Fields of the Black Hills, Powder River and Big Horn Countries . . . Accompanied by a New and Correct Map of Wyoming and Its Boundaries. 8vo, original printed wrappers. Omaha, 1876. $75.00

Barber Sale 1183. The author spent 12 years on the plains and in the Rocky Mountains. He describes the first settlement of Cheyenne, events in its early history, the Vigilantes, pioneer press, etc.

886 TRIPLETT, FRANK. Conquering the Wilderness; or, the Life and Times of Frontiersmen and Indian Fighters; Crockett, Houston, Carson, Wild Bill and other famous Plainsmen; Sutter, Marshall, Fremont, Kearney. With Sketches of Border Life; the Overland Route; the Gold Fever; the Filibustering Expedition; Vigilance Committee, etc. Plates, 716 pp. 8vo, cloth. N. Y., 1883. $5.00

887 TROLLOPE, MRS. Domestic Manners of the Americans. 8vo, original grey cloth, paper label intact (worn elsewhere at spine). Plates (foxed). London and N. Y., 1832. $7.50

888 TROW, JAMES M. P. A Trip to Manitoba. 86 pp., 12mo, original wrappers. Quebec, 1875. $6.50

889 TROW, JAMES M. P. Manitoba and the Northwest Territories. 100 pp., folding map. 12mo, cloth. Quebec, 1878. $4.50

890 TROWBRIDGE, M. E. D. Pioneer Days. The Life Story of Gershon and Elizabeth Day. 160 pp., front., 12mo, cloth. Phila. (1895). $7.50

Contains the overland journey of Day, who left St. Joseph, Mo., in March, 1849, for California.

891 TRUDEAU, JEAN BAPTISTE. Journal of Jean Baptiste Trudeau among the Arikara Indians in 1795. Translated by Mrs. H. T. Beauregard. (Missouri Historical Society Collections, Vol. 4, No. 1, 1912). 8vo. St. Louis, 1912. $3.50

Wagner-Camp 121 (note).

892 TRUMAN, MAJOR BEN C. Occidental Sketches. 212 pp., 12mo, cloth. San Francisco, 1881. $20.00

A very scarce work. The author gives an account of a trip to Alaska in 1869, an episode in Echo Canyon, adventures in Nevada, an account of the Wickenburg Massacre, etc. Major Truman was a Special Agent for the Post Office Department and this book is mainly an account of his experiences for the Post Office in the West. See Cowan.

893 TUCKER, EPHRAIM W. A History of Oregon, containing a condensed Account of the most Important Discoveries of the Spanish, American and English Navigators on the Northwest Coast of America; and of the different Treaties relative to the same . . . the Claim of the United States to that Territory. . . . 84 pp., 8vo. Buffalo: A. W. Wilgus, 1844. A photostatic facsimile. $17.50

Smith 4029.

894 TUCKER, J. C. To the Golden Goal and Other Sketches. Port. and illus., 303 pp. 12mo, cloth. San Francisco: William Doxey, 1895. $20.00

A scarce work of which only 50 copies were printed for the author's family and friends, according to Macdonald's bibliography. Macdonald was the son-in-law of Dr. Tucker. Relates to the gold fields, prospecting, vigilantes, with Walker, etc.

895 TUCKER, L. NORMAN. Western Canada. 164 pp., illus., map. 12mo, cloth. London (1908). $3.75

Handbook of English church expansion and historical sketches of western churches and missions.

896 TURNBULL, T. Travels Across the Plains to California. Maps. 225 pp., 8vo, original wrappers. Madison, 1914. $5.00

The author went from Chicago to Hangtown in 1852. He took the Mormon Trail on the North side of the Platte.

897 TURNER, FREDERICK J. Rise of the New West. 366 pp., map. 8vo, cloth. N. Y. (1906). $3.75

Smith 4034.

898 TURNER, FREDERICK J. Essays in American History. 293 pp., 12mo, cloth. N. Y., 1910. $3.50

899 TURNER, J. P. The Prairie Chicken. Its Distribution and need for Protection. 16 pp., 8vo. N.p., N.d. (1917). $3.50

900 TURNER, T. G. Turner's Guide from the Lakes to the Rocky Mountains, via the Cleveland and Toledo, Michigan, Southern and Northern Indiana, Chicago and Northwestern, and Union Pacific Railroads; Also, from Missouri Valley, via Pacific and Sioux City Railroad, and the Steamboats of the Northwest Transportation Co., including a Historical Account of the Railroads of the Country, Towns and Cities along the Route, and Notices of the Connecting Roads and Routes. 268 pp., 8vo, cloth. Chicago, 1868. $10.00

901 TURNER, WILLIAM S. Story of my Life, followed by an Appendix containing characteristic selections from his Writings and Public Addresses. 345 pp., port. 8vo, cloth. Cincinnati, N.d. $12.50

Smith 4037 cites but one copy. The author was a resident of Spokane and a pioneer in Methodism in California and Washington.

902. TURNER. Turner, J. Three Years Hunting and Trapping in the Great Northwest. Map and plates. 182 pp., 8vo, cloth. London, 1888. $7.50

Hunting adventures in the Big Horn Country, grizzly bears, British Columbia experiences, Indians, Fraser River, Caribou, etc.

903 TUTTLE, CHARLES R. Our North Land; being a full account of the Canadian Northwest and Hudson's Bay Route, together with a Narrative of the Experiences of the Hudson's Bay Expedition of 1884, including a description of the Native Inhabitants between the 50th Parallel and the Arctic Circle. Maps and engravings. 8vo, cloth. Toronto, 1885. $5.00

904 TUTTLE, REV. D. S. Reminiscences of a Missionary Bishop. 498 pp., illus. 8vo, cloth. N. Y. (1906). $20.00

A work dealing with life experiences in the west in the early days. It is seldom found.

905 TUTTLE, REV. E. B. The Book about Indians: Being What I Saw and Heard during Three Years on the Plains. 207 pp., 12mo, cloth. Phila., 1873. $17.50

A unique copy in that it bears the 1873 date. Most copies have the 1874 date. Dr. Tuttle's narrative is most interesting. He served as Post Chaplain at Ft. Sedgwick and Ft. D. A. Russell, Wyoming, from 1867 to 1870. His narrative records a trip across the plains, the Kearney Massacre, the Sweetwater Indian fight, trip to Ft. Laramie, Denver Stage Coach Indian Attack, the Plum Creek Massacre, etc.

906 TWISS, TRAVERS. Oregon Territory, its History and Discovery; including an Account of the Convention of the Escurial, also the Treaties and Negotiations between the U. S. and Great Britain, held at various times for the Settlement of a Boundary Line, and an Examination of the Whole Question in respect to Facts and the Law of Nations. 264 pp., 12mo, original wrappers. N. Y., 1846. $12.50

906a ——. The same. 12mo, original cloth, fine. N. Y., 1846. $7.50

907 TWISS, TRAVERS. The Oregon Question Examined in respect to Facts and the Law of Nations. 391 pp., 2 maps. 8vo, cloth. London: Longman, 1846. $15.00

"Mr. Greenhow's work has been exposed and answered ably and succinctly by Mr. Falconer and more at large by Dr. Twiss of the Commons, whose work is and will continue to be valuable independently of the Oregon Question as an able discussion of several important points of the law of nations"—Lon. Quar. Rev.

908 ——. The same. 8vo, cloth. N. Y., 1846. $7.50

909 TYLER, SERGEANT DANIEL. A Concise History of the Mormon Battalion in the Mexican War, 1846-1847. 8vo, original blind stamped cloth. (Salt Lake), 1881. $25.00

Wagner-Camp 165. Aside from its recording of hitherto unpublished facts relating to the Mormon Battalion, Tyler's work is of further importance for its account of the earliest wagon roads over the Great American Desert; of the Santa Fe Expedition and the march to San Diego; the Fremont-Stockton-Kearney controversy, and the account of the gold discovery.

910 TYRRELL, J. BURR. Report on the Doobaunt, Kazan and Ferguson Rivers and the Northwest Coast of Hudson's Bay, and on the Overland Routes from Hudson's Bay to Lake Winnepeg. 218 pp., illus., maps. 8vo, original wrappers. Ottawa: Dawson, 1897. $7.50

911 TYRRELL, J. BURR. Across the Sub-Arctic of Canada. A Journey of 3000 Miles by Canoe and Snowshoe through the Barren Lands . . . Including a List of Plants Collected on the Expedition, a Vocabulary of Eskimo Words . . . Map and illus. 8vo, cloth. N. Y., 1898. $15.00

912 TYSON, P. T. The Industrial Resources and Geology of California. With Reports of Explorations in California and Oregon, and also the Examination of Routes for Railroad Communication Eastward from those Countries. 198 pp., 12 large folding maps. 8vo, cloth. Baltimore, 1851. $12.50

Smith 4047. Presentation copy from Tyson with letter inserted. This is one of the most important works relating to actual conditions in California and Oregon which had up to the time appeared. Contains a minute account of the mines and mineral resources in general, vegetable products, animals, lands, land titles, government, routes, etc.

913 TYTLER, PATRICK F. Historical View of the Progress of Discovery on the more Northern Coasts of America, from the earliest period to the present time . . . with Descriptive Sketches of the Natural History of the North American Regions by James Wilson. Illus. and folding map. Edinburgh, 1832. $5.00

Original Edition. Russian and English voyages, Bering, Chirikov, Cook, Meares, Vancouver, Mackenzie, etc.

914 ——. Another edition. 12mo, cloth, map, plates. N. Y., 1833. $3.00

915 UDELL, JOHN. Incidents of Travel to California, Across the Great Plains; together with the Return Trips through Central America and Jamaica; to which are added Sketches of the Author's Life. Woodcut, port. 302 pp., errata slip. 12mo, original cloth. Jefferson, Ohio: Printed for the Author, 1856. $35.00

Wagner-Camp 281. This work is among the most fascinating of overland journeys in that Udell, a Norman Englishman of two generations in America went and came back three times via the Overland to Califorina. He kept diaries and they are printed verbatim. There is also a life of Udell. On his first trip he started from Iowa, May 1, 1850 and reached Placerville in Aug. 29th, started again for California from Missouri, arriving at Placerville in Sept. His 3rd journey was begun from Council Bluffs, April, 1854, and he reached California in Oct. He was born in 1795 and started his first trip at the age of 55. He was accurate and honest and seemed to carry his morals on his sleeve, as he records an incident where he actually got out of a train bought a new horse and rode it onward, because of "dirty stories" being told in his presence.

916 UNDERHILL, REUBEN L. From Cow Hides to Golden Fleece; a Narrative of California, 1832-1858. Based upon Unpublished Correspondence of Thomas Oliver Larkin, Trader, Developer, Promoter, and only American Consul. 273 pp., front., illus. 8vo, cloth. Sanford, 1939. $3.50

917 [UNION PACIFIC RAILROAD.] The Union Pacific Railroad from Omaha, across the Continent, making, with its Connections, an Unbroken Line from the Atlantic to the Pacific Oceans. Chartered by the U. S. Its Construction, Resources, Earnings and Prospects. 31 pp., map. 8vo N. Y., 1867. $7.50

The map shows cars running 305 miles west of Omaha, Jan. 1, 1867.

918 [UNION PACIFIC RAILROAD.] The Great National Highway between the Missouri River and California. 12 pp., 8vo, original wrappers. Chicago, 1868. $5.00

919 [UNION PACIFIC RAILROAD.] The Policy of Extending Government Aid to the additional Railroads to the Pacific by guaranteeing interest on their Bonds. 31 pp., 8vo, sewn. Washington, 1869. $3.50

The above is Sen. Rep. Com. Doc. 219, 40th Cong. 3rd Sess.

920 [UNION PACIFIC RAILROAD.] Wealth and Resources of Oregon and Washington, the Pacific Northwest; a Complete Guide over the Local Lines of the Union Pacific Railway . . . 256 pp., illus. 8vo, original wrappers. Portland, Ore., 1889. $5.00

Smith 4063.

921 [UNION PACIFIC RAILROAD.] The Great Pacific Northwest and Alaska. 47 pp., illus., map. 8vo, original wrappers. Chicago, N.d. $5.00

Smith 4058.

922 UPCHURCH, FATHER J. J. The Life, Labors and Travels of Father J. J. Upchurch, Founder of the Ancient Order of United Workman. Written by Himself. 12mo, cloth. San Francisco, 1887. $6.00

A scarce work containing accounts of trips to Oregon and California, and his work among the workingmen.

923 UPHAM, S. C. Notes of a Voyage to California, together with Scenes in El Dorado, 1849-50. With Reminiscences of Pioneer Journalism in California; Extracts from the Manuscript Journal of the "King's Orphan" in the year 1843; Pioneer and kindred Organisations. Plates, 594 pp. 8vo, cloth. Phila., 1878. $12.50

Cowan p. 236. "There is much contained in this interesting work that is not to be found in any other source, more especially regarding the early history of Sacramento, the history of the Territorial pioneers, and pioneer journalists in California".

924 [UTAH.] Acts, Regulations and Memorials, passed at the several Annual Sessions of the Legislative Assembly of the Territory of Utah. To which is prefaced the Constitution of the Provisional State of Deseret, the Deseret Laws, the Organic Laws of Utah, etc. 460 pp., 8vo, boards. Salt Lake City, 1855. $15.00

925 [UTAH.] Utah State Historical Society. Utah Historical Quarterly. Vol. 1, No. 1, Jan., 1928 to Vol. 9, No. 4, Oct., 1941. 8 vols., 8vo, original wrappers. Salt Lake, 1928-1941. $15.00

926 VACHEL, HORACE A. Life and Sport on the Pacific Slope. 393 pp., 12mo, cloth. N. Y.: Dodd, 1901. $4.00

927 VANCOUVER, GEORGE. A Voyage of Discovery to the North Pacific Ocean, and Round the World; in which the Coast of North-West America has been carefully examined and accurately surveyed. Undertaken by his Majesty's command, principally with a view to ascertain the existence of any navigable communication between the North Pacific and North Atlantic Oceans; and performed in the years 1790-1795, in the Discovery Sloop of War, and armed Tender Chatham. 3 vols., 4to, and folio Atlas. Complete with all the maps, charts and views, original boards, uncut, very fine copy. Partially unopened. London, 1798. $175.00

First Edition. One of the most important works for the history of California, Vancouver Island, British Columbia, Oregon and Washington. A unique copy in that both text and atlas are in the original state, entirely uncut and partially unopened.

928 ——. The same. 17 plates, 2 maps. 6 vols., 8vo, original tree calf. London: Stockdale, 1801. $65.00

929 VANCOUVER, GEORGE. Voyage de decouvertes, a l'Ocean Pacifique du nord, et autour du monde; dans lequel la cote Nord-Ouest de l'Amerique a ete soigneusement reconnue et exactement releve . . . execut en 1790, 1791, 1792, 1793, 1794 et 1795; tr. from the English. 3 vols. and folio of plates and maps. Par. l'Imprimerie de la Republique. Paris, An. VIII. $100.00

Rare French Edition. The maps and plates in this edition are equally as fine as those in the English issue of 1798. This fine French edition is unique in that the Atlas is rarely found with the set. See item 1472, Cat. 17.

930 ——. The same. 3 vols., 4to, original boards, paper label (lacks the Atlas). Paris, An. VIII. $37.50

931 VANCOUVER, GEORGE. Putshestvie v Sievernuiu chastj Tikhago Okeana i vokrug svieta, sovershennoe v 1791-5 godakh. Kap. G. Vankuverom, 1791-5. 6 vols., 8vo, calf. St. Petersburg, 1827-28. $40.00

Fine set. Wickersham 6288. See Cat. 17, item 1473.

932 VANCOUVER, GEORGE. Reisen nach dem Nordl. Theile der Sudsee, 1790-95. A. d. Engl. von J. F. V. Herbst. 2 bde mit 1 Karte und 2 Kupfern. 8vo, calf. Berlin, 1799-80. Cart. $25.00

The German edition of Vancouver is unique now in that it is rarer than the English edition, although printed two years later. See item 1474, cat. 17 in this Series.

933 VOSS, CAPTAIN. The Adventuresome Voyages of Capt. Voss. With an Introduction by Weston Martyr. Illus., map. 12mo, cloth. Boston, N.d. $1.25

Voss gives an account of Vancouver Island and the NW.

934 [VANCOUVER, GEORGE.] A New Vancouver Journal on the Discovery of Puget Sound. By a Member of the Chatham's Crew. Edited by Edmond S. Meany. iii-43 pp., 8vo, original wrappers. Seattle, 1915. $5.00

935 VAN DYKE, WALTER. Early Days in Klamath. [Wash.] Overland Magazine, Aug., 1891. 8vo, original wrappers. San Francisco, 1891. $2.00

936 VAN DUSEN, W. W. Blazing the Way; or, Pioneer Experiences in Idaho, Washington and Oregon. 199 pp., port. and plate. Cincinnati: Jennings (1905). $7.50

Smith 4178.

937 VAN GORP, LEOPOLD, S. J. A Dictionary of the Numipu, or Nez Perce Language. By a Missionary of the Society of Jesus in the Rocky Mountains. Part 1. English-Nez Perce. 242 pp., 8vo, original wrappers. St. Ignatius Mission Print, Montana, 1895. $37.50

This rare work is not recorded by Pilling or Smith or any other bibliography consulted. According to a letter received some years ago from Rev. Thomas M. Neale, of St. Joseph's Mission, Idaho, Part 1 was all that was ever published. Father Van Gorp was one of the founders of Helena having gone there to establish the Helena Mission at the instigation of Father De Smet. See item 1193, Cat. 18, wherein this has been wrongly attributed to Father A. Morvillo.

938 VAN TRAMP, JOHN C. Prairie and Rocky Mountain Adventures; or, Life in the West. . . . 655 pp., front., illus. 8vo, sheep. Columbus: Gilmore, 1866. $6.00

939 ——. Another edition. 8vo, cloth. 1869. $5.00

940 VAUGHN, ROBERT. Then and Now; or, Thirty-six Years in the Rockies. Personal Reminiscences of some of the First Pioneers of the State of Montana. Indians and Indian Wars. The Past and Present of the Rocky Mountain Country, 1864-1900. Port. and illus. 461 pp., 8vo, cloth. Minneapolis, 1900. $6.50

Embraces the James Stuart prospecting party, events in northern Montana in '65, Lewis's early days in Montana, battles in the Sun River Valley, John D. Brown's narrative, Warren C. Gilbert's early experiences, etc.

941 VENEGAS, MIGUEL. Noticia de la California y de su Conquista temporal, y espiritual hasta el tiempo Presente. Sagada de la Historia Manuscrita, formada en Mexico ano de 1739, por el Padre Miguel Venegas de la Compania de Jesus; y de Otras Noticias, y Relaciones antiguas y modernas. An adida de lagunos mapas particulares y ano general de la America Septentrional, Assia Oriental, y Mar del Sud intermedio, formados sobre las memorias mas recientes, y exactas, que se publican justamente. Complete with the four folding maps. 3 vols., 4to contemporary boards. Madrid, 1757. $150.00

Original Edition. Venegas labored as a Jesuit Missionary in Mexico and California, and while in the latter province, gathered much information from observation and from the archives of the various missions. The work contains much valuable historical, geographical and ethnological material not to be found elsewhere, and relates equally to Lower California, Southern Arizona and Northern Sonora, as well as to California proper. The Spanish edition is of further importance on account of the map and the Appendices which occupy the latter half of the third volume, and which deal with the pretended discoveries of Admiral De Fonte and the discoveries in the extreme Northwest between Alaska and the continent of Asia. "This work is considered the foundation of a library of California", Cowan p. 659.

942 VENEGAS, MIGUEL. Juan Maria de Salvatierra, of the Company of Jesus; Missionary in the Province of New Spain and Apostolic Conqueror of the Californias. Translated into English. Edited and Annotated by Marguerite Eyer Wilbur. 350 pp., illus., map. 8vo, cloth. Cleveland, 1929. $7.50

943 VERGNE, GEORGE H. DE LA. At the Foot of the Rockies. Stories of Mountain and Plain. 209 pp., 12mo, cloth. N. Y. (1901). $2.50

944 VESTAL, STANLEY. Kit Carson, the Happy Warrior of the Old West. A Biography. 297 pp., illus. 12mo, cloth. N. Y., 1928. $2.50

945 VICTOR, FRANCIS FULLER. The River of the West. Life and Adventures in the Rocky Mountains and Oregon; embracing Events in the Life-Time of a Mountainman and Pioneer; including an Account of the Fur Traders, the Indian Tribes, the Overland Immigration, the Oregon Missions, and the Tragic Fate of Rev. Dr. Whitman and family. Port. and plates. 8vo, cloth. Hartford, 1870. $10.00

Original Edition. The narrative is chiefly built about the strong figure of "Joe Meek," the fur-trapper; but Wyeth, Sublette, and many other heroes of the Yellowstone Country figure in it as well. Mrs. Victor's work was always conscientious and thorough.

946 VICTOR, FRANCIS FULLER. All Over Oregon and Washington, Observations of the Country, its Scenery, Soil, Climate, Resources and Improvements, with an Outline of its early History . . . 368 pp., 8vo, cloth. San Francisco, 1872. $5.00

947 VICTOR, FRANCIS FULLER. Eleven Years in the Rocky Mountains and Life on the Frontier; also a History of the Sioux War, and a Life of Gen. George A. Custer . . . 425-156 pp., illus., port., 2 vols. in one, 8vo, cloth. Hartford, 1877. $7.50

948 VICTOR, FRANCIS FULLER. The New Penelope and Other Stories and Poems. 349 pp., 12mo, cloth. San Francisco, 1877. $4.00

949 VICTOR, FRANCIS FULLER. Atlantis Arisen; or, Talks of a Tourist about Oregon and Washington. 412 pp., illus., port. 12mo, cloth. Phila., 1891. $3.75

950 VICTOR, FRANCIS FULLER. Early Indian Wars of Oregon, compiled from the Oregon Archives and other Original Sources; with Muster Rolls. 8vo, half calf. Salem, Ore.: Baker, 1894. $7.50

951 VICTOR, FRANCIS FULLER. A Scrap-Book of 58 4to pages containing numerous printed clippings of various writings of Francis Fuller Victor clipped from odd periodicals and newspapers. Presented to the San Francisco Woman's Literary Exhibit for the Columbia Exhibit of 1893 by Francis Fuller Victor "Florence Fane." 4to, cloth. V.p., V.d. $22.50

See Ore. Hist. Quar., Dec., 1941 for a note on this or another scrap-book by Victor.

952 VILLARD, HENRY H. Memoirs of Henry Villard, Journalist and Financier, 1835-1900. Ports., maps. 2 vols., 8vo, cloth. London, 1904. $7.50

953 VILLARD, HENRY. The Past and Present of the Pike's Peak Gold Regions. Reprinted from the Original Edition of 1860 with Introduction and Notes by LeRoy R. Hafen . . . 186 pp., map, illus. 8vo, cloth. Princeton 1932. $2.50

954 VILLIERS, BARON MARC DE. La Louisane de Chateaubriand. Extrait du Journal de la Societe des Americaiste de Paris. Nouvelle Serie, 16, 1924. Pp. 125-167. 8vo, original wrappers. Paris, 1924. $3.50

955 VILLIERS, BARON MARC DE. La Decouverte du Missouri et l'Histoire du Fort D'Orleans (1673-1728). 138 pp., maps. 8vo, original wrappers. Paris, 1925. $7.50

See the Canadian Hist. Rev., Sept. 1926, p. 262. This work while recently published is of considerable interest in relation to the discovery and exploration of the Mississippi and Missouri Rivers.

956 [VIRGINIA.] Report of the Portsmouth Relief Association . . . during the prevelance of Yellow Fever in that town in 1855 . . . tinted frontis. 8vo, cloth. 363 pp. Richmond, 1856. $2.50

957 VISSCHER, WILLIAM L. A Thrilling and Truthful History of the Pony Express; or, Blazing the Westward Way; and other Sketches and Incidents of those Stirring Times. Early Views, facsimiles, ports., etc. 8vo, cloth. Chicago, 1908. $5.00

958 VISSCHER, WILLIAM L., and McEWEN, W. H. A Souvenir of Washington's Third Legislature. 125 pp., illus. 12mo, cloth. Olympia, Wash., N.d. $2.00

959 VIVIAN, IMOGEN HOLBROOK. A Biographical Sketch of the Life of Charles Algernon Sidney Vivian, Founder of the Order of Elks. 103 pp., 12mo, cloth. San Francisco, 1904. $7.50

Vivian was an actor who appeared in various theatres along the West Coast and among inter-mountain states in the early 70's.

960 VORHEES, LUKE. Personal Recollections of Pioneer Life on the Mountains and Plains of the Great West. Port., 76 pp. 8vo, original cloth. Cheyenne: Privately Printed, 1920. $25.00

Original Edition privately printed in a few copies. Vorhees braved the frontier when it was a wilderness and lived a full life of adventure which makes his book one of the genuine narratives of the old plains' days. His narrative recounts a trip across the Plains to Smoky Hill and the Republican River Country in 1857; trip to Pike's Peak and the Gold Diggings in 1859; Montana in 1863; buffalo hunting; Indians in the Black Hills and Cheyenne Country, 1876-82; Early Stage Coach Days; the Metz Massacre; early days in Salt Lake; and the organisation of Wyoming Territory.

961 WADDINGTON, ALFRED. The Fraser Mines Vindicated; or, the History of Four Months. 49 pp., 8vo. Victoria: P. De Garro, 1858. (A photostatic replica). $12.50

Smith 4215 reports only the copy at Victoria. The above is an exact replica, bound.

962 WADDINGTON, ALFRED. Overland Route through British North America; or, the Shortest and Speediest Road to the East. With a colored map. 48 pp., 12mo, original wrappers. London, 1868. $50.00

Can locate no other copy. Waddington was the author of "The Fraser Mines Vindicated". All his published works seem to be rare.

963 WADDINGTON, ALFRED. On the Geography and Mountain Passes of British Columbia in connection with an Overland Route. (From the Royal Geographical Society Journal, 1868. Pp. 118-128). 8vo, sewn. 1868. $5.00

Smith 4216.

964 WAGNER, HENRY R. The Plains and the Rockies. A Bibliography of the Original Narratives of Travel and Adventure, 1800-1865. First Ed. Large 8vo, boards. San Francisco, 1921. $15.00

965 WAGNER, HENRY R. California Voyages, 1539-1541. Translations of Original Documents. 95 pp., maps. 4to, cloth. San Francisco, 1925. $7.50

966 WAGNER, HENRY R. Spanish Voyages to the Northwest Coast of America in the Sixteenth Century. 571 pp., illus., maps. 4to, cloth. San Francisco, 1929. $12.50

967 WAGNER, HENRY R. Fra Benito de la Sierra's Account of the Hezeta Expedition to the Northwest Coast in 1775. Trans. by A. J. Baker, with Introduction and Notes by Henry R. Wagner. 44 pp., 8vo, original wrappers. San Francisco, 1930. $7.50

Separate Printing from the Calif. Hist. Soc. Quar., vol. 9, no. 3, Sept., 1930.

968 WAGNER, HENRY R. George Davidson, Geographer of the Northwest Coast of America. 24 pp., 8vo, original wrappers. San Francisco, 1932. $5.00

Separate printing from the Calif Hist. Soc. Quar., vol. 11, no. 4, Dec., 1932.

969 WAGNER, HENRY R. Spanish Voyages to the Straits of Juan de Fuca. 323 pp., maps. 4to, cloth. Santa Ana, 1933. $7.50

970 WAGNER, HENRY R. The Plains and the Rockies . . . Revised and Extended by Charles L. Camp. 8vo, cloth. San Francisco: Grabhorn, 1937. $12.50

971 WALDO, FULLERTON. Down the Mackenzie through the Great Lone Land. 251 pp., illus. 8vo, cloth. N. Y., 1923. $3.50

972 [WALDSEEMULLER, MARTIN.] The Cosmographiae Introduction of Martin Waldseemuller in facsimile. Followed by Four Voyages of Amerigo Vespucci, with their Translation into English; to which are added Waldseemuller's two World Maps of 1507, with an Introduction by Joseph Fischer, S.J. and Prof. Franz von Wieser. Edited by Chas. George Herbermann. Front., illus., facsimiles. Small 4to, 151 pp., cloth. N. Y., 1907. $7.50

This beautiful work was printed by the Catholic Historical Society to commemorate the 400th Anniversary of the man who first used the name "America" on a map. He was a Lorraine geographer.

973 WALKER, C. B. Mississippi Valley and Pre-historic Events. Colored plates. 784 pp., 8vo, original sheep. Burlington, 1880. $8.50

Mound Builders, mineral resources, Spanish and English explorations, steamboats, southern planters, manners and customs, etc.

974 WALKINSHAW, ROBERT. On Puget Sound. 294 pp., illus. 8vo, cloth. N. Y., 1929. $3.50

975 WALL (OSCAR G.). Recollections of the Sioux Massacre: An Authentic History of the Yellow Medicine Incident, of the fate of Marsh and his men, of the Siege and Battles of Fort Ridgely, and of other Important Battles and Experiences. Together with a sketch of the Sibley Expedition of 1863. Port., 282 pp. and index. 12mo, cloth. [Lake City, Minn.: The Home Printery, 1909.] $10.00

Scarce. The author was a member of Marsh's company stationed at Fort Ridgely in '62, and with the Sibley Expedition in '63; he witnessed, from the beginning to the end, the stormy scenes attending the outbreak and its suppression, and from contact and observation became familiar with the history of the Sioux Massacre. He kept a diary of events, and no day was allowed to pass without the record being preserved. The author claims for the work a presentation of much material never before known, and among other things "the only detailed historical account of the Sibley Expedition of 1863 ever published."

976 WALLACE, JOSEPH. Sketch of the Life and Public Services of Edward D. Baker, U. S. Senator from Oregon, and formerly Representative in Congress from Illinois, who died in battle near Leesburg, Va., Oct. 21, A.D., 1861. 144 pp., port. 12mo, cloth. Springfield: Wallace, 1870. $4.50

Smith 4229.

977 WALPOLE, LIEUT. FRED. Four Years in the Pacific in Her Majesty's Ship "Collingswood" from 1844 to 1848. 2 vols., 8vo, cloth. London: Bentley, 1849. $17.50

The author arrived at Monterey July 16, 1846. He mentions the troubles of the times, especially the Ede and Bear Flag Fight.

978 WALTON, W. B. Eskimo or Innuit Dictionary, as spoken by all those strange People on the Alaska Peninsula, the Coast of Bering Sea and the Arctic Ocean, including Settlements on all the Streams emptying into these waters. 32 pp., 16mo, original wrappers. Seattle, N.d. $4.50

979 WARD, D. B. Across the Plains in 1853. Port. 55 pp. 12mo, original printed wrappers, with signed autograph presentation inscription from the author. Seattle: Privately Printed (1911). $42.50

This narrative is one of especial interest because of the route traversed, the hardships and perils encountered, and for its rich lore of the buffalo, the ox-team and the covered wagon. The Ward Party set out in March of 1853 from Arkansas, crossed through the Indian Territory, and journeyed by way of the Santa Fe Trail to Bent's Fort, the Spanish Peaks and the present site of Denver. Pushing northward they struck the main overland trail at the North Platt, which they travelled to the Green River, thence by way of the old Oregon Trail to the Dalles, which they finally reached in October.

980 WARD, H. G. Mexico in 1827. Two large folding maps, large folding lithographic views and illustrations. 2 vols., 8vo, half calf. London, 1828. $10.00

981 WARDNER, JAMES. Jim Wardner, of Wardner, Idaho. By Himself. Port. 154 pp., 12mo, cloth. N. Y., 1900. $4.50

Autobiography of the founder of Wardner, and one of the discoverers of the Bunker Hill and Sullivan mine in the Coeur d'Alenes. Also contains adventures in the Black Hills, Arizona, California, Nevada, Idaho, and the Northwest.

982 WARE, JOSEPH E. The Emigrant's Guide to California. Reprinted from the 1849 edition, with introduction and notes by John Caughty. Map. 8vo, cloth. Princeton, 1932. $3.00

983 WARRE, CAPT. HENRY J. Sketches in North America and the Oregon Territory. Map and twenty beautifully executed plates in colors, with the Account of his Journey Across the Continent from Canada to Oregon Territory and Pacific Ocean. Large folio, cloth. London (1848). $275.00

A choice copy of this rare work with the beautiful colored plates. See Barber Sale 887.

984 WARREN, E. SPALDING. Memoirs of the West; (Containing the Diary of Mrs. H. H. Spalding's Overland March Across the Continent, Feby., 1836, to March, 1838. Letters of Spalding, 1842-45, on Affairs at Vancouver, Walla Walla, Clear Water, etc. Reminiscences of Spalding's daughter, etc.). 153 pp., 12mo, cloth. Portland, Ore. (1917). $5.00

Wagner-Camp 68 (note). The author was the first American white child born in the Pacific Northwest who reached maturity, being born at Lapwai Mission (now in Idaho), in 1837. As a little girl of 10 she was at the Whitman Mission at the time of the Massacre and was an eye-witness of the butchery.

985 WARREN, GOUVERNEUR K. WARREN. Memoir to Accompany the Map of the United States from the Mississippi River to the Pacific Ocean, giving a brief Account of the Exploring Expeditions since A.D. 1800, with a Detailed Description of the method adopted in compiling the General Map. 120 pp., maps. 8vo, cloth. Washington, 1859. $7.50

986 WATSON, C. B. Prehistoric Siskiyou Island and Marble Halls of Oregon. 147 pp., 12mo, cloth. N.p. [Ashland, Ore.], 1909. $12.50

Smith 4326.

This work was privately printed some 35 years ago and has now almost disappeared.

987 WAUGH, LORENZO. Autobiorgaphy. Numerous ports. and illus. 12mo, cloth. 311 pp. Oakland, 1883. $15.00

Original Edition, giving the life and adventures of a California pioneer who crossed the plains in 1852; life in the Indian Country, historical events, etc.

988. ——. The same. 351 pp. San Francisco, 1885. $6.00

989 [WAR BETWEEN THE STATES.] Review of the Judge Advocate General on the Proceedings, Findings and Sentence of a General Court Martial held in the City of Washington for the Trial of Major General Fitz John Porter of the U. S. Volunteers. 31 pp., 8vo, original printed wrappers. Washington: Chronicle Press, 1863. $1.50

990 [WAR OF 1812.] Reports of Two Cases in the Prize Court for the New York District. By the Hon. William P. Van Ness. 59 pp., 8vo, unbound. N. Y.: Gould, Banks and Gould, 1814. $7.50

The outstanding legal case of the War of 1812 wherein Judge Van Ness decided against the American captors of a prize vessel. The latter, under American registry, owned by an American citizen but a native Britisher, sailed from England before war was declared and was captured in American waters after the declaration. The case attracted much attention at the time. The owners of the privateer were represented by the celebrated Colden and Ogden. From the library of Richard Rush. Not in Harbeck.

991 [WAR OF 1812.] Message from the President of the U. S., transmitting Documents relative to the Execution of the First Article of the late Treaty between the U. S. and Great Britain. Feb. 7, 1817. 103 pp., 8vo, unbound. Washington: Davis, 1817. $4.50

992 WASHINGTON, GEORGE. Washington and the West: Being George Washington's Diary of Sept., 1784 kept during his Journey into the Ohio Basin in the interest of a Commercial Union between the Great Lakes and the Potomac River. Edited by A. B. Hulbert. Front. and maps, 217 pp. 8vo, cloth. N. Y., 1905. $6.00

993 [WASHINGTON STATE.] Steilacoom Library Association. Constitution, Bylaws, and Rules and Orders of the Steilacoom Library Association . . . organised in March, 1858. 12 pp., 12mo, original wrappers. Steilacoom: Puget Sound Herald, 1860. $15.00

994 [WASHINGTON STATE.] The Everett Massacre, a History of the Class Struggle in the Lumber Industry. 302 pp., 12mo, original wrappers. Chicago: The Industrial Workers of the World Publishnig Bureau, N.d. $6.00

995 [WASHINGTON STATE.] Constitution of the State of Washington, with Marginal Notes and a full Index. By Andrew Wood. 74 pp., original wrappers. Seattle, 1889. $5.00

996 [WASHINGTON STATE.] Washington, the Evergreen State, and Seattle, its Metropolis. 59 pp., illus. 8vo. Seattle: Crawford, 1890. $2.50

997 WASHINGTON STATE. (Lincoln County). The Story of Lincoln County, Wash. By Richard F. Steele. 28 pp., 8vo, original wrappers. Spokane (1909). $4.50

998 [WASHINGTON STATE.] Rand McNally Sectional Map of Washington. 40x60 inches. Fine large map. Chicago, 1890. $4.50

999 [WASHINGTON STATE.] Report of the Joint Special University Committee of the House and Senate appointed to investigate the Title to the University Lands in the City of Seattle, under concurrent resolution of Dec. 5, 1889, together with Legal Opinion of Judge Struve Burke, of Seattle, as to Vested Rights of the State to the Ten Acre Tract. Also Testimony of John Arthur and John Kean. 93 pp., 8vo, original wrappers. Olympia, 1890. $15.00

Can't locate other copies in bibliographies consulted.

1000 [WASHINGTON STATE.] State of Washington. Enabling Act and Constitution, with side notes and index. 93 pp., 8vo, cloth. Olympia, 1891. $7.50

1001 [WASHINGTON STATE.] Laws and Regulations governing the National Guard of Washington. 597 pp., 12mo, cloth. Olympia, 1892. $4.50

1002 [WASHINGTON STATE.] Washington, the Evergreen State. By Julian Ralph. Contained in Harper's Monthly Magazine, Sept., 1892. 8vo, original wrappers. N. Y., 1892. $2.00

1003 [WASHINGTON STATE.] Second and Final Report of the Harbor Line Commission. 142 pp., 14 large folding maps. 2 vols., 8vo, original wrappers. Olympia, 1893. $6.50

Smith 4268.

1004 [WASHINGTON STATE.] Steel and Searl's Legislative Manual for 1895-1896; containing list of members of all Legislative Sessions, Territorial and State Officers, State Institutions and Boards of Government and other Information in relation to the State of Washington. 159 pp., illus., port. 8vo, cloth. Seattle: Koch, 1895. $3.50

Smith 4271. Contains many portraits paged in as text.

1005 [WASHINGTON STATE.] Port Townsend and Hadlock Directory, 1897. 95 pp., 8vo, boards. Seattle (1897). $7.50

1006 [WASHINGTON STATE.] Legislative Manual and Political Directory for 1899. 102 pp., 12mo, cloth. Olympia, 1899. $2.50

Smith 4271.

1007 [WASHINGTON STATE.] Glimpses of Pioneer Life on Puget Sound. By Rev. A. Atwood. 8vo, cloth, illus. Seattle, 1903. $6.00

Smith 138. History of Methodism in the Pacific Northwest.

1008 [WASHINGTON STATE.] Report of the Commissioner of Public Lands, 1901-2. 100 pp., 8vo, cloth. Seattle, 1903. $2.50

1009 [WASHINGTON STATE.] An Illustrated History of Southeastern Washington, including Walla Walla, Columbia, Garfield and Asotin Counties, Wash. 874 pp., 4to, sheep. The Western Historical Pub. Co., Spokane, 1906. $12.50

1010 [WASHINGTON STATE.] Railroad Commissioners' Map. Large folding, size 38x48 in. (Seattle), 1907. $2.50

1011 [WASHINGTON STATE.] Sketches of Washingtonians. 320 pp., 8vo, half morocco. Seattle, 1907. $7.50

1012 [WASHINGTON STATE.] Steele, Richard F. The Story of Lincoln County, Wash. 28 pp., 8vo, original wrappers. Spokane (1909). $3.00

1013 [WASHINGTON STATE.] Captain Pete of Puget Sound. By James Cooper Wheeler. 275 pp., front., illus. 8vo, cloth. N. Y. (1909). $5.00
Smith 4358.

1014 [WASHINGTON STATE.] State of Washington, its Resources, Natural, Industrial and Commercial. 104 pp., illus. 8vo, original wrappers. Olympia, 1909. $2.00

1015 [WASHINGTON STATE.] Surface Water Supply of the U. S., 1907-8. Part 12, North Pacific Coast. By J. C. Stevens and F. F. Henshaw. 418 pp., illus. 8vo, half morocco. Washington, 1910. $3.50

1016 [WASHINGTON STATE.] Water Powers of the Cascade Range. Part 1, Southern Washington. By John C. Stevens. 94 pp., illus., maps. 8vo, half morocco. Washington, 1910. $4.50

1017 ——. The same. Part 3, Yakima River Basin. By Glenn L. Parker and Frank B. Storey. 169 pp., illus., 20 folding maps. 8vo, half morocco. Washington, 1916. $4.50

1018 [WASHINGTON STATE.] Memorial Addresses in Joint Session of Senate and House, Thirteenth Legislature of the State of Washington, 1913. 107 pp., plates. 8vo, cloth. (Olympia, 1913). $2.50

1019 [WASHINGTON STATE.] Water Powers of the Cascade Range. Part 2, Cowlitz, Nisqually, Puyallup, White, Green and Cedar Drainage Basins. By Fred F. Henshaw and Glenn L. Parker. 170 pp., illus., maps. 8vo, half morocco. Washington, 1913. $4.50

1020 [WASHINGTON STATE-OLYMPIA.] Tillicum Tales. Early History of Thurston County, together with Biographies and Reminiscences of those Identified with Pioneer Days. By Mrs. George E. Blankenship. Numerous illus. 8vo, cloth. Olympia, 1914. $8.50

1021 [WASHINGTON STATE.] (Pierce County). Volume 2 of the State Historical Society Publications. [Commemorative Celebration at Sequalitchew Lake. Published by the Pierce County Pioneer Society.] 488 pp., 8vo, cloth. Olympia, 1915. $7.50

1022 [WASHINGTON STATE.] Pamphlet containing a copy of all Measures "proposed by Initiative Petitions", "measures passed by the Legislature and referred, by petition, to the People", "proposd to the Legislature and referred to the People", and "Amendment to the Constitution, proposed by the Legislature. To be submitted to the Legal Voters of the State of Washington . . . at the General Election . . . Nov. 7, 1916, together with all Arguments filed for and against such Measures". Comp. and issued by I. M. Howell . . . 64 pp., 8vo, original wrappers. Olympia: Lamborn, (1916). $3.50

1023 [WASHINGTON STATE.] Statutes of Washington Territory and State from the First Session, 1854 to the Session of 1915. Lacking 1858, 1859, 1861. 41 vols., 8vo, sheep and original wrappers. Olympia, 1854-1915. $137.50

1024 [WASHINGTON STATE.] Skagit County, Washington. 98 pp., 8vo, original wrappers. Mt. Vernon, Wash., 1921. $7.50

1025 [WASHINGTON STATE.] Washington for the Farmer. 77 ppp., illus. 8vo, original wrappers. N.p., 1924. $2.00

1026 [WASHINGTON STATE.] Williams, Lewis P. Chinook By the Sea. 136 pp., 12mo, cloth. Ridgefield, Wash., 1924. $7.50

The above work is a local history embracing the region bordering on the Columbia River and the counties of Pacific, Wahkiakum, Cowlitz, and Clark.

1027 [WASHINGTON STATE.] Halcyon Days in Port Townsend. By C. H. Hanford. 118 pp., 8vo, cloth. Privately Printed for the Author. Seattle, 1925. $7.50

Has the inscribed signature of Agnes C. Laut.

1028 [WASHINGTON STATE.] Williams, L. R. Our Pacific County. 110 pp., 8vo, cloth. Raymond, Wash., 1930. $5.00

History of Pacific County, Wash.

1029 [WASHINGTON STATE.] Views of Columbia River, Puget Sound and Alaska. By Ward Brothers, Publr. 8vo, cloth. N.p., N.d. $3.00

1030 [WASHINGTON STATE.] Watson C. Squires. By Clinton A. Snowden. 24 pp., frontis., 8vo, half morocco. N.p., N.d. $7.50

Squires was a Governor of Washington and a U. S. Senator. Can locate no other copies.

1031 [WASHINGTON STATE.] Chief Seattle's Unanswered Challenge. Spoken on the Wild Forest Threshold of the City that bears his Name, 1854. By John M. Rich. 45 pp., 8vo, original wrappers. N.p., N.d. $3.50

1032 [WASHINGTON HISTORIAN, THE.] Vol. 1, Numbers 1-4 incl. Vol. 2, Numbers 1-4 incl. Sept., 1899 to July, 1901, all published. 201-211 pp., 2 vols., 8vo, cloth. Tacoma, 1899-1901. $37.50

Smith 4314. The above work, which comprises the complete issue, has become very difficult to find. Bound in with the above is Vol. 1, No. 1, Oct., 1893, of the Washington Hist. Mag.

1033 WASHINGTON HISTORICAL SOCIETY. Vol. 1, No. 1, Oct., 1906 through Jan., 1914. Followed by the continuation, Vol. 1, No. 1, 1915 through Oct., 1935. Followed by the continuation The Pacific Northwest Quarterly, Jan., 1926 to date. In all 33 vols., 8vo, with the original wrappers bound in. Seattle, 1906-1942. $125.00

A complete set such as the above is seldom offered. This set is a storehouse of information relating to the discovery and settlement of the Northwest.

1034 [WASHINGTON MAGAZINE.] Pacific Magazine. Vol. 1, Sept., 1889. 11 numbers. [Should be 32 numbers.] 8vo. Seattle, 1889. $12.50

Smith 2955. The title to the above reads "Washington Magazine". No complete file of the work has been reported.

1035 [WASHINGTON PIONEER ASSOCIATION.] Transactions for the Years 1883 to 1889, inclusive, with Constitution and By-Laws; also Annual Addresses and other matters of interest to Pioneers, compiled by Charles Prosch. 154 pp., 2 ports. Seattle, 1894. Together with the Transactions . . . from 1905-1910. Compiled by Thomas W. Prosch. 65 pp., 2 ports. Seattle, N.d. Together with Proceedings of the Years 1903 and 1904, with a Historical Sketch of the Organization . . . 51 pp., Seattle, 1904. All bound together in one volume. 8vo, half morocco. Seattle, 1894, 1904 (1910). $22.50

Smith 4298, 4299, 4300.

1036 [WASHINGTON PIONEER ASSOCIATION.] Proceedings for the year 1903-1904, with Historical Sketch of the Organisation . . . 51 pp., 8vo. Seattle, 1904. $7.50

Smith 4298.

1037 [WASHINGTON TERRITORY.] Surveyor General Report. The Report and Decision of the Surveyor General of Washington Territory of the Catholic Mission Claim at Vancouver. 12mo, 16 pp., sewn. Printed at the Office of the Washington Standard: Olympia, 1862. $67.50

Can locate no other copy.

1038 [WASHINGTON TERRITORY.] Opinions of the Supreme Court of the Territory of Washington, in cases Argued and Determined in said Court from its organization to the Term ending Jan. 27, 1864. 256 pp., 8vo, calf (hinge cracking). Olympia: McElroy, 1864. $17.50

A rare work.

1039 [WASHINGTON TERRITORY.] Journals of the House of Representatives, as follows: 1st sess., 1854, 189 pp.; 2nd sess., 1854, 177 pp.; 3rd sess., 1855, 255 pp.; 4th sess., 1856, 153-cxxxiii pp.; 5th sess., 1857 (missing); 6th sess., 1858, 240 pp.; 7th sess., 1859, 293 pp.; 8th sess., 1860, 298 pp. (lacks first 8 pp.); 9th sess., 1861, 21596 pp.; 10th sess., 1862, 223-L pp.; 11th sess., 1863, 304 pp.; 12th sess., 1864, 341 pp.; 13th sess., 1865, 335 pp.; 14th sess., 1866 (missing). Volume 15 is the beginning of the 1st biennial sessions, as follows: 1st sess., 1867, 426 pp.; 2nd sess., 1869, 528 pp. (last page missing); 3rd sess., 1871, 359-240 pp.; 4th sess. (not printed); 5th sess., 1875 339 pp.; 6th sess., 1867, 334 pp.; 7th sess. (not printed); 8th sess., 1881, 359pp.; 9th sess., 1883(not printed); 10th sess., 1885 (missing); 11th sess., 443 pp. This is the end of the Territorial Sessions. Then follows the Journals of the House of Representatives of the State of Washington, from the 1st sess., 1891 to the 14th sess., 1915. Together with Washington Territory. Journals of the Council, as follows: 1st sess., 1854, 220 pp.; 2nd sess., 1854, 177 pp.; 3rd sess., 1855, 213 pp.; 4th sess., 1856 (missing); 5th sess., 1857 (missing); 6th sess., 1868, 232 pp.; 7th sess., 1859, 295 pp.; 8th sess., 1861, 323 pp.; 9th sess., 1861 (missing); 10th sess., 1862, 164-lxvii pp.; 11th sess., 1863, 200 pp.; 12th sess., 1864, 246 pp.; 13th sess., 1865, 264 pp.; 14th sess., 1866, 279-CI pp. Session 15 is the beginning of the Biennial Sessions, as follows: 1st sess., 1867, 279-[CI pp.; 2nd sess., 1869 (missing); 3rd sess., 1871, 237-240 pp.; 4th sess., 1873, 185-13 pp.; 5th sess. (not printed); 6th sess., 1877 (missing); 7th sess., 1879, 216 pp.; 8th sess. (not printed); 9th sess., 1883, 258 pp.; 10th sess. (not printed); 11th sess., 1887, 312 pp. This is the end of the Territorial Council Sessions. Then follows the Journals of the Council of the State of Washington from the 1st sess., 1891 to the 14th sess., 1915 Together 40 vols., 8vo. Olympia, Wash., 1855-1915. $375.00

1040 [WASHINGTON TERRITORY.] Descriptive Article of Whatcom County, Washington Territory, showing its Wonderful Natural Resources and Commercial Advantages. With a Short Sketch of the City of Whatcom, the future Pacific Terminal of the Great Canadian and Northern Pacific Railways on Belligham Bay. 11 pp., 8vo, original wrappers. Whatcom, 1885. $15.00

Can locate no other copies.

1041 [WASHINGTON PRESS ASS'N.] Proceedings of the Washington State Press Association. 1st-11th, 1887-1898. All bound in one volume. 8vo, cloth. V.p., V.d., 1887-1898. $27.50

Smith 4321-4322.

1042 [WASHINGTON, UNIVERSITY OF.] Association of Instructors. The Salary Situation at the University of Washington. 38 pp., 8vo, original wrappers. Seattle, 1919. $12.50

1043 WEBB, W. E. Buffalo Land: An Authentic Account of the Discoveries, Adventures, and Mishaps of a Scientific and Sporting Party in the Wild West; with graphic descriptions of the Country; the Red Man, Savage and Civilised; Hunting the Buffalo, Antelope, Elk and Wild Turkey, etc. Illus. 8vo, cloth. Cincinnati and Chicago, 1872. $7.50

1044 WEBB, WM. SEWARD. California and Alaska, and over the Canadian Pacific Railway. 268 pp., illus. 8vo, cloth. N. Y., 1891. $5.00

Smith 4330. Pages 140-161 deal with Montana; pp. 210-239, with Alaska.

1045 WEBBER, CHARLES W. Old Hicks, the Guide; or, Adventures in the Comanche Country in search of a Gold Mine. 12mo, cloth (rebacked). N. Y., 1848. $7.50

Wagner-Camp 158. Original Edition. The first 98 pages contain the Journal of an Overland Expedition to Western Texas. Webber later joined with Gen. Walker in his Central American Filibustering enterprise and was killed there in 1858.

1046 WEBSTER, E. B. The Ferns of the Olympics. 26 pp., illus. 8vo, original wrappers. Port Angeles, Wash., 1918. $5.00

1047 WEBSTER, E. B. The King of the Olympics. The Roosevelt Elk and other Mammals of the Olympic Mountains. 227 pp., illus. 8vo, cloth. Port Angeles, Wash., 1920. $7.50

1048 WEBSTER, E. B. Fishing in the Olympics. 227 pp., illus. 12mo, cloth. Port Angeles, Wash., 1923. $5.00

1049 WEBSTER, KIMBALL. The Gold-Seekers of '49. A Personal Narrative of the Overland Trail and Adventures in California and Oregon from 1849 to 1854. With an introduction and Biographical Sketch by George W. Brown. Illus., 12mo, cloth. Manchester, 1917. $3.50

1050 WEEKS, HELEN C. White and Red. A Narrative of Life among the Northwest Indians. 266 pp., front., illus. 8vo, cloth. N. Y., 1870. $5.00

1051 WELCH, WILLIAM. Report of a Visit to the Sioux and Ponka Indians on the Missouri River, 1872. 36 pp., original wrappers. Phila., 1872. $5.00

1052 WELD, ISAAC. Travels Through North America and Canada, 1795-1797. Folding colored map, engraved maps and plates. 488 pp., 4to, original half calf (worn and scuffed). London: Stockdale, 1799. $17.50

1053 WELLCOME, HENRY S. The Story of Metlakahtla [British Columbia]. Second Edition. Port. and plates. 12mo, original cloth. London, 1887. $7.50

Author's signed presentation copy. A history of the settlement from the time of Capt. Cook with an account of the conversion of the natives from barbarism to peaceful pursuits under the tutorship of William Duncan, the Missionary.

1054 WELLES, C. Three Years' Wanderings in California and South America. With a Detailed Account of Unusual Hardships, Sufferings, Privations, Disappointments and Dangers. 358 pp., plates. 12mo, cloth. N. Y., 1859. $7.50

The author went to California in 1854. He describes San Francisco, life in Sacramento; trip from French Creek across the Sierra Nevadas to Carson Valley; the Indian tribes; experiences among the Mormon Refugees; exploring tour through Petaluma and Santa Rosa Valleys; Vigilance Committee; and finally "hints to travelers" on the climate and resources of California and the routes thither.

1055 WELLS, EDWARD. A New Set of Maps, both of Ancient and Present Geography. Mit 41 doppelseitigen Karten in Kupferstich, Delin. M. Burghers, sculp. Univ. Oxon., R. Spofforth, sculp. Gut erhaltenes, breitrandiges, Exemplar. Halblederbd. Folio. London, 1718. $15.00

1056 WELZL, JOHN. Thirty Years in Golden North. Transl. by Paul Selver. 336 pp., map. 8vo, cloth. N. Y., 1932. $2.50

1057 WENTWORTH, MAY. Poetry of the Pacific and Original Poems selected from the Poets of the Pacific States. 415 pp., 12mo, cloth. San Francisco, 1867. $6.00

1058 WERNER, M. R. Brigham Young. 478 pp., 8vo, cloth. N. Y., 1925. $2.50

1059 WEST, JOHN. The Substance of a Journal During a Residence at the Red River Colony, and Frequent Excursions among the North-West Indians, in the years 1820-23. Plates. 210 pp. and leaf of errata. 8vo, original boards, uncut. London, 1824. $15.00

Brailin 1866. The personal narrative of life among the Indians and the fur traders of the Northwest and Hudson's Bay Country, with interesting particulars of the variout tribes, hunting adventures, the Russian settlements on the Northwest Coast, the Sioux War, etc.

1060 WEST, LEOTI L. The Wide Northwest. Historic Narrative of America's Wonderland as seen by a Pioneer Teacher. 286 pp., frontis. 12mo, cloth. Spokane, 1927. $5.00

1061 [WESTERN MISCELLANY, THE.] Volume 1 (all published), July, 1848 to June, 1849. Edited by B. F. Eels. 12mo, calf. Dayton, Ohio, 1848-49. $30.00

A rare work containing Slacum's History of Oregon and Dr. Gardiner's "Salmon of the Columbia River".

1062 [WESTERN PRESS ASS'N.] Who's Who in the Northwest. A Biographical Dictionary of Notable Living Men and Women in the Northwest. Illus. 12mo, sheep. Portland (1911). $6.00

1063 WHEELER, ARTHUR O. The Selkirk Range. 459 pp., frontis., illus. and an Atlas of folding plates and maps. 2 vols., 8vo, cloth. Ottawa, 1905. $10.00

Brief review of Franchere, Ross, Cox and other early travelers, the coming of the Canadian Pacific Railway, Rocky Mountain triangulation, etc.

1064 WHEELER, (COL.) HOMER W. Buffalo Days. Forty Years in the Old West. The Personal Narrative of a Cattleman, Indian Fighter and Officer. 361 pp., illus. 8vo, cloth. Indianapolis, 1925. $6.00

The Wheelers were a hardy mid-western and far western clan who struggled and died in the expanionist movement of America. The author was apperntly one of the sturdy Ulster County, N. Y., or Upper Hudson Valley New Yorkers. He apparently went west after the Civil War, roamed the frontier as a Scout-Cowboy and finally ended up as a Colonel.

1065 WHEELOCK, T. B. Journal of Colonel Dodge's Expedition from Fort Gibson to the Pawnee Pict Village. Pp. 73-93 of the Report of the Sec'y of War, attached to the President's Message, Dec. 2, 1834. Ex. Doc. 1, 23rd Cong., 2nd sess. (Washington), 1834. $22.50

Wagner-Camp 61. This contains an account of the expedition to Toyash Village and a council with the Indians, signed by T. B. Wheelock, first Lieut. of the Dragoons, and dated Ft. Gibson, Aug. 27, 1834.

1066 WHIPPLE, HENRY BENJAMIN. Lights and Shadows of a long Episcopate. 576 pp., 8vo, cloth. McMillan, N. Y., 1899. $4.75

1067 WHITE, STEWART EDWARD. The Conjuror's House. A Romance of the Free Forest. 260 pp., illus. 8vo, cloth. N. Y.: McClure, 1903. $4.50

Smith 4366.

1068 WHITE, STEWART EDWARD. The Silent Places. 305 pp., 8vo, cloth. N. Y.: Outing, 1904. $4.50

Relates to Hudson's Bay.

1069 WHITE, STEWART EDWARD. The Mountains. 282 pp., illus. 8vo, cloth. N. Y.: McClure, 1904. $4.50

1070 WHITE, STEWART EDWARD. Camp and Trail. vii-236 pp., illus. N. Y.: Outing, 1907. $4.50

1071 WHITE, STEWART EDWARD. The Cabin. 283 pp., illus. 8vo, cloth. N. Y., 1911. $4.50

1072 [WHITMAN COLLEGE.] The Story of Marcus Whitman. 7-32 pp., illus. Walla Walla, Whitman College, 1909. (Whitman College Quart., V. 12, No. Reprint from V. 1, No. 1, Jan., 1897). 8vo, original wrappers. Walla, Walla, 1909. $6.50

Smith 4370.

1073 [WHITMAN COLLEGE.] The Whitman College Quarterly, Vol. xvi, No. 2. 8vo, original wrappers. Walla, Walla, 1913. $6.50

Contains the unpublished journals of William H. Gray.

1074 WHITMAN COLLEGE QUARTERLY, Volumes 1-3, Jan., 1897 to June (?), 1900. 8vo. Walla Walla, Wash., 1897-1900. $40.00

Smith 4371. Contains much material relating to Marcus Whitman and his associates in the Oregon mission. It was discontinued with v.3, no. 4, commencement number, 1900.

1075 [WHITMAN MASSACRE.] Report of the Sec'y of Interior, communicating, in answer to the Senate Resolution, the Report of J. Ross Browne, on the Late Indian Wars of Oregon and Washington Territories. 35th Cong., 1st sess., Sen. Ex. Doc. 40. 66 pp., 8vo, ¾ crimson calf, fine. 1858. $12.50

1076 [WHITMAN MASSACRE.] The Early Labors of the Missionaries of the American Board of Foreign Missions in Oregon, commencing in 1836, and other Documents pertaining to the same. By Rev. H. H. Spalding. 81 pp., 8vo, sewn. Washington (1871). $20.00

(1) Oregon of 1834. (2) Helpless conditions of the territory under the Hudson's Bay Co. (3) Hostilities of the company to American citizens. (4) The Missions and their importance in securing the country to Americans. (4) The Whitman Massacre and the attempt to break up the American settlement. (6) Who intigated the Indians to murder the Missionaries and the Americans?

Rev. Spalding, who barely escaped the massacre, went to his grave bitter against the Hudson Bay's officials and certain members of Society of Jesus whom he claimed instigated the uprising against the Whitman settlement and mission. Bancroft and others long ago repudiated Rev. Spalding's charge.

1077 WHITNEY, ASA. Memorial of Asa Whitney, Praying a Grant of Public Land to enable him to construct a Railroad from Lake Michigan to the Pacific Ocean. Folding map. 8vo, unbound, 10 pp. (Washington, 1846). $25.00

This is Gov. Doc. 29th sess., 1st sess., sen. rep. 161. Whitney was the first business man in the country to suggest the feasibility of building a railroad to the Pacific. He was finally instrumental in securing appropriations in 1853 for the first surveys.

1078 WICKERSHAM, JAMES. The Alaska Railway Bill. Speech of the Hon. James Wickersham, of Alaska, in the House of Representatives, Jan. 14-28, 1914. 135 pp., 8vo, original wrappers. Washington, 1914. $1.00

1079 WILKES, CHARLES. Report upon the Territory of Oregon. No. 104. U. S. Ship Vincennes. N. Y., 1842. $7.50

The above is 40 pages of typescript of the original report which was never published as it was at the time considered incompatible with our national interests.

1080 WILKES, CHARLES. Narrative of the U. S. Exploring Expedition, during the Years 1838-42. Condensed and abridged. 8vo, cloth. London (1844). $4.00

1081 WILKES, CHARLES. Narrative of the U. S. Exploring Expedition, 1838-42. Illustrated with numerous maps and plates. Royal 8vo, and Atlas in 4to. 6 vols., cloth. Phila.: Lea and Blanchard, 1845. $22.50

1082 WILKES, CHARLES. Narrative of the U. S. Exploring Expedition during the Years 1838-42. 2 vols., illus., 8vo, cloth. London, 1852. $7.50

1083 [WILKES EXPEDITION.] Twenty Years before the Mast. With the more Thrilling Scenes and Incidents while Circumnavigating the Globe under the Command of the late Admiral Charles Wilkes, 1838-1842. By Charles Erskine. Illus. 12mo, cloth. Phila.: 1896. $7.50

Erskine was a member of the Wilkes Expedition to Oregon.

1084 WILKINS, J. H. The Great Diamond Hoax, and other Stirring Episodes in the life of Asbury Harpending; an Epic of Early California. Portraits. 283 pp., 8vo, cloth. San Francisco, 1913. $3.50

This work is really the life story of one of California's famous characters and early pioneers, Asbury Harpending.

1085 WILLIAMS, GEO. H. Occasional Addresses. 208 pp., port., 8vo, cloth. Portland, Ore., 1895. $6.00

Smith 4414. pp. 44-61, Pioneers of Oregon; pp. 129-137, Oregon and California railroad; pp. 138-148, Portland; pp. 167-172, Portland Exposition; pp. 172-175, Judge M. P. Deady.

1086 WILLIAMS, JOSEPH. Narrative of a Tour from the State of Indiana to the Oregon Territory in the Years 1841-2. With an Intro. by James C. Bell, Jr. 8vo, cloth. N. Y., 1921. $6.00

One of the 3 existing narratives of the Oregon migration of 1841. Although Williams, Bidwell and De Smet started overland for Oregon together, the latter two deserted the trail for different goals. Bidwell left the party on Bear River for California, while De Smet turned north at Ft. Hall to visit the Flatheads on the Upper Columbia. Williams held to his way and therefore his work becomes the first to tell the story of the trail.

1087 WILLIAMS, J. G. The Adventures of a Seventeen Year Old Lad and the Fortunes he Might Have Won. 308 pp., plates. 8vo, cloth. Boston: Privately Printed for the Author, 1894. $25.00

The author was a pioneer of '49, and his narrative of wanderings, adventure and life in the gold diggings in the early days is most interesting and readable. He describes San Francisco as it was in '49; tells of his experiences at the Carson Creek Mines; the great finds; questionable methods of the early traders; the Coulterville mines; encounter with Joaquin Murietta; Three Fingered Jack; the Vigilance Committee and their methods; the Fraser River Rush and adventures in British Columbia; prospecting on the Thompson River; Life among the Indians; winter in the mountains, etc.

1088 WILLIAMS, R. H. With the Border Ruffians. Memories of the Far West, 1852-1868. By R. H. Williams, Sometime Lieutenant in the Kansas Rangers and Afterwards Captain in the Texas Rangers. Illus. 8vo, cloth. N. Y., 1907. $7.50

1089 WILLIARD, DANIEL E. The Story of the Prairies. The Landscape Geology of North Dakota. 377 pp., 8vo, cloth. Chicago, n.d. $7.50

1090 WILLIARD, EMMA. Last Leaves of American History, comprising Histories of the Mexican War and California. 230 pp., flldg. map. 12mo, cloth (foxed). N. Y., 1849. $3.50

1091 WILSON, ELIJAH N. Among the Shoshones. Portrait and Plates. 22 pp., 8vo, cloth. Salt Lake: Skelton Pub. Co., (1910). $37.50

The Original Suppressed Edition with 222pp., the revised edition, after textual changes, contains 247pp. Both are scarce. The author crossed the plains in 1850, thenafter was trapper, Indian fighter, Pony Express Rider, Ox-Team freighter, Overland Stage driver, companion of Kit Carson, Howard Egan, Charley Webster, Jim Donaldson and Frank Mathis. He was also an adventurer in Wyoming, Montana, Idaho, Utah and throughout all the Rocky Mountain country. He was a guide for Gen. Albert Sidney Johnston; was interpreter during the Jackson Hole troubles; was a Mormon and knew the Mountain Meadows Massacre was about to take place and rode hard to warn the emigrant train but was too late. He refers to Gen. Harney and speaks with a bluntness of speech and plainness hard to come upon.

1092 WLISON, ELIJAH N. The White Indian Boy. The Story of Uncle Nick among the Shoshones. Revised and edited by Howard R. Driggs . . . xii-222 pp., illus., 8vo, cloth. Yonkers, N. Y., 1919. $2.50

Wilson crossed the plains in 1850. He gives a sketch of pioneer days in the west, Indian troubles, desert tribes, the gathering of the Shoshones in Deer Lodge Valley, Montana; story of buffalo hunts, Pony Express, Overland Stage, etc.

1093 WILSON, HARRY LEON. Ruggles of Red Gap. 371 pp., 12mo, cloth. N. Y., 1915. $4.00

The Original Edition. A story of the Northwest.

1094 WILSON, ROBERT A. Mexico, including California and Central America. 463 pp., 8vo, cloth. N. Y., n.d. $3.00

1095 WILSTACH, FRANK J. Wild Bill Hickok, the Prince of Pistoleers. 304 pp., illus., 8vo, cloth. N. Y., 1926. $3.00

1096 WINSER, HENRY JACOB. Great Northwest; a Guide-Book and Itinerary for the use of Tourists and Travelers over the Lines of the Northern Pacific Railroad, the Oregon Railway and Navigation Company, and the Oregon and California Railroad . . . 276 pp., illus., map in pocket. 12mo, cloth. N. Y., 1883. $6.50

Smith 4435.

1097 [WINSER, HENRY JACOB.] The Pacific Northwest . . . Oregon and Washington Territory . . . issued for the Information and Guidance of Settlers and Others. 88 pp., 11 plates. 12mo, cloth. N. P., n. pub., 1882. $7.50

Smith 4440. Apparently issued by the Portland Bureau of Immigration.

1098 WINSHIP, A. E. and WALLACE, ROBERT W. The Louisiana Purchase as it was and is. 175 pp., 12mo, cloth. Chicago, (1903). $3.75

1099 WINSOR, JUSTIN. Mississippi Basin: Struggle in America between England and France, 1697-1763. Maps. 8vo, 484 pp., 8vo, cloth. Boston, 1895. $7.50

1100 WINTHROP, ROBERT CHAS. Speech of Mr. Winthrop of Massachusetts on the Oregon Question, delivered in the House of Representatives of the U. S., Feb. 1, 1845. 16 pp., 8vo, sewn. Washington, 1845. $3.00

Smith 4442.

1101 WINTHROP, THEODORE. Cecil Dreeme. ix-360 pp., 8vo, cloth. Boston, 1862. $4.50

See Fullerton's "Bibliography of American Literature".

1102 WINTHROP, THEODORE. The Canoe and the Saddle. Adventures among the Northwestern Rivers and Forests; and Isthmiana. 375 pp., 8vo, cloth. Boston, 1863. $7.50

Original Edition. Contains a vocabulary of the Chinook Jargon, sketches of Indians and Indian life, etc. Smith 4444; and Fullerton's "Selected Bibliography of American Literature".

1103 WINTHROP, THEODORE. The Canoe and the Saddle; or, Klalam and Klicktat, together with Western Letters and Journals and Reminiscences of the men who knew Winthrop, with a biographical and historical introduction and notes by J. H. Williams. 8vo, half parchment, printed on antique paper. Tacoma, 1912. $7.50

The above work is illustrated with 16 page plates in color, 48 one-color page half-tones and 60 line etchings showing the scenery of the Northwest.

1104 [WISCONSIN.] Durrie, Daniel S. A History of Madison, the Capital of Wisconsin; including the Four Lake Country, to July, 1874. With an Appendix on Dane County and its Towns. Original photographs tipped in. 8vo, cloth. Madison, 1874. $12.50

1105 [WISCONSIN.] Letter of the Secretary of the Treasury communicating a Report of a Georgraphical Reconnoissance of the Chippewa Land District of Wisconsin, and the northern part of Iowa, by David Dale Owen. 134 pp., 24 fine engraved plates, large folding map, and 12 fldg. charts and plans. 8vo, sewn. Washington, 1848. $4.50

1106 WISLIZENUS, FREDERICK A. (M.D.) Memoir of a Tour to Northern Mexico, connected with Col. Doniphan's Expedition, in 1846 and 1847. With a Scientific Appendix and Three Maps (folding). 141 pp., 8vo, sewn, entirely uncut. Washington, 1848. $15.00

Wagner-Camp 159.

1107 WISLIZENUS, FREDERICK A. (M.D.). A Journey to the Rocky Mountains in the Year 1839. Translated from the German, with a Sketch of the Author's Life by Frederick A. Wislizenus, Esq. Port. 8vo, boards. St. Louis, 1912. $12.50

500 copies printed by the Missouri Historical Society.

1108 WISLIZENUS, FREDERICK A. (M.D.). Denkschrift uber eine Reise nach Nord-Mexico, verbunden mit der Expedition des Obersten Donniphan, in den Jahren 1846 und 1847. 3 fldg. maps, 211 pp., 8vo, original printed wrappers. Braunschweig, 1850. $7.50

A German translation of Wagner-Camp 159, in the Original Wrappers.

1109 WISTAR, ISAAC JONES. Autobiography of, 1827-1905. 526 pp. front., map. 8vo, cloth. Phila., 1937. $3.50

1110 WISTER, OWEN. Red Man and White. By Owen Wister. Illustrated by Frederick Remington. First Ed. 8vo, cloth. N. Y., 1896. $7.50

1111 WITHERS, ALEXANDER. Chronicles of Border Warfare, or a History of the Settlement by the Whites, of Nort-Western Virginia; and of the Indian Wars and Massacres in that section of the State; with Reflections, Anecdotes, etc. 12mo, old calf. Clarksburg, Va.: Published by Josef Israel, 1831. $25.00

1112 [WOLCOTT, OLIVER.] Memoirs of the Administrations of Washington and John Adams, edited from the Papers of Oliver Wolcott, Secretary of the Treasury. By George Gibbs. Port. 2 vols., 8vo, cloth. N. Y., 1846. $6.50

1113 WOOD, STANLEY. Over the Range to the Golden Gate. A Complete Tourist's Guide to Colorado, New Mexico, Utah, Nevada, California, Oregon, Puget Sound and the Great Northwest. Numerous illus. 8vo, cloth. Chicago, 1891. $1.25

1114 WOOL, JOHN E. Campaign in Mexico, 1846-48. By Francis Baylies. Port., 8vo, original printed wrappers. Albany, 1851. $7.50

Gen. Wool was the outstanding General in the Battle of Buena Vista. He did not seem to get his just rewards until Mr. Baylies wrote the above work. Gen. Wool later became head of the troops in Oregon and Washington Territory.

1115 WOOLEN, WILLIAM W. The Inside Passage to Alaska, 1792-1920; with an Account of the North Pacific Coast from Cape Mendocino to Cook Inlet, from the Accounts left by Vancouver and other early Explorers, and from the Author's Journals of Explorations and Travel in that Region; edited . . . by Paul Haworth. Illus., colored map. 2 vols., 8vo, cloth. Cleveland: Clark, 1924. $10.00

1116 WOOLEY, CLIVE PHILLIPS. Trottings of a Tenderfoot; or, a Visit to the Columbian Fiords. 8vo, cloth. London, 1884. $6.00

The author visited Portland, Puget Sound, Vancouver, and the Rocky Mountains.

1117 [WORLD WAR.] Collected Diplomatic Documents relating to the Outbreak of the European War. 561 pp., 8vo, original boards. London, 1915. $2.00

1118 WRANGELL, FERDINAND P. Narrative of an Expedition to the Polar Sea, in the years 1820-1823 . . . ed. by Edward Sabine. 137-413 pp., map in pocket. 8vo, cloth. London, 1854. $7.50

Smith 4471.

1119 WRAXALL, C. F. LASCELLES. The Backwoodsman; or, Life on the Indian Frontier. Illus., 12mo, original cloth, 302 pp., fine. Boston: Burnham, 1866. $7.50

Interesting accountt of a settlement on the Rio Grande, of hunting and Indian fighting throughout the southwest.

1120 WRIGHT, E. W. (Ed.). Lewis and Dryden's Marine History of the Pacific Northwest; and Illustrated Review of the growth and development of the Marine Industry, from the advent of the Earliest Navigators to the Present Time, with Sketches and Portraits of a number of well-known marine men . . . 49 pp., illus. Folio, cloth. Portland, Ore., 1895. $17.50

Smih 4473.

Early discoveries, Meares, Gray, Heceta, Vancouver, etc. Log books of the Beaver, Sulphur, etc. Early boats on the Columbia; Indian Massacres; Puget Sound History; San Juan Troubles; Fraser River Gold; steamboating on the Snake River; British Columbia and Alaska boating, etc.

Item 1120, Fifth line should read 494pp.

1121 WRIGHT, WILLIAM H. The Grizzley Bears. The Narrative of Hunter-Naturalist. Historical, Scientific and Adventurous. x-274 pp., illus. 8vo, cloth. N. Y., 1909. $6.00

Relates largely to the Pacific Northwest.

1122 WRIGHT, WILLIAM H. The Black Bear. 127 pp., illus. 8vo, cloth. N. Y., 1910. $6.00

Hunting in the Pacific Northwest.

1123 WRIGHT, WILLIAM. "Dan De Quille." History of the Big Bonanza: the Discovery, History and Working of the Comstock Silver Lode of Nevada. Illus. 8vo, cloth. Hartford, 1877. $10.00

Hagner Sale 1552.

WYETH'S "OREGON" IN ORIGINAL WRAPPERS, UNCUT

1124 WYETH, JOHN B. Oregon; or, a Short History of a Long Journey from the Atlantic Ocean to the Region of the Pacific by Land; Drawn up from the Notes and Oral Information of Joseph B. Wyeth, one of the Party who left Nathaniel J. Wyeth, July 28th, 1832, four days march beyond the Rocky Mountains, and the only one who has Returned to New England. 87 pp., 12mo, original printed wrappers, entirely untrimmed. Cambridge, 1833. $300.00

Wagner-Camp 47. As fresh and crisp a copy, with the original wrappers and half-title, would be hard to find.

1125 ——. The same. Lacks wrapper. $225.00

1126 WYETH, NATHANIEL. Correspondence and Journals of Nathaniel J. Wyeth, 1831-6. A Record of two Expeditions for the Occupation of the Oregon Country, with Maps, Introduction and Index . . . Edited by F. G. Young . . . 262 pp., 2 maps. [Sources of the History of Oregon, v. 1, pts. 3-6, Eugene, Ore., University Press, 1899.] $7.50

Smith 4480.

1127 WYOMING. Morris (Robert C.). Collections of the Wyoming Historical Society. Volume One (all published). Map, plates, early historical views, etc. 352 pp., 8vo, cloth. Cheyenne, 1897. $25.00

A treasure-house of out-of-the-way far western historical material written by the pioneers themselves. The volume is seldom met with. Among its rich contents we cite the following: Morris' "Sketch of Wyoming: early History, Explorations, Live Stock Industry, Mineral Wealth, etc.;" Col. A. G. Brackett's "Account of the First Settlements in Wyoming Territory;" "Fort Laramie in 1846;" Breckon's "Account of Washakie, Chief of the Shoshones;' Major W. H. Powells "Early History of Fort Laramie;" Capt. Nickolson's "Indian Depredations in Sweetwater County;" Baldwin's "Narrative of the Surrender of the Black Hills;" "The Custer Fight;" "Wounded in an Indian Fight" by Gen. Henry; 'Jim Bridger, the Famous Guide of the Rocky Mountains;" Carroll's "Pioneer Days of Cheyenne and Early Reminiscences of Bill Nye;" "The Overland Trail" by Charles Whitehead; "The History of Old Fort Casper;" Shaffer's "Early History of Evanston;' and "Recollections of Uinta County' by F. L. Arnold.

1128 [WYOMING.] The Nation and the State Civil Government of Wyoming. By Frank H. H. Roberts. 262 pp., 12mo, cloth. Syracuse, 1902. $3.00

1129 [WYOMING.] Guernsey, Chas. Arthur. Wyoming Cowboy Days. 288 pp., illus., 8vo, cloth. N. Y., 1936. $3.75

1130 WILD, JAMES. Voyages that have been attempted to Discover a Northern Passage to the Pacific Coast. Compiled by J. Wild and Printed from Stone in the Quarter Master General's Office, Horse Guards. 6 pp., folding map. 4to. London, 1818. $30.00

A scarce work by one of Britain's leading 19th century cartographers. The work is one of the earliest examples of printing from stone.

1131 [YELLOWSTONE PARK.] Yellowstone National Park; or, the Great American Wonderland. By W. W. Wylie. 99 pp., 8vo, cloth. Kansas City, 1882. $6.00

1132 YOUNG, EGERTON RYERSON. Stories from Indian Wigwams and Northern Camp-Fires. 293 pp., 8vo, cloth. Toronto: Briggs, 1893. $3.50

1133 YOUNG, EGERTON RYERSON. On the Indian Trail; Stories of Missionary Work among the Crees and Saulteaux Indians. 214 pp., illus. 12mo, cloth. Chicago, 1899. $3.50

1134 YOUNG, EGERTON RYERSON. The Apostle of the North. Rev. James Evans. 262 pp., illus., 12mo, cloth. Toronto: Briggs, 1900. $4.50

1135 YOUNG, FRANK C. Across the Plains in '65. A Journal from "Gotham" to "Pike's Peak." Large folding map of the route. 224 pp., 12mo, original cloth. Denver: Privately Printed, 1905. $30.00

Original Edition with the copyright pasted in. This copy is No. 117 of 200 copies printed. The journal is in day-by-day form and narrates the trip from Atchison, via the Little Blue and Platte Rivers to Julesburg, thence down the South Platte to Denver in 1865. Young's train made the trip in 42 days.

1136 YOUNG, COL. HARRY. Hard Knocks; a Life Story of the West. Photographic plates. 242 pp., 12mo, cloth. Portland, Ore.: Privately Printed, 1915. $12.50

Original Edition. An interesting personal narrative relating the early days of Dodge City, Laramie, Cheyenne and Deadwood; of dance halls and gambling saloons; border characters; frontier railroad building and army life; Indian fights; freighting and post trading; Wild Bill Hickok.

1137 ZIMMERMAN H. Reise um die Welt mit Capitain Cook. M. Protratvignette (Silhouette). 8vo, boards, fine, clean copy. 110 pp. Mannheim, 1781. $225.00

Original Edition of an excessively rare work. In 1930 the well-known authority, Judge F. W. Howay, made a world census of this work and was unable to locate more than four copies of this edition.

Zimmermann was a brass-founder who, after travelling through Europe, took part as a sailor in Capt. Cook's third and last voyage to the Pacific Ocean and to the N. W. Coast of America, 1776-80. He was assigned to the crew of the "Discovery," commanded by Capt. Clerke, and though only a simple workman he gives a lively description, in concise form, of all the important events during the voyage. He deals at length with the death of Capt. Cook and the characer of the great explorer. This is the first narrative of this great voyage that appeared in print, as the original English edition in three volumes was not issued until 1784. See Howay's "Zimmermann's Captain Cook" for further remarks on this work.

INDEX

INDEX

ALPHABETICAL AND SUBJECT INDEX TO THE FOUR PARTS OF THE GEORGE W. SOLIDAY COLLECTION OF NORTHWESTERN AMERICANA

——. Relacion del Viage 1792. II, 17b
Aldritch (H. L.). Arctic Alaska. 1899. I, 83
Aldritch (H. L.). I, 83
Alexander (H. B.). The Religious Spirit of the American Indian. 1910. I, 85
Alexander (P. F.). Northwest and North East Passage, 1576-1611. 1911. II, 18
Alexander (R. H.). Narrative of Incidents . . . Across the Rocky Mountains. 1862. Original manuscript, typewritten copy. N.d. I, 86
Alexander (T.). Experiences of a Trapper. 1924. I, 87
Alexander (W. D.). I, 641
Alelander (W. Earl of Stirling). I, 111
Alger (H.). Young Adventurer; or, Tom's Trip Across the Plains. 1878. II, 19
Alla (O.). Blue Eye. Story of the Plains. 1905. II, 20
Allen (A. J.). Ten Years in Oregon. 1848. II, 21
——. Ten Years in Oregon. Ithaca, 1848. II, 22
——. The Same. With Fremont extracts. II, 23
Allen (E. W.). North Pacific: Japan, Siberia, Alaska, Canada. 1936. I, 89
Allen (Ethan). I, 88
Allen (Joseph). Making of a Canadian. 1918. IV, 58
Allen (W.). The Army of Northern Virginia in 1862. 1892. I, 91
Allen (W. A.). The Sheep Eaters . . . Indians of Montana and Wyoming. 1913. II, 24
——. Adventures with Indians and Game. 1903. I, 90
Allen (W. B.). The Red Mountain of Alaska (1889). I, 92
Allen (W. W.) and Avery (R. B.). California Gold Books. 1893. I, 94
Alling (H.). Why We Vote. 1900. I, 93
Allsopp (F. W.). The Life Story of Albert Pike. 1920. III, 735
Alter (J. C.). James Bridger, 1804-1881. (1925). II, 25
Altowan. 1846. II, 1268
Alvord (C. W.) and Bidgood (L.). Explorations of the Trans-Allegheny Region, 1650-1674. 1912. I, 95
Alvord (C. W.). Publications of the Illinois State Hist. Society. 1907. III, 24
Ambler (C. H.). History of Transportation in the Ohio Valley. 1932. III, 25
——. Life and Diary of John Floyd, Governor of Virginia. (1918). II, 26
American Quarterly Register and Magazine. Vols. I-VI (all published). 1851. IV, 800
American Board for Foreign Missions Ann. Reports. 1834-1850. I, 849
American Journal of Science and Arts. Six Numbers from July, 1848 to May, 1849. 1848-49. I, 98
American Pioneer. Monthly Periodical. Logan Historical Society. 1843-4. III, 49
American Revolution. Debates in the Legislature of Pennsylvania on the Case of Gideon Olmstead. Reported by William and Hugh Hamilton. Printed and Published by William Hamilton, June, 1810. 1810. IV, 69b
Amherst (L. J.). Journal in America, 1758 to 1763. (1931). III, 184
Amoretti (C.). II, 1006-7
Anburey (T.). IV, 69
Anderson (A. C.). Dominion of the West, a Brief Description of British Columbia. 1872. I, 133
——. Handbook and Map of the Gold Region of Fraser's and Thompson's Rivers. 1858. I, 132
Anderson (A. D.). Silver Country of the Great Southwest . . . Mexico. 1877. III, 837
Anderson (A. W.). Heart of the Red Fir. 1908. II, 29
——. Rim of the Desert. 1915. II, 31
——. Strain of White. 1909. II, 30
Anderson (C. L.). Soldier and Pioneer: a Biographical Sketch of Lt. Richard C. Anderson. 1879. I, 106
Anderson (E.). Personal Recollections in the Revolutionary War. 1896. II, 27b
Anderson (G. H.). Vancouver and his Great Voyage: 1757-98. 1923. I, 134
Anderson (J. J.). Did the Louisiana Purchase extend . . . 1880. I, 135
Anderson (R.). History of the Mission . . . to the Sandwich Islands. 3rd ed. 1872. I, 136
Anderson (Lt. R. C.). I, 106
Andre (Maj. John). Major Andre's Journal. 1930. I, 101
Andreana. History of Major John Andre. 1865. I, 102
Andre (Maj. J.). I, 100, 102, 113, 124; IV, 77
Andreas (H. T.). Cook County, Ill. 1884. III, 231
Andrews (C. L.). Story of Alaska. (1931). I, 138
——. Story of Sitka. (c. 1922). I, 137
Andrews (C. M.). Colonial Period of American History. (1935). III, 26
Andrews (L.). Vocabulary of Words in the Hawaiian Language. 1836. I, 1057. II, 32 [Contents 132pp.]

Annales de la Propagation de la Foi. 1877-1923. IV, 410b
——. Complete run 41 vols. 1822-63. I, 139 [Lyon Edition.]
Annals of Harper's Ferry. 1872. IV, 117
Annals of Newtown. 1852. III, 386
Annual Register 1790. 1791. III, 405
——. Same. 1793. II, 1231
——. Same. 1793. I, 1326
Anson (G.). Atlas. N.d. I, 141
——. Voyage, 1740-44. 1748. I, 140
Anthony (C. V.). Fifty Years of Methodism. 1901. II, 35
Anti-Chinese Riots, 1885-6. III, 914
Apianus (P.). Cosmographia, siue Descriptio Universi Orbis. 1584. I, 156
Apple Growing in the Pacific Northwest. c. 1911). I, 96
Applegate (J.). II, 36, 352; IV, 593
——. Day with the Cow Column in 1843. 1868. II, 38
——. Recollections. By an Oregon Pioneer of 1843. 1914. II, 37; IV, 453
Appleton's Cyclopaedia of American Biography. 1888-9. III, 58
Archiv fur Wissenschaftliche Kunde von Russland. 1842-1859. IV, 561
Arctander (J. W.). Apostle of Alaska. Story of William Duncan of Mellokahtla. (1909). I, 12
Argonaut Press. I, 793
Argus, The. Alaska-Yukon Pacific Edition. I, 1433
——. Historical Edition. 1909. I, 1432
Argyle (A). Cupid's Album. 1866. II, 39
Arikara Campaign. General Gaines to the Secretary of War, July 28, 1823. II, 40
Armath (Capt.). II, 39
Armstrong (A. N.). Oregon: a Brief History. 1857 [dated wrongly 1867 in text]. IV, 444; I, 144
Armstrong (B. G.). Early Life among the Indians. 1892. I, 145
Armstrong (M. K.). Empire Builders of the Great West. 1901. I, 146; IV, 204
Arnold (B.). I, 100, 123, 125; II, 27e; III, 54; IV, 77, 173
Arnold (R. R.). Indian Wars of Idaho. 1932. I, 1243
Arnold (R. R.) and (Elta, M.). Outlines of the Constitution of the U. S., of the State of Idaho. (1928). I, 1241
——. Outline of the Constitution of the U. S. of the State of Idaho. N.d. I, 1242
Arnold (S. G.). History of Rhode Island. 1859-60. I, 1430; III, 792
——. History of Rhode Island and Providence Plantations. 1874. III, 63
Arrowsmith, A. Folio Atlas of North America. N.d. I, 157
Ashland Club, Ashland, Oregon. (c. 1905). I, 1336
Ashley-Smith Exp. I, 671; III, 361
Ashman (G.). Speech upon the Texas Boundary. 1850. III, 849
Astor (J. J.). I, 857-8, 1223, 1350; III, 673, 753; IV, 78, 533
——. Landlord of New York. 1929. I, 151
——. Notable Lawsuit. 1898. I, 152
Astoria, Astoria and Columbia River Railroad. N.d. III, 527
Astoria, Oregon and Clapsop County. (1905). I, 1337
Atchison and Eshelman. Los Angeles Then and Now. By Atchison and Eshelman. 1897. I, 496
Atego. History of Atego. (1907). III, 377
Atherton, G. Splendid Idle Forties. 1902. II, 33
——. Rezanov. 1906. II, 34
Atherton (W.). Narrative of the Suffering and Defeat of the Northwestern Army under General Winchester. 1842. I, 1274; III, 858
Atkin (B.). Sketches of Early Buffalo and the Great Lakes. Also a Sketch of Alaska. 1898. I, 153
Atkinson (G.). III, 268
Atkinson (G. H.). Fruits of the Oregon Mission. 1869. I, 154
Atkinson (Rev. G. H.). Northwest Coast, Including Oregon, Washington and Idaho. 1878. IV. 79; II, 41
——. Biography. 1893. II, 42
——. In Memoriam. 1889. II, 43
——. Missions on Pacific Coast. 1849. I, 155
Atlas of the Northwest. N.d. I, 965
Atwood (A.). Glimpses in Pioneer Life on Puget Sound. 1903. I, 164
——. Conquerors. Historical Sketch of Settlement of Oregon Country. (1907). II, 44
Atwood (J. M.). Travellers' Guide through the States of Ohio, Michigan. Map of Chicago, Detroit, St. Louis and Cincinnati. 1856. IV, 217
Aube (T.). Notes sur le Centre-Amerique Vancouver et la Columbie Anglaises. 1877. I, 165
Aubry (F. X.). I, 288
Audubon (I. L.). Scenes de la Nature. E. Bazin. I, 166
Audubon (J. J.). IV, 80
——. American Scenery and Character. 1926. I, 170
——. Life of. By Mrs. Audubon. 1901. I, 169

——. "Oregon." Struggle for Possession. 1885. II, 58

Barrows (Gen. Wm.). Three Thousand Miles up the Missouri. 1865. I, 234

——. To Idaho and Montana. 1865. I, 233

Barrows (W.). Struggle for Possession. 1885. I, 1343

Barry (J. S.). History of Massachusetts. 1855. III, 314

Barry (T. A.) and Patten (B. A.). Men and Memories of San Francisco in the Spring of '50. 1873. II, 60

Barsukov, (F. P.). II, 1270d

——. Tvoreniia. (Works of Innocent, Metropolitan of Moscow). 1886-88. I, 236

Bartlett (C. H.). Tales of Kankakee Land. 1907. I, 1263; IV, 363

Bartlett (J.). II, 61

Bartlett (J. R.). Personal Narrative of Explorations. 1854. I, 237

Bartlett (L. B. D.). Dictionary of Chinook. 1924. I, 238

——. Chinook-English Songs. (1914). I, 239

——. Student's History of Northwest and State of Washington. (1922). III, 62

Barton's Legislative Hand-Book of Washington, 1889-90. 1890. II, 1273

——. 1891-2. 1891. II, 1274

——. 1893-4. 1893. II, 1275

——. 1895-6. 1896. II, 1276

Barton's State of Washington. Legislative Hand-Book and Manual, 1893-94. 1893. I, 1495

——. Same, 1889-90. 1890. I, 1496

——. Same, 1891-92. 1892. I, 1497

Bartram (J.). Observations made in his Travels from Pennsylvania. 1895. III, 67

Barwick (G. F.). III, 421

Bashford (J.). Oregon Missions. 1918. I, 1344

Bashford (H.). Songs from Puget Sound. 1898. I, 241

——. Stories of Western Pioneers. N.d. I, 200

——. Tenting of Tillicums. (1906). I, 242

Bass (F.). Early Times in Great West. (1927). I, 243

Bass (S. F.). Gig-Tail Days in Old Seattle. (1937). I, 1437

——. Adventures in Canyons of Colorado. 1920. I, 244; IV, 74

Bates (D. B.). Incidents on Land and Water. 1858. II, 63

Bates (R. S.). Man on the Dump. (1909). II, 64

Batt-Crosley (J. L.). Last of the California Rangers. 1928. I, 461

Battay (T.). Life and Adventures among Indians. c. 1875. I, 245

Baudry Des Lobieres (Louis Narcisse). Voyage a la Louisiane, 1794-98. 1802. I, 246

Baughman (T.). Oklahoma Scout. N.d. II, 65

Baylies (F.). Campaign in Mexico, 1846-48. 1851. IV, 1114

——. Narrative of Maj. General Wool's Campaign in 1846-48. I, 247; II, 67

——. Northwest Coast of America. 1826. II, 66

Baywater (J. W.). Perils, Pastimes and Pleasures in Australia, Vancouver's Isl. and California. 1849. IV, 12b

Bazin (E.). I, 166

Beadle (J. H.). Life in Utah. 1870. I, 251

——. Undeveloped West. 1873. I, 249

——. Western Wilds. 1878. I, 250

——. Western Wilds, and Men who Redeem Them. (1879). IV, 90

Beale (E. F.). I, 323; II, 514

Beardsley (A. S.). Code Making in Early Oregon. 1936. II, 68

Beardsley (Com. L. A.). Affairs in Alaska, 1879. 1880. I, 14

Beaton (W.). City that made Itself: a Record of Seattle. (1914). I, 1436

Beattie (R. K.). III, 4634

Beauchamp (S. T. D.). Iroquois Trail, 1892. I, 248; IV, 321

Beaufoy (Col.). I, 229

Beaver. Journal of Progress . . . Hudson's Bay Company. Vol. 1, 1920 to date. II, 69

Bechdolt (F. R.). Tales of Old-Timers. (c. 1924). I, 253

——. When the West Was Young. 1922. I, 252

Becknell (Capt. T.). Journal. 1910. I, 254; II, 70

Beckwith (L. F.). III, 18

Beckwourth (J. P.). I, 321

Beebe (Mrs. I.). True Story of Swiftwater Bill Gates by his Mother-in-Law. (1908). II, 71

Beecham (R. K.). Sacajawa and Land of Oregon. 1905. I. 1345

Beecher (I.). II, 929-30

Beechey (Capt. F. W.). Narrative of Voyage to Pacific and Behring's Strait. 1831. I, 255

——. Same. 1832. I, 256

Beeson (J.). Plea for Indians. 1857. II, 72

——. Same. 1858. II, 73

——. Plea for Indians: 1857. IV, 445

Begg, A. Creation of Manitoba. 1871. I, 257

——. History of Northwest. 1894. II, 74

Beggs (S. R.). Pages from Early History of West and Northwest. 1868. III, 68

——. Pacific Railroad. 1869. I, 333
Bowman (Jacob). Archives of State of Washington. 1908. 1910. I, 334
Bowman (Major Jos.). III, 251
Box (Capt. M. J.). Adventures and Explorations, 1869. III, 61
Boyd (Joseph H.). I, 1244; II, 120
Boyd (Robert). History of Synod of Washington of Presbyterian Church in U. S. of A., 1835-1909. N.d. I, 335
Boyer (Lt.). Journal of Wayne's Campaign. 1866. III, 150
Boyer (Mary C.). Arizona in Literature. 1934. III, 79
Boynton (C. B.) and Mason (T. B.). Journey Through Kansas; with Sketches of Nebraska. 1885. IV, 99
Brabrant (A. J.). Vancouver Island and Its Missions, 1874-1900. N.d. I, 336
Brace (Charles Loring). New West. 1869. II, 121
Brackett (Albert G.). History of U. S. Cavalry. 1865. II, 122
Brackett (Linus Pierpont). Our Western Empire. 1881. II, 123
Brackenridge (H. M.). Views of Louisiana. 1814. II, 124
Bradbury (John). II, 124
——. Travels in Interior of America. 1809-11. 1817. I, 340
Braddock (Gen. Ed.). IV, 473
Bradford (Aleden). History of Massachusetts, 1620 to 1820. 1835. I, 1286
Bradford. Atlas of the U. S. 1838. I, 338
Bradford's History of Kentucky. 1932. IV, 266
Bradford (W. J. A.). Notes on the Valley of Upper Mississippi. 1846. I, 339
Bradford (Wm. J. A.). Notes on Northwest. 1846. IV, 402
Brady (Cyrus Townsend). Northwestern Fights and Fighters. 1913. I, 341
——. Indian Fights and Fighters. 1913. I, 343
Bradley (Glenn D.). Story of the Pony Express. 1913. II, 125
Bradley (Thomas H.). O'toole's Mallet. N.d. I, 342
Brady (Samuel). Sketches of Life and Adventures of Capt. Samuel Brady. 1891. IV, 471
——. Sketches of Life and Indian Adventures of. 1914. I, 1411
——. West Wind. 1912. II, 126
Brady (William). Glimpses of Texas. 1871. III, 844
Brainerd (Rev. David). Memoirs: Missionary to the Indians on the Borders. 1822. III, 80
Bramble (Charles A.). Klondike. Manual for Gold-Seekers. (1897). II, 127
Branch (E. Douglas). Westward. 1930. I, 344
Brant (Joseph). III, 53; IV, 790
Brassard (A. M.). Lettre du Pere Chiniquy. 1857. III, 229
Bratt (John). Trails of Yesterday. 1921. I, 345
Braughman (Theodore). [Vide Baughman.] Oklahoma Scout. N.d. IV, 407
Breckenridge (H.). III, 272
Breckenridge (John G.). III, 292
Bremer (F.). Homes of the New World. 1853. III, 81
Brenchley (Julius). I, 1428; IV, 497
Brent (John). III, 350
Brereton (Robert Maitland). Reminiscences of an old English Civil Engineer, 1858-1918. 1908. I, 346
Brewerton (G. Douglas). I, 1062
——. Ride with Kit Carson. 1853-1862. I, 347
Brice (W. A.). History of Ft. Wayne. 1868. III, 260
Bridger (James). I, 182; II, 25, 339; III, 90
Bridges (Robert). Rail and Water Facilities. 1916. II, 128
Bridges (Woodman). Shooting Skyward. 1912. I, 348
Brief Notice of Present Outrage Committed by Isaac I Stevens. 1856. IV, 767a
Briggs (Howard R.) and McConnell (William J.). Frontier Law; Story of Vigilante Days. 1924. II, 129
Bright (Gen. Michael). IV, 690
Brininstool (E. A.). I, 1076
Brinistool (E. A.). Trooper with Custer. 1925. II, 130
Bristol (Rev. S.). Pioneer Preacher. 1887. IV, 186
——. Pioneer Preacher. 1898. I, 349
Britannicus. 1427. I, 1407a
British-American Joint Com. for Settlement of Claims of H. B. C. and Puget Sound Agricultural Co. I, 350
British Columbia. Archives of. Memoir No. 8.
British Columbia Archives. House of Assembly Correspondence Book, 1856-59. 1918. I, 385
1928. I, 382
[British Columbia.] British Association for Advancement of Science. 1889. I, 371
——. British North American Act of 1867. 1873.
——. Days of Old and Days of Gold. 1922. I, 379
——. 11 docs. on Expl. Settlement. etc. III, 916

——. Lu Tel Kaimin tis Kolinzuten-Kuitlt Smiimii. 1879. (Should be 1876). (Some attribute this work to Father Giorda). I, 560

——. Paradigma Verbi Activi. Lingua Numipu. 1888. I, 561

——. Prayers Catechism Hymns in Numipu. 1909. I, 563

Catalogue of Books and Pamphlets Principally Relating to America. (The Bonn Library). 1870. IV, 92

Catholic Church. A.M.D.G. Canotle Rannaga Kelebak Delochet Roka. 1904. I, 565a

Catlin (George). North American Indian Portfolio scenes of Rocky M. and Prairies of America. 1844. I, 570a

Caton (John D.). Antelope and Deer of America. 1877. I, 572

——. Origin of Prairies. 1869. I, 571

Catlin (George). Last Rambles Amongst Indians. 1868. I, 569

——. Letters and Notes on N. American Indians. 1841. I, 570

Cattermole (E. G.). Famous Frontiersmen. 1883. I, 573

Caughty (John). IV, 982

Caverly (Robt. B.). Heroism of Hannah Duston. 1874. III, 364

Cawston (Geo.) and Keane (A. H.). Early Chartered Companies. 1896. I, 574

Cayuse War. Coll. of words. III, 927

Central Pacific Railroad across continent. 1868. I, 575

Central Pacific Railway of California. 1867. II, 1253

Central Point Commercial Club. (c. 1905). I, 1477

Certain Confidential Correspondence of the Foreign Office and of Hudson's Bay Company. 1899. I, 1200

Cession of American Territory; Pacific Coast Protest against yielding by U. S. of any portion of Alaska to Canada. [1899]. IV, 7

Chadwick (H. A.). Men Behind Seattle Spirit. 1906. I, 1444

Chadwick (S. F.). I, 1377

Chamberlain (A. F.). I, 1049

[Chamberlain, E. J.]. In the Beginning: Old Williamette Days. (1905). I, 576

Chambers (Margaret White). Reminiscences (1903). II, 197

Chambers Miscellany of Useful and Entertaining Tracts. 1845. I, 1353

Chambers Repository. Accounts of Fur Trade. 1853-54. I, 879

Champlain Society Publications. Complete Set. 1907-1942. IV, 170

Champness (W.). To Cariboo and Back. 1865 I, 577

Chandler (George). Textbook of Civics for State of Washington. (1910). II, 198

Chandler (Katherine). Bird Women of Lewis and Clark Expedition. 1905. II, 199

Chandless (Wm.). Visit to Salt Lake. 1857. II, 200

Channing (Wm. H.). III, 688

Chapleau (l'Hon. M.). Discours de sur les Resolutions du Shemin de Fer C. P. 1885. I, 532

Chapin (Louella). Round About Chicago. (1907). IV, 314

Chaplin (Ralph). Centralia [Wash.] Conspiracy. N.d. I, 578

Chapman (Chas. E.). Catalogue of Materials in Archive de Indias. 1919. II, 201

Chapman (Charles H.). Story of Oregon. (c. 1907). I, 1354

Chapman (J. T.). French in the Alleghany Valley. (1887). III, 131

Chapman (John W.). Alaska's Great Highway. 1909. I, 17

Chapman (Katherine Hopkins). The Fusing Forces. An Idaho Idyl. 1911. II, 202

Chappe d'Auteroche (Jean). Voyage en Siberia. 1769. I, 453

Chapell, (Lieut. Edward). Voyage to Hudson's Bay. 1817. IV, 308

——. Voyage to Hudson's Bay. 1817. I, 579

Chapman (W. O.). Diary of Amateur Explorer in Glacier Nat. Park. 1911. I, 580

Charlevoix (P. F. V. De). History and General Oescription of New France. 1900. III, 132

——. Voyage to North America. 1761. I, 581

Charter for Consolidation Cities of Portland, East Portland and Albina. 1891, III, 593

Chase (Geo. Washington). History of Haverhill, Mass. 1860. 1861. I, 1285

Chase (S. P.). Relations between U. S and Northwest British America. 1862. I, 582

Chastellux (Marquis de). Voyage en Amerique. 1788-91. III, 133

Chateaubriand (Le Vicomte De) Les Natchez. 1864. I, 583

——. Travels in America and Italy. 1828. III, 134

Cheadle (Dr. W. B.). II, 1130, 1132

Cheever (Henry T.). Life in Sandwich Islands. 1851. II, 203

Cheney (W. D.). Central Oregon. 1918. I, 584

Chenoweth (F. A.). Opinion on the return of Habeas Corpus for the Bodies of Chief Justice Lander and others, at Steilacoom, W. T. 1856. II, 204

——. Opinion on the return of the Marshall to Writs of Habeas Corpus. 1856. I, 1498

Colton (Walter). Three Years in California. 1850. II, 233

——. Deck and Port. 1850. II, 234

Columbia County, Ore. (c. 1905). I, 1536

Columbia River. Along Columbia River to Sea. N.d. IV, 749

Columbus (Christopher). III, 142-4, 767

Colvig (Wm. M.). Early Days in Southern Oregon. 1908. I, 1357

Colville (Frederick Veron). Botany of Death Valley Expedition. 1893. I, 620

Colvorcoresses (Lieut. G. M.). Four Years in Government Exploring Expedition. 1852. I, 621

——. Four Years in Government Exploring Expedition. 1855. IV, 184

Colyer (Vincent). Bombardment of Wrangel, Alaska. Report. 1870. I, 622

Coman (Katherine). Economic Beginnings of Far West. 1912. I, 624

——. Economic Beginnings. How we won land beyond the Mississippi. 1921. I, 625

——. Industrial History of U. S. 1910. I, 623

Combier (C.). Voyage au Golfe de California. (c. 1832). I, 459

Comerford (Mary Theresa). Memoir of. 1882. I, 460

Comstock (Henry S.). Recollections of a Busy Life. [1896]. II, 544a

Conard Howard L.). "Uncle Dick" Wootton, Pioneer Frontiersman. 1890. II, 235

——. Same. II, 236

Condon (John). II, 1077

Condon (Mary Alice). Mt. Hood our Indian's Pah-to. (1911). II, 237

Condon (Thomas). II, 947

——. Oregon Geology. Revision of "The Two Islands." 1910. II, 239

——. Two Islands and What Came of Them. 1902. II, 238

Congressional Globe and Appendix. New Series containing Sketches of Debates. First Sess. of 29th Cong. 1846. I, 632

——. New Series, containing Sketches of Debates. 2nd Sess. of 29th Cong. 1847. I, 633

——. 25th Cong., 3rd Sess., Vol. 7. 1939. I, 628

——. 1st Sess., 27th Cong. Vol. 10. 1841. I, 630

——. 2nd Sess., 26th Cong. Vol. 9. 1841. I, 629

——. 3rd Sess., 27th Cong. Vol. 12. 1843. 1, 631

Conkey (W. B.). Official Guide to Klondike and Gold Fields of Alaska. 1897. I, 634

Conn (William). Cow-Boys and Colonels. 1887. IV, 203

Connecticut Historical Society Collections. 1860-1823. III, 147

Connelly (W. E.).

Connelly (Wm. E.). War with Mexico, 1846-47. 1907. I, 1313

Connor (Gen. Patrick E.). Soldiers of the Overland 1938. IV, 268

Conover. Red Jacket, Birthplace of. 1884. III, 380

Conover (C. T.). In the Matter of Proposal to Change Name to Mt. Ranier. N.d. II, 242

——. Mirrors in Seattle. 1923. II, 243

——. Proposal to Change Name of Mt. Ranier. 1917. II, 241

——. Proposal to change the name of Mt. Ranier. 1917. I, 1480

——. Thomas Burke, 1849-1925. 1926. I, 1445

Conover (Geo. W.). Sixty Years in Southwest Oklahoma. 1927. IV, 846

Convention between His Britannick Majesty and King of Spain. 1790. 1790. III, 414

Cook (David J.). Hands Up; or Twenty Yars of Detective Life. 1882. II, 245

——. Same. 1897. II, 246

Cook (Dr. Fred'k.). II, 379

Cook (Capt. James). I, 282, 1071, 1191, 1502; II, 724, 818-9, 911; III, 148, 791; IV, 392 913-4, 1137

——. Voyage to the Pacific Ocean. 1785. II, 247

Cook (James). Fifty Years on the Old Frontier. 1923. I, 637

Cook (John R.). Border and Buffalo. 1907. IV, 334

——. Border and Buffalo. 1907. I, 638

Cook (Marion). Where Flows Hood River. 1907. I, 1358

Cooke (Belle W.). Tears and Victory. 1871. II, 249

Cooke (Geo. Willis). John Sullivan Dwight Brook-Farmer, Editor and Critic of Music. Biography. 1898. IV, 116

Cooke (Jay). III, 476

——. Northern Pacific Railroad. Its Land Grant. 1873. I, 1315

——. The Northern Pacific Railroad. 1873. II, 248

Cooke (Phil. St. George). I, 288

Cooke (P. St. George). Conquest of California and New Mexico. 1878. II, 250

Cooley (Harris Reed). First White Woman to Cross Rocky Mountains. 1890. I, 639

Coolidge (L. A.). Klondike and Yukon Country. 1897. II, 244

Coombs (S. F.). Dictionary of Chinook Jargon. 1891. I, 640

Cooper (J. C.). Military History of Yamihill County. N.d. I, 1361
——. Walnut Growing in Oregon. (1910). I, 1360
——. Yamhills. 1904. I, 1359
Cooper (James G.). IV, 806
Coos Bay. Nature Gateway, Oregon's Deep Sea Port. N.d. I, 1363
Copies of Treaties made May 3 and Aug. 21, 1871, between Queen and Chippewa and Cree Indians. 1873. II, 550
Corbett (Doris S.). II, 1254d
"Cormorant," H.M.S. I, 360
Coronado (Francisco Vasques de). Journey of. 1540-1542. G. P. Winship. F. W. Hodge. 1935. IV, 269
Copy of Correspondence between Chairman of the Hudson's Bay C. and the Secretary of State for Colonies (Earl Grey) re. colonization of Vancouver's Isl. 1848. 1, 1211
Cornelison (J. M.). Weyekin Stories. Titwatit Weyekishnim. N.d. I, 1339
Corney (Peter). Voyages in the North Pacific. 1896. I, 641
Cornish (George H.). Hand-book of Canadian Methodism. 1867. II, 251
Cornwallis (Earl). An Answer to Narrative of Clinton. 1783. I, 109; II, 27c
Cornwallis (Kinahan). New Eldorado; or, British Columbia. 1858. I, 642
Coronado, (Fr. Vazquez). I, 1077
Correspondence between this Government and Gt. Britain on Claims to Territory west of Rocky Mountains. 1928. II, 1289
Correspondence re. Agreement with Russia relative to Seal Fishery. (1895). I, 887
Correspondence re. Seizure of British Schooner "Araunah" by the Russians. N.d. I, 888
Correspondence re. an Agreement for Protection of Russian Sealing interests. (1893). I, 884
Correspondence re. Seizure of British Sealing Vessels by Russian Cruisers. (1893). I, 885
Corvallis and Benton County. (c. 1905). I, 1363a
Corwin (Revenue Cutter). Cruise in Alaska and Arctic Ocean. 1881. 1883. II, 266
——. Report of Cruise in Arctic Ocean, 1885. 1887. II, 267
——. Report in Arctic Ocean, 1884. 1889. II, 268
Costello (J. A.). The Siwash, their Life, Legends. 1895. I, 643
Cottage Grove, Ore. (1905). I, 1362
Cotterill (George F.). The Climax of a World Quest. (1927). I, 643a
Coues (Elliot). Birds of the Northwest. 1877. I, 646
——. Description of Mss. Note Books of Lewis and Clark, etc. 1893. I, 644
——. Description of the original journals and Field Note Books of Lewis and Clark 1893. II, 252
——. In Memoriam: Sergeant Charles Floyd. 1897. II, 849
——. Journal of Jacob Fowler. 1898. I, 645
——. I, 855, 893, 1087; II, 782, 848; III, 738
Coursey (O. W.). Beautiful Black Hills (of South Dakota), (c. 1926). I, 667
Coutant (C. G.). History of Wyoming and Far West. 1899. I, 647
Cowie (Isaac). Company of Adventurers. 1913. I, 647a
Conley (Chas.). Illustrated History of Lowell. 1868. I, 1288
Cox (John Henry). IV, 392
Cox (Ross). Adventures on Columbia River. 1831. I, 648
——. Same. 1832. I, 649
Coxe (William). Account of Russian Discoveries between Asia and America. 1780 II, 253
——. Account of Russian Discoveries between Asia and America. 1787. II, 254
Cozzens (S. W.). Marvellous Country. 1874. II, 255
Cozzens (Samuel Woodworth). Marvellous County. 1874. I, 143
Cradlebaugh (J. H.). Nyeena Kloshe Illahee. 1913. II, 256
Craig (Lulu Alice). Glimpses of Sunshine. and Shade in Far North. 1900. II, 257
Craig (Neville). Washington's First Campaign. 1848. I, 650
Craighead (James G.). Story of Marcus Whitman. 1895. II, 258
Crane (Florence B.). Faithful Indian of St. Ignatius. (1907). I, 1482
Crane (Lauren E.). Newton Booth of California. 1894. I, 462
Crane (Leo). Indians of the Enchanted Desert. 1925. II, 259
Crane (Wm. Carey). Life and Selected Literary Remains of Sam Houston, of Texas. (c. 1884). I, 1452
Capro (Thomas). Strange, but True. Life and Adventures of Captain Capro and Wife. 1893. II, 260
——. Strange, but True. 1893. I, 651
Craven (Herman W.). Errors of Populism. 1906. I, 99
Crawford (C. H.). Scenes Crossing Plains to Oregon. 1898. I, 652
Crawford (George A.). I, 935
Crawford (L. F.). Badlands and Broncho Trails, 1922. I, 653

Fourth line under Custer, Gen. G. A. 3rd figure is 1017.

Dale (H. C.). Ashley Smith Explorations. 1918. I, 671
D'Aligny (Henry F. Q.). Iron Hills Railway Company of Kentucky upon Value of Iron Lands. 1870. III, 282
Dall (Wm. H.). Alaska and its Resources. 1897. I, 673
——. Remains of later Pre-Historic Man from caves in Catherine Archipelago, Alaska T. 1878. I, 672
Dall (W. H.) and Gibbs (Geo.). Tribes of Extreme Northwest [Dall.). Also Tribes of Western Washington and Northern Oregon [Gibbs]. 1877. II, 84
Dalles Methodist Mission Cases. Matthew P. Deady. (1879). II, 285
Dalrymple (Alex). Hist. Coll. of Several Voyages. 1770-1771. III, 415
——. Hist. Journal of Exp. to North of California in 1768-70. 1790. II, 286
——. Milbank's Sound. 1789. I, 684
——. Plan for promoting Fur-Trade. 1789. II, 286a
——. Plan for Promoting Fur Trade. 1789. I, 675
——. Plan of Calamity Harbour. By James Johnstone. 1789. I, 679
——. Plan of Inlet of Bucareli. 1789. I, 680
——. (a) Plan of Port San Diego, 1782. (b) Fanya or Fango(?). Plan to Monterey. (c) Plan of the Road Principle of Santa Barbara. 1789. I, 676
——. Plan of San Francisco. 1789. I, 677
——. Plan of Snug Harbor Cove. 1789. I, 683
——. (a) Plan of St. Patrick's Bay. (b) Chart of part of Northwest Coast. (c) Track of the Snow Experiment. 1789. I, 681
——. Sketch of Ahouset. 1789. I, 678
——. Sketch of Entrance of the Strait of Juan de Fuca. 1790. I, 682
——. Spanish Memorial of 4th June considered. 1790. II, 286b
——. Spanish Pretensions Fairly Discussed. 1790. III, 154a
——. Spanish pretentions fairly discussed. 1790. II, 286c
——. Voyages dans la Mer du Sud. 1774. III, 416
——. Voyages dans la mer du Sud. 1774. I, 674
——. Voyages dans le Mer du Sud, par les Espagnoils and les Hollandois. Freville. III, 425
Daily News. History of Buchanan County and St. Joseph, Missouri. (1898). II, 1136
Damon (C. M.). Sketches and Incidents. 1900. II, 287
——. Trip from Sandwich Islands. 1849. I, 686
——. Same. I, 685
Dampier (Capt. Wm.). Voyages. 1906. II, 288
——. Voyages. 1906. I, 687
Dana (C. M.). The Great West. 1857. I, 688
Dana (Charles A.). U. S. Ill. (1850). II, 289
Dana (E.). Geographical Sketches of Western Country. 1819. IV, 205
Dana (James Dwight). I, 919
Dana (James D.). Corals and Coral Islands. 1872. I, 689
Dana (John Cotton). Far Northwest. 1906. I, 690
Dana. Notes on Upper California. I, 98
Dana (Richard Henry). Two Years before the Mast. 1840. II, 290
Danet (Guile). Map: l'Amerique Meridonale et Septentrionale. 1731. I, 691
Daniels (Joseph). Iron and Steel Manufacture. 1929. I, 692
D'Anville (J. B.). Nouvel Atlas de la China, de la Tartarie Chinoise et du Tibet. 1737 I, 161a
Darby (George H.). Phoenixiana. Collection of Burlesque and Sketches of John Phoenix, alias John P. Squibob. 1937. IV, 271
Darby (Wm) Geographical Description of Louisiana. 1816. II, 291
——. Geographical Description of State of Louisiana. 817. II, 292
——. New Gazetteer of the U. S. 1833. II, 295
——. Tour from New York to Detroit. 1819. II, 293
——. Universal Gazeteer. 1827. II, 294
——. View of U. S. 1930. III, 155
Darling (Esther Birdsall) Baldy of Nome. 1920. II, 297
——. Up in Alaska. (c. 1912). II, 296
Darnell (Elias). Journal. 1854. III, 156
Darlington (Mary Carson). Fort Pitt and Letters from Frontier. 1892. III, 705
Darlington (W. C.). III, 1063
——. III, 833
——. I, 924; III, 497
Daseggende Waschwerk bei den Sibirischen Goldseiben. 1845. III, 800
Dauphin County Historical Society Addresses, July 4, 1876. 1876. III, 706
Davenport (Homer). The Country Boy. (c. 1910). I, 693
Davenport (M.). Under the Gridiron. 1876. I, 694
David (Robert B.). Finn Burnett, Frontiersman. 1937. III, 90
Davidoff (G. I.). 1, 933
Davidson (Alex.) and Stuve. Complete History of Illinois. 1673-1873. 1874. III, 232

Darby, (George, H.) should read Derby.

——. Noticias de Nuka. (Information re Nootka). N.d. III, 417

De Fonte (Admiral Bart.) I, 715; II, 150a, 603, 605, 1903; III, 157a; IV, 941

De Fonte (Admiral Barth). A letter from. 1708. I, 711

De Fuca (Juan). III, 474

De Groot (Henry). British Columbia: its Condition and Prospects. 1859. II, 437

De Haas (Wills). History of Early Settlement and Indian Wars. 1851. I, 712; IV, 206

De Lacy (Capt. W. A.). IV, 376

Delaney (Mathilda J. Sager). Survivor's Recollections of Whitman Massacre. (1920). II, 318

Delano (Alonzo). Life on the Plains. 1854. I, 713

——. Pen-Knife Sketches, or Chips from Old Block. Grabhorn, 1934. IV, 270

Delano (Amasa). Narrative of Voyages and Travels. 1817. I, 714

Delisle (Admiral Jos. Nicholas). Nouvelles Cartes des Decouvertes. 1753. I, 715

Delisle (de la Croyere). III, 351a

Delisle (Guillaume). II, 150a, 603

——. Exploration de la Carte. 1752. With Carte des Nouvelles Decouvertes. (1752). III, 157a

——, III, 157a

Dell (Sidney). Astoria and Flavel, chief Seaport. (1893). II, 4248

——. Book of Clatsop County. 1899. I, 1249

Dellenbaugh (F. S.). Breaking the Wilderness. 1901. I, 719

——. Canyon Voyage. 1905. I, 718

——. Fremont and '49. 1914. I, 717

——. North Americans of Yesterday. 1901. I, 716

——. Romance of Colorado River. 1907. I, 710

Demers (L. J.). Esquisse Generale du Nord-Ouest du Canada. 1886. II, 319

Demers (Modeste). Mission de Vancouver. 1849. I, 721

——. I, 300; II, 98; III, 158; IV, 410a

De Mezieres (Althanese) and Louisiana-Texas Frontier. 1768. 1914. III, 159

De Milt (Alonzo). II, 320

Denison (E. S.). Pacific Coast Souvenir. (1888). I, 464

Denkschriften der Russicchen Geographischen Gesellschaft zu St. Petersburg. 1849. II, 321

Denman (A. H.). The name Mt. Tacoma. 1924. II, 322

——. The Name Tacoma. 1924. II, 1250

Dennett (John Frederick). Voyage and Travels of Capts. Parry, Franklin, Ross and Belzoni. 1826. I, 722

Dennison (E. S.). Pacific Coast Souvenir. 1888. IV, 134

Denny (A. A.). Pioneer Days on Puget Sound. 1888. II, 323

——. Genealogy of Denny Family in Europe and America. 1886. II, 1261

Denny (Emily Inez). Blazing the Way. 1909. I, 723

Denys (Ferdinand). Les Californies, l'Oregon. 1859. I, 724

De Peyster (John Watts). Personal and Military History of Philip Kearney. 1870. II, 671

Depredations in Florida, by U. S. Army, in 1814. 1814. I, 842

Der Fischanfg in Ost-Sibirien. 1848. III, 814

Derby (George H.). IV, 271

Des. of Country between Lake Superior and the Pacific Ocean. 1876. I, 531

De Smet (P. J.). I, 160; II, 326-7; IV, 728-733

——. Letters and Sketches. 1843. II, 316

——. Oregon Missions and Travels. 1847. II, 325

——. Pictures of Missionary Life. 1858. III, 160

——. Lettres Choisies 4 Series. 1875-8. IV, 733

——. Missions de l'Oregon. 1848. IV, 728

——. New Indian Sketches. 1870. IV, 731

——. New Indian Sketches. 1870. IV, 732

——. Western Missions and Missionaries. 1863. II, 324

——. Coll. de Precis Historiques. 1853. III, 729

De Soto (Ferdinand). IV, 245

Despatches from Sir R. Morier, inclosing Reply to Russian Government. (1893). I, 886

De Vaugondy (M.). Atlas of Maps. I to 10, relating to early voyages to North Pacific Ocean. Size of each map, 12 by 15 inches. Folio. 1772. I, 725

Deux-Ponts (Count Wm. de). My Campaign in America. 1780-81. I, 103

Devine (Edward J.). Across Widest America. 1905. II, 328

Dewar (J. Cumming). Voyage of Nyanza, R. N. Y. C. 1892. II, 329

Dewey (Henry B.). History of Education in Washington. 1909. I, 726

De Windt (Harry). Through Gold Fields of Alaska. 1898. II, 330

De Wolff (J. H.). Pawnee Bill (Major Gordon Lillie). His Experiences and Adventures. 1902. III, 516

Dickerson (Oliver M.). American Colonial Government, 1696-1765. 1912. III, 27

Ninth line from top, first column should read "Oregon Question 1846."

Gibbons (Phebe E.). "Pennsylvania Dutch" and other Essays. 1882. III, 710

Gibbs (G.). I, 909-911; II, 284

——. Dictionary of Chinook Jargon. 1863. I, 909

——.Memoirs of Administrations of Washington and John Adams. 1846. IV, 1112

——.Vocabulary of Chinook Language. 1863.

——. Physical Geography of North-West Boundary. 1871. I, 911

Gibbs Josiah). I, 912; IV, 254

——. Mountain Meadow Massacre. 1910. I, 912; IV, 254

Gibbs (M. W.). Shadow and Light, 1902. I, 913a

Gibson (A. E.). Silence. 1930. II, 460

Gibson (E.). III, 763

Gibson [listed as Gibbs] (J. W.). I, 913

Giffen (F. R.). Oo-Mah-Ha-Ta-Wa-Tha. Oamha City. N.d. II, 454

Gihon (J. H.). IV, 737

Gilbert (Benj.). III, 719

Gilbert (K. G.). Alaska. Glaciers and Glaciation. 1910. II, 454

Gilbert (J. H.). Trade and Currency in Early Oregon. 1907. I 1385

Gilbert (W. C.). IV, 940

Gilbert (W. H.). Schwatka's Search. 1881. II, 456

Gill (F. B.). Unfinished History of Transportation in Oregon and Washington. N.p. N.d. II, 457

Gill (J.). Dictionary of Chinook Jargon. 1909. I, 915

Gillam Co., Ore. 1905. I, 1386

Gillett (J. B.). Six Years with Texas Rangers. (1921). I, 1456

——. Six Years with Texas Rangers. 1925. I, 1457

Gilliam (A. M.). Travels in Mexico. 1847. I, 916

Gillmore (P.). Prairie and Forest. 1874. I, 917

Gill's Dictionary of Chinook Jargon. 1889. II, 206

Gilman (I. A.). Alaska, American Northland. 1923. II, 459

——. Great Northwest. 1909. II, 458

Gilpin (W.). Central Gold Regions. 1860. , 918

Gilman (D. C.). Life of James Dwight Dane. 1899. I, 919

Gilman (I. A.) Alaskaland. (1914). I, 920

Gilpin (W.). Notes on Colorado Territory. 1870. I, 921

——. Central Gold Region. 1860. IV, 255

Giorda (J.). Dictionary of Kalispel; or, Flathead Indian Language. 1877.

——. Szmimeie-s Jesus Christ. Catechism. 1880. I, 923

Girty's, The. I, 444

Gist (C.). Journals. 1893. I, 924

Glass (H.). III, 362

Glazier (W.). Ocean to Ocean on Horse-Back. 1899. II, 461

Glimpses of Pioneer Life of Okanogan County, Wash. N.d. III, 871

Glisan (R.). Journal of Army Life. 1874. I, 925

Gmelin (J. G.). Reise durch Sibirien 1733-1751-52. I, 926

——. (J.). III, 351a

Goddard (F. B.). Where to Emigrate and Why. 1869. IV, 256

——. The same. 1869. III, 194

Goddard (P. E.). Hupa Texts. 1904. IV, 257

Godwin (G.). Vancouver, Life. 1757-1798. 1930. II, 462

Goin (J. W.). Apprentice System for U. S. Merchant Service. 1855. III, 819

Gold Horizon. Life Story of Manson F. Backus. 1937. IV, 622

Golder (F. A.). Bering's Voyages. 1922-25. I, 929

——. Guide to Materials for American History in Russian Archives. 1917. I, 928

——. Russian Expansion on Pacific, 1641-1850. 1914. I, 927

Goldstone (L.). Memorial, May 20, 1870. Addressed to Senate and H. of Rep. 1870. IV, 8

Golovinin (V. M.). Begebenheiten des. 1811-13. I, 930

——. Puteshestvie vokrug svieta po poveleniiu Gosudaria 1817-19. I, 932

——. Sokrashchennyia zapiski flote 1811. 1819. I, 931

——. (Capt. Russian Navy). Memoirs of Captivity in Japan 1811-1813. 1824. I, 933

Gonzaga's Silver Jubilee. Memoir. (1916). I, 1491

"Good Tidings" Monthly Periodical. 1906-1911. I, 566

Goode (Rev. W. H.). Outposts of Zion. 1863. I, 934

Godell (Wm.). American Slave Code. 1853. IV, 258

Goodfellow (J. C.). Totem Poles in Stanely Park. N.d. II, 463

Goodlander (Geo.). I, 935

Goodnight (Charles). Pioneer Days in Southwest. 1850-1879. I, 936

Hannay, (James). History of Acadia. 1879. III, 119

Hannegan, of Indiana. Speech in Senate. 1846. I, 1402

Hannum, (Anna Paschall). IV, 465

Hans (Fred M.). Great Sioux Nation. n.d. I, 1021

Hansen (Marcus L.). Old Ft. Snelling, 1819-1858. 1918. II, 497

——. Old Fort Snelling, 1819-1858. 1916. I, 1022

Hanson (John). Map of South Eastern Washington. 1878. I, 1023

Hanson (Jos. M.). Conquest of the Missouri. 1909. I, 1024

Hanson (Ole). Americanism verus Bolshevism. 1920. II, 498

Hardin and Williard. History of Herkimer County. 1893. III, 395

Hardy (Lady Duffus). Through Cities and Priarie Lands. 1882. I, 1025

Hardy, R. Travels in the Interior. 1829. I, 1026

Hargrave (Jos. James). Red River. 1871. I, 1027

Hargraves (Edward Hammond). Australia and its Gold Fields. 1855. I, 1928

Hariot (Thomas). Narrative of First English Plantation of Virginia. 1893. III, 200

Harlan-Wimmer Expedition. 1, 94

Harlan (J.). California 1846 to 1888. 1888. II, 499

Hargraves (Sheba). Heroine of the Prairies. 1930. II, 500

Harlow (Fred'k Pease). Making of a Sailor. 1928. II, 501

Harmon (Daniel Wm.). Journal of Voyages and Travels. 1820. II, 502

Harmon (S. W.). Hell on the Border. 1898. I, 1029

Harnett, (Legh,). Two Lectures on British Columbia. 1868. I, 1030

Harney (Gen. Wm. S.) I, 1007

——. Correspondence, 1857-1860. 1860. III, 201

Harney (W. D.). Art Works of Seattle and Alaska. 1907. I, 1032

——. Art Works of Seattle and Washington. 1910. I, 1031

Harpending (Asbury). IV, 1084

——. Great Diamond Hoax Edited 1913. IV, 137

——. The same. 1913. I, 1033

Harper (Frank B.). Fort Union and its Neighbors N. d. I, 1034

Harriman Alaska Expedition. 1901. I, 37

Harriman (Alice). Man of Two Countries. 1910. I, 1035

——. Song o' the Olympics. 1909. II,503

——. The same. 1909. I, 1036

Harriman, (E. H.) II, 701

Harris (A. C.). Alaska and Klondike Gold. c. 1897. I, 38

Harris, (Dean). Catholic Church in Niagara Peninsula, 1626-1895. 1895. III, 126

Harris (Lawrence T.). History of Judiciary of Oregon. 1918. I, 1388

Harris (T. M.). Journal of Tour. 1805. III, 202

Harris (Thaddeus M.). Journal of Tour, 1803. II, 504

——. The same. II, 505

Harrison (Carter). Summer's Outing. 1891. I, 1037

Harrison (E. S.). Motnerey County. N.d. I, 483

Harrington (Dossie Elmer). Diary of Basil Nelson Longworth, 1853. 1927. I, 1038

Harrison (Martha Douglas). History and Folklore of the Cowichan Indians. 1901. I, 1039

Harrison (C.). Haida Grammar. 1895. 1895. I, 1049

Harrison (E. S.). Alaska Almanac, 1909. I, 1040

——. Alaska Geography, 1909. I, 1044

——. Alaska, Sportsman's Paradise. N.d. 1, 1043

——. Industrial Progress in Alaska. 1909. I, 1042

——. Nome and Seward Peninsula. c. 1905

——. The same. (c. 1905). I, 1047

——. Resources of Alaska. 1909. I, 1946

——. Scenic Alaska. 1909. I, 1045

Harrison (J. T.). Eulogy over the Remains of Griffith Davies. 12mo, sewn. Seattle, 1924. I, 1048

Hart, (I W.) II, 543

Harvey (Arthur). Statistical Account of British Columbia. 1867. II, 506

Haskell (William B.). Two Years in Klondike and Alaska Gold-Fields. 1898. I, 1050

Haskins (C. W.). Argonauts of California. 1890. IV, 299

——. The same. 1890. I, 1051

Hassell (Susan Whitcomb). Hundred and Sixty Books by Washington Authors. (1916).

Hastings (L. B.). Typewritten Mss. of Journey from Hancock County, Illinois to Oregon in 1847. N.d. I, 1052

Hart (Adolphus M.). History of Valley of the Mississippi. 1853. I, 1053

Harte (Bret). Tales of the Argonauts, 1875. I, 1054. II, 1104

Hastings (Lansford W.). Emigrant's Gunde, to Oregon and California. 1845. I, 1055

Hatton, (Joseph) and Harvey (M.) Newfoundland, Its History. 1883. III, 118
Haupt (H.). Yellowstone National Park.. 1883. I, 1056
Hawaiian Mission Children Society. Voyages to Hawaii before 1860. 1929. II, 508
Hawkes (Ernest William). "Inviting-in" Feast of Alaska Eskimos. 1913. I, 1058
Hawkeye (Harry). Tracy, Outlaw, King of Bandits. (1908). II, 509
——. The same. 1908. I, 324
Hawkins (W. W.) I, 244
Hawksworth, John. Account of Voyages in the Southern Hemisphere. 1775. II, 510
Hawley (A. T.). Portland, Oregon, n.d. I, 1059
Hawley (James H.). History of Idaho. 1920. I, 1255
Haworth (Paul L.). IV, 1115
——. Trailmakers of the Northwest. 1921. I, 1060
——. On Headwaters of Peace River. I, 1061
Hawthorne (Julian) and Brewerton (G. Douglas). History of Washington . . . 1893. I, 1062
Hay, (John). III, 297
Hayden, (F. V.) II, 1052
——. Sun Pictures of Rocky Mountain Scenery. 1870. I, 1063
——. Twelfth Annual Report of U. S. Geographical and Geographical Survey of Territories. A report of progress of Exploration in Wyoming and Idaho for Year 1878. 1883. I, 1064
Hayden, (Mary Jane.) Pioneer Days. 1915. IV, 300
Haydon (A. L.). Riders of the Plains (1910. I, 1065
Hayes (A. A.). New Colorado and Santa Fe Trail. 1880. II, 511
Hayes, (B.) IV, 150
Hayes, (Dr. I. I.) Open Polar Sea.. 1967. III, 69
Hayes, (Jack). The Intrepid Texas Ranger. (1905). IV, 850
Haymond (Creed). The Central Pacific Railroad. (1888). I, 1066
Hays (Jeff W.). Portland and Oregon, A.D. 1999. 1915. I, 1067
——. Looking Backward at Portland. 1911 I, 1068
Hayward (John). Civil and Political History of State of Tennessee, 1823. III, 203
——. The same. 1891. III, 204
——. Natural and Aboriginal History of Tennessee. 1823. III, 205
Stevens, (Gen. Hazard,) Brief Sketch of Life of. 1908. IV, 778
Hazard (Joseph). Glacier Playfields of Mt. Ranier Nat'l Park. 1920. I, 1070
——. Snow Sentinels of Pacific Northwest. 1932. I, 1069
Hazeltine (F. A.). Lost Ships. 1932. II, 512
Hazlitt (W. C.). British Columbia and Vancouver Island. 1858. I, 1071
Head (George). Forest Scenes and Incidents. 1929. I, 1072
Headley (C. P.). Life and Military Career of Maj. Philip Henry Sheridan. 1865. II, 513
Healey (W. J.). Women of Red River, 1923. I, 1073
Healy (Capt. M. A.) I, 149
Heap (G. H.) and Beale (E. F.). Central Route to Pacific. 1853-1854. II, 514
Hearne (Samuel A.). Journal from Prince of Wales Fort in Hudson's Bay to the Northern Ocean. 1795. I, 1074
——. II, 90A
Hearney (W. S.). Life and Military Services. 1878. VI, 301
Heath, (Maj. Gen. Wm.) Memoirs of. 1901. I, 115
Hebard (Grace Raymond). Pathbreakers from River to Ocean. 1911. I, 1077
——. Sacajawea. 1933. I, 1075
——. and Brininstool (E. A.). Bozeman Trail. 1922. I, 1076
Heckewelder (John). Gnadenhuetten Centennial, Sept. 29, 1798. 1898. IV, 302
——. Narrative of a Mission of United Brethren. 1907. I, 1078
Heclawa, (pseud.) In the Heart of Bitter Root Mountains. 1895. II, 519
Hedges (James Blaine). Henry Villard and Railways of the Northwest. 1930. I, 1079
Heer (Oswald). Flora Fossilis Alaskan. 1869. I, 1080
Hegg (E. A.). Souvenir of Alaska and Yukon Territory. 1900. I, 1081
Heilborn, (H. L.) II, 1058
Helm (Lt.). IV, 316
Helm (M. S.). Scraps of Early Texas History. 1884. I, 1549
Helms (Ludwig Verner). Pioneering in Far East. 1882. I, 1082
Helps (Arthur). 1869. III, 142
Hemphill, (Mr.) (1830). IV, 884
Henderson (Lester D.). Alaska. 1928. I, 39
——. Historical Sketch of Alaska. 1923. I, 1083
Henderson, (Sarah Fisher). I, 821
Henn (Bernhart) and William (Jesse). Township Map of State of Iowa. 1855. I, 1084
Hennepin (Father Louis). New Discovery of a Vast Country in America. 1903. III, 206

Henry, (Alexander). I, 3
——. Travels and Adventures in Canada Indian Territories, 1760 1776 . . . 1809. I, 1085
——. The same. 1907. I, 1086.
Henry (Alexander) and Thompson (David). New Light on Early History of Greater Northwest. 1897. I, 1087
Henry (Charles). History of Transportation in Ohio Valley. 1932. III, 487
Henry (Francis). Address of Feb. 23, 1865. 1865. I, 1089
——. Lodge Odes of Independent Order of U. F. F. U. 1858. I, 1088
Henry (Hon. Francis). The Old Settler. N.d. II, 515
Henry (John J.). Accurate and Interesting Account of that Band of Heroes against Quebec in 1775. 1812. III, 52
Henshaw, (Fred. F.) and Parker (Glen. L.) Water Powers of Cascade Range. Part 2, Cowlitz, Nisqually, Puyallup, White Green. 1913. IV, 1019
——. IV, 1015
Henty (G. A.). Redskin and Cow-Boy. N.d. II, 516
Herbermann, (C. G.) III, 125
Herbst, (I. F. W.) I, 1474
Heriot (George). Travels through the Canadas. 1807. I, 1090
Herman (Father). Ascetic and Enlightener of Alaska. N.d. I, 1091
Hermann (Binger). Louisiana Purchase. 1989. I, 1092
Herndon (Sarah Raymond). Days on the Road. 1902. I, 1093
Herne (Peregrine). Perils and Pleasures of a Hunter's Life. 1857. I, 1094
Herrick, (F. H.) I, 107, IV, 81
Herriff (E. L.). Pocket Map of Tacoma and Puget Sound. 1889. I, 1095
Herring (Francis B.). Among People of British Columbia. 1903. I, 1096
——. In the Pathless West. 1904. I, 1097
Herron (Jos. S.). Explorations in Alaska, 1899. 1901 I, 40
——. The Same. 1909. I, 41
Hewes, (David). I, 1098
[Hewes (Joshua).] New England Pioneer. 1913. I, 1908
Hewitt, Randall H. Across Plains and the Divide. 1906 I, 1099
Heylyn (Peter). Cosmographie. 1657. I, 1100
Hiatt (Isaac). Thirty-one Years in Baker County. 1893. I, 1101
Hibben (T. N.). Chinook Jargon. (1871). I, 1102
——. Guide to British Columbia for 1877-78. 1877. I, 1104
——. Picturesque British Columbia. n. d. I, 1103
Hickman (W. H.). Brigham's Destroying Angel. 1872. I, 1105
Hicks, (Fred. C.) III, 215
Higgins (Beth Bell). Memory Pictures of Puget Sound. 1900. I, 1106
——. Memory Pictures of Puget Sound Region. 1900. IV, 303
Higgins (D. W.). Mystic Spring and Other Tales. 1904. II, 517
Higginson (Ella). Alaska. 1908. I, 1107
——. Flowers that Grew in Sand. 1896. II, 518
——. From Land of Snow Pearls. 1897. II, 1109
——. Mariella: of Out-West. 1902. I, 1110
——. Vanishing Race and Other Poems. 1911. I, 1108
——. Voice of April-Land. 1903. I, 1111
[Hildreth, James.] Dragoon Campaigns to Rocky Mountains. 1836. I, 1112
Hildreth, (Richard). History of the U. S. A. 1851-56 III, 39
Hildreth, (S. P.) Contributions to early history of the Northwest. 1864. III, 490
——. Pioneer History. 1848. I, 1113
——. Pioneer History; and Account of first examinations of the Ohio Valley. 1848. III, 488
Hill (Alice Polk). Tales of the Colorado Pioneers. 1884. I, 1114
Hill (Geo. W.). Vocabulary of Shosone Language. 1877. I, 1116
Hill (James J.). Addresses. Thirty-four separate Addresses. 1902 to 1906. I, 1117
——. Highways of Progress. 1910. I, 1115
Hill, (J. L.) End of Cattle Trail. N.d. IV, 851
——. Passing of the Indian and Buffalo. N.d. I, 1118
Hilliard (Henry Washington). Speech 1846. I, 1119
Hill-tout (Charles). British North America. 1907. I 1122
——. Later Prehistoric Man in British Columbia. 1895. I, 1123
——. Oceanic Origin of Kwakintl-Nootka and Salish Stocks of British Columbia. N. d. I, 1124
——. Notes on the Cosmogony and History of the Spanish Indians of British Columbia. 1897. I, 1121
——. Notes on the Squamish Indians. 1897. I, 1120
Himes, (Geo. H.) I, 1408
Himmelwright (A. L. Artman). II, 519. [vide Heclawa.]

Hopkins (Mrs. S.). (Winnemucca). Life among Piutes; 1883. I, 1161
Hoppe (J.). California Gegenwart und Zukunft. 18 9.41, 1162
Horden. (J.) I, 415
Horetzky (C.). Canada and Pacific. 1874. III, 649
——. Canada on Pacific. 1874. I, 1163
——. Startling Facts Relating to the Can. Pac. Ry. and the North-West Lands. 1880. I, 1164
Horn (T.). Life. (1904). II, 527
Hornaday (Wm. T.). Camp-Fires in the Canadian Rockies. 1907. I, 1166
——. Our Vanishing Wild Life. 1913. I, 1165
Horner (J. B.). Oregon. 1919. I, 1392
——. Oregon Literature 1899. I, 1390
——. Oregon Literature. 1902. I, 1390
Horton (R.). Sooners; The Romance of Early Oklahoma. (1927). I, 1333
Hosmer, (J. K.) II, 852
——. History of Louisiana Purchase. 1902. I. 1167
Hough (E.). Story of the Cowboy. 1903. I, 1168
——. Story of the Outlaw. 1907. I, 1170
——. Magnificient Adventure. 1916. I, 1173
——. 54-40 or Fight. 1909. I, 1171
——. Way to the West and the Lives of Three Early Americans, Boone-Crockett-Carson. (1903). I, 1169
——. Young Alaskans. 1911. I, 1172
Houston, (Gen. S.). I, 761, 1452; IV, 855
——. Life of. 1855. IV, 852
Houstoun (Mrs.). Texas and the Gulf of Mexico. 1845. IV, 853
Howard (D. F.). Oregon's First White Men. 1927. I, 1174
Howard, (E. C.) IV, 540
Howard (F. P.) and Barnett (Geo.). British Columbian and Victoria Guide 1863. I, 1175
Howard (Jacob). San Juan Island. 1870. I, 1176
Howard (J. Q.). History of the Louisiana Purchase. 1902. I, 1177
Howard, (O. O.). IV, 410B
——. Autobiography of U. S. Army. 1908. I, 1178
——. Famous Indian Chiefs. 1912. I, 1179
——. My Life and Experiences among our Hostile Indians. (1907). I, 1180
——. Nez Perce Joseph;. 1881. I, 1181
Howay, (F. W.) I, 380, 1191, 1502; IV, 596
——. Attitude of Gov. Seymour Towards Confederation. 1920. I, 1185
——. British Columbia, the Making of a Province. (c. 1928). I, 1189
——. Dixon-Mears Controversy. (c. 1929). III, 429
——. Early History of Fraser River Mines. 1926. I, 1188
——. Gov. Musgrave and Confederation. 1921. I, 1186
——. List of Trading Vessels in Maritime Fur Trade, 1785. 1930. II. 528
——. Origin and History of the Great Canyon of Fraser River. 1920. I, 1184
——. Overland Journey of the Argonauts of 1862. 1919. I, 1183
——. Raison d'Etre of Forts Yale and Hope. 1922. I, 1187
——. Work of Royal Engineers in British Columbia, 1858 to 1863. 1910. I, 1182.
Howay (Judge F. W.). (Ed.). Voyage of the Hazard to Northwest Coast, 1810-1813. by Stephen Reynolds. 1938. IV, 306
Howe. (H.) III, 66, 370-1
——. Adventures and Achievements of Americans. 1864. II, 530
——. Historical Collections of Great West . . . (1851) II, 529
——. Historical Collection of Ohio. 1889.
Howe (O. T.). Argonauts of '49. 1923. I, 1191
Howe (M. A. De Wolf). Life and Letters of George Bancroft. 1908. I, 1192
Howell (I. M.). Pamphlet containing a copy of all Measures "proposed by Initative Petitions". (1916). IV, 1022
Howell (T.). Flora of Northwest America. 1903. I, 1194
Howells (Wm. C.). Recollections of Life in Ohio, 1813-1840. 1895. I, 531
Howison (J.). Sketches in Upper Canada. 1825. I, 1195
Howison (Lieut. N. M.). Oregon; Report of an Examination in 1846. 1848. I, 1196
Hoy (P. R.). Journal of an Exploration of Western Missouri in 1854, 1864. II. 532
Hrdlicka (Dr. A.). Remains in Eastern Asia of Race of that Peopled America. 1942. II, 533
Hubbard (B.). Memorials of a Half Century. 1887. II, 534
Hubbard, (G.) Autobiography. 1191. III, 346
Hubbard (J. N.). Sketches of Border Adventures in Life of Major Van Campen. 1842. III, 853
——. The Same. 1893.
Hubbard (Wm.). Narrative of Indian Wars. 1803. III, 208
Hudson (J. B.). Narrative of Christian Experience, Travel and Labor. 1838. III, 711
Hudson's Bay Co. Exhibition of Ancient Maps and Charts. N.d. II, 536

Kerr (J. B.). Biographical Dictionary of Well-Known British Columbians. 1890. II, 707

Kerr (John). History of Western Railroads. [1924-5.] II, 708A

Kerr (J. L.). Story of Southern Carrier. 1933. IV, 342

——. Story of Western Pioneer. 1928. IV, 341

——. Story of Western Pioneer. 1928. II, 708

Ketchikan, First City in Alaska. N. d. II, 9

Keyes (E. D.). Fifty Years Observation. 1884. IV, 343

——. Fifty Years' Observation of Men and Events. 1884. II, 709

Keyserling (A. von). III, 799

Khvostov (Nickolia Alexandrovich). I, 703

Kiahlik Ikso Nana- Aiymmika I Katikism. N.d. II, 213; 1, 568

Kimball (M. B.). Soldier-Doctor of our Army. 1917. III, 289

Kincaid (H. R.). Political and Official History and Register of Oregon. (1899). II, 710

King, (Capt. C.). Fifth Cavalry in the Sioux War of 1876. Campaigning with Cook. 1880. II, 711

——. Campaigning with Cook. 1890. II, 712

——. Mountaineering in the Sierra Nevada. 1874. II, 713

——. I, 637

King County History and Progress. 1916. II, 1284

King County (Seattle). Pamphlet descriptive of. 1884. II, 1272

King, (H. M.) Summer Visit to Three Rhode Islanders to the Massachusetts Bay 1651 . . . 1896. IV, 61

King (R.). Narrative of Journey to Shores of Atlantic Ocean in 1833-5. London, 1836. II, 714

King, (Stoddard). II, 467

King (T. S.). White Hills, their Legends, Landscape and Poetry. 1860. III, 365

Kingston (W. H. G.). Adventures among Indians. 1889. II, 716

——. Frontier Forts. N.d. II, 717

——. Adventures in Far West. N.d. IV, 344

Kinnear (G.). Anti-Chinese Riots at Seattle, Washington. 1911. II, 718

Kino (Father Eusebio F.). Historical Memoir of Pimeria Alta, 1683-1711. [Vide. H. E. Bolton.] 1919. II, 719

Kinzie (Mrs. J. H.). Wau-Bun; Early Days in Northwest. 1856. III, 243

——. Wau Bun. 1856. II, 720

Kip (Lawrence). Army Life on the Pacific. 1859. II, 721

——. Indian Council at Walla Walla. 1855; 1897. II, 722

Kip (W. I.). Early Jesuit Missions in North America. 1846. II, 723

Kippis (A.). Narrative of the Voyage Round World. N.d. II, 724

Kirby (W. W.). Journey to Youcan, Russian America. 1864. II, 725

Kirchoff (Theodor). Reisebilder und Skizzen aus Amerika. 1875-76. II, 726

Kirk (Robert C.). Twelve Months in the Klondike. 1899. II, 727

Kirkland (Caroline M.). Forest Life. 1842. IV, 364

Kirkland (Major). II, 235-6

Kirkpatrick (J. M.). Heroes of Battle Rock, 1904. II, 728

Kiser (F. H.). Pacific Coast Pictures. N.d. II, 729

Kitchin (E. A) Distributional Check-List of Birds of State of Washington. 1934. II, 730

Kitsap County, Washington Plot Book. 1909. II, 1281

Kittinger (Chas. M.). Seattle. Plates. N.d. II, 731

Kitto (F H.). Peace River District of Canada. 1920. II, 732

Klahhane Club. Annual, January, 1918. 1918. II, 1285

Klondike. Chicago Record's Book for Gold Seekers. (1897). II, 8

——. Chicago Record's Book for Gold Seekers. (1897). I, 586

Klotz (Otto). History of Forty-Ninth Parallel Survey. 1917. II 734

Klubo (Eldoinis Partlanda). Oregono Lando de Promeso. 1910. II, 1242

Knapp (Geo. L.). I, 546

Knower (Daniel). Adventures of a Forty-Niner. 1894. II, 735

Knickerbocker (Diedrich). III, 385

Knight (Wm. H.). I, 196

Knowles (Admiral Charles). I, 554

Kohl (Johann Georg). Asia and America. 1911. II, 736

Kolb (E. L.). Through the Grand Canyon from Wyoming to Mexico. 1914. II, 737

Konscak (Rev. Ferdinand S. J.). II, 746

Kootenai Catechism. 1892. II, 542

Kotzebue (A. von). Most Remarkable Year in the Lifetime of. 1802. IV, 345

——. I, 592A; II, 918A

——. Entdeckungs-Reise in Die Sud See und Bering's Strasse. 1821. II, 739

——. New Voyage round World. 1823-26. II, 740

——. Neue Reise um die Welt, 1823-26. 1830. II, 741, 740

——. Early Days in the Big Bend Country. 1926. II, 841, 842

Licenses to Trade with Indians. 1826. III, 341

Leinhard (H.). Californien. 1898. II, 858

Lincoln. (A.) II, 544A; III, 228, 238, 252, 255, 297, 498

——. Writings. 1905. III, 296

Linderman (F. B.). Indian Old-Man Stories. 1920. II, 860

——. Indian Why Stories. 1915. II, 859

——. Lige Mounts, Free Trapper. 1922. II, 861

——. Life Story of a Great Indian. (1930). II, 862

Lindley. (W.) and Widney. (J. P.) California of the South. 1888. II, 168

Lindsay (B.). Derelicts of Destiny. II, 863

Lindsey (A. L.). Sketches of an Excursion to Southern Alaska. (1880). II, 864

Lindsey (C.). Investigation of the Unsettled Boundaries of Ontario. 1873. II, 865

Linquist (G. E. E.). Red Man in the U. S. (1923). II, 866

Linforth (J.). Route from Liverpool to Great Salt Lake Valley. 1855. II, 867

——. Route from Liverpool to Great Salt Lake Valley. 1855. I, 1280

Linn (Mrs. E. A.) and Nathan Sargent. Life of Dr. Lewis F. Linn. 1857. II, 868

Linn, (J. B.) Annals of Buffalo Valley, Pa., 1755-1855. 1877. III, 712

Linn. (Dr. L. F.) II, 868

Linn (Lewis). Report on the Occupation of Oregon Territory. 1838. II, 869

Lionnet (J.). Chez les Francais du Canada. 1908. II, 870

Lisa. (Manuel). II, 350

Lisher (J. J.). Decline and Fall of Samuel Sawbones, M. D., on the Klondike. (1900). II, 871

Lisiansky (U.). Puteshestvie vokrug svieta v 1803-6. 1812. II, 872

——. Voyage Round the World. 1803-06. 1814. II, 873

Little. (J. A.) Jacob Hamlin, Narrative of his Personal Experiences. 1881. IV, 387

——. Kirkland to Salt Lake City. 1890. II, 874

Littlefield (L. O.). Reminiscences of Latter-Day Saints. 1888. II, 875

Lloyd (B. E.). Lights and Shades in San Francisco. 1876. II, 876

Lloyd (J. P.). Message of an Indian Relic. 1909. II, 877

Lloyd. (T.) Report on the Whole Trial of Gen. Michael Bright, and Others. 1809. IV, 69D

Lockley. (F.) II, 112, 348

——. Across the Plains by Prairie Schooner. N.d. II, 882

——. Oregon Folks. 1927. II, 880

——. Oregon Trail Blazers. 1929. II, 881

——. Oregon Yesterdays. 1928. II, 879

——. Talk with Edwin Markham. N.d. II, 884

——. To Oregon by Ox-Team in '47. N.d. II, 883

——. Vigilante Days at Virginia City.

Lodge. (H. C.) III, 199-9A

(1924). II, 878

——. Short History of the English Colonies. 1881. III, 298

Logan. The Last of the Race of Skikellemus. 1868. I, 1416

Lomax (J. A.). Cowboy Songs and other 895

London (Jack). Burning Daylight. 1015. II, 886

Long. (S. H.) II, 588-9; 672-3

Lopez. (R.) II, 895A

Longsworth (B. N.). Over the Oregon Trail. 1853. 1927. II, 894

Loomis (L. V.). A Journey of the Birmingham Emigration Company. Iowa to Sacramento, California. 1850. 1928. II,

Lord (J. K.). At Home in the Wilderness. 1867. II, 898

——. Naturalist in Vancouver Is. and British Columbia. 1866. II, 897

Lord (Mrs. E.). Reminiscences of Eastern Oregon. 1903. II, 896

Long (F. J.). Dictionary of the Chinook Jargon. 1909. II, 893

Lord. (Gov. W. P.) I, 1375

Lord (W. R.). Birds of Oregon and Washington. 1901. II, 899

——. Birds of Oregon and Washington. 1902. II, 900

Lorid (E. S.). Fort Bridger. 1890. II, 901

Loring (W. C.). Memoir of the Hon. William Sturgis. 1798. II, 902

Lorne (M.). Canadian Life and Scenery. 1886. II, 903

Lossing (B. J.). History of the United States. 1857. II, 904

——. Pictorial Field-Book of the War of 1812. 1869. II, 905

Lothrop (Thornton). William Henry Seward. (1890). II, 906

Louisiana. An Account of Louisiana. 1803. III, 299

Louisiana Purchase. State Papers and Correspondence upon the purchase of Territory of Louisiana. 1903. II, 907

Love (G.). Court of Claims Indian Depredations, No. 280. George M. Love, Administrator vs. Rogue River and Umpqua Tribes of Indians and the U. S. Evidence for Claimants. N.d. II, 908

Love (Nat). Life and Adventure. 1907. IV, 350

Love (Robertus). Rise and Fall of Jesse James. 1926. II, 910

——. Lewis and Clark Fair. 1905. II, 909

Lovejoy (J. C.) and (O). Memoir of the Rev. Elijah P. Lovejoy. 1838. III, 244

Low (C. R.). Captain Cook's Three Voyages. N.d. II, 911

Lowe (M.). Story of Chief Joseph (1881). II, 912

Lowe (P.). Five Years a Dragoon. 1906. II, 913

Lowery (W.). Spanish Settlements within Limits of U. S., 1513-1516. III, 302

Lucas (C. P.). War of 1812. 1906. III, 861

Ludington (F. B.). Newspapers of Oregon. N.d. II, 914

Ludlow (F.). Heart of the Continent. 1870. II, 915

Ludlow (W.). Report of a Reconnaisance of the Black Hills of Dakota. 1875. II, 916

Lugrin (N. de B.). Pioneer Women of Vancouver Island, 1843-1866. 1928. II, 917

Lake Wash. Canal. III, 920

Lummis. (C. F.) III, 96

Lundy. (B.) II, 390

Lush. (C. K.) The Federal Judge. 1897. IV, 66

Luigi (Duke of Abruzzi). Ascent of Mt. St. Elias. (1899). II, 918

Lusk (D. W.). Eighty Years of Illinois. 1889. III, 245

Lutke (F. P.). Puetschestvie vogrug Svieta Sovershennoe. 1835 7 vols. 1828-36. II, 918A

Luttig (J. C.). Journal of a Fur-Trading Expedition. 1812-1813. 1920. II, 920

Lyell (Sir C.). Second Visit to the U. S. 1849. III, 303

Lyman (A.). Journal of a Voyage to California. 1852. II,921

Lyman (C. S.). Around the Horn to the Sandwich Is. 1845-1850. 1924. II, 922

Lyman (Geo. D.). John Marsh, Pioneer. 1930. IV, 351

Lyman (H. S.). History of Oregon. 1903. II, 924

Lyman (R.). Beecher Island Memorial. 1905. II, 930

——. Beecher Island Memorial. 1904. II, 929

Lyman (W. D.). Columbia River. 1909. II, 927

——. Illustrated History of Walla Walla Co. 1901. II, 926

——. Indian Myths of the Northwest. 1915. II, 928

——. Lake Chelan. 1899. II, 925

Lynam. (C. S.) I, 98

Lynch (J.). David C. Broderick. 1911. II, 932

——. Three Years in the Klondike. 1904. II, 931

Lyndon. (J. W.) III, 751

Lyon. (E. W.) Barbe-Marbois, The Man Who Sold Louisiana. 1942. III, 65

Lyons. (E.) IV, 40

McAfee (R. B.). History of the late War in Western Country. 1816. II, 933

——. History of the Late War. 1816. III, 304

McAfee. (R.) Pioneer and the First Commodore on Three Principal Rivers of the West. Caput Mortum. III, 283

McArthur (H. N.). Recollections of the Rickreall. 1930. II, 934

McArthur (L.). Oregon Geographic Names. 1928. II, 935

McBeth (K.). Nez Perces since Lewis and Clark. (1908). II, 936

Macbeth (R. G.). Policing the Plains. 1921. II, 938

——. Romance of Western Canada. 1918. II, 937

McCain (C. W.). History of the SS. "Beaver." 1894. II, 939

McCaleb (W. F.). Aaron Burr Conspiracy. 1903. III, 305

McCall (G. A.). Letters from the Frontiers. 1868. II, 940

McCalla (W. L.). Adventures in Texas. 1841. I, 1460

McCarter (M. H.). Peace of the Solman Valley. 1911. II, 941

McCarver. (M. M.) II, 1073

McClellan (R. G.). Golden State. 1872. II, 942

[McClelland. T.] Inauguration of as President of Tulatin Academy June 15, 1892. II, 943

McClintock. (Rev. J.) III, 151

McClintock (Capt.). Voyage of the "Fox" in the Arctic Seas. 1860. II, 944

McClintock (W.). Old North Trail. 1910. II, 945

McClung (J. A.). Sketches of Western Adventure. 1832. II, 985

——. Sketches of Western Adventure. 1879. II, 986

Macombe (Capt. J. N.). Report of the Exploring Expedition from Santa Fe, N. M. II, 992

McConnell. (H. H.) Five Years a Cavalryman. 1889. IV, 856

McConnell (M.). Early History of Idaho. 1913. II, 946

McConnell. (W. J.) II, 129
McCormack (E. C.). Thomas Condon. 1928. II, 947
McCormick. (J.) I, 186
McCormick (S. J.). Almanac. 1862-1881. II, 948
McCoy (J.). Historic Sketches of the Cattle Trade. 1874. II, 949
McCoy. (S.) IV, 866
McCurdy (J. G.). By Juan de Fuca Strait. (1937). IV, 358
McDermott. (J. F.) IV, 874
Macdonald (Alex.). In Search of Eldorado. (c. 1880). II, 950
McDonald (Chief Factor). Peace River, Canoe Voyage from Hudsons Bay to the Pacific. 1872. II, 951
MacDonald (Duncan Geo. Forbes). Lecture on British Columbia and Vancouver's Is. 1863. II, 952
Macdonald (C D. F.). British Columbia and Vancouver's Island. 1862. II, 953
McDonald. (Capt. B.). III, 839
McDonald (J. L.). Hidden Treasures; or Fisheries Around the North-West Coast. 1871. II, 954
MacDonald (Ranald). II, 955
McElroy (R. McN.). Kentucky in the Nation's History. 1909. III, 284
——. Winning of the Far West. 1914. II, 956
McElwaine (E.). Truth about Alaska. 1901. II, 957
McEwen. (W. H.) IV, 958
Macfie (M.). Vancouver Island and British Columbia. 1865. II, 958
MacGahan. (J. A.) Under the Northern Lights. 1876. III, 59
McGhee (M.). Rough Times in Rough Places. 1891. II, 959
McGibbon (E.). Leaves of Knowledge. 1904. II, 960
McGillivray (D.). Journal. 1929. II, 961
McGillivray. (S.) II, 962
MacGillivray. (W.) IV, 312
McGilvre. (J. J.) Addresses upon the Life and Character of. 1904. I, 1449
McGraw. (J. H.) In Memoriam. 1911. IV, 635
McGunnigle. (J.) IV, 377A
McIlhany (E. W.). Recollections of a '49er. 1908. II, 963
McIlvaine (E.). III, 246
McIntire (J.). Early Days in Texas and New Mexico. 1902. II, 964
Mackay (A.). Western World. 1850. II, 965
McKay (D.). History of Hudson's Bay Company. (1936). IV, 239
McKeeby (L. C.). Memoirs of. 1924. II, 966
McKeevor (T.). Voyage to Hudsons Bay. 1812. 1819. II, 967
McKenny (T. L.). Sketches of a Tour to the Lakes. 1827. III, 306
——. Memoirs, with Sketches of Travel. 1846. II, 968
Mackenzie (Alex.). I, 3, 291; II, 90A; IV, 360-1, 913-A
Mackenzie (Alex.). Voyages from Montreal. 1801. II, 970
McKinstry. (G. Jr.) Thrilling and Tragic Journal. 1846-47. (1913). IV, 359
McKinstry (C.). Thrilling and Tragic Narrative! Journal kept by aSuffering Emigrant. N.d. II, 972
Mackintosh. (A.) IV, 636
McKenzie (N. M. J.). Men of Hudson's Bay Company. 1921. I, 969
——The same. 1902. II, 971
——. I, 1417
McKnight (C.). Our Western Border. 1876. III, 307
McKnight (T.). Thirty Years of Foreign Policy. 1855. II, 974
——. Our Western Border One Hundred Years ago. 1879. I, 1282
McKonochie (Capt. A.). Summary View of Existing Commerce of Principal Shores of Pacific Ocean. 1818. II, 975
McLain (J. S.). Alaska and the Klondike. 1905. II, 976
McLaughlin. (A. C.) III, 750
——. Lewis Cass. N.d. II, 977.
McLaughlin (James). My Friend, the Indian. 1910. II, 978
McLaughlin (John). II, 979-80, 1153
Maclauries (Mr.). Narrative of Travels through Northwest in 1789 and 1793. 1802. II, 981
MacLean. (J. P.) Mound Builders. 1904. III, 495
M'Lean (J.). Notes of Twenty-Five Years' Service in the Hudson's Bay Territary. 1849. II, 982
McLeod. (M.) I, 1407A, 1427; II, 951
——. Oregon Indemnity. 1892. II, 984
Macleod (X. D.). History of the Devotion to the Blessed Virgin Mary. 1866 II, 983
McLoughlin (Dr. J.). I, 1148
McLung (J. W.). Minnesota as it is in 1870. 1870. II, 987
McMaster (J. B.). History of the People of the U. S. 1886-1913. III, 40

Thirteenth line from top, first column should read Minto, not "Minot."

Should read Josiah Mooso, not "John."

Mullan (Capt. J.). Report on Construction of a Military Road from Fort Walla Walla to Fort Benton. 1863. II, 1210

——. Miners' and Travelers Guide. 1865. II, 1211

Muller, (G. F.) III, 157A

——. Nachrichten von Seereisen. 1758. II, 1211A

——. Sammlung Russicher Geschichte. Nachricht den dreyen in Gebiete der 1758. III, 351A

——. Voyage et Decouvertes Mer Glaciale. 1766. II, 1211B

——. Voyages from Asia to America. 1761. II, 603

Muller (H. G.). Oregon and seine Zukunst. 1872. II, 1212

Mumey (N.). Life of Jim Baker, 1818-1819. 1931. II, 1213

Munro (W. H.). Tales of an old Sea Port. 917. II, 1214

Mulvaney (C. P.). History of the Northwest Rebellion of 1885. II, 1215

Munson (Lyman E.). Pioneer Life on American Frontier. 1907. II, 1216

Murch, (A. B.) IV, 367

Murchison (R. I.). Address to the R. G. S., 27th May, 1844. 1844. II, 1217

Murdock (Harold). The 19th of April, 1775. 1923. III, 51

Murieta (J.). Life and Adventures. 1925. II, 1218

——. IV, 127

——. Life of, being a Complete History from the Age of Sixteen. 1923. IV, 278

Murphy (H. C.). Anthology of New Netherland. 1865. I, 1323

Murphy (J. M.) and Harned. Puget Sound Business Directory. 1872. II, 1219

Murphy (J. M.). Sporting Adventures in the Far West. 1880. II, 1220

Murphy (T. D.). Oregon the Picturesque. 1917. II, 1221

Murray (A. H.). Journal of the Yukon, 1847-48. 1910. II, 1222

Murray (C. A.). The Prairie Bird. N.d. II, 1225

——. The Prairie Bird. 1844. II, 1224

——. Travels in North America. 1839. II, 1223

Murray (H.). Historical and Descriptive Account of British America. 1844. II, 1226

Murrelet, The. Vol. 1, May, 1920 to Vol. 13, No. 2, May, 1932. 1920-32. II, 1227

Myers (Capt. J.). Life, Voyages and Travels. 1817. II, 1228

Myers (Harriet W.). The Bird's Convention. (1913). II, 1229

Myrick (H.). Cache la Poudre. 1905. I, 1327

Nahl, C. I, 503; II, 85

Narrative of Occurrences in the Indian Countries. [McGillivray]. 1817. II, 962

Nash (Wallis). [Note: First name given incorrectly as "Ogden" in text]. Oregon, there and Back in 1877. 1878. III, 557

——. Settler's Hand-Book to Oregon. 1904. III, 559

——. Two Years in Oregon. 1882. III, 558

——. Farm, Ranch and Range in Oregon. 1904. II, 560

National Cyclopaedia of American Biography. 1898. III, 352

National Democratic Executive Committee, Breckinridge and Lane Campaign. 1860. III, 292

National League for Woman's Service. Washington State Report, 1917-1919. N.d.

Native Sons of British Columbia. Romance of Vancouver. 1896. III, 85

Navarette (Martin F. de.). III, 426

Neah Kah Nie Commercial Club. The Neah-Kah-Nie Mountains. 1905. III, 872

Nebraska. Journal of the Council of the Legislative Assembly. 1855-1875. III, 353

Nebraska State Hist. Soc. Transactions and Reports. 1885-1893. III, 354

Neidhardt (J. G.). The River and I. 1910. II, 359

——. Song of Hugh Glass. 1922. II, 362

——. Song of Indian Wars. 1925. III, 363

——. Song of Three Friends. 1919. III, 360

——. Splendid Wayfaring. 1920. III, 361

Neill (E. D.). Materials for the Future History of Minnesota. 1856. III, 335

Nelson (Denys). Fort Langley, 1827-19297. 1927. III, 84

Nesmith (J. R.). Branch Mint of the U. S. Mineral Resources. (1864). III, 564

Neville (E.). The Smugglers. A Story of Puget Sound. N.d. III, 873

Newberry (J. S.). II, 992

Newcombe (Chas. Francis.). Menzies' Journal of Vancouver's Voyage, 1792. III, 358

——. The McGill Totem Pole. 1919. III, 357

——. Petroglyphs in British Columbia. 1907. III, 355

——. Victoria, B. C. Guide to Anthropological Collection. 1909. III, 356

Newell (C.). Indian Stories. (1912). III, 271

New England Assoc. of Railway Superintendents. Report. 1851. I, 1420

New England Club. Souvenir Edition. With Wellesley, Harvard, Yale and Brown Alumni. 1910. III, 368

New Highway to the Orient across the Mountains, etc. of Canada. N.d.

Ostrander Army Boy of the Sixties, should read vol. 3, not vol. 2.

Portsmouth, Virginia. Report of the Portsmouth Relief Association . . . during Yellow Fever in 1855. 1856. IV, 956

Post (C. C.). Ten Years a Cowboy. 1903. III, 754

Potter (E. R.). Address delivered before the Rhode Island Historical Society. 1851. III, 795

Potter (T. E.). Autobiography. 1913. III, 755

Poussin (G. T.). The United States, its Power and Progress. 1851. III, 38A

——. Question of L'Oregon, 1846. 1846. III, 623

Powderly, (T. V.) The Labor Movement; The Problem of Today. 1890. IV, 65

Powell (A.). Echoes from the Frontier. 1909. III, 756

Powell, (F. W.) Hall Jackson Kelley, Prophet of Oregon. 1917. II, 685

Powell (J. W.). Exploration of the Colorado River. 1875. III. 757

——. Introduction to the Study of Indian Languages. 1880. III, 758

Powell, (J. J.) Nevada, the Land of Silver. 1876. III, 399

Power (T.). Impressions of America, during 1833-35. 1836. III, 759

Powers, (J. C.) History of the Early Settlers Sangamon County. 1876. III, 252

Powers (L. B.). Missions of California. 1897. III, 108

Powers (S.). Aborigines of California. 1874. III, 761

——. Afoot and Alone. 1872. III, 760

——. Afoot and Alone. 1884. I, 505

Pratt, (J. J.) Hesperian Tree, Souvenir of Ohio Valley, 1900. 1900. III, 498

Pratt, (J. W.) IV, 644

——. The City of Seattle. 1893. III, 822

Pratt (O.). Series of Pamphlets: Complete Collections. 1851. III, 763

——. 1884. III, 764

Pratt, (P. P.) Autobiography. 1874. III, 350A

Prayers in the Crow Indian Language. 1891. II, 195

Prentiss, (N. L.) Kansas Miscellanies. 1899. III, 279A

Prentiss, (S. S.) A Memoir of. 1855. II, 338

Presbyterian Church, Portland, Ore. Dedication Services. 1899. III, 606A

Prescott, (W. H.) I, 223

Price, (J. M.) From Euston to Klondike. 1898. III, 20

Price (Major Sir R. L.). The Two Americas. 1877. III, 765

Prichard (J. C.). Natural History of Man. 1855. III, 766

Priest (J.). American Antiquities. 1835. III, 768

——. American Antiquities. 1835. III, 767

Priestley, (H. I.) IV, 94, 140

Pringle (L. M.). Yukon-Tamana Region, Alaska. 1905-1908. III, 21

Pringle, (O. M.) Magic River Deschutes. N.d. III, 647

Proceedings Conference of Western Governors held at Salt Lake City, Utah, June 5, 1913. 1913. I, 626

——. Same. Held at Seattle, May 18, 1915, and at Portland, Ore., Sept. 22, 1915. I, 627

Proceedings of a Meeting of the Bar Washington on Arrest of Hon Edward Lander. 1856. IV, 767

Proceedings of the Second Annual Meeting of Cairo and Fulton R. R. Co. 1855. II, 1268C

Proceedings of the 16th Annual Encampment, Independence, Oregon, 1897. 1897. II, 470

Proceedings of the Sixteenth Annual Encompment of the G. A. of the R. Independence, Oregon, 1897. 1897. I, 1399

Proceedings of Sundry Citizens of Baltimore, convened for the purpose of devising the Most Efficient Means of Improving the Intercourse between the City and the Western States. 8vo, sewn. 1827. I, 1422

Progress of the Catholic Church in America. N. d. I, 565

Prosch, (C.) IV, 1035

——. Reminiscences of Washington. 1904. III, 771

Prosch, (T. W.) IV, 629, 1035

——. Chronological History of Seattle. 1850-1897. [Seattle, 1900-01]. III, 770

——. Dr. D. Maynard, the Pioneer Physician of Seattle. 1904. III, 772

——. The Conkling-Prosch Family. 1909. III, 774

——. Insane of Washington. 1914. III, 775

——. McCarver and Tacoma. 1906. III, 773

Prosser, (Wm. F). History of the Puget Sound Country. 1903. III, 885

Protestant Episcopal Church. Proceedings of the Second Convocation of Clergy and Laity of Oregon and Washington. 1854. III, 886

Proud. (R.) History of Pennsylvania. 1797-8. III, 715

Under Sir John Richardson and Swainson should read vol. IV, 501.

Rockwood (Eleanor Ruth). Books on the Pacific Northwest for Small Libraries. 1923. IV, 519

Roe (Francis M.). Army Letters from an Officer's Wife, 1871-1888. 1909. IV, 520

Rogers (Archibald). Out of Doors Library Hunting. 1897.

Rogers (John). Sport in Vancouver and Newfoundland. 1912. IV, 521

Rogers (John R.). The Irrepressible Conflict; or, An American System of Money. 1892. IV, 522

Rogers (Thomas H.). Nehalem, a Story of the Pacific. (1898). IV, 523

Rogers (William). Memoranda of the Experiences, Labors and Travels of a Universalist Preacher. 1845. IV, 524

Roggeween (Arnoldo). III, 308

Rohrbacher (C. A.). Seattle Spirit. (1907). IV, 648

Roland (Walpole). Algoma West, its Mines, Scenery. 1887. III, 195

Rolle (Denys). I, 841

Rollins (Alice Wellington). The Three Tetons. (1887). IV, 525

Rollins (Philip Ashton). The Cowboy, 1936. IV, 526

——. Discovery of the Oregon Trail. 1812-13. 1935. IV, 527

Ronan (Peter). Historical Sketch of the Flathead Indians, 1813 to 1890. [1890]. III, 344

Roosevelt (Theodore). Good Hunting in Pursuit of Big Game. 1907. IV, 529

——. Hoofs, Claws and Antlers of the Rocky Mountains. 1894. IV, 528

——. Thomas Hart Benton. N.d. IV, 530

Roquefeuil (Camille de). Journal d'un Voyage autour du Monde, 1816-1819. 1823. IV, 531

——. (English edition). 1823. IV, 532

Rosenberg (C. G.). I, 416

Ross (Alexander). Adventures of the First Settlers on the Oregon or Columbia River. 1849. IV, 533

——. Fur Hunters of the Far West. 1855. IV, 534

——. Red River Settlement. 1856. IV, 535

Ross (Edward C.). III, 637

Ross (James Clark). IV, 536

Ross (Sir John). Memoir of Admiral Adam John de Krusenstern. 1856. IV, 537

——. Voyage of Discovery, 1819. Second Voyage, 1829-33. . . . 1835. Appendix to Second Voy., 1835. 1819-35. IV, 536

Ross (Patrick H. W.). Western Gate. 1911. IV, 538

Ross (Victor). History of the Canadian Bank of Commerce. 1920-1922. IV, 162

Ross (W. P.). Life and Times of. 1893. I, 150

——. Remarks in Opposition to Bill to Organize T. of Oklahoma, 1874. IV, 408

Ross (W. W.). 10,000 Miles by Land and Sea. IV, 139 [author given wrongly in text.]

Rossi (Louis Abbe). Six Ans en Amerique. Californie Oregon. 1863. IV, 539

Rossiter (Harriet) and Howard (E. C.). Indian Legends. 1925. IV, 540

Rouhaud (H.). Les Regions Nouvelles. Histoire du Commerce au Nord de l'Ocean Pacifique. 1868. IV, 541

Rothensteiner (J.). Flat-Head and Nez Perce Delegation to St. Louis, 1831-39. N.d. IV, 542

Rothrock (T. J.). Sketch of the Flora of Alaska. 1868. IV, 13

Rottschew (A.). Schreiben eines Russen aus Californien. 1852. III, 109

Rowan (Capt). II, 902

Rowan (James). The I.W.W. in the Lumber Industry. N.d. IV, 543

Royal Society of Canada. Proceedings and Transactions of. 1895. IV, 544

Royce (Alice C.). III, 381

Royer (Edgar). Benaiah Longley Whitman, 1862-1911. (1911?). IV, 545

——. Financial Record: Vol. 1-12. 1908-1919. IV, 546

Rubio (pseud.). II, 595

Ruffner (W. H.). Report on Washington Territory. 1889. I, 1481

——. Report on Washington Territory. 1889. IV, 547

Rubeau (C. E.). Une Page d'Histoire Decouverte des restes de Trois Missionares de la Compagnie de Jesus. 1898. IV, 167

Rumiantev [Romanov] (Vladimir). Two Original Ms. in Russian, between 1832 and 1835. 1832. III, 806

Rupp (I. Daniel). Early History of Western Pennsylvania. 1754 to 1833. 1847. III, 716

——. History of Berks and Lebanon Counties. 1844. IV, 549

——. History of Lancaster County, Pa. 1844-45. IV, 548

——. History of Northampton, Lehigh, Monroe, Barton and Schuylkill Counties. 1845. IV, 550

——. History of Berks and Lebanon Counties. 1844. III, 717

——. History of Northampton, Lehigh, Monroe, Barton and Schuylkill Counties. 1845. III, 718

Rush (Richard). Memoranda of a Residence . . . Oregon Question. 1845. IV, 551

Sherrard (R. A.). Narrative of Escape and Sufferings of Col. James Paul. 1869. IV, 691; III, 828
Sherwood, (E.) Buffalo Bill and the Pony Express. N.d. IV, 121
——. Buffalo Bill's Boyhood. N.d. IV, 120
Shields, (G. O.) Battle of the Big Hole. 1889. I, 1297
——. Battle of the Big Hole. 1889. IV, 695
——. Big Game of North America. 1890. IV, 697
——. Cruisings in the Cascades. 1889. IV, 696
——. Hunting in the Great West. 1890. IV, 698
——. Rustlings in the Rockies. 1883. IV, 694
Shiels (A. W.). Alaska, its Early History. N.d. IV, 702
——. Alaska, its early History. (1925). IV, 699
——. Early Voyages to the Pacific. 1930. IV, 700
——. Seward's Ice-Box. 1932. IV, 701
Shinn (C. H.). Mining Camps. 1885. IV, 703
——. Story of the Mines. 1896. IV, 704
Shippen, (M.) III, 54
Shirley Letters, (The.) California in 1851, by Shirley. IV, 281
Shirley, (J. M.) Route and Distances to Oregon and California. 1846. IV, 705
Shortfield, (L.) Wild Western Scenes. 1849. I, 130
Shuck, (O. T.) California Anthology. 1880. IV, 707
——. Representative and Leading Men of the. 1870. IV, 705
Sibley, (Gen. H. H.) IV, 507, 708, 975
Sierra, (F. B. de la.) IV, 967
Silingsby (M.). Buckskin Joe; or, the Trapper's Guide. (1879). IV, 709
Silverton, Oregon. 1910. Also, Coos Bay, Ore., (1905). IV, 427
Simms (J. R.). Frontiersmen of New York. 1882. III, 389
——. Frontiersmen of New York. 1862-83. IV, 710
Simms (Wm. G.). History of South Carolina. 1860. III, 829
Simpson (A.). Life and Travels of Thomas Simpson. 1845. IV, 712
Simpson (G.). Journey Round the World. 1841-42. 1847. IV, 711
——. Overland Journey Round the World 1841-42. 1847. IV, 713
Simpson (T.). I, 972, 1011; II, 951, 1100, 1217; IV, 72
——. Narrative of Discoveries on the North Coast. 1836-39. 1843. IV, 714
Sinclair (B. W.). North of Fifty-Three. 1914. IV, 715
Siringo (C. A.). Cowboy Detective. 1912. IV, 717
——. History of Billy the Kid. 1920. IV, 719
——. Lone Star Cowboy. 1919. IV, 718
——. Texas Cow Boy. (1886). IV, 716
Sitgreaves, (Capt. L.) II, 1231B
——. Expedition down the Zuni and Colorado Rivers. 1853. IV, 721
Sitka Times, First Published on September 19, 1868. 1868. IV, 720
Six Lessons on Missions in Alaska. 1907. I, 596
Skagit County, Washington. 1921. IV, 1024
Skagway Commercial Club. N.d. IV, 51
Sketch of Geographic Rout of a Great Railway to Which to Connect the Canals and Navigable Waters of the States of New York . . . and Missouri Territory. [By W. C. Redfield.] 1839. I, 1425
Sketch of the Reign of George the Third, from 1780-90. 1791. IV, 403
Sketches from the North. 1858. III, 867
Skinner, (A.) The Mascoutens. 1924. IV, 323
Skinner (Constance L.). Adventures of Oregon. 1920. IV, 722
Slacum, (W. A.) II, 479
Slaves. Census of Slaves in 1755. N.d. III, 379
Sloan (W. N.). Spiritual Conquest along the Rockies. 1913. IV, 723
Slocum (Wm. A.). II, 272; 1061. [Note: Should be Wm. A. Slacum in text.]
Sloss, (L.) Reply of the Alaska Commercial Co. to Charges of Gov. Alfred P. Swineford. 1887. IV, 47
Slover, (J.) III, 272
Small (F. B.). Autobiography of a Pioneer; 1916. IV, 724
Smet (Pierre J. De). [Vide De Smet.]
——. Western Missions and Missionaries. 1863. IV, 730
Smith (A. D.). John Jacob Astor. 1929. I, 151; IV, 78
Smith,(C. W.) Journal of a Trip to California. 920. IV, 454

Stanier, (W.) The Gentleman Emigrant . . . in Canada. 1874. III, 37
Stanford's Map Shewing the Position of the Yukon Goldfields, 1897. 1897. IV, 53
Stanhope, (R.) II, 798
Stanley (E. J.). Life of Rev. L. B. Statler. 1916. IV, 378
——. Rambles in Wonderland. 1878. IV, 755
Stanley, (W. S.) A Mile of Gold. Strange Adventures in the Yukon. 1898. IV, 54
Stark (J. H.). Loyalists of Massachusetts. 1910. III, 47
Statement of Facts pertaining to Proclamation of Martial Law over Pierce County. 1856. IV, 769
Statement of the Oregon and Washington Delegation in relation to the War Claims of Oregon and Washington. N.d. IV, 450
Statement of the Oregon and Washington Delegation in relation to Indian War Claims of Oregon and Washington. (1857). IV, 767B
Statement on the Part of the U. S., in Pursuance of Convention of 29th Sept., 1927. between U. S. and G. Britain. 1829. III, 450
States and Territories of our Western Empire. 1858. III, 645
Statistik der von 1822-33 erfolgten Verbannumgen nach Sibirien. 1845. III, 810
Steam Duck (The Great) . . . Invention for Aerial Navigation. 1841. 1928. I, 7
Steamer Corwin. Report of the Cruise. 1884. 1889. I, 149
——. Report of the Cruise 1885. 1887. I,148
——. Report of the Cruise. 1888. 1888. I, 147
Stearnes, (J. F.) Historical Discourse First Presbyterian Church of Newark. 1853. I, 1312
Stearns, (R. C.) Remarks on death of late Dr. Philip P. Carpenter. (1877). IV, 130
Stebbing, (W.) Sir Walter Raleigh. 1899. III, 34
Stedman, (J. W.) Norwich Jubilee. 1859. III, 145
Steel and Searl's Legislative Manual for 1895-1896, in re State of Washington. 1895. IV, 1004
Steel, (J. V.) New Guide to the Pacific Coast, Santa Fe Route. 1893. IV, 452
Steel, (W. G.) Mountains of Oregon. 1890. IV, 428
——. Steel Points. 1906-1907. IV, 414
Steele, (H. R.) Reminiscences of a Long Life. (1927.) III, 789
Steele, (J. P.) The Wyandotte Cave of Crawford County, Ind. 1864. I, 1265
Steele (J. W.). Frontier Army Sketches. 1883. IV, 758
Steele, (R. F.) Story of Lincoln County, Wash. (1909). IV, 1012
——. Story of Lincoln County, Wash. (1909). IV, 997
Steele, (Col. S. B.) Forty Years in Canada. 1915. IV, 105
Steilacoom Library Association. 1860. IV, 993
Steller (G. V.). Beschriebung von dem Lande Kamtschatka. 1774. II, 1261k
——. II, 742-3, III, 351A
Stennett (W. H.). North and West Illustrated (1875). IV, 759
Stephens (H. N.). Memorial Biography of Adele M. Field. (1918). IV, 764
Stephens (J. L.). Incidents of Travel in Central America. 1841. III, 841
Stephens (L. D.). Life Sketches of a Jayhawker of '49. 1916. IV, 762
Stephenson (R. L.). Across the Plains. 1892. IV, 763
Stephenson, (Wm. B.) Land of Tomorrow. (1919). IV, 21
Sterling, (E.) Story of the Files. 1893. I, 521
Stevens (A. H.). Admission of Oregon. 1859. IV, 760
Stevens, (F. E.) III, 256
——. Black Hawk War. 1903. III, 255
——. Speech on Washington and Oregon War Claims. 1858. IV, 774A
——. Vindication of, for Proclaiming and Enforcing Martial Law. Washington Territory. 1856. IV, 772
Stevens, (H. M.) IV, 97
Stevens (Hagard). Life of Isaac Ingalls Stevens. 1900. IV, 779
Stevens (Horace). III, 777
Stevens (Gov. I. I.). Address on the Northwest. 1858. IV, 773
——. Campaign on the Rio Grande. 1851. IV, 765
——. Letter from Secretary of State communicating Report of Governor Stevens, of Washington, property of the Hudson's Bay and Puget's Sound Company. 1855. IV, 766
——. 1856. IV, 770A
——. Message. Also Correspondence with Secretary of War, Maj. Gen. Wood. 1857. IV, 771
——. Minority Report of showing growth upon which Regular Southern Delegation were entitled to seats in the Convention at the Front Street Theatre, Baltimore. 1860. IV, 776
——. Pacific Railroad, Northern Route. Letter from Isaac I. Stevens, to Railroad Convention of Washington and Oregon, May 20, 1860. IV, 775

Stutfield (H. E. M.) and Collie (J. Norman). Climbs and Explorations in the Canadian Rockies. 1903. IV, 805

Suckley (G.) and Cooper (J. G.) et al. Natural History of Washington Territory and Oregon. 1859. IV, 806

Suffling (E. R.). Fur Traders of the West. 1896. IV, 807

Sullivan (M. K.). Trail of a Sourdough. 1910. IV, 23

——. Woman who Went to Alaska. 1903. IV, 22

Sullivan (Maurice). IV, 725-6

——. Jedediah Smith, Trader and Trail Breaker. 1936. IV, 808

Sulte (B.). Melangs Historique. 1919. IV, 809

Summer Saunterings. 1882. 1882. III, 610

Summerbell (N.). Autobiography of Elder Mathew Gardner . . . 1875. III, 502

Summerhayes (M.). Vanishing Arizona. 1908. IV, 810

——. N.d. IV, 811

Sumner (C.). Speech of . . . on the Cession of Russian America. 1867. II, 1268A

Sumner Excursion Routes. Day Line Steamers on the Hudson River. 1886. III, 214

Sundby-Hanson (H.). Norwegian Immigrant Contributions to America's Making. 1921. III, 168

Sunset Library. No. 1, Oct. 1893. 1893. IV, 652

Sutre Collection, II, 485

Sutter (J. A.). IV, 603

Sutter (J. A.). General Sutter's Diary. 1939. IV, 282

Swainson (W.). IV, 504

Swan (J. G.). Amoor River. Countries drained by the Amoor River. 1885. IV, 815

——. Indians of Cape Flattery. 1868. IV, 814

——. The Northwest Coast. 1857. IV, 813

——. Notes on the Fisheries, Puget Sound. 1894. IV, 815A

Swan (O. G.). Frontier Days. 1928. IV, 816

Sweetser (A. R.) and May E. Kent. Key and Flora. 1908. IV, 817

Swift (Lindsay). Brook Farm. I, 393

Swineford (A. P.). Alaska. 1899. IV, 818

Swineford (Gov. A. P.). IV, 47

Swisher (J.). How I Know; or, Sixteen Year's Eventful Experiences. 1880. IV, 819

Swisshelm (J. G.). Half a Century. 1880. IV, 339

Symons (T. W.). Report of an Examination of the Upper Columbia River. 1882. IV, 820

Tabor (Clarence W.). Breaking Sod on the Prairies. Early Days in Dakota. 1924. IV, 200

Tache (Mgr. Alexander A.). Esquisse sur le Nord-Ouest. 1869. IV, 822

——. Vingt Annees de Missions dans le Nord-Ouest. 1866. IV, 821

Tacoma Ac. Sc. II, 1283

Tacoma Illustrated. 1889. IV, 824

Tacoma and Vicinity. 1888. IV, 823

Tailhan (R. D.). III, 690

Tale of Two Cities: Minneapolis and St. Paul Compared. 1885. III, 336

Tallmadge (Benj.). Memoir of. 1858. I, 124

Tarr (Ralph S.) and Butler (Bert. S.). Yakutat Bay Region, Alaska. 1909. IV, 24

Tarr (Ralph S.) and Martin (Lawrence). Alaskan Glacier Studies. 1914. IV, 25

Tasse (Joseph). Les Canadiens de l'Ouest. 1878. IV, 826

Tate (C. M.). Chinook as Spoken by the Indians of Washington T., British Columbia and Alaska. (1889). IV, 827

Taverner (P. A.). Birds of Western Canada. 1926. IV, 828

Taylor (Bayard). Colorado. 1867. IV, 831

——. Eldorado. 1850. IV, 829

——. 1854. IV, 830

Taylor (Charles M.). Touring Alaska and the Yellowstone. (1901). IV, 832

Taylor (Elder). III, 763

Taylor (J. G.). Some New Light on the Last Resting Place of Benedict Arnold. 1931. III, 54

Taylor (J. W.). I, 582; II, 144

Taylor (James W.). History of the State of Ohio, 1650-1787. 1854. III, 503

——. History of the State of Ohio. 1854. IV, 406

Taylor (Joseph H.). Beavers, Their Ways, and Other Sketches. 1904. IV, 836

——. Kaleidoscopic Lives. 1901. IV, 835

——. Sketches of Frontier and Indian Life. 1863-1899. IV, 834

——. Twenty Years on the Trap Line. 1891. IV, 833

——. History and Government of Washington. 1898. IV, 837

Taylor (Samuel). III, 292a

Taylor (William). California Life Illustrated. 1867. IV, 838

Tebienkov (Capt. M. D.). Atlas Siev. Zapadnykh Beregov Ameriki. 1852. 1268b

Tecumseh. III, 164

Teit (James). European Tales from the Upper Thompson Indians. 1916. IV, 842

Traugott Bromme's Hand-und Reisebuch fur Auswanderer nach dem Vereinigten Staaten von Nord-Amerika. 1849. I, 1464

Travels in the Interior Parts of America; in a Series of Letters. By an Officer. 1789. IV, 69

Treadgold (A. N. C.). An English Expert on the Klondike. 1899. IV, 49

Trevenen (Capt. James). III, 148

Trexler (Harrison A.). Flour and Wheat in the Montana Gold Camps, 1862. 1918. IV, 382

Triggs (J. H.). History of Cheyenne and Northern Wyoming. 1876. IV, 885

Trimble (William). The Mining Advance into the Inland Empire. 1914. IV, 383

Triplett (Frank). Conquering the Wilderness. 1883. IV, 886

Trollope (Mrs.). Domestic Manners of the Americans. 1832. IV, 887

Trow (James M. P.). Manitoba and the Northwest Territories. 1878. IV, 889

——. Trip to Manitoba. 1875. IV, 888

Trowbridge (M. E. D.). Life Story of Gershon and Elizabeth Day. 1895. IV, 890

Trudeau (Jean Baptiste). Journal among the Arikara Indians in 1795. 1912. IV, 891

Truman (Major Ben C.). Occidental Sketches. 1881. IV, 892

Trumbull (Benj.). Complete History of Connecticut. 1818. III, 146

Tschitsghagow (Herrn V.). Russich: Kayserlichen Admirals Reise nach dem Eismeer. 1793. II, 1268g

Tucker (Ephraim W.). History of Oregon. 1844. IV, 893

Tucker (J. C.). To the Golden Goal. 1895. IV, 894

Tucker (L. Norman). Western Canada. 1908. IV, 895

Turnbull (T.). Travels Across the Plains to California. 1914. IV, 896

Turner (Frederick J.). Essays in American History. 1910. IV, 898

——. Rise of the New West. 1896. IV, 897

Turner (J.). Three Years Hunting in Great Northwest. 1888. IV, 902

Turner (J. P.). The Prairie Chicken. 1917. IV, 899

Turner (T. G.). Guide from the Lakes to the Rocky Mountains. 1868. IV, 900

Turner (William S.). Story of my Life. N.d. IV, 901

Tuttle (Charles R.). Our North Land. 1885. IV, 903

Tuttle (Rev. D. S.). Reminiscences of a Missionary Bishop. 1906. IV, 904

Tuttle (Rev. E. B.). Book about Indians. 1873. IV, 905

Twain (Mark). Letters from the Sandwich Islands. 1937. IV, 284

Twiss (Travers). Oregon Question Examined. 1846. IV, 907

——. 1846. IV, 908

——. Oregon Territory. 1846. IV, 906

——. 1846. IV, 906a

Tyler (Sergeant Daniel). Concise History of the Mormon Battalion in the Mexican War, 1846-1847. 1881. IV, 909

Tyler (Sydney). San Francisco's Great Disaster. 1906. IV, 147

Tyrrell (J. W.). David Thompson. Canada's Greatest Geographer. 1922. IV, 862. (First name misgiven as "J. Burr" Tyrell in the text)

——. Report on the Doobaunt, Kazan and Ferguson Rivers. 1897. IV, 910

——. Across the Sub-Arctic of Canada. 1897. IV, 911

Tyson (Martha E.). II, 526a

Tyson (T. P.). The Industrial Resources and Geology of California. 1851. IV, 912

Tytler (Patrick F.). Historical Views of . . . the more Northern Coasts of America. 1832. IV, 913

——. 1833.

Udell (John). Incidents of Travel to California. 1856. IV, 915

Ueber die Schiflahrt auf dem Omour in Jahre 1857, 1858. III, 809

Uebersicht der Hydrographischen Expeditionem 1846. III, 804

Ulrich (Charles). The Honor of a Cowboy. 1908. IV, 188

Umfreville (Edward). II, 349

Underhill (Reuben L.). From Cow Hides to Golden Fleece. 1939. IV, 916

Underwood (John). Alaska, an Empire in the Making. 1913. IV, 30

Union Pacific Railroad from Omaha. 1867. IV, 917

Union Pacific Railroad. Report of Chief Engineer, with Reports of Division Engineers for 1866. 1868. IV, 456

Unitarians. IV, 412

University of Wash. Coll. 12 reports. III, 937

Upchurch (Father J.). Life, Labors and Travels. 1887. IV, 922

Upham (S. C.). Notes of a Voyage to California, 1849-50. 1878. IV, 923

Wickersham (James). Changing name of Mt. Ranier. II, 1283

Utah. Acts, Regulations and Memorials, passed at the several Annual Sessions of the Territory of Utah. 1855. IV, 924

——. Letter of the Delegate in Congress, enclosing a Constitution. 1858. II, 1269a

Under Wurttemberg line 4 should read III, 911.

P9-DBI-448

THE GARDEN
SOURCEBOOK

Caroline Boisset & Fayal Greene

THE GARDEN SOURCEBOOK

A PRACTICAL GUIDE TO PLANNING AND PLANTING

CROWN PUBLISHERS, INC.
NEW YORK

Edited and designed by
Mitchell Beazley International Ltd
Michelin House
81 Fulham Road
London SW3 6RB

Published by the Crown Publishers, Inc. 201 East 50th Street, New York, New York 10022. Member of the Crown Publishing Group.

Random House, Inc. New York, Toronto, London, Sydney, Auckland

CROWN is a trademark of Crown Publishers, Inc

Typeset in Plantin by SX Composing Ltd, Rayleigh, Essex
Colour reproduction by Mandarin Offset, Hong Kong
Produced by Mandarin Offset, Hong Kong
Printed and bound in Hong Kong

Library of Congress Cataloging-in-Publishing Data

Boisset, Caroline.
The garden sourcebook/Caroline Boisset.
p. cm.
Includes index.
1. Landscape gardening. 2. Gardens. 3. Plants,
Ornamental-Selection. 4. Garden Structures. I. Title.
SB473.5548 1993
635.9-dc20 92-30874
CIP

10 9 8 7 6 5 4 3 2 1
First American Edition

Editors Emily Wright, Simon Ryder, David Joyce, Richard Rosenfeld
Designers Jeremy Roots, Geoff Fennell
Senior Art Editors Larraine Lacey, Mike Brown
Editorial Assistant Jaspal Bhangra
Production Controller Sarah Schuman
Commissioned Photography Sue Atkinson, Paul Barker
Commissioned Artwork Tony Graham, Andrew Macdonald, Coral Mula, Gillie Newman, Sandra Pond, Will Giles
Picture Research Christine Rista

Executive Editor Sarah Polden
Design Director Jacqui Small

The gardens shown on pages 20-25 were designed by Alison Coleman and illustrated by Vivien Monument.

Please note: for guidance on the hardiness zones given in **The Plant Selector** see page 7.

ʟ10.0ᴄ

Contents

FIRST
STEPS

FIRST STEPS

Anyone can have a dream garden. No matter where you live, or how undeveloped your horticultural skills, creating the perfect garden is not only feasible, but much easier than you might think. Few are lucky enough to inherit an ideal site but hardly anyone finds a truly hopeless situation. The art of gardening is evaluating what you have got and transforming it into what you want. And above all knowing exactly how to do it. One simply cannot visit enough different, specialist gardens to see the full range of available effects. Investigate the formal Renaissance style, cottage garden informality (or even chaos), Mediterranean courtyards, one-color borders, water features, and gardens with inventive examples of topiary. On seeing something you like, note down how the effect is achieved. As a vital complement to these records, keep enormous lists of plants.

All good gardeners cheat. The more you borrow ideas the better. If it works recreate it. If you cannot provide exactly the same growing conditions then play around with the idea and reinvent it. Amend it to your own needs. If you like formal gardens then the range of tricks is huge, more or less everything can be whipped into art. Hedges can be given windows onto contrasting areas, with "doors" leading into corridors and alleys. Never settle for the obvious.

You have to be equally imaginative with plants. When you find a particular plant that you like the next step is to visit a national collection. Most countries have them. See if there is a variety with even better color and/or scent. Also get into the habit of visiting major horticultural shows. Thereafter start visiting small specialist nurseries which invariably sell a wider range of rare plants than garden centers.

Far left: Sunshine filtering through a heavily clad archway lights up the evergreen foliage of *Elaeagnus* × *ebbingei* 'Gilt Edge', adding a touch of warmth in winter.

Left: This garden perfectly complements the house. Perennials provide quick interest, giving shrubs like *Cupressus macrocarpa*, by the fence, time to develop.

While at times one relishes getting carried away, beware of totally overdoing it. Creating a garden is one thing, time-consuming and expensive though it can be. But looking after it year after year is something else. Shrubs are a godsend if only because they tend to require relatively little attention. One of the biggest pitfalls is collecting tender perennials. Because so many are exotic, they need to be kept in pots in a frost-free greenhouse over winter, or indoors. It is easy to run out of space and money for fresh compost and eventually even bigger containers.

But given some basic knowledge, a clear idea of the do's and don'ts, and three key ingredients – time, patience, and the will to make it work, then everything will go according to plan. Your dream garden can become a reality. And sooner rather than later.

ASSESSING THE SITE

Whether the site is brand new or an old established plot, the same principles apply to planning and designing your ideal garden. First, assess what is at your disposal, then decide what kind of garden you want and whether you can provide its requirements. For example, a kitchen garden needs fertile soil and full sun, whereas woodland species need shade; alpine and rock plants need less space than an arboretum, when nothing less than about four acres (1.6 hectares) will do justice to a collection.

For most purposes, one needs reasonably fertile soil and a sunny, sheltered position, but even without these ingredients do not give up. Assess your garden's potential, its strengths and weaknesses, and then decide how to take advantage of the former while minimizing the effects of the latter. It is the surest way to successful garden design.

Dimensions

The first step with a new garden is to familiarize yourself with its dimensions. Size matters, but only in so far as it might limit the number of different areas you can create, and the size and number of plants and features within them. If the garden is on the small side, there are several ways of putting the available space to more efficient use. Vertical surfaces, for instance, offer scope for climbers, wall plants and hanging baskets. The range of plants is enormous. One small area could contain the dark red flowers of *Clematis viticella* growing up through the long catkin-like racemes of *Itea ilicifolia*, with a *Cytisus battandieri* nearby bearing early summer, pineapple-scented yellow flowers. Though the latter is strictly speaking a freestanding tree, it can also be grown against a sunny wall. Raised beds and terraces also extend the growing areas, and containers make maximum use of sterile locations such as paving and window sills. Furthermore, the *illusion* of size is easily achieved. Clever design demonstrates how even the most cramped plots can, with crafty positioning of screens in the form of hedges and trellises, give a spurious impression of size and stature. The secret is to have a surprise around every corner, and to make the visitor think there are more corners than really exist. One of the most sophisticated forms of illusion is *trompe l'oeil* (see page 212). At its most developed, it involves painting a scene on a wall suggesting an extra area beyond, but "receding" trelliswork and the clever use of mirrors can easily give an impression of depth that does not exist.

Incidentally, too large a garden can also cause problems, although they are easily solved by strategic planting, with the emphasis on trees and shrubs underplanted with ground cover. However, since the great majority of gardeners find themselves with limited space rather than too much, this text will concentrate on that extreme rather than coping with extensive acres. By itself smallness is not a problem, what counts is how it is used.

Planning considerations

When planning your garden, once you have accepted the size of the site, begin by considering these four factors: shape, topography, division and ambience.

Shape This influences design considerably. Few plots are symmetrical but that really does not matter. Indeed, an L-shape or a triangle offers more design potential than a rectangle. Perhaps the most difficult shape of all is a square, particularly when it is too small to subdivide, but even this problem has solutions (see pages 22 and 23).

Topography Surprisingly, a level site is less desirable than one with interesting, gradual changes, and the attraction of a slope is that it often provides the possibility of terracing. Since steep slopes are unstable, especially when cultivated, devices such as retaining walls, steps or buttresses are needed.

Division Hedges, walls and fences make ideal screens and can introduce different moods and styles as you walk through the garden. They are also invaluable for screening off unsightly but essential areas like the compost heap and refuse storage areas, but do not just erect screens and forget about them. They ought to be attractive, architectural features. Hedges, for example, in addition to decorative entrances and exits, can be given scalloped or battlemented tops. Alternatively, you could plant a tapestry hedge consisting of hornbeam and *Lonicera nitida*.

A design for an awkward garden shape needs to be carefully thought out. A long thin area, for example, can be divided into contrasting sections (the Mediterranean garden, the black and white garden, the ornamental kitchen garden) by means of barriers across its width, but by leaving a narrow view running through from one end to the other you create an additional vista. Furthermore, by placing an ornamental feature – for example, a statue, seat or urn – at the far end, you gain the full benefit from the site's length while the screens minimize the disadvantages.

Ambience The atmosphere of a potential garden is an important consideration. Even when you are working on a bare site the potential of the space needs to be assessed and compared with the "feel" you want to achieve. Walk around the area, take measurements, and observe natural features such as wet spots, bumps or edges, and any other quirks and oddities because they may well have the potential to become focal points. The emphasis is on making use of your natural resources, and converting the apparently insignificant into eye-catching attractions.

CLIMATE AND MICROCLIMATE

Geographical location

Climate is all-important because it dictates the kinds of plants you can grow and exerts an immense influence on design. If you have moved to a new area it is easy to discover average temperatures and rainfall, but you must always allow for extremes.

Regional climate is influenced by fundamental geographical factors like latitude, altitude, proximity of large land masses and the sea and the influence of major ocean currents. Every district has its own special quirks too, such as the Mistral, a cold wind funnelled down the Rhône Valley in France, the "Fremantle Doctor", a cooling wind that relieves the inhabitants of Perth in Western Australia from heatwaves, and the high altitude of the Alps and Rockies that shortens the growing season.

Then there are microclimates, natural and artificial. For example, in most winters central London is nearly frost-free because of the artificial heat exuded by the city. Consequently many tender plants like certain abutilons can be kept outside while in colder country areas they have to be secured in a conservatory over winter. More surprisingly, given the northerly latitude, gardens on the northwest coast of Scotland can grow subtropical plants outdoors with minimal risk of damage because of the moderating effect of the Gulf Stream. In the Pacific Northwest of the United States the climate is made more temperate and wetter than adjacent regions by warm Pacific currents, giving milder winters than are found in the more southerly Kansas.

Though it is wise to learn about your local climate, it is equally important to set about creating your own special microclimate. You cannot do much about the weather but you can do a great deal to minimize its effects, perhaps by erecting a protective windbreak against slicing, icy winds. Often, famous established gardens succeed because their creators have taken great care to improve conditions, enabling them to grow a wider range of delicate and more interesting plants. In cold areas frost and snow do no harm provided you are growing hardy plants and no tender perennials have been left outside. A much bigger problem is wind. It dehydrates soil and stunts growth, while constant buffeting bruises young, emerging plant tissue, impairing growth and development. The first task, therefore, in trying to influence the climate in a new garden is to eliminate or at least reduce the potentially destructive wind.

Creating shelter

If the site is badly exposed, conditions may be too unpleasant for even shelter plants to establish themselves, in which case you will need to erect either temporary or permanent windbreaks. Although it may seem like a good idea to build a solid wall, this does more harm than good. The wind will eddy over the top of the wall and swirl down, creating a whirlwind effect in the garden. The only solution is to create a filtering windbreak that is approximately 40 percent porous, which reduces wind speed but does not stop it dead. Since the screen should become an attractive garden feature rather than a simply functional object, plants are preferable to fencing, but they do, of course, take longer to develop.

Windbreaks usually protect an area ten times their height, so they will produce an immediate change to the growing conditions within the enclosure. For example, two of them running from east to west on either side of a garden will create a dark, cool side and a warm, well-lit one. The advantage of such a windbreak is that it provides an opportunity for two contrasting garden areas, each with its own range of plants, each with its own character.

The type of screen chosen depends on personal preference. Walls will need to have trees or shrubs planted nearby to minimize the eddying effect of the wind; evergreens or matching shrubs successfully complement such solid structures. Alternatively, consider hedges, whether clipped formally or kept in trim with an annual haircut. For a more natural look, thickly planted shrubs, interspersed with taller trees, create a good shelter belt. The selection of plants should ensure a changing pattern of interest running through the seasons with spring blossom, fresh, exciting contrasting foliage in summer, autumn berries and interesting twigs, branches and bark over winter. Pay particular attention to color, texture and outline. With thoughtful planning you will be able to create an outstanding garden feature which is also functional. This does not have to be formal and symmetrical; a seemingly random planting will blur the garden boundary and give the illusion of space.

Above: Besides forming boundaries, walls and hedges provide essential shelter, improving the climate within the garden. When choosing hedging or building materials, make sure they harmonize with foreground planting.

Frost

Frost in winter is seldom a problem unless you want to grow bananas outdoors in upstate New York or daturas on the Cotswold hills. Given that there are in excess of 60,000 hardy plants to choose from, even the coldest areas can be planted up to suit most tastes.

Frost at the wrong time of year, on the other hand, is disastrous. It kills tender young growth, destroys spring blossom and, in extreme cases, wipes out whole plants, especially the marginally hardy. The most likely scenario for unseasonal frost is a clear, still night which follows a calm, bright day. Without wind currents to move it, cold air accumulates in low places, like water forming a pool at the lowest level. The problem with erecting shelter is that it increases the danger of untimely frost by damming up cold air. This is particularly likely on a hillside or in a hollow and is known as a frost pocket. A natural frost pocket cannot be eliminated, but you can at least reduce the problem by creating perimeter gaps so that the cold air flows out of the garden and away.

Having said that, though, it is worth stressing that winter frost can be a fantastic advantage. This is particularly true of gardens strong on structure, with topiary or with clipped low hedges roping in different areas. Not only can the form of plants be more clearly appreciated than in summer when they are usually part-hidden by flowers, but such architectural shapes look quite sensational when crested with frost. The same goes for the herbaceous border. Many gardeners cut down the straggly growth in autumn, but this can easily be left until the following spring so that it, too, will give a fine display of mid-winter, frosty outlines.

SOIL TYPES

How inappropriate and demeaning that, in certain parts of the English-speaking world, soil is known as "dirt". First-rate gardens cannot exist without excellent soil. If yours is poor and infertile then it has to be improved. Drastic steps may be necessary, but first, since soils vary hugely in texture, structure and quality, it is vital that you begin by assessing its

Right: In a very informal setting aim for naturalistic planting. This woodland scene includes groups of shade-tolerant plants such as hostas. Spring bulbs and winter flowering species would give excellent year-round interest.

character. The soil in any area is the product of local geology. During the ice ages glaciation transported huge quantities of rock across the globe. Each type of rock responded differently to weathering so that limestone bedrock, for example, broke down to a very different material than volcanic rock. Some areas, such as the Rhine Valley in Germany, benefit from loess, a fine, fertile soil formed by wind erosion. However, the most fertile soils are found in flood plains, being the sediment deposited by rivers.

Soil is a living material. If healthy it contains billions of micro-organisms which live off the organic content which mainly consists of decaying vegetation. Good soil must also contain moisture and oxygen, and usually carries a high proportion of mineral particles. When very fine, the soil resembles clay; when coarse, a sandy loam. On marsh and peatland the topsoil may be composed almost entirely of organic material, the result of millennia of sedges or mosses living and dying, gradually forming a thick layer of fibrous material.

Most gardeners need only know whether their soil is clay-like or sandy. Clay retains moisture, is difficult to work and sticky when wet, and sets very hard with surface cracks in a dry summer. It needs regular breaking up over winter with a soil conditionier (for example, mushroom compost), although it is often very fertile in its own right. Sandy soil is easy to work and dries out quickly, but needs plenty of well-rotted manure or compost to improve moisture retention. Alluvial silt in a flood plain is an exception to the sandy rule; it is easy to work, fertile, and though free-draining, excellent at retaining moisture.

Acidity and Alkalinity

Plants manufacture their own food by converting carbon dioxide in the atmosphere into carbohydrates. Other essential ingredients come from mineral salts dissolved in the water that coats the soil particles. Nitrogen, phosphorus and potassium are needed in fairly large quantities, with minor but vital additions of magnesium, calcium, sulphur, oxygen, iron, manganese, boron, molybdenum, copper and zinc.

Plants differ in their ability to take up these mineral nutrients. Some are only efficient at absorbing iron, for example, in acid soil. Others can obtain everything they need even in the most alkaline conditions. That is why it is essential to know the character of your soil. If it is alkaline you will not be able to grow limehaters such as rhododendrons or camellias. In very acid soils limestone plants such as philadelphus, clematis and dianthus will flounder. You can easily buy cheap pH testing kits which you should apply to different parts of the garden since conditions will vary. (The pH refers to the negative decimal logarithm of hydrogen ion concentration expressed in moles per liter). A pH of 7 is neutral; anything higher, and the scale goes up to 14, is alkaline, and anything lower acid. Generally, most plants thrive at 6.4-7, vegetables preferring 7-7.5. To confirm your readings look around the neighborhood to see what plants are growing well in other people's gardens. If you want to increase soil alkalinity add lime. But note such a step tends to be irrevocable so think carefully before you act. It is not so easy to increase the acidity. The best way is to create raised beds, or special enclosures, filled with acid soil for ericaceous plants.

Improving the soil

There are a number of ways to improve the quality of the soil; drainage can be made more efficient and the substance and fertility of the soil enhanced.

Drainage The most important consideration on any land that is to be productive is drainage. This fact has been recognized almost as long as gardening has been a practise. The ancient Roman poet Virgil, a keen horticulturist, waxed lyrical about it. While soil must contain water if it is to sustain plant growth, saturation or waterlogging can be as harmful as drying out. This can be fatal. If water fills all the interstices between the soil particles there is no room for air, and so the essential oxygen, and the plant roots begin to rot. Good drainage enables water to pass through the soil and run away to its natural level. In well-drained soils, root development is unimpeded and roots will grow to surprising depths, improving the plant's efficiency at absorbing nutrients and therefore maximizing growth and vigor.

Some soils drain naturally, but not all can be relied upon to do so. In a particularly damp garden it may be worth considering installing a drainage system. The most effective consist of underground pipes laid in trenches at regular intervals and backfilled with gravel, but this is an expensive procedure. Cheaper but less effective methods include digging organic material or sand and gravel into the soil. Such measures may not assist deep drainage, but they do improve soil condition just below the surface. Raising borders slightly to produce a trench along their edges also improves drainage, particularly for shallow-rooted plants. Some species are more tolerant of wet feet than others, but there is still no substitute for truly efficient, beneficial drainage.

Building up the soil Soil that has been well managed will be rich in organic matter and therefore rich in beneficial micro-organisms. If you are lucky enough to inherit a garden in good condition then rejoice, but remember you have got to keep working at it. If the soil is poor do not despair, but start digging in whatever rotted or rotting vegetation you can find – manure, leaf mold, compost, and so on. Thereafter, treat your soil as a hungry beast and feed it with compost or manure every year. After three summers you should notice a considerable difference.

Fertility This is different from soil condition, though often confused with it. To thrive, plants need adequate levels of every essential plant nutrient, but in the act of gardening you automatically remove vital plant material, such as crops and prunings, so these lost minerals need replacing. Furthermore, many garden plants have been bred to grow faster and larger than their wild counterparts and therefore need higher levels of nutrients.

Manure used as a soil conditioner also tackles this problem, but it is not always available. Fortunately plant foods are easy to come by, either organic (such as fish or bone meal) or inorganic (in the form of proprietary products). The concentration of nutrients in inorganic fertilizers varies, the exact ratio sometimes being indicated by the letters NPK. The accompanying numbers, say 10:11:27, indicate 10 percent nitrogen, 11 percent phosphorus, and 27 percent potassium. Nitrogen promotes leaf growth, phosphorus ripens fruit, and potassium produces good fruit and flowers. Generally a balanced, all-in-one fertilizer is adequate, but sometimes a plant needs extra quantities of one nutrient. For example, leafy vegetables such as spinach require heavy nitrogen application.

High fertility, once achieved, needs to be kept at that level. I use dried poultry waste at roughly a double handful per square yard (square meter) once a year on my mixed borders. This works well as a source of nitrogen, phosphorus and potassium. (Occasionally I have missed a year but the garden has not suffered because the general level of fertility in the soil is high.)

Soil structure and damage

Inexperienced gardeners often fail to recognize the fragility of soil structure. While some soils are less stable than others, all are liable to damage. The main problem is compaction. This results from mechanical pressure which forces the particles together, driving out air and spoiling the environment for micro-organisms. In extreme cases roots will be unable to penetrate and water will not drain away. Light, sandy soils may not suffer but heavier soils with a high clay content can be ruined and are particularly prone to compaction if walked on when wet. It is like stepping on, and sinking into, semi-hard concrete, and does plant roots no good whatsoever. The best way to avoid this problem involves creating beds never more than one footstep wide, so there is no need to walk on the soil, with stone paths running between. The ideal is rarely practical in the flower garden, but you can minimize difficulties when undertaking winter projects by laying planks on the soil surface. These reduce the pressure on the ground, distributing weight more evenly, and are more pleasant to tread on than mud.

A hard compacted layer below the surface is known as a "pan". It can be created by the weight of a mechanical cultivator, although you may not be aware of the problem because the surface soil can still look friable or crumbly. One of the worst instances occurs when a garden has previously been used as a building site. The contractors will have churned up the subsoil and afterwards, as a cosmetic exercise, spread a load or two of imported topsoil over the plot, hiding faults and problems. Standing water after rain is a sure sign, but even without it, investigate the state of the soil sooner rather than later.

Once the pan forms it impedes drainage and needs to be broken up. Various tools are available, those particularly worth considering being mechanical cultivators which have an extension at the back designed to crack through the pan as the machine drives forward. Otherwise compaction is best repaired by deep digging and by incorporating bulky material, particularly in heavy soils, to open up the structure and let in oxygen. In cold areas, deep digging can be undertaken in autumn and the ground left rough throughout the winter, allowing the action of frost and thawing to convert clotted land into a more manageable tilth.

To conclude this section, three examples of problem soils are given with suggested treatments.

Heavy, sticky clay The problem with clay is that it does not forgive abuse, being easily damaged and difficult to repair. Any means of making it more porous and getting more air into the mix will improve growing conditions. The prime objective is to build up the humus by digging in bulky compost. As the garden develops, be assiduous in your composting, hoarding every scrap of organic refuse from rose prunings to kitchen waste. Farmyard manure, if you can obtain it, is beneficial, adding humus as well as nutrients. Further additions of coarse grit, sand and even ash will also open up the texture and give a crumbly, more manageable texture in which plants thrive.

In many respects the plants themselves help to improve heavy soils. The roots penetrate and open the structure while falling foliage increases the organic content so that gradually, over the years, the surface soil becomes easier to work.

To establish new plants in the heaviest soils you must improve conditions around their roots. When digging planting holes incorporate extra quantities of leaf mold enriched with bone meal or a slow release fertilizer at the bottom to ensure rapid establishment. The one huge compensation for having heavy clay is that once the plants have settled they succeed much better than in less fertile ground.

Fine, blowing sand In some areas, particularly near the coast, shifting sands or sandy soil may cause problems. Unlike clay which stays put, sand at its worst can literally blow away, leaving roots exposed, or it can blow in, depositing a desert-like dune over the entire surface of the garden.

The main advantage of sandy soil is that it is easy to work and difficult to damage. The drawback is that water runs straight through it, flushing away dissolved mineral salts, leaving plants dry and undernourished. It may seem contradictory to suggest that organic matter is the best way of adding body when it also lightens heavy clay, but it works. The addition of humus in the form of leaf mould or rotted manure improves moisture retention. In the case of existing beds which need bulking up, it may be necessary to remove all the plants, transferring them to a temporary bed, while the soil is treated. Most sands tend to be acid, so if you want to grow food, mix lime into the soil.

Thin topsoil over chalk or bare rock In such conditions, moisture retention will be impaired since there is very little soil to hold the water (made worse with chalk as it is so porous); as a result, plants are likely to suffer from summer drought. Also, pure chalk or pure rock are poor sources of plant nutrients. As an additional problem, soil over chalk is likely to be strongly alkaline, restricting the choice of plants to the most lime-tolerant.

The solution to these difficulties is simpler than you might think. Wise plant choice is the first consideration. Species which thrive in the wild on chalk hills or rocky outcrops will be natural choices and many have superb garden cultivars. Flowering trees, such as crab apples and hawthorn, do well, and among chalk-loving herbaceous plants are pinks, carnations and many campanulas.

It also makes sense to build up the topsoil as much as possible with imported material. Extra loam will help, as will generous additions of leaf mold and organic matter or manure. As for moisture retention, building up the soil's humus content will enable it to hold more water, and a thick mulch either of compost, tree bark chippings or similar material spread generously over the surface helps reduce the evaporation rate from the ground.

SHADE AND SUN

After soil type, climate and topography, comes the final key consideration, light quality. Sunlight is essential because it is absorbed by chlorophyll in the plant cells and converts moisture absorbed through the roots and carbon dioxide absorbed through the leaves into sugar and water. This vital food-making process is known as photosynthesis. Generally, the sunnier a plant's position the more it reaches its full potential, but there are many notable exceptions. Thousands of plants have adapted to various kinds of shade. You only have to consider the darkness of a jungle floor and the abundance of lush vegetation growing there to realize how successful these plants are. Indeed, far from restricting choice, shade provides plenty of planting options and the chance to create a contrasting area of garden. It makes an excellent foil to bright areas with hot colors, so much so that, in a large, open, sunny garden it is worth planting a small tree simply to create an area of shade.

Types of shade

Before completing a garden design, and certainly before planting, assess what kind of shade you have. The degree varies according to the amount of light received, which itself is dependent on the time of year.

Dappled shade This is thrown by the leaf canopy of trees overhead. It can be quite cool and dense in summer but non-existent in winter. This creates good woodland conditions where spring flowers bloom in full light before the tree foliage emerges, followed by a summer in cool shade.

Partial shade Such shade is created when an area is in shadow for part of the day and receives direct sunlight at other times. A wall or building is the most likely cause. The further the site is from the equator, the lower the sun in winter, so that in London or Oslo, New York or Chicago, such obstacles throw more shadow than in Rome, Madrid or Los Angeles. This makes no difference in mid-winter but has a considerable influence in spring, when even as little as an hour of direct sunshine is sufficient to tempt a crocus or an aconite into bloom.

Full shade Full shade refers to an area which is always in shadow but which, nevertheless, has enough diffused daylight to support a reasonable plant collection. For example, the space between two buildings might be in constant shadow, as would the area of ground directly behind a wall running east to west (this, in turn, produces a cooler microclimate).

Dense shade This type of shade is the most likely to cause problems. There may appear to be too much gloom to grow anything but the dullest evergreen which even then languishes and looks miserable. But even dense shade is plantable.

The most challenging problem is dense, dry shade where surrounding buildings also restrict the amount of rainfall. Although there are plants that will cope with such surroundings, they seldom look as good as when growing in more suitable locations. There are, however, ways of minimizing the disadvantages. Container-grown plants can be moved here for a number of hours each day, provided at other times they get plenty of sun. Another good choice is spring bulbs which have their own food supplies and flower well in their first season even in the densest shade, but they must be replaced each year since they are unlikely to bloom again. Improving the soil to minimize moisture loss and maximize fertility will also help.

Reducing shade

There are three particularly useful ways to minimize the presence of shade. They are garden design, tree selection and tree thinning.

Garden design One of the side effects of creating shelter is that windbreaks may well impede light. This is particularly so if they enclose a long, thin garden running east-west and are approximately 5ft (1.5m) high. The solution involves a compromise between wind shelter, creating privacy, and letting in daylight. One obvious answer, if the site is large enough, is to enclose part of the garden creating sheltered, private shade, while leaving the remainder more open to ensure higher light levels. Alternatively, use trelliswork above a low white wall.

Tree selection Since evergreens create permanent shade, they frequently make it impossible to grow plants beneath them. Deciduous trees let in winter light, but the choice of species makes an enormous difference. Those which come into leaf late create better lighting conditions beneath their canopies. *Robinia pseudoacacia*, for example, does not begin to

Above: Shade makes for special planting opportunities and effects. Glossy, evergreen foliage is an asset while pale leaf variegations show up better than strong colors, like the magenta flowers of *Geranium psilostemon* here.

sprout until late spring and even then its foliage is frail and lacy, letting in a fair amount of daylight until it is fully developed in mid-summer. Large-leaved trees such as paulownia and catalpa also open late but they produce a dense canopy.

Tree thinning Many trees lend themselves to artistic pruning, which is another means of reducing the effect of dappled shade. With practice it is possible to remove whole branches cleanly instead of crudely lopping off their ends, producing a shapely, balanced tree with a smaller, more open arrangement of limbs. Please note this can be tough, even dangerous work, and you may prefer to employ a professional tree surgeon or a very experienced gardener.

Plant selection

There is a far wider choice of plants for cool, moist, woodland-type shade than for the dense dry kind, but in both cases the same planting principles apply. Since shady areas are usually sheltered from the wind, plants with large, soft leaves can be selected, with special attention to contrasting textures and colors. A light touch is necessary to avoid fussiness. A good example of plant combination features the broad, blue-green foliage of the plantain lily, *Hosta sieboldiana* (which produces violet flowers in late summer), spreading in front of the feathery fronds of the Lady fern, *Athyrium filix-femina*. Place an evergreen shrub at the back, perhaps a camellia, or a *Mahonia japonica* for its fragrant primrose-colored winter flowers and glossy foliage, and complete the picture with a foreground cover of sweet violets.

Flowers that open in shade are plentiful but try to select pale colors because they show up much better than do dark reds and blues. Subtle suffusions of pink, mauve or cream, lost in full light, are more obvious in darker areas, so use plants whose flowers exhibit gentle contrasts and harmonies of hue rather than stark differences. Furthermore, since the air is often still in shady areas, scent tends to linger. This is the ideal site for a good range of fragrant plants like honeysuckle and lilies in pots, which can be moved here from sunnier areas for at least part of the day. Plants for dry shade are few and far between, and in really severe cases there is not much choice. You could train a white *Clematis montana* over the offending wall, or try *Euphorbia amygdaloides robbiae* beneath it, with *Iris foetidissima*. Bulbs are the best idea, particularly beneath deciduous trees, with Solomon's seal, lily-of-the-valley and bluebells well worth trying for a delightful display.

Sun and heat

The diversity of planting possibilities in full light is so vast that it would be impossible to do justice to the subject here. However, it would be useful to point out some of the hundreds of plants that tolerate extremes of heat and drought. The base of a sunny wall, a dry bank, and the "hot" side of a rock garden provide conditions which suit the kinds of plants that grow naturally in the maquis of the Mediterranean and the semi-desert-like conditions in Australia and North America. Such plants, with their toughened, often silvery foliage, easily cope with heat.

Many have beautiful and distinctive flowers, others have stately architectural shapes. The tall, creamy flower spikes of yuccas, for example, make superb living sculptures in a garden and are fully drought-tolerant. Most of the wormwoods (artemisias) have filigree foliage in silvery tones, and gems like the delicate flowered *Convolvulus cneorum* are exquisite with their silver foliage and pinkish white blooms.

Many bulbs and corms thrive in hot, dry conditions too, from Mediterranean anemones and dwarf irises to various green, brown and purple fritillary species. Later in the season, the alliums relish heat, as do autumn-flowering amaryllis and crinum.

The Mediterranean look Gardens with a reliably dry, bright, sloping area are ideal for a wide range of scented Mediterranean shrubs like lavender, myrtle, thyme and rosemary (both the upright forms and the trailing *Rosmarinus officinalis* 'Prostratus'). Many cystus do equally well in such conditions (for example *C. crispus*, which has gray foliage, and *C. albidus*, with leaves verging on white).

Unless you can guarantee frost-free conditions over winter the tender, heat-loving plants will have to be put into containers and brought inside. This is certainly true of *Nerium oleander*, which is never going to be as big in temperate regions as one growing in the Mediterranean or California where it makes a massive flowering hedge; even so it is definitely worth its place on a hot patio.

Some plants, like the prolific, white-flowering *Osteospermum ecklonis*, can be risked outside over winter in most areas except for the very coldest, though it is still best to take cuttings in case the temperatures dip well below freezing and kill the parent plant.

Besides the ornamental plants, also consider fruit bushes like *Citrus limon* 'Meyer'. Discovered in China at the turn of the century it gives good size fruit and is hardy enough to stand outside even in a disappointing summer. In contrast, the European olive tree can be surprisingly hardy, and ought to be grown more widely in unusually warm city centers like London.

HOUSE AND GARDEN

Having assessed the garden's advantages and disadvantages, the next task is to consider your special needs and what you want from the garden as a space and as a reflection of your lifestyle.

Garden designers are now very fond of pointing out that the garden is an extension of the house. The term "extra room" keeps cropping up. But which room? One in which to rest and relax, enjoy a barbecue, grow vegetables, play games and sports, or build up a specialist collection of plants? In a large garden the

Left: Tall, evergreen hedges provide welcome shade in a Mediterranean summer. Agapanthus bloom prolifically in climates with hot dry summers and winter rainfall. Here, their characteristic cool blue flowers have matured to lilac.

problem does not exist – the only concern is how much space to assign to each room, and how to divide the one from the other. But with a smaller area you simply have to be ruthless, limiting yourself to one or two rooms, and be particularly crafty, accepting the need for compromise. The less space there is to play with, the more ingenious the design must be.

The potager is a brilliant example of a dual-purpose room. The word means a decorative or ornamental kitchen garden, and features different color vegetables (for example the reddish leaves of 'Lollo Rosso' lettuces as well as the traditional green), herbs (basil 'Ruffles Green' and 'Ruffles Purple'), and flowers. Herbaceous penstemons come in a wide range of colors from white (*Penstemon* 'Snowflake') to dark purple (*P.* 'Blackbird') and bloom from mid-summer until late autumn, even early winter in mild seasons. They mix well with vegetables, are usually contained in separate beds, and can be set off with topiary; for example, balls of clipped box in Versailles tubs. The Renaissance garden at Villandry in France has a particularly good, formal potager, and, although it is enormous, it is worth visiting to see how many ideas can be incorporated in a far smaller garden.

The second kind of compromise means beginning with one kind of garden, say predominantly lawn where children and animals can play, later converting it into another when there is no longer risk of damage to plants. Lawn can easily be replaced with paving and flower beds. The one advantage of making such changes is that at least you have time to visit scores of different gardens and work out exactly what kind of look you finally want, and the most appropriate combination of plants that will achieve these ends.

The third compromise involves children. Beware of ponds since a person can drown in even a few inches of water. Instead use a water feature which has no depth: a fountain dribbling into a dish in the wall for instance, or a cascade which disappears into stones.

Planting

In small gardens the most important rule is that each and every plant must earn its keep. Only the best forms should be planted and your choice should be tempered by such questions as: Will this plant give more than one display? Does it repeat flower? What is it like in winter? Are there good seed heads, or fruits as well as spring or summer blossom? What is its autumn foliage like? Does it have good scent?

Good planting and clever design should allure, keeping the visitor's curiosity alive. What goes on behind that screen? Where does this path lead? What is that flash of pink in the shrubbery? As you move around the garden you want to create changing moods and styles. Part of the key is sensitive, imaginative planting, but having learned the basic rules do not be afraid to play with and even break them. Try introducing a few surprises. For instance, an ivy-leaved pelargonium can easily be turned into topiary. Grow a single stem up a 4ft (1.2m) high cane and then around a circular piece of bamboo attached to the top. Or create a yellow area and finish it off in high style with pots of *Lilium* 'Citronella' which twirl butterfly-like flowers to a height of 4ft (1.2m).

Linking house and garden

From indoors, the view through the windows into the garden is at least as important as the view from any vantage point outside. The garden design must therefore include vistas or scenes which look tempting from inside, from the room where you spend most time. If you are lucky enough to look out over open countryside or a fine cityscape, make sure the garden design blends with the background: for example, in a wild valley a cottage garden is most appropriate.

Looking back to the house from the garden, it should be an integral part of the design and not an alien presence. A conservatory, for instance, can be designed to open on to a terrace or patio so that in summer, when the doors are open, the garden feels as though it is extending into the house and vice versa. Climbers and wall plants can soften the harsh outline of a building and, where pergolas lead to and echo the style and fabric of the house, the link between indoors and outdoors is sealed.

GARDEN DESIGNS: SITE ONE (*right and far right*)
A south-facing garden, 20 × 50ft (6 × 15m), with a slight slope from north to south. Neutral soil

INHERITED FEATURES

In some way it is best to begin with a bare site. You can more or less do what you like with it, providing there are no overwhelming restrictions. Far trickier is reworking an established garden. But before you demolish it, do wait one full season. It really is essential. Even the apparently most hideous layout is likely to have some feature worth preserving, though it may not be immediately obvious. Note down the existing spring bulbs, shrubs for winter color, colorful autumn seedheads, boggy winter areas, particularly dry hot summer beds and then you can decide which features to keep.

Plants

In the case of an overgrown garden, dig out known weeds and give established plants a chance to show what they can do. In cases of serious neglect this may be difficult because of the urgent need for renovation, but even so it pays to be circumspect.

Overgrown shrubs and trees can be pruned and tidied up without damage – indeed many shrubs respond well to being cut hard back. Furthermore, do not be afraid to impose shape on the apparently shapeless. The Japanese are particularly good at it. For example, *Ceanothus thyrsiflorus* can be converted from shrubbiness to a shapely, weeping tree. Again, *Prunus laurocerasus* 'Magnifolia' can be turned from a floppy specimen into something more statuesque and upright. When it comes to transplanting, mature woody plants can be difficult, but perennials are easy to lift, divide and replant into temporary nursery beds, perhaps while new borders are being laid out. In such cases, it pays to plan a new design carefully, to avoid heaving up plants again.

Large natural features

Objects such as large trees or natural water courses, which make prominent features, could push you on to the horns of a dilemma: how will they look when incorporated into a new design? It is impossible to suggest general solutions, but the basis for your decision should be tempered by the following considerations: is the tree or natural feature particularly fine, rare or special in any other way? Could you reshape your design to work around the feature? Since maturity is lacking in a new garden, and since the established look is going to be the aim, is it possible to keep the feature for the medium term until the garden has mellowed and matured, and then think about replacing it with your ideal specimen tree or sculpture?

INFORMAL GARDEN

This design recaptures the spirit of an old cottage garden, using both traditional and modern plant species, combined with natural materials. The landscaping is of blue-gray stone, slate and gravel; most of the pathways are designed to allow plants to spill over at either side. The east-facing wall includes (top to bottom) *Pittosporum* 'Garnetti', *Polygonatum* × *hybridum, Rheum alexandrae, Hosta sieboldiana, Lupinus* 'Inverewe Red', *Amelanchier lamarckii, Papaver bracteatum* 'Goliath' and *Thalictrum delavayi*. An apple tree provides a focal point; underplanting includes *Milium effusum. Verbascum olympicum* and *Digitalis purpurea* 'Alba' give height to the bed beyond the terrace which is lined with tubs of fragrant *Lilium regale*. A cold frame, compost container and shed are set apart.

FORMAL GARDEN

A linear, symmetrical form has been given to the space by means of clearly defined surfaces and structures and controlled planting. The terrace is framed by ivy, ferns and containers planted with *Trachycarpus fortunei*; this has an architectural quality. The facing benches lead the eye into the garden. The small parterre is planted with *Buxus sempervirens* which will frame seasonal planting in restricted colors. Bay trees (*Laurus nobilis*) sit at each corner. The central, raised summer house gives a focus to the vista; espalier pears or pleached quince are trained at either side. A well-clipped *Taxus baccata* hedge encloses a seat and hides the compost area and cloches at the end of the garden. *Actinidia kolomikta* plants shroud the greenhouse and shed. The surfaces are yellow-ochre gravel and pink granite.

Structural and ornamental features

Hard landscaping and architectural and ornamental features present less of a problem than natural features because in most cases they can be dismantled and relocated. The advantage of re-using such existing materials – stone walls and troughs, paving slabs, millstones and so on – is that they will be weathered and worn, as compared to the rather sterile appearance of new materials. If you want to dispose of existing features, it is worth looking to auction houses to sell ornaments and the small advertisements in local newspapers for building materials. Many garden details have a surprising value.

TIME AND MONEY

The joy of gardening is that it suits every pocket. Landscaping a small area with choice materials and lavish, mature plants is expensive; by contrast, using inexpensive materials, propagating as many plants as possible, and being prepared to wait is the best way to develop a fine garden on a shoestring.

Interim measures have their uses: beds can be filled with annuals until you can afford more expensive shrubs; an arrangement of pots can provide the focal point until a statue or sculpture has been added. For example, an architectural *Cordyline indivisa* can be set in a tall or raised pot with pots of scented flowering heliotropium, such as the fine 'Chatsworth', 'Princess Marina' or 'White Lady', and the yellow-orange flowers of echeveria around the base.

From the gardening point of view phasing the work has many advantages, but the question is which major structures should you complete first? Clearly the answer depends on your own priorities but it is logical to begin with the basic layout. Lawns, pathways, main borders and the seating area provide the garden skeleton and take priority. Later, when your pocket has recovered, you can add a little more flesh to the bones by adding special features like a pond, conservatory, gazebo and so on. Usually, the biggest cost item is the hard landscaping: structures such as walls, terraces, buildings and paving. There may be earth-moving exercises too, such as digging ponds or creating different levels. These, especially if done by contractors, will be costly but are one-off expenses.

Inexpensive plants

Mature trees are the costliest plants to buy, and the bigger they are, the more expensive. In effect you are buying the time taken to grow specimens. If you are prepared to nurture them, most small, immature

GARDEN DESIGNS: SITE TWO *(right and far right)*
A west-facing, walled town garden, 20 × 20ft (6 × 6m). Acid soil

plants grow very quickly and are much cheaper. The important point to remember is that they will grow just as large as their bigger, more expensive counterparts, and need spacing out according to their potential and not their current size.

The cheapest plants of all are those that you propagate yourself. Shrubs grow surprisingly fast from cuttings and many are easy to root. Space is too limited to cover the subject here but there are dozens of specialist books on propagation. The skill needed to strike cuttings is so basic that anyone can learn it in minutes. Essentially, all that is required is a piece of healthy young stem, a pot of compost, and a warm, moist atmosphere that prevents the shoot wilting. Within a few weeks you should have a new plant.

A clear plastic bag and a windowsill will suffice for small numbers of cuttings, but results are quicker and better with an electrically-heated propagator. The most basic types are widely available in a range of sizes and are easily affordable. The crudest consist of a large open tray with low sides, a plastic cover and a heating pad. If you have a cold frame or a cold greenhouse you can wait for temperatures around 60°F (15.5°C) and raise cuttings there. Place them in a sheltered, shady position, and remember to close the greenhouse to keep in the heat. A cold frame is not essential when it comes to acclimatizing the young plants to outside conditions but it helps. Alternatively, stand the pots outside for an increasing amount of time during the warmest part of the day; eventually you should be able to leave them out over a mild night, but whatever you do, do not rush the process.

Nor should you be afraid to ask neighbors for cuttings of plants or for seed. You should have a good success rate with both, as with layering (bending a branch down to soil level, pegging it in place, waiting for it to develop its own root system, and then separating this new, young plant from its parent), dividing one plant into several (each with top growth and roots), and stooling (building up soil around the base of a japonica or lilac, for example, which encourages rooting higher up the stem so that ready-rooted pieces can be removed and replanted).

MAINTENANCE

The labor-free garden does not exist, but there are ways in which such chores as weeding and tidying can be kept to a minimum. Clearly, what you get out of a garden is in proportion to what you put in, and it will never be possible to expect a plantsman's paradise to thrive on neglect. Those who want beauty without effort are being unrealistic, but there is no need to become a slave. Any means of reducing the more troublesome tasks to a minimum is worth pursuing.

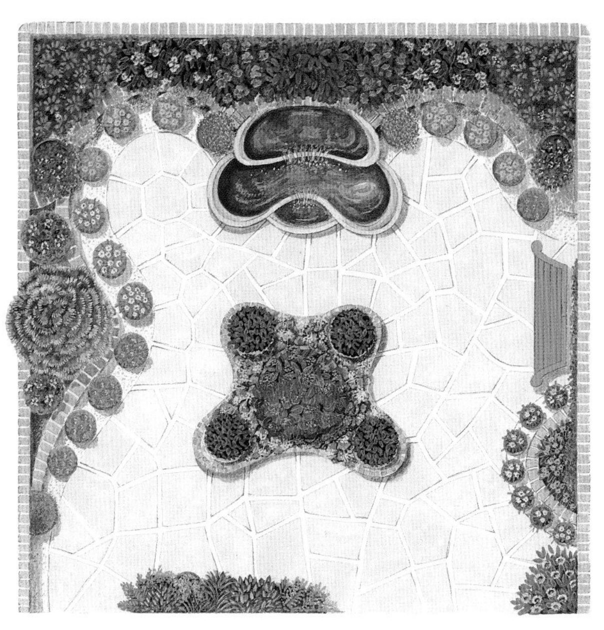

CONTAINER GARDEN
Shrub roses, small rhododendrons and foliage plants set off the containers in this grotto-like space. The late spring display shows blue hyacinths and white and pink tulips on a gravel sweep. (In summer impatiens, lilies and fuchsias can be used; in autumn, dahlias.) Pots of *Phygelius aequalis* 'Yellow Trumpet' stand either side of the large *Acer japonicum* 'Aureum'; herbs and ferns are placed beside the house. The central feature has four specimens of the evergreen *Ligustrum japonicum*, with hydrangeas in the middle (bergenias in winter) and gap-filling *Alchemilla mollis*.

Design

Much labor can be saved by thoughtful design. All parts of a border, for example, should be accessible without having to walk on and damage the soil surface. This is achieved by laying stepping stones or pathways along the back as well as in the more visible areas. Paving is easier to maintain than lawn and, in a small garden, flagstones can look better than grass.

Gravel, as a mulching device, is gaining popularity, easing maintenance and providing plants with a friendly environment. Plants growing in gravel or small stones seed freely; to prevent this, lay the mulch over a woven polypropylene sheet; water will still pass through. To plant shrubs or specimens, a crisscross slit is made in the sheet, the plant inserted and the gravel carefully replaced.

The vertical surfaces in a well planned garden will be covered with a wealth of climbing and wall plants. To encourage them to grow up and sideways and not flop over the plants in front of them, tie in all growths to horizontal wires. These should be attached to vine eyes or large nails inserted into the masonry at regular intervals. With this permanent anchorage, it is easy to display wall plants to their best advantage.

MODERN GARDEN
The theme here is cool greens and whites, with scented flowers for evening entertaining. Marbled tiles swirl around a fiberglass table and seat, protected by a parasol (cut away in this view). The planting uses tender species, including *Lonicera splendida*, *Hedera helix* 'Telecurl' and *Wisteria floribunda* 'Alba' around the walls. The central beds have a pleasing symmetry: *Ficus benjamina* with its variegated form grow hydroponically in the raised triangle; *Camellia japonica* 'Commander Mulroy', *Phanerophlebia falcata* and nicotiana are either side of a raised mirror pool.

Planting

Choice of plants, and their arrangement, exert an enormous influence on the amount of time needed for maintenance. The aim, in a carefree garden, is to make the plants themselves do as much of the work as possible. Thus, shrubs which need little pruning are preferable to those like hybrid tea roses which require more attention. Disease- and pest-resistant plants will always be desirable and, unless a species is especially glorious, vigor takes preference over delicacy.

Among herbaceous varieties, those which self-seed freely without becoming invasive are ideal in the low-maintenance garden. Ground cover plants are perfect for filling the spaces between shrubs and give excellent weed control, provided the ground in which they are planted is completely free of perennial weeds. There are so many to choose from that dull planting is inexcusable. It is perfectly possible to arrange a weed-proof ground cover which changes in color, texture and mood month by month.

STARTING THE DESIGN

Once you know all about your site, exactly what you want from your garden, what inherited features are worth preserving and how much time you want to spend on maintenance, you can begin the design. To do this you will need squared or graph paper and a pencil, but to generate any useful ideas, first stand in the garden – or on the patch of wasteland that is to become your garden – and think. Turn the area into a dream space in your mind's eye. Think not of specific plants but in terms of shapes and colors. As ideas begin to form, you can then explore practicalities and solve problems. Finally, you should measure the plot and trim your dream to fit the area, and your pocket.

Preparing the plan

The practical business of designing – preparing drawings to scale, organizing plant lists, and so on – appears to be far more daunting than it really needs to be. Accuracy is important but it is not that difficult to achieve; if you are methodical and careful, the site can be measured and a true plan drawn. You should include all important details: architectural features, the herb garden, beds and borders, pond, large trees, topiary, key shrubs, and the like. If you find it difficult to visualize designs from lines on a piece of paper, there is really no reason why you should not use the garden itself as your drawing board. The site, if not already clean, will have to be cleared of any rubbish or unwanted objects before you begin. Then, using sticks and lengths of string (preferably strong and very visible baling twine) as markers, it is possible to indicate where everything should go. Keep making adjustments to these markers until you have the layout you want. A length of garden hose is very useful for marking out curving border fronts. I certainly feel much more comfortable working on the design in the garden itself, juggling my sticks, string and hose until I feel I have laid out all the features and details in the best order and proportions.

Complicated details, like a parterre, may require a more striking outline. This can be achieved with whitewash, brushed over the grass or surface of the proposed location. Eccentric though this may sound, any step between planning and planting is invaluable and saves subsequent heartache. It is also worth visualizing height where this is a vital factor. A stepladder erected to the height of a mature hedge will give you a good idea of the ultimate effect. If this looks too tall, obscuring a fine view and casting too much shade, select a different hedging plant. Again, if you intend to include a lengthy pergola, you could draw on a clever technique of an earlier era. In the 1920s, wealthy house owners placed cardboard cut-out pillars in various positions until they looked exactly right. Another eccentricity, but useful and potentially great fun if enough people are involved. Improvise in such a manner wherever possible: put a chair in a

GARDEN DESIGNS: SITE THREE (*right and far right*)
An east-facing, irregular garden, between 35ft (10.5m) and 10ft (3m) wide, and 65ft (19.5m) long. Alkaline soil

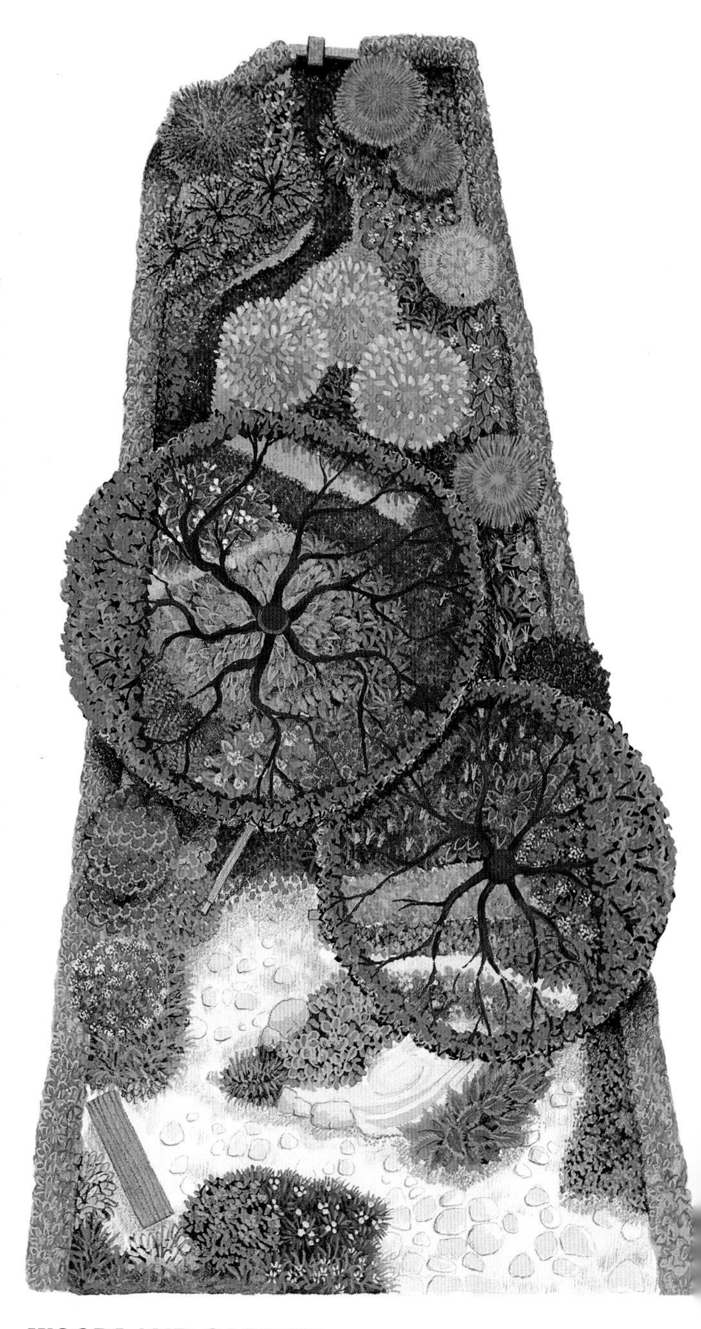

proposed seating area and try it out. Is this the best place, or will it be ruined by an unpleasant view?

When you have a clearer idea of the arrangement of your site it will be easier to transfer the details onto paper; this will be essential for reference once the heavy work has begun. Before you draw up the plan, leave the markers in place for a week or so to ensure that the idea really is going to be practical. Then, when you are finally happy with the main elements of the design, draw up the plan.

The proposed planting

With the outline in hand, start filling in planting details on the plan – shapes, colors, texture and scent, leaving the choice of most plants until last. Scent is most easily dealt with. Tobacco plants, pots of lilies, *Choisya ternata* and the like, need to be in sheltered positions where the fragrance will hang in still air. Ideally such plants should surround the seating and eating areas where they are really going to be appreciated. A bench or patio can be backed by a semi-circular, enclosing trellis threaded with scented climbers. The plants should be chosen so they flower in succession right through the summer and you get a prolonged spell of delightful perfumes, not one over-powering blast for two weeks in August.

The next stage is to ensure that the planting line-up is going to provide color and interesting shapes right through the year. Use four different colored pens (signifying winter, spring, summer and autumn) to mark blocks of plants on the plan and, if possible, grow a star plant for every season in each area. (When planting, leave space around the young specimens to accommodate their ultimate spread. Annuals and bedding plants can fill the gaps temporarily.) Many gardeners are drawn to the idea of an all-white garden at some point, but it is important to remember that they generate a lot of extra work as faded blooms present a glaring eyesore.

Foliage

One key point rarely mentioned is that most plants only flower for a relatively short period, which means foliage and shape ought to be rated just as highly as flowering interest. Palm trees are impressive on both counts. They *do* grow in mild areas, with the advantage that their fronds will not turn the frazzled brown seen in hotter climates. Agaves are much hardier than generally realized and make good focal points, having the additional benefit of a dramatic flowering spike something like once every 20 years! Much smaller but

WOODLAND GARDEN

Tranquil woodland gardens come into their own in spring, when bulbs and woodland herbaceous plants provide a riot of color, as here. The two pin oaks, *Quercus palustris*, are about fifteen years old but will cast only dappled shade even when mature (they are cut away to reveal the underplanting). The right-hand tree stands in front of a hedge of *Prunus spinosa*; a drift of yellow *Primula vulgaris* sweeps up into the garden, past a dark holly. Corsican pines (*Pinus nigra*), three *Betula utilis jacquemontii* and an *Acer saccharum* 'Temples Upright' are surrounded by cyclamen, honesty and bluebells. A stile leads into a wood beyond. On the other side of the path a *Crataegus oxycantha* 'Plena' is grouped with three *Hamamelis* × *intermedia* 'Jelena'. Beneath the second oak is an *Epimedium* × *perralchicum*, surrounded by trillium, bluebells, foxgloves and ferns. Primulas and hazels grow beside the gate. Around the log bench are snowdrops, chamomile and *Rosa rugosa* 'Fru Dagmar Hastrup'. The pond is planted with yellow *Primula florindae*, giant cowslips and *Myosotis scorpioides*.

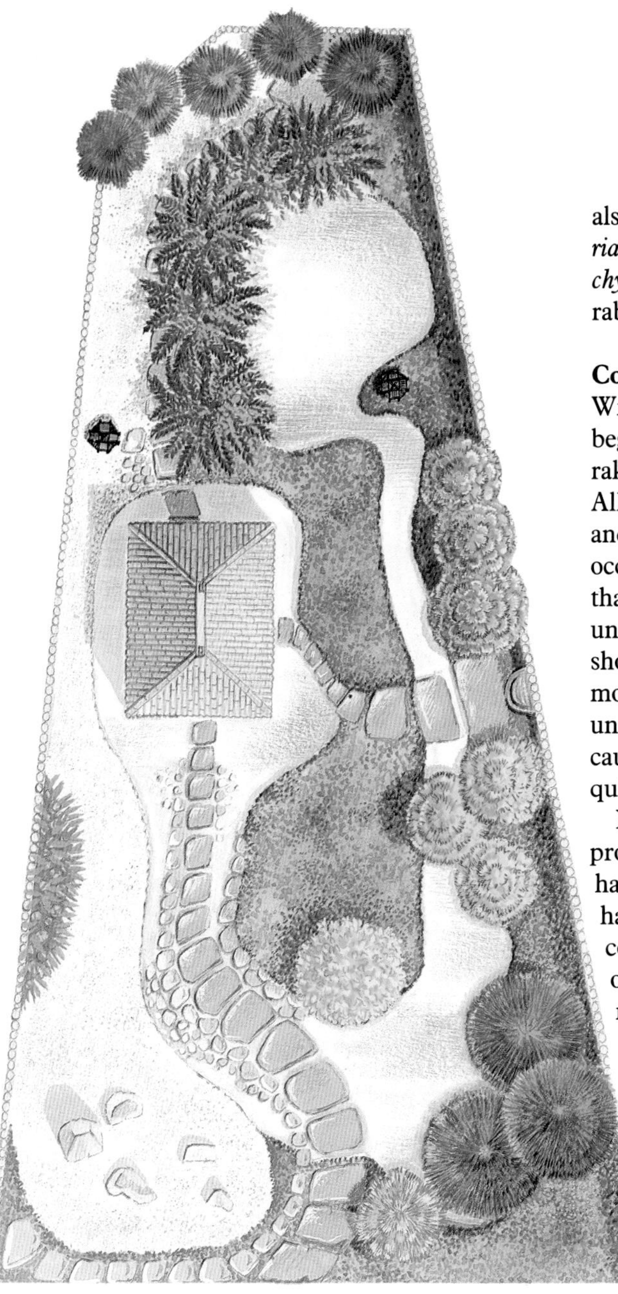

JAPANESE GARDEN

The distinctive flavor of a Japanese garden is achieved by combining a traditional layout with special features, such as lanterns and a washing basin, included here, and sculpture with a Japanese theme – dragons, temples and shrines. This strictly contrived, restful landscape includes the central elements of water and rocks, making a perfect setting for the small tea house which provides a charming focal point. Opposites run through the design, with moving and tranquil water, jagged rocks versus smooth boulders, and gravel against moss. The planting is essentially Japanese, in the selection and groupings. Around the water, from the house front, a *Cryptomeria japonica* 'Vilmoriniana' leads to groups of *Pinus parviflora*, *Acer palmatum* 'Ozakazuki' and *A. p.* 'Senkaki'. Spring-flowering white cherries (*Prunus* 'Tai-Haku') curve around the top of the pool, with a strong accent supplied by the Japanese black pines (*Pinus thunbergii*). Bamboo is used in a tied cane fence and as a planted hedge and curving clump. Japanese gardens can take a long time to mature; they demand patience and careful training.

also effective are the white spotted leaves of *Pulmonaria longifolia* and the velvety, light gray foliage of *Stachys byzantina*, appropriately called lamb's tongue or rabbit's ears. Hunt out other, eye-catching examples.

Construction

With your well-considered plan complete, work can begin. Borders can be dug out, areas for lawns dug, raked and rolled and foundations for paving installed. All the time this is going on, keep reviewing the scene and be prepared to make any changes that might occur to you. This is much easier to do at the outset than later when more permanent construction is under way. With regard to heavy equipment, you should always be sure to hire well-maintained, modern and safe machinery. Make sure you fully understand how to use it, taking all necessary precautions, and leave no harmful devices to hand for inquisitive children to discover.

Needless to say, there is always the option of using a professional garden designer and a contractor. If you have ambitious plans, limited time or an aversion to hard physical work, such experts should be seriously considered. Their involvement could raise the cost of a project quite dramatically, but equally costly mistakes could be avoided. You will not have the complete satisfaction of knowing that all you survey is your work, but you might have come that much nearer to achieving your dream garden. It is a matter of weighing up the advantages and disadvantages to both approaches. A good designer will be sensitive to your preferences and tastes as well as to the context: the style of your house and the surrounding view, quite apart from the size, shape and contours of the space.

Perhaps the key point about a garden is that it is never complete. As with a sitting room, owners occasionally get bored with a particular look and rearrange things. Then, a plant that succeeded in its previous place may, for no known reason, fail in the new, apparently more appropriate site. Another plant must be sought, and the color scheme suddenly leaps from pink to yellow and different, complementary features become desirable. It is a matter of being aware of the alternatives and gauging whether they can be made to work. The six garden designs included on these pages give you some impression of the range of options available. The idea is not to copy them slavishly – some of the design elements are solutions to very specific problems – but to apply similar principles of design to serve your own needs and tastes.

THE LOOK OF THE GARDEN

SHAPES

The use of different shapes is perhaps the single most important element in designing a garden. It is the chief tool with which a gardener defines the spaces and structures of a garden – his working vocabulary. In a really good garden, consideration will have been given to the shape and purpose of every component, from broad issues such as the outline of a path or lawn to the details such as the contrasting shapes of miniature shrubs in a particular stone trough. It is the sum of all these parts, large and small, which gives a garden its character.

The garden's perimeter is the first shape to consider in relation to the site as a whole. The internal structure can complement the shape through a geometrical composition, using straight lines and circles, with the emphasis on hard landscaping (the walls, paths, steps and so on). Alternatively, natural flowing forms with no straight lines may be preferred. Again, a blend of the two approaches might be more suitable. In making this decision, the practical requirements of the garden must be considered: the need to get from one place to another, to create enclosures and the like. All the components of a garden – from lawns, borders, island beds and parterres to paths, topiary, pergolas and water features – can be treated in a geometric or an organic way. There is no right or wrong, only a variety of options with which the imagination can experiment.

Within the layout, the shape of the plants themselves comes into play. All plants fall into one of a number of basic shape categories, the plants in each category fulfilling a similar role in the overall scheme. There is the tall upright shape of fastigiate trees and conifers which leads the eye upwards and commands

Left and right: The first shapes to consider in a garden are those of the ground plan. Here, two perfectly geometric schemes are achieved, one by the formal planting of hedges and lawns, the other largely by the use of hard landscaping. Both gardens show remarkable attention to the detail of shapes. The planting is noteworthy. An orderly yet imaginative series of beds compares with symmetrical but strong forms that soften the modern design.

Below: A woodland garden begins life under mature trees, on organic rather than geometric lines. Unless the shapes of an organic plan are broad and simple, the effect is fussy and appears just as contrived as a formal garden, even though the scheme is non-symmetrical.

Top far left, top left and right: Strong shapes, such as tall upright conifers, make an even greater impact when repeated, and usually strong horizontals and more earthbound shapes are needed to balance the effect. Horizontal lines of great substance are most often gained from hard landscaping, such as walls and paths, reinforced by plants with a naturally tiered, architectural habit, or those that have been trained to form striking, flattened shapes. Notice the clever use of an espalier-trained weeping blue cedar (*top left*). The combination of horizontal and vertical lines will weave a design together, forming unifying connections. This is demonstrated by the strategically placed ornaments – the obelisk and pots – that point up from the flat lines of the retaining walls (*right*).

Bottom left: Shapes repeated often enough provide a large-scale texture, as do these domes of lavender. When shapes are repeated in a straight line, like the mounds beneath the pergola, they are almost more effective than a clean straight line in leading the eye forward. In summer, these bushes would provide a glorious, aromatic display of flowers, giving a very different face to the garden. The cypress arch and the trimmed laurels (either side of the steps) present different but connected forms. The climbing roses have an altogether freer disposition and open effect.

attention, especially when used repeatedly in a group or row. The effect is the same whatever the scale: notice how the excellent red salvia dominates in this way when used in a bedding scheme. Low rounded shapes or domes are equally arresting, but in a more earthbound way. They sit heavily upon the ground and fix the eye. Think of clipped spheres of box or chunky potentilla bushes. Fans or fountain shapes offer a softer touch, lifting the eye but in a gentler lighter way than a conifer. Grasses, bamboos and irises all shoot up in a fan, and many then droop over at the top, like a subsiding firework. A more extreme version of this effect is the weeping shape, less visually static than the sphere and less busy than the fountain. Finally, there are the horizontal shapes, found in plants like the striking, architectural *Viburnum plicatum* 'Mariesii', *Cornus controversa* and some of the low junipers, for example *Juniperus horizontalis* and *J.* × *media* 'Pfitzeriana'. They keep the eye peacefully arrested, moving neither up nor down, forward nor backward. Obviously there are endless variations within and between these categories, but when planning a layout they are very useful tools.

It is the arrangement of these typical shapes that gives movement, balance and punctuation to a garden design. For example, movement can come from the repeated use of upright shapes which takes the eye away into the distance. The effect will work either in a formal symmetrical context, as in an avenue, or in a more informal zigzag fashion. Balance will help the garden to look restful to the eye. For instance, a dramatic upright shape can be countered by an adjoining

Below: The main contrasting elements here are the fans of iris leaves, the closed shape of a clipped euonymus and the airy form of the variegated *Acer negundo* trees.

Top right: Shape is relevant in every aspect of the garden. It is expressed in the ground plan – lawns, beds, borders, paths, hedges, walls and containers. Also important are the outlines of single plants and groups of plants, and even the shape of flowers. Shape, however, must work hand in glove with texture and color: none exists in isolation.

Bottom right: Much can be made of the interaction of color and shape. A somber walk of tall cypresses is brightened and balanced by a horizontal streak of pebbles.

low mound, and the two held together by some horizontal shapes. Strong shapes can be used to focus and punctuate the different areas within a garden, perhaps by closing an avenue with a tight specimen tree or by flanking a gateway with two strong mounds or sentinels of foliage.

Apart from these structural uses of shape, a garden is kept alive through its detail, by the constant interplay between neighboring plants. Shape is just as important here as texture or color. It is the continuous interplay between shape, color and texture which makes a mixed or herbaceous border so fascinating, and so difficult to achieve over a long period, presenting a challenge to the gardener.

It is often helpful in the planning stages of a garden, or even a border, to make simple sketches that block in the most important shapes and lines (as well as the main color effects). This will enable you to envisage the composition in advance and allows the main refinements to be made before planting begins. It is also useful for considering the mature aspect of the garden, which should include appropriate spacing of trees and large shrubs. This is an excellent tool for clarifying your ideas; on paper, the imagination can run riot, but once planting begins, changes become much more difficult. A plan can bring you that much closer to your ideal, well balanced garden. (See page 23 for further advice on starting the design.)

CONTOURS

Not everyone is blessed with an easy, level site for a garden, and those who are often long for a more varied terrain. Whatever your preference, there is no doubt that level ground makes gardening easier and that changes of level create a set of problems, both in planting and with access. But however steep the site, so long as you work within its limitations, it is perfectly possible to have an interesting and fulfilling garden. Virtue must be made of necessity.

Steeply sloping gardens lend themselves to different treatments depending upon their aspect. South-facing slopes receive the maximum heat from the sun and are especially suitable for Mediterranean plants or make good scree gardens. Drainage will be fast, which is an advantage to many slightly tender plants. These slopes also offer the possibility of creating streams or waterfalls, which can be made to be as formal or informal as required. Terraces can be constructed across the slope, as in the great villa gardens of Italy, to maximize the potential for planting, using either retaining walls or turf banks.

Cold north-facing slopes make good woodland gardens, but will equally make an ideal site for a terraced alpine garden because they are naturally well drained, fully exposed to light, but without the drying heat found on a south-facing slope.

The approach used on a sloping site also depends on its relationship to the house. A garden that slopes up from the house will be far more dominant than one that slopes away: it will fill the whole view and offer the opportunity for a real *tour de force*, whether formal or informal. It could be perfectly symmetrical with pairs of circular steps or an idealized Japanese mountain waterfall. Sites which slope away from the house are less imposing in themselves and throw the eye outward into the view beyond. It might be Mount Fuji, a power station or just your neighbor's garden. Whether this view should be consciously incorporated

Left: This change of levels has been made less daunting and more interesting by the use of intermediate levels. A shallow circular podium makes a gentle approach to the lower steps, while a landing halfway up accommodates a seat for restful contemplation, with a view of the garden.

into the garden's design or excluded to produce an enclosed oasis will depend on its merits or demerits. If the view is good, and it can be relied upon to remain so, then make the most of it. If the focus needs to be kept within the garden then try using a formal arrangement of large pots or upright conifers. These may not mask a poor view but they will give details of some substance to attract the eye.

Irregular changes of level within a garden can make it more interesting and offer the chance to create surprise views and features. The move from one level to another does not necessarily have to be negotiated at once; a flight of steps can be split up and intermediate levels inserted in between. Steps are one of the most significant built features of a garden and deserve to have plenty of attention given to their detail. If the garden contains large mounds or hollows, consider enlarging them to create a major feature, such as a pond or a mount or rockery.

During the planning stage always keep in mind the maintenance implications of the finished garden. Steps are attractive, but they can stop easy access with a wheelbarrow or lawn mower. Terraces are fine, but will there be suitable access to take away prunings? Should the compost heap be positioned at the bottom or the top of the slope? Where access is limited, it is often better to opt for a style of planting that requires little pruning, such as an alpine or heather garden.

Finally, soil erosion can be a problem on banks and can be solved in a variety of ways. Turf banks will hold the soil once they are established, but ruts can soon develop where people constantly walk. Ground cover plants such as *Hypericum calycinum*, which have underground stems to bind the surface soil in a tight mat, can be used to stabilize a bank, but they may take some years to become effective. In extreme cases, terracing and channeled drainage may be essential.

Top right: Changes of level break up a garden. Here a sense of open space is retained by avoiding the use of steps and letting a grass bank link the lower and upper lawns to form one space. The grass flows around the contours.

Center right: Terraces always present problems of access. Here a grass ramp allows a mower to be driven onto the terrace, but steps also make it visually more satisfying and close the vista.

Bottom right: A long flight of shallow steps is awkward to walk on and is generally not the best solution on a gradual slope. A path with a gentle gradient is usually more satisfactory, although you will need to make provision for water running off fast and hard when it rains. This detail is a fine illustration of a well conceived design. The mixed border has been planned to show every plant to its best advantage. It is backed by an attractive plant-clad wall.

Top left: Steps provide a good opportunity for interesting planting. There is no reason at all why you should not plant into the steps themselves, so long as they remain safe.

Top right: On terraced sites, sprawling evergreen perennials soften the edges of retaining walls, even in winter.

Above: Terrace walls and steps lend themselves easily to a very formal treatment, especially in front of an imposing symmetrical house. A formal planting with evergreens offers greater winter interest than an informal scheme. This clever planting affords very varied textures and shapes.

Opposite, top: Even in a small, flat garden changes of level can be introduced by building raised areas like this circular platform. The seat gives it an added *raison d'être*. Repeated motifs can be used in subtle ways in garden designs. The gentle bend of the steps and wall and the circles of the urns echo the curving theme.

Opposite, bottom: This grass terrace has been introduced as a means of separating the garden from grazed fields without the need for a solid, stock-proof fence. The wall has been built at an angle to help it resist the weight of soil pushing from behind. It presents a pleasing sweep, perfect for strolling along.

MANIPULATING SCALE

It is a rare gardener indeed who wishes to make a garden look smaller than it is, unless he or she is motivated by an underlying passion for bonsai landscapes. Most wish to increase the apparent size; others to make a broad site with little depth appear longer than it is, or to make a long and narrow garden seem less tunnel-like; or the aim may simply be to make a small garden seem less confined. A way to do all these things is through the manipulation of scale.

Making a small garden appear less cramped is often best achieved by avoiding a single unified design; rather, the space can be broken down into even smaller portions, where the attention is focused onto the detail of planting and hard landscaping. These spaces or garden rooms can each be given different characters which are presented as a series of little surprises. There is no golden rule which says a garden must have an open lawn in the middle; if space is really tight it is usually better to go for a fuller, heavier planting. One possibility is to turn the garden into a miniature ornamental jungle, where paths wind in among the plants in such a way as never to reveal the full extent of the site.

Long thin gardens can also be treated this way, so that it is never possible to see down the full length of the long axis. If this is unavoidable, then try to arrest the eye with some major feature in the foreground or middle distance, such as a circular lawn or a specimen tree, or place horizontal features such as low walls, wide steps, paving or hedges across the axis. Tiered plants like *Viburnum plicatum* 'Mariesii' have the same effect. In a less symmetrical garden, features can be placed down the sides, causing the eye to swerve and pause – perhaps a painted seat in a formal arbor or the striking trunks of a multi-stemmed tree. In all of this it is a good idea to begin by making a sketch plan of the garden and drawing in the sight lines to see where the visual emphasis lies.

There are many ways of increasing the sense of depth in a garden. Vistas can be emphasized and

Far left: Clever transitions, from one part to another, increase the feeling of variety and size within a garden. One area can be used like the hall of a house, giving access to different "rooms" that may or may not pick up motifs and materials from the useful linking areas.

Left: Even in informal gardens, vistas can be emphasized by careful planting. A solid screen of shrubs would be much less effective than the golden foliage and the elegant, upright blue cypress that form the focus of this vista.

Right: The lines of tile detail on this plastered wall lead the eye on and succeed in increasing the false perspective through the two arches, making the second seem further away. The glimpses of plants and steps beyond enhance this impression.

Below: The stripes produced by a lawn mower can be used to draw the eye according to the direction of the cut. Here they emphasize the vista, counteracting the cross-banding of the steps and leading the eye to the statue.

Left: Still water and the mirrored sky give a feeling of light and air, while reflections emphasize the vertical lines of upright forms. A large space that is given a carefully designed treatment needs to be handled with care to avoid great "lost" expanses jarring with highly finished parts of the garden. Transitional areas are essential in the design if the scheme is not naturally compartmentalized.

Top right: Long narrow gardens can be made more interesting by deliberately closing the central vista with a bold feature, such as this pergola, set at right angles to the main thrust of the site. This device effectively creates two separate gardens, each of which can be given a different character.

Top far right: In small gardens it is often better to dispense with views altogether and to go for a closely-planted jungle-like effect. In a garden of this scale paving makes a much better surface than lawn.

Bottom right: Foreground detail can be used to arrest the eye. Here the view to an unremarkable field is lightly screened by wonderful clipped trees and hedges so that the focus is brought forward to the circular lawn of chessmen. The large formal bands of gravel provide a border to the elaborate central design, setting apart the imaginative array of shapes more dramatically than would be achieved with grass.

"lengthened" by stressing the distant perspective. Eye-catching features can be used to draw the eye away into the distance, and there is no need to rely solely on the contents of your garden to do this. Make use of the landscape outside: let a distant hilltop or church spire become the focus of a garden vista. On the other hand, a door in a garden wall 20ft (6m) away will work in the same way for a smaller garden. It is a matter of degree and using opportunities.

Creating a false perspective is another useful technique. By placing large plants in the foreground and smaller ones of the same shape in the distance, at a glance they all appear to be the same size but receding into the distance. It is possible to do the same with foliage, by planting thin airy foliage close by and denser foliage further away.

Lawn-mower stripes in a lawn can be used to give direction to a view or to pull the eye in a particular direction, lengthening or shortening the perspective. Arches and pergolas will enhance perspective, while fences and trelliswork have a strong linear impact. Trellis can also create *trompe l'oeil* effects, giving the impression of three dimensions where only two exist. Even mirrors have been used in garden doorways to double the length of a vista. *Trompe l'oeil* can be used to highly sophisticated ends, with false scenes and features painted onto flat surfaces. Such tricks can be very restrictive to a whole design so they should be used with care. Simpler devices might be preferable; the reflective surface of a pool of still water offers tranquillity and a vertical dimension (its own depth and the reflection of the sky above).

SEASONAL PLANNING

A garden can never be as colorful in winter as in summer, but there is no reason why it should not be just as interesting but in different ways. This is simply a matter of planning so that there is always something attractive to be seen. Each season needs thinking about in terms of the color of flowers, foliage and fruit, form, texture, perfume and the uses to which the garden will be put. Even if a grand slam of summer color is desired, it is still possible to underplant and interplant for other times of the year.

There is almost no season in which bulbs do not flower and most of them are easy and trouble-free to grow. Use dry shade under trees for winter aconites and spring and autumn cyclamen. Plant the early dwarf daffodils and the very late, scented pheasant-eye types as well as the mid-season hybrids. Tulips in all their variety have a long season from March to May. There are spring- and autumn-flowering crocuses, as well as the colchicums (meadow saffron) which flower in September. Lilies and galtonias will fill the middle of the summer. Remember that bulbs do not need to occupy a space solely for themselves; they can be tucked in among other plants, almost as a bonus. Bulbs naturalized in grass are a delight.

Perfume can be present in the garden throughout most of the year. There are headily scented, late winter and early spring shrubs such as *Azara*, *Sarcococca*, *Chimonanthus*, *Viburnum* and *Hamamelis*. Even heather is very sweet on the air in March. Try to make room near to a door for a shrub with good perfume in winter, and have those with summer perfume by windows or sitting-out areas, especially if they produce

Left: Autumn color should be planned for at all levels of the garden, from the tree canopy down through shrubs (such as the Japanese maple shown here), to herbaceous plants with berries or colorful foliage. It is not just trees and shrubs that color in autumn.

The foliage of herbaceous plants, including bergenias, gillenias and *Euphorbia cyparissias,* can color just as beautifully as the leaves of the larger plants. The euphorbia, for one, also has delightful spring interest, bearing umbels of lime green flowers.

Top: Summer showpiece borders, awash with color as here, steal all the limelight for a few months, but gardens need to compensate elsewhere to give interest throughout the year. The focus of interest can move round the garden as the year progresses.

Bottom right: In the depths of winter, late berries and flowers, colored bark, evergreens and even snow itself lend color to a garden. It would be hard to better these "flowers" of ice. The skeletal forms of plants are central to the winter garden.

their strongest scent in the evening. There are also plants with scented foliage to consider, such as *Artemisia abrotanum* and *Helichrysum italicum*, a delightful quality, rarely considered by many gardeners, but a great bonus nonetheless.

In many places herbaceous perennials can be found in flower for almost 11 months out of the 12, and by planting a good cross section it is possible to get a long season. Hellebores are invaluable in late winter and are soon followed by pulmonarias. Both of these have an unseasonal lushness. Spring and summer are well supplied with colorful perennials, but there are plenty more which flower in the autumn such as *Rudbeckia*, *Persicaria*, *Schizostylis*, asters and dahlias.

In the winter the focus shifts to evergreen foliage, and there is a great variety of textures and colors to choose from including the glossy spiny leaves of holly, the soft gold of some variegated yews, or the blue of spruce needles. The interest supplied by colored bark is also invaluable. Dogwoods offer scarlet, purple and yellow bark; while that of willows is orange, bloomy gray or glossy brown. Some species of birch have brilliant white or coppery-pink bark and there are cherries with glorious, dramatic bark that resembles purest polished mahogany.

Autumn color can be found in trees like maples and rowans, but there are vines of equal brilliance and even herbaceous plants such as euphorbia and gillenia. Fruits and berries need not just be an autumn feature. Many roses carry their hips and *Mahonia aquifolium* bears its blue berries in late summer. Later come the reds, yellows and oranges of holly, rowans, cotoneasters and pyracantha. Usually the paler the berry, the later the birds will descend to eat them.

In winter a garden falls back on its structure to make itself interesting, and it is then that the most benefit is gained from light and shade and the clarity of the design. Think of the long low shadows from an orange winter sun cast by pencil cedars or a castellated hedge; a tremendously satisfying effect.

Right: Heathers and conifers can be very bright in winter, seen in the selection here. Their evergreen colors are best woven subtly into the entire fabric of the garden.

Other things to consider are the provision of privacy for the summer and of open spaces for children to play. They will need grass for the lively games of summer and a hard surface to avoid mud and damage in the winter. To get the most out of a garden, think of the luxury of a sitting area in a sun-trap, which could be comfortable on a sunny day in early spring or in autumn. Every detail has seasonal significance; if water features are included as part of the seasonal plan, then it is possible to have the sound of running water in the heat of summer and the still mirror-like surface of a pool to reflect scudding clouds in winter.

Far left: Bark like that of this red-stemmed dogwood (*Cornus alba*), can be an important feature of winter gardens. Many other trees and shrubs, especially birches, cherries and pines, have colored bark that is a great bonus in winter.

Left: Most autumn foliage colors are complementary, as in the case of *Cotinus coggygria* 'Royal Purple' and *Acer palmatum*. There is no need to worry too much about color schemes in this season, except to take into account possible clashes with highly valuable late season flowers.

Above: Fruits are just as much a part of the autumn scene as colored leaves, so try to find room for some fruiting plants in your garden, even if it is on a wall. Here the rich tints of a medlar glow with seasonal promise. There is little to match the pleasure of harvesting home-grown fruit.

Right: This yellow border is infiltrated with golden-leafed evergreens, which will maintain color and substance in the border long after the leaves on other plants have fallen. In summer they play a more discreet role.

COLOR

As harmony is to a tune, so color is to a garden: it gives a more precise feeling and mood to the underlying design. Color alone cannot make a garden, but it can enrich the design and highlight different parts of the scheme at different times. It can attract attention by means of bright harmony or by shocking contrasts; it can produce tranquillity through quiet harmonies or monotones, or create movement within the design by means of flowing harmonies and contrasts (which is perhaps the most ambitious and difficult part of gardening). Edwardian herbaceous borders were so magnificent precisely because of their fine tuning of color on a grand scale over a long season. Use color purposefully, to your own ends and tastes, but never underestimate its power. Right and wrong may be in the eye of the beholder, but almost everyone recognizes chaos for what it is. Above all, color in gardens is a means to an end like any other garden-design tool, rather than an end in itself.

Regardless of the effect sought through color selection, there is no getting away from the need for green. It is the backbone of any color scheme and should always be in evidence. There is a whole range to choose from: fresh apple greens will complement white and yellow, and warm bronzy greens will set off orange and scarlets. In a single-color garden the presence of greens is particularly important and should be used to maximum effect.

Everything in a garden has color, not just flowers, but foliage, walls, buildings, paths and seats. Together they offer the opportunity for endless experimentation and variety. If the hard landscaping has been inherited with the garden, the color of brick walls, gravel and so on must be taken into account before embarking on a color scheme to which they might be unsympathetic. A new site offers a rare opportunity: a chance to create the design, with the colors, of the gardener's dreams.

Left: Color on its own cannot make a garden, but it is one of the most powerful instruments in the gardener's hand. It can shock, soothe or seduce; the gardener is in control.

Top left: Geranium × oxonianum 'Claridge Druce' under roses and border phlox contributes to a running variation on a theme of pink and mauve. A precise and limited color scheme allows for subtle shifts of tone.

Bottom left: Foliage can be just as much a source of color as flowers. Here, variegated hostas, meadowsweet, bamboo and golden catalpa form the basis of the color scheme, while highlights of the same color are provided by day lilies and helianthus.

Top right: Single-color gardens are deservedly popular. Variety must come from a range of shapes and textures rather than color. Here, white 'Blizzard' tulips, grape hyacinths, forget-me-nots and pansies nestle beneath *Viburnum × carlcephalum*. It is the geometic rank of tulips which keeps the composition alive and anchors the display.

Bottom right: Some colors have to be used sparingly because they are so strong. In this detail the bright red of *Lychnis chalcedonica* is isolated in front of a delicate curtain of the cool gray weeping pear. Both plants benefit from the juxtaposition.

Harmonizing Colors

Each of us sees color differently, and one person's idea of bright harmonies may be another person's chamber of horrors. Nevertheless, there are certain basic guidelines which will help to produce harmonizing colors. Thereafter it is up to the individual to satisfy his or her tastes and to find the combinations that do most justice to the size, style and situation of a garden, a garden "room" or a flowerbed.

With color, almost more than any other element in garden design, economy is the key. A few colors used carefully will be far more effective than a fussy mixture. Too many colors, used indiscriminately, will tend to cancel each other out and look either muddled, frantic or simply unattractive.

Color harmonies can be made by several means. The simplest way is to use several varieties and tones of one color, plus greens of course. This can be fun, but it is rather limited. Alternatively, one main color can be combined with closely related colors – think of late summer borders of scarlet, oranges and browns or those intriguing mixtures of steely blue and gray foliage spiked with flowers of white and midnight blue. Another way, which is perhaps the hardest, is to

Above: On the color wheel, blue and gray are neighbors and offset each other well. Gray is accommodating and will act as a foil for many other colors.

Above right: Blue and gold are contrasting colors, but can be made harmonious by using one in a pale form and one in a dark form. Here the rich blue of *Geranium himalayense* is combined with the paler blue of *Veronica gentianoides* and the soft yellow leaves and heads of Bowles' golden grass (*Milium effusum aureum*).

Below left: Different tones of one color make a harmonious combination. Here, yellow is the dominant theme leading through the border, from *Achillea* 'Moonshine' on the left, through golden-leaved shrubs and trees, to *Rosa* 'Golden Wings' on the right.

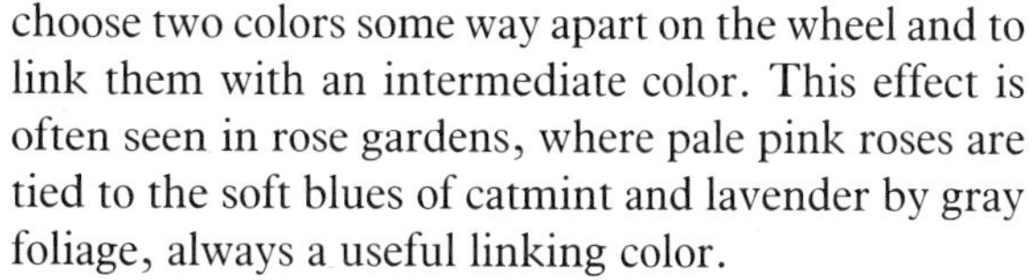

choose two colors some way apart on the wheel and to link them with an intermediate color. This effect is often seen in rose gardens, where pale pink roses are tied to the soft blues of catmint and lavender by gray foliage, always a useful linking color.

Color harmonies can also be used to allow a large part of the spectrum to appear in one garden, by progressing from cool creams and yellows through warmer reds and oranges to purples and blues. Along the way it is possible to make a whole range of small contrasts and variations depending on taste and space, but the general progression will remain the same.

Color relationships work not only through their relative positions in the spectrum but also through the strength and amount of color used. A good guide is to have one or at most two colors that are dominant in strength but not in area, with other colors supporting in decreasing ranks.

Never forget the importance of green. It is often spoken of as if it were one color, overlooking the fact that there is a whole range of different shades which can be just as useful in creating harmonies as any other color which has a range of tones.

Below: Blue and red make a bold contrast, but here they are drawn together by intermediate colors such as pink, lavender and mauve. Using intermediate colors allows the creation of schemes that pass through several strong colors; if the design is well paced the effect can be wonderful. Gertrude Jekyll used intermediate colors in this way in her grand Edwardian flower borders.

Below right: Strong colors need to be used sparingly, as the culmination or highlight of a color scheme. Here, deep red azaleas form a dense and dark base, leading upwards into lighter-textured pale pink, and finally into the airy, white structure of a magnolia tree. Strong colors used in tiny flashes have a very different, less startling effect than dense blocks of color which tend to hide every leaf.

One-color Gardens

These have become popular in recent years in the wake of such famous examples as the wonderful white garden at Sissinghurst Castle in Kent, England. They represent an extremely disciplined form of gardening in that the gardener has to work with a very limited palette. This can have its advantages: the emphasis is thrown back on to the elements of shape and texture, which is never a bad thing, and it suits small gardens because the simple and economic use of color saves them from the clutter trap of having too many colors squeezed into a limited space. Larger gardens may use the single color theme in just one small area, and in a garden where color is used in an extravagant and complicated way this can come as a moment of relief from the hurly-burly. This is certainly true with a white garden which seems so clean and neutral to an eye that has been romping through the whole spectrum. Above all others, a white garden allows the viewer to appreciate the forms of the plants and the flowers: by removing the element of strong color, which tends to dominate, the white palette gives a unique clarity and purity to a planting scheme.

Single-color gardening can be based on any color – red, yellow, gray, blue, brown have all been used, as have black and white. Parallel herbaceous borders have been divided up into single color sections facing each other across a path. Whichever color is chosen, three things will remain paramount: the need for many shades of the chosen color, the occasional contrasting color, and the liberal use of greens.

Above: In the famous "White Garden" at Sissinghurst gray and green are used as foils. The very formal design gives substance to the garden in winter, and there is much underplanting of bulbs to extend the season.

Left: Rosa rugosa 'Blanche Double de Coubert' has a relatively brief flowering period but it makes a delightfully cool combination with snow-in-summer (*Cerastium tomentosum*).

Right: Roses, pinks and peonies make a scrum of compatible pinks. The hard landscaping of steps and verandah, rather than contrasting foliage, provides the structure.

Even within a single color there are many variations and degrees of density with which to make contrasts. A blue garden will almost certainly be improved if it contains the gamut of blues, from the midnight purple of *Salvia × superba* through the royal blue of agapanthus to the lavender and palest amethyst of violas and crocuses. It may contain more gray and silver foliage than green, but the overall effect will be a fanfare of blueness. There is no reason why a blue garden should not contain the occasional splash of another color. Nature may do it for you, just as the dense blue-gray of rue will always throw up its crop of yellow flowers into your color scheme. The occasional splash of white will never seem out of place in a blue garden, while a steely autumn picture of juniper, rue, *Euphorbia characias wulfenii* and santolina can be greatly enhanced by a streak or two of screaming or soft pink schizostylis.

Top right: Experimentation is needed when finding different shades of a color to put together. Scarlet and pink are not automatically comfortable bedfellows, but with the chaperones of rich greens and plentiful grays to keep them apart, the effect is one of warm harmony and unity.

Right: There is no need to take too strict an approach to single-color gardens. A little latitude will positively improve the look of a scheme, provided the principal color (and therefore mood) remain dominant. Here, an array of blue, white and mauve delphiniums combine perfectly to produce an effect that is more than just an exercise in monochrome.

All-green Gardens

From time to time most gardeners long for an all-green garden. It is a longing for clarity and simplicity, for a rest from the business of gardening. The inspiration may be found in a formal garden: picture a white-painted clapboard house with a long verandah overlooking still trees and emerald lawns striped with the shadows of beautifully clipped hedges. Or a more intensively planted garden may appeal, perhaps a dappled grove carpeted with choice woodland plants. Whatever the inspiration, an all-green garden is almost certain to be restful and easy on the eye. There is an easy-going naturalness about green gardens, even when made in a formal style.

Green gardens happily lean toward formality because in the absence of other colors they are free to fall back on the elements of texture and design. Some of the most striking green gardens are exclusively topiary gardens, which can be breathtaking displays of trained and tailored evergreens.

In a less formal context there is a huge range of all-green plants to choose from; plants, that is, which have green flowers as well as green foliage. Look at all the different greens in a flowering plant of *Euphorbia amygdaloides robbiae* or *Alchemilla mollis;* there is everything from dark green to pale gray-green and lime. A good green garden can incorporate every shade; emerald, olive and khaki all have their uses.

A green garden is a way of making the most of the simplest palette on offer, but it will also benefit from other discreet colors such as brown. There are many brown, black and green barks to be had, and there is the russet and silver indumentum underneath the

Left: A green garden can throw the emphasis back onto the line, color and texture of nearby buildings and paths. Here it highlights the configurations of the brickwork, the gateway and the floating forms of the "lollipop" bay trees. A shady courtyard is made into a delightful haven by this cool, formal approach.

leaves of some species of rhododendron. Gray foliage is not always sucessful in a green garden, as most gray-leaved plants are sun lovers and come from more naturally colorful plant communities.

Do not banish color from a green garden. As with any single-color garden, a little of the color's close relatives (yellow and blue) can be incorporated with good effect. White also blends in very comfortably with green. *Tiarella*, *Aruncus*, Solomon's seal and primroses all offer a gentle touch of color without moving away from that green-upon-green woodland feel. For the palest pinks, add Tellimas or dicentras.

Variegated foliage has a place in a green garden, but can by contrast look very artificial when surrounded by simple greens. It should be used sparingly. Most variegated foliage shows its best colors in full light and tends not to be successful in shady gardens. Slight shade is less of a problem to these plants and a dull corner will benefit from bright variegations.

Far left: Any one-color garden is always improved by a touch of another color. White or pale blue are the most discreet and perhaps best additions to green, as they enhance the feeling of purity and simplicity. Green itself has a whole range of tones, from the yellows of box and spiraea, as here, to sea greens, grays and blues, to virtually black. A mostly green garden is relaxing compared to an over-fussy floral display.

Left: Clipped shapes within the hedges echo the forms beyond: box spirals and tall conifers, box balls and stone balls, spiky phormium leaves and complementary patterns in the pathway.

Above: Variegated foliage has a most useful role to play in green gardens. It can add variety and provides a means of highlighting certain shapes and areas. Ivy and euonymus can be particularly useful.

Contrasting Colors

The color wheel shows how the principal contrasts in color are made – red with green, blue with orange and yellow with purple – but countless bold combinations can be used. These are strong effects, highlights to be used in garden design in a similar way to harmonies, but more sparingly. If a garden is overloaded with severe contrasts they cease to be effective. For instance, a golden-leaved conifer can make a brilliant highlight in the all-green days of winter, but plant a dozen of them and the effect is devalued.

A variety of smaller contrasts, in color as in texture, are the stuff of interesting gardening. They keep the eye entertained and moving along. Sharp contrasts, like purple hazel next to yellow elder or a blue spruce with a yellow cypress, can draw attention and focus a garden, but they also hold up the progress of the eye, whereas smaller, gentler contrasts allow the eye to flow along. Indeed, the most harmonious of planting schemes will need a little contrast to keep it alive and add that certain spark of the unexpected. A garden without enough contrast becomes a dull affair.

Colors which at full strength would war with one another can make good companions when one of them is used in a paler tint. The strong, creamy yellow of *Anthemis* 'Wargrave' would look crude beside royal blue delphiniums, yet if the misty lavender of *Thalictrum delavayi* were to be substituted for the delphinium there would be an interesting contrast, and the speck of yellow in the heart of the thalictrum flower would tie the two colors together. For a more gradual contrast, the thalictrum could be placed between the anthemis and the delphinium.

Contrast of foliage color can be just as telling as that of flower color, and this should be borne in mind when planning a garden. Those schemes which are

Above: Strong colors can have strong effects. This deep scarlet rose contrasts just as much with blue as it does with shell pink, when all colors are delivered in the same volume. The tiered effect – blue rising to red, rising to pink – is clear and most satisfying.

Below left: Red has the ability to make green, its opposite on the color wheel, all the more intense. Here, one form of the excellent, vibrant climber parthenocissus changes color after another form, the autumn contrast being used to emphasize the line of the wall.

intended to carry a great deal of bright flower color will not require so much contrast or variety in the foliage: a reliable matrix of good stable greens will provide the best platform for floral pyrotechnics. By contrast, a garden which relies more on permanent shrubby plantings and evergreens will benefit from a greater range of contrasts in foliage color.

Color contrast can be made part of the whole garden design with certain areas set aside for strong hot colors, in direct contrast to other pale, cooler areas. These color pools need not be kept separate in enclosed areas of the garden; instead, contrast can be used to enhance and distinguish the different sides of a more open prospect.

Remember that the effects made by color depend upon the light in which they are seen. A really startling contrast may be devalued by siting it in shade, but, conversely, this effect can be used to temper an unwanted, unavoidable clash of colors.

Above: In a largely yellow color scheme, a contained touch of deep maroon presents a strong highlight and focus that emphasizes the different lighter shades. The maroon is made more intense by the contrast, and the yellow is saved from being uneventful.

Below right: Contrasts of color can be heightened by simultaneous contrasts of form. The solid green bulk of yew here acts as a foil to the light shape and texture of the airy lemon *Euphorbia characias wulfenii*. White blossom adds another subtle note.

Left: A gentle color scheme of mauve and lemon can be given a sparkle by the addition of some rich blue and bright yellow, forming a greater contrast on the fringe. Gray helps to tie together the lemon and mauve. This late summer border gives a good impression of the flower and foliage effects that can be achieved with a planting of perennials and annuals. The main emphasis falls on the yellow *Achillea taygetea* and *Helichrysum* 'Sulphur Light', with their respectively flat and clustered flower heads and texturally interesting foliage. A companula, to the right, gives height, while the delightful floriferous annual, *Xeranthemum annuum*, fills the foreground. Although it is drawing to the end of the growing season, the plants remain attractive. Fading flowers and mature foliage can have their own charm – subtlety compared to the vividness of high summer extravagance. The whole makes an enchanting scene. Notice the discreet supports around the established rose bushes at either side.

TEXTURES

Texture works with shape and color in a garden to create movement and harmony for the eye. In contrast with themselves and each other, these three elements produce a constantly changing variety of interest, bringing the detail of the garden to life. The greater the range of textures, the greater will be the interest throughout the space.

It is easy to forget that everything in a garden has its own texture; not only are there the textures of foliage, grass, flowers and bark, but also those of water, paths, walls, gravel and all the other areas of hard landscaping. Texture is a more discreet element than color or shape, and a wide range of textures will not clutter a garden so much as highlight its other elements. So it is worth trying to incorporate plenty of different textures in all aspects of the garden.

We are made aware of texture in different ways; partly through direct sight and touch – we can see and feel if a leaf is rough and hairy – and partly through the way light falls on surfaces – we expect shiny rhododendron leaves to be smooth and firm or a glistening, wet stone-flagged path to be harder than gravel. This indirect visual appreciation of texture needs to be part of the planning of texture in a garden as much as the tactile element.

Hard landscape features can be softened by the use of textures. Consider the use of "green" steps, where the risers are planted with ivy or some tiny cotoneaster; think of deep cobbles or precise herringbone bricks with emerald green moss in every joint. The features themselves also offer a wide range of textures, from hard concrete to fine footstep-deadening grit. In a precise, formal garden, where much of the design is dictated by architectural features, large quantities of polished marble can look perfect on walls or underfoot, most usually in the form of a well-proportioned staircase. By contrast, in a minimalist style, where incidental details are more appropriate

Above: Texture and form work hand in hand. Here, smooth circles of hard and rugged paving contrast with the brittle hard lines of yuccas and the architectural, blue-grey Atlas cedar. The domes of golden yew are soft in detail and texture but have a hard form when clipped.

Above: Textural contrasts need not be extreme to be effective. The roughness of this gravel is suitably offset by a gentle mixture of soft shapes and textures, seen in both the foliage and the adjacent surfaces. The delicate, mounding Japanese maple rightfully takes center stage.

Left: The tall Chusan palm has its own internal contrast of textures. Hard, flapping leaves stand above a rugged hairy stem. A woodland floor, rippling with bluebells, complements the softness of the trunks to produce a calm, gentle aspect. Although the tree is distinctly exotic in appearance it is frost hardy. It does, however, need full sun, fertile, well-drained soil and shelter from strong winds.

Above: Texture can be a matter of scale. Here the spiky flowers of the dwarf laurel *Prunus laurocerasus* 'Otto Luyken' combine *en masse* to form a soft carpet of green and white. As a contrast, the light glossy texture of box is clipped into a hard wheel shape to be doubly effective. Color and form underline the textural contrast. The whole effect shows the highly original nature of garden design.

than clearly delineated patterns, a great river-washed boulder will combine a gentle shape with a hard texture without imposing uncompromising order.

The range of textures to be found in foliage is immense, but they can reasonably be grouped into the following categories: feathery, soft, felty or hairy, rugged, spiky, hard, smooth or shiny.

Feathery leaves make you instantly want to touch them. Some, like fennel and artemisia, release a perfume when touched. There are the green or purple domes of the dwarf maple, *Acer palmatum dissectum*, the tougher birch 'Trost's Dwarf' or the fern-leaved elder. There is the billowy foliage of 'Boulevard' cypresses, the brittle delicacy of dicentras or the flowers themselves of the smoke bush, *Cotinus coggygria*, which is smothered in panicles of wonderful, fluffy blossoms during summer.

Softness comes in many guises, from the swaying fountains of bamboos and ornamental grasses to the simple eloquence of moss. Ferns offer some deliciously soft textures over a long season. Meadow grass rippling in the wind must surely be one of the garden's most seductive softnesses, while in a border plants like *Alchemilla mollis* will act as a gentle foil for more vigorous shapes.

Feltiness or hairiness is often to be found on large leaves, like those of *Hydrangea sargentiana* and *Bergenia ciliata*, or on the undersides of some species rhododendron leaves which can have a rich indumentum of gray or russet. Lambs' ears (*Stachys byzantina*) is a favorite with children, and many people like to stroke the cerise velvet flowers of *Salvia buchananii*.

Ruggedness shows up well in the bold, corrugated leaves of veratrums, rogersias, *Viburnum davidii* and

V. rhytidophyllum, and the vast umbrella leaves of *Gunnera manicata*. There are barks too, flaky, deeply corrugated, striped, or even peeling in shreds and tatters.

Spikiness appears most often in the sword-like foliage of irises, crocosmias, phormium and yucca, and in the prickles of holly and eryngiums. Acanthus, morina and eryngiums also have spiny flowers.

Hard textures are found in shiny broad-leaved and needle-bearing evergreens, in the rigidity of yuccas and in the tight surfaces of topiary and cushion plants like *Bolax* or *Hebe* 'Boughton Dome' (which is as crusty-looking as a new loaf of bread).

Glossy leaves grace evergreen shrubs like laurel, aucuba and griselinia, but there is just as much shine on the foliage of herbaceous plants like galax or asarum. Remember that some barks can be shiny too, especially some species of cherry and birch.

Opposite: Amid a generalized soft planting of ferns and primulas, the striking textures come from the shiny surface of the water and the rugged bark of the silver birch. These elements together produce a balanced effect.

Top left: In a planting of soft shapes and textures, the hard lines of stepping stones can be used to give clarity to the structure of the garden.

Top right: The combinations of texture and form can vary greatly. The shape of this pampas grass is undeniably stiff, yet the flower plumes are soft and yielding. The dome of 'Jackman's Blue' rue has a broad, draping form that matches its soft texture.

Bottom left: Texture is often deceptive. The purple euphorbia is far softer than the surrounding cotoneaster branches, yet their geometric structure would lead you to expect them both to be hard. Greater contrast of form would benefit these textures.

Bottom right: The leaves of this purple cordyline and the surrounding griselinia are equally hard, yet the contrast of form is extreme.

STYLES

The style of a garden is largely responsible for its atmosphere, whether it is neat and geometric, relaxed and informal, busy and colorful, or still and discreet. The choice of style is often influenced by other gardens that have been seen and admired. Try to be open-minded about the styles you look at, and consider not just their personal appeal, but also how they would suit your house and family use, and how much maintenance they would create and when. Styles which rely on a very detailed planting to look correct will require a great deal of summer attention which you may not be able to give. On the other hand, a style which is architecturally complex may be more expensive to construct but far easier to maintain during the growing season. Some of the great historic garden styles have been extremely simple in terms of plant material, relying more on the form of the land, on water and buildings, and such staples as grass and trees. This restrained approach can produce stunning results, whatever the scale of the site. Let period styles be a source of inspiration, a starting point rather than something to copy slavishly. It is too easy to let period style become a cliché: draw the best from it and make it your own. After all, every style was modern once. By giving serious consideration at the outset to style, ideas are often enriched and crystallized and the temptation to simply fill the garden with a mass of favorite plants avoided.

Left top and bottom: Classical formality or cottage garden? You must decide what suits your house, your household (children and pets as well as adults) and your pocket. It is also important to consider how much time you are prepared to put into gardening and the length of time you are likely to stay before moving. Choosing the right style will maximize the pleasure you receive.

Above left: Select a design appropriate to your interests. The clear lines of a modern designer garden can be obscured by rich planting so may not suit the plant lover.

Above right: With care, you can make your own style by mixing unlikely elements. The combination of classical urn, cottagey pots and modern paving works as a satisfying composition of shapes and color. The attention given to the paved design allows other details to be simpler.

Below: If time and money are plentiful, the Victorian style may be for you. But would you always want a garden so rich in detail in all its parts, so formal, so ostentatiously gardened? Might you prefer a simpler, classical approach to formality, that gives order to a space without such abundance?

Wild

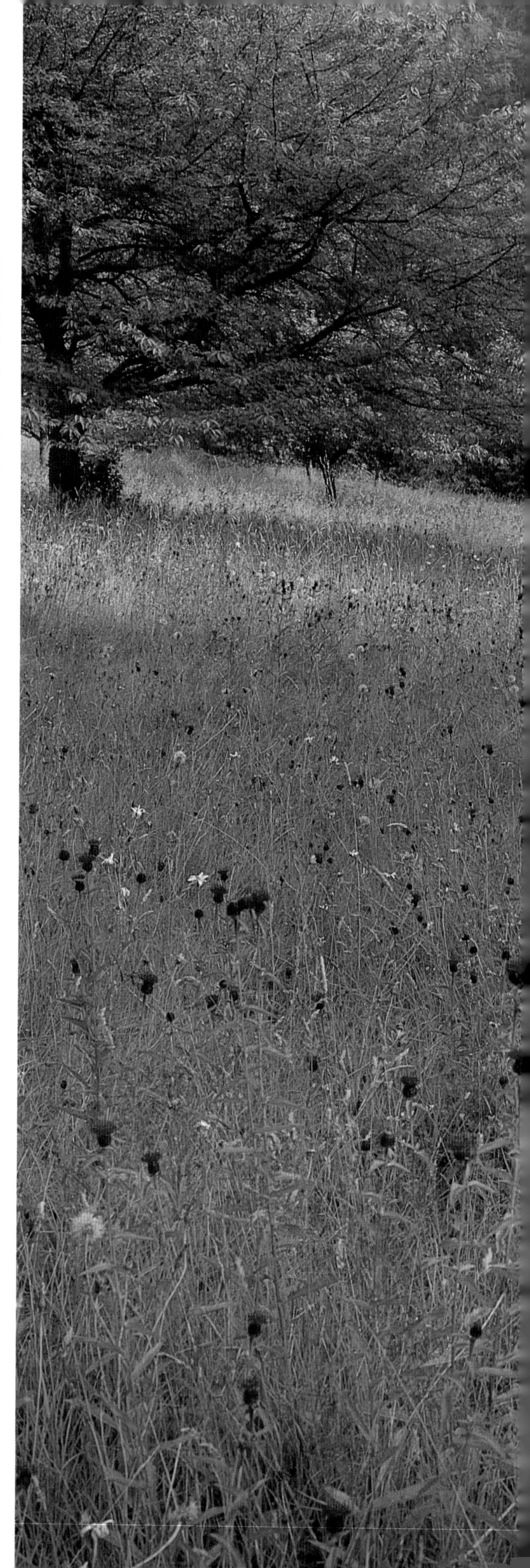

Most gardeners understand what is meant by a wild garden even though it is really a contradiction in terms. How can a garden, a man-made creation, be truly wild? The main characteristic is that nature is apparently allowed to have the upper hand over the gardener, but in a successful wild garden this is never actually so. The gardener produces this illusion by keeping maintenance to a discreet minimum and by choosing plants which will not take advantage of this kind of freedom. It is a quiet lyrical style of gardening, a balance between the truly natural and the contrived which is surprisingly difficult to achieve.

The fashion for a more relaxed approach to gardening first appeared in the late seventeenth century, when large gardens often included a "wilderness": an intersecting network of paths and vistas running between areas of trees and shrubs, and sometimes hedges. This was wild only in that it contrasted with the more rigidly formal gardens nearer the house. Wild gardening as we know it today was pioneered in the late nineteenth century by the writer William Robinson as a reaction to the ostentatious formality of the high Victorian period. In *The Wild Garden* (1870) he advocated naturalizing "perfectly hardy exotic plants under conditions where they will thrive without further care". It was he who first persuaded the hybrid daffodil out of the bed and into the long grass; yet even he was content to have areas of more closely managed formality around the house.

Today, the notion of wild gardening has become associated with the idea of nature conservation, and one hears more of putting back native plants than

Far left: Naturalized bulbs, like these anemones and small early daffodils, are perfect for creating decorative drifts of color in a wild garden. The grass here would not be cut until mid-summer, allowing the foliage of the naturalized plants time to feed the bulbs and die down first. Wild daffodils self-seed readily in these conditions.

introducing foreign ones. We have become aware of gardens as living communities, not just of plants but also of birds, animals like hedgehogs and squirrels, insects, fungi, and even lichens.

Certain rules of thumb are worth remembering when creating a wild garden. First, the garden needs to be big enough to have its own identity to avoid looking like a small shabby part of an otherwise well maintained garden. It may be advantageous to separate the wild area visually from the rest of the garden. Second, it is usually more appropriate to keep wild gardening at some distance from the house. Close contrast with a neat house will make a wild garden look muddled rather than relaxed and comfortable.

The wild garden should be planned for minimum maintenance. Lawns may even become flower meadows, cut as hay in late summer, with paths mown through them for access. Safe old trees should be left to decline gracefully and woodland plants should be cultivated beneath them. Use plenty of bulbs and shrubs which can compete with grass and require next to no pruning or spraying. It may be a good idea to introduce a pond if the time is available to maintain it. Above all, do not overplant: nature is an economical gardener and gains her best effects very simply, with just a few plants.

Left: A wild-flower meadow makes a superb transitional zone between garden and country. Wild gardening, when it is successful, can be sheer magic.

Below: In damp woodland, primulas, ferns, bluebells and forget-me-nots multiply. Such a display needs weeding in spring but later in the year requires minimal attention.

Left: This early summer scene has a wonderfully fresh and relaxed quality. Vigorous roses look well in turf, and can be allowed to sprawl freely. Try to choose mildew-resistant varieties, and then leave them.

Below left: Much of wild gardening is a matter of keeping the peace. Having established wild flowers where you want them, the general maintenance regime should allow them to increase freely, apart from the most vigorous.

Below right: An informal pond cannot be beaten for imparting that wild look, even when, as here, exotic plants are combined with native ones. Ponds also provide a habitat for wildlife, including fish, amphibians, insects and certain birds.

Right: A simple hazel-nut walk can be transformed into a garden with a minimum of planting. Self-seeding bluebells are given that little extra spark by the addition of a few scarlet tulips.

Below left: Wild gardening should be simple, but can still be subtle. Here, native foxgloves and the wild *Rhododendron ponticum* make a perfect early-summer combination alongside a soft path. Purples can be all the more opulent in shade.

Below right: Wild flowers may often be small, but *en masse* they are just as effective as larger garden flowers, if a little less precise. These buttercups contribute just as much to this scene as the pink pokers of the cultivated bistort.

Topiary

Despite the vituperations of those who regarded topiary as "pastry cooks' gardening", it has always had a loving following somewhere. Whatever topiary might do for the style of a garden, there is always pleasure to be taken in the sheer craftsmanship of creating and maintaining it. In manageable quantities, making topiary is fun.

The clipping of yew, holly and box played an important part in seventeenth-century gardens and came to the fore again in the grand formal gardens of the high Victorian era. Large gardens of the twentieth century have often made bold use of topiary, and it has long been a part of the cottage garden tradition.

The continuing appeal of topiary stems from the fact that it is an effective (and also inexpensive) means of creating the structure of a garden. A fine hedge with knife-edged finials marching on top is every bit as much a part of the garden's structure and ornament as a stone wall would be. A well-placed and freestanding topiary specimen, in whatever style, will command just as much dramatic attention as a fine statue.

Topiary is essentially a formal style of gardening. It is the imposition of the gardener's will upon the plant, a living sculpture. This degree of artificiality immediately commands the onlooker's attention and makes competition from mere flowers seem rather petty. Consequently, topiary is best used where it has the space to be seen on its own terms. The faintly comical mixture of topiary and a gentle jumble of flowers in cottage gardens is perhaps why topiary there has tended to be humorous in inspiration.

Whole gardens of topiary are best kept simple. The point of concentration should be in the contrast of curves and straight lines, of light and shadow, of earthbound or floating forms. A lawn or clean gravel is all that is needed to set off these living sculptures, but you can extend the interest by adding a little colored foliage such as golden yew, or some simple washes of color provided by bedding plants.

Topiary is not in itself a labor-intensive craft. Only the amount of topiary you have will make it a chore, especially if ladders are needed. Patience and skill are the keys. Once the shapes are fully formed, an annual clipping is sufficient for yew and box, carried out at the gardener's convenience during autumn or early winter. Topiary can be made out of holly and bay too, but there is no doubt that yew is much the best. Good topiary is slow to take shape, which is why so many topiary gardens conveniently begin life with a more diverse planting until the topiary develops its own singular authority.

Left: This great topiary cartwheel is almost a garden in itself. It is made entirely of box, both the green and yellow forms, giving structural contrast throughout the year. Interplanting is restrained.

Below: Strong, towering forms produce a maze-like effect, which offers new vistas at every turn. A bold structure like this can cope with a loose, informal underplanting.

Above: Single-color bedding emphasizes the geometric design in this scheme of great clarity and simplicity. There is contrast in the hard paths and the play of sunlight on the imaginative shapes.

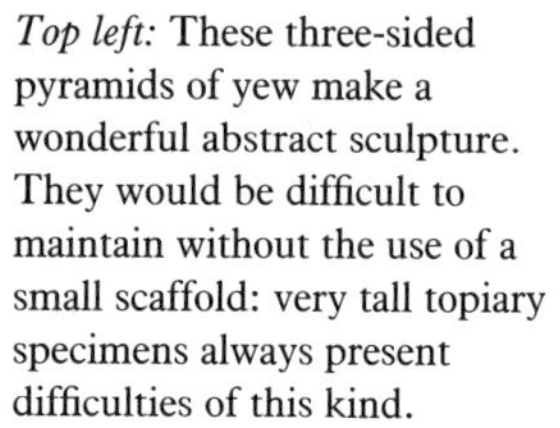

Top left: These three-sided pyramids of yew make a wonderful abstract sculpture. They would be difficult to maintain without the use of a small scaffold: very tall topiary specimens always present difficulties of this kind.

Top right: Box bushes will respond well to hard pruning. This old specimen has been cut back to its framework of branches and the new growth has been cloud-pruned to form a clever vegetable poodle of considerable charm.

Below: Spiral box sentinels of this size require many years of skilful training on a wire frame. Specimens that have already been trained are expensive: weigh your means against your patience.

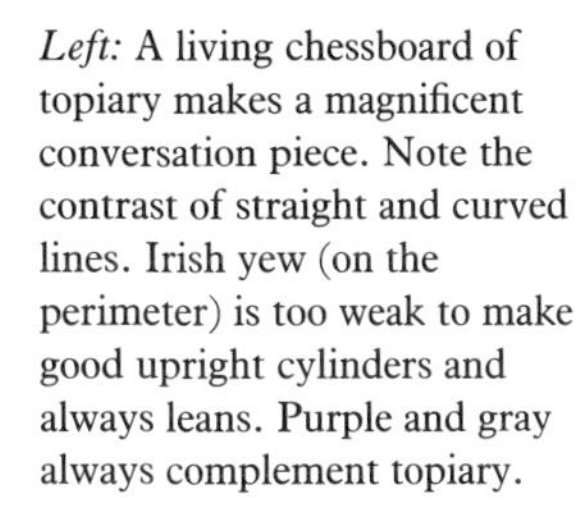

Left: A living chessboard of topiary makes a magnificent conversation piece. Note the contrast of straight and curved lines. Irish yew (on the perimeter) is too weak to make good upright cylinders and always leans. Purple and gray always complement topiary.

Top left and right: The precise hedging of a parterre or knot garden is just as hard to maintain well as more fanciful pieces of topiary. In topiary it is always the straight lines that take time to perfect. The job is made easier if a stretched line is used as a cutting guide.

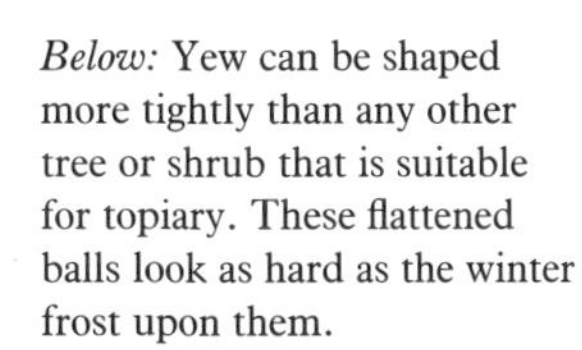

Below: Yew can be shaped more tightly than any other tree or shrub that is suitable for topiary. These flattened balls look as hard as the winter frost upon them.

Cottage

The best words to sum up the cottage garden style might be unpretentious or unsophisticated. It is a style in which a random variety of plants is grown, not particularly for the subtleties of careful plant association but simply as favorites, because they are loved for their own sake or are useful in some way. The garden in which they grow will have a small-scale, purely functional framework, without any grand vistas or extravagant hard landscaping. This is because a cottage garden is essentially an elaboration of a working

garden, a fruit and vegetable garden made pretty by flowers with the minimum of expense.

The cottage garden was developed by people who could not afford designer gardens, in the days when cottage meant a humble dwelling in a rural setting rather than a desirable small house in the country. So, for instance, paths were of simple local materials, no wider than absolutely necessary, and lay where necessity required – for instance, from the front door to the garden gate, from the front door round to the back door or from the back door to a garden shed. Gates were simply made, perhaps of painted wood rather than metal. A rustic fence or boundary hedge kept passing farm animals out and would have been of native plants such as holly and hawthorn, forming a transition from garden to country.

Pursuing the theme of a productive garden, in a modern cottage garden the trees should be fruit trees wherever possible, or at least blossom trees of some kind. Apples, pears, plums and cherries will all help

Left: In the soft light of evening this cottage garden seems to merge with the countryside beyond, with the fields seen through a screen of old espalier apple trees and roses trained over a rustic arbor and fence. Free-seeding has helped to produce the relaxed plant groupings in the foreground; it also quickly gives a look of maturity.

to create the right atmosphere, as will nut trees such as hazel or almond. If there is space for a large tree, a walnut might do. Try to avoid large upright conifers. Evergreens such as holly or yew will look more appropriate and they can be clipped into shapes which add a touch of fun and formality to the garden if required. Lawns should not play an important part in a cottage garden. Open spaces suitable for lawns would in a real cottage garden be used for vegetables, so if you need grass for children grow it under fruit trees.

Colorful plants, or perhaps herbs, in simple pots by the door will look right. Make the most of vegetables and fruit bushes, letting them be part of the garden design. Do not be afraid of using rows of vegetables, herbs, bedding plants or flowers for cutting, especially alongside a path. There is no need to grow only old fashioned flowers because it is how the flowers are used and grouped that creates the cottage style not what type they are. Choose as many scented plants as can be fitted into the space available, especially climbing roses and honeysuckle.

The overall effect should be of fussy well-tended order, a comfortable mix in which all the plants are allowed to run together. There will be plenty of weeding, but also an opportunity to grow all your favorite plants in rich profusion.

Far left: Foxgloves, clematis and lovage grow freely in an informal border, backed by low, simple architecture that seems at one with nature.

Below: This arbor is engulfed by a luxuriant growth of mixed climbers; plants drape over the path, giving the scene an intimate mood.

Left, top right and centre right: In cottage gardening, the planting is visually more important than the structure. Paths can be overwhelmed with plants – just so long as you can get by – and the built structure of the garden should be made of simple materials. Very sophisticated materials look out of place. Local stone or brick are ideal materials for walls and paving. Rough-cut timber or rustic logs are most suitable for arches.

Bottom far left: Built features in a cottage garden should be well made but simple, like this wicket under a nut arch.

Bottom left: Topiary, often whimsically shaped, is a traditional feature of many cottage gardens.

Below: This excellent example of dry-stone walling shows high quality construction and the use of sympathetic materials. The pink hue in the stone complements the foxgloves. Simple furniture is entirely appropriate.

Bottom right: Showy wild flowers, like foxgloves and herbs, strike a suitably unpretentious note in a cottage garden. Lavender makes an attractive lining to paths, tempting passersby to pick it. Flowers for drying, like helichrysums, honesty and Chinese lanterns, fit in well.

Modern

It is ironic to think that every historical garden style was once the latest thing, fresh and exciting. But what makes a garden modern today? Certainly not the plants themselves, for the world contains no more unexplored continents to offer us startling new introductions as it did during the last 400 years; and while we can reconstruct or draw inspiration from period styles to make something new, the result would not immediately be called a modern garden.

The most clearly modern tendency in gardening is to follow the leads of modern architecture and painting towards a minimalist style, using plenty of clean, modern hard landscaping materials and a much reduced palette of plants. The plants, such as grasses and bamboos, are often chosen more for their foliage and architectural qualities than for their flowers, because the modern style springs precisely from the contrast of shapes and textures between plant and plant, and between plant and hard landscaping.

Due to this predominance of hard landscaping, the modern style is especially suitable for town gardens and courtyards. Here sculpture can bring life to this kind of precise, discreet garden, and it looks more at home than in some traditional styles. Water can be used in mirror pools, trickling over pebbles or in fountains to bring light and movement to the design.

Below: Modern gardens tend to use few plants and there is an emphasis on line and hard landscaping. These pebble arabesques are unashamedly modern, yet are inspired by the parterres of earlier periods and the decorative style of Spanish and Moorish architecture. Could this open space happily stand further complication of its lines?

Left: High-quality materials, such as marble and slate, deserve the attention drawn to them in this angular garden. The fountain and the stylish, sweeping pergola add movement to the design.

Above: An "outdoor room", complete with tiled floor, cleverly uses the contrast between the rough texture of grass and the smooth texture of stone. The linear pattern lengthens the garden.

There are so many different modern paving materials that the possibilities for interesting effects are endless. Concrete paving slabs come in all sizes and colors, from simple rectangles to hexagons. Bricks offer a wonderful range of colors and opportunities for patterned textures. Wooden decking is increasingly used as a means of surfacing outdoor areas, and it can easily accommodate sudden changes in level through the interplay of platforms and steps.

Another development of modern architecture has been the large plate glass window, which has helped to bring the garden into the house. Equally, everyone likes to have a living area outside in the garden, where the family can eat, read or amuse themselves when the weather permits. These two factors have combined to blurr the distinction between indoors and outdoors. Swimming pools have further emphasized this ambiguity and have also introduced another form of hard landscaping into the garden, a feature that requires careful placing and design. Materials usually found indoors have come to be used outside, and it is not unusual to see ceramic tiles on the floor and walls of a patio, as well as in swimming pools. Where shade is needed for outdoor living, modern gardens have made use of specimen trees with ornamental bark set off by a gravel surround, so that the beauty of the trunk becomes a feature in itself.

It is in the modern garden that the curve, the organic shape, has found its proper home. Curved lawns, curved pools and curved paving marry in well with this flowing, informal style.

Above left: Unashamedly artificial curves are perfectly at home in the hard landscaping of a modern garden. The angular pattern of the paving only serves to accentuate the curves of the low retaining wall. Modern gray slabs and a sweep of old dark bricks are effectively juxtaposed.

Above: The modern style suits small courtyards and town gardens. In this example, the relationship to the house is enhanced by the use of quarry tiles on the steps; they give warmth to the scene and are probably seen from a vantage point inside the house as often as from the garden.

Left: The large simple shapes, made possible in modern architecture by the use of concrete, find a complement in natural forms: the spiny disks of cacti contrast splendidly with the smooth rectangles of paving. Gravel is a discreet foil to both.

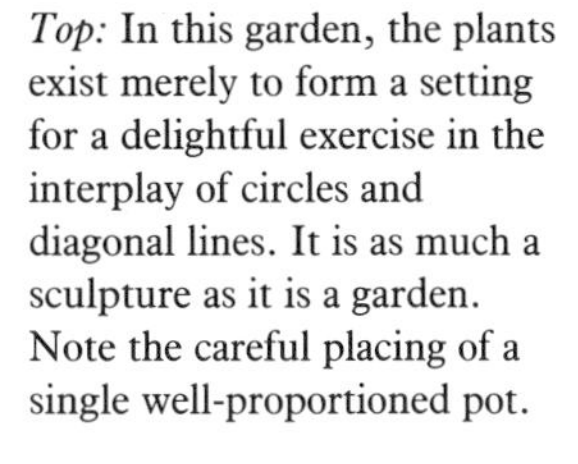

Top: In this garden, the plants exist merely to form a setting for a delightful exercise in the interplay of circles and diagonal lines. It is as much a sculpture as it is a garden. Note the careful placing of a single well-proportioned pot.

Bottom left: Sculptural foliage, water, and hard landscaping blend well together. The clever tunnel-stepping-stone contributes liveliness and a sense of direction to this carefully poised composition of mixed materials.

Bottom right: Here a rather ordinary back yard has been transformed into an attractive outdoor room. The emphasis is on gravel, paving and the wooden supports for the "roof", which gives a feeling of privacy and seclusion without making the space dark. The pale gravel also helps to keep it light, as does the delicate statue on tip-toes. Modern gardens make a good setting for modern sculpture; a sympathetic environment can be made around it.

Victorian

The interiors of Victorian houses were known for their fussiness and crowding detail; so it was with the gardens of the high Victorian period. Labor was cheap and numerous gardeners could be employed, removing worries about whether a garden style might be labor intensive or not. The period was also marked by a passionate interest in scientific discovery and the cultivation of those plants which were being introduced from far-off countries. These two factors led Victorian gardening away from eighteenth-century debates on the aesthetics of design towards an interest in plants for their own sake, for their collectability as specimens. The result was a style of gardening as formal and ostentatious as gardening has ever been. Everything was kept very dressy indeed.

Above: The Victorians loved to use formal vases, and to plant them up with striking specimens for the summer. Yuccas have been used here, to top off two already enormous vases that have been raised on pedestals to frame the hedges and the path. The Victorians were not in the least afraid to be a little pompous, or to gild the lily.

What the gardens of the great houses did one day, the villa gardens of the new suburbs did the next but on a smaller scale. Whereas in the eighteenth century country landowners had vied with each other for supremacy in good taste, the new one-upmanship was in the material contents and the sheer quantity of plants used in a garden.

Typical features of the period include close-shaven lawns, frequently changed bedding schemes, parterres, extravagantly winding paths, iron pergolas and arches, cast iron seats, urns and balustrades, and

Below: Victorian gardens made the most of ironwork, and of roses. The elegant top of this gazebo and the swags of roses between its pillars make a fine wedding-cake feature.

the very generous use of specimen trees at the expense of open space. Conservatories, glasshouses and vegetable and fruit gardens were beautifully and precisely maintained. Formality was the keynote in all things, whether the garden was full of curves or straight lines. Nothing was discreet: all the work was for show.

Even specimen trees were clipped and evergreens such as holly and yew were used a great deal for the purpose. Weeping trees were especially favored as specimens, not least of which was the weeping holly. Monkey puzzles sprouted on every lawn with a pretense to fashion. Evergreen shrubberies were common and made much use of three laurels: spotted laurel, Portugal laurel and cherry laurel, largely because they withstood the sooty Victorian town

Left: Grandeur in miniature was the keynote of Victorian villa gardens. Here there are terraces with imposing central steps, but all in rather light materials. The planting is used to emphasize the central axis, with pairs of clipped box and griselinia flanking the steps. The use of colored gravel and rope-tile edging adds to the sense of order.

atmosphere so well. Roses were the great favorite and could be trained hard. Small, perfectly-edged island beds would be cut into lawns to house specimens such as a potted cabbage palm or a mass of red-hot pokers, surrounded by rings of brightly colored annuals. Gravel paths were popular, kept perfectly clean and well raked with a rope-tile edging. Even tarmac came to be used for its precise looks. Urns were common and were planted rather than used as ornaments in themselves. In short, the Victorian style can offer some unforgettable eye-opening effects.

Above: Victorian gardens were places of entertainment and education, as much as havens of peace. Aviaries like this were common and were used to house collections of newly discovered, extraordinary birds. Conservatories housed exotic plants in a similar way.

Left: The Victorians loved formal fountains, especially when they were set in a large pool. With electric pumps and countless reproduction fountains, similar effects can readily be achieved today.

Below: Fashionable Victorian gardens never shied away from complicated features. Economy of design, or of labor, was not respected: in the great country houses of England, entire bedding schemes could be changed overnight, while weekend guests dined and slept.

Above: Roses, bedding, a planted urn and lots of white paint make a typically Victorian combination. The late nineteenth century saw a considerable fashion for the idea of charming cottage gardening and roses around the door. Here, a modern interpretation of picket fencing is successfully coupled with a chinoiserie bench (a style popular from the 1760s) and Victorian-style planting.

Top right: A box-edged parterre in Victorian style complements a good cast-iron seat and elaborate jardinière. Centerpieces like this were common in formal gardens. The contents could be changed regularly as plants came into flower under glass.

Bottom right: No lawn could be too well maintained for Victorian taste, so, if you have the patience, a fine lawn should be your aim. Specimen trees were used a great deal, including forest conifers and, of course, the monkey puzzle. Bedding was often used under the canopy of young specimen trees or on its own, in small, well-planted island beds.

Parterre

A good parterre is about as stylized a piece of gardening as you will ever find. It turns the surface of the garden into a picture, a pattern complete in itself. In principle it is one of the simplest of garden styles, however complex the geometry of the pattern itself may actually be.

Knot gardens were a feature of seventeenth-century gardens and consisted of a square plot upon which lines of dwarf shrubs were interwoven to form a symmetrical pattern. The style developed, under French influence, into the parterres of the early eighteenth century. Here a larger area was divided with small hedges into all kinds of shapes, such as animals, crests, arabesques and leaves. The areas between the hedges were filled variously with grass, flowers, shrubs, or colored substances such as gravel, fluorspar, sand, coal, crushed brick and even glass. Clipped evergreens were also used, in pots or in the ground, to add a further dimension to the patterns. Much later, in the mid-nineteenth century, the grand parterre was revived in England by designers such as Nesfield and Barry, and fountains were regularly used as animated centerpieces.

The parterre may not be a style which will appeal to a keen plantsman, as the opportunities for growing a large range of plants are few. Its appeal lies instead in the precision of its lines, its contrasts of color and its relation to the adjoining architecture of the house.

Below: Strictly speaking, parterres are filled with blocks of a single color. However, an alternative approach is to use them as island beds filled with a mixture of shrubs and perennials. These will give varied color and interest in summer, and still leave you with an ornamental pattern of hedges in winter. The garden will have two distinct identities, the one abundant, the other linear.

Left: Part of the attraction of a parterre is the wide variety of surfaces that can be combined with the structural planting and the different effects that can thereby be achieved. Paths can be gravel – discreet or highly colored – or paved, as here, or even of grass. The object is to make a pleasing pattern with whichever materials you select.

Above: Plain blocks of color help to emphasize the shapes and structure of a parterre and to draw attention to the overall pattern by the way colors are repeated. The choice of colors is endless, from subtle pastel shades or single-color schemes to outrageously bright contrasts. All can be made to work in different, appropriate situations.

A parterre will complement even the most modern of houses because it is a pure geometric design. The modern style of heather-and-conifer garden of the last twenty years is simply a form of arabesque parterre.

A parterre needs to be kept separate from the hurly-burly of a mixed flower garden so that its lines can be appreciated without distraction. An encircling hedge is often all that is required to do this. The Victorians loved to use a grand balustrade to mark the perimeter. With a hedge all round it, a small parterre garden could be made a part of a much larger garden at some distance from the house, but the symmetrical facade of a house is undoubtedly the best backdrop for this sophisticated style of gardening.

Dwarf box is the traditional hedging material for parterres, but yew, santolina, berberis, germander and lavender can all be used. There is no reason at all to be limited to a traditional range of plants, either for hedging or for in-filling. The spaces between hedges could even be filled with water or pebbles instead of the usual bedding plants or bulbs. The same opportunities are offered in the use of the great array of modern hard-landscaping materials that are available, producing a wealth of detail in the surface of the paths in a small-scale parterre. Modern sculpture or a modern fountain can be used instead of topiary specimens. Parterres are an unashamed contrivance, to be enjoyed for their bold structure and artistry.

Left: In this modern knot garden the gravel background has been kept deliberately simple to emphasize the pattern of the box hedging.

Below left: Part of the pleasure of a parterre is to be able to walk among the beds, making your own patterns as you cross. A parterre that has no central axis has the appeal of an open-ended maze.

Right: This parterre, in the Victorian manner, has typical vibrantly colored spring bedding that will be changed again before summer. There is a lot of work in maintaining grass paths but, in a garden of this size, gravel might seem very stark. The huge vase centerpiece could be replaced by topiary, a traditional ornament of parterre gardens.

Below: Vegetables and herbs do not have to be grown in straight rows. They can be surprisingly ornamental in a parterre, and access for picking could not be easier.

Japanese

Japanese gardens have throughout history set out to provide a tranquil environment around the house. They possess an aura of calm which is rarely matched in western garden styles, and almost every element in their composition is symbolic of some aspect of nature or human life. Today the symbolism is not so strong and many gardens in Japan tend to use these symbolic elements for traditional and aesthetic reasons rather than for their meaning. For a westerner, perhaps the best approach to Japanese gardens is to draw from

them the means of arriving at that special stillness and to use it like any other garden tool, instead of trying to produce faithful copies in a foreign land.

Much of that tranquillity derives from an economical, almost minimal use of materials. Each element, whether built or planted, seems heavy upon the ground and settled there. Even water is still or flows gently downwards; you do not find fountains in Japanese gardens. The garden is designed to give the impression of the natural landscape at its most serene. The man-made geometry of some western garden styles is abhorrent to the Japanese.

It is precisely because Japanese gardens discreetly suggest nature, instead of copying it, that they can be created in a space of any size, however small. (At its most extreme, this becomes the miniature landscapes of bonsai.) Western gardeners can learn much from this clever use of small spaces.

The key elements involved are stone, water and a wealth of greenery, arranged in asymmetrical but well-balanced configurations. Flowers, such as irises,

Left: A true Japanese garden is calm and discreet, full of light and shade and contrasts of hard and soft. The paths are gentle and indirect and there is minimal planting.

Far left: Restful Far Eastern gardening can be a wonderful source of inspiration, even when there is no intention to fully reproduce the style in a Western garden.

peonies, lilies and chrysanthemums, play a relatively unimportant part. Groups of stones or boulders can be used to represent mountains and evergreens are clipped to depict boulders, while flat stones may form a gently weaving path. Straight lines are avoided. Water will be present, either as a waterfall, a pool with islands or simply suggested by flowing white sand. Commonly used plants include trees such as plums, cherries and maples and bamboo. Coniferous trees such as pines and juniper are often clipped to form floating cloud shapes, or they can be encouraged to take on a weatherworn appearance. Most significantly, all these plants are used sparingly and are rarely allowed to rub shoulders with one another.

Fences and screens, of materials such as bamboo or grasses, are more common than walls for dividing the garden. Often a loggia is provided from which to view the garden and a lantern of stone or metal is carefully placed to light the path at night or to offer reflections in the water of a pool.

Essentially, a garden in the Japanese style is intended to offer peace and quiet contemplation to its owner and his or her guests, a designer's garden rather than a plantsman's garden. Restraint is everything, with order, harmony and decorum as the guiding principles behind a scheme.

Above: Waterfalls and watercourses are a major element in Japanese gardens and are intended to suggest high mountain streams. Bridges and stone lanterns are also important, symbols of a safe pathway. The cut-leaved, domed Japanese maple (*Acer palmatum dissectum*) is a popular plant for Western versions of Japanese gardens.

Above and bottom far right: Japanese gardens contain many traditional elements which can be used to suggest an Oriental style. Water is vital. Favorite plants, such as maples, plums, pines and bamboos, will produce the right flavor, especially when set in a carpet of moss. Low mounding evergreens can be used as a substitute for mosses. It is a style that can be adapted to any size garden, as can be seen here, where a small courtyard and an expansive landscape have been equally well served.

Bottom right and above right: When there is no real water, an impression of a stream or waves can be created by raked sand or gravel or a bed of small stones. Where there is real or imaginary water there are stepping stones; here, wood, stone and foliage combine to present a crisp, clean effect.

Above far right: Bamboo is commonly used to make screens and bridges and well constructed features like this example would be an asset to any Japanese-style garden. Stone lanterns of traditional design are an emphatic Japanese statement.

Classical

In all art forms the classical style is one in which a logical, well-considered form is used as the structure upon which to hang the individual expression of the artist – and so it is with gardens. A classical garden is one which has a structure designed to be pleasing in itself, rather than the largely functional layout of the traditional cottage garden. Within that structure, the planting may be as unrestrained and romantic as you wish, but it will always be seen in relation to the structure of the garden as a whole.

It is no surprise to find that most of the formal period styles of gardening have come under the heading of classical gardens, and there is no denying that symmetry and formality lend a garden the strongest of structures. However, the planting can be vibrantly colorful and extravagant or contained, minimal and quiet. This is the great advantage of a classical garden: its good bones will support all manner of fleshing out.

Throughout history it has been the classical gardens which have survived, from the green simplicity of an eighteenth-century landscape park with its lakes and temples to the geometric razzmatazz of Baroque gardens. But the twentieth century has seen the development of classical gardens on a much smaller scale, where the blend of domestic architecture and plantsman's gardening have complemented each other perfectly. English gardens like Sissinghurst

Below: Classical gardens have strong bones – a clear and attractive structure which can then be enriched by planting. Light and shade and the qualities given to a design by the inclusion of water are almost more important than the overlay of planting, which need not be colorful.

Left: Symmetry plays an important role in classical gardens, repetition of parts being the easiest way of producing balanced arrangements that are strong and visually satisfying.

Above: The formal structure of a classical garden, frequently composed of walls, hedges, paving and sculpture, should be coupled with a sympathetic, complementary selection of plants.

(designed by Vita Sackville-West and Sir Harold Nicolson) and Great Dixter (by Sir Edwin Lutyens) and Dumbarton Oaks (by Beatrix Farrand) in the United States have proved that gardens rich in architectural and structural detail will happily support the most exuberant of planting and win the affections of all serious gardeners. In gardens like these, form and content reach a most satisfactory balance, which surely is the essence of a classical garden.

A well-designed garden deserves to be well planted, and when making a classical garden it is worth planting carefully with an eye for shape, color and texture. The plants may form part of the structure itself, in hedges or recurring patterns of specimen plants. Water, either standing, running or as a fountain may form part of the design. Even within a small garden it is possible to make use of vistas and focal points, while ensuring that the open spaces intended to be part of the design do not fall prey to a clutter of specimen plants. It is too easy to let the planting obscure rather than enhance the design.

Well-built walls, doorways, arches, steps, paths and pergolas will all enhance the quality of the garden structure, and occasionally a good-sized urn or vase will add distinction. So will an attractive garden bench carefully placed. Good quality hard landscaping can be expensive, but it is undoubtedly the key to success when making a classical garden. Few great gardens, however, were made in a season, but were built up gradually over the years. This is the best way to approach your own plans for a classical garden.

Left: Classical gardens, in relying on a strong structure and plan, tend to use a good deal of hard landscaping, often of antique appearance.

Right: Period features such as parterres can be introduced into classical gardens. The twentieth-century idea of separate "garden rooms" fits in well with the classical tradition, allowing different planting styles to be used within the various sections of the overall design.

Bottom right: Simplicity of structure is one of the keynotes of classical gardens. The emphasis here is linear.

Below: High quality materials skilfully combined with simple planting, as here, will always produce a classical garden.

Subtropical

The so-called subtropical garden is really a trick. We are used to seeing in our gardens plants from all over the world, from the most extravagant rhododendron to the most delicate alpine primula; but usually these plants come from a climate broadly similar to our own. In the subtropical garden, the aim is to present a picture of a totally different climate in which the usual range of temperate plants will not grow. To do this is inevitably a deception, but a satisfying one.

The subtropical style of gardening involves using a range of plants which might seem more at home in a much hotter climate, although they must of course be able to grow in our own gardens. It is achieved by selecting those plants with the most appropriate foliage; but perhaps more importantly, it is achieved by avoiding those plants which are commonplace in temperate gardens. The absence of certain plants is just as telling as the choice of plants used.

By the same token, subtropical gardens are often best sited in an enclosed area where the presence of the temperate world outside cannot dilute the effect you are trying to achieve. The same goes for garden architecture, furniture and hard landscaping. It is better to avoid the hallmarks of other garden styles such as classical urns and familiar, traditional garden seats and paving techniques. Instead, try to keep hard surfaces as informal as possible. Gravel is the most discreet option but clay tiles are another possibility. Stay with unsophisticated materials wherever possible. Cane or bamboo seats will look right.

Water can be important in creating a subtropical garden. If you want to give the impression of a hot dry climate, then a pool or a fountain is ideal. If the aim is

Left: The great paddle-shaped leaves of cannas always look suitably exotic, especially those forms with bronzed foliage. Although in temperate parts of the world cannas are grown mainly for their impressive leaves, their large flowers can produce a brilliant tropical effect, coming in bold shades of red, orange and deep pink, taking complex forms.

to reproduce a jungle effect, running, trickling or dripping water may be more appropriate, with moss and ferns growing alongside to enhance the effect.

Subtropical climates tend to produce large, lush foliage and this should be imitated in your choice of plants. The paddle-shaped banana leaf is to be found in cannas and lysichitums; spiky rosettes are found in yuccas, cordylines and potted agaves; araucarias can be useful too. For sheer size of leaf, there is no beating the Chusan palm, *Trachycarpus fortunei*, and paulownia and ailanthus trees can be pruned hard back to produce huge leaves. Gunnera and *Rheum palmatum* both produce huge herbaceous leaves in damp soil and in similar conditions bamboos and phormium can be used to give an exotic touch. In dryer conditions, *Melianthus major* offers lush blue-gray foliage. Climbers such as passion flowers, gourds and menispermum can add a tangled, jungle flavor, and daturas in pots will provide wonderfully exotic trumpet flowers rather like a hibiscus. In general, however, foliage is a better tool than flowers in creating the effect of an alien climate: it can offer the promise of subtropical flowers without ever giving the game away.

In some climates it is necessary to create the subtropical effect under glass or at least partial cover, where the higher temperatures and reduced winds will better suit many large-leaved plants.

Far left: As long as plants look exotic and foreign, they can be used, no matter how many continents the result actually represents. The jungle effect is enhanced by running water.

Below: The combination of potted aspidistra, Chusan palms and a reflecting pool helps to create an "oasis" look. The palms produce fragrant yellow flowers.

Right: Palm fronds and handsome large leaves are the hallmarks of the colonial-style subtropical garden. Tall, mature palms create the ideal, lush impression.

Below left: Even where the climate is temperate, and especially in coastal gardens, there is scope for using plants that impart an exotic flavor, such as the yuccas flanking these steps. Simple touches like this, combined with the use of suitable hard landscaping materials, can make all the difference to a design. Such strategic use of plants and features is a device that will serve any garden style; one ideal element can crown the effect.

Below right: Given overhead cover, you can grow a wide range of large-leaved plants, both hardy and not-so-hardy, which in the open would not look as lush and exotic because of the wind and the drier atmosphere. *Rodgersia podophylla* (as underplanting in the center) is perfectly hardy in an open space, but looks and is at home in the cool, moist shade beneath taller foliage plants.

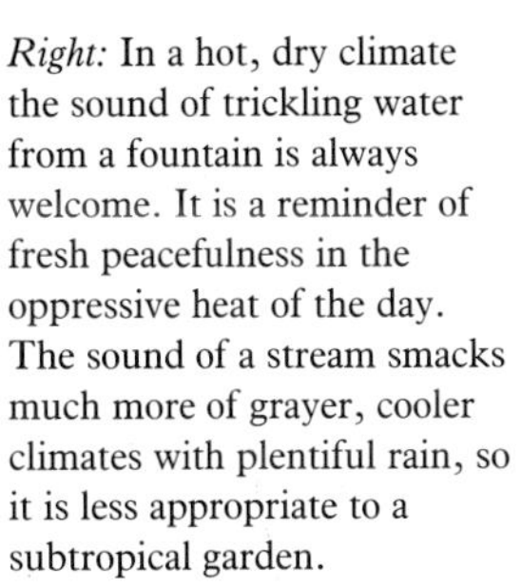

Right: In a hot, dry climate the sound of trickling water from a fountain is always welcome. It is a reminder of fresh peacefulness in the oppressive heat of the day. The sound of a stream smacks much more of grayer, cooler climates with plentiful rain, so it is less appropriate to a subtropical garden.

Above right: The dry heat of central America and Africa can be simulated by the use of succulents and cacti. Where soil would be expected to look dry, gravel or pebbles can be successfully used as ground cover. Select light shades of stones and other surfaces to suggest arid conditions.

Container

Never let it be said that container gardens are second best to gardens in the soil. They may be fairly labor-intensive, but, as a reward, they can be as rich and extravagant as your pocket and patience will allow.

Containers solve many problems for would-be gardeners. They are the answer for a paved town courtyard and a roof terrace ten stories high, and an excellent solution for people who cannot bend easily to dig. They are an ideal finishing touch: an array of window boxes can complete a house front. Whatever the reason, the choice of containers is enormous.

However, certain ground rules need to be borne in mind. You need to consider the work involved in occasional changes of soil and the ease of access; most important of all, you need to consider watering. Do

Above: Pelargoniums provide a bright summer display in this formal garden. Pots of flowers are set into permanent containers allowing for change during the season. The empty pots provide winter ornament.

Right: Potted citrus trees are a feature of Italian gardens. The orangeries of English historic gardens were built to overwinter such trees which were then displayed outdoors during the summer.

the containers have adequate drainage? Is there a water supply nearby? Will you be able to use liquid feeds? What will happen if you are away for a week-end or on holiday? Watering is by far the greatest chore of container gardening and it needs to be done generously and regularly. Rain is never adequate on its own and can fool you into thinking the containers are wetter then they really are. Automatic irrigation is well worth considering for a large container garden.

Below: Alpines are the perfect plants for stone or imitation stone troughs. Although most of these plants need perfect drainage they will still need watering in dry weather.

It is important to decide whether to plant for a 12-month display or to let the containers remain empty during the winter. Remember that many plants which would be hardy enough in the ground may succumb to the cold when their roots are raised up in a container open to frosts. Frozen, waterlogged soil can also burst containers as it expands. Conversely, containers in sun can get very hot in summer and your choice of plants needs to be governed by this fact: it is all too easy to bake the roots of plants.

With these practical points in mind, you are free to choose from the gamut of container gardening styles. Formal courtyards can be graced with potted bays, sentinel cypresses, camellias or bamboos. In addition, some especially beautiful pots may look best not

planted but used as an architectural contrast. Large concrete planters can be filled with trees and shrubs, almost as if they were in the ground. Stone troughs can be planted as miniature gardens of alpines or screes, but they can equally be filled with a single carpeting plant as a piece of living sculpture.

In a more cottagey style, tubs, pots and even baskets of all shapes and sizes can be clustered to form splashes of color, by doorways or lining steps. Window boxes and hanging baskets blend in well with this style and provide an opportunity for bold or restful incidental planting in prime locations.

With the aid of a circulating pump, even water can be a feature of container gardens, either as a small fountain or trickling over pebbles from one container to another. Certainly such details add great charm.

Right and below: Container gardening need not be formal. A glorious clutter of interesting, well-filled pots can look splendid and can give a Mediterranean air to your garden. Only remember that every pot you use is another one to water. Hanging baskets are the hardest of all to keep moist. All sorts of containers make interesting planters so there is no need to stick to commercially available ones, as long as you remember to provide drainage holes. Copper wash-tubs or plastic-lined baskets make attractive tubs, and bought pots can be painted and decorated to suit the style of your garden, be it formal or informal.

Bottom: An arrangement of containers that is loosely symmetrical is a very appealing way of arranging a busy mixture of pots and harmonious plants.

Opposite, top and bottom left: A rigidly formal arrangement of containers is a useful way of accentuating strong, adjoining architectural features.

Opposite, bottom right: Pots and troughs, when well placed, are a form of sculpture in themselves. The effect is enhanced here by simple, single-species planting. The row of tulip-filled containers is sited to echo the curve of the parterre behind.

THE STRUCTURAL FRAMEWORK

Gravel and Bark

Gravel can be used to create practical and attractive garden surfaces. It has a smooth look about it and is easy to lay; it also has the advantage of being relatively cheap. Many people enjoy the satisfying crunching sound that it produces under foot, indeed, some use it as an early warning for anybody approaching the house. Gravel does, however, need a bit more care and attention than some other surfaces to keep it neat and in place as it is easily spread to adjacent lawns and flowerbeds, spoiling the effect.

Being a soft material, gravel flows around corners and is ideal for filling irregular shapes. In small gardens or courtyards, the whole ground can be covered with it, with plants growing through in one or two places for a natural look. Gravel can also be used to complement other materials such as brick, stone or grass, providing interesting textural contrasts.

The warmth of orange and brown gravels has a lot to recommend it in the garden, but there are also many gray and yellow chippings to choose from. In addition, plenty of gravels are made from local stone, and these are useful for tying up paved areas or walls made from the same material.

Gravel areas can benefit from a solid, fixed edge, such as a curb of stone or lengths of wood, to keep it in place, although for a less formal effect it can be left to merge in with surrounding areas, or the edges can be softened with overhanging plants.

Chipped or shredded bark is another popular material for creating visually and physically soft surfaces. Its somewhat unruly appearance and tendencies make it unsuitable for formal areas and, because of its natural affinity with wood, it is generally used in wilder parts of the garden. Bark is particularly suitable for woodland areas, where its color and texture blend in well with the trees.

Bark is one of the best materials to use in areas where children play as it is relatively soft. Heavier pieces of bark are better than composted bark, which is more like peat in consistency, and tends to be more difficult to control.

Bark and wood chips will not necessarily stay in place, even with curbing of some kind, as regular use by pedestrians and birds searching for worms will scatter it far and wide. Logs can be used to edge the area to provide some restraint, and these will be in keeping with the natural look of the surface.

The Japanese make the most of the amorphous nature of gravel in their tranquil gardens which are especially designed for contemplation. Here, a deep layer of gravel is laid and then raked into patterns, often swirling to resemble water flowing around stones. With sensitive treatment, these ideals can easily be transferred to any garden, provided that the surrounding areas conform with the stark, minimal approach of the Japanese original.

Left: In informal settings, gravel makes an ideal surface, flowing around flowerbeds.

Below: In a woodland setting, dark stones or bark make a soft, sympathetic path.

Gravel in formal gardens
Gravel is particularly effective when used in formal patterns where it can be mixed with other materials, such as brick (*left*). It fills the spaces naturally and lacks the harshness of concrete or other hard surfaces, and it has a visual affinity with grass. Different colors (*below*) can be used to enhance the pattern, but care must be taken to avoid the different gravels getting mixed up. Gravel should be raked regularly to maintain an even pattern and to remove debris such as leaves and twigs; any weeds should be uprooted.

Bottom right: Practical stepping stones can be incorporated into paths that are composed of gravel.

Above: Gravel is a versatile material, suitable for formal and informal settings. This elegant parterre is perfectly highlighted by the neat gravel path. The main disadvantage of the material is that stones tend to spread onto adjoining surfaces like lawns.

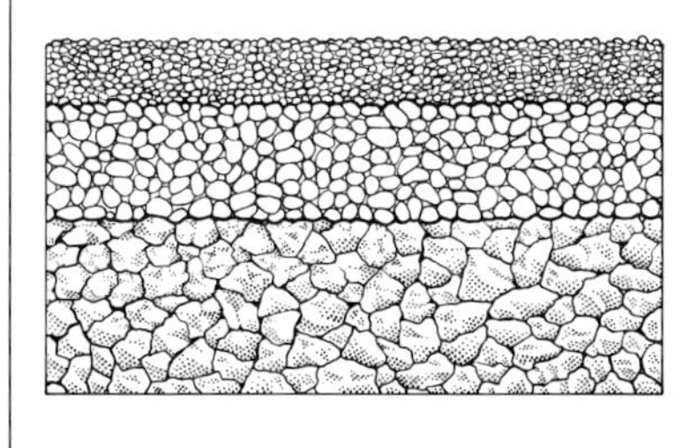

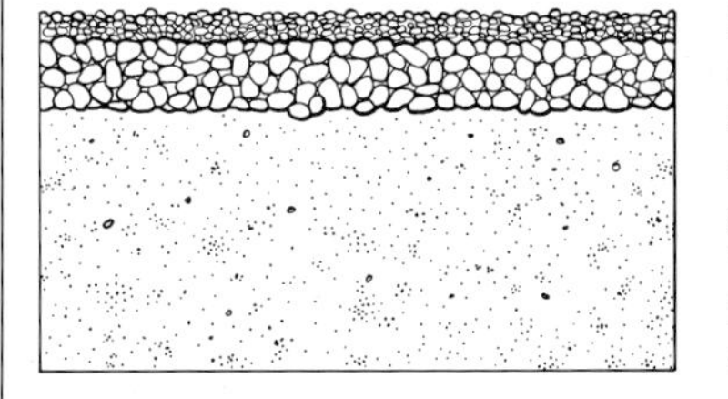

LAYING GRAVEL

Gravel can be laid in three ways; the last technique is the most durable. The first method consists of a 3in (7.5cm) base of well rammed coarse gravel covered with a 2in (5cm) layer of compacted coarse gravel, with a final 1-2in (2.5-5cm) top covering of finer gravel, rolled flat for a good finish. The second involves a 3-4in (7.5-10cm) layer of mixed clay and stones over which is spread and rolled about 1in (2.5cm) of compacted gravel, scattered with loose gravel. The third method, for a hard-wearing finish, involves a base of concrete covered with tar and gravel.

Gravel Although the individual stones in gravel vary in color and size, they present a very uniform surface which usually looks fresh and uncluttered. This clear-cut quality can be seen in the surround to this pool (*left*). The band of gravel helps to emphasize the clean lines and serenity of this formal feature; few other materials would be as effective. The gravel surround of the circular flowerbeds (*below right*) also produces a clean finish, the surface providing an ideal background for the hard lines of brick and the softer inner circle of hedge. As well as being decorative, the circular brick edging is a functional barrier that prevents the gravel from spreading.

Bark Bark is not an elegant surface material but it has a soft appearance that can be reassuring to the eye. Its physical properties correspond to the visual impression it makes. It can be particularly useful where children run and play. Bark is also a good material for creating contrasts with hard surfaces. Where beds are top-dressed with gravel, as in rock gardens (*above*), bark makes a good choice of pathing material. It can also be used to create a bridging area between two different surfaces, such as decking and grass (*right*).

Decking

Part way between a hard surface and a soft one, timber is very much in harmony with the garden, and timber decking (areas of wooden planking) is used a great deal for constructing areas of relaxation. Decking can provide terrace space either at ground level or, in some cases, higher up.

Timber is a versatile material and it can easily be cut and shaped to create a wide variety of designs. Most decks are built just above ground level, but they really come into their own when built on hillsides so that they project out as high platforms, giving elevated views of the garden and the surrounding countryside. With such platforms, it is possible to leave holes in the decking through which the branches and tips of the trees below can emerge, giving the impression that you are sitting high up in the tree tops. With houses that are built on steep slopes, this is the only realistic way of creating a flat area immediately outside the house without major earthworks being involved to level the site.

As decking is relatively light, it can be used at an even higher level on the roof to make an ideal sitting-out area or roof garden, and the added advantage here is that it protects the roof below from wear and tear. Decks at all levels can also have pergolas constructed above them to give the feeling of a veranda. If climbing plants are grown over at least part of the structure, they will provide a cool and shady area to enjoy during hot, sunny days.

A much more exotic kind of deck can be built in trees, usually in the form of tree-houses. These have a special appeal for children, but people of all ages find them fascinating. Of prime importance is safety, both in the strength of the structure and the construction of safety rails around the edges. It goes without saying that the tree must be sufficiently large, sturdy, healthy and mature to take the weight of the deck and a number of occupants.

Structures at ground level are well within the capabilities of most people. The decks should be supported on joists which in turn need to be supported by brick or concrete piers or walls; a damp-proof membrane should be placed between the joists and the piers or walls. All the wood must be treated with preservative, which is available in a variety of colors. Higher structures, especially those on sloping hillsides, are likely to need the aid of an architect or structural engineer in their design. If in doubt, seek professional advice when constructing any deck, so as to avoid accidents.

Wooden decking The versatility of decking means that it can be used as a single surface (*left*) or stepped over several levels on sloping ground (*below*). It can merge into the rest of the garden or it can be enclosed and used as a courtyard. If a large expanse of decking is used in combination with groups of tables and chairs, it can serve as an open-air room, with a floor but no containing walls.

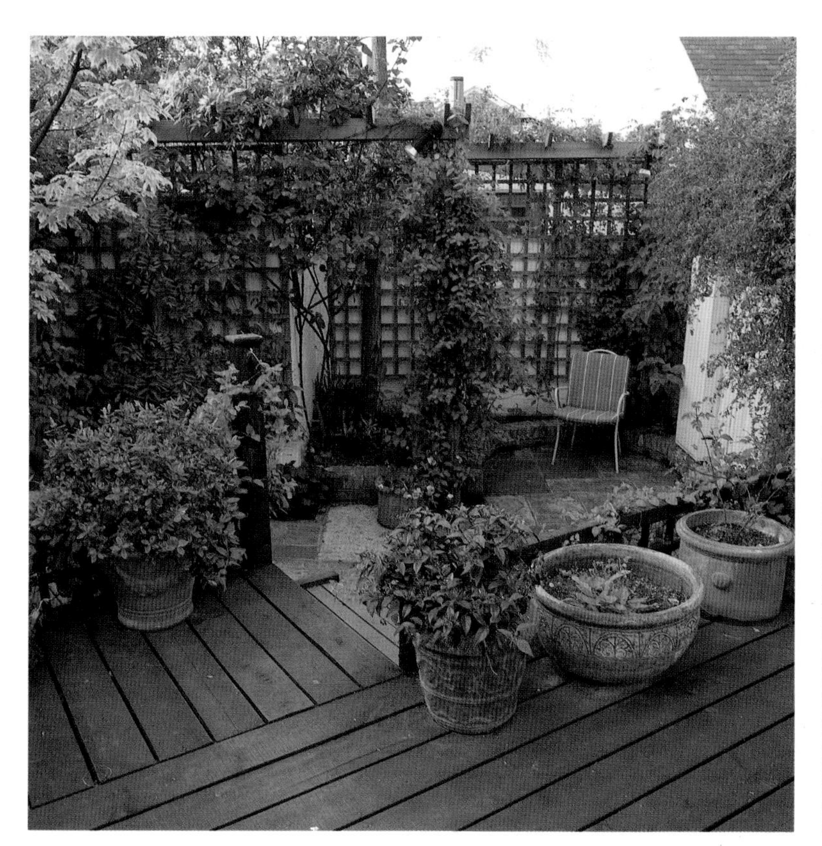

Left and below: Decking makes an excellent surface for roof gardens and can form the basis of an attractive retreat. It is pleasant to look at and, because it spreads the load, can prevent the underlying roof from being damaged. There is no reason why decking, like other surfaces, should not be decorated with containers (*left*). Plants can be grown in pots and tubs, and these can be moved around and replanted with the changing seasons. Climbing plants can be grown up posts and trellis. Decking can also be used as an extension of the living area (*below*); there is plenty of room for outdoor furniture.

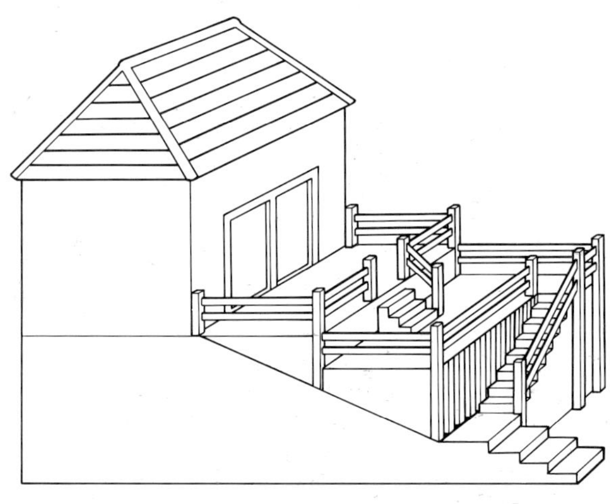

Variations on decking Wood is a very versatile material and can be used in situations where it would be difficult to use other materials. Deck construction is relatively easy and, compared with building materials such as concrete, timber is light. This means that structures and level surfaces, often as platforms, can easily be erected on problem slopes in the garden that might otherwise be difficult to maintain. On a steep site it may be desirable to create a series of terraced decks to cover most of the slope (*left*). Various additions can be made to the platform of a deck. More interest can be created with guard rails that are not only functional but decorative (*below left*). Built-in furniture – seating and possibly a table – can also be added. Either the whole or part of the deck can be covered with slats, in the style of a pergola (*below right*); this is particularly appealing in hot climates where cross-pieces can support a variety of climbing plants.

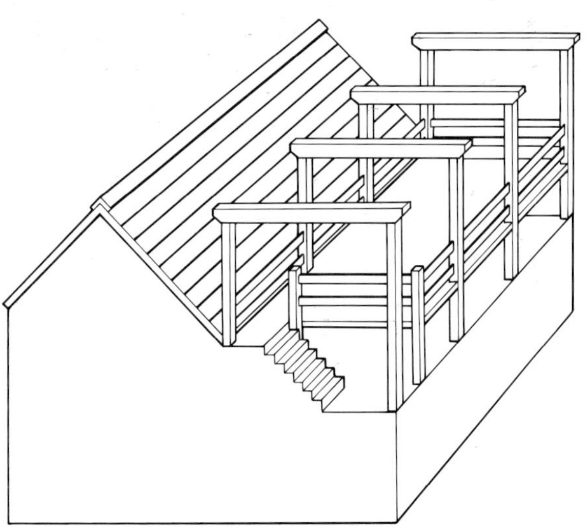

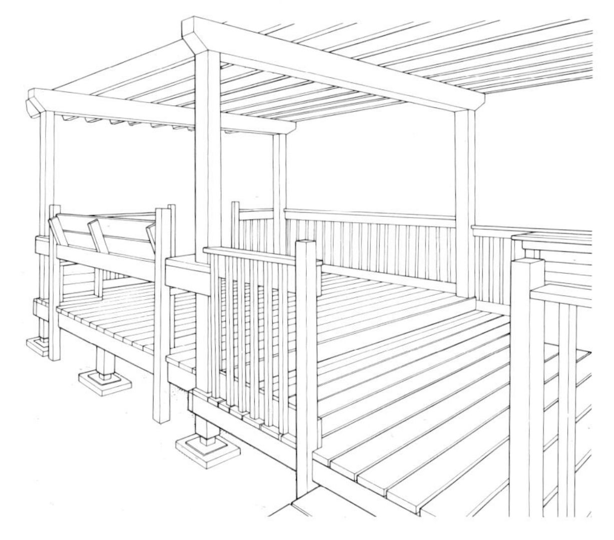

SAFETY AND CONSTRUCTION

Great care must be exercised in the design and construction of decks since they can be very dangerous, especially in wet weather. They must be well-built, made with the best and strongest materials, and securely attached to firm foundations. Those decks built above ground level should have a handrail, and any steps and planting holes should be well-illuminated or edged with a painted white line.

Most decks are likely to be built of softwood; cedar is a good choice as it is hard wearing and splinters relatively little. The natural resins in softwoods act as an effective preservative against rot. If a deck becomes slippery in shady areas and wet weather, the addition of a wood preservative will help to keep moss and algae at bay. Alternatively, brush the surface regularly with a stiff garden broom or apply an algicide, or nail small-mesh galvanized chicken wire over the deck. Treat steps in a similar manner. Any broken or rotten boards must be replaced immediately.

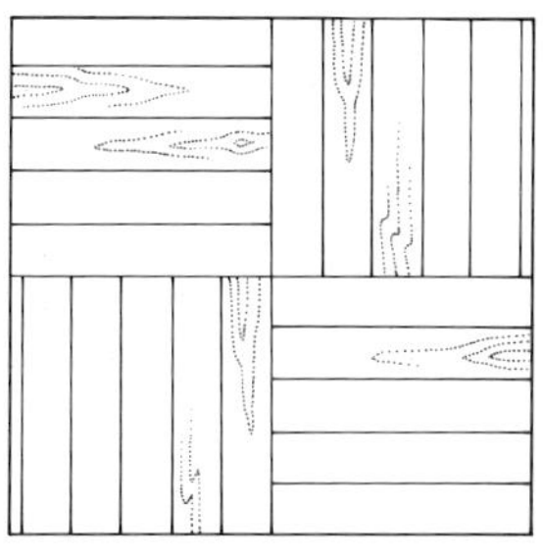

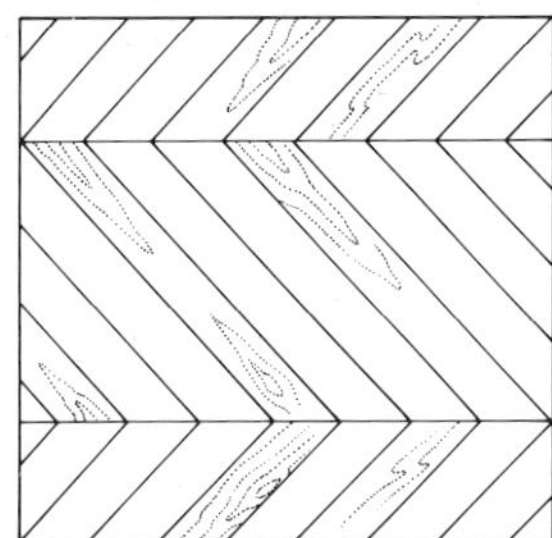

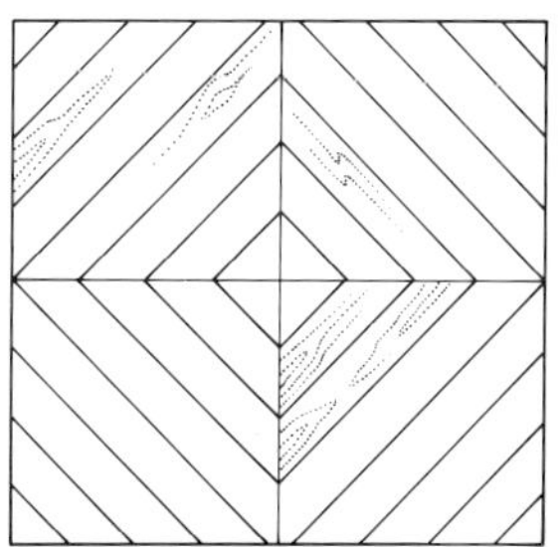

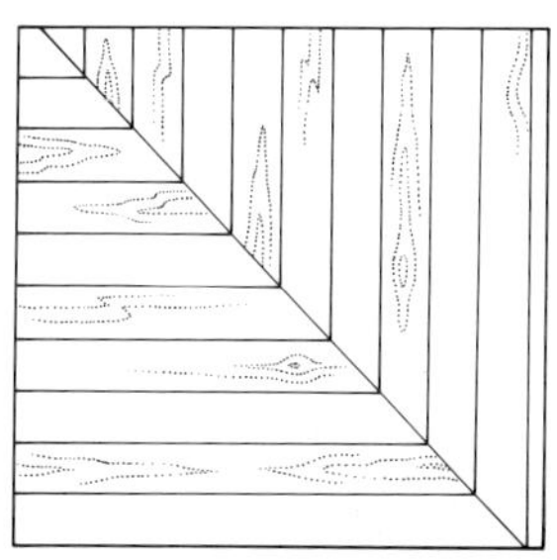

Patterns *(left)* The planks of decking do not have to be laid in simple parallel lines. There are numerous patterns to choose from and these can be highly decorative. With complex patterns it is essential to work out the framework below the deck so that all the planks are supported.

Top left: Decking can be used to create a clean, neutral finish that is easy to live with. Here, an uncluttered deck, sporting some modern furniture, provides a sitting-out area beside a pool. The simple parallel lines of the planking are offset by the planting of pampas grass beyond.

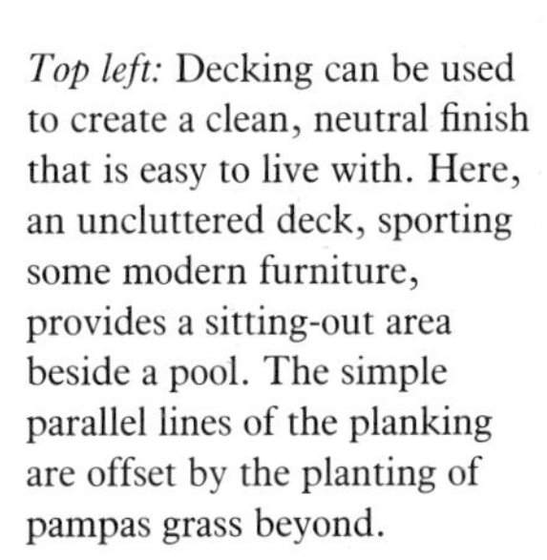

Left and above: It is much better to define the edge of an area of decking rather than allowing it to tail off. These two treatments are very different. The straight line *(above)* mixes well with the foliage, while the log-palisade finish *(left)* blends perfectly with the stones and water.

Paving Stones

Areas that are constantly used, like paths and patios, are best made with a hard surface. Paving stones are a convenient and relatively cheap method of covering both large and small areas.

The choice of paving will depend on many factors, including the character of the garden and other materials used, as well as cost. The best slabs are undoubtedly of real stone which are often particularly attractive. Unfortunately this, and stone in general, is very expensive, although occasionally it is possible to buy second-hand slabs at a more reasonable price. Reconstituted stone and concrete slabs are readily available and much cheaper, but imitation natural stone and colored stone should be used sparingly as they can look rather garish. Brightly colored slabs are visually uncomfortable to live with in gray climates, where their brilliance is likely to jar with the rest of the garden; accordingly, they tend to look better in hot, sunny climates. When they are used, colors should not be mixed as this will create a restless pattern in what should be a restful area. Plain concrete slabs will make a more subdued surface, especially when they have begun to weather and take on the patina of age, which, as a rule, is a very useful quality.

Paved areas should be almost level, with enough slope to allow water to soak away, either to a drain or into the garden. The larger the slabs, the easier they will be to lay, although weight may prove a hindrance. Avoid using small slabs if covering a large area, to reduce the amount of work and time involved. Slabs can be laid in regular patterns, either like a chessboard or offset from each other, like brickwork. Varying sizes can be employed to create irregular but more interesting designs, and broken slabs can be used to create crazy paving, but this must be done well in order to be a success.

The difficulty with using paving stones is that they are not easy to lay in irregularly-shaped areas. One way around this is to fill as much of the space as possible with whole slabs, and leave the edges free for an alternative material, such as cobblestones embedded in concrete. In larger areas of paving, it is possible to break the monotony by leaving out the occasional stone and planting the space instead. Alternatively, large tubs or urns can be placed in appropriate positions, but if the containers are heavy and the paving is not laid on a base of coarse gravel, the slabs may sink, creating an irregular, dangerous surface.

Left and above: Paved areas in the form of patios and terraces are indispensable close to the house (*left*). These surfaces should be level and even, and suitable materials for such surfaces include paving slabs and bricks. Different colored slabs can be used if the tones are muted. Concrete is practical and easy to lay, but a large expanse of it can be hard on the eye. Solid foundations are needed for most main pedestrian areas and wherever heavy plant pots and furniture are likely to be positioned. Leave uneven surfaces (*above*), however attractive they might be, for areas that receive little traffic; they are excellent for an informal finish.

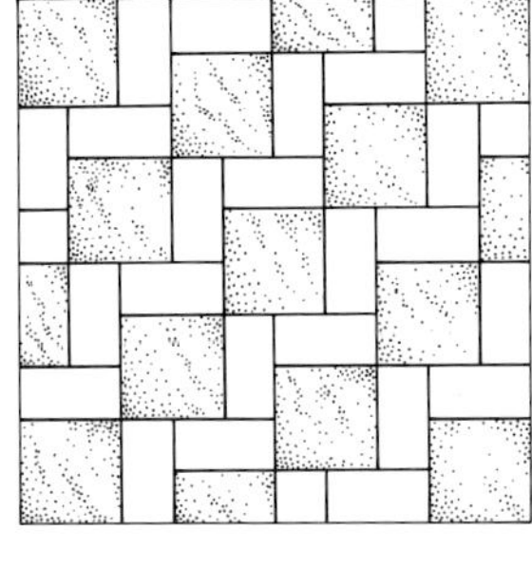
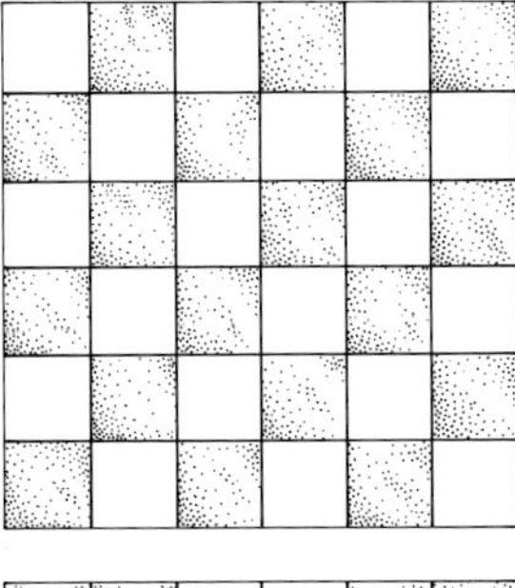

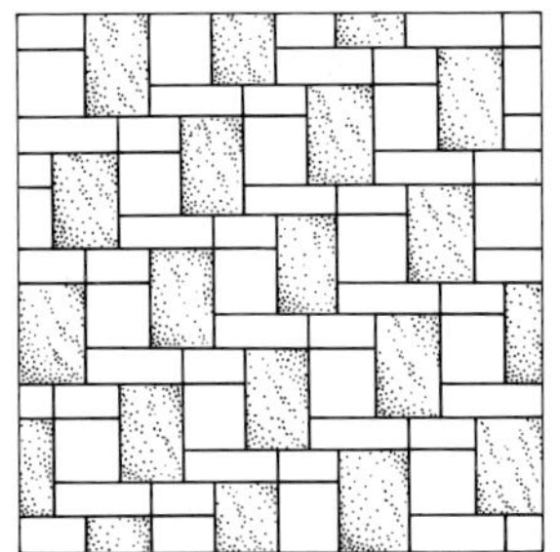
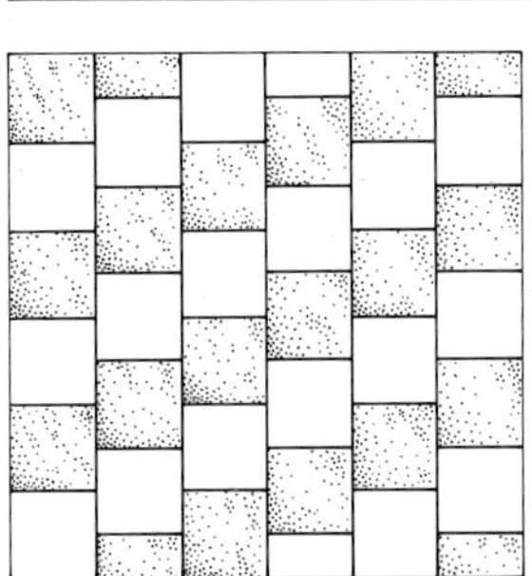

Paving slabs *(above)* Concrete slabs are available in a wide variety of sizes and colors. The simplest designs *(top right and bottom right)* have the advantage of being easy to lay. They blend in with their setting more readily than complicated and difficult patterns *(top left and bottom left)*, a point that is relevant in areas designed for relaxation. In the right place, however, detailed patterns can be interesting to look at and their creation can give a lot of enjoyment. It is best to work out the pattern on squared paper before buying slabs so that the exact requirements can be calculated. Lay out all the slabs before securing them, then the whole pattern can be seen. Only cement them into place when you are happy with the effect.

Left and above: Paving slabs are suitable for surfaces in both formal *(above)* and informal *(left)* garden designs. When paving has been newly laid it can stand out rather starkly; it tends to look better if covered with lichen, which gives it the patina of age. An informal effect is created when plants are allowed to flop over the edges and grow between the cracks of the paving.

LAYING PAVING

If the surface of the ground is well compacted and the paving slabs large, it is possible to lay them directly onto soil using sand to level them. However, if there is any risk of the slabs sinking then it is best to lay a base of coarse gravel first.

Take off the sod, dig down to below the frost line, and lay any drains that might be necessary. Next, level the site, allowing a gentle slope as little as ½in per 3½ft (1cm per 1m) in one direction, preferably away from any buildings, towards a drain or flowerbed. To level the site, place a peg in one corner of the area so that the top is at the desired level of the surface of the sand that will support the paving slabs. Mark the proposed levels of the soil and coarse gravel on the peg. Place similar pegs at 6ft (1.8m) intervals across the site, and check they are level by spanning adjacent pegs with a length of wood bearing a spirit level. The tops of the series of pegs should reflect the line of the gentle drainage slope.

Once the ground is level, compact the soil and ram down a 4in (10cm) layer of coarse gravel to form the foundations of the paved area. Next, lay a 2in (5cm) layer of sand, raking and rolling it until it is level with the tops of the pegs. The slabs can then be laid directly onto the sand. Check that each slab is level using a spirit level, making allowance for the drainage slope, before going on to the next one.

Do not set the slabs too close together as this will draw attention to any irregularities in their shape. Short strips of wood can be used as spacers between them so that an even gap is left around each slab, but check the slabs by eye to make certain that they are aligned in all directions. The joints can be pointed to help prevent grass and other weeds growing up between the slabs: brush dry cement or sand over the surface until all the gaps are filled.

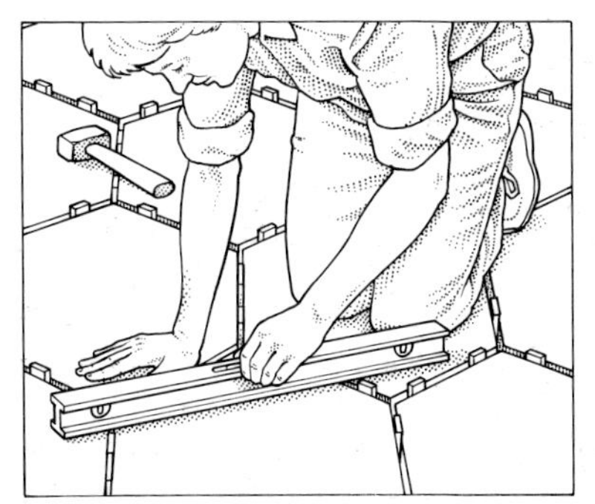
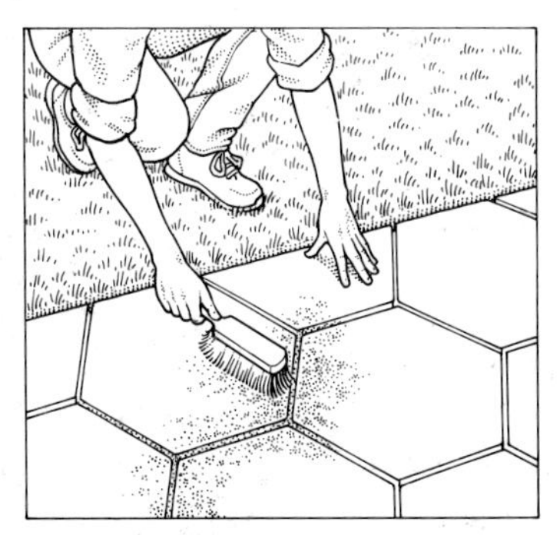

LAYING CRAZY PAVING

Choose the pieces of paving carefully so that they fit together reasonably well, like a jigsaw puzzle. This will create a more attractive surface as it will reduce the amount of cement needed to fill the joints in between each piece. Try and use the same type of material throughout; any variations in color and texture have to be handled well to look good.

Bed down each piece in cement and make sure each paving stone is level before laying the next one. Try not to use small pieces around the edge of the area as they can easily become detached. Alternatively, lay some form of curbing or edging.

Once in position, point the joints between the slabs with mortar.

The shape of paved areas When laying out paving there is no need to restrict yourself to rectangular shapes. Broken and irregularly-shaped slabs can be used to make crazy paving (*top and bottom middle*), which can be fitted into almost any shape. Rectangular slabs can themselves be shaped or interstices can be filled with other materials. There is great variety in the paved areas illustrated above, although rectangular slabs have been used in most of the designs.

Bricks and Tiles

Brick is ideal for surfaces and paths within the garden. It is a sympathetic and versatile material and its color and texture mellow well, blending in with most designs. Bricks can be laid in a variety of patterns, both simple and complex, either used on their own or in conjunction with other materials.

Bricks are available in a wide range of colors; if possible, select a tone which fits in well with the color of the house and any other nearby structures. Avoid white bricks as these are likely to stain and become rather unsightly with time, while frost-proof housebricks are a good choice as they are readily available and should last well. Clay brick pavers offer more scope in shape and design than housebricks; they come in a variety of colors and textures and are best used for decorative surfaces. Granite blocks can also be used, either on their own or mixed with other materials; these are extremely hard-wearing cubes of gray stone which are similar to bricks but slightly irregular in shape. They can be laid in many herringbone, weave and circular patterns in the same way as brick, but the resulting surface will be a little uneven, which can make chairs and tables unstable.

From a safety point of view, bricks can be very slippery, especially if they fall in the shadow of a north wall, which encourages the growth of moss and algae. These can be removed by vigorous and regular sweeping or with an algicide. Tiles too can be very slippery, and for large outside areas it is best to use non-slip ones to avoid any accidents.

Tiles are made of hard-fired clay and, depending on the composition of the clay and the temperature of the firing, they can be very durable. Quarry tiles are popular for paving; these are unglazed, geometric in shape (usually square or octagonal) and regular so they can be used to make formal, smooth surfaces. However, they are very difficult to cut and should be reserved for areas with long, straight edges rather than complicated, curved perimeters.

For a more decorative effect, use glazed paving tiles which come in different shapes and colors, often with painted motifs or designs. The more decorative tiles look best in the strong sunlight of hot climates. As glazed tiles are both fragile and relatively expensive, they should only be used in small quantities. Fragments of tiles can be used to make floor mosaics.

Brick and tile patterns It is easy to create a wide range of patterns and designs with bricks and tiles because the units are relatively small. Specially shaped and colored tiles (*above*) can be used to make unusual three-dimensional patterns. More conventional bricks (*right*) can be used to produce quite complex designs, although it may be necessary to trim them. The use of more than one color extends the range of design possibilities.

Concrete

Concrete is a hard, unyielding material that is used in the garden as a foundation for structures as well as a surface in its own right. Like tarmac and asphalt, it is mainly used for drives and other hard-wearing areas, particularly those around sheds or greenhouses to make large, flat surfaces for storing or mixing materials. In spite of its rather cold and unattractive appearance, it does have the advantage of being cheaper than most other paving materials; it is also very strong – particularly if it is reinforced – and relatively easy to lay compared to other surfaces.

Concrete does not look attractive enough to be used on its own in areas intended for relaxation, especially if it is introduced in large, unrelieved expanses. It will eventually acquire the patina of age, but this will take several years and will never fully disguise the harsh appearance of the material. However, concrete can be made to look much more acceptable and less harsh if its surface is brushed while still damp to reveal a pebble or gravel aggregate. This mellow, soft appearance is better suited to a garden setting.

There are other ways of texturing concrete to make it look more interesting. On some even surfaces it is possible to press objects, such as strong-veined leaves, into the freshly laid concrete so that a decorative impression is left when they are removed. Alternatively, designs, abstract or otherwise, can be drawn in the semi-wet concrete, but these must be done well to be successful. Do not forget that it is virtually impossible to remove any marks once the concrete has set. Avoid making the impressions too deep as they will only create an uneven surface, unstable for furniture, and the grooves will collect dirt and water. Make sure there are no rough edges.

Concrete can be used in association with other materials; small areas can be decorated with large pebbles or cobblestones which are embedded in the wet concrete to create a pattern (see page 123). This may be uncomfortable to walk on, but it does make an attractive surface for a little-used spot. Concrete can also be tarred and covered with gravel while the tar is still wet, giving it a permanent gravelled surface. Alternatively, it can also be colored by the addition of special pigments, but this is rarely satisfactory as the finished result can look too garish and artificial for the natural garden environment and its plant life.

Improving concrete Concrete is a harsh material for the garden but it will look softer and more sympathetic if treated before drying to expose its aggregate, thereby creating a patterned, textured surface (*left*). Another way to make concrete blend in more effectively is to split it up into small units (*above*). Here, the use of long slabs, softened with plants and interspersed with stones, is a very effective way of breaking up the surface.

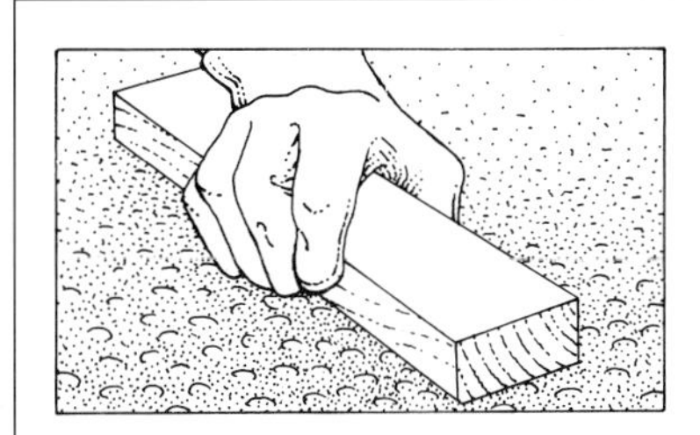

EXPOSED AGGREGATE

Scatter dampened pebbles or gravel over the freshly laid concrete and tamp them down. After the concrete has hardened, but not quite set, use a stiff scrubbing brush and a gentle spray of water and brush away the concrete to expose the aggregate.

Above: These textured square concrete blocks look like granite blocks.

Below: Circular concrete stepping stones make attractive small units.

Right: A large area of concrete can be brushed while wet, to expose the aggregate, and impressed with lines, thus suggesting crazy paving.

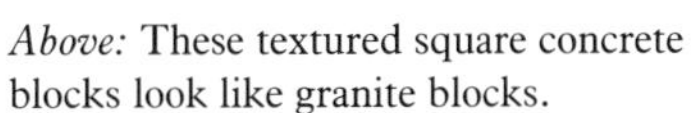

LAYING CONCRETE

The area to be concreted should be dug out to below the frost line and the final extent should be marked out on all sides using wooden forms. These are made from planks of wood nailed to upright posts and they enclose the ground that is to be covered. The top of the planks marks the finished level of the concrete, therefore it must be accurate, allowing for a slight slope for rain water to run off.

Coarse gravel is laid and rammed down to a depth of 3in (7.5cm), on top of which is laid the same depth of concrete. The concrete must be levelled-off; this is done by tamping it down with a length of wood that extends right across the width of the site, with the form as a depth guide. Pebbles or cobblestones can be embedded or simple patterns made in the semi-wet concrete for a more decorative finish.

In wet or frosty weather, the concrete must be covered until it has set. The wooden forms can be removed after about a week, and the concrete can be walked on once it is fully set, a few days after the forms have been taken out.

If the area is extensive, it may be necessary to lay the concrete in several sections, each one being laid in turn with a separate form. After the planks have been removed, the gaps left behind must be filled with a proprietary expansion compound for a smooth finish.

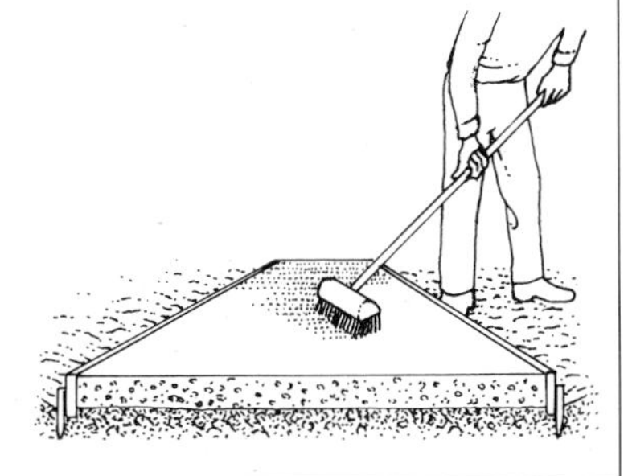

Mixed Materials

An exciting way of using materials is to mix them. Different materials are particularly useful for emphasizing various aspects of a design; they can break up large expanses into smaller plots and accentuate different levels, as well as defining a change of purpose in an area. Contrasting materials set in geometric patterns can act as guidelines; parallel lines of bricks set lengthways in paving will lead the eye towards some focal point, a statue or a view for example, but laid in intricate patterns, they will act as a focal point in their own right. Either will enhance the design.

Whatever is done, the imaginative use of materials will give the garden a unique and personal character, but mixed materials should be handled sensitively and not overdone for the greatest effect.

There are many combinations of materials that can look very pleasing, creating areas of excellent textural contrast. Brick and stone slabs, for instance, complement each other, as do brick and gravel, and stone and gravel. Blocks of tiles can be laid on their edges in a paved area; cobblestones set in concrete can be used on their own to cover small areas or they can be mixed together for a patterned surface. They can also be combined with other materials such as brick, granite blocks and stone in durable, attractive designs.

Scraps of left over materials from other projects can be combined and used in much the same way as crazy paving. Be careful not to make a main path too irregular and avoid combining materials that deteriorate at different rates as this may make an uneven, dangerous surface; wood is likely to rot before any surrounding brick or stone has crumbled.

Sometimes artefacts can be incorporated with dramatic effect. For example, a millstone can be embedded in the center of an area of gravel or cobblestones and surrounded by radiating circles of bricks, granite blocks or tiles set on their edges.

Mixed materials look better once the surface has aged and mellowed. Often the brashness of new materials can clash, the brightness of newly-cut sandstone with raw brick, for instance, but once they have weathered, they will become aesthetically more compatible. Lichen and moss will help to blend materials together; these can be encouraged by coating the appropriate surface with a thin solution of cow dung and water or liquid seaweed fertilizer.

Left and above: A paved area can look interesting if more than one material is used in its construction. A certain amount of skill is required to visualize the finished surface, but working it out on paper beforehand helps a lot. These circles of brick and crazy paving (*left*) are very effective but need careful laying. Pebbles of different colors can be laid in a great variety of designs, including flowers and triangles (*above*).

Above left: Paths that are not main thoroughfares can be more incidental in appearance. Stepping stones set in gravel are ideal for an informal path. Use stones with flat surfaces and try to ensure that they are set at a distance of a stride apart for comfortable walking.

Above right: An informal path of small paving slabs has been set directly on the earth. This casual method of laying means that the path can easily be moved, but it does create an uneven and therefore potentially hazardous surface, especially in wet weather.

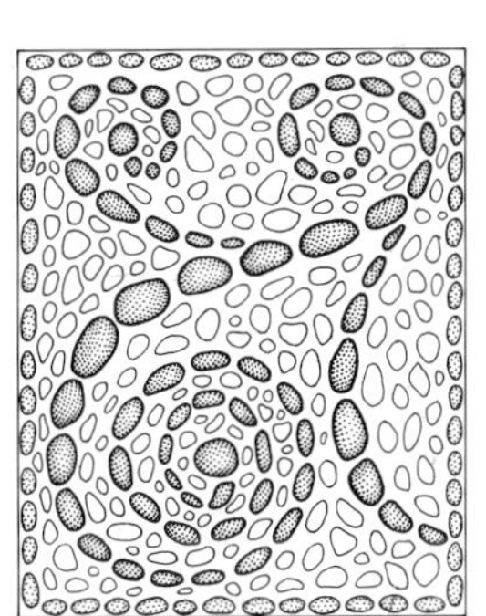

MOSAICS

Both abstract and figurative mosaics can be created using a variety of pebbles and cobblestones. Work out the design on graph paper, and recreate the pattern using different colored pebbles and stones in a mixture of sizes. These should be set in cement and firmed down.

Above: A delightful informal area has been created around a formal layout of circles and straight lines. This has been achieved by laying pebbles and intersecting them with paths of bricks radiating from a central water feature. The containers of plants have been placed on the brick lines for aesthetic reasons and they can be moved to make different patterns. The green of the foliage enlivens the surface.

MIXED MEDIA SURFACES

Some areas of the garden, such as large expanses of patio or terrace, or courtyards, can benefit from decoration to break up the monotony of an otherwise uniform surface. A combination of materials can be used to make attractively patterned and textured surfaces. Given the number of different materials available, the choice of colors and patterns is myriad. Surfaces can be laid to take pedestrian traffic or to form hard areas that are largely ornamental. Variations in shape and thickness have to be taken into account when laying and bonding materials. Large, heavy objects, such as millstones (*bottom*), can be laid directly on compacted earth or sand. In areas where there is light pedestrian traffic, bricks and whole paving slabs can be laid directly onto a sand base. In general, however, a firm foundation should be provided with a base of rammed coarse gravel. Bricks, pieces of stone slab, tiles, blocks or pebbles should be bedded in concrete laid over such a base. Smaller stones, such as gravel, can be left loose, but these, too, should be spread over a base of rougher, compacted stones. In pedestrian areas, the surface should be as near level as possible so that there is no risk of people tripping up. Unless they are flat, large pebbles bedded in concrete are very uncomfortable to walk on and are best confined to surfaces where there is little or no traffic.

Uncomfortable and hazardous surfaces Mixed materials can look very attractive but can be uncomfortable to walk on in anything other than heavy shoes. Avoid using irregular stones (*left*) or large pebbles (*below left*) in areas where there is a good deal of traffic.

Wood (*below*) can be mixed with other materials – bark is appropriate – but wooden surfaces can become very slippery and are best used on paths away from trees and shrubs. A covering of small-meshed galvanized wire netting is rather ugly but it gives a good grip.

Granite blocks Granite blocks are a very versatile and decorative form of paving. They can be used as solid paving on their own or mixed with other materials of a different color or texture. They can look particularly good with gravel or stone chips. The smallness of each individual unit allows granite blocks to be laid in various patterns, including complicated geometric designs (*left*) as well as much simpler linear schemes. The effective concentric circles of blocks (*below right*) echo the curve of the lawn and are cleverly complemented by the shaped bush; the circular bench around the tree adds the finishing touch. The principal disadvantage of granite blocks, however, is that they are not very pleasant to walk on in thin-soled shoes.

Above left: An advantage of materials that come in small units, such as bricks, granite blocks or pebbles, is that they can be used in a wide variety of patterns. With complicated geometric designs it is often sensible to draft the proposed configuration on paper first. An alternative course is to work the pattern out on the ground. Once the pattern is complete, a mixture of sand and cement can be worked into the gaps between each piece to bond the units together for an even surface.

Left: Interesting patterns can be made using large pieces of irregularly shaped stone. Usually the pattern can only be worked out on the ground with the available pieces of stone. Begin by selecting one or two key pieces and then fit other pieces around them, finishing off with some form of edging. This can be heavy work, even when lifting is minimized by the use of levers. The imaginative gardener can, however, produce a feature unique to his or her garden.

PATHS

Paths are important elements as they direct the eye as well as the foot. They are used in the garden for both practical and visual reasons. As well as providing a way for people to circulate, paths also form a framework, delineating lawns and individual flower beds or defining various parts of the garden.

As a practical feature, a path can be used regularly as a means of getting from one place to another; for example, from the gate to the front door. This type of path will receive a lot of heavy use, irrespective of the weather, and should be built of hard weather-proof materials so that it will stand up to the constant wear. On the other hand, a garden path is often more decorative than practical, to be used for slowly strolling along while admiring plants or chatting to a companion. This tends to be a fine weather activity and presents no real hardship to the surface; soft materials, such as bark, grass and gravel can be used.

From a visual point of view, the choice of materials will depend on what is sympathetic to the house and other structures in the area, and what is appropriate to the style of the garden. Paths must be constructed on solid foundations, with a slight camber (upward curve) to drain rain away from the surface.

Formal Paths

Most formal paths are intended to be used frequently and their construction should reflect this. One great fault with many paths is that they are too narrow. As a rule of thumb, such thoroughfares should be wide enough for two people to walk comfortably side by side. This is particularly true of paths that are made for ambling along, as nothing is worse than having to talk over your shoulder as you progress around a garden. Functional paths should be even more generous in width to allow easy access, and if you want to have plants spilling over the edges of the path, do not forget to make allowance for these decorative effects; pushing past wet or thorny bushes on the way to a gate or doorway is not pleasant and can be dangerous.

The shape or direction of a formal path will mainly depend on the overall design of the garden, but paths with a definite function should, on the whole, be straight and direct, otherwise people will start taking short cuts, especially between well-used areas such as the back door and the garbage cans, or the house and the garage. Paths meant for wandering along can be more serpentine; it is always rather exciting not to know what lies around the next corner. A meandering path can also give the impression that the garden is longer and wider than it really is.

Formal paths can be constructed from a wide range of materials. Close-clipped grass can look very stylish, but for a more hard-wearing finish, one of the most traditional and best-loved materials is brick. The relatively small size of each unit allows for a wide range of patterns to be used. If they are laid in lines along the length of the path they tend to accelerate the walker's pace and at the same time make the garden appear longer than it really is; bricks laid widthwise across the path have the opposite effect: they slow the walker down and make the garden seem smaller.

Stone slabs are another traditional material, one well-suited to older houses. The only drawback is that they are rather expensive. Concrete slabs can be used instead, but these tend to be harsh and unsympathetic to the eye. Concrete itself makes a very practical, if not particularly attractive, path; it is certainly more acceptable used in small rather than larger areas, but it should be left for the more functional paths. Its appearance can be improved by brushing the surface before it has completely set to reveal the aggregate (see page 121). Gravel, in spite of being loose, can be used for both formal and informal paths, but if it is to form the main pathway it must be well contained by edging or a curb of some sort.

All formal paths should be regularly checked for any weeds growing in or through them. The weeds can be removed by careful hand weeding, or an appropriate herbicide can be applied instead.

Straight paths Paths play an important role in the garden's design, as these three examples show (*left, above and right*). The treatment of paths can vary considerably and their impact will vary accordingly. All three of these paths are straight and yet they have quite a different effect on their surroundings. The materials, the edging and the positioning are all important factors in shaping a garden and creating its atmosphere. The gravel path (*left*) is the least formal of all the paths, the herringbone motif (*right*) is the most decorative, while the entrance path (*above*) is primarily functional, leading through the front garden to the gate.

Above: Granite blocks make a simple but effective diamond pattern in a gravel path.

Paths of mixed materials (*below*) The combination of two or more materials can totally transform a path into a very handsome feature. The attraction may lie in the pattern formed, the varying textures of the materials, their different colors or a mixture of all three. Care needs to be taken in getting a level surface; the path should preferably be laid on a solid concrete base. An edging that gives the path solidity can enhance the pattern.

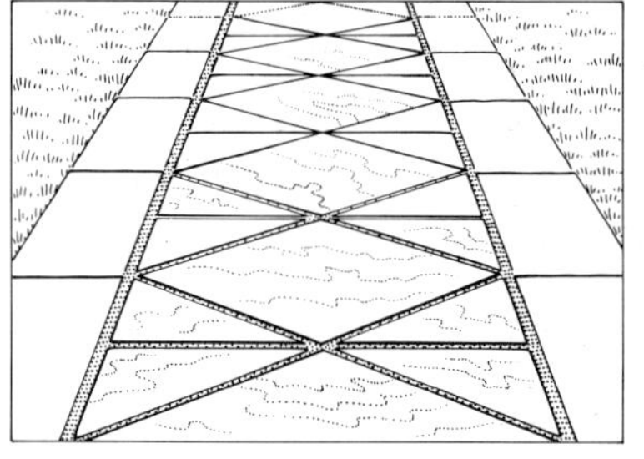

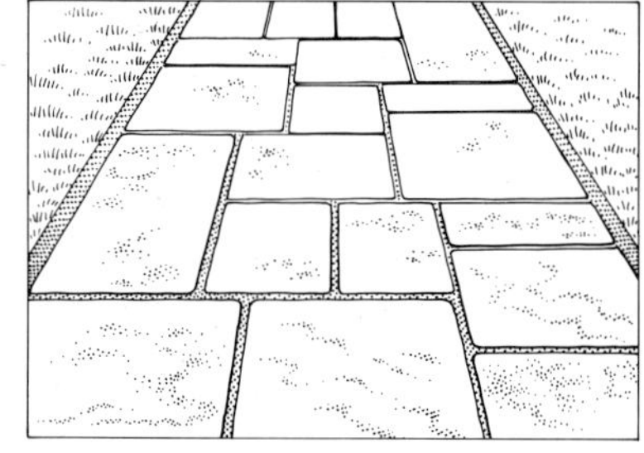

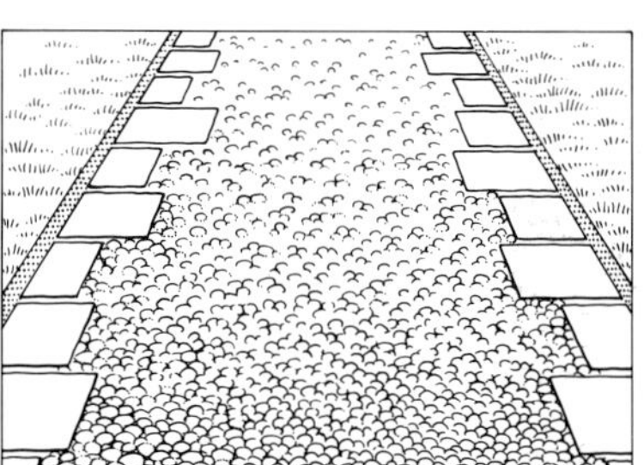

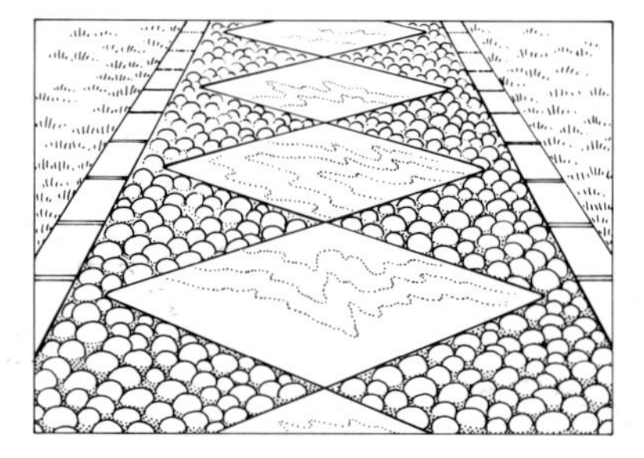

Above: When grass paths are well maintained, they are wonderfully soft to look at and blend sympathetically with plants.They are also relatively cheap to create. However, they do need constant mowing if they are to be kept in good condition. Such paths are not at their best in wet weather, being unpleasant to walk on and easily damaged. Plants cascading over them create brown patches and make mowing difficult, while paths that lie under trees can become bald. In spite of these drawbacks, in many situations grass is the only obvious material for paths; it is one of the best choices of pathing to use among shrubberies and borders for an informal, natural look. Paths that curve away, like the one above, are especially attractive, drawing the viewer on to see what is growing around the corner in the neighboring part of the garden.

Informal Paths

Some paths are markedly informal, both in use and in appearance, and they play a large part in giving a relaxed and casual feel to a garden.

One of the most informal pathing materials is chipped or shredded bark. This has a loose, shaggy appearance and looks very much at home in wilder or more neglected parts of the garden, especially woodland. Paths through woodland areas always look best if they are as informal and as natural as possible. This also applies to pathways through large areas planted informally with bushy shrubs.

Gravel or other stone chippings can look informal and decorative, especially if the path has no defined edges or if it is swamped with flowering plants. Indeed, planting has a lot to do with the style of a path, and the more the edges and line of the path are blurred, the more informal it will look. Gravel paths in particular look very good with a few plants spilling over them from neighboring borders. For safety reasons, regularly trim or cut back any vegetation that has become too abundant.

Delightfully informal paths can be created in an orchard, a meadow or a patch of wild garden by simply mowing a swath through the long grass. No preparation is needed for this natural pathway and the beauty of it is that you can change the direction of the path to create different routes and vistas every year without any trouble.

On a rather more practical level, many large flower borders need some form of access so that they may be tended. Such paths only have to be wide enough to allow the gardener to slip between the plants without causing damage to roots or growth. A similar path can be constructed along the back of a border in front of a hedge; wading through a lush growth of plants makes cutting a hedge very difficult and clearing up the resulting clippings all but impossible. The surface should not be made of any permanent material as there may be a need to change the route from time to time; a beaten earth track with a gravel topping is both simple and appropriate and cinders, a traditional country material, can also be used.

Left and above: Informal paths may make a more humble contribution to the garden than formal, main highways, but they help to create a relaxed and restful atmosphere. There is no urgency in their given course and they allow the garden to be enjoyed at leisure. They can be constructed of simple, plain materials, crazy paving being especially appropriate, as is rough-cut grass, ideal for wild, meadow-like areas.

Above, right and below: Informal paths appear to wander at will, leading into the heart of the garden's growth. Their natural flow helps to create a romantic atmosphere, which can be heightened by planting that softens their edges, merging vegetation and paths into an organic whole. Yielding surfaces, such as gravel, soft bark and grass, are more suitable than paving of stone, brick or concrete, materials which convey an impression of purposefulness that is more appropriate to main paths which are used a great deal.

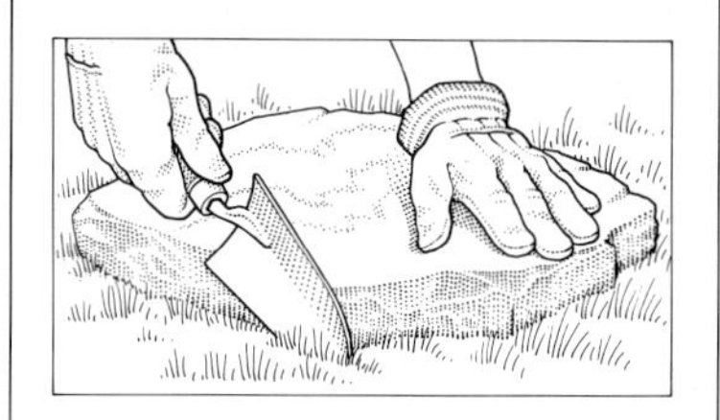

STEPPING STONES

Position whole or broken pieces of paving slabs and test the stride-length. Mark out the shape of each stone using a trowel and remove the sod. Lay the paving ¾in (1.5cm) below the surface of the lawn on a 1in (2.5cm) bed of sand.

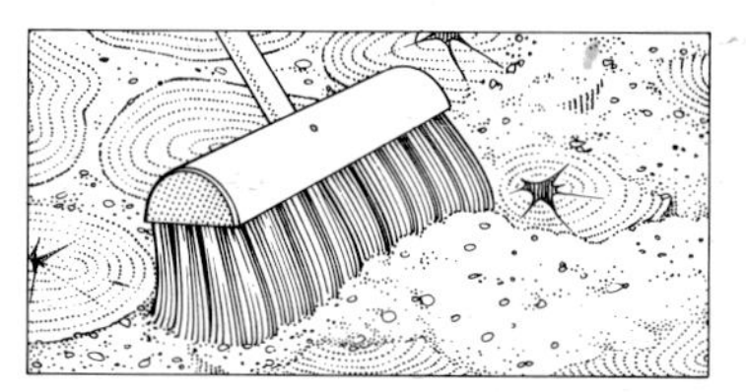

WOOD AND GRAVEL PATHS

An informal and attractive path can be made from logs and gravel; the wood should be treated with preservative. Make sure all the logs are the same height to ensure that the surface is even. Lay them close together, almost touching, on a sand and gravel base, and firm them down. The gaps between the logs should be filled with a mixture of sand and gravel, and the surface brushed with a stiff outdoor broom.

STEPS

Having more than one level, whether natural or man-made, can add considerable interest to a garden, but either ramps or steps are necessary to move from one point to another. Where the slope is gradual, a ramp or sloping path may be sufficient, but for steeper slopes steps are necessary, a curved flight being best for unusually steep ascents.

Steps make an exciting and dramatic feature in the garden. Standing at the top of a flight the lower area spreads before you, but approaching from below, the upper area may be wrapped in mystery until the steps have been ascended. Steps that curve up and away through bushes, with the top out of sight, give a touch of enticing secrecy to the garden, and few can resist the impulse to climb them to find out where they lead and what lies beyond.

It is important that steps should fit in with the look of the garden, and informal steps should be much more fluid and less severe than formal ones. Formal flights of steps are a structural feature, part of the basic framework of the garden, while informal flights are more of a decorative accessory. Formal staircases can be straight and angular or almost sculptural in concept, with double flights curving around to meet the lower level, or diverging to finish some distance apart. Informal steps can produce a gentle curve or a sharp zigzag, and they are usually less exposed than formal steps, perhaps hidden away in a corner of the garden, winding up a gradual slope.

As well as being functional, steps can also act as important focal points, drawing the eye towards them in expectation. It is essential, therefore, that as well as being structurally sound, such steps should be attractive and well designed.

A wide range of materials can be used to construct steps. Apart from cost, the main consideration should be to use materials that blend in well with the paths and other structures within the garden. Another vital factor to consider is safety; in certain places, most notably moist and shady sites, non-slip surfaces should be used whenever possible. As long as safety is not impaired, it is perfectly acceptable to plant up the sides of steps, even occasionally on some of the treads, although make sure enough of the tread is showing to enable the climber to ascend easily and securely, with a sure, uncluttered foothold.

Above: Informal steps have a "take-it-or-leave-it" air, but they are likely to lead somewhere interesting, like a hidden walled garden or a wooded area. They are most tantalizing when their full extent cannot be seen.

Left: Formal steps link different levels of a garden on a clearly defined axis in a definite and self-conscious way, even when the edges are softened by planting.

Formal Steps

Steps can either be built into a bank or slope or they can be constructed as freestanding structures that project out from a rise. The latter is a particularly formal device associated with a regular design, and is usually used in conjunction with highly finished retaining walls and terraces.

Formal projecting steps should be built on a grand scale as a small flight will look insubstantial and give the impression of being merely an afterthought. Since projecting steps form an integral part of the surrounding structures, they must be planned in advance. They are more difficult to construct than built-in steps because, being freestanding, they have to be self-supporting, whereas those built into a bank have their weight catered for.

Projecting steps are usually constructed from stone or brick and must be tied well into the adjoining structure. They are often constructed as part of a retaining wall and built at the same time. It is important that they are well built on good, firm foundations so they are safe and sturdy.

Stone and brick are the most appropriate materials for formal steps. Stone steps are undoubtedly the most visually satisfying but stone is an expensive material. Brick is very popular because, among other reasons, the small units make it very versatile to use. They must be frost-proof and match the materials of any nearby structures.

On a truly grand scale, grass can be used. It is best if grass steps are reinforced on the leading edge with bricks or some other solid material. They are very difficult to maintain because of the problem of mowing them, and they are also prone to wear and tear; depressions can be dangerous, making it easy to trip over the top of the solid riser. Wood is another option; leading up from decking, a flight of wooden steps is an excellent finishing touch. They should be made using a timber framework so that the treads are not in contact with the soil. Concrete, in the form of slabs or pre-formed step units, is suitable for formal designs, and it is possible to buy non-slip slabs which are useful for shady areas of the garden.

Above: There is no mystery in a short flight of steps but the materials used and the positioning of features can give it an individual character.

Left: A long series of steps is visually exciting, drawing the eye and enticing the garden visitor to ascend and explore. The mystery deepens when, as here, bushes obscure the full sweep of the steps. It is a good idea for long stairways to have flat "resting" areas at regular intervals. These can be more interesting if they correspond with cross-paths.

Ramps *(below)* In gardens where it is only possible to move from area to area by ascending or descending steps, it is often useful to incorporate a ramp. This may be to give access to wheelchairs (when a wide ramp would be needed), but it is more likely to facilitate gardening needs like moving wheelbarrows about.

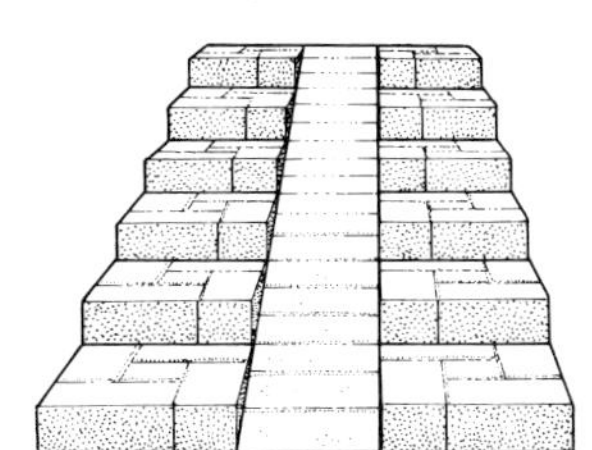

Above: Grass steps generally need to be on a grand scale; here, they look splendid with formally clipped hedging.

Left: Wooden steps have a light, ordered appearance that contrasts with foliage.

Below: Stone steps nearly always have a solid, safe appearance because the treads tend to be deep and the risers shallow. Here, the curved shape creates the impression that they are flowing through the gate, into the courtyard.

TYPES OF STEPS

There are two basic types of steps: freestanding and cut-in.

Freestanding steps are built between one flat area and another, and they are keyed-in to the retaining wall so that the two structures do not pull apart. They must be well-constructed and sturdy, built on a firm foundation. The steps should be laid on a base of approximately 4in (10cm) of coarse gravel and covered with a 4in (10cm) layer of concrete.

For cut-in steps, each step should have a foundation of well-rammed gravel. If you are using small paving material, such as brick or granite blocks, these should be set in concrete or cement and the joints securely bonded with cement. Concrete or stone paving slabs need to be bedded down on pads of cement on top of the gravel base.

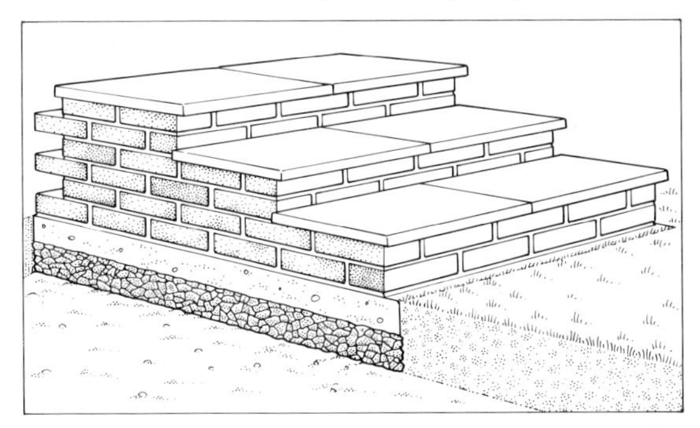

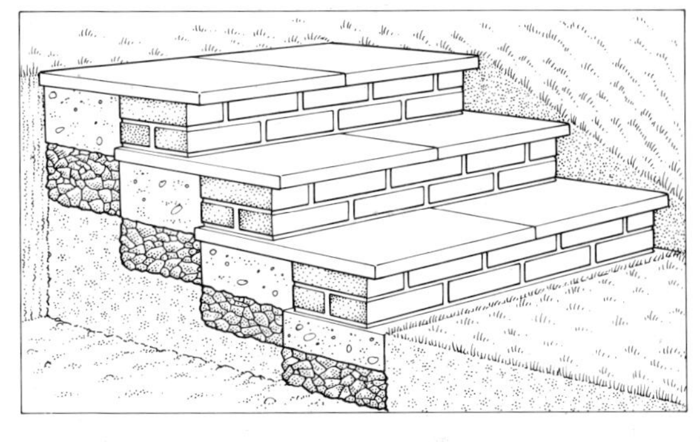

EDGING

Not all surfaces need to be edged but it often adds the finishing touch. In some cases, edging is used for purely ornamental reasons, but in others, edging is required to help keep the surface material in place, or even to hold back soil in flowerbeds. With brick surfaces, edging has a dual function. On the practical side, it helps to prevent the edges breaking away or sinking, and from a visual point of view, decorative edging can add considerably to the effect of a path or a more expansive paved area.

A brick surface can be edged in a variety of ways (see page 119), according to the look of the garden. A level course of bricks can be set in cement or concrete, but a more decorative effect can be created by sinking bricks into the soil at a 45° angle, to give a toothed effect. Many special edging tiles can be purchased for brick paths, especially mock Victorian styles which include those with scrolled tops, known as barley sugar tops, and those with a castellated finish. These look particularly good in small town gardens and in association with weathered brick or gravel.

Concrete is more difficult to edge. The most commonly seen edging is round-topped lengths of concrete, but these are rather municipal and not very attractive. A better finish is to use a row of granite blocks or even bricks positioned around the edge of the concrete area. Paving slabs need some form of edging, and a line of bricks or granite blocks can often add to the interest of the material. These should be laid flush with the surface rather than raised.

Gravel requires a raised edge to prevent the stones mixing with bordering soil. Any of the materials already mentioned can be used, although brick and granite blocks look the most handsome. In a more informal setting, use thin logs of wood.

Plants themselves can be used as edging. Low clipped hedges of box (*Buxus*) make very effective edging, especially to brick or stone. Other plants can be used for a more informal edge; lavender (*Lavendula*), for example, is ideal as it can be clipped into neat shapes; it is also deliciously fragrant and will perfume the air along the border or path.

Left and above: The linear or sinuous quality of a path is emphasized if it has a uniform edge. The line is broken if plants are allowed to flop over it at irregular intervals, although a row of a single species of plant, such as these hostas (*above*), will soften the line but highlight the whole sweep. Here, the rounded shape of the abundant leaves complements the geometric brickwork. Clipped hedges, for example of box (*left*), produce a harder line, ideal for a parterre or the borders of a knot garden.

Solid edges A solid edge of logs (*above*) gives a neat but soft finish. It can also act as a support for adjacent beds, to prevent them encroaching on the path. These colorful ceramic bricks (*right*) separate the soil from the gravel and complement the flowers. Individual stones (*below left*) also help to define a path precisely, while sunken edging (*below right*) allows for a well finished lawn.

Decorative edging Various forms of decorative edging (*right*) can be used for paths. Second-hand, frost-free bricks (*top row*) are among the cheapest materials; they can be laid in a flat row or angled for a serrated effect. The gaps between the vertical bricks can be filled with cement to make a small wall. The diagonal bricks can be left resting on one another with or without bonding. Bricks and tiles (*middle row*) define the edge of the path and also give it some support, especially if they are concreted or cemented into place. Edging tiles can be plain or ornate, with pretty decorative tops. They are ideal for a Victorian garden. Wire edging (*bottom row*) is versatile and can simply be pushed into the soil.

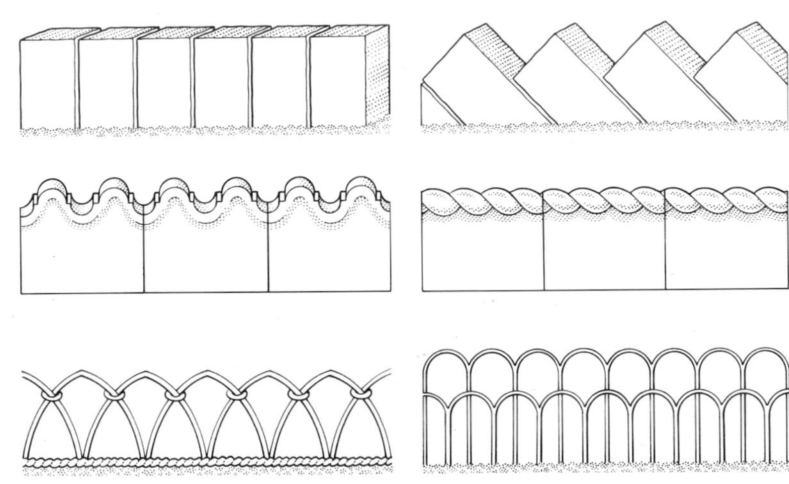

Left: Loose stones provide an effective surface for a sunken edge to a grass path; this recess allows a lawn mower to be run right along the edge.

Above: The barley sugar twist on Victorian tiles makes a lively boundary to a path, helping it race away out of sight.

Below: Edging to irregular paving can be soft, with plants used to disguise the irregularities, or pronounced, as shown by this strikingly shaped lawn.

Below left: Plants help to soften hard architectural lines. A mixture of plants makes an irregular edging while using a row of the same kind creates a more formal effect. Here, the bushy lavender almost forms a hedge containing the steps.

Below right: Edging is used to finish paths and paved areas and also to confine beds and borders. Here, uncemented bricks are used to form a circular surround to a small bed, with concentric circles of foliage and flowers.

BOUNDARIES

Unless you are lucky enough to have a ha-ha – that is, a sunken fence or deep, steep-sided ditch – around your garden, you will need to construct some form of boundary. The beauty of a ha-ha is that, unlike a barrier, it allows uninterrupted views, visually merging the garden and the countryside beyond into one continuous, harmonious vista.

Most gardens must have some form of physical barrier around them, partly to keep the world out and partly to keep the garden in. A boundary also defines the limits of a garden, and at the same time provides a backdrop for displaying plants and other features such as statues and decorative garden furniture. With the exception of hedges, most forms of boundary can be used to support climbing plants of one sort or another for a decorative effect. This allows the gardener to pick his own colors and textures to soften the harsh outlines of walls and fences.

The choice of boundary material will greatly affect the overall appearance of the garden. Although many fences, walls and hedges are used as screens, they should not always turn the eye inward; any vistas beyond the garden should be framed with well sited gaps in the boundary.

Hedges

Hedges make both good and bad barriers. On the positive side, they form a marvellous background to plantings, the colors and textures being fully complementary. They also allow the wind to filter through rather than creating a solid barrier which can cause wind turbulence. Hedge plants are relatively cheap to buy and no real skills are required in planting them. On the negative side, hedges may take several years to reach maturity and, having done so, they need regular maintenance in the form of trimming and feeding. It is also difficult to grow climbers over a hedge as this will interfere with clipping.

There is a wide range of hedging materials from which to choose. Some, such as yew (*Taxus*) and holly (*Ilex*), are evergreen and will form a permanent screen. Others, for example, hazel (*Corylus*) and hawthorn (*Crataegus*), are deciduous and so lose their leaves in winter, although some deciduous trees, notably beech (*Fagus*) and hornbeam (*Carpinus*), retain their brown and withered leaves throughout the winter. These make a dry rustling sound when the wind blows them, which appeals to some people but is thought to be rather menacing by others.

The color of hedges can vary considerably. There is a range of both coniferous and deciduous hedging plants that will give different shades of green, from dark to light and on through to yellow and even purple. Yellow and purple should be used with care; large blocks of light yellow can be too bright as a general background, while purple can be too solid and leaden. Yew and holly provide a somber green that is very good in a formal setting but can be a little oppressive in a small garden.

Tapestry hedges are an interesting option, but these are best used as a feature of the garden rather than just a background, since they are visually very lively and can be a little distracting. Here, a mixture of hedging plants are used, planted in alternating colors. Common green and copper beech are a popular choice for such hedges, but there are other equally pleasing color combinations.

Not all hedges need to be neatly trimmed and manicured. In gardens with plenty of space, informal hedges of rose (*Rosa*) or barberry (*Berberis*), for example, can be grown and left to take on their natural, wild-looking shapes.

Holly and thorny hedges like hawthorn and barberry deter unwanted visitors, but the thorns are a menace to the gardener if the hedges are planted near a border that needs weeding.

Previous page, left and above: As well as forming physical barriers, hedges help to define spaces, preventing the eye from being distracted by what lies beyond, thereby forming private secluded areas. They can also create a sense of mystery by hiding other parts of the garden; openings through them provide tantalizing and enticing glimpses. The autumnal coloring of certain hedging plants is another asset.

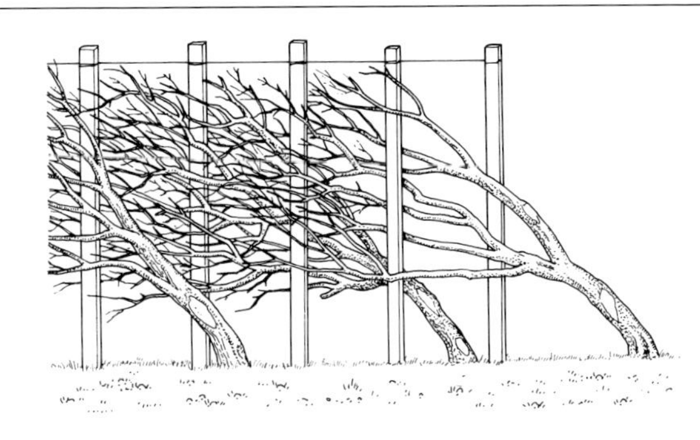

LAYING A HEDGE

An overgrown deciduous hedge can either be pruned back into shape or relaid as a new hedge. To relay the hedge, cut out any dead wood and thin the hedge (which will promote new, dense growth). Then cut halfway through the main stems, bend the tops over and weave them through a row of stakes. This will train in the old growth.

Top right and above: Although hedges are composed of living plants, they can be architecturally massive and dense, particularly evergreens, making wall-like enclosures that can create a feeling of isolation and security.

Above: An attractive, almost floating hedge can be created by planting trees behind a conventional hedge and then training them to form an upper tier. This creates an unusual and interesting hedging feature, one that emphasizes the horizontal element of the garden and allows only a partial view of what lies behind it. The horizontal layers will initially need to be trained along wires and branches from adjacent trees will need tying together. Lindens (*Tilia*) make ideal trees for this kind of training, which is known as pleaching. A heavier stilt hedge can be made from hornbeam (*Carpinus*). For this layered effect, the lower hedge is best planted on the sunny side; if a hedge does not get sufficent light it will be drawn and thin. This type of hedge casts an area of dense shadow so plants beneath must be shade tolerant.

TRIMMING

A hedge should be shaped as it matures. This is normally done by sloping the sides inwards slightly so that the top is narrower than the bottom. This shape is known as a batter.

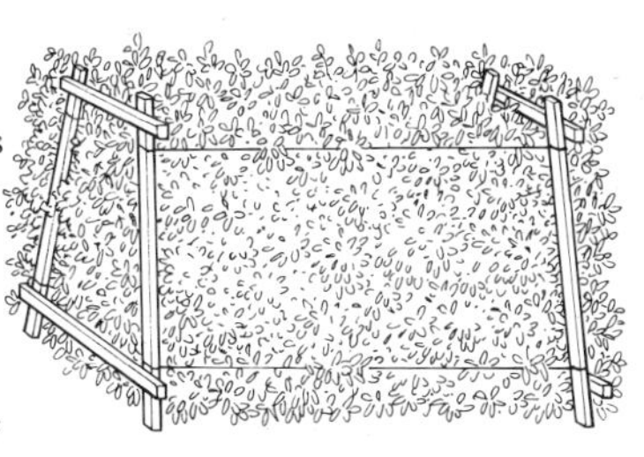

The reason for having a batter is to allow maximum light to reach the lower leaves so that they remain healthy and the hedge grows evenly. It also prevents too much snow weighing on the top and splitting the hedge open in winter.

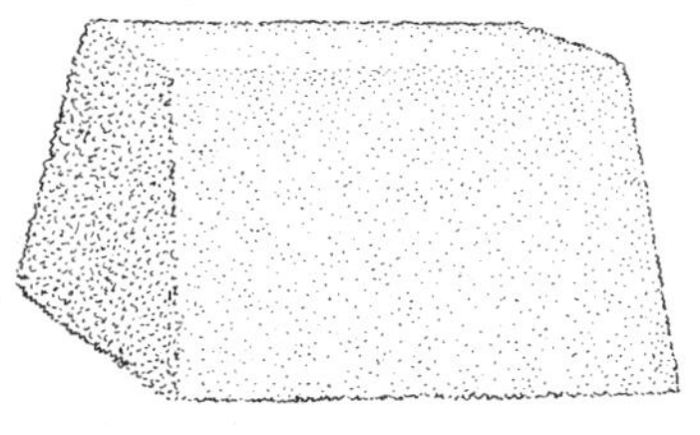

With formal hedges, the slope should be even along its whole length. To do this, frames known as formers are constructed with the desired batter, and strings are stretched between them along the hedge. These act as a guideline to create a level surface.

Above: A stilt hedge makes an impressive canopied entrance to a garden.

Left: Dense, dark hedges make good backgrounds against which to see light foliage and flowers, but they also take moisture and nutrients from the soil.

PLANTING AND MAINTAINING HEDGES

Hedges should be well cared-for if they are to look their best. The soil along a new hedge-line should be well dug, even double-dug if possible, with all perennial weeds removed and plenty of organic compost or farmyard manure incorporated. Choose plants that are about 2ft (60cm) tall and plant them in autumn or spring. A single row planted 1-2ft (30-60cm) apart, depending on type, is usually sufficient for most gardens, but for a thick hedge, a double row with the plants staggered is necessary.

Water the plants well and lay a mulch of grass cuttings or some other organic material. With the exception of conifers and slow-growing evergreens, the plants should be cut back as soon as they have been planted to promote bushy growth. Water regularly, especially in dry weather, until the hedge is established and the plants have developed good root systems.

Once a hedge has reached its full size, it should be trimmed regularly, the number of annual clippings depending on the speed of growth of the plant. Hedges of large-leaved plants, such as Portugal laurel (*Prunus lusitanica*) or holly, look better if they are pruned with hand pruners rather than a hedge trimmer, as the latter tends to cut leaves in half, giving an untidy finish.

Not all hedges need cutting. Informal hedges of rose or barberry can be left to their own devices apart from some general pruning to keep the plants healthy and vigorous.

To help maintain the hedge in good condition, regularly clear out the bottom and feed it in spring with a general fertilizer or organic material.

Above: Archways and gaps through hedges are always inviting and their positioning should be well thought out. Often only a glimpse of what lies beyond is needed.

Right: Hedges of uniform color are best as backdrops. Avoid mixed or tapestry hedges and variegated leaves as these tend to make the background look too busy.

Walls

Walls are a popular choice of boundary, ideal for the utmost privacy. They give a solid, secure feeling and, at the same time, provide a uniform but handsome background for plants. Their colors and textures often make them attractive in their own right, and their warmth and strength make them suitable for climbing plants. They need not be confined to external boundaries, and can equally well be used as internal screens or as supports for hillsides, raised beds or terraces. Internal walled gardens offer the opportunity to create a miniature garden and peaceful haven within a larger whole.

Walls have their drawbacks, high costs being one of them. In small gardens they can also be rather claustrophobic, especially if they are tall and cut out a lot of light. When built in certain positions, walls can also create turbulence as they cause strong winds to eddy, which plays havoc with border plants.

Brick is still the favorite construction material for walls, and it should be chosen to match the walls of the house or any other existing buildings. Stone is another sympathetic walling material, although it tends to be rather expensive. If possible, local stone should be used to conform with the character of the area; this will also be much cheaper as lower transport costs are involved. Stone is a versatile material that can be bonded with cement or constructed as a drystone wall. Tufa, an unusual, porous rock, is appealing as it can be planted up. Only use it to build retaining walls which support little pressure.

Concrete blocks are relatively cheap and easy to use but they can look severe and unyielding in a garden setting. For a less solid wall, use geometric pierced blocks. These are light and airy but they tend to have a coldness about them, although their appearance can be softened with climbing plants.

Above: This low retaining wall divides two levels of a garden. Although it is essentially functional, holding back the earth of the upper level, the choice of materials and the planting make it a decorative feature. Aubrieta and heather grow in abundance here.

Left: A solid boundary wall makes a splendid support for climbing plants. Wires need to be fixed to such walls so that plants can be trained up them. When such a wall is well exposed to sun, a microclimate is created at its base in which relatively tender plants that might not survive in more open positions are likely to thrive. This allows for a much greater variety of plants.

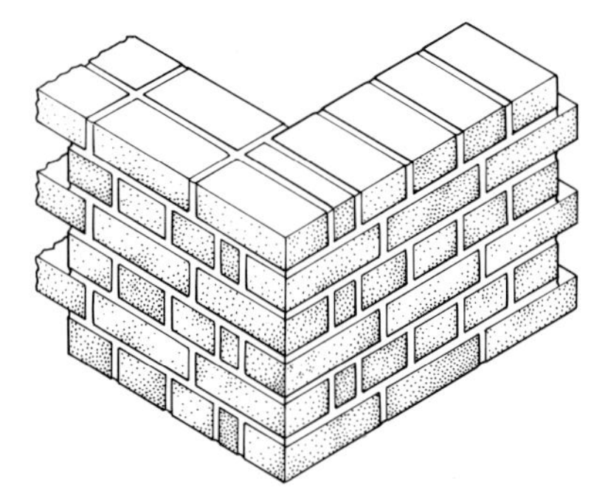

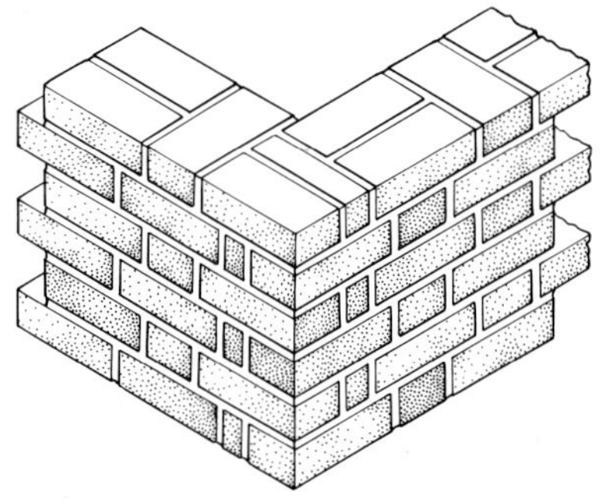

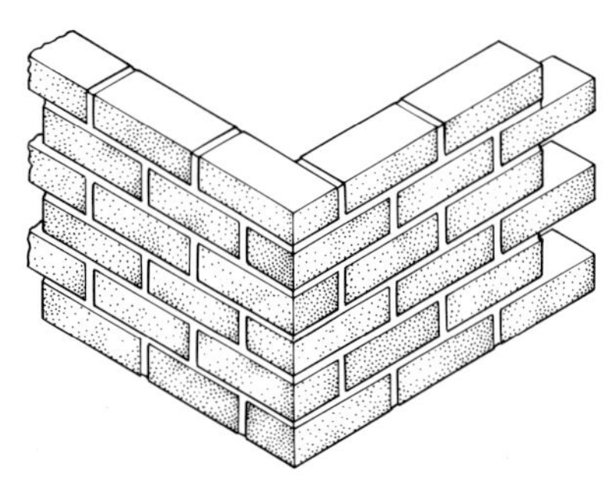

The construction of brick walls Brick walls can be constructed in several different ways (*above*). The different bonds that can be used are chosen partly for their decorative quality and partly for the strength they give a wall; for example, a retaining wall supporting a hillside must be a double thickness, whereas one supporting a shallow flowerbed can be a single thickness. A wall consisting of more than one thickness of brick must have ties through the wall to prevent the two layers from pulling apart. The tie bricks, which show their ends, are known as headers. Those that are laid lengthwise are known as stretchers. The various bonds illustrated (*above, left to right*) are English bond, Flemish bond and running bond, all different combinations of headers and stretchers. The running bond is used for single skinned walls.

Decorative treatment of walls Brick and concrete blocks are most widely used in the construction of walls but many other materials are also suitable. Furthermore, there is great scope for adding decorative finishes through a range of varying textures and colors. Some of the most attractive finishes are achieved using local materials. Split flints and other decorative stones (*below left*) lends themselves to various treatments and sandstone (*below*), which varies in color from region to region, is much used where it is available. Decorative tiles (*left*) are attractive but may pose problems. They may look altogether too busy for the garden environment, and their glazed surfaces are not hard-wearing. Their permanent coloration and patterns mean that any plants will have to be carefully selected.

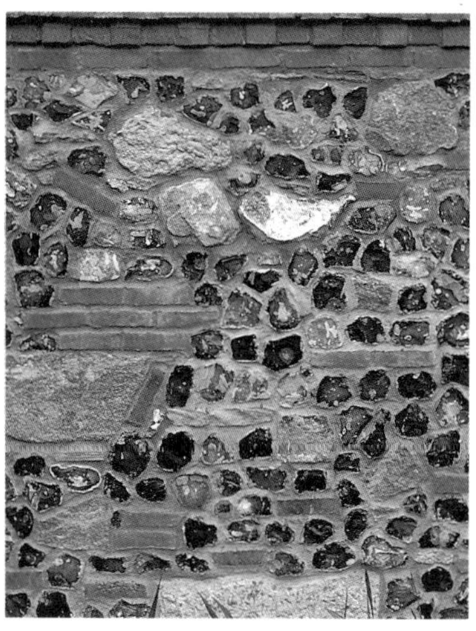

Above left: A fence topping a low wall forms an effective barrier but is much less heavy to look at than a solid wall to the same height. A railing fence, as here, allows light to reach plants in the border at the base of the wall.

Above right: Painting walls a light color helps to cover up any blemishes in brickwork and creates a surface that reflects light into the garden. This is particularly useful in small or basement gardens in part or full shade.

Below left: Tall brick walls form a very good background for a garden, especially if the bricks are of a sympathetic coloring. As well as providing a backdrop for border plants, they can also provide support for climbers.

Below right: Planting in beds and borders backed by walls should take into account the color and texture of the materials the walls are made of. The orange and yellow primulas bring out the red in the stone wall.

PLANTING AGAINST WALLS

Using nails and ties to secure plants against a wall is not a recommended practice, as the nails will need to be replaced regularly and this will damage the wall. Instead, attach horizontal wires between vine eyes. These are wedge-shaped pieces of metal with holes in the top, through which the wire passes. The wire can then be tightened with tensioning screws so it does not sag.

Wooden trellising is an attractive alternative. Fix the trelliswork to the face of the wall with screws and plugs, using 1-2in (2.5-5cm) thick wooden blocks as spacers so the trellis is held clear of the wall.

For a more informal look, use wire mesh. Wire livestock fencing can be used on large walls behind borders; if you are growing very heavy, dense climbers, use plastic or plastic-coated metal mesh for good support.

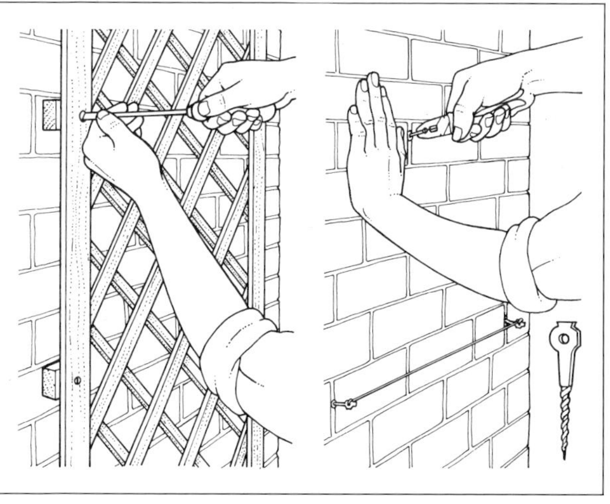

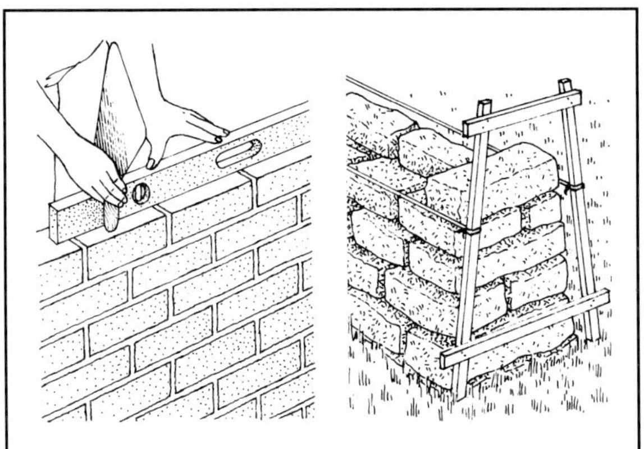

BRICKLAYING TECHNIQUES

When bricklaying, lay a ½in (1.25cm) layer of mortar along each course and butter the head of each brick with the same amount of mortar. Firm down each brick and check that it is level. Level the whole course before building upwards by spanning it with a spirit level and, with the end of the trowel, tapping down any bricks that are not level. Also check vertically with a spirit level that each course is exactly above the previous one.

For dry stone walling, use a former as a guide when placing the stones so that the sides slope slightly inwards. Construct the ends with several courses of uniform edging stones alternated with through stones, and fill in the cavity formed between the front and back facing blocks with small stones, tightly packed in the space.

Below left and below right: Walls in formal gardens are often used as supports for climbing plants. In more informal or rural situations, strands of ivy make an appropriately casual cover. However, care must be taken that this vigorous climber does not become too rampant and take over. Although both these walls are fairly low, they provide some protection for plants as well as giving them encouragement in the form of radiated heat.

Rustic stone walls Such walls have a charm that is difficult to beat and they rarely look inappropriate, especially in a cottage garden. Ornaments, such as urns, will make the walls look more formal. A capping of some sort, whether it be flat slabs (*top*), blocks set on end (*above*), or simply a rough dome of cement (*left*), helps to finish off the feature. Without it, a wall tends to look incomplete. Capping also serves the practical function of shedding rainwater, thus protecting the internal fabric of a wall. Steps associated with walls should be constructed of a sympathetic material and built in an appropriate style for an integrated effect.

Fences

Fences make slightly less solid boundaries than walls, but this is not necessarily a disadvantage, especially in attractive country areas where short fences will allow good views of the scenery. Fences tend to be easier and cheaper to construct and install than walls.

There are many attractive forms of fencing, handsome picket fences being a prime example. These are generally quite short and so are of little use for providing privacy, but they do have a delicacy that makes them particularly suitable for small cottage gardens in either town or country. They are often painted white, which adds to their charm.

There is a wide range of more solid wooden fences that can be purchased from garden centers, most of which are sold as pre-prepared panels that can be quickly erected between vertical posts that have been fixed into the ground. These include lap board, wavy-edge and woven panels.

A more formal and solid look can be achieved by constructing a close-boarded fence. Here, overlapping, vertical boards are nailed to two or three horizontal bars which are then attached to the secured vertical fence posts.

All wooden fencing should be treated with preservative, preferably not creosote as this may harm nearby plants. Alternatively, they can be sealed and painted. Erect the fencing so that the panels do not touch the ground; this will prevent the bottom being permanently damp and so prone to decay. Fill the gap between the bottom of the panel and the soil with a gravel board, a separate length of wood that can easily be replaced should it rot.

Old-fashioned iron fencing can look very elegant, while the more recent chain link, although not particularly appealing in its own right, can be quite acceptable if it is well covered with climbing plants. It does have the advantage of being relatively cheap, easy to put up and long-lasting.

Many fences can be extremely unattractive in spite of their obvious efficiency. This is particularly true in the country where they are designed to keep animals at bay rather than to create an attractive garden boundary. It is best to avoid fences that simply consist of livestock netting stretched between posts with one or two strands of barbed wire pulled taut along the top, although this can serve as a temporary measure while a hedge is growing.

Fences can be covered with plants, but this may introduce one or two problems. The extra weight of the plants and the wind resistance will increase the stress on the supports. Consequently, the fence should be as solid as possible in order to withstand such pressures. Furthermore, unless the climbing plants are species that can be cut to the ground annually, the fence cannot be re-painted, or re-treated with preservative to keep it in good condition.

Left and above: These two fences are markedly different in character. One (*left*) has been erected on a low wall. This is very much in character with the Victorian house beyond and is nicely in proportion with the wall. It gives some feeling of security, as well as allowing a view of the garden inside. The other example (*above*) is a simple post and rail fence. It is made from chestnut or oak that has been split lengthwise, giving it a rustic air that is entirely in keeping with the country setting. If well secured, it will keep out large animals in rural areas.

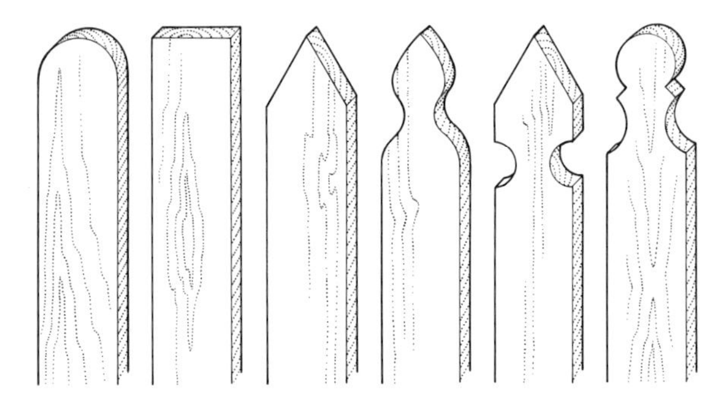

Decorative paling (*above*) For a more decorative finish, shape the ends of palings. The simplest designs are square, pointed or rounded, but more complex ones include intricately carved Gothic and ornate Queen Anne styles.

Fences Fences make less solid barriers than walls. They define a space but do not necessarily totally enclose it, allowing the planting within to relate to that beyond the demarcated boundaries. They can be informal (*above*) or formal (*below left and below right*). Often they are decorative features in their own right (*left*) and there is enormous scope for varying the construction and using different materials to make them highly ornamental. As a general rule it is advisable to keep formal fences free of climbers, especially those that need to be painted regularly. More informal ones, such as woven wooden hurdles, although decorative, can be clothed in plants and still remain functional.

Simple and sophisticated fence designs Although the appeal of many fences is their simplicity, such as a plain fence made of wooden stakes (*left*), they can be handled in a very imaginative way (*below left*). Here, the curve of the fence echoes the details on the adjacent benches. Specially commissioned fences can be expensive, but when they are custom-made they contribute to the unique character of a garden. Amateur carpenters can make their own (*below right*), suiting the style to the situation and using materials according to their means. The bottom rails of this fence almost touch the ground and will be liable to rot unless the ground underneath them is kept clear.

FIXING A FENCE POST

Drive a fence spike into the ground and check that it is vertical by holding a spirit level against each side. Install the post in the collar of the spike and tighten the integral bolts to secure the post.

Alternatively, set the post in concrete, with at least a quarter of the post below ground. Lay a coarse gravel base, position the post and brace it with battens. Before finally filling the hole with concrete, ram more gravel around the base of the fence post.

Wooden fencing (*below*) This selection covers six types of wooden fencing. The three panels in the bottom row could be constructed at home but they are almost certainly cheaper to buy ready-made. The three in the top row are more individual designs but they are still within the scope of many amateur carpenters. The fence on the left is the easiest to construct, and is simply a matter of nailing horizontal planks to vertical posts. If rustic timbers are available, the fence on the right is probably the cheapest to make. Treat all wooden fencing with a preservative that is not toxic to plants.

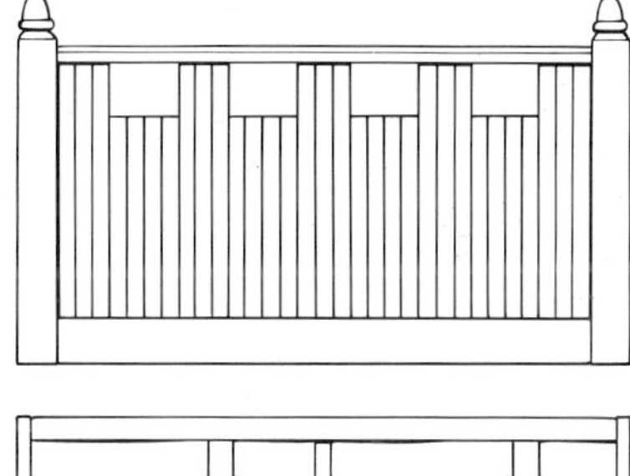

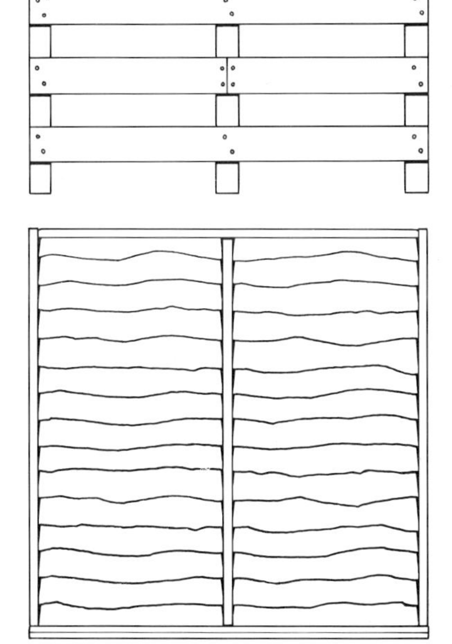

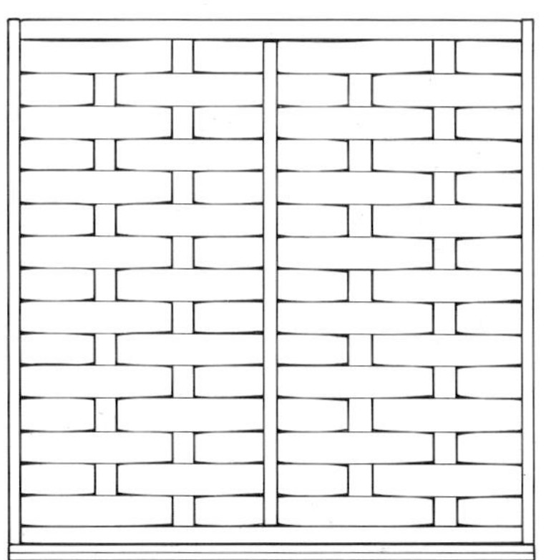

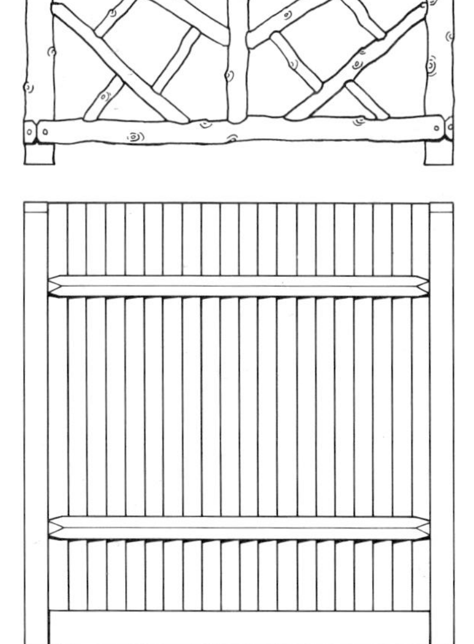

GATES AND GATEWAYS

The approach to a house or garden is often through a gate or gateway, and it is important that this first impression is given due consideration. The general principle in choosing a gateway is to select one that matches the hedge, fence or wall through which it gives access. If it is near the house or any other building then the gateway should be architecturally and stylistically in keeping.

The most popular materials for gates are wrought iron and wood. As a very general rule of thumb, the former looks better in town gardens and the latter in country gardens. Iron gates can look very handsome when they are associated with brick or stonework; a tall, fine wrought-iron gate set in a high brick wall with tantalizing glimpses of a garden beyond will be a beautiful object in itself but, being strong, it is also practical and will provide good security. If privacy and security are needed, the gate should be a tall and solid wooden one, affording no views of the garden beyond to the passer-by.

Wooden gates can look very attractive set in hedges and fences, especially picket fences. They can be painted; black tends to be more popular in towns and white in the country, but it is really a matter of personal taste. Only choose a bright color if it fits in with the setting. Alternatively, wooden gates can be treated with a preservative and left plain (creosote may be used if there are no plants near the gate), or stained with wood stain to bring out the grain.

Gates are heavy and need to be well supported, especially if there are children about who often delight in swinging on them. If the gate is set in a wall there should be no problems as long as well-secured, heavy duty hinges are used. Freestanding gates in hedges or fences should have strong wooden posts that are securely embedded in the ground, preferably in a 1ft (30cm)-deep bed of concrete, to stop them moving. For small gates the posts should be at least 4in (10cm) square and for larger gates, those leading to a drive or a field, for example, the posts should be approximately 8in (20cm) square.

The key to constructing a wooden gate is to make certain that the frame is rigid and will not sag, which will prevent the gate from shutting properly. This is normally done with the use of diagonal cross braces. Always use strong hinges and catches, and make sure all the gate furniture is in keeping with the style and status of the gate, be it simple or grand.

Left and below: The delicacy of iron gates allows the eye to pass through them to the enticing sight of the gardens beyond (*below*); the filigree metalwork is particularly attractive. Such views are invitations to step inside but the gates make effective barriers, especially if spearhead finials are used (*left*).

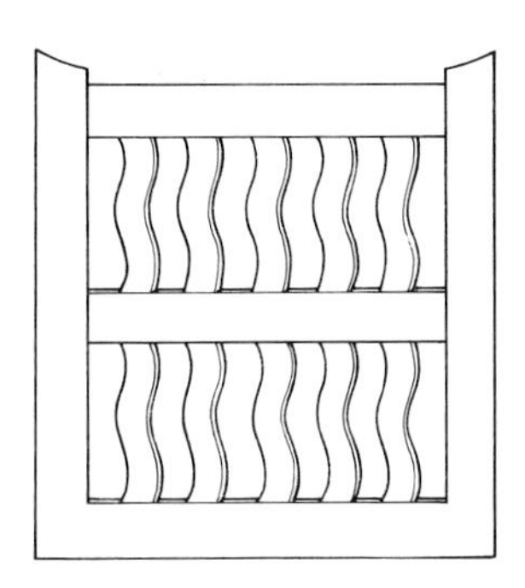

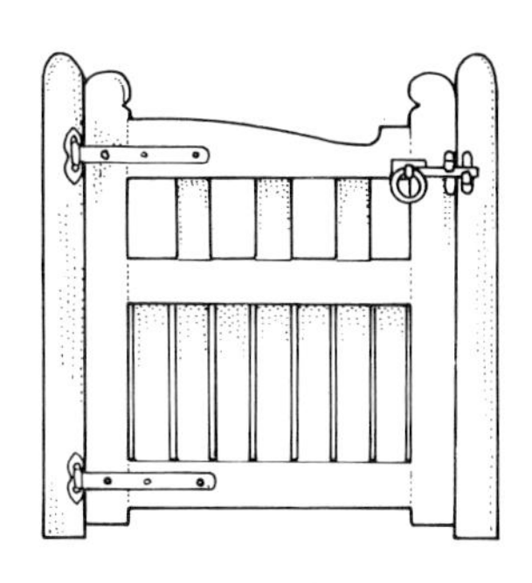

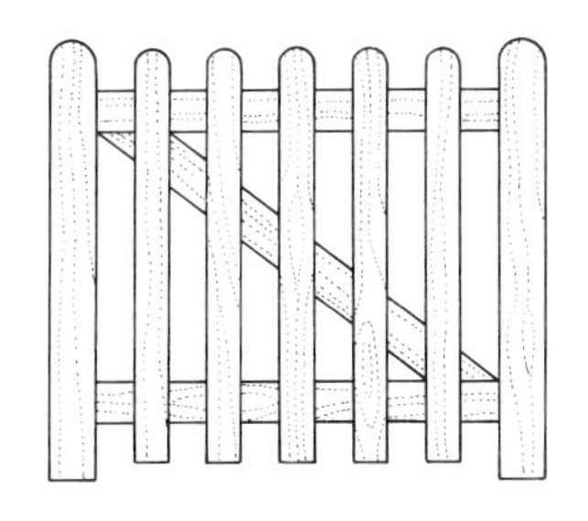

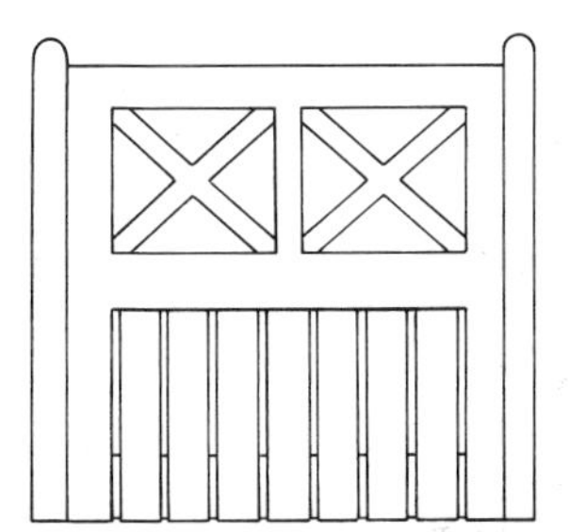

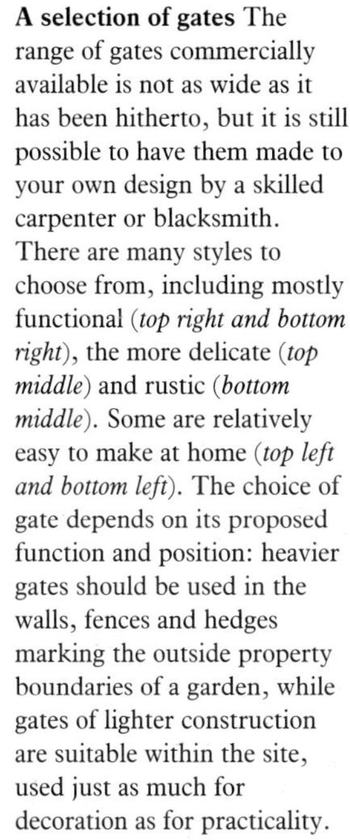

A selection of gates The range of gates commercially available is not as wide as it has been hitherto, but it is still possible to have them made to your own design by a skilled carpenter or blacksmith. There are many styles to choose from, including mostly functional (*top right and bottom right*), the more delicate (*top middle*) and rustic (*bottom middle*). Some are relatively easy to make at home (*top left and bottom left*). The choice of gate depends on its proposed function and position: heavier gates should be used in the walls, fences and hedges marking the outside property boundaries of a garden, while gates of lighter construction are suitable within the site, used just as much for decoration as for practicality.

Fitting gates to their setting Gates in fences (*top left and top right*) should be designed, if possible, in the style of the fence. The gateposts should also be in keeping, as in both of these examples. For gates in hedges and walls there is much more choice of style and material. However, they should suit the weight of the boundary and be appropriate to what lies beyond. Delicate ironwork has the advantage of allowing a view of the garden and, although rather elegant, it complements wilder, meadow-like areas (*bottom left*) as well as more formal paths (*bottom right*). Gateposts should be substantial but not out of scale. Finials and palings can be highly decorative and add character and finish to the gate.

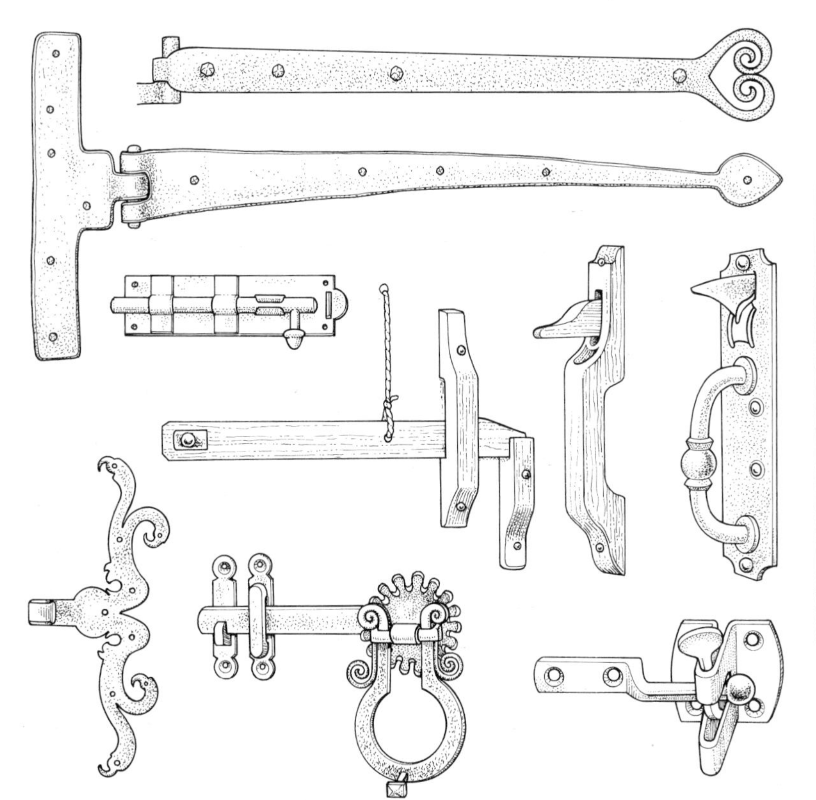

Above and below: It is important to choose a style of gate that is in keeping with its setting. These two wooden gates, in contrasting styles, would not be interchangeable.

Gate hardware (*above*) The choice of hardware can make or mar the appearance of a gate. Many hinges and bolts are designed to be decorative as well as functional but even those that are essentially practical should be in keeping with the style of the gate. When buying hardware, carefully choose a style that is durable and is in scale with the gate for which it is intended. Skimpy hardware will look wrong and will be short-lived. Hardware is either made of metal or wood. Examples of the latter are not commonly seen, but should be within the capabilities of many adept handymen. To last a long time they need to be made of a hardwood, such as oak. Most metal hardware is made of iron or steel, but occasionally items can be found in brass or bronze. Iron or steel hardware can be either galvanized or painted. Blacksmiths may accept custom-made orders.

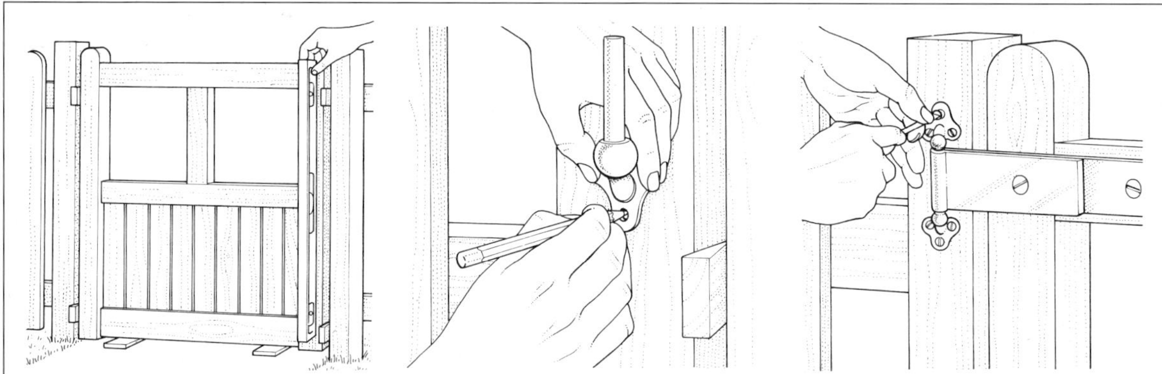

HANGING A WOODEN GATE

Prop the gate up 2in (5cm) above the ground, between the posts. Check that there is a clearance on either side of at least a ¼in (0.5cm) between the gate and the posts, so that it will swing open and shut without jamming; if necessary, plane off any surplus wood. Temporarily but accurately hold the gate in place with wooden wedges, and mark the position of the hinges on the gate and the appropriate post. Remove the gate and attach the hinges. Drill the pilot screw holes into the post, position the gate, ensuring that it is vertical and sits correctly in the space, and securely attach the butt end of the hinges to the post. Oil the hinges if they are stiff.

Decorative gates The design of ready-made gates is generally dull but, as all these examples show, gates can be very decorative objects in their own right. If a gate is needed, it is well worth going to the trouble of either making one or getting one made. Cast-iron gates (*above left*) are difficult to come by, but forged ones (*bottom left and bottom right*) can be made by blacksmiths, who often welcome the chance to fashion something different. Wooden gates (*right and below left*) may well be within the range of skilled individuals, or they can be commissioned from carpenters. Gates should always be made from the best materials and must be well maintained to ensure a long life. A neglected gate gives a garden a dejected, uncared-for appearance and mood.

GARDEN FEATURES

Retaining Walls

Retaining walls are used in two ways in the garden; either they shore up a bank or slope to prevent it from slipping, or they form the containing walls of a raised flowerbed or lawn. Raised flowerbeds are particularly popular as features bordering patios and terraces; they will suit a wide range of plants, including alpines, which can be grown in the walls as well as in the beds. While both types of retaining wall are fundamentally functional, being in a garden they should also have some decorative merit; thus the choice of materials and style are of great importance.

In a formal situation, the best materials to use are brick, dressed stone or plastered concrete, either cast or in blocks. For a more informal garden, appropriate materials include wood, dry-stone walling and also various decorative concrete blocks. If using brick, it should match or complement the color of other structures and blend in well with the planting. Any of the various brick bonds can be used, but for walls that retain banks a double thickness of brick is required, with piers if necessary. A low wall built around a raised bed can be built using a single thickness, although a double layer will often look better. Foundations are required in both cases.

Dressed stone is attractive but expensive; dry-stone walling is a cheaper, less formal option that is best employed in areas where it is widely used. This is partly because it will look more in keeping with the surroundings, and partly because stone is likely to be cheaper and more abundant. Both reconstituted and imitation stone are popular choices, but these can look unnatural and garish, even though the colors do become more muted with age. Concrete is a harsh and unattractive material to use, but rendered with cement, incised with lines to give the effect of stone blocks, it can be more acceptable. Pierced concrete blocks are a relatively cheap way of building retaining walls, but such walls tend to look more functional than attractive.

It is also possible to decorate retaining walls by pressing objects, such as pebbles, shells, colored glass or broken pottery, into cement on the surface. This must, of course, be done with sensitivity to the rest of the garden, its style and all the seasonal colors.

Wood can be used in less formal settings. Although a versatile material, it is less hard-wearing than stone and is prone to decay. All supporting timbers should be thick, in good condition and well soaked in preservative – avoid creosote if plants are to be grown up the wall or nearby. Old railroad ties can be used to construct very solid retaining walls, and these will last for a long time because they contain tar. For a more natural look, use logs laid horizontally one on top of the other, the whole stack being well supported by vertical posts to stop the logs rolling forward. Alternatively, construct a retaining wall from logs driven into the ground vertically, like a palisade. In both cases, the logs should be as straight as possible so that they butt together snugly, preventing soil from spilling out between the cracks.

Left and above: In formal walls (*above*) as well as in dry-stone walls (*left*) holes and crevices can be left for inserting plants. This helps to soften these features, giving them a less functional, more decorative look, and it gives a vertical dimension to the planting.

Variations on retaining walls
There are retaining walls for every situation. This rustic stone wall (*right*) fits in well with the rough hillside and the woodland setting. The low brick wall (*below right*) reflects the brickwork of the terrace and pergola above it, and creates a flowerbed alongside the path in which a variety of plants soften the precise brickwork. Without the raised bed, the terrace wall would look too tall and stark. Thick and boisterous planting (*below left*) is kept in check by low retaining walls that surround the beds. Railroad ties are easily used and are particularly suitable for straight-sided beds. They form stable, informal walls and are still relatively cheap to buy.

Above and right: As well as containing beds, retaining walls are used to hold back the soil from different levels of the garden. Often there is little or no pressure on the wall (*right*) and a largely decorative structure can be built. Steps are often necessary to gain access to the upper levels. A retaining wall can also be built into a sloping lawn (*above*).

Right: Some retaining walls are simply low surrounds to raised beds. Others, however, are constructed between two levels where the alternative would be a sloping bank. Sometimes a strong, massive construction is needed to hold back the earth of the upper level. In order to disguise its functional nature, a retaining wall, especially one that incorporates a number of features, can be a highly ornamental component of the garden. In this Italianate example, there is a grotto-like recess containing seating and a table, with a sweeping stone staircase linking the two levels. There are niches for statues as well as for plants, and cascading vegetation breaks up the sturdy, stone-built structure.

BUILDING A RETAINING WALL

If the wall is to support a great deal of weight, such as that exerted by a slipping hillside, it is essential to employ a civil engineer to plan and supervise the operation as it could be too difficult and dangerous for amateurs to tackle by themselves. The same safeguard applies to all retaining walls over 3½ft (1m) high.

Dry-stone walling can be used for retaining walls, but because there is no mortar to hold the wall together, only low walls should be attempted if the builder has no previous experience. If in doubt, employ a professional waller. Simple retaining walls, however, are relatively easy to build and well within most gardener's capabilities.

The earth must be removed from immediately behind the wall and, if necessary, held back by a wooden form. All retaining walls, apart from those built of wood, must have concrete foundations which extend below the frost line, with a width approximately three times the width of the wall. If the retaining wall has any weight behind it, the front section of the foundations must be deeper than the back, but low retaining walls that are built around a raised bed will be sufficiently safe with shallower foundations.

With brick and stone retaining walls occasional gaps must be left in the mortar on the lowest level to allow water to drain from the bank or bed. Fill the area immediately behind these drainage holes with rubble to prevent them getting clogged-up with soil. Other gaps higher up in the wall can be left as planting niches and filled with colorful trailing plants such as aubrieta.

Allow the mortar to harden for about a week before back-filling the area behind the wall with soil. If the wall is to support a flowerbed, use a good potting compost for small areas, or for larger areas a home-made mixture of one part loam or good garden soil, one part grit and one part peat, coconut fiber or leaf mold, measured by volume. Put drainage material such as rubble in the bottom, and fill the bed with the compost, pressing it down firmly. The surface should be heaped up above the level of the wall, and this should be left to subside naturally before planting. If alpines are grown, add a top dressing of gravel or small stones.

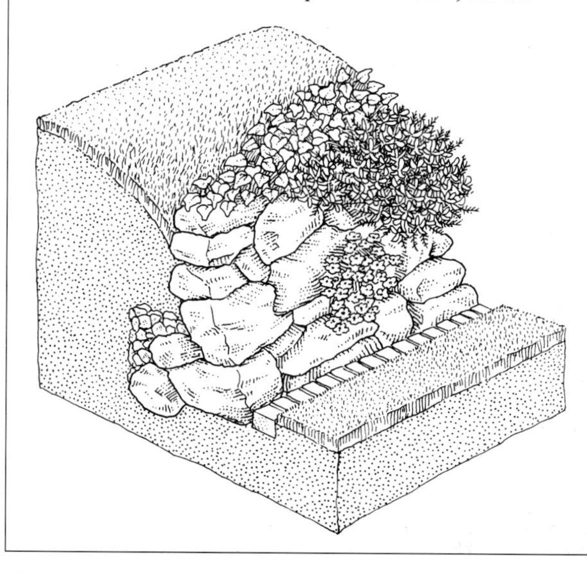

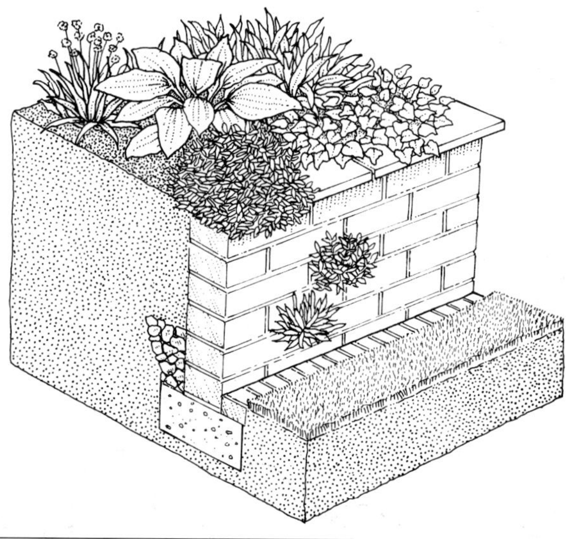

Materials for retaining walls
Irregular stones and dry-stone walling (*left*) make a very informal wall, much akin to a rock garden. Such walls are very suitable for planting in because of the gaps between the stones. This stone wall, surrounding a pool fed by a small cascade, suits the atmosphere and informality of this tropical-looking garden. A retaining wall of mortared brick (*below left*) is a complete contrast as it is much more structured and formal. Here, the regular brickwork echoes the wall of the terrace and pergola behind it, producing a unified appearance. The function of this retaining wall is to create a bed beneath a sunny wall that will hold its warmth and provide suitable conditions for tender plants.

Stone blocks can be used to make a regular, rather formal wall (*above*). This retaining wall, which has made a bed from a low rise in the garden, is attractively draped with plants; careful plant selection based on color and form is needed to achieve this effect. Although regular in shape, rustic logs create a very informal wall (*left*), especially when the bark starts to peel off. This type of wall is particularly suitable for a woodland border; note the top covering of bark which ties in with the wooden wall. The logs will eventually rot and need replacing.

Rock Gardens

Rock gardens are usually planted with alpine plants. The rocks create a natural and decorative setting against which the alpines look at home; indeed, the rocky site provides the perfect, free-draining habitat with a cool root-run which alpines require if they are to thrive. Rockeries can be any size; they can vary from small arrangements built on patios where paving stones have been removed, to large features that take up most of the garden.

The site can be of any aspect but an open one with plenty of light and air is preferable. Although alpines will tolerate high winds they do not like drafts, so avoid constructing a rockery where wind is likely to be funneled between buildings or trees. Rock gardens look best on sloping sites, but they can also be built on flat ground to make horizontal features.

The soil must be carefully considered. A free-draining loam is best if it can be obtained, otherwise a mixture of one part good garden soil, one part coconut fiber, peat or leaf mold and one part grit or gravel, as measured by volume, can be used; the grit or gravel is important as it will aid drainage. The soil used must be completely free of weeds, otherwise the rock garden may have to be dismantled so that the gardener can thoroughly weed the site.

Rockeries are attractive features in their own right and the choice of rock is important. If possible, use a local stone which will not only be cheaper but will also look more natural. Do not use lumps of concrete as these rarely look right, and in particular avoid using a soft stone that is more than likely to shatter and flake during the first frosts.

The rocks should be arranged so that they resemble the strata of a rocky outcrop rather than being dotted around on the surface of the soil. Each rock should be partially buried in the ground. This will create a more natural look and provide the plants with a cool root-run, as well as making the feature more stable so that people can walk across it to admire the plants.

For a more varied feature, certain areas of the rock garden can be given different soils so that a wider range of plants can be grown. Areas shaded from the sun during the hotter part of the day should have more organic material, such as peat or leaf mold, incorporated into the soil to make it more moisture-retentive; primulas love damp soil and these and other plants suited to moist conditions can be grown. Crevice plants can be worked into the vertical cracks between the rocks which will provide the sharp drainage that they require.

There is a vast range of plants that can be grown in rockeries but the majority flower in the spring. Try and include some summer- and autumn-flowering plants as well to give as much seasonal interest as possible. Rock garden plants need not be restricted to those from high alpine regions; many dwarf lowland plants are excellent choices. Small bulbs in particular can look very attractive in rocky settings.

Left and above: Rock gardens resemble miniature free-draining natural habitats. The rocks, stones and gravel of which they are made allow surplus water to drain away quickly and plants, especially alpines, seek out the moisture retained under the rocks.

Natural rock gardens Natural rock formations (*left*) make the best rock gardens; the small cushions of plants growing on this rock cliff appreciate its sharp drainage. However, few sites have a suitable outcrop, so natural-looking arrangements need to be constructed using imported rock (*above*). If possible, use local stone as this is more likely to harmonize with its setting than foreign material, which will look out of place.

Scree beds A natural scree consists of stones and pieces of rock that have fallen from a cliff and accumulated at its base. The free-draining conditions that are found in a scree suit a number of plants and can be created in an artificially constructed scree bed (*right*). The bed is best created on a slope but can be constructed on flat ground by building the bed up at one end. Dig out the soil and include a drainage channel to prevent any water collecting. Fill the hole with rubble or with pebbles. On top of this put a thick layer of gravel or small stones. Incorporating a few random outcrops of rock will help give the bed a natural appearance. Plant the scree bed with appropriate plants for a natural look.

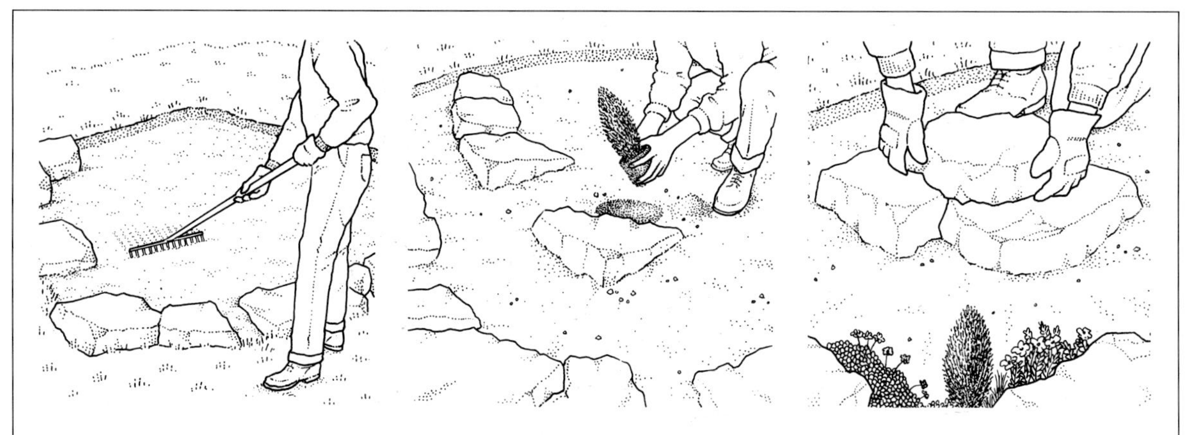

BUILDING A ROCK GARDEN

Clear the site and eradicate all weeds, especially pernicious ones, either by hand-weeding or using weedkiller.

Rocks are very heavy to move and the help of a second person is useful. If the pieces are quite large, hire a miniature mechanical digger. Roll or lever the rocks rather than lift them if possible; a soil or stone ramp built between different levels can be helpful. Always bend your knees when lifting.

Before building the rockery, assemble all the materials. Spread the rock around the site with the best side of each piece facing you. This will make the choice of pieces easier and lessen the number of times each stone will have to be moved as all the rocks are clearly displayed around you.

Arrange the first layer, burying each rock up to at least a third of its depth. If the pieces have any visible strata lines, they should all run in the same direction, preferably horizontally. Slope the rock backwards into the ground so that it gives the impression of an outcrop emerging from the garden; this will also ensure that rainwater runs back into the bed rather than cascading over the rocks, eroding the soil and bed beneath. Each piece of stone should be firmed in very well so that it cannot move, even when stepped on.

Crevice plants can be planted while the rock garden is being built. Place them between two rocks as they are pushed together, making sure that the plant roots are in contact with the soil behind or beneath the rocks. Build up the outcrop, staggering each layer further back to form a series of terraces, allowing plenty of spaces for planting.

Once the structure is finished, arrange the rest of the plants, still in their pots, among the rocks. When satisfied with the arrangement, plant them, watering them well.

All exposed soil will need a top dressing of grit or stone chips. This will act as a mulch, keeping in moisture, as well as providing a free-draining surface around the bases of the plants. It also makes a tidier finish.

Contrary to popular opinion, alpines do need watering, especially in dry weather. Keep the rock garden free of weeds; if they do become established, it may be necessary to demolish that section of the rockery and thoroughly weed it before rebuilding the site. Preserve the plants.

Above: This rocky outcrop has been colonized by self-seeding plants; the planted stone container successfully complements the texture of the rock.

Left: Rock gardens need not be confined to rocky outcrops and slopes. Here, the combination of a rock garden and water feature allows for a wide range of plants.

Raised beds The conventional rock garden is constructed on either a natural or an artificial slope (*below left*) although alpines (the most usual rock garden plants) are increasingly being grown in raised beds (*left and below right*). These consist of walls enclosing a free-draining compost, covered with gravel and rocks. The strategically placed rocks create a more natural look and also provide plants with a cool root-run. If dry-stone walls are used, plants can also be established in the vertical sides. Even bonded walls can have planting gaps in them.

Below: It takes some skill to construct a natural-looking rocky outcrop using large blocks of stone; a covering of lichen and moss will give the rocks a weathered look. Allowance has to be made for planting pockets, not only in horizontal niches and ledges but also in vertical crevices.

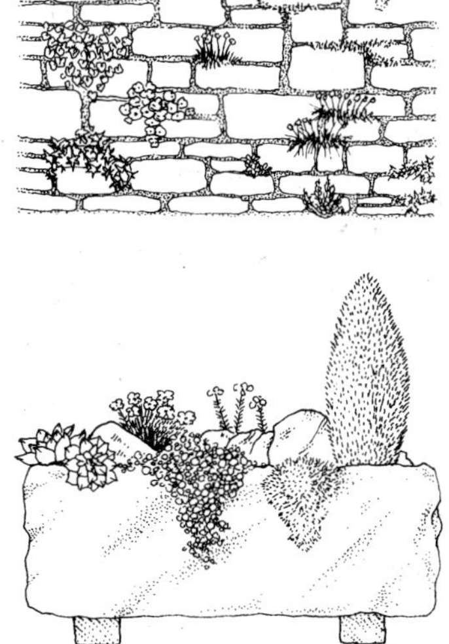

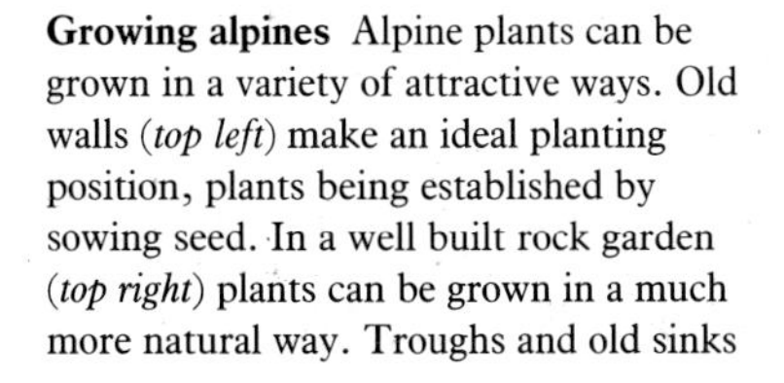

Growing alpines Alpine plants can be grown in a variety of attractive ways. Old walls (*top left*) make an ideal planting position, plants being established by sowing seed. In a well built rock garden (*top right*) plants can be grown in a much more natural way. Troughs and old sinks (*bottom left*) provide ideal conditions and look good on patios. Paving with gaps (*bottom right*) can reproduce the conditions of a rock garden, the plants' roots spreading beneath the stones. Such surfaces are especially good in association with aromatic plants such as thyme.

Screens and Trellis

Screens and trellis are similar to fences. They are principally used for concealing or dividing one area from another, and they can be decorated with climbing plants for a more attractive finish.

Solid screens are often used to hide an eyesore, such as an oil tank or a garbage can. They can also be used to mask off part of the garden, with only an archway cut into the screen that allows further exploration of the garden. These dense screens are usually made of wood and they are available in a variety of different sizes and designs, to suit most styles of garden.

Other screens, made of wrought iron or wire netting, are open so that light can filter through, silhouetting the foliage or flowers that grow up the vertical surface. This type of screen will also provide a tempting glimpse of what lies beyond. Wrought-iron screens look particularly good used in association with brick or stone. For a more solid, permanent screen, pierced concrete blocks can be used, but the overall effect may look harsh and fussy, and the geometric patterns do not always complement the fluid lines of plants or the sweep of a lawn.

For a simple screen, stretch a length of wire netting between upright posts and cover it with climbers; evergreens will ensure that little of the netting is visible. Screens can also be constructed out of other materials such as bamboo canes; placed close together they will form a solid, ribbed barrier; set further apart, they will make a more open and decorative screen. For less solid screens, it is also possible to weave bamboo and other softwoods, while rough hurdles made from thin strips of softwood are also available. These make attractive and appropriate rustic screens for less formal gardens.

Lengths of trellis tend to look more elegant than screens, and a great deal of thought should go into their design. The most elementary types consist of square or rectangular panels comprising horizontal and vertical laths that create a squared pattern. Common variations include laths that cross each other diagonally and laths that move on opposing diagonals from a central upright, to create a chevron effect. The panels are held between upright posts that should be concreted into the ground.

If the trellis is to support climbing plants, it must be made from relatively thick, strong laths, but as a decorative feature it is better to use a thinner wood so that the overall appearance is graceful and stylish. The more ornamental trelliswork is often associated with archways or pergolas laid in sweeping lines with finials on each post. Rustic trellising can be constructed from rough poles.

All screens and trellis must be well secured to posts concreted into the ground as the wind can exert considerable pressure on them, particularly if they are covered with plants. If they are not painted then they should be treated with a preservative other than creosote, which is harmful to plants.

Screens and trellis Screens and trelliswork can be used to create visual barriers, partially or completely blocking a view. They can also provide supports for plants. When an example is highly decorative (*left*), it is often better left plain, uncluttered by plants, but in most instances it is the planting that makes the structure ornamental (*above*). Tantalizing glimpses through a screen or trellis are often more appealing than a full view, encouraging the viewer to explore futher.

Above left, above right and right: Screens and trellis can be highly decorative or quite plain. There is great scope for the imaginative gardener to produce something unusual.

Ready-made panels (*below*) These are commercially available in a variety of designs. Many are made of wood but some can be created from concrete blocks (*top center*). Rustic hurdles (*top left*) are rather rough and informal in appearance and look best in rural situations. These and other rustic and woven panels (*top right*) cannot be cut to length as easily as other forms of wooden trellis, which come in many patterns (*bottom row*).

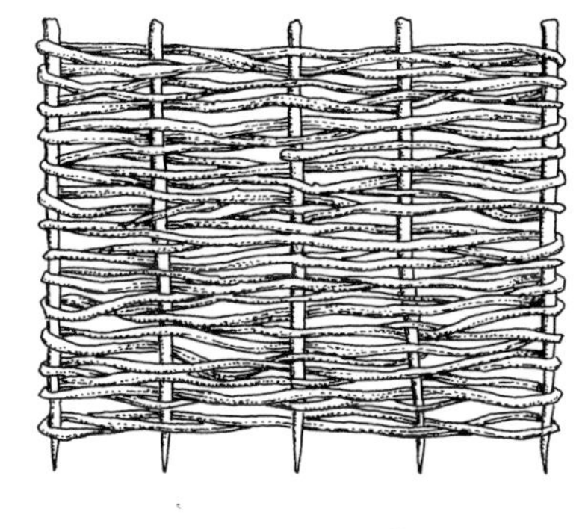

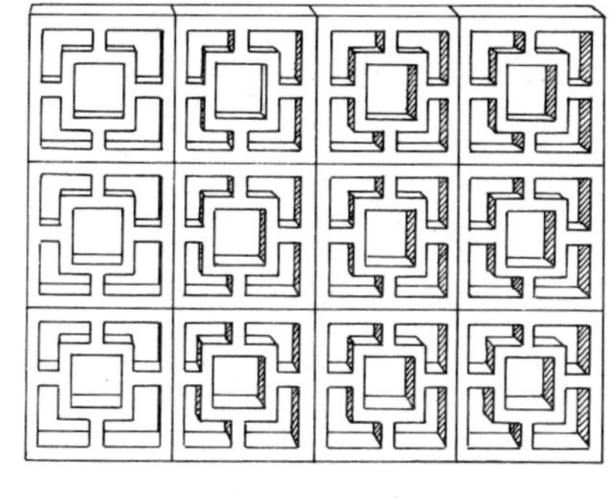

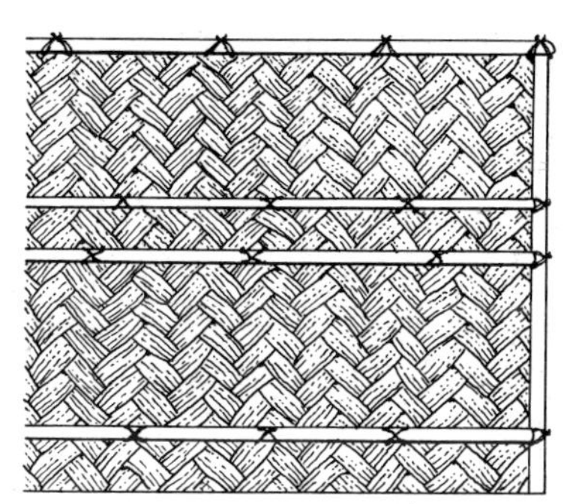

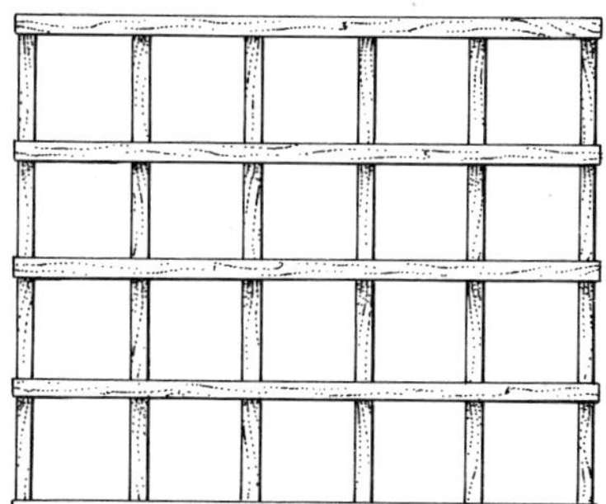

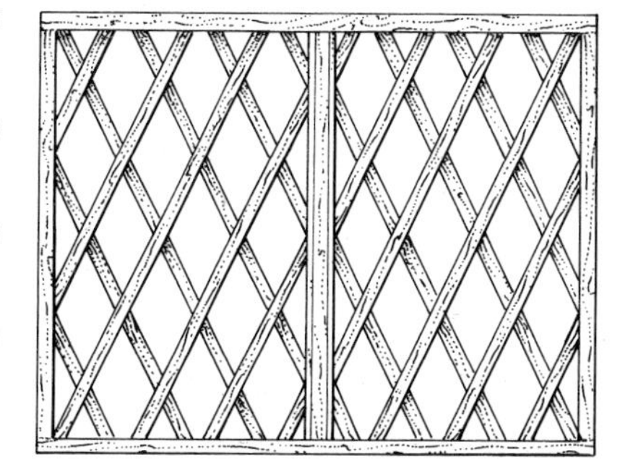

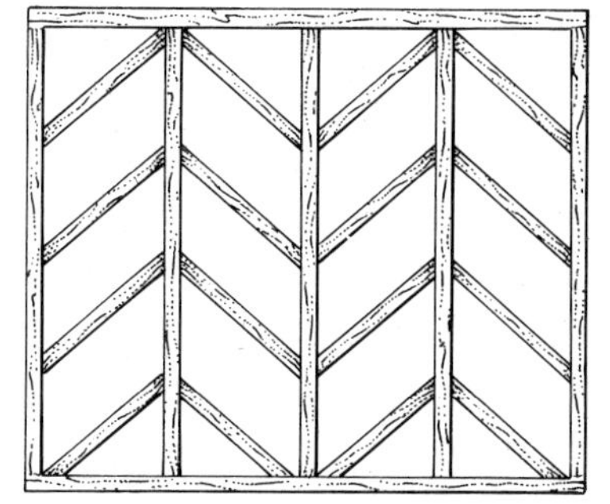

Pergolas

Ornamental walkways are often covered with wooden or wrought-iron frameworks holding climbing plants; these structures are known as pergolas. Although they are mainly used as decoration, in hot climates they have an additional, more functional role of providing shade. From the point of view of design, they add a vertical element to the garden and a texture that is light and airy and full of interest.

Pergolas can either consist of a series of disconnected arches or they can be one continuous tunnel. In hot climates they are more likely to stretch along a network of paths to give protection from the sun, but they can equally well be used in shorter lengths, covering a single path or even a small part of one. They must be well integrated into the surroundings so as not to look out of place; a pergola placed in the middle of a garden with no obvious purpose or sense of direction will look totally wrong. If it covers a main path, or marks the beginning or end of such a path, it will take on more significance. The effect of a long pergola can be enhanced by a point of focus at the end, such as a piece of sculpture, a view, a bold planting scheme or a simple seat.

In order to create areas of shade, pergolas must be well covered with climbing plants. A single species often produces the greatest impact: a dramatic golden tunnel of laburnum or frothing masses of headily-scented climbing roses can be breathtaking and spellbinding, enticing the viewer to walk through the pergola. Many climbing plants are suitable, but make certain that any thorny ones, such as roses, are properly trained and well tied in. Pergolas do not necessarily have to display ornamental plants; they can equally well be used in the vegetable garden to support runner beans or squash.

Depending on style, pergolas can be constructed out of brick, wood or metal. Ready-made, highly decorative wrought-iron pergolas must be bought but brick and wood structures can be home-made. When building a pergola, be generous with the width as this will narrow once the structure is covered in plants.

In formal settings, brick piers look elegant and imposing. They must have concrete foundations and it is a good idea to place an iron scaffold pole up the center of each column to reinforce it. The wooden cross-members must be of a substantial thickness, otherwise they will look out of character with the piers. This is a solid structure that will bear a considerable weight of plant cover.

Wooden pergolas are easy to construct. Use thick timber so the framework will not only be able to support the weight of the climbers, but it will look as if it is able to do so; psychologically, no-one will enjoy walking under a structure that looks flimsy even if it is not. Make certain that the uprights are well embedded in the ground, concreting them in if necessary, so that the wind does not push the structure over or move it out of line. A more informal pergola can also be made out of rustic poles, but this will look lighter so should carry delicate climbers.

Formal and rustic pergolas Pergolas add a delightful geometric element to a garden; they also provide additional planting possibilities to sites that do not have wall space for vigorous climbers. Structures can be rustic and made from whole or split logs (*right*), or they can be more formal, made from smooth timber (*above*). Both examples support roses.

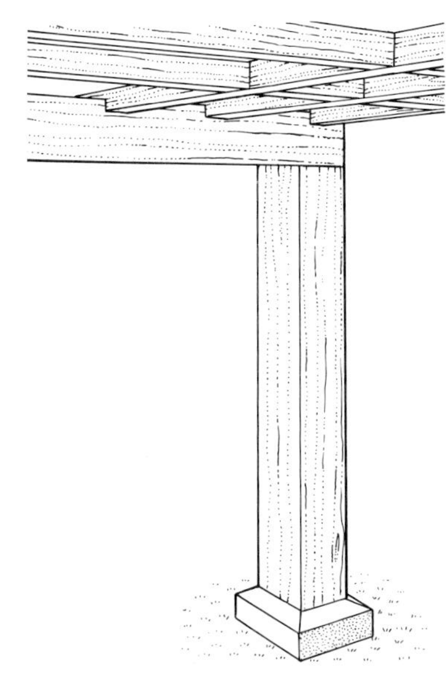

Supports for pergolas There are many different pergola designs, each with different construction methods. All supports must be very strong in order to carry the weight of vigorous climbers and withstand strong winds. Wooden supports (*left*) need to be made of sound wood. Hardwoods, such as oak, are the best, but softwoods can be used as long as they are treated with an effective preservative. Creosote is poisonous to plants and not suitable. The base of each column should be sunk at least 2ft (60cm) into the ground and embedded in concrete. Brick or stone columns (*right*) need to have foundations. To give extra strength, it is advisable to insert a steel rod in the center of the column when the foundations are laid; a galvanized scaffold pole is ideal. Cap any stone or brickwork to prevent water getting inside the cavity.

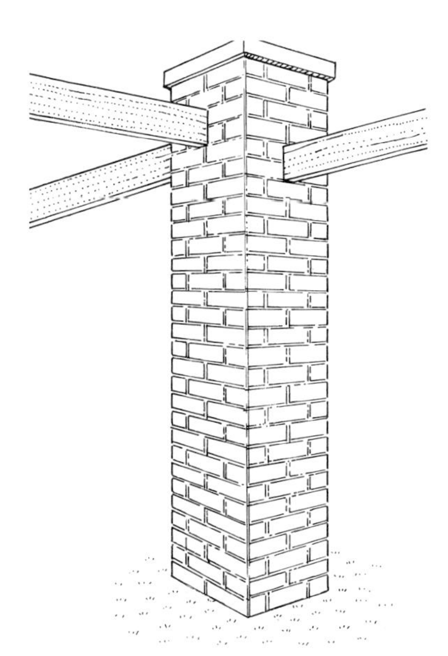

Pergolas with a purpose A pergola that is simply stranded in the middle of a garden, leading nowhere, usually looks forlorn. It is only when a pergola forms part of a real or visually important axis in the garden that its full potential can be realized. These three examples show how important the focal point of a pergola can be. Seen in winter, one pergola leads purposefully to a gate that gives access to an orchard (*left*). Another wooden pergola, wonderfully decked in roses (*below right*), ends at the edge of a garden. Brick-piered pergolas tend to be the most solid and robust-looking. The vista through this example (*below left*) terminates at a fountain, which cuts across the line of vision. Grass is only suitable underneath if there is enough light; where a pergola supports a dense canopy, lay a paved or gravel path.

Scale and weight Pergolas tend to look best when they have been designed on a generous scale. The grace of the shallow arch and the gentle curve along the length of this pergola (*above left*) creates a wonderful atmosphere, even when the covering climbers are out of leaf. Sturdiness also adds to the character of a pergola (*above right*). Even with delicate trelliswork there is an underlying feeling of strength here, mainly because of the substantial beams used for the roof. However, many pergolas are little more than a framework to stroll under, and these rely on the plants that climb up and over them for their attraction (*right*).

Pergola design (*left and right*) Pergolas are designed to be seen as an architectural whole from outside as well as from within, framing a vista. There are many variations of shape, scale and degree of ornamentation; the two examples shown here are particularly ornate. In both cases, the detailing might be too small to be seen if plants are allowed to climb all over the pergolas. Iron frames (*left*) have the disadvantage of needing to be painted at regular intervals, which can present problems when the structure is carrying a mass of climbing plants. The plants will need to be removed before painting can take place. The chinoiserie pergola (*right*) has an ornate roof which should only be lightly covered with plants.

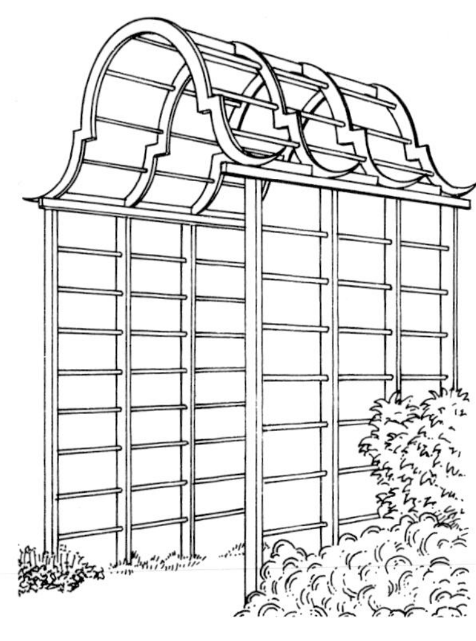

Left: A trellis pergola has several points in its favor. Despite looking light, a structure made in this way is surprisingly strong as the members are mutually supportive. Furthermore, it has the great advantage of providing plenty of fixing points for tying in scrambling climbers. Roses are the ideal plants to train over this sort of structure. Although they are vigorous, their foliage is not so dense as to obscure the pergola.

Below: Pergolas constructed of stone piers create quite a different impression from those made of box sections of trellis. These look sturdy and walking beneath them inspires confidence in their strength. They require less maintenance than pergolas of trelliswork, but a disadvantage is that they lack convenient tying points. Climbers must be tied either to eyes secured to the stonework or to wires attached to the columns. These should be checked regularly to be sure they offer plants the necessary support.

Pergolas from the inside The interior of a pergola is as important as the view of it from outside; indeed, the very sight of one draws you towards and into the defined space. The appeal of many pergolas is that they provide shady walks and, if large enough (*above left*), places to sit in dappled shade. In some, the cross members are too far apart to provide much shade (*left*), but the repetition of the columns and horizontal bars along their length creates the impression of a tunnel. If a pergola is too enclosed by foliage, it is difficult to grow plants under it. On the other hand, if too many plants are grown along the inside of a pergola, or if they are too vigorous, the path can become difficult to negotiate (*right*).

Arbors

An arbor is the name given to a structure, natural or otherwise, over which plants grow, creating an enclosed area of dappled shade, often containing a seat. It is a romantic, decorative feature suitable for gardens of any size.

Both wood and wrought-iron arbors can be bought ready-made, but some models are insubstantial and flimsy, so manufactured units should be carefully inspected before being purchased. Arbors are also relatively easy to make. To a certain extent it does not matter what they look like because the framework can be covered up with climbing plants.

The simplest arbors do not involve any framework at all but are carved out of solid bushes or thick, healthy hedges. These take time to grow to a sufficient size, and they should be trained from the start to ensure an even coverage of foliage. If an existing bush is opened up it might take a while for the areas that have been cut to grow more leaves. Yew (*Taxus*) is an ideal material for a natural arbor but many other faster-growing evergreens can be used. It should be remembered, however, that the faster the growth, the more clipping will be required to keep the arbor neat. A suitable climber can be trained over an arbor to highlight and embellish the feature.

Wood is the most practical, versatile material to use for arbors as it is relatively cheap and the arbor can be constructed on site. Ready-cut, prepared wood is ideal for making smart, elegant structures, especially if thin wood is incorporated into the framework. This type of wood can also be used to build a much more functional, less decorative feature and, being a strong material, it will take the weight of a mass of climbing plants. The alternative is rustic wood in the form of poles; these will provide a strong but less regular framework, one that is more in keeping with rural or wild settings. It is also possible to use panels of trellis as the basis of the arbor, but these will need strong supporting posts.

All the joints must be well made and fastened with galvanized bolts and nails. Strength is important as the framework will not only have to bear the considerable weight of climbing plants but also the force of the wind. The main uprights should be well embedded in the ground, preferably in concrete.

Arbors can be used to support a wide range of plants, but particularly decorative arbors, such as those made from wrought iron, should only be partially covered. The more delicate and thin-leaved the plants, the more sunlight they will admit. Plants with open habits, such as roses, will provide the right density of cover, so the ornamental metalwork can be enjoyed as well as the flowers. Less formal wooden arbors can have a thick covering of foliage and flowering plants; this will create more shade and give greater protection from the elements.

Above: Typically elegant gazebos and belvederes are purely architectural features that need to be well sited.

Left: Foliage creates shade and a sense of intimacy, as seen in this unusual, informal arbor built in an area of stonework and evergreens, where the roof is constructed out of living plant material.

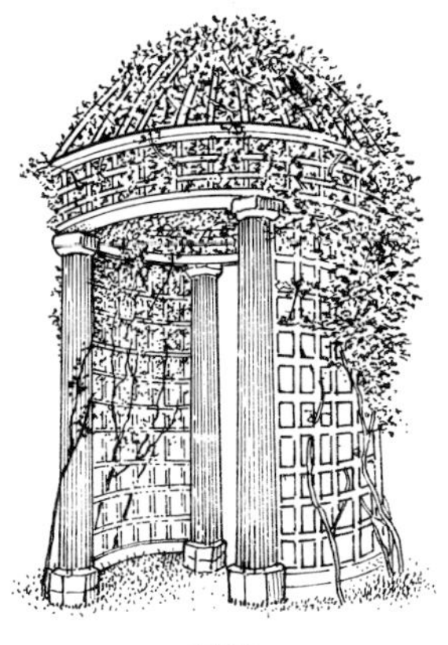

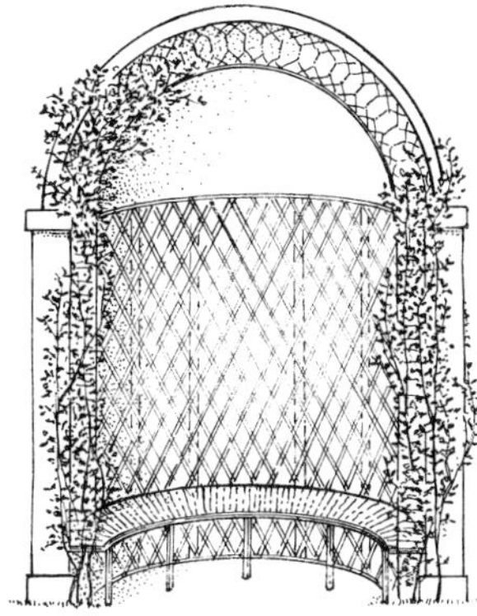

Above: Arbors are suitable features for quiet, secluded parts of the garden, a cover of foliage and flowers adding to their appeal as places of retirement. Although the clothing of vegetation may be quite dense, it rarely makes these structures rainproof.

Trellis arbors (*above*) Pretty arbors and airy summer houses can be constructed out of trelliswork, a versatile material that can be adapted to a variety of shapes, whether open or relatively enclosed. The use of trellis simplifies the tying in of climbing plants.

Above: Not all arbors need to have a framework. They can be constructed entirely out of trees and shrubs that have been trained or shaped appropriately, like this wisteria. Some of the most romantic are carved out of single bushes. Arbors should always be large enough to accommodate seats and, if there is room, a table.

Right: The most commonly seen arbors are built frameworks with climbers scrambling over them, the amount of shade offered depending on the density of the foliage. Roses create a dappled shade, heavier when used in conjuction with climbers like honeysuckle. Such scented flowers are particularly appealing.

WATER FEATURES

Water was one of the earliest features to be introduced to the garden. It is considered particularly precious in countries with hot, sunny climates, but it is just as appropriate in more temperate conditions under much grayer skies.

Water adds sound and texture to a garden and, as ornamental details, water features will attract attention, drawing the eye towards them. Water can be spread in a vast sheet or it can be kept to a smaller area, such as a pool or rill, partially hidden by vegetation. Running water, either splashing in a stream or playing in a fountain, introduces a pleasing sound and creates a lively atmosphere. It brings movement and moving images that sparkle with every ripple and splash. Conversely, the mirror-like surface of still water has a superb reflective quality which adds further scope to a design. Another benefit of water in the garden is that wildlife will be more plentiful.

It takes a certain amount of planning and effort to introduce a water feature in a garden, and such a project should not be undertaken lightly or without a firm commitment to success; a wrinkled black or graying plastic liner, half-filled with dirty water, does little towards producing an attractive garden. If in any doubt about your construction abilities, employ a water garden specialist to do the job for you.

Below: The addition of a water feature can transform a garden. Most people find it relaxing to be near water, enjoying the calming influence of the reflections in a still or broken surface. A water garden, especially one with moist margins, offers an opportunity to grow a wide range of beautiful and colorful plants. Furthermore, features associated with water, such as bridges and stepping stones, make attractive additions to the garden. Water can be introduced on any scale, from a large area of the garden devoted to a series of streams or waterfalls to a small pond or even an ornamental container.

Pools

Pools are one of the most popular garden features. They can be any size, from a small, formal raised structure built on a patio, to a full-sized lake. They must be sited where they will receive plenty of light; the water plants themselves will provide ample shade and protection for wildlife.

Formal gardens are best served with ponds that are regular and geometric in shape: circles, squares, ovals and rectangles are all suitable. For an elaborate feature, use a more complex shape such as a cross, a hexagon or a dumbbell shape. Triangular pools can be constructed, but these tend to look better in modern gardens where they are more likely to fit in with asymmetrical designs. The pool should be edged in a formal way, with paving stones or bricks. Any planting should be within the pool itself and is best restricted to one or two choice water lilies or a few marginal plants with impressive foliage.

Informal ponds can be of any shape but they are usually sinuous in outline. They should be well integrated into the surroundings and blurred at the edges with waterside planting that starts on the banks and moves down into the water. Informal ponds are often constructed in association with bog gardens, and once fully planted, these wet, spongy features will help merge the pool into the landscape.

There is a wide choice of construction methods and materials to choose from, the major ones being concrete, plastic or PVC liners and pre-formed shells. As a general rule, more irregular shapes are easier to construct using liners or pre-formed shells rather than concrete; concrete is best reserved for formal and raised structures. The disadvantage of pre-formed shells, however, is that you are restricted to the shapes on offer and it is difficult to blur their edges with planting; once installed, they should be edged with stones and plants. It is much easier to disguise the edges of pools made with plastic or PVC liners, and these flexible liners can accommodate virtually any shape of pool, sinuous or angular.

Plant the shallows of the pool with marginal plants, keeping the marshy area around the pool for bog plants. Place water lilies on the pool floor, along with other deep water aquatics; these should be planted in planting baskets and carefully lowered into the water. Introduce several clumps of submerged plants and floating aquatics to help keep algae at bay and to encourage all manner of wildlife.

Above: Splashing fountains, waterfalls or more lively cascades add the pleasure of sound to the light-catching qualities of moving water.

Left: Marginal aquatics usually look out of place in a formal pool, where water lilies are the most appropriate plants. With less formal pools, however, marginals make a distinctive contribution.

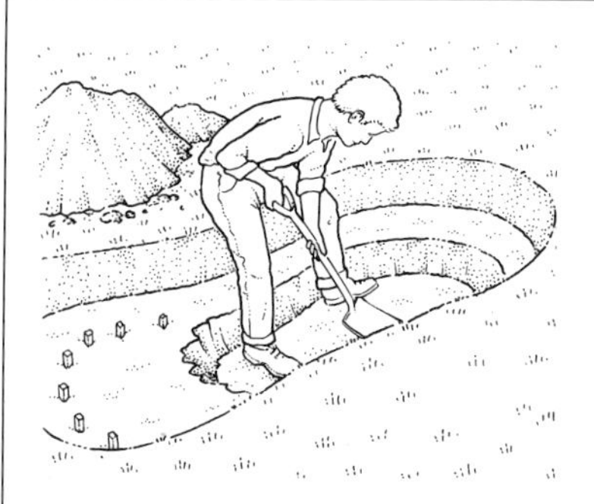

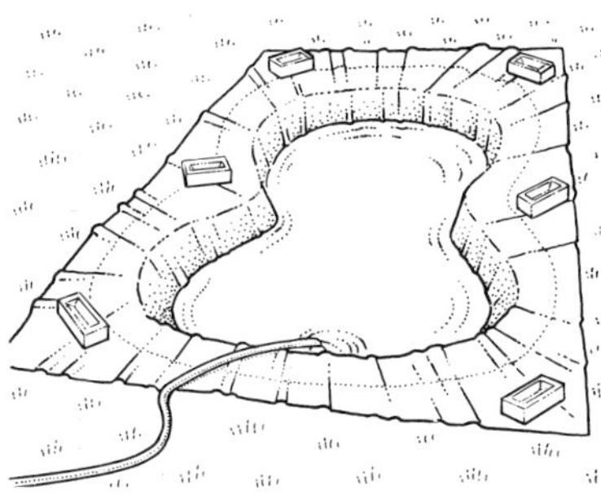

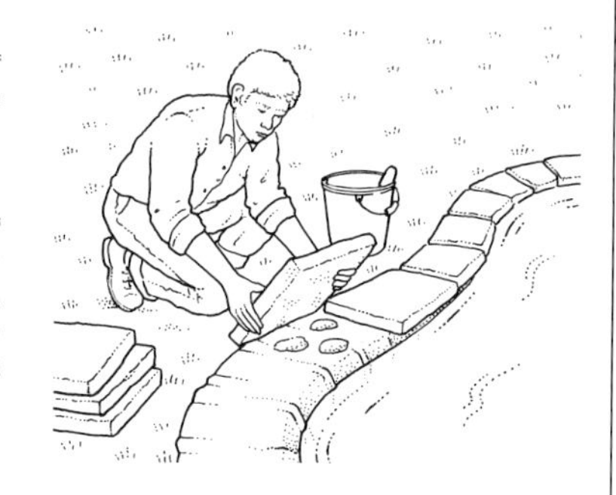

USING A PLASTIC OR PVC LINER

Create the outline of the pool on the ground using a garden hose. Excavate the site, keeping the topsoil for use elsewhere, but discard any heavy subsoil. Build up or reduce the sides so that they are all level; if the garden is on a slope, it may be necessary to construct a strong bank using some of the spare soil. Make some areas of the pond deeper than others to allow for plants that require different depths.

Once satisfied with the excavation, line the pond with a 2in (5cm) layer of soft sand to prevent any stones from puncturing the lining once it has been filled with water. If any vertical faces are too steep for the sand to adhere, use damp newspaper (you can use this alone for small ponds).

The dimensions of the liner should be as follows: the length of the pool multiplied by twice its depth will give the length of the liner; the width of the pool multiplied by twice its depth will give the width of the liner, plus about 18in (45cm) in every direction to allow for overlap into the ground around the pool margins. The liner must be well secured.

Stretch the liner across the pond, holding it in position with slabs of stone placed around the edges. Slowly fill the center of the liner with water from a hose; as it fills, the liner will sink into the hole, taking shape as it does so. Once the pool is full of water, trim the liner, leaving an 18in (45cm) margin all the way around. Smooth this down and dig a trench in which to bury the edge of the liner. Cover the margins of the pool with stone or concrete paving slabs so that the edges of the liner are well masked; alternatively, add a layer of soil to accommodate plants. It is also possible to use pieces of sod but these are likely to go brown where they come into contact with the liner unless they extend right down into the water; grass edges are also difficult to mow. Be careful never to puncture the lining; although repair kits are available, the patch will always be a source of weakness.

Pool shapes and surrounds In the design of pools, like that of many other garden features, there are great possibilities for varying the shape. In addition, there is considerable scope for treating the surrounds of pools in different ways, as these examples show. A hard surround with flagstones makes an interesting stepped edge (*above*). A more natural finish is created by grass, plants and stone running right up to the pool edge (*above right*). The rim of the raised pool (*right*) is cleverly disguised by a closely clipped hedge, an attractive option. The delicate irises are perfect for this design. Care must be taken in planting small pools such as these; an incautious approach can soon lead to overcrowding.

Marginal planting There is great scope for the imaginative planting of the margins and bog areas of pools and ponds (*right and below left*). A great number of plants thrive in moist conditions; bog plants require a wet environment but will not tolerate periods of inundation, while marginal plants prosper in standing water. Both types of plants are useful for masking and softening the area where land and water meet, integrating the feature into the adjacent landscape. Many of these plants look particularly attractive when planted in large drifts. Foliage is often more important than flowers. Around a big pond, large-scale planting always looks better than the restless effect produced by dotting plants about at random.

Reflections Much of the appeal of water lies in the way its surface reflects sky, clouds, surrounding vegetation and waterside features such as statues. Water also reflects light back onto surrounding plants and features, the flattering illumination enhancing their appearance (*right*). If there is no room for a pool, a simple tub of water can be used to create a small-scale watery mirror (*below left*). Although best if the surface is kept clear, it is possible to grow a few plants in a small container.

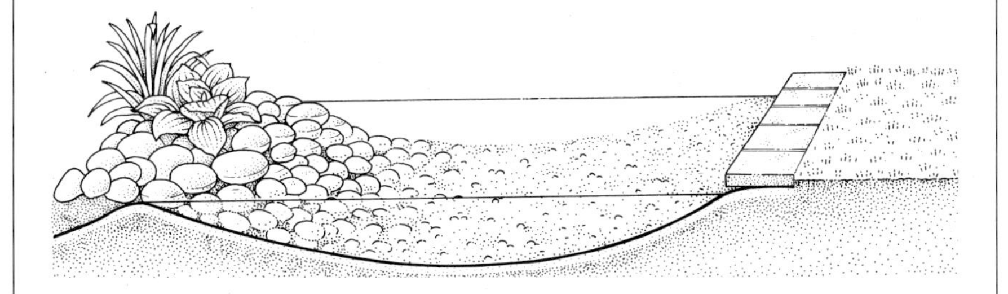

MARGINS

It is important to get the margins of a pool right, making a suitable interface between two different surfaces – water and grass for example – and disguising the edge of the liners that are commonly used. Many potentially attractive pools are spoiled because the wrinkled edge of the liner is visible. This can be hidden by plants, paving slabs (*right*) or by a beach of pebbles and gravel (*left*); the last will encourage wildlife.

Right: A pool and bog garden together form a natural-looking association. The hard edge of a pool betrays its artificiality, but this is blurred when the moisture-loving plants of the bog garden hang over the water's edge. Water lilies and similar plants enhance the natural effect. The red and yellow flowers add a splash of color in what is predominantly a foliage-led area; much interest is generated by the contrasting shapes of the different types of water plants and shrubs.

Left: A wide range of plants can be grown in the permanently moist conditions of a bog garden, many with superb leaves that are interesting for their forms and colors. Flowers are often an attractive bonus. Good foliage plants generally have a long period of interest and are likely to make a contribution for the whole of the growing season. Irises are among the many plants enjoying the moist conditions around this pool. Their long, narrow leaves contrast well with the rounder shapes of water lily pads, hostas and the umbrella-like marsh marigolds.

Above: Bog gardens are sometimes extensive but they need not cover a large area. Because they are recreations of natural habitats, it is important that bog gardens have an organic shape; rows of plants rarely look good. A sinuous line of moisture-loving plants can create the illusion of running water even where there is none.

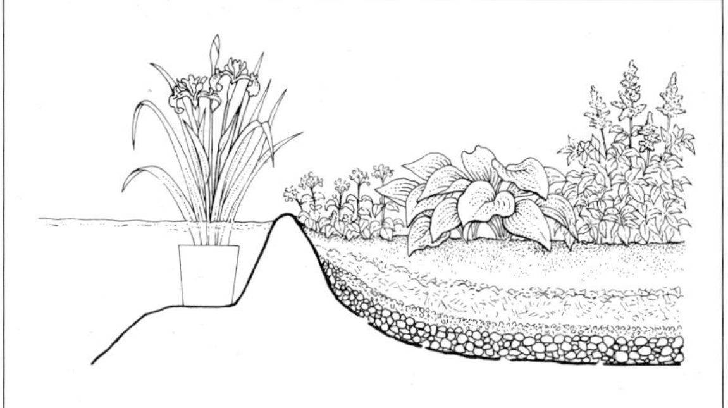

MAKING A BOG GARDEN

The bog garden should be constructed at the same time as the pool, using one large piece of liner for both features.

Excavate a 12in (30cm) basin next to the pool. Its edges must be the same height or a little higher than the bank of the pond, but the interconnecting lip must be a little lower than the pool. Spread a layer of coarse grit or gravel over the soil to aid drainage.

When the pond is lined, continue the liner over the lowered bank and across the bog area, and then tuck in the edges in the same way as for the pond. Puncture the liner in a few places and cover the floor with a layer of gravel to prevent the holes becoming clogged-up. Add a layer of well-rotted farmyard manure before filling the basin with a mixture of loam and leaf mold.

Canals and Streams

A garden with naturally-running water is a rare blessing; most people have to be content with constructing artificial streams using pumps to recycle the water. However, impressive and realistic results can still be achieved by artificial means.

The design of a canal or stream very much depends on the garden and whether there are any natural slopes down which water can flow. Running water does not require a steep gradient, and if no slopes exist it is quite easy to construct one with a sufficient incline to keep the water moving. Informal streams can be incorporated into rock gardens or natural, wooded banks; install a pool or create a spring at the top of the slope and construct another pool at the bottom of the stream, from where the water is recirculated by means of a submersible pump.

Streams that are irregular in width, depth and direction can be made with a strip of plastic or PVC liner, much in the same way as the construction of pools or, if the watercourse is very irregular and includes waterfalls, it may be easier to use several pieces of liner instead of one large strip. The joints should have a minimum overlap of 6in (15cm) depending on the steepness of the slope, the uppermost piece pointing in the same direction as the flow of the stream.

It is also possible to construct streams using concrete and waterproof cement. The ground beneath the feature should be well compacted, with a layer of coarse gravel for extra support to ensure that the finished, set concrete does not crack.

When using either a liner or concrete, be certain that the bed of the stream is flat so that the flow of water will cover and disguise it completely. If using concrete, you can implant rocks in the semi-wet concrete along the margins to give a more natural appearance. With a liner, any rocks must be placed on the bank overhanging the channel so that they do not come into contact with the liner and risk puncturing the material in any way.

For a more formal feature, a straight-edged canal built of concrete and cement can be built between regularly shaped pools.

Left and above: A natural stream flowing through a garden makes a superb feature. Simple planting on the margins, for example of ferns (*left*), is often the best way to integrate a stream into the landscape. There are, however, a large number of plants that relish moist waterside conditions, and more detailed planting can produce charming effects with foliage and flowers (*above*). Hostas and irises in particular lend themselves to streamside planting, especially when clustered together in groups.

Below: A canalized stream can look particularly attractive if there are small fountains placed at regular intervals along its length. Such a watercourse needs a formal setting, although the straight lines of the canal can equally well be softened by adjacent planting.

Above left and above right: Moving water always adds a touch of sparkling excitement to a garden, especially if it is bouncing off rocks and plunging down waterfalls. The visual effect is important but so, too, is the sound generated by running water. This can pervade the whole garden, giving it a unique atmosphere. If there are no natural waterfalls in a flowing stream, it is well worth creating small artificial falls by constructing dams or forming miniature rapids by the careful placing of stones and large rocks.

Left: A slow stream quietly meandering through a garden can be just as attractive as a fast moving torrent, although its appeal is very different. Because the flow is gentle, plants can be allowed to spread out into the water with no fear of them being washed away. The floating margin creates a natural look. Plants and the sky are reflected in the calm surface. Note the very effective stone edge.

Left: Rustic logs make an attractive bridge that is suitable in an informal setting. The logs must be checked periodically to ensure that they have not decayed.

Below: Some form of non-slip surface is a wise precaution on wood, especially if the bridge has no safety rails. Wire mesh is best; nail it securely in place over the boards.

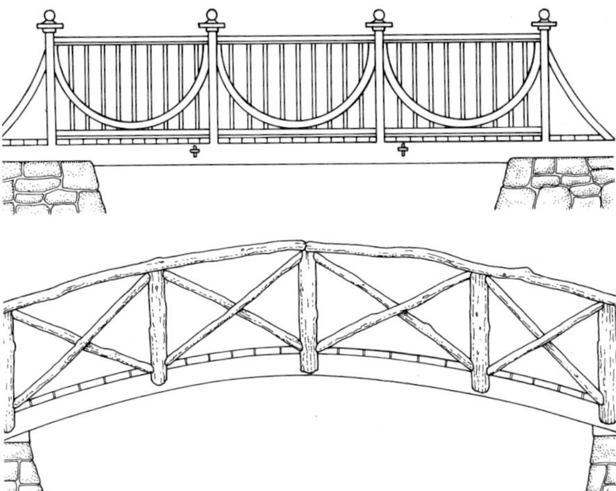

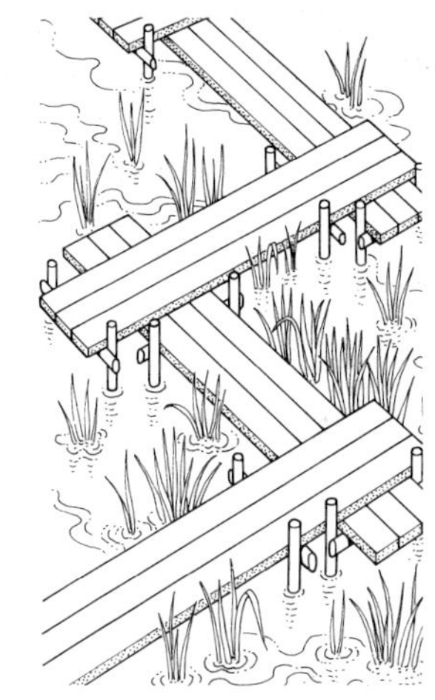

Duckboards Duckboards (*left*) are a simple but effective means of bridging broad stretches of water and, more particularly, of creating paths through extensive bog gardens. The supporting posts should be driven well into the ground, so this is not a technique to use if the pond or bog has a plastic or PVC liner. Both the posts and the planks need to be treated with a preservative. They should also be checked regularly to ensure that they are sound. The boards can be laid in patterns.

Bridge design There are many ways to vary the design of a simple wooden bridge (*above*). The crossing can be flat or curved, a curved design adding to the bridge's strength by thrusting the weight towards the banks. Handrails are generally necessary for the safety of pedestrians, and there are a variety of different ways in which the posts and rails can be treated in a decorative manner.

Right: A crossing such as this colorful bridge will enhance the unique character of a garden. A custom-built bridge, on a scale appropriate to the path it is carrying and the water it is crossing, is more likely to add a distinctive touch than a ready-made one.

Fountains

The sound of falling water is soothing and gives the impression of coolness. A fountain also keeps water moving and this will help prevent the growth of algae in a pond, as well as oxygenating the water for fish and other aquatic animals.

Fountains are most usually associated with pools. The simplest kind consists of a pump submerged under the water with the fountain nozzle just above the surface; various spray patterns are available. Stand the pump on a pile of bricks or a wooden framework, if necessary, to bring the nozzle up to the correct height. The fountain head will not be obtrusive as interest is focused on the water, but it is possible to disguise it by burying it in a pile of stones with the water emerging from the top. For more of a feature, install a sculptural fountain, which can be placed in the center or at the edge of the pool. It is essential that such fountains are attached to a secure base and care must be taken not to puncture the pool liner.

The height to which the water is thrown should be carefully calculated in relation to the size of the pool; even the slightest breeze can blow the spray sideways and possibly right out of the basin. For this reason, do not be too ambitious with small areas of water.

Not all fountains are freestanding. Water spouts can be attached to a wall or any other vertical surface, perhaps built into a sculpture, mask or gargoyle, from where they will shoot water into a pool or basin below. When installing such a device, provision must be made for draining it during the winter or when hard frosts threaten, with their punishing effects.

A bubble fountain is another option. This produces a simple, low bubble of water and, placed within a rocky outcrop edged with flowers, it can successfully imitate a spring. A bubbler can also be placed in the middle of a millstone set in a bed of pebbles; the water will emerge from the center of the stone and wash over the edge, through the stones.

Figurative fountains Fountains come in numerous guises. A classical figure pouring water from an amphora (*left*) is an attractive if well-used motif; the single trickle of water and the green vegetation produce a lovely cool effect. In another figurative fountain (*above*), the liveliness of the water seems to express the exuberance of the figure. The cherub is best placed in the middle of a pool, and the classical figure to one side, as here.

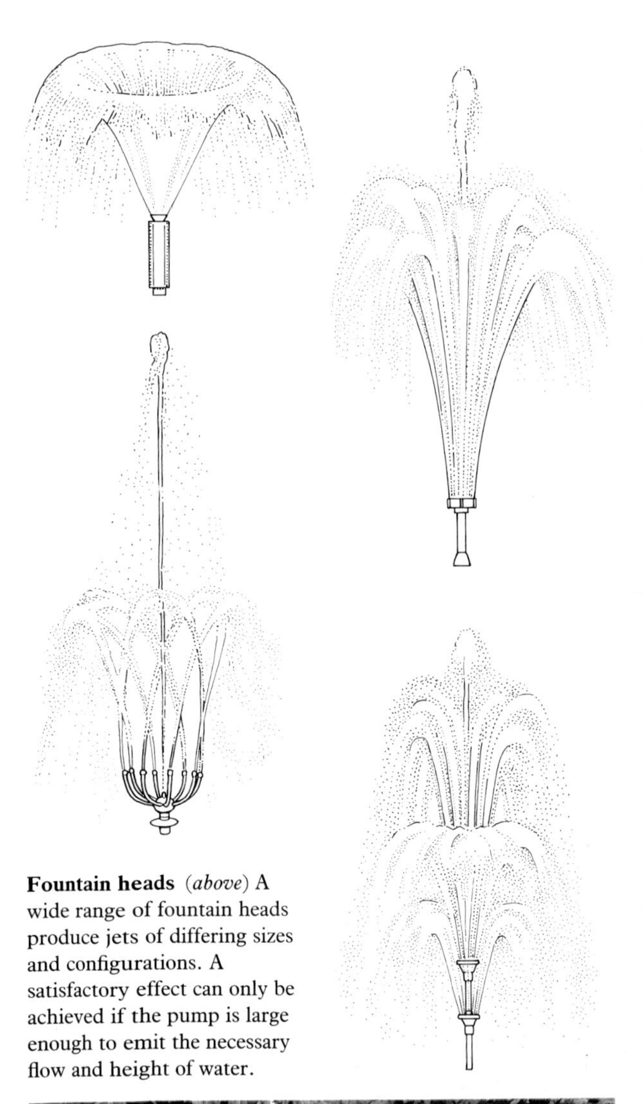

Fountain heads *(above)* A wide range of fountain heads produce jets of differing sizes and configurations. A satisfactory effect can only be achieved if the pump is large enough to emit the necessary flow and height of water.

Below left: The water of a fountain is not necessarily collected in a pool. Here, water splashes onto stones and pebbles before draining into a reservoir located below them. The variety of different stones used adds much interest.

Above: Stainless steel is a material much used in modern fountains. In this example, water flows out of the tallest cylinders filling those below till they brim over, spilling into a pool below: a pyramid of moving water.

PUMPS

A pump is the power behind all artificially moving water, giving the impression of an uninterrupted flow.

There are two types of pump: submersible and surface. Advice should be sought from the supplier as to which pump will supply the required rate of flow. Submersible pumps are suitable for small water features: they will operate a fountain or lift sufficient water for a modest stream. They are quiet and easy to install; simply place the pump on the floor of the pool, on a pile of bricks if necessary to bring it up to the right level. Surface pumps are much more powerful and should be used to shift large quantities of water over considerable distances or heights. A surface pump can operate a large fountain or a waterfall and, with the addition of a T-piece, it can operate more than one feature at the same time.

The power supply must be provided by a shielded cable that is buried in a trench at least 2ft (60cm) deep. As an extra safety precaution, the cable should be fitted with a circuit breaker which will cut off the supply should there be a short circuit. Any outdoor sockets must be completely weatherproof. As a word of warning, water and electricity can be a fatal mixture, and if there is any doubt on the part of the gardener as to his or her ability to install an electric pump, then a qualified electrician must be called in for this part of the procedure.

Left: Woodland is an ideal setting for this piece of sculpture, the twisting, slender forms of the entwined figures reflecting the shape of nearby tree trunks.

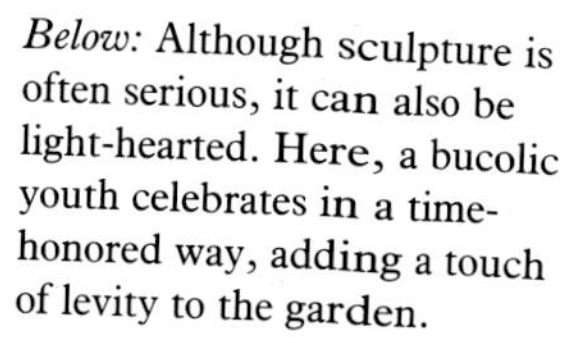

Below: Although sculpture is often serious, it can also be light-hearted. Here, a bucolic youth celebrates in a time-honored way, adding a touch of levity to the garden.

Small-scale sculpture Small figures rarely look right in isolation as they tend to be dwarfed by their surroundings and so lose their impact. They frequently need to be placed on a pedestal to lift them up to eye level (*above*), which will make more of a feature of them. Another way to give small figures emphasis is to place them on a low base, surrounding them with plants grown in flower beds and in urns (*left*). This figure seems to dance, floating above brightly-colored flowers.

Above: A substantial plinth takes the weight of this massive kneeling figure; the base also provides a visual anchor for the sculpture.

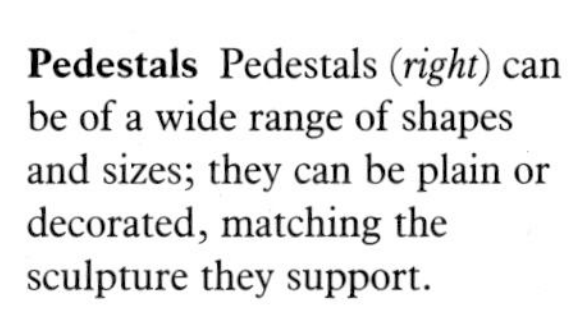

Pedestals Pedestals (*right*) can be of a wide range of shapes and sizes; they can be plain or decorated, matching the sculpture they support.

Above: This sculpture depicting two figures is itself quite small, but the pedestal doubles its height, transforming it into an imposing and handsome formal garden ornament.

Sculpture and foliage The worked surfaces of pieces of sculpture contrast well with the texture and shapes of foliage and bark. This is never more apparent than when a figure (*above*) or a more abstract piece (*left*) seems to be wandering out of the greenery; then the effect is particularly subtle. The contrast can also be strong, even when the plants are a little more distant (*above left*).

Decorative Details

Apart from sculpture, there are other ornamental features which can be used to liven up and decorate the garden in all manner of ways.

Columns can be employed for purely aesthetic purposes, or they can be functional, acting as supports and pedestals. They may be simple, with a smooth surface, or fluted to accentuate their length, with either plain or highly ornate capitals (the molded crowns). Used as decoration, columns can be positioned in such a way as to frame another feature, such as a gateway or view; a tall Grecian column flanking a doorway will look elegant and imposing. Columns can also be used to form colonnades and as supports for pergolas.

In many small gardens, a complete classical column will look out of place, but a section of a column that includes the capital, hidden in a corner and half covered with ivy, can blend in well and look very effective. In a large, leafy garden which has a timeless quality, columns can be used to create an interesting feature. They need not stand upright; they can be placed on their sides, either whole or in a number of pieces, to simulate a classical ruin.

Obelisks are four-sided columns, usually made from stone, that taper to a pyramidal form. They often have inscriptions on one or more of their faces, an arcadian ode or, in the case of a commemorative monument, an elegy. They make interesting and elegant decorations when used in pairs to mark doorways, or at the top or bottom of a flight of steps. Larger examples make good focal points, especially set at the end or intersection of a series of paths or avenues, or in the centre of a circular lawn.

For the finishing touch, add a finial to a wall or column. These ornamental pieces, often in the shape of a fleur-de-lys or a pineapple, or a more simple spherical or pointed design, can stand on gateposts and other features. Urns can be used instead of finials, either as containers or simply as ornamentation. Unless they are very large, they usually look best on some sort of pedestal. There is an extremely wide range of different styles of urn available. Antique examples come in a number of materials including stone, terracotta, bronze, copper and lead, although reconstituted stone reproductions are a popular alternative.

Above: Urns need not be filled with plants to have visual impact. Here, the rounded empty pot contrasts well with the slender, linear planting around it. The raised position of the urn allows its decorative surface to be appreciated.

Left: The contrast of the solid but spiky growth of the plant with the shape and decoration of the urn in which it grows is perfect as they fully complement each other. The background planting makes the picture even more satisfying; a frothy collection of bedding plants would not be at all effective.

Urn selection There is an almost inexhaustible range of urns on offer from which to choose. In this selection (*below*) all have strong character. The central three, the largest representing autumn, are decorative in themselves and could not be planted up; they would look best standing on pedestals. The smaller two would make ideal adornments placed on walls, and the top and bottom urns can be used either by themselves or containing plants. If large enough, they could stand directly on the ground, but both would be displayed better if they were raised on low pedestals.

Urns for planting Urns for planting always look best if they are on the generous side so they can be filled with a mass of plants (*top and right*). However, large pots are heavy and should be placed in position before they are filled with compost. Smaller urns (*above*) make ideal objects with which to ornament the tops of walls, although they may need to be secured on high walls so that they are not swept off by the wind.

Below: The gateposts flanking a gate give an impression of the style of the garden beyond. In this example, the stone balls topping the gateposts help to make an impressive entrance.

Obelisks Their smooth, geometric shape makes obelisks stand out from their surroundings in the garden. These architectural forms make strong focal points; this can be seen in the example of an obelisk positioned in a border among colorful, spiky agapanthus (*left*), and in the very different example (*below left*) of an obelisk set in isolation in a formal pool, repeating the shape of the tall, slender trees close by.

Right: The clean lines of these columns inevitably lead the eye to the sculpture in the garden beyond. The columns are themselves ornamental because of the effective, well-proportioned ball finials that add a finishing touch.

Classical columns Although both these columns (*below*) have the same physical function, one looks solid and heavy while the vertical flutes make the other look much lighter.

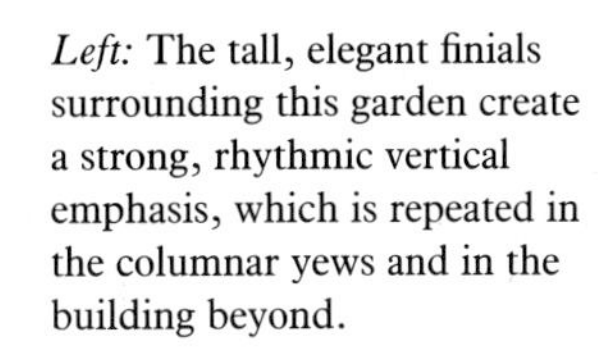

Left: The tall, elegant finials surrounding this garden create a strong, rhythmic vertical emphasis, which is repeated in the columnar yews and in the building beyond.

Above: The mysterious character of this narrow, almost claustrophobic garden compartment is intensified by a curious spiral column topped by an oversized ball.

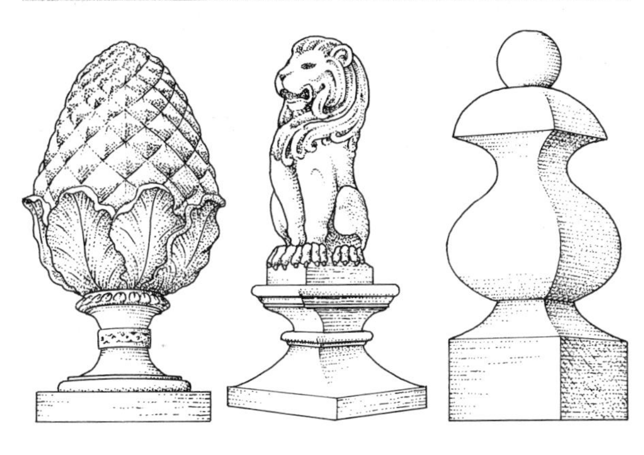

Finials (*above*) There is a very wide range of finials available, many of which, like the three illustrated, take traditional, refined forms. New examples are usually made from reconstituted stone or cement. Because of their weight, they need to be fixed to the tops of walls or columns securely, so that there is no risk of them being dislodged by strong winds. Increasingly they can be found made from lightweight fiberglass, but this does not weather like stone.

Above: Finials can often be used to create links between different areas of a garden. Here, the ball on the gable is picked up on the column in the foreground. The repeated use of softening creepers makes the echo more obvious.

Niches

A niche is a decorative alcove and, when built into a wall, it can also provide a place for displaying a piece of sculpture or an urn.

To incorporate a niche into a wall, the wall must be thick enough to take the depth of the niche, that is to say, more than one brick deep. It is also advisable to build the niche into the wall at the time of construction, rather than have to partly demolish the wall at a later date to accommodate the niche.

There are many designs suitable for niches. The most popular is semi-circular with a domed top, but the sides can equally well be straight and the niche box-like; a number of ornamental examples have fluted surfaces with shell-head tops. Niches are frequently set flush with the brick or stonework but can be delineated with a decorative raised edging around them. This can be extended to create a sill at the base of the niche and a canopy over the top. While the conventional niche is smooth-sided and formal, it is possible to create a rougher finish, perhaps a little irregular in shape, more similar to a small grotto. This should not be decorated but left to weather; in a cool, damp, shady position, it will soon develop a thin coating of moss and lichen and take on a natural, informal appearance.

A niche does not have to be restricted to a stone or brick wall; with careful design and skilful management, an alcove can be cut into a hedge to liven up an otherwise flat surface. For the best results, use a compact, small-leaved hedging plant like yew (*Taxus*) and create a simple arched shape. This needs to be well maintained for the most dramatic effect.

To a certain extent, the position of a niche will be determined by its intended contents. A figure, religious or otherwise, can be set high up looking down on the viewer, but while a full-length statue can be placed at ground level, other sculptures require an eye-level location; an urn full of plants, for example, should be positioned at a height where it can be fully appreciated as well as easily watered.

Larger niches can be created at ground level to house a bench or even seats and a table, although these tend to be more appropriate in large, formal gardens. Ground-level niches of any size can also contain a flowerbed planted with shade-tolerant species. Niches can also be incorporated into water features; they make handsome wall fountains with the spout emerging from the back of the alcove and falling into a pool or basin below. For a more decorative feature, install a figurative fountain.

Above and right: If a wall is deep enough, niches are a valuable way of adding decoration to the garden. A small one set in a wall at eye level or above might accommodate a bust (*above*) or a similar small sculpture but, on a grander scale, niches can become major features in their own right (*right*), lavishly planted and ornamented with large scale sculpture.

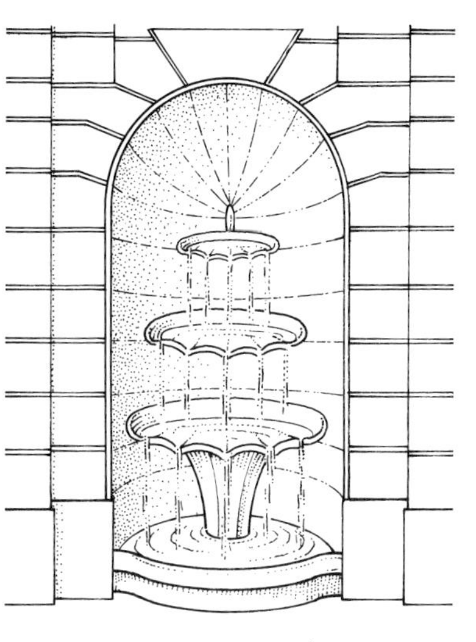

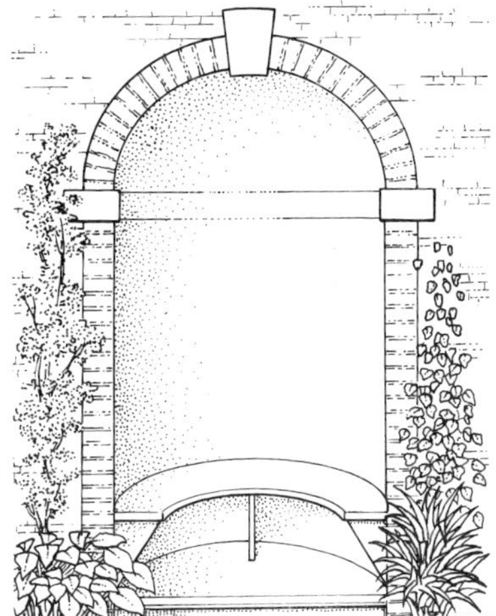

Above left: Many niches have curved crowns and these can be decorated in various ways. The shell shape, dating back to the seventeenth century, has been much used.

Above: Large niches are almost apsidal in scale and can be used to house water features, such as the tiered fountain (*top*), and even seating (*bottom*).

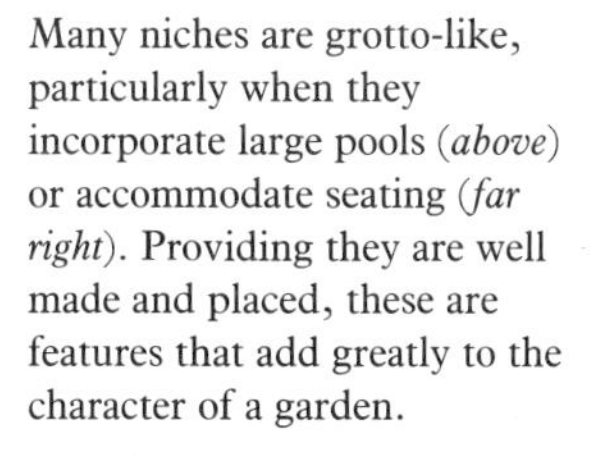

Many niches are grotto-like, particularly when they incorporate large pools (*above*) or accommodate seating (*far right*). Providing they are well made and placed, these are features that add greatly to the character of a garden.

Right: Architectural detail in brick or stonework can be used to make a niche look more conspicuous.

Grottoes

Grottoes are mostly small caves, either natural or artificial, some of which are highly decorative, often housing an ornament of some kind. Buildings that are obviously not caves but are adorned with plentiful stones or shells are also known as grottoes. It is believed that they were originally sacred shrines that housed gods, goddesses or water nymphs. In the past these features have mostly been constructed in large, formal gardens as picturesque features and cool retreats from the sun, but today they are no longer associated with such grandeur and can be accommodated very successfully in smaller sites.

Among garden features, grottoes call for the greatest imagination and flair in their design. True grottoes should either be sculpted out of a rock face or cliff, or dug into the ground, perhaps in association with a mound or a suitable grassy bank. As few gardens have the benefit of a rocky outcrop, it is most likely that the gardener will have to construct a small hill out of which the grotto can be carved.

At their simplest, grottoes are shallow caves, not much more than hollows, while complex ones can involve a warren of tunnels and underground chambers. Those built either totally or partly below ground should have walls and domed roofs of stone or brick. These grottoes should be provided with a drainage system to take away any water that may accumulate on the floor. Above ground, structures can be built of preserved wood or brick.

It is a good idea to leave a vent in the roof, not only for ventilation but to admit a shaft of sunlight. If all or part of the walls are then covered with glass bottle-bases, a most effective atmosphere can be created as they will reflect the light and produce an eerie glow. The structure should also be surrounded by trees and bushes to give an authentic, dark, cool effect. Finally, an ornament, a statue of a god or goddess, or some kind of water feature, such as a wall fountain, can be introduced to enliven the interior.

Potentially, grottoes can be one of the most dangerous garden features, especially if built below ground, and so great care must be taken in their construction to ensure that they are safe and sturdy. Caves in particular should be given much attention, to ensure that they do not collapse. The most complicated grottoes are major projects which should not be undertaken lightly, and professional help should be sought to ensure that roofs and walls are totally secure. The internal decoration, however, is enjoyable and well within the grasp of most gardeners.

Left and above: Although both these grottoes are likely to have similar dark and damp interiors, their exteriors are very different. One, appearing as a black hole in the hillside, is like the original grottoes, which were either natural or man-made caves. The other has an ornate and classical architectural entrance with an iron gate, which gives little idea of the interior.

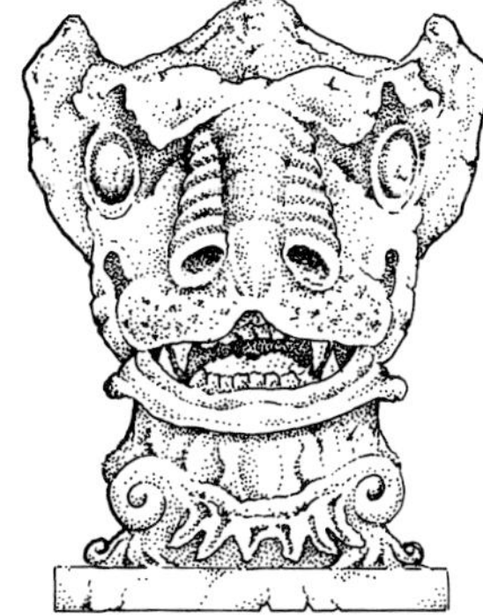

Right and below: Many grottoes have facades in keeping with their interiors and sunken entrances. It is typical of many that they have a Gothic flavor (*right*) which seems to pay homage to their primitive origins, but these are often rather run down or decayed (*below*). This is mainly because they are old and have not been maintained, but as long as they are safe, this suits the character of the feature; indeed, many of the grottoes that have been built or refurbished in recent times have emulated this state of decay. Grottoes are best set out of the way in an isolated part of the garden.

Above: These four faces are typical of keystones set in the entrance arches of grottoes. They epitomize the character of these garden features, which have their origins in pagan places of worship. The figures represented guard the grotto and also act as a forewarning of the earthy, primitive world within. Carvings of this kind are also found inside. A certain degree of skill is required to make these grotesque masks, but cement reproductions are readily available. They can be adapted into wall fountains, with water spouting out from their mouths into a pool or decorative sink below.

DESIGN AND DECORATION

Authentic grottoes are mysterious and secretive. For the greatest effect, they should be hidden away in a corner of the garden, off the main track so that they are suddenly chanced upon. Vegetation and rough stonework will help hide the entrance, which might be approached by a winding path that inevitably draws the inquisitive towards the unseen grotto. If possible, a damp situation should be chosen, as this will allow ferns, mosses and other lush, green growth to surround the approach and doorway, adding to the sense of adventure. If a grotto has a waterfall or stream flowing by the entrance, with careful engineering, this could be diverted inside to provide a delightful water feature.

The entrance itself can be protected by a gargoyle or the head of a mythical beast. Once inside, decoration can be anything from the bizarre to the primitive, or it might reflect the religious origins of the form. Grottoes provide a unique opportunity for the imagination to run riot without the gardener having to re-design the rest of the site to match or accommodate them.

The walls can be decorated with murals or they can be covered with mosaics of odds and ends, shells being especially popular. The use of glittering materials that pick up any rays of light is very effective; broken pieces of glass or mirrors, faceted if possible, and pieces of broken porcelain will supply a charmed atmosphere. Not only can the walls be decorated but the ceiling as well, creating a room without boundaries, again, part of the grotto's mystical quality. The floor can be left as trampled earth or it can be covered with cobblestones laid in a pattern.

Odd shafts of light can be allowed into the interior through small roof lights or long pipes leading out through the walls into the open air. When visitors are expected, candlelight will add to the romance. Water can be introduced, and masks and small figurines enhance the Gothic feel of a grotto, which should still retain much of the mysticism and idiosyncrasy of a holy shrine. Strange, artificial stalactites can be made out of cement, as can a mass of other three-dimensional effects. Not everybody likes to create a bizarre illusion however, and many prefer to keep the grotto simple, with just one or two mysterious touches such as a hidden niche or dimly-lit statue of a god or goddess.

Such places are often damp and cold, even on a hot day, and few people remain inside for long. However, a grotto could contain a bench, possibly built into the wall, for those who wish to linger in the special setting.

Left, top right and bottom right: Grottoes are usually decorated with sculpture, shells and other small objects, including pieces of glass and mirrors, that catch and reflect any light that penetrates the gloom. Water is also often a feature, an allusion to sacred springs.

Wall Ornament

As structural components of gardens, walls have more to offer than just protection and privacy. They can be used to display a variety of ornamentation, although attractive old walls are best left unadorned. Some forms of ornament can be built into the wall while it is being constructed; these are likely to become permanent features as they will be difficult to remove without damaging part of the wall.

A modest form of built-in decoration is a simple coping placed on the top of the wall, often used to complement fine stone or brick. More of a feature can be made if tiles or slate are used to complement the fabric of the wall. Piers or columns are a means of creating a functional but decorative structure: they may be there primarily to support the wall, but they are also ornamental and can be used to break the monotony of a flat surface. Another way of decorating a wall is to create a small round or square window, which can be left as an open space or covered with a metal grille. This will allow a glimpse of the area beyond, encouraging the observer to explore further, while from a distance the feature will look like a picture hanging on the wall.

Fixed patterns and designs using different colored bricks can be incorporated into the wall at the time of building, and certain bricks can be left slightly proud of the wall surface to form a raised pattern. A less subtle form of decoration is to use pierced concrete blocks in a geometric pattern. These can be used on their own or built on top of an existing low wall, their angular appearance used as an asset in a suitable, linear design or softened by climbing plants.

Applied decoration does not need pre-planning and can be used to add variety to existing walls. Urns, balls, obelisks and finials all look effective placed on the tops of walls, and framing columns or piers next to gates or doorways can be highly decorative. A more creative approach is to attach items to the wall. These can be in the form of ready-made pieces of sculpture, such as decorative masks, or perhaps a few unique pieces found in an antique shop. Another possibility is to make a mosaic out of fragments of colored tiles and porcelain embedded in cement.

None of these effects should be overdone or allowed to become too dominant; they need to be subtle in order to blend in well with the garden.

Left and above: When decorating walls, many gardeners are happy to use only plants. However, a variety of different kinds of sculptural decoration can be applied, both on the face of a wall and on its top, and these help make blank architectural features more interesting. Sometimes a decoration is most effective when combined with plants. The mask (*left*) seems to be commenting on what is taking place above its head. The decorative circular niche (*above*) may originally have housed a sculpture.

Sundials

Sundials make popular and attractive garden ornaments. These days they are primarily used as decoration rather than as timepieces, but as such they add a tranquil air of historic timelessness to the garden. Although old sundials are expensive to buy, there are many good reproductions available, and sculptors and blacksmiths will often be delighted to take commissions to produce original works.

There are two types of garden sundial: one that is placed in a horizontal position on a pedestal, and one that is fixed vertically to a wall. Essentially, each one consists of a dial and a gnomon — the sloping piece that casts the shadow. The gnomon is usually made of metal, either brass or bronze, although stone ones are sometimes seen, and the dial can be made of metal, engraved stone or slate; the smooth texture of the latter makes it particularly popular. More contemporary designs made of metal and perspex can also be found. If freestanding, the sundial should be placed on a pedestal made of stone or cast cement; this must be low enough to enable the observer to look down onto the face of the sundial. If the sundial is fixed to a wall the dial should be clearly visible.

The basic structure of a sundial is very straightforward, but there is plenty of room for imaginative decoration. The gnomon can be made of plain metal or decorative wrought iron; numbers denoting time can be simple or ornate, following any preferred design. Quotations can be engraved on to the dial; anything about the passing of time is appropriate. On a wall, the dial can be painted.

Sundials need careful positioning at a particular time of day, with the shadow of the gnomon showing the correct hour. From a functional point of view they must obviously be sited in a location which receives full sun throughout the day; even if a sundial is to be used for purely ornamental reasons, it should still be placed in a sunny spot as it will look out of place in the shade. A prominent location will take full advantage of their aesthetically pleasing qualities.

Sundials make ideal central features in open, circular, paved or gravel areas, and they can look particularly handsome when placed in the middle of a series of radiating paths or borders. Set in the heart of a herb or rose garden they add true character. They also make an interesting focal point in an otherwise uninterrupted expanse of lawn. Used as an accessory rather than a centerpiece, a sundial can be placed on a terrace or in a sunny courtyard.

An attractive alternative to sundials are armillary spheres, globes of concentric metal hoops showing the progress of the planets across the sky.

Left and above: Some of the best sundials are the simplest. All they need is a stable plinth and somewhere to stand in the sun; this last point is particularly important but is often overlooked. A patina gives them the romance of age but, if they are to be used to tell the time, make certain that the face does not become so moss-covered that it obscures the numbers and the time cannot be read.

Fixed sundials Some sundials are portable but most are mounted in fixed positions. In garden settings they are conventionally placed on a horizontal plane (*above*), but they can also be vertical (*right*), as is more frequently seen on the side of buildings. The armillary sphere (*below right*) is an attractive alternative to the sundial.

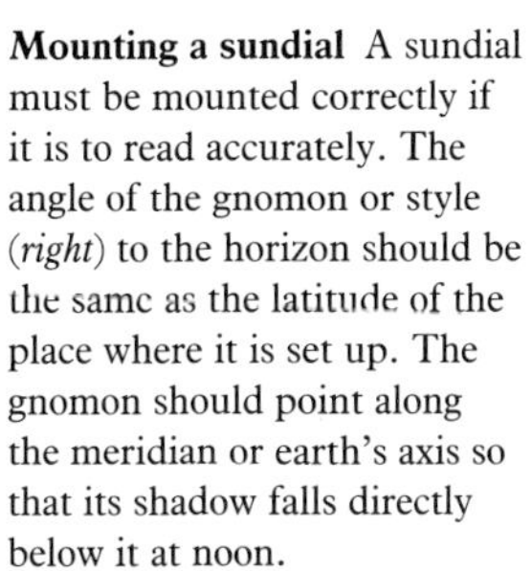

Mounting a sundial A sundial must be mounted correctly if it is to read accurately. The angle of the gnomon or style (*right*) to the horizon should be the same as the latitude of the place where it is set up. The gnomon should point along the meridian or earth's axis so that its shadow falls directly below it at noon.

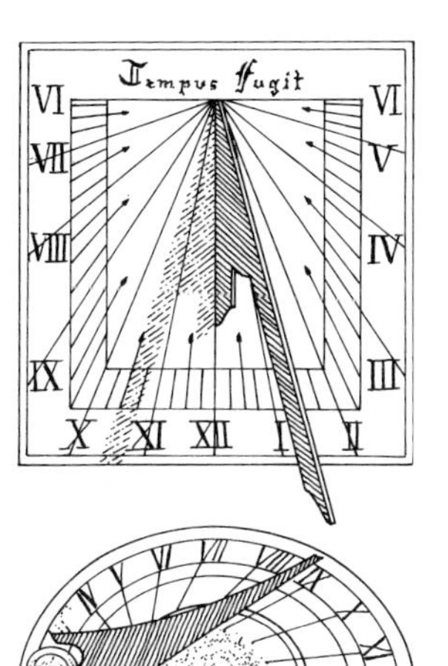

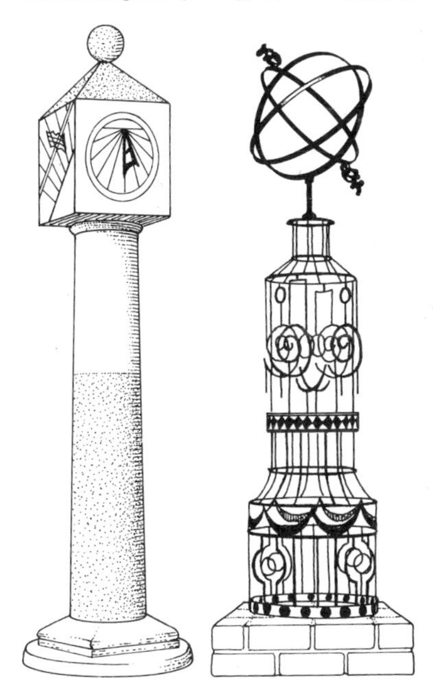

Columns for sundials Stone or a stone substitute are the usual materials for sundial columns (*above left*), although fancy wrought iron (*above right*) can be used for a more decorative effect.

Variations on sundials Sundials need not just be conventional flat dials with gnomons (*below*). They can also be multifaceted (*above*); such sundials must be made specifically for the area where they are to be installed. Alternatively, three-dimensional designs (*left*) can be constructed, and these give great scope for unusual and imaginative treatment.

Above: The armillary sphere is more sophisticated than the sundial, doing more than telling the time. It also demonstrates the movement of the heavenly bodies and, among other things, gives information on the equinoxes. Armillary spheres are set with the gnomon, (here, the straight line passing through the center of the sphere), along the meridian; that is, it points due north at midday. A sphere needs to be mounted at eye level.

Right: Do not be deceived: some pieces that superficially resemble armillary spheres are simply sculptures.

Topiary

Topiary can be considered a living sculpture, not only in the sense that it is made up of living material which grows each time it is clipped, but also because it sways and changes shape when blown by the wind. As long as you have the patience to wait until it is mature, topiary is the cheapest form of sculpture and can be had for the price of the original plant. However, buying ready-formed topiary can be expensive because of the amount of time it has taken to bring the plant to maturity and to train it.

Topiary as a form of garden sculpture is expressive of the gardener's tastes, and the range of shapes and designs are infinite, as wide as the gardener's imagination. They can be purely geometric — cones, pyramids, spheres or spirals – or they can be representational, depicting a bird or an animal. Simple shapes can be carved directly from mature shrubs, but more complex shapes need a form which will act initially as a training frame and then as a guide for subsequent trimming; pieces that stick out, such as animals' tails, particularly need some kind of support until the plant is mature.

There is a wide range of trees and shrubs that can be used for topiary. Slow-growing species are best because, although a bit more patience is needed to await their maturity, the plants will need less clipping and retain their shape better. While fast-growing plants can be used, they quickly become loose and ragged and need a lot of attention in order to keep any consistent and recognizable pattern. Fast-growing plants, such as privet (*Ligustrum*), should only be used for simple shapes, while slow growers, for example yew (*Taxus*) or box (*Buxus*), have a much tighter habit, good for more complicated figures.

Topiary need not be confined to plants growing in fixed positions, it can equally well be practiced on container-grown shrubs placed singly or in small groups. This means that even in a small garden where the majority of space is devoted to paved areas, it is possible to have miniature pieces positioned at strategic points, and these can easily be moved around to create different arrangements. Bay (*Laurus*) can be successfully accommodated in containers, with the growth shaped into spheres or cones.

Left and above: Topiary is one of the most delightful forms of garden ornament, often lovingly created by gardeners themselves. There is great scope for the imagination as well as skill with the shears. Some specimens are representational, like these birds sitting enthroned in regal majesty (*left*). Others are more geometric in shape, such as this spiral (*above*).

MAZES

In the long history of maze making, hedges, stones and turf have been used to form intricate patterns. Two of the many possible patterns are illustrated above. The most familiar planted mazes consist of a complex of paths walled by hedges, trimmed to head height or above. These may take years to reach full maturity.

Below: This row of topiary could almost represent chessmen lined up for a game. Yew, one of the most suitable trees for topiary, only needs trimming once a year. However, if time is available, two cuts will keep it neater. Scaffolding will be needed to trim the taller pieces.

Above and right: Topiary need not be restricted to pieces on a grand scale (*above*). It can equally well be created on the much smaller and more intimate scale of these animals shaped from box (*right*). These have been grown in Versailles tubs and make an interesting contrast alternating with the box "tubs". Simple shapes are easier to maintain than more intricate designs, and this is particularly relevant when it comes to clipping large specimens. Pot-grown topiary can generally be moved easily to different settings.

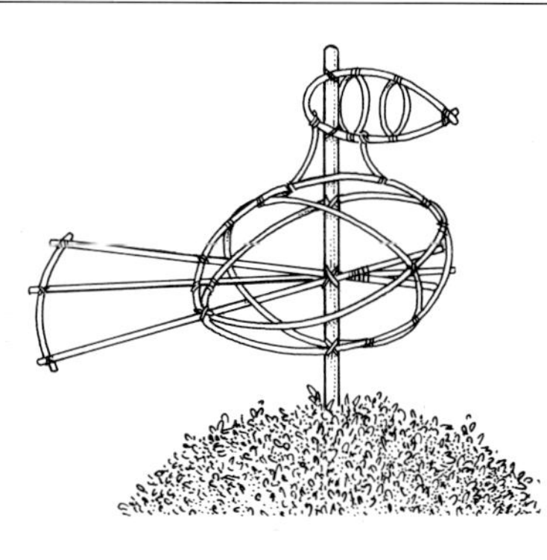
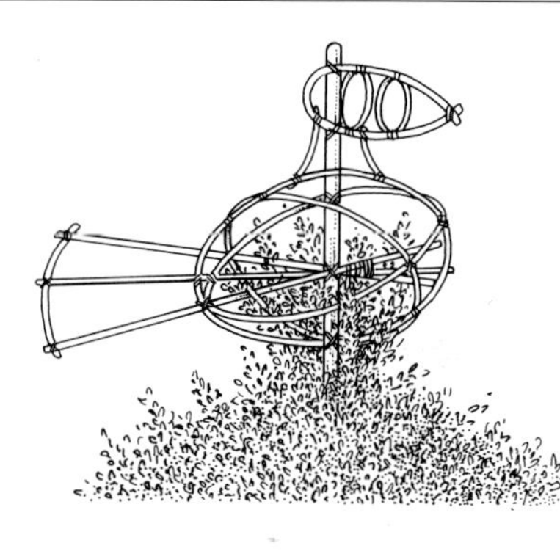

CREATING TOPIARY

The first step to creating successful topiary is to choose a suitable site. This should be done carefully as topiary can take up to ten years to mature, a time-consuming mistake if it is in the wrong position.

Next, the shape must be decided upon. Sometimes an existing bush, or the configuration of the young growth on a new bush, will suggest a form. In such cases, shaping will be easier as it will follow the natural lines of the plant. Solid and simple forms can be clipped from existing trees or started from scratch. Cutting into bushes will expose bare areas of wood, but these will soon leaf over and within a year or so the piece will be quite presentable. Geometric shapes are deceptively difficult to clip, especially those with flat surfaces. Use plumb lines to get vertical faces; wooden templates and jigs are also very helpful in getting the correct line. Spontaneous, asymmetrical shapes are easier to create and can be done by eye.

Figurative works are in some ways easier because any accidental variation, short of cutting off a tail or head, is much less likely to show. These can be shaped from a solid bush if they are not too complicated, but the most detailed figures are best created from young bushes trained from the beginning over sturdy wire forms.

Train a few thick stems along the main elements of the form. Loosely tie in the shoots with tarred string to allow them to grow. Do not try to force older shoots in a direction in which they do not want to go as they are likely to break; young pliant growth is better for complicated shapes. Growth is rarely uniform, especially when shoots have been bent downwards, and the side facing the sun is likely to grow fastest. Try to accommodate such quirks of nature into an asymmetrical, irregular design.

Topiary does not have to be a single color; plants of different shades can be planted and trained together.

Clipping is best done with garden shears. Use the tips rather than the full length of the blades, as the latter are likely to create flat areas. For intricate details use pruning shears, which are more adept at fine pruning. It is best to start at the top of a figure, cutting out and downwards.

Above left and above: Topiary often introduces elements of fun and humor, even in grand, formal gardens.

Left: Pleaching is another way of training plants, as seen in this row of trees forming a screen on stilts.

Trompe l'oeil

A *trompe l'oeil* is a painting or decoration that creates an illusion, tricking the viewer into seeing something that is not really there. With a bit of imagination and ingenuity, it is possible for the gardener to create any number of original, deceptive devices using plants, paintings and sculpture.

As practical features, they are mainly employed in small gardens to give the impression of space, so that the garden seems bigger than it really is. However, they can be used in any garden in a jocular way to create an amusing and witty trick of the eye.

Classic *trompe l'oeils* are created by painting pictures that look three-dimensional. It is possible to use this technique in a small garden by painting windows on a wall that reveal an apparently pastoral vista; this will be especially effective in a town garden where the painted scene will contrast with the true urban surroundings. Similarly, doors or gateways can be painted; a half-open gate with a glimpse of what lies beyond will deceive the observer into thinking the garden has another part to it.

Another example of *trompe l'oeil* is the careful positioning of a large mirror on the wall of a small basement garden or other enclosed area to give the impression that the garden is twice its actual size. Again, another trick is to attach trellis to a wall so that it gives the illusion of perspective: the typically horizontal battens should be arranged so as to point towards some imaginary vanishing point, taking the eye with them into the supposed distance. This is most effective when the impression given is that of a tunnel or corridor. A further method is to use a single panel on a side wall that narrows towards the far end, again in the direction of an imaginary vanishing point, making the space look longer. Plants can be used in a similar fashion: tall trees in the foreground with progressively shorter, thinner ones behind will give the illusion of distance. Pale flowers, misty blues for example, planted at the end of a border will make the border seem longer; conversely, brilliant colors planted at a distance will draw the end of the garden towards the viewer.

More illusions can be created by painting murals, of woods for example, that form a backdrop against which the garden is viewed, but the problem with this is that a painting does not change with the seasons. It is possible to create whole borders on a flat surface, with one or two real plants in front to add to the three-dimensional effect. Three-dimensional *trompe l'oeils* can be created by using artificial flowering plants and trees made from plastic or silk. This kind of illusion should be used with care and is only suitable for certain types of quirky garden where such materials can be assimilated into the overall style. Real statues and other ornaments such as urns can also be placed in front of a decorative mural.

Left and above: The illusions created by *trompe l'oeil* can introduce an element of fun into the garden. Flat walls can be transformed by painting (*left*) or by trelliswork (*above*) so that they present an impression of three-dimensional architecture.

Above left and above right: The use of trellis to distort perspective has a long history. It has often been combined with elaborate architectural features (*above right*), although the wooden laths are simply attached to flat walls. Planting can enhance the impression created by *trompe l'oeil*, but the perspective should not be obscured (*above left*).

Illusions of perspective At its simplest, *trompe l'oeil* creates an illusion of depth by using painted lines or trelliswork (*below*) that suggest a receding perspective within necessarily uncomplicated architectural forms. These architectural fantasies can be elaborated so that even a tiny garden can seem like a courtyard in a palatial complex.

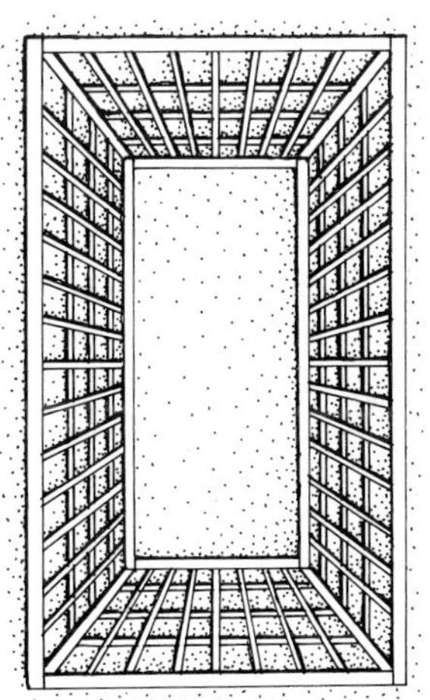

Left: Painted *trompe l'oeil* allows more scope for inventive decoration than trellis does. Dull blank walls can be enlivened with views that you might expect to see there, such as a window or door, or the image of a landscape can create the illusion in an urban setting that countryside lies just beyond the garden. The technique is particularly useful for increasing the apparent size of a small garden. The use of large mirrors, although not strictly *trompe l'oeil*, can also make a garden seem larger.

OBJETS TROUVES

Many less conventional garden ornaments start life as quite ordinary, often functional, objects. The range is limitless, but they should be chosen with care; incongruity can have its place and often makes a welcome impact, but it can be overdone and detract from the garden.

A surprising number of man-made objects, such as old wooden wheels, millstones, disused beehives or dog kennels, can fit well into the landscape, and chimney pots, either used on their own or as containers filled with plants, are often seen. The more esoteric railway signal posts and road signs feature in some gardens, and old tools also have their devotees. Not all *objets trouvés* are man-made, some are natural items: a carefully placed stack of logs, stones or old weather-worn tree stumps can all be used effectively. Tree stumps can be left on the surface of the ground with their interesting, tangled roots exposed, or part of the stump can be buried to give the impression that it has been there for a long time. Shells and antlers are other favorite decorative ornaments that are often seen.

The placement of *objets trouvés* must be considered with great care. Some pieces are best in formal settings, used perhaps as focal points; others work well in informal designs, apparently carelessly abandoned. The more surrealistic objects should be positioned in such a way as to create witty or amusing scenes that possibly tell a story.

Recycled objects Recycled objects have long been used as ornaments for the garden. Many old jars from a pre-plastic era (*right*) make attractive plant containers. This example has a spigot hole that allows for drainage. If there are no drainage holes, old jars can be used to hold planted plastic pots. The millstone (*far right*) has been converted into a table that looks at home in a garden setting. Terracotta pots and jars, including those once used in the house, are ornamental, even without plants (*below*). This medley includes old rhubarb forcing pots, which are no strangers to the garden.

Above: Home-made sculpture can be made from all kinds of recycled objects and *objets trouvés.* The springs here may well be a witty reference to "spring in the garden". The scope for this type of sculpture is infinite, but avoid overwhelming the garden with too much junk as it will lose its impact.

Containers

The use of containers for growing plants has a long history and their popularity has never diminished. Containers are decorative objects in their own right, but they are also practical. They allow the gardener to introduce plants to soilless areas like steps, patios and terraces, and facilitate a variety of fresh, seasonal changes in the garden.

The range of containers available is almost inexhaustible. There are ornamental and plain, informal and formal ones, and it should not be difficult to find a suitable container for any position that is required. The material of the container is relatively unimportant except as an aesthetic consideration, although some types of terracotta are susceptible to damage from frost and this should be borne in mind in cold areas. If the containers are to be on a balcony or roof garden then those of fiberglass or plastic will be much lighter than stone, terracotta or metal, and will reduce the load on the structure.

Containers can be placed on their own or used in groups; larger ones look better in isolation while smaller ones look best collected together, especially if they are all different shapes and sizes. The appearance of a lone container is important, while in a group, it is possible to hide one or two that are not so attractive. Classical urns tend to look more appropriate in formal settings, while wooden containers are more informal in design, although an arrangement of carefully-planted, painted Versailles tubs can look very smart.

Wherever it is positioned, a container should always have a firm base as a pot full of moist compost is very heavy. In most cases, particularly with very large tubs, it is best to put the container in the final position first and then fill it with compost and plants to save having to move it when it is full.

Virtually any plants, including vegetables, can be grown in containers, but all will need more care than those grown in the open garden. The key to success is not to let the containers dry out, but at the same time never to allow them to become too wet. They will need constant watering, which will leach nutrients out of the compost, so the plants will also need regular feeding during the growing season.

To facilitate drainage, all containers should have holes in the bottom, preferably covered with a layer of stones, shards or coarse gravel to prevent them from clogging up and to provide an easy passage for excess water. The compost should be free-draining but capable of retaining sufficient moisture for the plants' needs from one watering to the next.

Left and above: Container-grown plants add much to a garden, and wide range of vessels can be used, either singly or in groups. Some containers, including recycled copper tubs (*above*), are so impressive that they deserve to be displayed in isolation. Often, however, the appeal of plants is enhanced by the way containers are brought together. An old stone sink makes a lovely arrangement with clay pots containing different species and varieties of sempervivum (*left*).

Left and below: The ornamental quality of a container is often as important as that of the plants growing in it (*left*). Some containers can simply be used to house less attractive containers, including plastic pots, in which plants are growing. Pot-grown plants can just be dropped into decorative containers during their peak display and then replaced when their season is over. An attractive box for this purpose (*below*) is not difficult to make.

Troughs and sinks Old troughs and sinks (*below and right*) are particularly suitable for growing alpines. Glazed sinks can be made to look like weathered stone by coating them with a mixture of peat and cement. Sinks and troughs look best mounted above ground level.

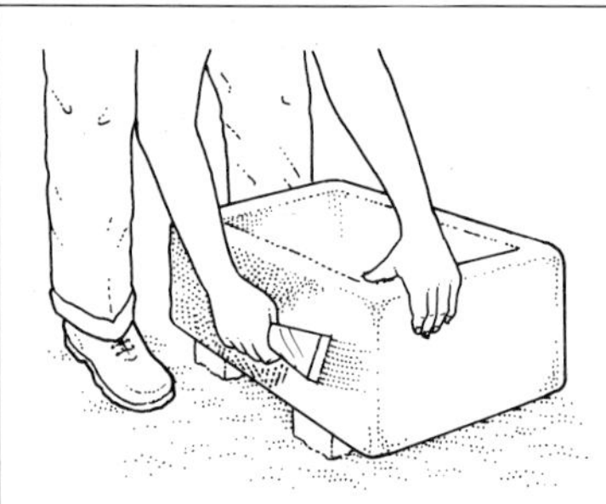

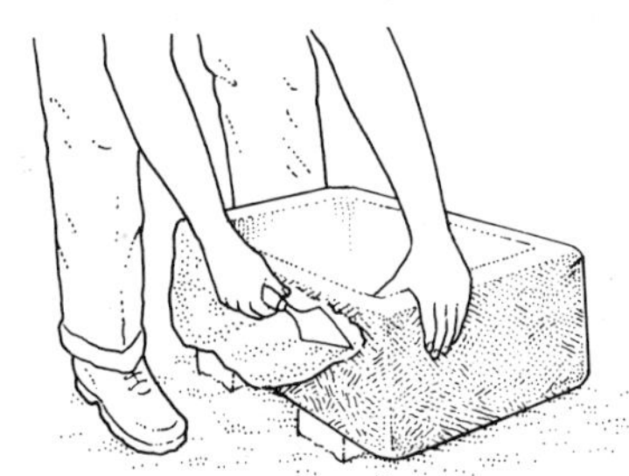

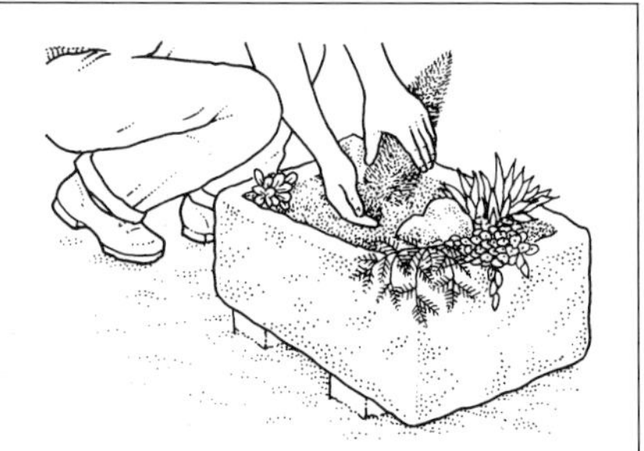

RECYCLING A SINK

A sink can be turned into a trough by covering it with a mixture of cement and fine peat. Clean the sink and apply a layer of adhesive. Apply the mixture to the sides, including the inside down to just below the intended soil level. When completely dry, paint the sink with mud, liquid seaweed fertilizer or a stiff mixture of cow manure and milk to encourage the rapid development of moss and algae. Place the sink in position before filling it with a free-draining potting compost and planting it up.

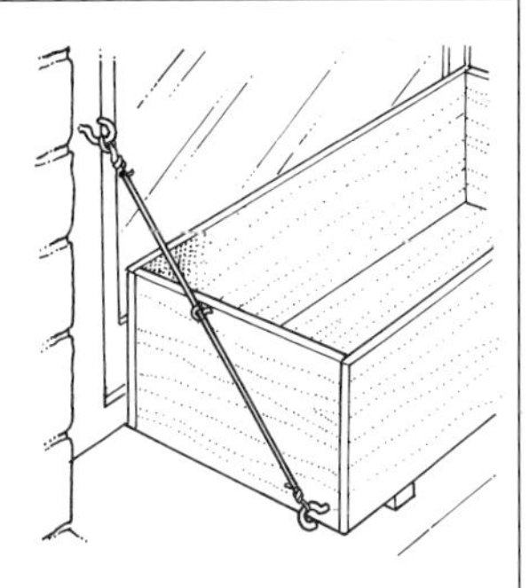

WINDOW BOXES

Window boxes are all but constantly wet and therefore need to be made of marine ply or hardwood, or a softwood that has been treated with a preservative (not creosote). Corrosion-free screws and fixings should be used. It is essential that holes in the base and some form of feet are provided to facilitate drainage. Firmly secure boxes in place.

Above: Troughs and rough-hewn stone containers are normally planted with alpines, but they are also suitable for dwarf conifers and bulbs, provided they are deep enough to hold sufficient compost.

Below: Terracotta flower pots can be painted in striking patterns, as seen in these examples. Here, the contrasts between the shapes and textures of the foliage are an integral part of the effect.

Above and right: Groups of container-grown plants look good when assembled on patios, especially in corners or to one side of a door. However, they should not be allowed to encroach on paths to the extent that they pose a hazard to pedestrians. Variety in the containers, and in the planting, will greatly increase the interest of a collection. Regular watering is essential, especially during hot weather, and feeding during the growing season will ensure good plant growth.

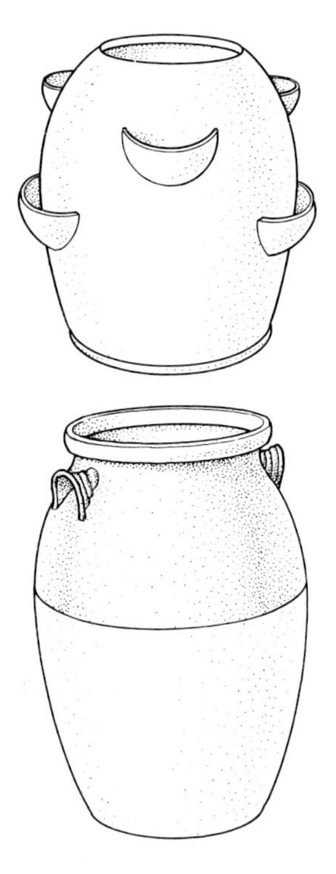

Terracotta Terracotta is a traditional material for containers and remains popular because the color and texture of the material is sympathetic to plants. Almost any plant looks good in a terracotta pot, whether grown in the garden, the greenhouse or indoors. There is a very wide range of shapes and sizes available, both plain and decorated (*left and below*). Firing at high temperatures is needed to make pots frost resistant, so not all pots can be safely left outdoors in areas that experience cold winters. The principal disadvantage of terracotta pots is that they dry out fairly quickly in hot summer weather. If planted up, the containers must have drainage holes; otherwise, fill them with plants still in their original flower pots.

Herb pots and planters (*above*) Herb pots and strawberry pots have apertures in their walls to take plants at different levels. They can be used for a wide variety of ornamentals as well as the plants they are designed to take. The pots should be rotated on a regular basis to ensure that all plants get sufficient light. These pots look attractive with tall planters, which can be glazed or partially glazed.

Below: Many terracotta pots have molded decoration, such as this basket pattern, and a suitable planting is needed to complement it.

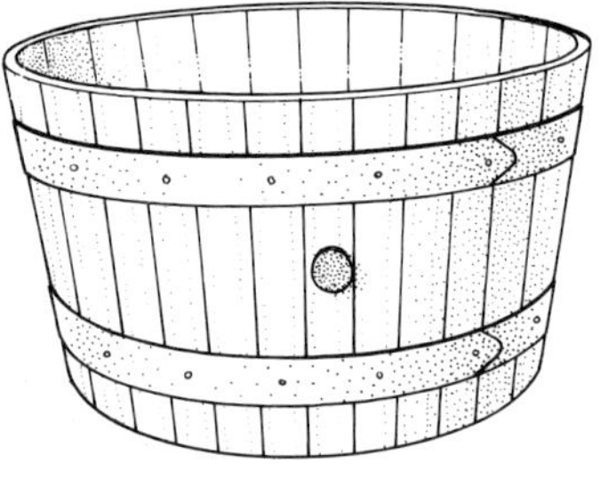

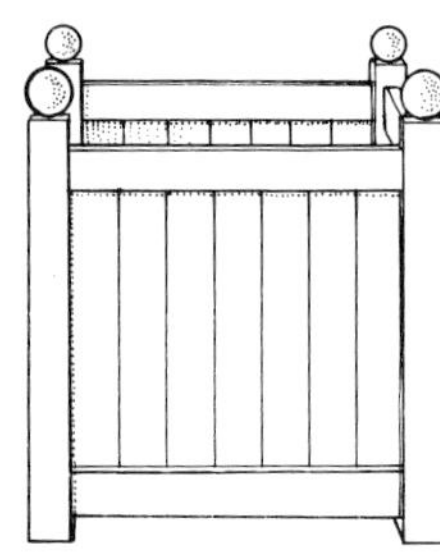

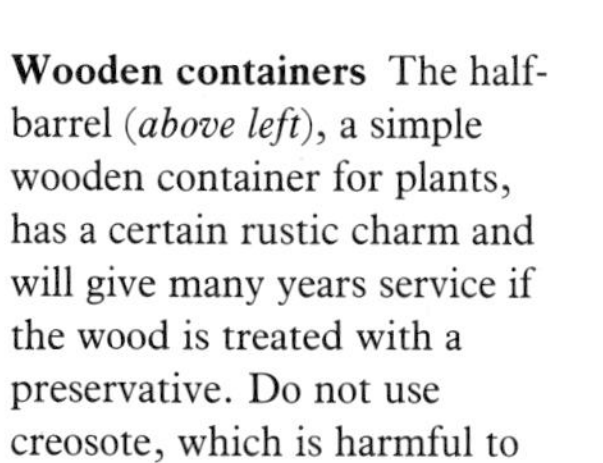

Wooden containers The half-barrel (*above left*), a simple wooden container for plants, has a certain rustic charm and will give many years service if the wood is treated with a preservative. Do not use creosote, which is harmful to plants. Versailles tubs (*above right*) suit a more sophisticated setting. These are often made of cedar and, as with half barrels, there should be drainage holes in their bases. Ready-made tubs are also available in fiberglass.

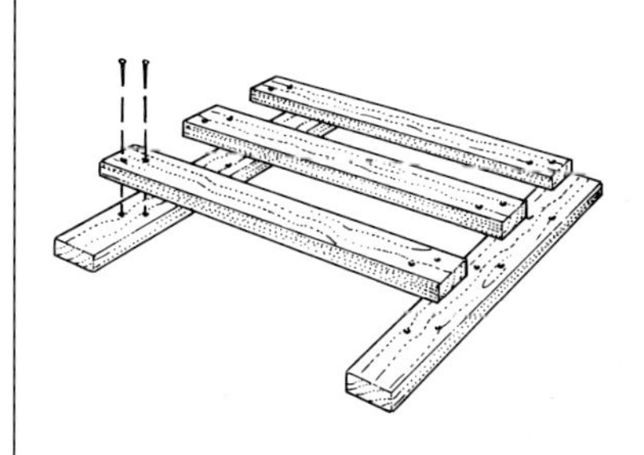

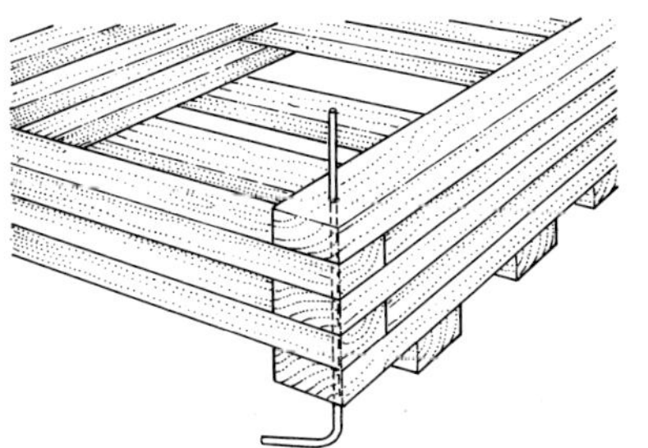

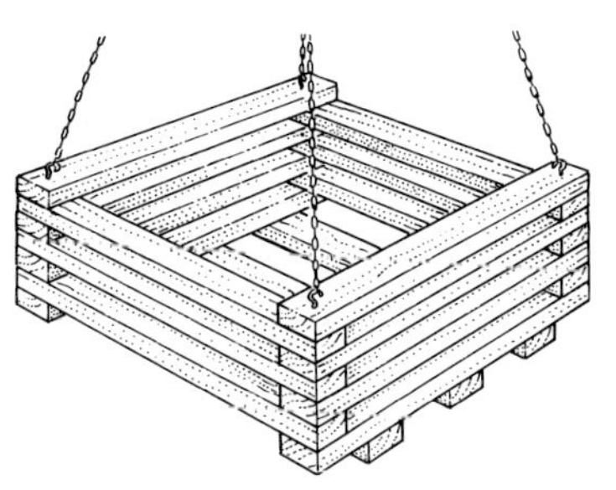

MAKING A BASKET

An attractive wooden hanging basket can be easily constructed from a few slats of wood. The slats should all be of the same length; about 30cm (12in) will do. The wood must be treated with preservative (not creosote) to prevent it rotting, and the base strips attached with corrosion-free screws. The slats for the sides should have a hole drilled in each end, just large enough to take a stout galvanized wire, which, when passed through, holds them together. Turn the wire over on the underside of the container and secure it with staples. Thread on alternate side pieces, as shown, and bend the remaining wire into a loop.

Below: Terracotta pots often look attractive combined with recycled containers. Here, a container is combined with ornamental chimney pots.

Right: Careful positioning is often needed to make the most of a container. The pendulous habit of a fuchsia is shown off in a pedestal-mounted pot.

Left: Attractive arrangements of spring bulbs such as tulips can make a splendid display in terracotta pots. Summer and autumnal planting can follow.

Above: Long-flowering plants for containers include pansies and the Mexican daisy (*Erigeron karvinskianus*), an effective combination of flowers.

LIGHTING

If the garden is to become an important part of the home and used in the same way as other rooms, it is necessary to provide outside lighting so that the space can be used in the evenings, especially in the warmth of summer weather. Outdoor lighting is also important from a safety point of view so that people can see where they are going in the dark; it should also help deter intruders, denied their cover of darkness.

There are many types of lighting, including blanket cover from a lamp high up on the house. This will provide general illumination and act as security lighting as well. By contrast, a series of lamps set along a path or drive will light that area but the rest of the garden will be dark. Alternatively, different features can be spotlit: trees, ponds or statues can all be lit in isolation to give the garden interest and form at night. Highlighting features in this way creates a dramatic backdrop that is not only seen from the garden itself but also from within the house through key windows. These lights are generally installed low down so that they shine up at the chosen feature. Water can be lit from below the surface as well as from above; illuminated fountains and waterfalls make exciting and spectacular night-time features.

Treat outside lighting as you would lights inside and avoid overall coverage, restricting it to particular areas. Allow for different circuits so, for example, you can have a private meal on a terrace with soft lighting, without the surrounding area being lit up around you. Smaller, softer lights, such as fairy lights, are no more difficult to install than other lights, and candles and torches can be very effective.

There is a large selection of external light fixtures on sale that will supply just the right amount of light in the right place, and many of these are unobtrusive during daylight hours, especially if they are hidden in the vegetation. All light fixtures must be specially designed for outdoor use; never try to adapt lamps originally intended for use indoors.

While the gardener should be encouraged to choose the location of lights and to work out the general design of the scheme, if there is any doubt at all as to his or her ability to carry out the actual wiring then it should be passed over to a professional, as electricity is particularly dangerous in the damp environment of the garden. Any mains feeds should be of shielded cable and this must be buried at a minimum depth of 2ft (60cm) below the ground.

The garden at night Gardens are rarely used at night, except in summer, but an imaginative use of lighting can open up a whole new world (*left and above*). Lighting can be functional or it can be atmospheric; functional lighting allows people to find their way around and see what they are doing, whereas atmospheric lighting illuminates various parts of the garden, possibly individual plants, to create a relaxing ambience in which people can enjoy themselves. Electricity is now widely used for garden lighting but gas and oil can be used as well. Candles and flares can also be employed if adequate precautions are taken.

Light fixtures A wide range of light fixtures (*below*) is available for use in the garden. A standard, hard-wearing, general-purpose light (*top*) can be used to floodlight drives or paths, good for security reasons. The two below are movable fixtures that can be pushed into the earth. These are generally battery operated, although there are some that work on gas. Below these is a lantern; these old fashioned-looking lights are decorative and functional fixed outside a door or marking a gateway. The bottom set of spotlights are for immersion in ponds, under fountains or on side walls, to illuminate the water.

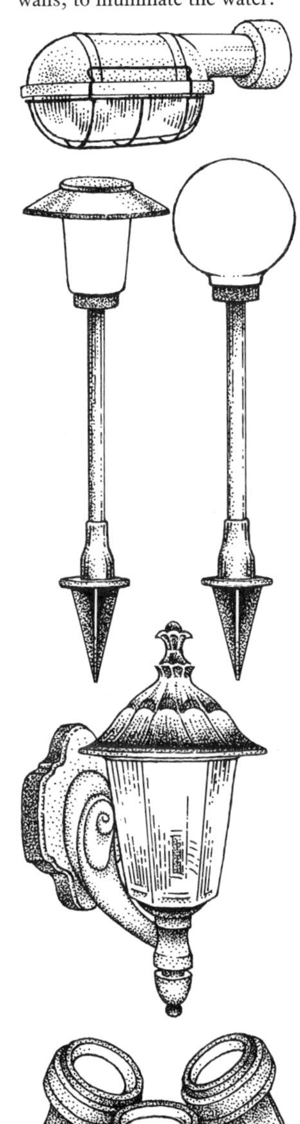

Above: Floodlighting certain features in the garden can create dramatic night-time vistas from the house and from within the garden.

Right: Lighting posts are a good method of obtaining localized light along a path.

Below left: Spotlights or floodlights shining through plants can magically transform their daylight appearance.

Below right: Soft light filtering through from other areas that are illuminated can create an intimate atmosphere.

GARDEN FURNITURE

As the garden is an extension of the home, a place to sit and enjoy the surroundings rather than somewhere to just grow flowers or vegetables, it is important to have good, comfortable garden furniture which looks as attractive as possible.

There is a vast range of chairs, benches and tables to choose from; some are sufficiently robust and weatherproof to remain outside throughout the year, while others need to be taken inside for the winter and during inclement weather.

Permanent furniture is usually made of wood or wrought or cast iron; both are quite unyielding and may need cushions if they are to be used for any length of time. Inside summer houses, which get a certain amount of protection from the weather, cane furniture can look very effective, especially once it has begun to age.

Movable furniture comes in a range of materials, including plastic. Many of the modern designs are quite comfortable but their visual appearance leaves much to be desired. For example, folding aluminum chairs and tables are practical but generally look temporary and add little to the overall appearance of the garden, although they are useful as a back-up in case of a sudden influx of people. Traditional deck-chairs, on the other hand, give the impression of leisure and blend in well with their surroundings. Unfortunately, they can be dangerous if children are around as it is easy to trap fumbling and inquisitive fingers when putting them up or dismantling them.

It is also possible to have built-in furniture in the garden, for example, around a barbecue. Seats or benches can be constructed out of stone or brick as part of a wall, or they can be made using thick wooden slats suspended between parts of a low wall; tables can be constructed in a similar way. This type of seating will be very hard and often cold and will certainly need cushions. Much thought should go into their design and placement, however, because once they are in position they cannot be moved easily.

As well as placing seats in obvious sites, on a terrace for example, some should also be set in key positions where certain aspects of the garden can be enjoyed, such as beside a pond or a fragrant climber. Position a seat to catch the early morning or evening sun. Seats in the shade are always welcome, especially in the summer, as are those tucked away in an arbor that provides protection from light showers. Garden tables should be sited in shady spots as they are mostly used in summer for dining alfresco.

Opposite: Furnishing an area near the house with a table and chairs simplifies outdoor eating and entertaining. A paved patio with an even surface makes an ideal location, although the climate will dictate the extent to which the area is used throughout the year. Furniture not used during winter should be stored under cover.

Strategic seating Seats and benches need careful placing (*above left, above right and right*). The top of a flight of steps or the end of a path are natural resting places. A warm wall makes a good backing, as do beds of scented plants. Whether seating is in sun or shade, commanding a view or hidden away will depend on personal taste.

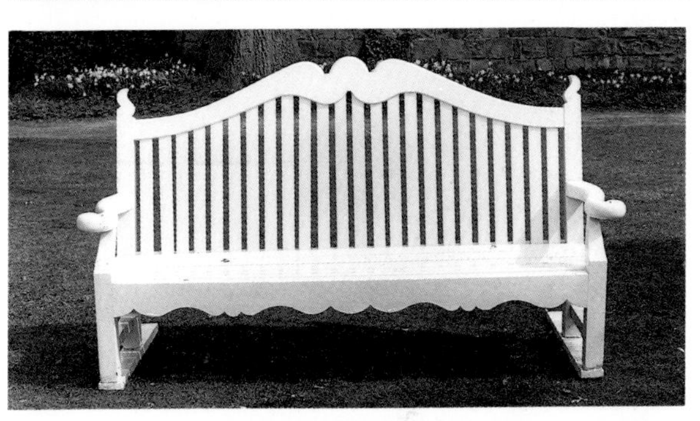

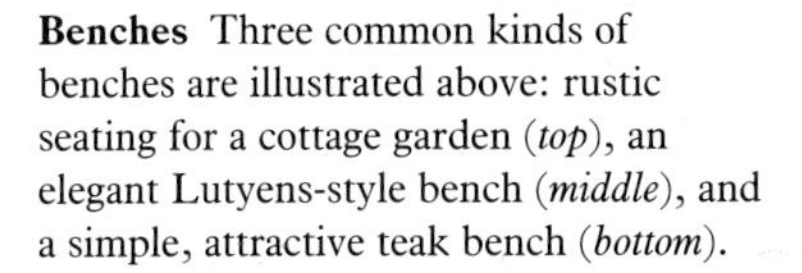

Benches Three common kinds of benches are illustrated above: rustic seating for a cottage garden (*top*), an elegant Lutyens-style bench (*middle*), and a simple, attractive teak bench (*bottom*).

Above: Seating that can easily be moved about has many advantages. Its position can be altered to suit the changing seasons and to take advantage of shelter and sun. The wicker canopy of this movable seat is functional as well as decorative, giving additional protection from the weather; it is an unusual, pleasing piece that would make a focal point in a garden. Some benches and chairs are fitted with wheels.

Simple seats Seats need not be of very complicated construction. It is perfectly possible to make them out of a single slab of stone (*left*) or a timber beam (*below*) (note the topiary "back" and "arms"). Whatever material is used, the supports must be sturdy and firmly bedded. Carved or plain supports would suit a stone slab. A simple wooden seat is easy to make using wooden blocks as supports.

LESS CONVENTIONAL SEATING

Not all seating need be purchased at the local garden centre; there are many types of seats that the gardener can construct by hand, often with the minimum of effort.

The easiest seat is simply a log or large piece of stone placed in a suitable position to provide a resting place. Another simple seat is a thick plank of wood supported on two pieces of tree trunk or timber posts inserted into the ground; the uprights should be solid and treated with preservative. Grass or herb seats make delightful features: construct a hollow seat from wood, stone or brick which has draining holes in the bottom, covered with a thin layer of drainage material, such as rubble. Fill the seat with compost, water well, top up with more compost and firm the surface; it is now ready for planting. Grass seed can be sown or sod laid; these will give the quickest result. Aromatic herbs can also be used; thyme is a fragrant and wonderfully resilient plant, while mint and chamomile are popular alternatives. Grass needs regular trimming, herbs demand less frequent attention; all need watering during dry spells.

Another type of resting place is the hammock. It is possible to buy modern swing seats on frames, but a hammock slung between two trees can hardly be bettered on a warm summer's day. Such hammocks can be bought or easily made from canvas or knotted from string or rope. Do not forget that the most important part of the hammock is the supports; these must be very strong and the hammock firmly secured. Healthy, mature, solid trees are ideal.

Combining seats and plants Seating that is built in conjunction with plants can make an interesting feature in the garden. Delightful, plain tree-seats (*above*) can be constructed to encircle a tree trunk, which acts as a back rest. A hole should be left in the center of the seat large enough to allow the tree to grow. Other seats can be built using shrubs as part of the framework (*left*). These need regular clipping to keep them neat. Shrubs can also be used as a backdrop (*opposite*), here emphasizing the color of the stone and creating a very interesting focal point.

Left: This beautiful tree-seat has been built over pebbles and tiles. Grass gets badly worn around permanent seating and can be difficult to mow.

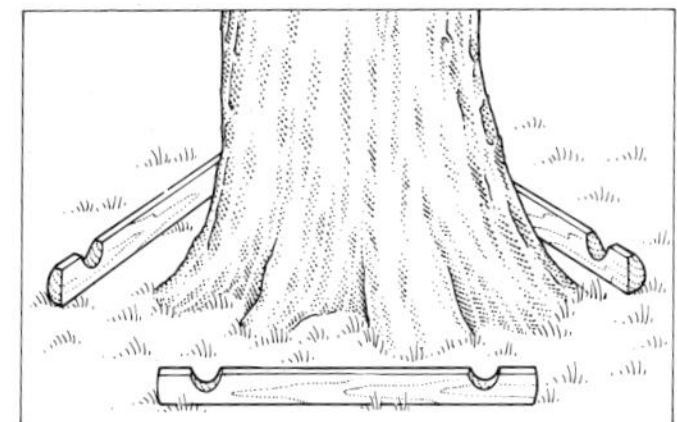

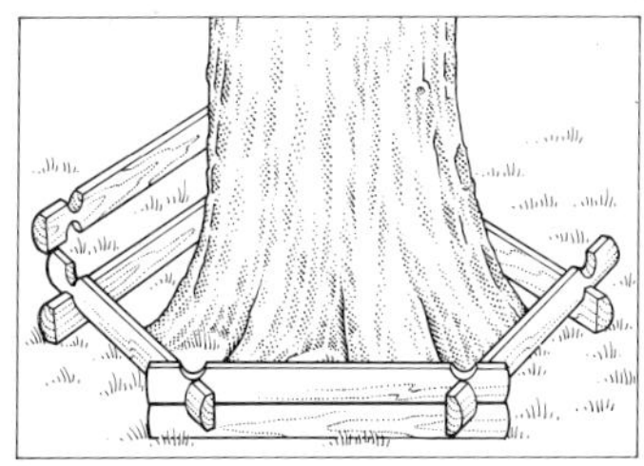

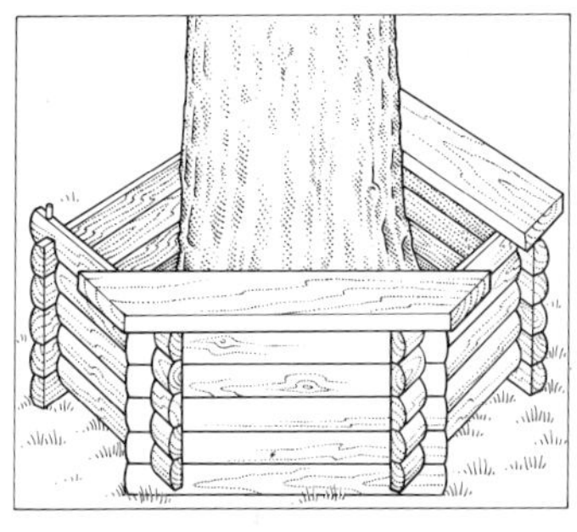

MAKING A TREE SEAT

Create a shady seating area under a favorite tree by building an attractive and practical tree seat. This simple design can be made from split lengths of logs and three lengths of planking. The logs should be treated with a preservative, but not creosote, which could kill the tree. Cut the logs to length, allowing room for overlap, so that they will form a hexagon around the tree. Make notches in one edge only of the first three logs and last three logs. Other logs should have notches cut on both edges, shaped so that they fit snugly into one another. Plane the top edges flat if necessary so that the planks will not rock and then drill holes to accommodate dowel pegs. Drill matching holes in the planks, position them and insert the dowels for a tight, secure bond.

Above and left: An ornate, leafy chair, wittily painted green, and an elegant seat are fine examples of old, highly decorative wrought iron furniture. These deserve good care and should be washed and repainted regularly.

Right: There is a comfort and price advantage to seats made with cast-iron end-pieces and simple wooden slats.

Cast-iron furniture In the Victorian period, cast-iron garden furniture was manufactured in a wide range of designs, such as these gothic and romantic examples (*left*). Old pieces are expensive and difficult to come by, but reproductions are available.

Right: A variation on the traditional wooden deckchair, this elegant set of chairs with a matching table is made from wrought iron, the chairs having canvas upholstery. Because of their light construction, these pieces can be moved about as needed. They are, however, best on a good, level surface. To prolong their life, they should be put away when not in use so the canvas does not rot.

Below: Although much furniture of cast cement and artificial stone is very plain, these materials can be treated in a highly imaginative way, as this set of chairs and table demonstrate. Both these materials are long lived and they are fairly maintenance free, although with very fanciful designs there is the risk that comfort will be sacrificed to visual appeal. Cushions on the seats would help to make these chairs more welcoming.

Above: When painting garden furniture, decide whether you want pieces to stand out from or blend with plants and other features. This ornate wooden bench has been painted white and blue to show off its detail.

Left: A seat running round the edge of a Japanese gazebo provides a seating area that is shaded from the midday sun, but it cannot be moved.

Below: Well used furniture, like the collection of wicker chairs in this paved bay, adds a touch of homely comfort to a garden scene.

Below: This wrought-iron chair once had a refined elegance, but it now takes on the guise of a modern piece of sculpture. Even when furniture is old and possibly too unstable to use, it can still look attractive in the garden when employed in a decorative rather than practical way.

GARDEN STRUCTURES

Most gardens have at least one structure in them apart from the house itself. Some, such as sheds and greenhouses, are practical, while others, summer houses for instance, are more for pleasure. These structures should be chosen to blend in with the style of the garden and any buildings in the vicinity.

Sheds often have little aesthetic appeal but can be effectively disguised with a trellis or screen supporting climbing plants. Wood is more sympathetic than most other materials, but if you are building on a grand scale, brick or stone sheds can be constructed. Such structures can be covered with climbing plants, as can those of wood, but the latter will have to be stripped of creepers to carry out maintenance.

Greenhouses can be difficult to site. Although they need an open, sunny aspect, for visual reasons they should be tucked out of the way rather than placed in a prominent position. Wooden-framed greenhouses are better insulated, but those with aluminum frames are easier to maintain.

Summer houses, either totally enclosed or with one open side, can look very handsome when they are found nestling in a secluded corner of the garden. Make sure they are big enough for two or more people to sit comfortably, preferably at a table. Pavilions are an original and exciting alternative; they are usually constructed to cover a bench or seat and are often set at the end of a path or avenue of trees.

There are plenty of smaller structures that can be used around the garden, partly as decorative features and partly as practical objects. Dovecotes are popular; the design is up to the individual and, although good examples can be bought, the gardener can always make his or her own. Beehives are also attractive, especially the old-fashioned white ones which add a cottage atmosphere to the garden. These can be functional – a home to bees – or purely decorative.

Follies can be built but, generally speaking, the garden must be quite large in order to accommodate them. They come in many forms including buildings, monuments and ruins. Ruins are easy to construct; rather than completely dismantling an old disused brick or stone shed, do so only partly and allow it to become overgrown with ivy and moss.

Left and below left: Summer houses, gazebos, belvederes and pavilions are all evocative names for a romantic type of building that forms an ornamental feature in the garden. Large summer houses are often functional pieces of architecture used for sitting in, to admire a view or a fine piece of planting. They are sited where they allow a more intimate appreciation of the garden than is possible from the house. Although many summer houses are open-sided and airy, they do need a roof to provide some protection from both sunshine and sudden rainy outbursts.

Opposite: A summer house can be an important architectural feature of the garden, its significance underlined by the way it is sited. Here, a highly ornate summer house forms part of an elaborate scheme, terminating a pergola that covers a pathway running beside a large pool.

Above right and right: Many small summer houses are used as purely ornamental features. Such structures, clothed in climbers like ivy, often form a focal point along an axis of a garden. They can also serve as a quiet retreat in a shady, wooded area, where the planting is wilder.

Above: A summer house can be incorporated into a garden of almost any size but care must be taken in getting the scale right. In a really small plot, a scaled down summer house can still take up too much room, even appearing oppressively dominant, if it is solid-sided. In this situation, and even in the larger garden, it is often better to build an open-work structure. This can provide a shady area in which to sit, although it will not give protection from wind and rain in the way a more solid structure can. The open-work summer house can be left unplanted but provides an ideal support for climbers. Being light and airy, it blends in with the garden and is an important architectural feature, adding much to the character of a design.

Garden sheds Every garden needs its shed (*above left, above right and below*). There are many items that need to be stored, including hand tools, lawn mowers, potting composts and pots, chemicals and fertilizers, as well as overwintering plants. Much garden furniture also needs to be stored during winter or when not in use. Since a shed is so indispensable, it is worth making an effort to integrate or decorate it. One solution is to disguise a plain shed by training creepers over it (*below*), but unless they are kept on trellis slightly away from the building they can be difficult to keep in check and can make the building damp. The addition of architectural details such as decorative bargeboards can transform an ordinary shed, as can bright or delicate paintwork (*above left and right*). Louvers are attractive and useful; they help to maintain a free flow of air through a shed without allowing rain to penetrate.

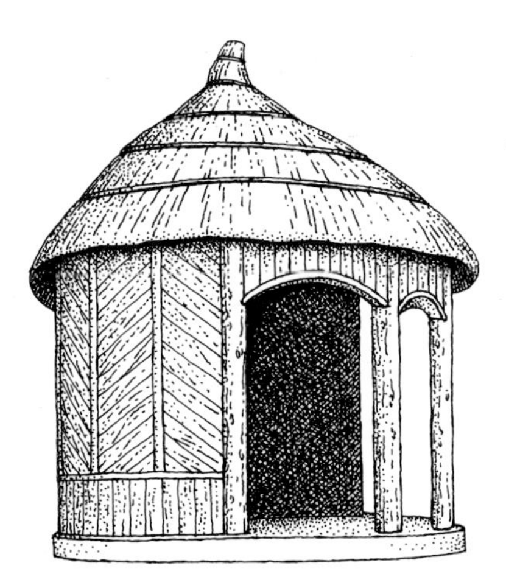

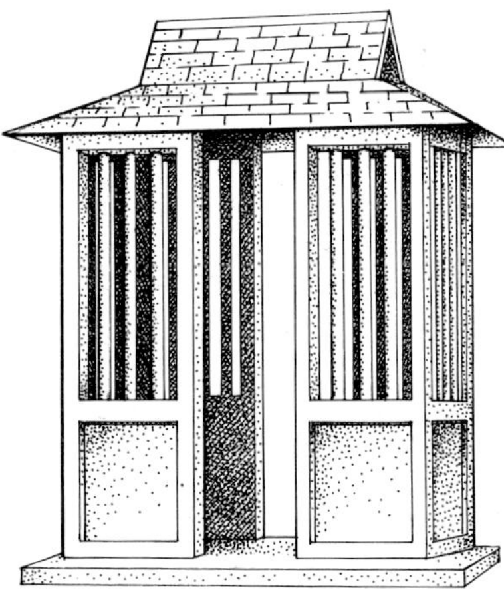

A wide range of materials is used for roofing. Thatching can be used in highly rustic designs (*above left*), while more conventional summer houses may have tile or slate roofs (*above middle*).

Above right: A Japanese-style open-sided summer house is roofed with sheet metal.

Conservatories A conservatory can make an elegant, useful extension to a house, combining the warmth and comfort of a room with uninterrupted views of the outside world. It need not be restricted to the conventional garden, as this one on a roof garden demonstrates (*left*); the siting of the conservatory affords breathtaking views of the city. With the use of modern materials it is not necessary to stick to straight, small-paned pieces of glass. This allows the use of sinuous curves to create attractive roof shapes (*below*). These materials are light as well as flexible.

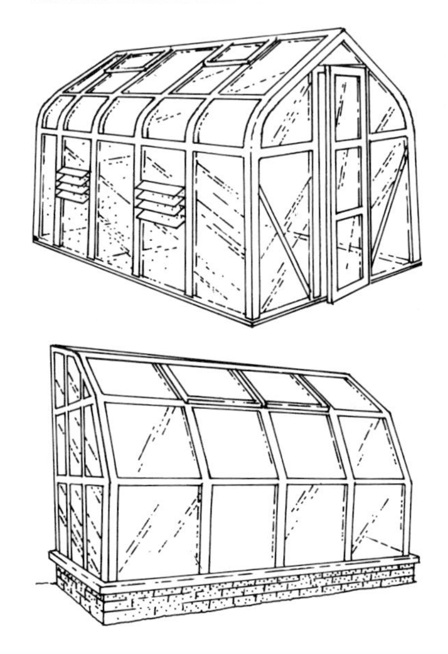

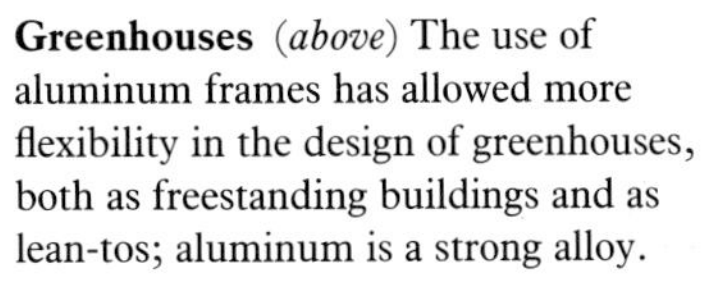

Greenhouses (*above*) The use of aluminum frames has allowed more flexibility in the design of greenhouses, both as freestanding buildings and as lean-tos; aluminum is a strong alloy.

Above: Dovecotes have long been a feature of European gardens. Now they are usually decorative structures to house ornamental birds, but previously they were built for pigeons that were bred for food. Some dovecotes are elaborate freestanding buildings, but those most commonly seen are made of wood, erected on poles, as here, or attached to walls.

Follies and ruins Follies and ruins (*above*) help to create a romantic landscape. A ruin can be constructed from recycled materials, or an existing building – such as an old brick or stone outbuilding or a pigsty – can be distressed. Although conveying an impression of decay, a ruin must be securely built; make sure there are no loose bricks or unstable piers.

Left: Shrines and temples, sometimes plain but often ornamental, provide an opportunity for highly personal expressions of taste and homage.

Above: The original function of some highly ornamental buildings is obscure. This was probably the public side of a gardener's bothy (living quarters).

Above: The competent amateur carpenter could easily make dovecotes of simple, traditional design.

Right: Buildings beside water should fit in with the tranquillity of the setting. This circular boathouse sits squat and protected among the trees, with its doors facing towards the water.

Below: An imposing shrine is set at the top of a flight of stone steps. The shape of its pediment echoes the steps below.

THE PLANT SELECTOR

TREES AND SHRUBS

The design of every garden, whatever its size, should include trees and shrubs. Even in the smallest plot there will be a suitable location for a tree, which will introduce the valuable element of height, and there are good compact selections of many shrubby species which will give substance to the overall composition. In addition, trees and shrubs create shade and a superstructure which allows a whole new collection of plants to be grown.

The choice of plant depends on the function it is expected to fulfil within the design. It is important, particularly in small gardens or where a single specimen is required to create a focal point, to be certain that the plant will justify the space it occupies. Size and shape are factors that should be considered for year-round effect: there are small compact strains of many plants as well as larger, vigorous ones; forms range from tall and columnar to pendulous. The foliage, flowers and fruit, bark and color of young twigs all influence the visual scene while fragrance is always an added bonus.

Larger species should be positioned with care as they will create shade and block out light as they grow. Some of the most vigorous ones may interfere with the foundations of buildings and nearby drains if sited too close to them. For example, *Populus* species can be particularly problematic.

Left: Evergreen conifers – including cultivars of abies, chamaecyparis, cupressus and picea – create a stunning picture in golden- and blue-greens all year round. Changing light and atmospheric conditions will show the wide range of shapes, sizes, colors and textures to good effect. The flowering heaths used here add a bright seasonal note. A pleasing pattern, enhanced by the healthiness of the plants.

If blocking out an undesirable view outside the garden or breaking the linearity of a wall is a priority, then use quick-growing species. These plants often make large trees when mature, so a strict pruning regime will need to be carried out regularly. Quick-growing species are also very useful in creating an air of maturity early in the life of a garden. Often, as in forestry, a quick-growing tree is planted alongside a slower-growing species as a nurse and is removed as the latter gains size. I have seen balsam poplars (*Populus balsamifera*) coupled with a beech tree. The poplars grew quickly and, as the beech gained height, the lower branches of the poplars were removed. Once the beech had made 15ft (4.5m), the poplars were felled. Another slow-growing species which benefits from a nurse is English oak (*Quercus robur*).

Left: Three birches make strong vertical accents as they snake up through an understorey of ceanothus. Even in winter the trunks will remain arresting features of a simple composition.

Right: The appeal of this planting relies on contrasts of habit as well as of flower and foliage color. The pink flowers of the hibiscus and foreground heather harmonize with the maroon foliage of *Cotinus coggygria* 'Royal Purple'. In habit and leaf shape the cotinus contrasts with the *Eucalyptus gunnii* behind it. Spiky heather and rosemary contrast with the broad, variegated leaves of the impressive dogwood.

Above: The foliage of the fine, spreading *Acer pseudoplatanus* 'Brilliantissimum' opens pink and later turns bronze and then greenish yellow. Here the lobed leaves make a sharp contrast against the tight, controlled shapes of clipped *Chamaecyparis lawsoniana* 'Fletcheri' behind.

Left: The bright red autumn foliage of *Acer palmatum* makes a strong focal point in a relaxed planting of shrubs, ferns and perennials. A well planned seasonal effect.

Large trees already present in the garden can create considerable shade. Try to work with rather than remove the tree; it is possible, through careful pruning, to significantly reduce and raise its canopy, letting in light without markedly altering the tree's impact.

There are many shrubs and small trees that are adapted in the wild to growing in the shade of taller trees and require these conditions to thrive in the garden. These include both evergreen and deciduous species: *Aucuba japonica*, *Juniperus* × *media* 'Pfitzeriana' and *Prunus lusitanica* provide good, all-year-round dense foliage. To this quality mahonias, some viburnums and many rhododendrons add blossoms in winter and spring. *Acer palmatum*, *Philadelphus coronarius* 'Aureus' and *Pieris* species are also grown for their foliage which colors spectacularly for extended periods, adding an additional season of interest to that provided by the flowers.

When designing a garden it may be that a plant is needed that is of interest throughout the year. Alternatively the garden, or a specific section of it, may need to be designed to be at its best during one season of the year. Many trees and shrubs have interesting features in at least two seasons and there are some outstanding ones that are attractive in three seasons. Among the best are many viburnums, particularly *V. opulus* 'Aureum' with its beautiful golden foliage, large panicles of white flowers in late spring and bunches of translucent red berries from late summer into the autumn. Other outstanding plants are sorbus, crataegus and prunus species that combine good foliage with flowers, fruit and bark; dogwoods with flowers, autumn or variegated foliage, and fruit; and witchhazels with winter flowers and autumn color.

In winter the main feature is the bark. This may have a shiny, polished appearance as in some cherries;

a peeling or flaking texture that reveals layers of differing hues as in birches, *Acer griseum* and *Pinus bungeana*; or brightly colored twigs from the previous season's growth as found on many willows (*Salix* species) and shrubby dogwoods. To get the best effect from willows and dogwoods it is necessary to prune them hard in early spring at least every other year.

There are many trees and shrubs that flower in early or late winter when frosts are at their worst. These always perform most successfully if planted in a sheltered spot away from the morning sun which can damage frozen flowers by thawing them too quickly. Remember that the blooms will be shown to their best advantage against a solid backcloth, so grow winter-flowering species near conifers or broadleaved evergreens or in front of a wall of a contrasting color.

Spring is the time for flowers. They range in color from the pale yellow racemes of *Stachyurus praecox* to the bright pinks of the flowering cherries. Choose the most garishly colored ones with care so as not to clash with other spring-flowering plants. Young foliage can also have an impact, with delicate cream, pink and coppery leaves unfurling in the sun.

In summer the vegetation is at its height. Flowers are at their most abundant with lilacs, mock oranges and buddleias covered in a mass of blooms. The dense cover of leaves makes a rich background to all the other plants in the garden. Colors range from the dark maroon of *Cotinus coggygria* 'Notcutt's Purple' or 'Royal Purple' to the blue-green of *Cercis siliquastrum*, the gray-green of *Pyrus salicifolia* 'Pendula' and the yellow-green of *Robinia pseudoacacia* 'Frisia'. The shape of the leaves – varying from the perfectly rounded to very narrow and feathery – and their size – they may be large or very small – are characteristics that affect the visual impact of the garden and can be used in very effective juxtapositions.

Autumn is the time when the canopy thins out and the garden begins to wind down, but still there are late flowerers such as *Abelia × grandiflora* and *Hydrangea paniculata; Clerodendron trichotomum* and *Callicarpa bodinieri giraldii* make a show with many berries that complement their startling foliage color. Pyracanthas, cotoneasters and berberis are also good in berry, while maples, amelanchiers and euonymuses have beautiful foliage.

Right: Quercus coccinea 'Splendens', the only named form of the scarlet oak, colors gloriously in autumn. Arboreta and the many other plant collections throughout the world are often the best places to evaluate the ornamental qualities, speed of growth and ultimate size of trees when assessing their suitability for the garden. This oak will eventually make a tall tree in excess of 90ft (27m).

Quick-growing

Acer platanoides z 3
Norway maple
This rapid-growing deciduous tree reaches 80ft (24m), spreading 50ft (15m). In spring, clusters of bright yellow flowers clothe the bare stems. The lobed leaves are held in pairs; they are deep crimson-purple in 'Crimson King'. 'Drummondii' has creamy-white margins to its leaves, while those of 'Schwedleri' emerge bright crimson in spring, mature to a crimson-green and turn orange-red in autumn. The more erect, smaller 'Columnare' is useful for restricted spaces. Suitable for most soils.

Ailanthus altissima (*above*) z 5
Tree of heaven
This deciduous tree rapidly reaches 45ft (14m) with a spreading habit. The ash-like leaves are 1-2ft (30-60cm) long and turn yellow in autumn. Female trees bear small panicles of yellow-green flowers in late summer and early autumn, followed by bunches of bright red, winged fruits. It grows from seed in most soils and in some areas is rather a weed. For a tropical-looking bush cut back hard each spring; the strong shoots carry leaves over 3ft (90cm) long. Resistant to atmospheric pollution.

Alnus glutinosa **'Aurea'** z 4
All alders grow easily in virtually any soil and are especially suited to moist conditions. This cultivar has pale yellow leaves, which are most conspicuous in spring and early summer, fading to pale green as the summer progresses. With similar features is *A.incana* 'Aurea', the gray alder, the young yellow shoots contrasting well with the bright, red-tinted catkins during spring. It makes an attractive shelter-belt subject for an exposed garden. Alders bear woody cones which stand out in winter.

Betula platyphylla japonica **'Whitespire'**
Japanese white birch z 4
This moderately fast-growing tree develops a slender pyramidal shape with remarkable pure chalky-white bark. It will grow to 40ft (12m) and spreads 15ft (4.5m). The glossy deciduous leaves turn yellow in autumn. This fine birch needs well-drained soil and will tolerate extremes of both heat and cold. It is resistant to the borers and miners that attack so many birches. For damp areas, the river birch, *B. nigra*, is preferable and distinguished by its flaking dark bark. It can grow to 80ft (24m).

× *Cupressocyparis leylandii* z 6
Leyland cypress
This forms a noble tree of a dense, columnar habit. It is one of the fastest growing of all evergreen conifers, capable of reaching 100ft (30m) when mature. It makes a fine specimen in a large garden providing it is correctly sited and tended. The foliage is borne in irregular, slightly drooping sprays and is aromatic if crushed. Useful as a screen or windbreak, it grows well even in poor soil and tolerates alkaline soils and coastal conditions. 'Castlewellan' has yellow foliage.

Liriodendron tulipifera (*above*) z 5
Tulip tree
Fast-growing and deciduous, this tree can reach 40ft (12m) in 20 years. The peculiar leaves are four-lobed, glossy green in summer, turning to clear butter yellow in autumn. The tulip-like flowers are greenish-yellow with orange centers and are sometimes followed by woody fruits. Young trees flower less readily. The leaves of 'Aureomarginatum' have greenish-yellow margins. Succeeds in all fertile soils, including chalky.

Pinus strobus z 3
Eastern white pine
Native to the northeast of North America, this tree can grow to 200ft (60m), although such huge specimens are rare. Growth is rapid during its early years. Like most pines, this tree will flourish in dry or poor soils in full sun, even when it is exposed to strong winds. For this reason, a row of *P. strobus* makes a fine windbreak. *P. s. fastigiata* has upright growth so is useful in a more restricted site. *P. s. umbraculifera* is a much more compact plant, only 6ft (1.8m) in height, but rounded and bushy. *P. s. prostrata* trails.

Populus deltoides z 2
Cottonwood
This tree grows in every temperature zone from Canada to Florida and can withstand very harsh conditions, including heat, cold and high winds, as long as the roots can reach ample moisture. Growing to 90ft (27m), it has deeply-grooved bark and bright green fluttery leaves which turn yellow in autumn. Female cottonwoods bear huge quantities of fluffy seeds which can be extremely messy; it might be preferable to plant only male specimens, often sold as "cottonless". Never plant near house foundations or drainage pipes.

Ribes odoratum (*below*) z 2
Buffalo currant
This ornamental currant is a vigorous, deciduous shrub that grows to 5ft (1.5m) with a loose, erect habit. The shiny, dark green leaves are carried on upright stems, along with golden-yellow, clove-scented flowers during spring. Shiny black currants contrast with the rich orange-yellow autumn foliage. Prune out some of the oldest shoots in late winter.

Shade tolerant

Acer palmatum *(above)* z 5
Japanese maple
This plant will slowly make a small tree of 20ft (6m) with a low, rounded crown, but is best treated as a shrub. The species has palmate leaves, 2-4in (5-10cm) across, with five or seven lobes; these turn scarlet in autumn. Small, purplish summer flowers are followed by winged fruits. 'Senkaki' has coral red winter bark; 'Atropurpureum' is smaller, growing to 6ft (1.8m), with rich purple-red summer foliage. Grow in cool, moist loam, possibly in a tub or raised bed, sheltered from cold winds. Succeeds in dappled shade.

Aucuba japonica *(below)* z 7
A shade-loving evergreen shrub that makes a dense, rounded bush, 6ft (1.8m) tall, with large, laurel-like, glossy leaves. Female plants bear red berries. 'Crotonifolia' has golden speckled leaves, 'Variegata' (spotted laurel) has gold blotches. For berries, grow the narrow-leaved, all-green female 'Salicifolia', with its sea green stems. Variegated forms retain their color best on an open site, but all thrive in sunless positions in most soils.

***Juniperus × media* 'Pfitzeriana'** z 5
Pfitzer juniper
Ideal for growing as a lawn specimen or to break up the outline of a bed or border, this evergreen shrub is also useful as a tall ground cover. It reaches 10ft (3m) and spreads 10-15ft (3-4.5m); arm-like branches are set at an acute angle with drooping shoot tips. It has glaucous, scale-like juvenile leaves. 'Pfitzeriana Aurea' has golden-yellow young shoot tips and foliage; the latter turns yellowish-green in winter. Very versatile; good for alkaline soils.

Lonicera fragrantissima z 5
The flowers of this semi-evergreen shrubby honeysuckle give off a strong scent during the coldest winter months. The small cream blossoms appear on part-naked branches from winter to spring, followed occasionally by red berries. Liven up the dull summer phase with a fast-growing clematis or other climber; this will scramble over the bush which can reach 6ft (1.8m). The deciduous *L. standishii* is similar and *L.* × *purpusii* is more vigorous. Prune out old wood in spring.

Mahonia aquifolium *(above)* z 5
Oregon grape
This vigorous, spreading, suckering evergreen shrub reaches 2ft (60cm) in height and makes good ground cover. In spring, dense terminal clusters of fragrant yellow flowers appear, followed by black, bloomy berries that give the plant a bluish sheen. The spiny, glossy, leathery leaves can turn orange-red in winter and are up to 1ft (30cm) long. 'Atropurpurea' has rich reddish-purple winter and early spring foliage. 'Moseri' has bronze-red young leaves which turn apple green and then dark green in summer. Needs well-drained soil.

***Philadelphus coronarius* 'Aureus'** z 4
(above)
Golden mock orange
The leaves of this deciduous plant are bright yellow in spring, ageing to greenish-yellow. It makes a dense bush 6ft (1.8m) high, covered in scented, creamy-white flowers from early summer. Use in a mixed border, masking the lower stems with herbaceous plants such as *Euphorbia griffithii* 'Fireglow', which has orange-red flowers. Cut back the flowered stems immediately after the blooms have faded. Tolerates dry soils. Direct sun may bleach the leaves.

Pieris japonica *(below)* z 6
This evergreen shrub can reach 4ft (1.2m) and has a compact, bushy habit. The young leaves are coppery-pink in spring, turning a darker, glossy green. Flower buds are decorative in winter, the long-lived waxy flowers opening in drooping panicles in spring. 'Daisen' has pink flowers, deeper when in bud; the leaves of 'Bert Chandler' turn from salmon pink to cream, white and then green. Needs moist acid soil; protect from cold winds and early frost.

Lawn specimens

Prunus lusitanica *(below)* z 6
Portugal laurel
This can make an excellent specimen tree of 20ft (6m), doing particularly well on thin alkaline soil. The evergreen leaves are dark glossy green with red stalks. Small flowers appear in long, thin racemes in summer and have a sweet fragrance. Mature plants often fruit following a hot summer, the red fruits turning deep purple as they ripen. The less vigorous 'Variegata' has white-splashed leaves, flushed pink in winter; *P. l. azorica* has larger, brighter green leaves which are red as they unfold; *P. laurocerasus*, the cherry laurel, is less hardy and often used in hedging.

Rhododendron viscosum z 4
Swamp honeysuckle
Clusters of funnel-shaped, sticky flowers appear on this deciduous shrub in early summer. They have a sweet fragrance and are white, sometimes pink-tinged. The dark green glaucous leaves open earlier; they color up beautifully in autumn. Despite its common name, this plant does not need moist conditions, although it will tolerate damp soil. It reaches 8ft (2.4m). Avoid alkaline soils; add organic matter before planting.

Viburnum rhytidophyllum z 5
A large rhododendron-like evergreen that grows in the dappled shade of trees. The drooping, long leaves are dark glossy green above with a thick gray tomentum underneath. Shoots are felty gray-brown. Upright clusters of white spring flowers are followed by small oval fruits which turn from red to black. Two or more specimens must be planted together to ensure fruiting. Plants can reach 6ft (1.8m) or more. 'Roseum' has rose-tinted flowers. Ideal for alkaline soils.

Acer cappadocicum *(above)* z 6
Notable for its brilliant autumn color, this elegant maple makes a fine specimen, up to 70ft (21m) high, with a rounded crown. The broad leaves are bright green, five- to seven-lobed, and turn a rich butter yellow in autumn. 'Aureum' has leaves which turn from red to golden-yellow over several weeks. For attractive blood red young foliage grow 'Rubrum'; the leaves turn green in summer and reddish-gold in autumn. Needs fertile, well-drained soil.

Betula ermanii *(below)* z 6
Grown largely for its stem color, this Asian birch also has attractive yellow autumn leaves. A tree can reach 70ft (21m) when fully grown, but it is just as useful as a young garden specimen. The small glossy leaves have deep, parallel veins. The trunk has pinkish-white peeling bark while the branches are an orange-brown. On old trees the bark hangs from the branches. Plant with some thought as the beautiful bark colors are easily lost if not set against a dark backcloth such as evergreen shrubs. Grows well on most soils except shallow, calcareous types.

Cedrus atlantica **'Glauca'** z 6
The blue-gray form of the atlas cedar is pyramid-shaped when young, with ascending tips to its branches, and reaches 110ft (33m) when fully mature. The silvery-blue, needle-like leaves are held in rosettes on plentiful short lateral shoots. The pale brown cones are up to 3in (7.5cm) long and sit topside of the branches. *C. deodara*, the deodar, has drooping tips, while the cedar of lebanon, *C. libani*, has level branches: both have gray-green foliage. All three trees develop a flatter habit when mature. Grows in most fertile soils.

Cornus controversa **'Variegata'** z 5
This spectacular deciduous dogwood is ideal for a lawn where its horizontal, tiered branches can spread fully, giving it an architectural quality. The leaves have silver variegations, enhanced by clusters of creamy-white flowers in summer. In autumn the foliage turns purple-red and small black fruits may form. This species grows in most fertile soils, and benefits from shelter and sun. It can reach 15ft (4.5m) or more in height, and can spread to 10ft (3m), making this one of the most impressive of all foliage plants.

Davidia involucrata *(above)* z 6
Pocket-handkerchief, dove or ghost tree
The extraordinary inflorescences of this tree are its chief glory. Each small flower is protected by two paper-thin white bracts which hang below the branches in summer. These bracts are between 4in (10cm) and 8in (20cm) long. The deciduous leaves are fresh green, heart-shaped and felted beneath. Green fruits litter the ground in autumn and winter. Plants can reach 30ft (9m), need rich, moisture-retentive soil and prefer a sunny, sheltered position.

Fragrance

Ginkgo biloba *(below)* z 5
Maidenhair tree
This deciduous conifer is slow to establish but can reach 80ft (24m) with an open habit. The leaves are fan-shaped and two-lobed, pale green in summer, yellow in autumn. Plants are single-sex: male trees produce small catkins, females bear tiny flowers. The hard, yellow fruits smell of rancid butter when ripe. The nut-like seeds are edible. 'Pendula' has spreading, weeping branches. It is resistant to atmospheric pollution.

***Laburnum × watereri* 'Vossii'** z 6
In late spring and early summer the golden chain tree is massed with hanging racemes of golden-yellow, pea-like flowers. This cultivar reaches 25ft (7.5m) and has extra-long racemes at 2ft (60cm). The deciduous leaves have three leaflets. It does not produce seed pods, which are poisonous in other laburnums, as are all the genus' parts. Train a late summer-flowering clematis, such as 'Ernest Markham', through its branches. Laburnums can be trained to form tunnels. Grows in most soils.

Magnolia stellata z 5
Star magnolia
A fine shrubby magnolia that is covered with fragrant white blooms in spring which burst from silky, gray buds. Slow-growing to 10ft (3m), it has a rounded, compact habit. 'Rosea' and 'Rubra' have pink flowers. Plant in a sheltered position in rich, well-drained soil that receives plenty of moisture. Mulch regularly with organic matter. Avoid disturbing the roots and only prune if essential. Underplant with dwarf bulbs such as *Narcissus bulbocodium*. Tolerates alkaline soil and atmospheric pollution.

Metasequoia glyptostroboides z 5
Dawn redwood
This deciduous conifer was known only as a fossil until it was rediscovered in 1941. It grows in a pyramid-shape, reaching 36ft (11m) in 25 years and ultimately 100ft (30m). The tapering trunk bears a light, airy canopy of feathery foliage, carried in opposite rows on short branches. The leaves are bright green in spring, turning golden-yellow in autumn. The shaggy, cinnamon-brown bark is attractive during winter. This tree grows well in moist soil and is resistant to pollution.

Salix caprea 'Weeping Sally' z 4
Rarely growing to more than 6ft (1.8m), this small weeping willow is a female form of the larger goat willow, *S. caprea*, grafted on to a straight-species rootstock. It grows slowly into a graceful umbrella-shaped tree, the branches growing down to the ground, and bears soft silvery-white catkins in spring. The deciduous leaves are glossy green with woolly undersides and form a dense mass in summer, allowing little to grow under the tree other than spring-flowering bulbs.

***Viburnum plicatum* 'Mariesii'** z 4
(below)
This form of the Japanese snowball tree is best grown as a specimen shrub. Horizontally tiered branches make it a fine architectural plant reaching 6ft (1.8m) in height and spread. The flowers are made conspicuous by white, sterile, ray florets which form heads 2-3in (5-7.5cm) across. These are held above the branches in early summer and persist for many weeks. In autumn the leaves turn a rich burgundy-red. Grows in most soils including those over chalk; needs no regular pruning.

Cercidiphyllum japonicum *(above)* z 5
Katsura tree
As the leaves of this tree take on their grayish-pink, vermilion and yellow autumn tints they release a delicious caramel-like fragrance. They begin coral-pink in late spring, turning sea-green above and bluish beneath. Small flowers appear before the leaves. In cultivation this large tree normally forms a small- to medium-sized specimen. *Helleborus orientalis* makes a good underplanting. Grow in a sunny, sheltered position, in any moist soil, preferably against dark evergreens.

***Clethra alnifolia* 'Paniculata'** *(above)* z 4
The sweet pepper bush grows to 6ft (1.8m) and is prized for its late-summer flowers which fill the air with a sweet fragrance. 'Paniculata' is a superior form with the near-white flowers held in terminal panicles. Its deciduous foliage is attractive year-round and turns a bright yellow-orange in autumn. 'Rosea' has flowers flushed pink. In warm areas black, peppercorn-like seeds follow the flowers. Succeeding in damp, acid soils, this plant is useful for woodland gardens. Good at the back of a border.

***Daphne* × *burkwoodii* 'Carole Mackie'** z 4
Raised in New Jersey, this unusual and beautiful daphne is a striking evergreen shrub noted for its variegated leaves; each rich green leaf has a golden yellow margin which fades to cream. In summer there is the added attraction of clusters of pink, highly fragrant flowers. These dense, well rounded bushes grow to 4ft (1.2m) in height. Although easy to cultiivate in humus-enriched soil in sun or light shade, the plants are difficult to propagate and seed only occasionally. Named after an American gardener who discovered it as a sport in 1962.

Fothergilla monticola z 5
This deciduous shrub makes a rounded 5 × 5ft (1.5 × 1.5m) in ten years. Small, bottlebrush flowers appear in spring, creamy-white and sweetly scented. The coarse, dark green leaves are up to 4in (10cm) long and turn orange and yellow in autumn, blending with the scarlet autumn hues of *Acer palmatum*. The leaves of *F. major* begin golden-orange then deepen to crimson-reds. Grow in moist, acid soil, in sun or partial shade, among heathers or evergreen azaleas. No regular pruning is necessary.

Oemleria cerasiformis (*above*) z 6
Oso berry
A suckering deciduous shrub which bears male and female flowers on different plants. The small, bell-shaped, fragrant white flowers appear in very early spring, carried in pendulous racemes on erect stems some 8ft (2.4m) tall. The sea green leaves emerge on vigorous young shoots. Of little real interest during the summer, plant towards the back of a border. Fruits are plum-like, turning from brown to purple as they ripen.

***Philadelphus* 'Virginal'** (*above*) z 5
In early summer the plentiful double flowers of this vigorous mock orange fill the air with their rich fragrance. It produces upright shoots 10ft (3m) tall and has deciduous leaves, 4in (10cm) long. The compact 'Belle Etoile' reaches 6ft (1.8m). It has 2in (5cm)-wide scented flowers with a reddish-purple blotch in the center. This patch can be picked out in the mixed border with mauve-flowered herbaceous plants such as hardy geraniums. Easily grown, even on poor dry soils, it should be pruned straight after flowering.

Sarcococca hookeriana z 8
Christmas box
This spreading, shade-tolerant, evergreen shrub has erect stems that reach 3ft (1m). In late winter the small, pink-tinged white male flowers release a distinctive scent which is strongest on moist, mild days. Leaves are lance-shaped. The insignificant female flowers are followed by shiny black berries in early spring. *S. h. digyna* has narrower leaves and reddish-tinged stems. This species grows in any fertile soil, including that over chalk.

Styrax japonica z 5
This graceful plant makes a small tree which may reach up to 25ft (8m) and has slender drooping branches. It requires protection from cold spring winds and late frosts that damage the opening buds. The fragrant white flowers are pendulous and open in early summer. The roundish to oval deciduous leaves are dark shiny green. In cooler climates it is best grown in full sun, but some shade is necessary in sunny areas. Can be slow to establish but thrives in deep moisture-retentive soil with plenty of organic matter.

Syringa vulgaris (*below*) z 3
Hundreds of forms of the common lilac exist in cultivation as shrubs or small trees. They reach 5-10ft (1.5-3m) and have a tendency to sucker. The large, spring flowers, held in dense pyramidal panicles, have a delicious scent and can be white, pink, cream, purple or mauve, single or double. The heart-shaped deciduous leaves are fresh green in spring. Plant in any fertile soil in a sunny position, preferably towards the back of a border as it tends to become bare at the base. Deadhead, but avoid hard pruning which encourages growth.

Viburnum carlesii (*below*) z 4
The heavy daphne-like scent of this popular viburnum permeates the air in spring. Clusters of pink buds make pure white flowers, followed by jet black autumn fruits. The leaves are dull green above, gray below, and often take on orange-red autumn hues. A rounded shrub, 4ft (1.2m) high, it makes a fine specimen plant. 'Diana' and 'Aurora' have red flowers which turn pink; 'Charis' has red flowers which turn pink then white. Cut out suckers sent up by grafted plants. Easily grown in most soils, it requires little pruning.

Winter color

BARK

Acer griseum *(above)* z 6
Paperbark maple
This slow-growing, lime-tolerant tree grows to 40ft (12m) with an open, rounded crown. The polished, orange-brown peeling bark is fully developed on wood three or more years old. In spring the trifoliate leaves emerge buff yellow. They turn dark green, reaching 2-4in (5-10cm) across, and become deep scarlet-orange in autumn. Greenish-yellow flowers appear in early summer. Needs a moist soil. Grouped plants should be well-spaced.

Betula papyrifera *(above)* z 4
Paper bark or canoe birch
During its first five years this deciduous tree develops a smooth, white bark which then peels away in sheets. This peeling continues throughout the tree's life, revealing new glistening bark beneath. It grows to 60ft (18m) but the canopy casts only partial shade, allowing other plants to grow at the base. The irregularly toothed leaves turn a rich yellow in autumn. *B. jaquemontii* is similar but has brown peeling bark. Grows in most soils.

Cornus alba **'Sibirica'** *(below)* z 2
The bright red, glossy, upright stems of this winter dogwood form a thicket some 6ft (1.8m) high; they are stronger in moisture-rich soils. The leaves are up to 5in (13cm) long and turn shades of plum-red in autumn before falling. For deep purple, almost black stems, grow 'Kesselringii', striking if combined with red- and yellow-stemmed forms. Plant in groups for the best effect, avoiding shaded positions. Cut the stems very hard back in early spring to encourage fresh growth; flowers and fruits will be sacrificed as a consequence.

Cornus stolonifera **'Flaviramea'** z 2
(below)
This dogwood is grown for its bright yellow and olive green stems which can grow to 6ft (1.8m) if cut hard back in early spring. The growth is vigorous and suckering, forming a dense thicket if left unpruned. The light green deciduous leaves are up to 5in (13cm) long and turn yellow in autumn. Choose a site where the stems can be illuminated by the winter sun. It will tolerate waterlogged conditions. Grow with the red-stemmed dogwoods for beautiful winter color.

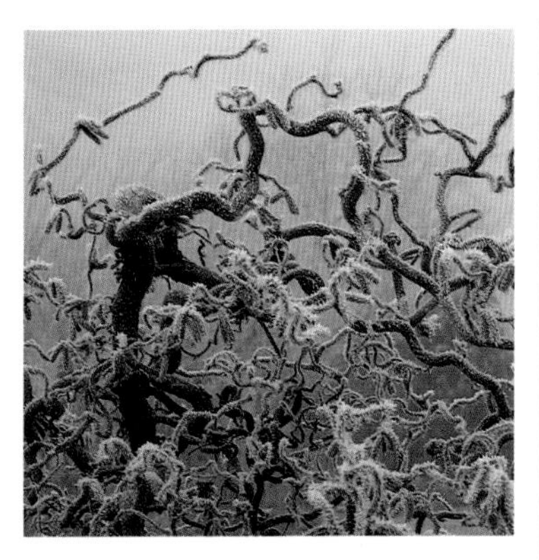

Corylus avellana **'Contorta'** *(above)* z 5
Corkscrew hazel or Harry Lauder's walking stick
The branches and the thread-like twigs of this deciduous bush are twisted and looped in a knotted mass. Reaching 10ft (3m), the plant is covered in spring with yellow male catkins and tiny, red, tufted female flowers. The leaves are up to 4in (10cm) long and more crinkly than the ordinary hazel; they turn yellow in autumn. Grows in most soils. Cut out vigorous suckers from the base. Plants look striking when seen against snow or covered in frost.

Leycesteria formosa z 7
Himalayan honeysuckle or pheasant berry
This deciduous shrub has bright sea green stems which are hollow, upright and reach 6ft (1.8m) in a season. The young stems are covered with a glaucous bloom. Olive green pointed leaves are 2-7in (5-18cm) long; they turn yellow in autumn. In summer the white flowers emerge from purple-red bracts and hang in heavy racemes. These are followed by purple-brown fruits which smell of caramel. Grow in moist, fertile soil. Cut back to ground level in spring.

Parrotia persica z 6
Persian ironwood
Grown mostly for its vivid red, orange and yellow autumn leaf color, this plant also has beautiful flaking gray bark on its older stems. It grows as a spreading large shrub or small tree and can reach 25ft (7.5m) with a similar spread, the stiff, horizontal tiers of branches making an excellent winter silhouette. The flowers appear in late winter, conspicuous for their bright red stamens and lack of petals. Grows in most soils apart from highly alkaline.

Pinus bungeana z 5
Lace-bark pine
An unusual evergreen conifer, this slowly forms a low-branching specimen shrub or tree up to 40ft (12m) tall. The gray-green bark flakes away, leaving a beautiful jigsaw-like pattern of white, olive green, yellow, brown and purple. The colors change as more flaking occurs. The yellow-green, needle-like leaves are about 3in (8cm) long. *P. gerardiana*, Gerard's pine, has pinkish-gray bark that flakes to reveal brown, green and yellow wood. Grow both in full sun, avoiding shallow alkaline soils.

Prunus serrula *(above)* z 6
Tibetan cherry
The smooth bark of this tree resembles polished mahogany. It peels horizontally between large, pale brown lenticels which ring the trunk and stems. A tree is at its best after ten years when it is 15ft (4.5m) tall. Ideal for a lawn, underplanted with *Narcissus* 'February Gold' or similar. It grows in all soil types including alkaline. Plant in full winter sunlight, removing lower branches to gain trunk length. Polish the bark with a soft cloth to enhance the beautiful sheen.

Rhododendron barbatum z 8
Dense heads of crimson red flowers appear in spring on this evergreen rhododendron. It has deep purple, peeling bark, large leaves with sunken veins, and bristly young branches and petioles. It forms a very large shrub or a tree 30ft (9m) high. *R. thomsonii* has cinnamon-colored bark and blood red flowers. Plant in semi-shade in moist, acid soil, mulching with leaf mold. This species is ideal for woodland. Water well until established. No regular pruning needed.

Rubus cockburnianus *(above)* z 5
Whitewashed bramble
A whitish bloom covers the arching, purple stems of this deciduous rubus. The lower surfaces of the pinnate, fern-like leaves are also bloomy. Small flowers are sometimes followed by black fruits. All shoots should be cut to within 1in (2.5cm) of the ground in spring to encourage new growth; this can reach 6ft (1.8m) on established plants. Will grow in shade or sun in most soils. Plant against a dark background in full winter sun, with *Eranthis hyemalis* beneath.

Salix alba **'Chermesina'** z 2
Scarlet willow
Similar to the winter dogwoods in habit, the young shoots of this shrub are bright orange-red. Deciduous, pale green leaves open in summer. Prune hard back at least twice in spring to encourage fresh growth. Plants will reach 6ft (1.8m) in two seasons, considerably more if left unpruned. *S. alba* 'Vitellina', the golden willow, has bright yellow shoots. For contrast, plant with dogwoods such as the dark purple-stemmed *Cornus alba* 'Kesselringii'. Best in moist soil, especially near water.

Salix matsudana **'Tortuosa'** z 4
Corkscrew willow
The twisted shoots and branches of this willow are dramatic against the winter sky. It makes a narrow, pyramidal tree and, once settled, grows to 20ft (6m) in ten years. The olive green twisted stems carry narrow, contorted, bright green decidous leaves in spring, as well as small yellow-green catkins. Train *Clematis* 'Bill Mackenzie' through it for yellow flowers and fluffy seed heads. Quickly regrows if cut hard back. Prefers moisture-rich soil, near water.

FLOWERS AND BERRIES

Camellia **'Salutation'** z 7
This hybrid evergreen shrub grows to 6 × 6ft (1.8 × 1.8m) in ten years. The silvery-pink flowers are semi-double, 5in (13cm) across, and appear in late winter and spring. The leaves are matte green. Grow camellias in humus-rich, acid soil and mulch regularly with organic matter. Choose a sheltered spot, out of strong winds and protected from the early morning sun which can damage the flowers after frosts: a woodland garden is ideal. Water in the summer, especially until established.

Corylopsis pauciflora z 6
Winterhazel
The arching stems of this deciduous shrub can reach 6 × 6ft (1.8 × 1.8m). The leaves emerge pink and open a dull green, with good autumn color. Drooping racemes of scented, bell-shaped yellow flowers are carried in early spring. *C. spicata* is larger, with yellow flowers and purple anthers; *C. willmottiae* 'Spring Purple' has purple-red winter shoots. Plant in deep, lime-free, humus-rich soil in some shade. Underplant with *Narcissus cyclamineus.*

Cotoneaster lacteus *(above)* z 7
This plant bears large clusters of small red fruits which last throughout the winter if they survive the attention of birds. Evergreen, leathery, oval leaves have deep-set veins and felted gray undersides. Creamy-white flowers appear in summer. It can be pruned to make a short, single-stemmed tree, but is more usually a free-growing shrub up to 12ft (3.6m) tall, with similar spread. The mauve flowers of *Clematis viticella* 'Abundance' will give interest in late summer. Grows in most soils.

Hamamelis mollis *(above)* z 5
Chinese witch hazel
One of the first winter-flowering shrubs, this has sweet-scented, golden yellow flowers with hardy strap-like petals, borne on bare, upward-growing branches. The light, open canopy reaches 10ft (3m). Hazel-like deciduous leaves are up to 5in (13cm) across, turning deep yellow in autumn. 'Pallida' has larger, sulphur-yellow flowers; *H.* × *intermedia* 'Diane' has rich copper-red flowers and good autumn color. Slow-growing; do not prune. Plant in humus-rich acid soil in full sun.

Ilex verticillata z 3
Winterberry
This holly is quite unlike all others because of its deciduous nature. It forms a rounded shrub reaching 13ft (4m) in ten years. In winter the bare green-purple stems are clothed with long-lasting, bright red berries. An unusual shrub, also noted for its purple-tinged 1⅔in (4cm)-long leaves, which are particularly well-colored in spring, turning yellow in autumn. The female form 'Christmas Cheer' has many persistent fruits. Needs acid soil.

***Malus* 'Red Sentinel'** z 5
With fruits lasting into mid- and late winter, this crab apple is a valuable small- to medium-sized tree. The deep red fruits hang in large clusters from bare branches. They are preceded in summer by groups of white flowers. The deciduous leaves are 2in (5cm) long. It forms a round-headed tree 20 × 10ft (6 × 3m) after ten years. 'Golden Hornet' carries bright yellow fruits and is a useful pollinator for dessert apples. Thrives in most soils except those which are waterlogged; needs little pruning.

Pernettya mucronata z 7
Small, cup-shaped, white flowers appear in summer on this evergreen shrub, followed by dense clusters of shiny, marble-like fruits. 'Mulberry Wine' has large magenta berries, 'Pink Pearl' lilac-pink, and 'Alba' white. They grow to 2ft (75cm), making a rounded mass of wiry stems. The small evergreen leaves are held close to the red stems. Grow in acid soil, in sun or semi-shade; good in peat beds and for growing with heathers and callunas. Plant in groups, ensuring one plant is a male. Prune back straggly shoots. Makes useful ground cover.

***Prunus* × *subhirtella* 'Autumnalis'** z 6
(above)
Autumn or winter flowering cherry
This tree grows to 16ft (5m) in ten years. Small, white, semi-double flowers appear throughout the autumn, winter and spring on bare branches; the blooms may be damaged by severe weather conditions. The 2in (5cm)-long leaves have yellow-bronze autumn colors. 'Autumnalis Rosea' has rose pink flowers. Plant in fertile, moist soil, avoiding frost pockets or very exposed positions. Can also be grown as a multi-stemmed shrub. Slow to establish.

Rhododendron mucronulatum z 6
Normally evergreen, this slender shrub has small lanceolate leaves that form a backcloth to the clusters of purplish-rose flowers. These are funnel-shaped, up to 2in (5cm) long. The flowers appear from late winter to early spring. The cultivar 'Winter Brightness' has richer flowers, its name giving an obvious clue to its value. Plant away from exposure to cold winter winds which can damage the flowers, in humus-rich, moist, acid soil; add mulch to retain moisture during summer.

Sorbus cashmiriana z 2
Kashmir mountain ash
From autumn onwards pearl white fruits are borne in dense clusters on the bare branches of this ash. They are ⅖in (1cm) across, have reddish stalks and last well into winter. The pinnate leaves are 9in (23cm) long with numerous gray-green leaflets that turn yellow in autumn. Soft pink flowers appear in spring. Makes a small rounded tree or large shrub, reaching 10ft (3m) in ten years. *S. hupehensis* (z 5) has smaller fruits tipped pink. Does not need pruning. Suitable for most soils.

Symplocos paniculata z 5
Sapphire berry
The ultramarine, jewel-like fruits of this plant are dazzling. Carried in dense clusters, they follow the fragrant, white spring flowers. Small leaves turn yellow in autumn. It forms a dense, twiggy shrub or small tree up to 10ft (3m) tall in ten years. Plants need cross-pollination and only fruit fully after several seasons. Grow in rich, deep, non-alkaline soil, in a sheltered spot in sun or shade. Fruiting is most prolific after a hot, dry summer.

***Viburnum* × *bodnantense* 'Dawn'** z 6
(above)
This deciduous viburnum has a strong, upright habit and grows to 8ft (2.4m). Clusters of sweetly scented, tubular, pink flowers appear from early winter through to spring. In 'Deben' the flowers are pink in bud opening white. Leaves are bronze-tinted in spring, maturing to green and turning reddish in autumn. The purple-green stems darken as they age. Thin out some of the oldest flowering stems each spring when fully established. Suitable for any soil; reasonably frost-tolerant.

Spring color

FLOWERS

Berberis darwinii (*above*) z 7
Clusters of double, cup-shaped, orange flowers are borne by this evergreen barberry from early spring onwards. The dark green, spiny leaves have silvery undersides. In autumn dark purple, bloomy fruits appear and some older leaves turn fiery orange and fall. Grows to 6 × 6ft (1.8 × 1.8m) in ten years. Underplant with the bright blue-flowered *Brunnera macrophylla*. Grow in sun or shade; avoid dry soils. Use at the back of a border or as a hedge.

Cercis siliquastrum (*below*) z 6
Judas tree
In spring the branches and trunk of this plant are covered with clusters of pea-like, pink flowers. These are followed by kidney-shaped glaucous leaves, which turn yellow in autumn. Purple-tinged seedpods appear in late summer. Makes a small tree but gives more flowers as a multi-stemmed shrub, reaching 8 × 7ft (2.4 × 2.1m) in ten years. Grow in full sun and well-drained soil. Plants need little pruning until they are five years old. *C. canadensis* is hardier (z 4).

Chaenomeles* × *superba z 5
Japanese quince or japonica
Forms of this vigorous, small- to medium-sized thorny shrub include 'Knap Hill Scarlet', with orange-scarlet flowers, and 'Pink Lady', rose-pink. Loose-petalled flowers appear in mild winters, but the main flush is in spring. Dark green deciduous leaves follow. The fragrant, yellow fruits can be used to make jelly. Grow freestanding or as a wall shrub in sun or shade; avoid alkaline soils which cause chlorosis. Prune back the previous season's growth after flowering.

***Cornus* 'Eddie's White Wonder'** z 5
This plant is much prized for its large white flower heads which appear in spring. It forms a small tree or large shrub up to 16 × 16ft (5 × 5m) and is very hardy. The leaves turn brilliant shades during autumn before falling. In winter the flower buds are only party protected by the bracts, evidence of this cornus's hybrid origins. Plants have a compact, upright habit and succeed best in moist acid soils in sun or light shade. An ideal subject for a woodland planting.

Cytisus* × *praecox (*above*) z 5
Warminster broom
The spindly, green stems of this shrub form a mass that makes 4 × 4ft (1.2 × 1.2m) in eight years. In spring the stems are weighed down by pea-like, light yellow flowers. 'Allgold' has long-lasting yellow flowers, 'Albus' pure white and 'Buttercup' golden-yellow flowers. The small deciduous leaves drop early in the season. Grows in full sun in most soils. Plants tend to be short-lived; they have weak root systems and need staking in exposed sites. Prune if necessary after flowering, removing one-year-old wood: never remove mature wood.

***Erica arborea* 'Alpina'** z 7
During spring this form of the evergreen tree heath is awash with frothy white flowers which complement the feathery foliage. The blooms have a strong honey-like fragrance. Making 6ft (1.8m) in ten years, it is a fine specimen shrub and gives height to a heather garden. Works well with a basal planting of *Erica carnea* or *Calluna vulgaris* in their various forms. 'Riverslea' has purple flowers but is less hardy. Needs acid soil and full sun or very slight shade. Prone to damage by high winds or snow: only prune to remove damaged growth.

***Exochorda* × *macrantha* 'The Bride'** z 5
(*above*)
The graceful stems of this deciduous shrub are covered with racemes of small, white saucer-shaped flowers in spring. Each flower has five petals. The light green, lanceolate leaves are 3in (8cm) long and turn yellow in autumn. Plants grow upright for the first few years and then develop arching shoots, making a rounded bush, some 6ft (1.8m) high and often wider. Grow in a sunny position, avoiding alkaline soils. Remove a third of the old wood after flowering to encourage new growth.

Forsythia* × *intermedia z 5
Forsythia carries masses of early spring, yellow flowers before the leaves emerge. This vigorous hybrid will grow to 12ft (3.6m) in ten years, but can be kept smaller with regular pruning. Plants have an upright habit when young but form a rounded shrub when mature. 'Spectabilis' is the most floriferous form. Cut back one third of the oldest wood immediately after flowering to encourage new shoots. Easy to grow, it succeeds in sun in all soils.

Magnolia × _soulangiana_ (*above*) z 6
Tulip magnolia
Large, loose-petaled, sweetly scented flowers appear on bare branches in spring, the white petals shaded pink with purple bases. Oval leaves open later. A small tree or a multi-stemmed shrub, it reaches 16ft (5m) in 20 years. 'Brozzonii' has huge white flowers, 'Rustica Rubra' reddish-purple, goblet-shaped flowers and 'Lennei' has rose-purple flowers with white insides; it may have a second flush in early autumn. Needs shelter and a heavy soil, enriched with compost. A superb specimen plant.

Prunus 'Okame' z 7
This cherry is renowned for its display of clear pink flowers, which are carried in profusion in early spring. The flower buds are equally attractive. Trees bloom over a period of 2–3 weeks, and in autumn the leaves turn attractive shades of reddish-orange. In winter there is the added attraction of brownish-red bark. Plants grow to 25ft (8m) and have an upright oval shape. Quick growing in most soils in a sunny position.

Rhododendron luteum z 5
Also known as *Azalea pontica*, this deciduous shrub can grow to 5 × 5ft (1.5 × 1.5m) in ten years. It tolerates poorer and drier conditions than most deciduous azaleas but still requires acid soil. The winter buds and young shoots are characteristically sticky. Funnel-shaped, yellow flowers appear in round heads, in advance of the leaves; they have a very strong fragrance. The leaves are oblong, 4in (10cm) long, and turn rich shades of orange-crimson in autumn. Growth tends to slow with age. Pruning is usually unnecessary.

Stachyurus praecox (*below*) z 6
From early spring onwards this deciduous shrub bears plentiful frost-hardy, pale yellow flowers in small rigid racemes. Long, oval leaves with dark veins open later and turn yellow in autumn. Stems are purple-green. It makes a domed bush 6 × 6ft (1.8 × 1.8m) in five years. Underplant with *Helleborus orientalis* and *H. niger* or use it at the rear of a border. *S. chinensis* has smaller, more numerous flowers. Plant in sun or semi-shade in fertile soil. Once established, prune out a third of the older wood every few years.

Viburnum × _carlcephalum_ (*below*) z 5
This deciduous viburnum carries large heads of scented, white, tubular flowers, pink in bud. The gray-green leaves often take on orange-red colors in autumn. A rounded bush of compact habit, reaching 5 × 5ft (1.5 × 1.5m) in ten years, it makes a good specimen, or can be grown in a border or large tub. Grows well in most soils, but avoid extremes of dryness or wetness, which damage the surface root system. Plants need sun or partial shade to thrive. Remove any suckering growths that appear at the base.

FOLIAGE

Acer pseudoplatanus z 5
'Brilliantissimum' (*above*)
This sycamore is a slow-growing, small deciduous tree, reaching 12ft (3.6m) in ten years. The spring foliage emerges bright shrimp pink, turns pale yellow-green and then green during the summer. Autumn leaves are usually yellow. It has an architectural quality, forming a rounded, mop-headed shape after three or four seasons. Succeeds in most soils, in full sun. Remove wood affected by coral spot disease.

Aesculus neglecta 'Erythroblastos' z 5
Sunrise horse chestnut
A beautiful, slow-growing, medium-sized tree with spectacular spring foliage. The leaves are composed of five leaflets, each up to 6in (15cm) long. They unfold bright pink in spring, then fade over a period of weeks to a pale yellowish-green and finally turn yellow-orange in autumn. Pale yellow flowers appear in summer. It can reach 25ft (7.5m). Grow in any good soil; choose an open position in spring sun, with some protection from larger trees.

Cryptomeria japonica 'Elegans' z 7
This cultivar of the evergreen Japanese cedar has small, drooping, awl-shaped leaves that make a dense head. In spring the foliage turns blue-green, also the color of fresh new growth. It assumes brown-bronze tints in winter; the change is sometimes so dramatic the plant appears to be dead. A rounded coniferous bush or small tree, it grows to 8 × 8ft (2.4 × 2.4m). The reddish, peeling bark is only really noticeable on older plants. 'Elegans Aurea' turns green-gold in winter. Grows best in moist soils.

Summer color

Larix decidua *(below)* z 3
European larch
This deciduous conifer is beautiful in spring as the leaves emerge; light green and needle-like, they are held in rosettes along the shoots and are set off by the yellowish-brown bark. In autumn they turn golden-yellow. Mature trees produce pink-purple female cones, along with smaller yellowish male cones. Quickly forms a large cone-shaped tree, reaching 60ft (18m); the branches droop with age. Avoid wet soils.

***Photinia* × *fraseri* 'Red Robin'** z 7
(below)
This evergreen shrub makes its boldest statement in spring. Red leaves appear in autumn, the color intensifying during winter, so that by spring the plant is covered with flaming foliage. Leaves continue to appear until mid-summer, when they turn bronze and then green with age. White flowers may open in spring. Plants can grow to 6ft (1.8m) in height in ten years, with a rounded habit. Mature specimens are a good support for a summer-flowering clematis. Plant in full sun, and add plenty of compost to the soil. Prune hard every few years.

Pieris formosa forrestii z 7
'Forest Flame'
An acid-loving evergreen shrub, ideal for a woodland garden. Fiery red foliage opens at the shoot tips in spring. The small lanceolate leaves change to shrimp pink, then white, and finally to dark green as summer progresses. Sprays of slightly fragrant, white, lily-of-the-valley-like flowers appear in late spring. Plants can reach up to 6ft (1.8m) in height when mature, and need little pruning. Avoid full sun and alkaline soils; add leaf mold at planting. Protect from cold winds.

***Spiraea japonica* 'Goldflame'** z 5
An easily grown, deciduous shrub that reaches only 2ft (60cm) in height after ten years, this plant is a useful addition to the shrub or mixed border. In spring the brownish-red stems are adorned with new apricot-orange leaves; these turn orange-red and then golden-yellow as the season progresses. Reddish-pink flowers appear in summer. Grow as a specimen or in groups, avoiding strong sun (which can scorch the leaves) and dry and alkaline soils. Prune plants to ground level in spring to encourage healthy re-growth.

***Viburnum opulus* 'Aureum'** *(above)* z 3
This yellow-leaved form of the guelder rose is useful in moist soil and for wilder parts of the garden. The deciduous leaves are 2-5in (5-13cm) long with five lobes. New spring growth is bright yellow, ageing to greenish-yellow during summer. It reaches 6ft (1.8m) in ten years and can be left unpruned; alternatively, a third of the oldest shoots can be cut to ground level every two or three years once the plant is established. Protect from strong, direct sun which scorches the leaves.

FLOWERS

***Aesculus* × *carnea* 'Briottii'** z 4
This compact form of the red horse chestnut will reach 20ft (6m) in ten years, forming an oval-canopied tree. It has upright, 10in (25cm)-long panicles of deep reddish-pink flowers in early summer. The dark deciduous leaves are digitate and up to 1ft (30cm) across; they turn deep orange-yellow in autumn. The "conkers" (fruits) are smooth-coated. Plant in moist soil, avoiding high alkalinity, in full sun. Casts deep, unfruitful shade so best-suited to the larger garden.

Buddleia davidii *(above)* z 5
Butterfly bush
Fragrant, tubular flowers, held in large racemes, appear on this arching shrub from summer to early autumn. Deciduous lanceolate leaves are 4-12in (10-30cm) long and are light green with silvery-gray undersides. Forms include: 'Black Knight' (velvety-purple flowers) and 'Peace' (white with orange eyes). Grows to 10ft (3m) in five years in the poorest soils. Spreads by seed; can become a weed. Prune hard back in early spring to 4in (10cm) from the base.

Calycanthus floridus z 4
Carolina allspice
During summer this shrub bears red-brown, star-like, scented flowers on wood that is more than two seasons old. These are set off by the light green, deciduous leaves, which have downy undersides and are aromatic if crushed. In autumn the foliage turns yellow. It reaches 6 × 6ft (1.8 × 1.8m) in ten years, with a rounded habit. Grow in deep, rich, alkaline-free soil, in diffused shade, as found under a light tree canopy. Pruning is not necessary.

***Crataegus laevigata* 'Crimson Cloud'** z 4
(above)
Also listed as *C. oxycantha*, this hawthorn is a deciduous, spiny tree that reaches 20ft (6m) with a rounded crown. The small leaves are lobed, gray-green, and often have attractive yellow tints in autumn. However, the flowers are the greatest asset. Held in dense clusters, they are deep red with a white patch at the base of each petal. 'Paul's Scarlet' has double flowers. Bunches of shiny red berries follow in autumn and persist for at least six weeks. Prune only to remove suckers. Avoid over-dry soils.

***Deutzia* × *elegantissima* 'Rosealind'** z 5
(below)
The arching stems of this shrub are covered with dense corymbs of pink, five-petaled, fragrant flowers from late spring to early summer. The oval, deciduous leaves are slightly rough. Plants reach 6ft (1.8m) and should have a third of the oldest wood removed after flowering. Train a large-flowered clematis through the branches. Plants need moist fertile soil and regular watering during periods of drought. Select a sheltered spot.

Enkianthus campanulatus z 4
A member of the heather family, this deciduous shrub flowers in early summer, producing clusters of waxy, bell-like blooms, creamy-yellow with red stripes. Growth is bushy and upright, reaching about 13ft (4m) with a spread of 8ft (2.4m); the base of mature plants is open. The glossy green leaves turn shades of orange, red and scarlet in autumn. 'Red Bells' has more prominent stripes. Cut back one or two shoots each season. Plants need lime-free soil and grow best in partial shade in moist, deep, acid soil. They are excellent for a woodland garden.

Halesia carolina z 5
Snowdrop tree or Carolina silverbell
This spreading deciduous shrub grows 12ft (3.6m) tall in ten years. Clusters of nodding, pure white flowers cover the branches in early summer. Four-winged fruits follow as the flowers fade. The deciduous oval leaves are pale green, yellow in autumn. *H. monticola vestita* has larger flowers that can be tinged pink. Grows well in moist, acid soil, high in organic matter in a protected site. Takes two or three seasons to establish; needs no pruning.

Kalmia latifolia *(above)* z 5
Calico bush or mountain laurel
This rhododendron-like evergreen shrub is one of the most beautiful summer-flowering plants for an acid soil. In early summer the striking buds open into clusters of pink flowers. These last for several weeks, framed by the narrow, glossy, mid-green leaves. It makes a rounded bush, 10 × 10ft (3 × 3m). Full sun is needed for maximum flowering. Soil should be deep and moist. Does not need pruning, except for shaping when young.

Koelreuteria paniculata z 6
Golden rain tree, Chinese rain tree or Pride of India
This excellent tree reaches upwards of 20ft (6m) in 20 years. Upright terminal panicles, 1ft (30cm) long, hold small, yellow flowers in mid- to late summer. These are followed by three-lobed, bladder-like fruits which are pale green with a reddish tint, turning yellow-brown in autumn. The light brownish-green bark is also attractive. Needs full sun and a well-drained soil; tolerant of heat and drought, alkaline soil and atmospheric pollution.

Kolkwitzia amabilis *(above)* z 4
Beauty bush
A hardy shrub with slender, drooping branches, clothed in bell-shaped, pink, yellow-throated flowers in summer. The calyxes and flower stalks are hairy. It forms a vase-shaped bush of 6ft (1.8m) in ten years, and is suited to the rear of a border. The small, deciduous leaves are tooth-edged. Peeling, silvery-brown bark gives winter interest. 'Pink Cloud' has larger flowers. Grows in most soils, needing full sun. Cut a third of the old wood to ground level after flowering.

Paulownia tomentosa z 6
Princess or foxglove tree
Panicles of brown buds form in autumn on plants that are at least five years old; these open the following spring as blue-mauve, foxglove-like flowers. Lobed, deciduous leaves, up to 10in (25cm) long, appear after the flowers. Reaches 16ft (5m) in 20 years. If only foliage is required, cut stems hard back in spring to produce vigorous shoots with enormous leaves, 2ft (60cm) across. Some damage to buds is likely in severe weather, even in a sheltered site. Needs deep, rich, soil and full sun.

***Rubus* × *tridel* 'Benenden'** (*above*) z 5
This vigorous, shrubby rubus has arching, thornless, reddish canes and grows to 10ft (3m). The blackberry-like, deciduous leaves are lobed and turn yellow in autumn. In summer it carries 2in (5cm)-wide white flowers with clusters of yellow stamens. Good on most soils and happy in some shade. Prune a third of the oldest shoots out after flowering; new growth will reach 6ft (1.8m) in a year. This form has larger flowers than the type. Old shoots have peeling bark.

***Syringa meyeri* 'Palibin'** z 3
Korean lilac
This smaller-growing relative of *S. vulgaris* is suitable for planting in a container as well as in the open garden. It grows slowly, forming a low, neat shrub 4ft (1.2m) high. During summer it is covered with small trusses of pale lilac-pink, fragrant flowers; this is particularly true of younger plants. The deciduous leaves are rounded, up to 3in (8cm) long, with a velvety texture; they turn yellow in autumn. Succeeds in any fertile soil and flowers best in partial shade. Pruning unnecessary.

***Viburnum opulus* 'Roseum'** z 3
Snowball shrub
Also classified as *V. opulus* 'Sterile', this form of the guelder rose has creamy-white, snowball-like heads of sterile flowers which weigh down the spreading branches in summer. The light green deciduous leaves often turn attractive shades in autumn. Quickly reaching 12ft (3.6m), it can be left to form a mound; alternatively, a third of the oldest shoots can be pruned back in spring. Grows in all soils, even with extremes of dryness or wetness. Non-fruiting.

FOLIAGE

***Berberis* × *ottawensis* 'Purpurea'** z 5
A vigorous, deciduous barberry which reaches 12ft (3.6m), it carries large, purple, ovate leaves along the upright, thorny shoots. Racemes of golden-yellow flowers form in spring, hanging clusters of red berries in autumn. Useful as an informal hedge or planted with white or gold variegated shrubs such as *Rhamnus alaternus* 'Argenteovariegata'. *B. thunbergii* 'Rose Glow' is smaller, with pinky-white leaves. Grow in full sun; avoid over-dry soils. Prune out a few old stems occasionally.

***Cotinus coggygria* 'Royal Purple'** z 4 (*above*)
Smoke tree or bush
The leaves of this deciduous shrub open a deep wine red, changing through the growing season to a velvety maroon. They are rounded and turn shades of orange, scarlet and red in autumn. Plume-like panicles of pink blossom are at their best in late summer. The plant reaches 10ft (3m) if left unpruned, or it can be cut back each spring to produce vigorous 6ft (1.8m) shoots with large leaves but no flowers. Plant in rich, deep soil, in a sunny position.

***Gleditsia triacanthos* 'Sunburst'** z 5
Golden honey locust
Vibrant, golden-yellow, late spring foliage characterizes this plant. The leaves are pinnate or bipinnate. It makes an elegantly branching tree, 13ft (4m) tall after five years; on older plants the bark is deeply fissured. It does not bear the vicious spines of the species. An ideal host for *Clematis macropetala*. Needs rich, well-drained soil, full sun and protection from winds as branches are brittle. Prune for shape when young.

***Pyrus salicifolia* 'Pendula'** (*above*) z 5
Weeping silver pear
Few small trees are as graceful as this specimen plant. In spring the small, lanceolate leaves open with a silvery down and are followed by small clusters of creamy-white flowers. Reaching its full height of about 15ft (4.5m) in 15 years, its pendulous branches sweep to the ground. Mature plants have a mop-headed appearance. In summer the foliage is a cool greenish-gray. Spring-flowering blue or purple clematis make excellent companions. Grows in most soils and needs full sun.

Rhododendron yakushimanum z 6
This dome-shaped evergreen rhododendron has unusual young leaves that resemble silvery shuttlecocks. They appear from a collar of older, dark green, leathery leaves which are 2in (5cm) long and have brown, felted undersides. The silver hairs disappear as the leaves mature. Trusses of flowers open earlier, apple-blossom pink, fading to white. Very slow-growing, reaching 3-4ft (90-120cm) in ten years, it needs a well-drained, acid soil in some shade but no pruning.

***Robinia pseudoacacia* 'Frisia'** z 4
Golden false acacia
Similar to, if more slender than *Gleditsia triacanthos* 'Sunburst', this tree has 6in (15cm)-long pinnate leaves that open bright yellow-green in late spring, turn green during summer and butter yellow in autumn. The petioles are orange. Mature trees bear clusters of pea-like white flowers in mid-summer. It grows rapidly, achieving 20ft (6m) in 20 years. Container-grown specimens establish themselves best. Needs moist, well-drained loam and shelter from winds.

Autumn color

***Sambucus racemosa* 'Plumosa Aurea'** (*below*) z 4
This form of the red-berried elder is one of the finest deciduous shrubs for golden-yellow foliage. The fern-like, dissected, pinnate leaves are 3-6in (8-15cm) long and wide. The largest leaves are produced by plants that are pruned hard back each spring: unpruned plants bear large panicles of white flowers, followed by translucent red berries. It can reach 6ft (1.8m) but annual pruning will reduce height and spread. Most soils are suitable; some shade is good, to protect the leaves from sun-scorch.

Sorbus aria z 5
Whitebeam
In spring leaves emerge grayish-white on this tree and turn bright green above, with dense silvery-gray hairs beneath. Autumn leaves are brownish-yellow. In early summer 4in (10cm)-wide panicles of white flowers appear, followed by bunches of scarlet fruits. It reaches 20ft (6m) in ten years with a rounded crown. The leaves of 'Lutescens' have creamy-white hairs. A fine specimen tree, it can also be trained over a wall, archway or pillar. Most soils are suitable; tolerates alkalinity.

***Weigela florida* 'Foliis Purpureis'** z 5
The leaves of this deciduous shrub are flushed purple in spring and darken during summer. Foxglove-like purple-pink flowers appear in late spring along the arching branches. 'Variegata' has leaves with creamy-white margins and pink flowers, while 'Looymansii Aurea' has golden foliage and pale pink flowers. Plants grow in all types of soil, reaching 2 × 2ft (60 × 60cm). To maintain good leaf color on established plants, prune out a third of the old wood in early summer after flowering.

FOLIAGE

Acer japonicum (*above*) z 5
Japanese maple
The large, lobed, red-veined leaves of this tree turn red in autumn. 'Aureum' has golden-yellow summer foliage and darker autumn color; 'Vitifolium' has fan-shaped leaves that turn plum-purple; 'Aconitifolium' has dissected leaves with orange-red autumn tints. Groups of reddish-purple flowers form from early spring. The spreading open habit reaches 10ft (3m). Needs slightly acid, moist soil; best in partial shade.

Amelanchier lamarckii (*below*) z 4
Shadbush or juneberry
Crimson, orange and red autumn foliage adorns this plant. The small leaves open coppery-pink. Plentiful sprays of star-shaped, white spring flowers become scarlet fruits in summer; these turn black in autumn. 'Ballerina' has more abundant pink-tinged flowers but less striking autumn foliage. Makes a small cone-shaped tree or multi-stemmed shrub of 20ft (6m) in 20 years. Use against a dark background or as a lawn specimen. Plants need moist soil and little pruning.

Euonymus sachalinensis (*below*) z 5
This shrub has large leaves which turn orange-red in autumn, enhanced by red fruits with deep pink seeds. The leaves open dark green and have a reddish tinge in summer. Makes 13 × 13ft (4 × 4m) in ten years. *E. europaeus* 'Atropurpureus' has purple summer foliage and red autumn color; *E. e.* 'Aucubifolius' has yellow and white mottled leaves, tinted pink in autumn. *E. alatus* 'Compacta' is the dwarf form of 'Burning Bush' and has scarlet autumn foliage and red fruits. Needs sun; will grow on alkaline soil.

***Fraxinus oxycarpa* 'Raywood'** z 6
Raywood ash
This ash is beautiful in autumn when its 10in (25cm)-long pinnate leaves turn reddish-purple. Clusters of creamy-white, petaless, fragrant flowers appear in late spring, developing into small, orange-brown, key-like fruits. The canopy broadens with age and makes it a fine specimen tree, reaching 35ft (10.5m) in 20 years. It casts only slight shade, useful for underplanting. 'Flame' has brilliant red autumn leaves. Grow in any soil, in full sun.

Hydrangea quercifolia z 5
Oak-leaf hydrangea
The large, deciduous, oak-shaped leaves of this shrubby hydrangea turn bright reddish-orange to purple in autumn. From late summer the plant carries conical panicles of white flowers which fade to pink as they age and turn brown in winter. Growth is slow, making a rounded bush of 4 × 4ft (1.2 × 1.2m) after ten years. Shoots tend to be brittle. Thrives in sun or shade and grows in most fertile, moist soils. Can be wall trained. Pruning is unnecessary, but plants will re-grow if cut back.

Liquidambar styraciflua (*below*) z 5
Sweet gum
Similar to the maple, this tree differs in having alternate lobed leaves which release a distinctive aromatic fragrance when crushed; they turn red with hints of yellow, orange and purple in autumn. Slow to establish, it can reach 20ft (6m) in 20 years with a regular, conical canopy. Older trees have fissured bark. 'Worplesdon' and 'Lane Roberts' have more upright-growing branches and deep crimson-purple autumn foliage. Grow in full sun in rich, moist soil.

Malus tschonoskii (*below*) z 6
Of all the crab apples, this species has the most spectacular autumn colors, the leaves turning yellow, then shades of red, crimson and orange. Clusters of rose-pink spring flowers are followed by yellow-brown fruits. This species has an upright habit, growing up to 25ft (7.5m) in height in 20 years, with a spread of 5-10ft (1.5-3m). Enliven the gray-green summer foliage with the climbers *Clematis macropetala* or *C.* 'Bill Mackenzie', which have bluish-mauve macropetals and yellow flowers respectively. Grow plants in sun in moist, rich soil.

Prunus sargentii (*above*) z 5
Sargent's cherry
One of the first trees to color-up in autumn, this has brilliant orange and crimson foliage. In spring the abundant pale pink flowers are followed by the leaves which open bronzy-red and turn dark green with strong veins. Chestnut-brown bark is a feature of older trees. It can reach 20 × 16ft (6 × 5m) in ten years. Grow singly or in a small group; underplant with spring bulbs such as *Narcissus triandrus* 'Thalia'. Best in full sun; needs moist, rich soil.

Quercus coccinea z 4
Scarlet oak
During autumn the foliage of this tree turns scarlet, branch by branch, before falling; some leaves often persist until mid-winter. The leaves are up to 6in (15cm) long, deeply-lobed with bristly tips; they are light green in summer. Slow to establish, the tree reaches 23ft (7m) in ten years and ultimately 70ft (21m), with an open, broad crown. The red oak, *Q. rubra*, is over 100ft (30m) tall when mature, with 10in (25cm)-long matte leaves. Best in full sun, on acid soil. Tolerates pollution.

Spiraea prunifolia z 4
Bridal wreath spiraea
The arching branches of this dense-growing shrub are ablaze with color in autumn when the finely toothed leaves turn bright orangey-red. The branches can reach 6ft (1.8m) and are clothed in spring with button-like, double, white flowers. The leaves are mid-green in summer. Stands out against dark plants and works well with an underplanting of low-growing bamboos. Grows in moderate shade or full sun; avoid alkaline soils. Prune out a third of the older wood after flowering.

BERRIES AND FRUIT

Callicarpa bodinieri giraldii (*below*) z 6
Clusters of lilac-purple fruits form on this deciduous shrub in autumn and can last for several months. The dull green, lanceolate leaves turn purplish at the same time. Small, mauve flowers appear in late summer. The upright stems reach 6ft (1.8m) after ten years. 'Profusion' is a particularly reliable form with larger fruits. Plant in acid soil with added leaf mold; may suffer in hot, dry summers on thin soil. Grow more than one plant to guarantee berries.

Clerodendrum trichotomum fargesii (*below*) z 6
This shrub is a remarkable sight when mature. In late summer the delicate buds open into fragrant, star-like, white flowers, set in maroon calyxes. Electric blue fruits follow, held in the now deep red calyxes. The large, deciduous leaves have a fetid smell if crushed; they take on purple tints in autumn. It makes 8 × 8ft (2.4 × 2.4m) in ten years. Grow in some shade, in moist, non-alkaline soil. Prune out winter damage. The fruits glow in sunlight. Prone to whitefly, mealy bug and red spider mite.

***Cotoneaster* × *watereri* 'Cornubia'** z 6
(*above*)
This semi-evergreen vigorous shrub is one of the finest tall cotoneasters. In autumn its branches are weighed down by bunches of bright red berries. These are preceded in early summer by clusters of white flowers. The small dark green leaves are lanceolate. Graceful with spreading branches, it makes 10 × 10ft (3 × 3m) in ten years. 'Rothschildianus' has clusters of yellow fruits and can make a small, single-stemmed tree. *C.* × *watereri* has large crops of orange-red berries. Grow in full sun or part shade in moist, fertile soil.

Malus hupehensis z 4
This crab apple is one of the best for garden use, making a free-growing small tree 25ft (7.5m) tall when mature, with spreading, stiff and ascending branches which reach out from the trunk. In spring, small flowers appear along the entire length of the branches. They are soft pink in bud, opening white and have a strong fragrance. The flowers are followed in autumn by tiny yellowish fruits which ripen to red. Plant in sun or light shade.

***Pyracantha* 'Mohave'** z 6
This stiff-growing, evergreen shrub makes a 6ft (1.8m) vase-shaped specimen in ten years. Abundant small, white summer flowers are followed by orange-red berries that persist into winter, birds permitting. Leaves are dark green and shiny. It is good for windy areas and resistant to fireblight and scab. 'Orange Glow' has dark stems and large clusters of orange fruits. 'Shawnee' has orange-yellow berries that color early. Full sun gives the best berries, on moist, rich soil.

Sorbus commixta (*below*) z 5
Scarlet rowan
This tree not only has clusters of large, bright red berries in autumn but also dramatic foliage color. The large pinnate leaves emerge coppery in spring, turn glossy green in summer, then purple and finally flaming scarlet during autumn. It has a columnar habit when young, broadening with age, and reaches 16ft (5m) in ten years. *S. aucuparia* 'Beissneri' has shiny coppery-orange stems. Needs full sun and grows on most soils, including alkaline.

***Viburnum opulus* 'Fructuluteo'** z 3
(*below*)
This form of the guelder rose carries bunches of translucent, lemon yellow, pink-tinged fruits in autumn. They are preceded by corymbs of white flowers. Large, lobed, light green leaves take on warm shades in autumn. For larger flowers and golden-yellow fruits which darken as they ripen, grow the cultivar 'Xanthocarpum'; 'Notcutt's Variety' has red fruits. The spreading habit reaches 8ft (2.4m) in ten years. Plants are tolerant of most soils, dry or wet. Prune out one-third of old wood annually, or leave to grow freely.

FLOWERS

Abelia* × *grandiflora (*above*) z 6
This semi-evergreen shrub carries pale pink, slightly scented flowers on its arching branches from late summer into autumn. It grows to 5 × 5ft (1.5 × 1.5m) in ten years, rarely any taller. Olive green ovate leaves are up to 2in (6cm) long. 'Francis Mason' has gold-variegated leaves. A good companion for autumn-flowering bulbs such as *Schizostylis coccinea*. Prune out a third of the old shoots in early spring; take care as the branches are brittle. Grow in moist soil, in full sun.

Caryopteris* × *clandonensis z 5
A sub-shrub which is at its best in early autumn, this hybrid caryopteris is prized for its violet-blue flowers and fragrant, silvery foliage. Plants grow to a height of 3ft (90cm). Prune back to within 3in (8cm) of the basal stump each spring to encourage vigorous new shoots. Plants grow best in full sun and well-drained soil, doing well in alkaline conditions. For paler flowers grow 'Arthur Simmonds', while 'Heavenly Blue' and 'Kew Blue' both have rather darker violet-blue shades.

***Hydrangea paniculata* 'Grandiflora'** z 4
Flowering from late summer into autumn, this makes a spectacular specimen plant. The huge panicles of white, sterile florets fade to pink before turning brown. Each panicle can be 18 × 12in (45 × 30cm). The broad leaves turn yellow in autumn. For the best flowers, cut back all shoots in spring to within two buds of the base: regrowth will be 10 × 10ft (3 × 3m) in ten years. Protect from strong winds if grown as a standard as the stems are brittle. Needs slight shade and deep, rich, moist soil.

CLIMBERS AND WALL SHRUBS

Garden walls present the best opportunities for growing climbers and shrubs that benefit from the support and protection offered, whether it be from the cold, the wind or the sun. Trellis, screens, pergolas, arcades, arbors and summer houses (see pages 164-173, 228-233) also provide good support for climbers and have an immediate impact on the garden while introducing a valuable vertical element.

Certain plants are better suited to specific structures according to their vigor and means of attachment. Reasonably vigorous twining climbers that provide adequate cover without swamping the structure are suited to pergolas and arbors. Either a single species, such as wisteria, can be used to create a spectacular display at one time of the year or a collection of plants, including *Clematis armandii* and *Vitis vinifera* 'Purpurea', can be used to provide a succession of flowering and foliage interest.

Slow-growing scramblers, such as roses and *Jasminum nudiflorum*, that require careful tying in because they do not actually attach themselves to the structure, work well on small trellis screens; while self-clinging climbers such as ivies, *Schizophragma* and *Hydrangea petiolaris*, are best suited to walls which provide a suitable surface for their aerial roots or suckers to adhere to. The habit of a plant may also make it suitable for growing against a wall. *Kerria japonica*, *Pyracantha coccinea*, *Chaenomeles* species,

Right: Parthenocissus tricuspidata, the Boston ivy, is a vigorous climber that turns crimson-purple in the autumn. It attaches itself to walls by means of sticky tendrils and is tolerant of shady conditions.

Left: Pyracantha coccinea is a vigorous, evergreen shrub of stiff, erect habit suitable for training against a shady wall. In late spring or early summer it is covered with small, white flowers, which are followed by a plentiful crop of orange berries. These specimens, trained to great effect like espalier fruit trees, should be trimmed in early autumn.

Forsythia suspensa and *Robinia hispida* all have fairly stiff, upright stems that grow close to the wall and can be pruned and trained to fill the available space.

Climbers that hook their stems onto the support with the help of coiling tendrils need wires to wrap themselves around, or alternatively are well adapted to threading their way through other plants as they do in their wild state. When choosing a host plant the climber's vigor should be taken into account.

Many other factors will govern the choice of plants. The style of the garden dictates whether the plants should be slow-growing and neatly tied in to give a controlled form or whether they should be given a fairly free rein to grow at will. For example, the relaxed effect that is achieved by allowing honeysuckle to cascade over a structure with its scent mingling with that of other vigorous climbers, such as rambling roses and summer jasmine, is perfect for a cottage, romantic or wild garden. In contrast, a strictly pruned and flat-trained *Magnolia grandiflora* with its large, smooth, architectural leaves and single, stiff, waxy-white summer flowers, would be a fitting focal point in an enclosed courtyard.

It may be that a fast-growing climber is required to camouflage an ugly building or cover a trellis screen placed in front of an eyesore: *Polygonum aubertii* (the mile-a-minute or Russian vine), *Parthenocissus quinquefolia*, Virginia creeper and the related *P. tricuspidata* (the Boston ivy), *Vitis coignetiae* (the crimson glory vine), *Celastrus orbiculatus* (the Oriental bittersweet), *Akebia quinata* and *Clematis montana* are all suitable for this purpose. However, these plants need a lot of space and require constant pruning or have to be replaced in order to prevent them from swamping all other nearby plants, lifting tiles or blocking gutters. Their speed of growth, which can be their greatest asset, has also earned them a bad reputation.

In fact most climbers are fast growers which need pruning and tying in to keep them under control. Some need near constant attention, others can be attended to once a year, either in the winter or in early spring or after flowering, depending on the requirements of the plant. It is always advisable to ensure that the structure is sound before the plant starts to cover it and that it is large enough to accommodate the plant when mature.

The aspect of the wall is an important consideration when choosing suitable plants to clothe it. A protected wall that receives the sun for most of the day is likely to be several degrees warmer than one that receives little direct sunlight. Marginally hardy plants can survive when grown against such south-facing, warm walls. For example, in areas where *Clematis montana* is perfectly hardy, *C. armandii* will require a southern aspect. Many Californian and Central American species such as the attractive *Ceanothus* and

Below: Climbers are particularly useful in the garden to create quick screens and an instant vertical element. Here, a large-leaved evergreen ivy, *Hedera colchica* 'Dentata Variegata', mingles with the autumnal foliage of *Parthenocissus quinquefolia*, the Virginia creeper, to create a "volcanic" effect. On the left is the herbaceous golden hop, *Humulus lupulus* 'Aureus'.

Right: Wisterias are fast-growing climbers with flowers that are generally violet-blue to mauve. There are also white- and pink-flowered forms of the commonly grown species which are attractive alternatives, as can be seen from this salmon pink variety.

Fremontodendron californicum will flourish in temperate climates when grown against a wall. *Magnolia grandiflora* makes a large freestanding tree in Mediterranean climates but will also survive and flower in areas where the summer rainfall is higher and season shorter when placed against a wall. The way in which a wall absorbs and then releases heat produces not only additional winter warmth and hotter summers but also extends the season, allowing the wood to ripen well and survive the winter cold.

In contrast, there are many plants that prefer shady situations – including *Jasminum nudiflorum*, *Kerria japonica*, *Garrya elliptica*, *Berberidopsis corallina* and *Lapageria rosea* – but this does not necessarily mean that they are frost-hardy; many shade-loving climbers are still tender. There are also a number of plants that tolerate the poorest conditions and are able to clothe seemingly inhospitable walls. These include ivies as well as the climbing *Euonymus radicans, Parthenocissus* species, and *Hydrangea petiolaris*.

Camellias, winter sweet (*Chimonanthus praecox*) and *Jasminum nudiflorum* which blossom early in spring, when there is still a risk of frost, benefit from growing against a wall that does not receive direct morning sun, because this would defrost the blooms too quickly and damage them.

A notable way of extending the season of certain plants and adding a new dimension to a design is to grow climbers through other plants. The most vigorous climbers such as *Vitis coignetiae*, *Celastrus orbiculatus* and *Wisteria sinensis* are successful only in tall trees, but there are a number of other species that grow happily through shrubs without swamping them. Clematis are the most frequently used in this instance. Herbaceous climbers such as *Codonopsis convolvulacea*, *Tropaeolum speciosum* and *Lathyrus grandiflorus* are also well suited.

Left: Clematis 'Perle d'Azur' is an outstanding large-flowered cultivar, which is covered in blossom in late summer.

Below: Wisteria has traditionally adorned the warm, sunny face of many country houses. The scented, pea-like flowers are produced abundantly if specimens are pruned in summer, after flowering, and again, more severely, in winter, when plants are dormant.

***Rosa moyesii* 'Geranium'** z 4
One of the finest forms of this species rose, 'Geranium' is grown for its large, bright crimson-red fruits in late summer and autumn. The flowers appear in early summer and are bright red and single with overlapping petals. Plants form open-centered bushes, each with a few stout stems when mature. Some of the older shoots can be removed after flowering on established plants. The vigorous arching shoots are armed with sharp thorns and carry the light green foliage. Slightly more compact than the species and valuable for autumn color.

***Rosa rugosa* 'Roseraie de l'Haÿ** z 2
Named after the rose garden of the same name to the south of Paris established by Jules Gravereaux, this richly-scented rugosa flowers throughout the season and is best planted in small groups. The vigorous growth can reach 8ft (2.4m), with an equal spread, carrying very large, semi-double loose flowers of deep crimson-purple with a velvety sheen and a strong scent. Each bloom is 4in (10cm) across carried among luxuriant, typical rugosa foliage. This form stands out among the rugosa group because of its distinctive wine-colored flowers.

Rosa virginiana (*above*) z 4
Grown for its autumn leaf colors and brightly colored hips, the young leaves of this species rose emerge bronzed, then turn glossy-green during summer and finally to fiery reddish-orange and yellow shades in autumn. They are accompanied at the end of the season by persistent, rounded, bright red hips. The stems are reddish-brown. The rather late flowers are pink with pale centers. Plants form dense rounded bushes with many shoots growing from the base to a height of 6ft (1.8m).

BUSH

'Allgold' z 4
Unsurpassed for the stability of its flower color and for its numerous long-lasting flowers, 'Allgold' is a neat, compact, moderately vigorous grower which reaches to just over 2ft (60cm) high. The flowers of this floribunda open in early summer and last until late in the season. They are semi-double and of a deep golden yellow that never fades, even in hot sunny weather. The leaves are dark glossy green and resistant to disease. Plants resists rainy weather well, the flowers remaining unblemished by the water.

'Europeana' z 4
This vigorous growing floribunda may well need its flowers supporting if heavy rain threatens. This can be overcome by close planting so the plants give each other mutual support. Although this cultivar is susceptible to mildew in some areas, it is well worth growing for its striking, deep crimson flowers which are rosette shaped and carried in heavy trusses. Plants grow to 3ft (90cm) and have glossy, bronze-green foliage, which is coppery when young.

'Just Joey' (*below*) z 4
Unique for its coppery-orange flowers with lighter and deeper flushes, this hybrid tea is very free flowering and has an open spreading habit. The petals are often veined red, paling toward the edges which are wavy. The flowers appear singly or in clusters on plants growing up to 3ft (90cm) high and have some scent. Each one is fully double and can be up to 5in (13cm) across. The leaves are leathery and dark green. Flowers stand up well to rain and are excellent for cutting in the bud stage.

'Queen Elizabeth' z 4
One of the commonest pink floribundas with a tendency to produce a few blind shoots in the early part of the season, which eventually revert to flowering normally. It is a vigorous grower reaching 5ft (1.5m) or more in height with almost thornless stems and dark green glossy leaves. The flowers are very weather resistant and open a clear pink, fading as they age. They appear throughout the summer and autumn, carried either singly or in trusses, and are useful for cutting. Plants make an effective informal hedge.

'Starina' (*above*) z 4
A miniature rose achieving only 10in (25cm) in height, this plant is a vigorous grower with glossy green foliage and fully double, scarlet-orange flowers. This rose should be positioned carefully in a border so as not to allow it to become swamped by other plants. It is suitable for use as a pot plant, for bedding or as a miniature standard. As with all miniatures, 'Starina' resents root disturbance. The flowers are well-formed and last for a long time when used as cut flowers.

'Whisky Mac' z 4
The shapely blooms of this hybrid tea are gold with tints of bronze and orange; they are freely produced throughout summer. The flowers are quite fragrant, which is unusual among roses of this color. Plants grow vigorously to 3ft (90cm) and carry holly-like, dark green glossy leaves which are tinted bronze as they unfold in spring. It is susceptible to mildew and damage by frost; this should be borne in mind when choosing a suitable position for planting, a protected, warm site producing the best results.

"Landscape" roses

GROUND COVER

'Nozomi' *(above)* z 4
This miniature climbing rose will form excellent ground cover if left unsupported and planted 2ft (60cm) apart, as well as scrambling effectively along the top of a low wall. Its low arching habit means that it rarely achieves more than 18in (45cm) in height, but when supported it can reach 4ft (1.2m). Small, pale pink, single flowers appear in massed trusses. The leaves are glossy. Plants will also grow as weeping standards.

Rosa* × *paulii *(above)* z 2
A hybrid between *R. arvensis* and *R. rugosa* that is excellent for smothering weeds because of its sprawling habit. A vigorous trailing rose, it will form a 3ft (90cm)-high shrub if hard-pruned. The long shoots are very thorny, carrying in mid-summer the single white or pink flowers with wedge-shaped petals, each one being 3in (8cm) across, with a central mass of golden stamens. The flowers are produced freely and have a slight scent of cloves. 'Rosea' has deep pink flowers with white centers.

'Max Graf' *(below)* z 2
A hybrid between *R. rugosa* and *R. wichuraiana*, the long growths of this rugosa shrub lie prostrate along the ground unless trained. The dense foliage is effective at smothering weeds, but it can be difficult to weed among the prickly shoots before the leaves emerge. The scented flowers are single, pink, fading to white at the base of the petals, with yellow stamens. They are the size of large dog roses and appear once, but over a long season. Flowers sometimes appear in the autumn. The leaves are a glossy bright green.

'Snow Carpet' *(below)* z 5
Also known as 'Maccarpe', this prostrate, creeping miniature bush rose was introduced to cultivation in 1980. It grows to a height of only 6in (15cm) with a spread of 20in (50cm), making it ideal for low ground cover. It carries fully double, pompom-like white flowers which are 1 ¼in (3cm) across. They appear in clusters, mainly during summer with some into autumn. The small glossy leaves are plentiful, adding to the usefulness of 'Snow Carpet' as ground cover as they smother weeds very successfully.

'The Fairy' z 5
A weather-resistant and vigorous spreading plant which attains a height of 3ft (90cm). It is ideal as tall ground cover or as a low informal hedge and can also be grown as a standard. The small box-like leaves are deep green and shiny with a very healthy sheen. Large trusses of double soft-pink flowers appear later than most floribundas, and fade if the weather is hot. This is one of the few polyanthas available.

HEDGING

'Coupe d'Hébé' *(below)* z 4
This vigorous shrub rose, which can grow to 7ft (2.1m), is usually described as a bourbon but is actually of mixed parentage; this gives it a rather loose growth pattern which makes it suitable for an informal hedge. Copious fresh glossy leaves form a dense barrier. The medium-sized double flowers are pink inside, almost white outside and fragrant, appearing quite late in the summer. The weak flower stalks cause the heads to hang downwards. Although this plant was introduced as long ago as 1840, its shapely outline is reminiscent of more modern cultivars.

Rosa eglanteria z 2
Sweet briar or eglantine
Also listed as *R. rubiginosa*, this species rose has small leaflets which give the whole plant a spicy aromatic scent during damp weather. Plants grow with vigour to a height of 8ft (2.4m) and are excellent as dense informal hedges or as boundary plantings. The single pink flowers appear in clusters. Hips are bright red. 'Amy Robsart' has semi-double pink flowers and gold stamens; 'Lady Penzance' has fragrant leaves when wet and salmon-pink flowers.

Climbing roses

***Rosa pimpinellifolia* 'Hispida'** z 2
Scotch rose or burnet rose
A moderately fast growing form which suckers freely but grows little over 4ft (1.2m) high. The stems are bristly, but not very prickly. Freely-produced white or creamy-white single flowers appear in late spring or early summer in one flush. The rather delicate foliage is bluish-green and much toothed around the leaf margins. The rounded hips are a deep shining purple during autumn. A row of plants will make a good informal hedge. Cut out dead and damaged stems in winter for the best effect.

***Rosa rugosa* 'Fru Dagmar Hastrup'** z 2
(*above*)
Sometimes seen as 'Frau Dagmar Hartopp', this rugosa shrub rose is more compact than other rugosas, making it suitable for hedging with the added attraction of bright red hips throughout summer and autumn, the size and color of small tomatoes. The leaves are fresh apple green with impressed veins. Plants respond well to winter clipping. They flower over a long period, beginning in mid-summer. Each bloom is up to 3in (8cm) across, single, pink with golden stamens, cup-shaped then saucer-shaped when fully open. In autumn the leaves take on attractive golden-yellow shades.

'Sea Foam' z 4
Clusters of double flowers, shading from white to pinkish-cream, cover this broad, low-growing modern shrub for the entire summer; the fragrance is light. Leaves are small, dark green and glossy. This is a vigorous grower with long trailing canes which make it suitable for training over a trellis, wall or tree as well as for hedging. It can also be used as a ground cover.

FOR GARDEN STRUCTURES

'Aloha' (*above*) z 4
This moderately vigorous climbing or shrub rose reaches 5ft (1.5m) if grown as a shrub or up to 10ft (3m) if grown on a pillar. Plants grown as large shrubs need regular pruning. The scented flowers are like those of hybrid teas. They are large and double, pink with darker centers, changing to a salmon-pink as they age. The flowers are produced freely, appearing throughout the season. This cultivar derives its free-flowering habit from 'New Dawn' which is one of its parents. The stiff stems perfectly suit its climbing habit.

'American Pillar' (*above*) z 4
A vigorous rambler, it should be pruned by cutting the flowering shoots hard, down to ground level, in late summer: the new shoots are then tied in. Each quite large, pinkish-blue single flower has a white eye and is produced in a large cluster. The flowers are unscented. Plants bloom once in the summer but are very floriferous; they are susceptible to mildew. They reach a height of 15ft (4.5m) and may be trained up arches and pergolas as well as pillars.

'Blaze Improved' z 4
This American climber, introduced in 1932, is one of the most commonly grown in the United States because of its unfailing reliability. The large bright scarlet flowers are 2-3in (5-8cm) across and cover the plant in early summer and again in early autumn with a spattering in between. It grows quickly to 12-15ft (3.6-4.5m), making it ideal for trelliswork and pergolas. The dark glossy green foliage complements the flowers. Tolerant of most soils and shade, it is an excellent, versatile garden plant that well merits its popularity.

'Bobbie James' (*above*) z 2
One of the best ramblers, this vigorous plant reaches 25ft (7.5m). It is related to *R. multiflora* and was named in 1960 after the Hon. Robert James who cultivated a beautiful garden in Yorkshire. The fragrant flowers are cream in bud, opening white with gold stamens. Huge clusters are freely produced in one flush in mid-summer. The sturdy stems bear abundant glossy green foliage. Ideal for a pergola or for growing through a tree.

'Constance Spry' z 4
The large and extremely fragrant flowers are produced in a single display in mid-summer, to spectacular effect. With its open, arching growth, this plant is suited to growing either as a 6ft (1.8m) shrub or as a climber, reaching 15ft (4.5m) with a 6ft (1.8m) spread. The flowers are a glowing pink in the center, tending to be paler on the outside. They are fully double, 4in (10cm) across and held in groups of three or four. The foliage is deep green. Plants tend to throw up long vigorous growths which need support. Effective against a gray brick wall or on a pillar.

'Félicité et Perpétue' (*above*) z 4
To maximize flowering on this semi-evergreen rambler, leave the prickly overlapping growths unpruned, cutting out only dead, diseased or damaged wood. The long strong-growing shoots can reach 18ft (5.4m) in length, making it ideal for pergolas or for training into an old tree. The fragrant, small creamy-white flowers with a hint of pink are double and globular, held in large clusters. They appear from mid to late summer. Grows well even in light shade and has small, dark, shiny green leaves.

Rosa filipes **'Kiftsgate'** z 2
A vigorous Himalaya rambler clone, this plant was bred in the garden of the same name in Gloucestershire. It needs a large and robust pergola for support as it can reach 50ft (15m) and is capable of covering buildings and trees. In mid-summer the plant is spectacular, covered in sweetly scented, small, creamy white single flowers which cascade in corymbs over the gray-green foliage. Few roses can rival the huge cascades of flowers.

'Golden Showers' z 4
A very popular yellow rose which flowers continuously from early to late summer and is tolerant of wind, rain and some shade. This floribunda climber is ideal for trelliswork. It can reach 10ft (3m) in height with its stiff upright growth, carrying rich lemon-colored flowers which are large, double, with a lemony fragrance and pointed when in bud. They fade in strong sunlight and should be regularly deadheaded. In winter cut out one older stem to ground level to promote new growth, as well as removing dead or diseased wood.

'Joseph's Coat' (*below*) z 4
Considered by different authorities to be either a tall floribunda or a large-flowered climber, this plant can be effectively trained as a pillar rose. Its growths reach 8ft (2.4m) high and it is repeat-flowering. The semi-double flowers are bright yellow with red and orange flushes, especially at the petal edges, and are produced in large trusses. They appear over a long period and well into autumn. The leaves are dark glossy green. Equally at home grown as a shrub or, with hard-pruning, as a bedding rose.

'Lawrence Johnston' z 4
A large-flowered climber growing to 10ft (3m), it produces bright yellow blooms in mid-summer, followed by a succession of smaller displays. The semi-double flowers are strongly scented and the leaves are a glossy rich green. The first specimen was bought by Major Lawrence Johnston and planted at Hidcote Manor in England. It was originally named 'Hidcote Yellow', although this name is no longer valid. Can also be grown as a shrub.

'Mermaid' z 4
Rarely happy in cold situations, where it may die back in severe winters, this modern climber is a vigorous grower which thrives in sun or in a north-facing position in a warm area. Growths reach up to 30ft (9m) and carry clusters of single sulphur-yellow blooms with amber stamens, the latter remaining for a few days after the petals have fallen. The flowers appear repeatedly through the summer, are slightly scented and do not require deadheading. Plants resent root disturbance and should be pruned only to remove dead, diseased or damaged wood.

'Souvenir de la Malmaison' (*above*) z 4
Named in memory of the Empress Josephine's private garden just to the south of Paris, this bourbon rose is suitable for growing on a pillar or as a shrub. It has vigorous shoots which can reach 10ft (3m) in length. The large flowers are pink fading to white, double, cup-shaped when opening, flattening as they mature. Each bloom is up to 5in (13cm) across and strongly scented. The flowers have two flushes, one in mid-summer and a second in late summer. They dislike wet weather, the rain spoiling the petals.

'Swan Lake' (*above*) z 4
This cultivar was introduced in 1968 and is also listed as 'Schwanensee'. It is one of the best white climbers available and is very resilient in poor weather, which is unusual for a white rose. 'Swan Lake' forms a strong free-growing plant which is well-suited to trelliswork, but can also be grown on pillars and arches. The large flowers are double, white with pinkish centers. They have little scent and appear throughout the season. The leaves are mid-green and are prone to the blemishes of blackspot.

FOR WALLS

Rosa banksiae banksiae z 7
Plant this vigorous climbing species rose on a south-facing wall where it can grow to 30ft (9m). Several forms of the banksian rose exist, all being early and free-flowering with almost thornless stems. Young plants should be allowed to reach their desired height before any pruning starts. The white or pale yellow flowers appear in the second or third year on the older shoots, which tend to trail. Prune to ripen the wood. The leaves have a yellow tint.

'Climbing Iceberg' (*above*) z 4
Discovered by B.R. Cant in 1968, this is a climbing sport of 'Iceberg' or 'Climbing Schneewittchen' (as it is also known) and is a spectacular sight when well trained. It will reach 12ft (3.6m) on a wall and carries a profusion of white flowers early in the season, with more flowers appearing throughout the season on mature plants. The flowers are lightly scented, opening flat to reveal a cluster of brownish stamens. Plants grow well in shade, but are prone to mild attacks of mildew and blackspot.

'Danse du Feu' z 4
Also known as 'Spectacular' and well suited to both its names, this strong climber which will reach 10ft (3m) in rich, well-drained fertile soil which contains plenty of humus. In early summer this cultivar is massed with bright scarlet, slightly scented, semi-double flowers, with a few blooms appearing through the rest of the season. Young foliage is bronzed, ageing to dark glossy green. Suitable for a north-facing aspect, it will grow on a wall, pillar or pergola; benefits from light shade. Deadhead regularly.

'Desprez à Fleurs Jaunes' z 6
Also known as 'Jaune Desprez', this cultivar was raised by Desprez in 1830 and is probably the earliest yellow climbing rose. Choose a high wall for this plant. Growths can reach up to 15ft (4.5m) and have few prickles. The flowers are held singly or in small clusters, and are beautifully fragrant, appearing from mid-summer through to autumn. They are double, rather flat, pale yellow with peach shades. Plants need some shelter and thrive in sun. Prune in late winter, removing old, weak or diseased wood.

'Dortmund' (*below*) z 4
The bright flowers of this climbing *kordesii* hybrid are reddish-crimson with a white eye surrounding the central golden stamens. The single flowers appear in large clusters and will keep being produced with deadheading; this restricts the production of the large number of striking but energy-consuming hips. Good for the shaded wall, but also valuable for pillars and as a large shrub. The abundant foliage is a healthy, glossy, dark green. This is a very hardy rose with little scent.

'François Juranville' z 4
When young the foliage of this vigorous rambler is bronzed, turning to a rich glossy green as it ages. The strong growths can reach 25ft (7.5m) and are ideal for a large shaded wall. Plants have a rather weeping habit. They flower only once with some later blooms after the main flush. The strongly scented flowers are salmon-pink, double, opening large and flat, with deeper-colored centers, and are held singly or in clusters. They are paler in dry summers and on dryer soils. Also useful for a large pergola or tree.

'Gloire de Dijon' (*below*) z 6
The double flowers of this hardy climber are up to 4in (10cm) across, of an apricot-orange color with some darker and lighter petals, and strongly fragrant, especially in hot still weather. This cultivar is very popular and is often seen growing to 15ft (4.5m). It likes sun, but will also grow on north-facing walls and can be grown as a pillar. The bottom half of older plants tend to become bare and needs obscuring with other plants. Blooms appear continually from mid-summer onwards in great numbers.

'Handel' z 4
The unusually colored flowers of this climber make it popular: each flower is composed of petals which are creamy edged with pink, making an attractive combination, and are beautifully shaped. The flowers are carried on vigorous shoots capable of growing to 20ft (6m) in a hot sunny summer, about half this in cooler seasons, and are weather-resistant. They are only slightly scented and tend to fade in hot weather. The dark green leaves have coppery shades; they are prone to mildew. Blooms appear throughout the season.

'Hume's Blush' z 6
This clone of the vigorous hybrid climber *R.* × *odorata* originated in China and was introduced to England from the East Indies by Sir A. Hume in 1809. It flowers on wood grown in the previous season so should only be pruned lightly. The flowers are a blushing pink, very strongly scented, large and double, and open from mid-summer onwards. It needs a sunny position to thrive. *R.* × *odorata* is an important cross in rose history, with *R. chinensis* and *R. gigantea* for parents.

'La Follette' z 4
Raised by Busby at Cannes around 1910, this half-hardy but vigorous climber is often grown into trees on the Italian and French Rivieras where it flowers early. It requires a sheltered wall (or in colder areas the protection of a cold greenhouse) and sun to achieve 20ft (6m). The huge, double, loose flowers appear in early summer in one main burst and are rose pink with shades of salmon and cream, especially towards the outside of the petals. The flower buds are long and pointed.

'Leverkusen' z 4
A useful plant which can be used either as a climber for a wall or pillar or grown as a shrub. Plants grow to 10ft (3m) in height and are very hardy with moderate vigor. The semi-double, pale creamy-yellow flowers with darker centers have their main display in mid-summer, followed by fewer recurrent blooms during the rest of the season. The smallish leaflets are a deep glossy green. An extremely useful rose for its abundant flowers.

'Madame Grégoire Staechelin' z 4
(below)
Thriving on shaded walls, this very vigorous climber can grow to 20ft (6m) in a sunny position. The thorny shoots need careful pruning to prevent flowers forming only at the top of the plant: cut some of the most vigorous shoots to the base in the winter after planting, and when mature remove one or two of the old woody stems completely each season. The pink flowers appear early in the season and are slightly pendent which is an advantage on taller plants. They have a fragrance not unlike sweet peas. In autumn the hips turn light orange, adding to the plant's interest.

'Maréchal Neil' *(above)* z 7
Popular in Victorian conservatories, this rather tender climber will grow better under glass in cold areas, with the roots planted outside the greenhouse. Elsewhere, train it against a warm sheltered wall in a sunny spot, where it can grow to 15ft (4.5m). Large tea-scented flowers are produced during summer. They are golden yellow and are held on weak flower stalks which give the plant a nodding habit. In Britain, this cultivar is only sufficiently hardy to be grown in the open in southern England.

'New Dawn' *(above)* z 4
This disease-resistant hardy rose is useful for shady pergolas, walls and fences. A vigorous lateral grower, given space the stems can exceed 15ft (4.5m). The medium-sized flowers are profuse during early summer, of apple-blossom pink with deeper pink centers and a very strong fragrance. A second flush of flowers appears in late summer. The flowers tend to fade to white during hot weather. The foliage is shiny light green. It also grows well into small open-canopied trees.

'Royal Gold' *(below)* z 7
Also suited to growing as a pillar, this climber is rather tender and will only succeed on a sheltered sunny wall in warmer areas. Die-back is common after a severe winter in colder regions: any dead shoots should be pruned out in the following spring. Deep yellow flowers appear from mid-summer onwards; they are large and double, scented and held singly or in clusters. Only moderately vigorous, this cultivar will give poor results unless planted on rich and fertile soil, where it can grow to 10ft (3m). The flowers resemble those of a hybrid tea.

'Veilchenblau' *(below)* z 4
A distinctive plant among ramblers because of its blue-purple flowers and sometimes listed as 'Violet Blue'. It is virtually thornless and has small semi-double flowers which open purplish, with white centers, maturing to dark blue-violet and finally grayish-mauve. They produce a scent of apples. The flowers appear in large clusters in mid- to late summer; there is no repeat flowering. Often called the "blue" rose due to the color of its blooms, this plant is best grown in shade as the petals fade in direct sun.

HEDGES AND WINDBREAKS

The way in which a hedge is intended to be used in the garden, whether it be for its aesthetic qualities or for purely practical reasons or a combination of the two, influences the species chosen to make the hedge.

Aesthetically, hedges compartmentalize a garden creating a number of distinct areas that can each be given an individual style and character with a feeling of intimacy and seclusion from other parts of the garden. However, with a clever use of openings, either "windows" or "doors", an element of surprise and invitation is introduced which gives the illusion that the whole garden is larger than it really is. In addition, hedges form a valuable backdrop against which any composition of other plants stands out and in a relatively short period of time they give the garden a satisfying air of maturity.

As windbreaks, hedges generate a precious microclimate which enables a wider range of plants to be grown. Often in an exposed new site it is necessary to use the fastest growing species. If there is the space, it may be a good idea to choose trees, such as poplars, alders or scots pines, that do not require any pruning and maintenance as this can make for heavy and time-consumming work. In the last 25 years or so the Leyland cypress has been used in many small gardens to create quick screens, but is invariably left to grow too

Right: Rhododendron ponticum is an evergreen that grows vigorously in cool shady conditions. It makes a tall, windproof, informal hedge that is a blaze of color in late spring and early summer.

Left: A tightly clipped cypress hedge makes a fast-growing backdrop to a traditional herbaceous border, giving good protection from wind. Yew would be slower growing, requiring only one clip a year. Even when this border is dormant, the hedge remains interesting because of the way the top has been shaped.

Below: Privet is a semi-evergreen that is commonly used as a fast-growing hedge. To the right of the golden form shown here is a tiered topiary specimen of holly and, behind this, a formally trained beech hedge.

big before it is pruned severely and left looking like a skeleton. In many cases a good solid hedge of yew, for example, requiring only one cut a year, would have been achieved in less than eight years and is exceedingly long lived. If there is any risk of livestock eating any part of the hedge then use thuja instead of yew.

Yew and thuja make dense evergreen screens that are usually kept tightly trimmed, both responding to this treatment by generating plenty of new shoots after being cut back. The structural quality of a tightly clipped hedge gives a garden a strong form, whatever the season, and is best used in formal designs. A variety of textures and colors are available to the gardener through the choice of species. For example, a beech or hornbeam hedge offers a soft green color which turns to russety brown in the autumn lasting through the winter and into spring, in contrast to the evergreen broadleaves of the Portugal laurel, *Prunus lusitanica*, or the English holly, *Ilex aquifolium*, which make a strong, glistening, dark green hedge all year round. For those who live in very cold climates, the choice of evergreens may be limited to the hardiest conifer, the western hemlock, *Tsuga heterophylla*, or a number of deciduous plants such as *Ilex verticillata* (z 3), which has rounded leaves that are smaller and less prickly than those of the English holly or sea buckthorn, *Hippophae rhamnoides*.

Left: The frost-hardy *Fuchsia magellanica* is deciduous but makes a good informal hedge, flowering over a long season in summer and autumn. The pendulous flowers are followed by black fruits. Pruning in early spring will help to keep plants strong and compact.

Below: Several spiraeas are good shrubs for informal hedges, the arching stems being wreathed in glorious white flowers in late spring or early summer.

Some plants that respond well to tight clipping, such as linden and hornbeam, can be used for pleaching, creating what is sometimes referred to as a hedge on stilts. This is a useful technique for making a boundary without reducing the sense of space. Others, such as the small-leaved box 'Suffruticosa' and wall germander (*Teucrium*), are small enough to use for edging and parterres. Box and yew are the best choice for topiary. They are slow-growing, with small, dense leaves, and respond well to very specific, intricate cutting. Patience is vital with topiary, and dedication to maintaining the chosen forms. It is important to select shapes and designs well within your capabilities.

A hedge can also be used informally, such as in a cottage or landscape garden, where it introduces a free-flowing line to the design. For example, *Rhododendron ponticum* makes a tall, windproof evergreen hedge, that is covered with purple blossoms in spring. Where space is at a premium compact forms need to be chosen. In most cases informal hedges are made of flowering and, in some instances, fruiting species giving them seasonal interest. Some, like the laurustinus, *Viburnum tinus*, combine glossy evergreen foliage with pink winter flowers that are followed by blue-black fruit. There are a number of flowering plants that flower on old wood, such as forsythia and *Cornus mas*, that can be lightly pruned to make an informal hedge. They can also be clipped hard back to make a formal hedge, although flowers will be lost.

Quick-growing

Alnus cordata z 4
Italian alder
An extremely useful plant for wet conditions, this quickly forms a barrier against the wind and reaches 40ft (12m) in twenty years with a narrowly conical habit. In spring the crown is hung with clusters of yellow, male catkins. The tiny female flowers form small, round, woody fruits which persist throughout winter. The deciduous leaves are a shiny dark green above, paler beneath and up to 3in (8cm) long. Thrives in all moist soils, acid or alkaline; dislikes dry conditions. Needs sun or partial shade.

Chamaecyparis lawsoniana *(above)* z 4
Lawson cypress
One of the fastest-growing evergreen conifers used in gardens, this can be free-grown, reaching 60ft (18m), or clipped for formal use. Drooping, deep green leaves with grayish undersides set off small pinkish-red male cones in spring, then (on mature plants) woody cones. Forms have blue, gray, green or yellow foliage: 'Green Hedger' is ideal for screens. Excellent for exposed, windy sites and heavy soils; succeeds in shade. Plant 2ft (60cm) apart. Trim in late summer if used formally.

Crataegus monogyna z 4
Common hawthorn
This deciduous shrub has extremely spiny stems which act as a deterrent to unwanted animals. If free-growing it reaches 20ft (6m) in ten years and produces large clusters of single white flowers followed by red berries. For a formal hedge, plant 1ft (30cm) apart and clip monthly from late spring to late summer. The small, lobed leaves turn yellow in autumn. Useful for coastal sites and all exposed, windy gardens; excellent for heavy clay soils.

Cupressus macrocarpa z 7
Monterey cypress
One of the best evergreen conifers to grow for shelter in coastal areas, this species has bright green foliage that grows in upright, dense sprays. The leaves smell of lemons when crushed. Left unclipped, the Monterey cypress makes a tree 25ft (7.5m) high in about ten years. The conical habit broadens with age. Yellow-foliaged forms such as 'Goldcrest' must be planted in full sun or they fade to green. Older plants carry clusters of small, shiny brown cones. Plant 2ft (60cm) apart.

Elaeagnus × ebbingei *(below)* z 6
A fast-growing evergreen that reaches 6ft (1.8m) in ten years. The large, oval leaves are dark green above with round, silvery scales beneath. Yellowish-silver, fragrant flowers appear in autumn, followed by orange, silver-specked fruits in spring. 'Gilt Edge' has gold-margined leaves that need protection from cold winds. Plants dislike their roots being disturbed, which leads to the sudden death of entire limbs. Cut back long shoots by two-thirds in spring to promote bushiness.

Escallonia macrantha z 8
Plant specimens of this evergreen tender shrub 2ft (60cm) apart for a semi-formal, 6ft (1.8m)-tall hedge in five years. The small, scented, sticky leaves have indented margins. In summer it is covered with masses of rose red flowers. It thrives in most soils, resists drought and tolerates alkalinity: a good choice for exposed coastal gardens in warmer regions. Cut out a third of the oldest wood after flowering and trim back long shoots. Overgrown plants can be cut back to the ground and will take two to three seasons to regrow.

Hippophae rhamnoides *(above)* z 3
Sea buckthorn
This shrub is the perfect choice for a coastal windbreak. The silvery, narrow leaves are 2in (7cm) long and give good yellow autumn color. Male and female plants must be grown together to ensure fruiting; the orange-yellow berries last into winter. Reaches 10ft (3m) in ten years, spreading rapidly by seed and suckers if well-established. Grow in full sun and, ideally, in light, sandy soil. Pruning is unnecessary but the plant will regenerate if cut hard back to ground level. It can become invasive.

Ligustrum ovalifolium *(below)* z 5
Privet
This species grows quickly, is evergreen or semi-evergreen, ideal for exposed sites, and will tolerate alkaline soils as well as atmospheric pollution. It reaches 8ft (2.4m) in eight years but is prone to sudden die-back in patches. The roots may deprive neighboring plants of nutrients and water. For a bright yellow hedge grow 'Aureum'. Plant 1ft (30cm) apart. Clip at least monthly from mid-spring to late summer for a pleasing formal appearance.

Formal

***Populus alba* 'Richardii'** *(below)* z 4
This form of the white poplar makes 33ft (10m) in ten years if free-growing. It has bright, golden yellow lobed leaves with white undersides and wavy margins. Trees make excellent windbreaks if pollarded; alternatively, grow the plants as large shrubs, cutting them back every two to three years. Valuable for exposed sites and for coastal areas, it tolerates some waterlogging but fails in dry soils. Grow in full sun to keep foliage color. Plant well away from buildings and drains.

Thuja occidentalis *(below)* z 3
American arborvitae
An evergreen conifer with a broad, conical habit and reddish-brown peeling bark, this species makes 10ft (3m) in ten years. The smaller 'Rheingold' has coppery-gold foliage that darkens to orange by winter. *T. plicata* 'Atrovirens' (z 5) has flat sprays of shiny foliage, and will tolerate shade and thin alkaline soil. The Chinese arborvitae, *T. orientalis*, has a formal habit, producing its foliage in vertical sprays. Plant 2ft (60cm) apart and trim during late summer. The foliage of the American arborvitae releases a fruity aroma when crushed.

Buxus sempervirens *(above)* z 7
Common box
This slow-growing evergreen shrub makes only 4ft (1.2m) in ten years. It has small leaves and is able to withstand severe pruning, making it an ideal subject for a formal hedge; it is also used extensively for topiary. Mature, free-growing plants make small trees or large shrubs 8ft (2.4m) high. For a low edging along a path or for a knot garden or parterre, choose the dwarf form 'Suffruticosa'. Grows in most types of well-drained soil.

Carpinus betulus *(above)* z 4
Common hornbeam
On heavy, damp soils, unsuitable for beech (*Fagus sylvatica*), hornbeam makes a good alternative. Bright green summer foliage turns yellow-brown in autumn. It retains its dead leaves during winter, providing an effective wind-filter throughout the year. As the new leaves unfold the old ones fall. Plant 18in (45cm) apart and trim frequently to form a dense hedge 8ft (2.4m) high in ten years. Hornbeam succeeds in sun or shade and makes a fine backcloth for the herbaceous or mixed border.

Fagus sylvatica *(below)* z 4
Common beech
Beech grows best on well-drained, sandy or chalky soil and is intolerant of damp conditions which are better-suited to *Carpinus betulus*, the common hornbeam. Leaves open bright green but darken. The dead leaves are carried throughout winter. Susceptible to late spring frosts, it will only make 8ft (2.4m) in ten years in a sheltered spot; in the longer term, it is useful for windy sites. Plant 18in (45cm) apart and prune in late summer.

Ilex aquifolium *(below)* z 4
Reaching only 5ft (1.5m) in ten years, this holly makes an excellent dense hedge with very prickly, dark green leaves. The leaves of 'Golden Queen' have yellow edges, while those of 'Silver Queen' are white-edged (both of these cultivars are male). 'J. C. Van Tol' has spineless leaves. The hardiest hollies are *I.* × *meserveae*, the blue holly, and the deciduous winterberry, *I. verticillata*. Plant 18in (45cm) apart in fertile soil; useful for heavy soils and coastal gardens. Trim plants in late summer. For berries, female forms need a pollinator to ensure setting.

Lavandula angustifolia (*above*) z 7
A fine shrub for a low hedge, both the mauve flowers and the silver-gray, evergreen leaves are aromatic. 'Hidcote' is dense with violet flowers. Thrives in full sun, in well-drained soil and is useful in coastal areas. Clip the plant several times during the growing season for a formal shape; this effectively stops flowering. Unclipped plants reach 2ft (60cm) with an equal spread. Discard leggy plants and replant every five to six years. Complements blue and gray borders, rose gardens and stonework.

Lonicera nitida (*above*) z 7
This evergreen shrubby honeysuckle needs careful and regular clipping into a wedge-shape to prevent bare patches developing, particularly at the base of the plant. The stiff, twiggy branches are clothed with tiny, glossy green leaves which are golden in 'Baggessen's Gold'. Plants grow quickly to 5ft (1.5m). An old or neglected hedge can be renovated by being pruned hard back in early spring to stimulate fresh growth. Grow plants 1ft (30cm) apart, in any soil; prune back to 1ft (30cm) immediately after planting.

Prunus laurocerasus z 7
Cherry laurel
This evergreen shrub quickly makes a dense hedge 20ft (6m) high if free-growing. It has large, dark-green, glossy leaves. 'Rotundifolia' has leaves half as broad as long. Succeeds best in acid soil with some shelter; tolerates shade and dripping water from overhanging trees. Plant 2ft (60cm) apart and trim in summer with hand pruners: shears or hedge trimmers cut through the leaves which turn brown at the edges. Useful as a dark backcloth for a border.

Rosmarinus officinalis (*above*) z 6
Rosemary
A fast-growing evergreen shrub which can be clipped into a low, formal hedge or left as an informal hedge, making 5 × 5ft (1.5 × 1.5m) when mature. The leaves are deep green, off-white below and aromatic when rubbed. Flowers are blue. 'Benenden Blue' is smaller-growing with dark, very narrow leaves and bright blue flowers. Plant 18in (45cm) apart in a sunny, sheltered spot in well-drained soil. Clip often when young to induce bushiness. Rosemary is useful in herb gardens, as an edging, or in knot gardens.

Taxus baccata z 6
Yew
This popular plant makes a dense hedge if regularly clipped. The narrow, glossy, evergreen leaves are poisonous, as are the seeds (surrounded by a fleshy red aril). *T.* × *media* 'Hicksii' is hardier, with a broadly columnar habit. A fairly rapid-grower if top-dressed annually with fertilizer, it reaches 8ft (2.4m) in ten years. Plant 2ft (60cm) apart: tolerant of shade, exposed windy sites and heavy or chalky soils. Trim in late summer. Much-used for topiary.

Teucrium chamaedrys (*above*) z 6
Wall germander
This shrub has a dwarf, bushy habit and grows from a creeping rootstock. It has dark gray-green, toothed leaves. Useful for edging and in parterres where, with regular clipping, a neat low hedge can be produced. If plants are left untrimmed they produce whorls of rose pink flowers from mid-summer onwards. Grow in sun in well-drained, fertile soil. Can reach 3ft (90cm) if free-grown. A good alternative to box, *Buxus sempervirens*.

Tilia* × *euchlora (*below*) z 5
Lindens are tolerant of hard pruning and are often seen as pleached specimens. While free-growing trees can exceed 50ft (15m) in height, plants can be kept to the required height with regular clipping. The 4in (10cm)-long rounded leaves are a shiny, dark green above and pale and glaucous below, with brown tufts between the veins. This form is not susceptible to attack by aphids. Grows well in full sun on all but the poorest soils. Prune in spring before growth begins. Plants can be trained to form a tunnel or arbor.

Informal

Acer campestre *(below)* z 5
Field maple
This deciduous plant is an excellent choice for a country or cottage garden. It is moderately fast-growing and reaches 35ft (10.5m) if left free-growing. The lobed leaves are green in summer and turn reddish-yellow in autumn. The trunk and stems of older plants develop corky, raised ridges. Plant 18in (45cm) apart in alkaline soil, in an open, sunny position, or in some shade. Prune to restrict growth in winter or, preferably, in summer.

Arbutus unedo *(below)* z 8
Strawberry tree
An unusual ericaceous plant in that it is tolerant of alkaline soils. This species makes a shrub or small tree some 20 × 20ft (6 × 6m). It is often gnarled or twisted when mature, with deep brown, peeling bark. The evergreen leaves are narrow, dark and glossy. Panicles of white, pitcher-shaped flowers and edible fruits are carried together in autumn and winter. 'Rubra' has pink-flushed flowers. The strawberry tree is a good choice for exposed coastal gardens. Pruning is necessary only to keep the plant to the desired height.

Berberis thunbergii *(above)* z4
This deciduous, spiny barberry reaches 5ft (1.5m) in ten years, 6ft (1.8m) when mature. It makes a dense hedge of small, bright green leaves with gray undersides. Red-tinged, yellow flowers open in spring, followed by bead-like, shiny red fruits. The reddish-brown bark is striking in winter. 'Rose Glow' is illustrated; *atropurpurea* also has reddish-purple leaves, which take on good colors in autumn. Plant 18in (45cm) apart. Grows in alkaline or clay soil, in sun or shade: suitable for an exposed position. Prune in winter.

Camellia × williamsii *(above)* z 7
Camellias need shelter and are unsuitable for very cold and exposed positions; this is one of the best and hardiest. In winter and early spring velvet-petaled flowers in shades of pink, red and white are set off by the evergreen, dark, glossy leaves. Cultivars include 'Donation' (dark pink double flowers) and 'Francis Hanger' (white). Can grow to 10ft (3m) in ten years in humus-rich acid soil; will not tolerate a trace of lime. Plant in partial shade. Prune out long, leggy shoots.

Cornus mas *(below)* z 4
Cornelian cherry
Usually seen as a free-growing large shrub or densely-branched small tree, this dogwood can be grown as a closely-pruned hedge if clipped in early summer. Clusters of small yellow flowers appear on bare branches in early spring. The dark green, oval leaves turn orange-red in autumn. After a warm summer, small, red, edible fruits form. Enliven with *Tropaeolum speciosum* or *Clematis* 'Perle d' Azur'. Grows in sun or partial shade in most fertile soils.

***Forsythia × intermedia* 'Spectabilis'** z 5 *(below)*
The golden bell bush is covered with rich yellow flowers in spring. This vigorous deciduous hybrid is particularly floriferous. It has stout growths and can make a wide-spreading hedge 12ft (3.6m) tall by 10ft (3m) wide in ten years if left unpruned. The summer foliage is mid-green and sharply toothed, unfolding as the flowers fade. Other notable cultivars are 'Lynwood', 'Beatrix Farrand' and 'Spring Glory'. This bush tolerates most soils and is suited to exposed sites. Cut back after flowering if necessary.

Hibiscus syriacus *(above)* z 5

This shrubby mallow carries large cup-shaped flowers from summer into autumn. The red, pink, purple, blue or white flowers last only a day before fading. Gray-green stems give winter color; lobed leaves appear in late spring. 'Blue Bird' has dark-eyed, violet-blue flowers; 'Woodbridge' is the best large, single, pinkish-red form. Plants grow to 5 × 5ft (1.5 × 1.5m) in ten years, unless they are pruned in spring to keep them within bounds. Best in rich, well-drained soil in a sheltered, sunny position in the garden.

***Hypericum* 'Hidcote'** *(above)* z 5

One of the most popular flowering shrubs, this hardy, semi-evergreen has slender, low-growing, arching brown stems which can grow to 5 × 5ft (1.5 × 1.5m). The leaves are bright, apple green; the large yellow summer flowers are noted for their prominent golden stamens. This cultivar has the largest flowers. Grows equally well in dry or humus-rich soil, in full sun or semi-shade. Reduce plants if necessary by pruning hard back in late winter or early spring to the desired shape.

Osmanthus delavayi *(below)* z 6

Grow this evergreen shrub for a wonderful fragrance in spring. The small, sweetly scented flowers are creamy-white and trumpet-shaped; they are held in plentiful clusters. The small, oval, dark green leathery leaves are fringed with minute teeth. It will grow to 5 × 4ft (1.5 × 1.2m) in ten years in well-drained soil, in sun or partial shade, with some shelter from other evergreens. Slower growth can be expected in cold areas. Any trimming should be carried out straight after flowering, using hand pruners.

***Potentilla fruticosa* 'Goldfinger'** z 2
(below)

In ten years this shrubby cinquefoil can grow to 5ft (1.5m), forming a rounded bush with twiggy stems. The deciduous pinnate leaves are deep green and hairy. A profusion of large, deep yellow, five-petaled flowers appear from summer into autumn. Other forms include 'Katherine Dykes' (pale yellow flowers), 'Farrer's White' (white with yellow stamens) and 'Red Ace' (vermilion flowers with yellow centers). Plant 18in (45cm) apart in most soils. Prune in early spring to control growth.

Rhododendron ponticum *(above)* z 6

This very resilient rhododendron will succeed in deep shade and is excellent for hedging. An evergreen shrub with large dark green ovate leaves, it grows to around 6ft (1.8m) in ten years. In late spring and early summer it is covered with tubular, lilac-pink flowers. 'Variegatum' has creamy-white margined leaves and is one of the few variegated rhododendrons. Needs a moist, acid soil and will benefit from a humus-rich mulch in summer. When the desired height has been reached, prune selected shoots after flowering.

Viburnum tinus *(above)* z 7
Laurustinus

The stems of this adaptable plant carry dark, glossy, evergreen leaves and flat cymes of flowers at the tips. Pink in bud, these open white from late autumn to mid-spring. Shiny blue-black fruits often coincide with some flowers. Plants reach 10 × 10ft (3 × 3m) in ten years. 'Eve Price' is denser and smaller with pale pink flowers. Tolerates most soil conditions, shade, pollution and salt spray. Remove weak growth and prune lightly to maintain the shape.

GROUND COVER

For most people, the aim of ground cover in a garden is to minimize the number of weeds that seed themselves and grow rapidly, marring the appearance of the planting and competing with cultivated plants for moisture, nutrients and, in some cases, light. In the last 40 years or so, as labor has become more expensive, densely leaved low-growing plants have been widely used to accomplish this aim and the term "ground cover plants" has been applied to them. They are comparatively cheap to buy, easy to plant and available in many different forms: quick or slow to increase; suitable for sun or shade; thriving in freely draining or moisture retentive soils; appropriate to formal or informal schemes, according to species or cultivar. Ground cover plants can be prostrate conifers, shrubs or herbaceous plants, evergreen or deciduous: something to satisfy every need, taste and planting plan.

Ground cover plants quickly colonize sizeable areas and build up a thick thatch of vegetation that suppresses most weeds. The one exception is woody weeds, but these usually appear singly and are easily removed. The perennial quality of most ground cover plants ensures that, with a minimum of pruning and splitting during the winter months, maintenance during the growing season is negligible. Once they are established, there is no longer any necessity to dig and hoe the areas of the garden that are planted with them. The chances of success are maximized if the ground is cleared of perennial weeds before planting. This can be a time-consuming task but it pays dividends.

The art of ground cover lies in spacing the plants correctly to ensure that the ground is covered quickly but without the plants competing for space or losing their characteristic habits from having to spread too far. The estimated spread of a plant can be used as a guide, taking into consideration the means by which it spreads. Those plants that spread by underground or overground runners are, as a rule, the most vigorous. They can be useful when a large area needs to be covered, but the larger plants, in particular, tend to suffocate and choke everything in sight. Clump forming plants are much more containable and there are a number that self-seed as well. These days, when a plant becomes a pest it is possible to eradicate it by painting it out with a non-persistent herbicide that is deactivated as soon as it comes into contact with the ground; this should be used sparingly, over limited areas. However, most plants can be kept at bay by digging them up regularly.

The value of leaves cannot be overemphasized when looking at ground cover plants, the different textures and colors being so closely juxtaposed that they create an intricate tapestry. There are greens in every hue, yellow-flushed plants and white-variegated cultivars that prefer shade (for example, *Hosta fortunei* 'Aurea', *Lysimachia nummularia* 'Aurea' and *Lamium maculatum*); while silvery, yellow-variegated, purple and glaucous foliage perform best in sunshine (*Heuchera* 'Palace Purple', *Stachys olympica*, *Ruta graveolens*). Flowers must be woven into the whole scheme, bringing seasonal interest to the composition (*Geranium endressii* 'Wargrave Pink', *Helleborus orientalis*, *Phlox subulata*).

Ground cover plants can be used in great informal drifts, covering large areas of the garden. A suitable scheme for a moist shady position would include hostas in variety, pulmonarias, hellebores, bergenias, solomon's seal and epimediums; in direct sunlight catmints, pinks, thrifts, snow-in-summer, jerusalem sage and thymes thrive. A steep bank, where it may be difficult to grow grass, can be successfully clothed in a thick mat of St John's wort (*Hypericum calycinum*) which carries bright yellow flowers throughout the summer, or periwinkle (*Vinca*) that raises starry blue eyes over a dense carpet of green leaves in spring – both require pruning in late winter.

In formal designs, where labor-intensive bedding plants might have been used in the past, it is possible to associate neatly clipped cotton lavenders, colored leaved sages, blue leaved festuca, ivies and chamomile for a pleasing effect.

Left: A sunny well-drained sloping site is completely clothed with low-growing perennials, including *Convolvulus sabatius*, helianthemums, pinks and thrift. Dense planting suppresses weeds and creates a rich tapestry effect.The conifers introduce a discreet vertical element that emphasizes the flatness of the ground cover. This planting demonstrates the wealth of color and texture provided by ground cover plants.

Below: Ivy is a thorough and accommodating ground cover in shady, cool conditions, creating a dense and weed-proof carpet.

For flowers

Arabis caucasica z 3

Often listed as *A. albida*, this useful plant forms loose mats of gray-green oblong leaves with bright white, slightly fragrant flowers carried in lax racemes 8in (20cm) tall in spring. It succeeds in dry situations and combines well with *Aubrieta* hybrids and *Alyssum saxatile*. The best forms are the double 'Flore-Pleno', 'Rosabelle' with its single, deep pink flowers, and the green-and-yellow leaved 'Variegata'. Propagate from cuttings taken in the summer or raise from seed sown during the autumn; plants may also be divided. Deadhead after the flowers have faded.

Asperula odorata z 4
Sweet woodruff

Also listed as *Galium odoratum*, the whole of this carpeting perennial is aromatic. It bears whorls of star-shaped white flowers during summer and reaches a height of 6in (15cm), with a spread of 12in (30cm). When in ideal conditions – partially shaded and in moist but well-drained soil – sweet woodruff needs to be kept in check as it tends to be invasive. Propagate either by softwood cuttings or raise from seed sown in early summer.

Cerastium tomentosum (*above*) z 6
Snow-in-summer

This widely-spreading, extremely vigorous perennial is an excellent for dry, sunny banks. It will become straggly if grown in the shade. From late spring the star-shaped white flowers are held above the foliage in a dense bright display. The spreading, prostrate stems are clothed in a mat of very small, gray shiny leaves. Plants reach a height of 6in (15cm) and tend to be rampant when established. Propagate by division or sowing seeds during spring.

Cotoneaster dammeri z 6

In well-drained soil, this low evergreen cotoneaster makes excellent ground cover, especially beneath other taller shrubs. It reaches 4in (10cm) in height, spreading to 2ft (60cm) or more, and needs hand weeding until a dense canopy is formed. The prostrate stems carry oval alternate leaves which are 1in (2.5cm) long, with small white flowers appearing in late spring and bright sealing-wax-red fruit in autumn. The deciduous *C. horizontalis* reaches 2ft (60cm); it has a variegated form.

***Geranium endressii* 'Wargrave Pink'** (*above*) z 3

Originating from the Pyrenees, this geranium is ideal in a mixed border between large evergreen shrubs. 'Wargrave Pink' is a vigorous plant which produces flowers (bright salmon-pink with pale veins) throughout the summer and into the autumn, if cut back. The stems can reach 2ft (60cm) in height; the deeply divided leaves are 2-3in (5-8cm) across and form neat clumps. Plants will grow in most soils, in sun or light shade, and are useful as a weed-suppressant. Propagate by division in autumn or spring.

Helleborus orientalis z 3
Lenten rose

Choose a sheltered spot to grow this beautiful, evergreen hardy perennial. The flowers are extremely variable, ranging from creamy-white to deep-purple with yellow stamens, as plants readily cross-pollinate. They open from mid-winter onwards on stems 12-18in (30-45cm) high, above divided, mid-green leathery leaves. Plants self-seed very easily. Combines well with galanthus (snowdrop) and the perennial *Brunnera macrophylla*.

Iberis sempervirens (*above*) z 4
Candytuft

With its compact, cushion-like growth of dark green, evergreen leaves and dense smothering in late spring of white flowers, this sub-shrub makes ideal ground cover. It is also often grown as edging or in rock gardens. For best results plant in well-drained, slightly alkaline soil. Plants can reach 9in (23cm) in height and spread to 2ft (60cm). 'Snowflake' has larger-petaled, brighter flowers; the smaller 'Little Gem' has more erect growth. Propagate from softwood cuttings in midsummer.

Hypericum calycinum (*above*) z 5

The suckering habit of this dwarf evergreen shrub allows it to cover large areas quickly, even on poor and impoverished soils. The solitary flowers appear at the end of shoots up to 20in (50cm) tall. They are 4in (10cm) across and golden-yellow with a central boss of yellow stamens tipped by red anthers. Once established, cut hard back in spring to promote fresh growth, which is vital if plants have been affected by rust disease. Makes effective ground cover in shady areas.

Lamium maculatum (*below*) z 3
Spotted deadnettle
In deep shade this rampant perennial will establish quickly where other plants might struggle. It has the characteristic "square" stems of the Labiate family, cream-striped, pungent leaves and mauve-pink flowers which appear in early summer. Plants can spread to 3ft (90cm), reaching a height of 8in (20cm). The cultivars tend to be less vigorous: 'Beacon Silver' has green-edged silver leaves and pink flowers; 'Aureum' has pale yellow leaves with pink flowers.

Lysimachia nummularia (*below*) z 3
Creeping Jenny
In moist, sunny conditions this plant is especially rampant and needs to be checked by regular pulling and thinning of wandering shoots. 'Aurea', which has yellow-green leaves, is less invasive and makes an excellent low-growing perennial ground cover; it is also used in hanging baskets, containers and for edging. The leaves are opposite on the prostrate stems, barely 1in (2.5cm) long and an ideal foil for the bright yellow flowers in summer. Plants reach only 1in (2.5cm) in height but can spread for 3-4ft (60-90cm).

Phlox subulata (*above*) z 2
Moss phlox
In spring, mats of bright flowers hide the narrow, spiky leaves of this evergreen, mound-forming perennial. Color variations include the clear blue 'G.F. Wilson' and 'Scarlet Flame' with its deep red flowers. Plants need sun and fertile, well-drained soil. They reach 6in (15cm) in height and spread up to 20in (50cm). Propagate by taking 2in (5cm) cuttings through the summer. 'Marjory' is illustrated.

Polygonum affine **'Donald Lowndes'** z 3
This evergreen perennial is outstanding when planted in bold drifts on large banks. It produces small rose-red flowers in dense spikes in summer which fade and pale as they age. Plants grow to a height of 6in (15cm) and spread up to 6in (15cm). The narrow, pointed green leaves often take on attractive bronze tints in autumn and winter. For a larger plant grow *P. bistorta* 'Superbum' which has 2ft (60cm)-tall pokers of pink flowers in late summer. Grow both in sun or partial shade, where they will succeed in most fertile soils. Divide in autumn or spring.

Saxifraga × urbium z 6
London pride
An evergreen spreading perennial with spoon-shaped leaves held in rosettes, this makes excellent ground cover, reaching a height of 1ft (30cm), and quickly forming a dense, weed-suppressing mat of leathery, toothed leaves. In spring and summer the plants produce sprays of small whitish-pink, red-spotted flowers. Plants grow best in light shade and need moist soil. Increase by detaching healthy rosettes or divide plants.

Vinca minor (*below*) z 4
A trailing evergreen perennial of use in shady positions and on inaccessible, steep banks. The bright bluey-mauve flowers appear from early spring to autumn, with the main flush in summer, among glossy, dark green, lanceolate leaves. To encourage a second flush, cut back after the main display. Plants need well-drained soil. The arching shoots can reach 8in (20cm) in height, spreading to 2ft (60cm). There are a number of cultivars; 'Variegata' has creamy-white splashed leaves and 'Multiplex' double plum-purple flowers.

Waldsteinia ternata (*below*) z 4
Also listed as *W. trifolia*, this semi-evergreen creeping perennial is notable for its trifoliate leaves and saucer-shaped, yellow flowers. In autumn, the leaves turn golden which is an added attraction. Plants grow to a height of 4in (10cm) forming loose spreading mats in well-drained soil in sun. Useful on banks where it soon spreads by fast-growing runners. Propagate by division in spring. Similar is *W. fragarioides* which has deeper toothed, strawberry-like leaves. Both are uncommon but well worth growing.

Long flowering

Liatris spicata *(above)* z 3
Gayfeather
Also known as *L. callilepis*, this is something of an oddity among flowering border perennials in that its flower spikes, which look like thick pinkish bottlebrushes, open from the top downwards. The spikes grow from clumps of dark green grassy foliage. Good forms include 'Kobold', with rosy-purple spikes up to 18in (45cm) high, and 'Alba' for white flowers. All are easy to grow, needing full sun and regular deadheading in summer.

Nepeta × faassenii z 3
Catmint
Cats will roll in this wonderfully aromatic herbaceous perennial – hence its common name. The leaves are gray-green, soft and downy. In late spring and early summer blue-purple flower spikes appear, with a second flush of blooms in autumn if the plants are sheared back after the first flowering. Catmint will grow even in the poorest of dry soils. Ideal for edging beds and borders. Propagate by tip cuttings in summer or division in spring.

Phlomis russeliana z 4
An evergreen perennial which makes excellent ground cover, growing to 3ft (90cm) high when in flower. The strong flower stems appear in summer carrying several whorls of soft butter-yellow hooded flowers above the foliage. The large hairy leaves are heart-shaped. In winter the dead flower heads add interest. Plants can achieve a spread of 2ft (60cm). The leaves are aromatic if rubbed. They need full sun and are ideal for baked, dry positions. Divide plants in spring or take softwood cuttings during summer.

Ruta graveolens *(below)* z 3
Rue
If not grown in full sun in an open spot, rue tends to become drawn and floppy. It is an excellent border plant and very useful as edging. Clusters of mustard-yellow flowers appear above the foliage during early summer, at which time plants can reach up to 3ft (90cm) in height, with similar spread. 'Jackman's Blue' is illustrated, with blue-gray fern-like foliage. The leaves release a pungent odor. Contact with the foliage or sap can cause a skin rash. Clip back shoots in spring; take semi-ripe cuttings in summer.

Santolina chamaecyparissus **'Nana'** z 7
Cotton lavender
This dwarf and compact form has finely toothed, narrow leaves which are covered with a woolly white coating. Plants form low mounds of silvery fragrant foliage topped in summer by small, yellow button-like flowers. Blends well with the true English lavender, *Lavandula officinalis*. Deadhead in autumn and cut older plants hard back in spring. Propagate by semi-ripe cuttings in late summer.

Stachys byzantina z 4
Bunnies' or lambs' ears
Also listed *S. lanata* and *S. byzantina*, this popular evergreen perennial makes good ground cover. It forms thick mats of deeply felted, silver-gray leaves. In summer the flower spikes, which are also covered in silver hairs, grow upright from the mats carrying clusters of tiny pink-purple flowers. Lamb's ears is at home in hot dry soils and loves to be baked next to paving in full sun. It goes well with old fashioned roses and pinks and with *Sedum* 'Autumn Joy'. Divide clumps in spring or autumn.

Achillea filipendulina **'Gold Plate'** z 3
(above)
Yarrow or milfoil
Thriving on dry, poor soils, this plant flowers throughout the summer. The bold flat heads of tiny, golden-yellow daisy-like flowers face upwards on stiff stems 4ft (1.2m) high. The foliage has an elegant feathery nature and is aromatic if rubbed or crushed. For paler yellow flowers and gray foliage grow *A.* 'Moonshine'. Plants can spread to 2ft (60cm) across. Divide them in spring or autumn, or take cuttings in summer.

Anemone × hybrida **'Honorine Jobert'** z 5
This Japanese anemone flowers for three months from mid-summer to autumn, producing saucer-shaped flowers with clear white petals and yellow stamens. Even though the branched flowering stems are up to 3ft (90cm) tall, they do not need staking. The deeply lobed leaves form a neat mound, 2ft (60cm) across, in heavy soil; in lighter soils these anemones can be quite invasive. Plants grow well in full sun or light shade. Divide in spring or take root cuttings in winter.

Bupthalmum salicifolium z 6
Yellow ox-eye
While tending to be invasive in borders, the yellow ox-eye is worth growing for its deep yellow flower heads carried singly on thin stems. Its vigorous nature can be curbed somewhat by regular division and by digging out unwanted growth. Plants grow to a height of 2ft (60cm) when flowering, and have dark green, narrow leaves. They thrive on slightly starved, infertile soil in full sun. The flowers appear for many weeks. Increase by division in spring.

Spring flowering

Chrysanthemum maximum *(below)* z 4
Shasta daisy
Even after bad weather, the flowers of the shasta daisy will show little sign of damage. This old border favorite grows 2-3ft (60cm-90cm) tall, the stems being topped with large, white daisy-like flowers with yellow button-like centers. The dark bottle-green leaves form a dense carpet in spring from which the flowering stems emerge throughout the summer if regularly deadheaded. Fine cultivars include the frilly-petaled 'Aglaya' and the pale yellow 'Cobham Gold'. Plant in sun. Divide clumps in spring or autumn.

Erodium manescavii *(below)* z 7
One of the most useful heronsbills for the border, this species will flower for several months during the summer. It forms mounds of blue-green, divided fern-like foliage topped by clusters of single lilac-pink flowers. Plants need a sunny position. They reach a height and spread of 20in (50cm) and self-seed quite readily, from which good forms can often be selected if the seedling plants are allowed to flower. As an alternative, semi-ripe cuttings can be taken in summer.

Patrinia gibbosa z 5
This unusual Japanese plant emits a rather unpleasant smell. It produces long-lasting flowers during late summer each with one long greenish-yellow petal. The flowers are small, appearing in massed heads above a clump of broad basal leaves, and are attractive even when they have faded. The roots need to be kept reasonably cool and moist. Plants grow to 18in (45cm) tall and spread to 1ft (30cm). Divide in spring or grow-on self-sown seedlings.

***Penstemon* 'Lady Alice Hindley'** z 9
The greatest asset of the penstemons is their long flowering season – from early to late summer – which can be extended through regular deadheading. They are also available in a wide range of colors, from white to deep red, with many intermediate shades of blue and mauve. Hardiness is also variable: it is often said that the wider the leaf the more tender the plant. This cultivar has the characteristic tubular flowers which are pale lilac, and is more or less evergreen with rich green leaves. Plants can grow to 4ft (1.2m) and may need staking. Take cuttings in summer.

***Sedum* 'Autumn Joy'** *(above)* z 3
This large stonecrop is prized not only for its display of large, flat pink flower heads in autumn, but also for its dried seed heads in winter. The young leaves are also attractive and grow to 2ft (60cm) by late summer. In full flower the plants attract clouds of bees, butterflies and other insects. Plants will soon form bold clumps 2ft (60cm) across on fertile soil, and must be in a warm sunny spot. As the flowers age they turn to shades of coppery red. Cut back the old flowering stems in late winter. Divide the crowns in spring.

***Aquilegia vulgaris* 'Nora Barlow'** z 4
(above)
This unmistakable cultivar of columbine is a spring favorite in the border, noted for its double spurred flowers with red petals which are pale green at their tips. The gray-green foliage is deeply divided and forms a loose clump below the 2½ft (75cm)-long flowering stems. Plants spread to 20in (50cm). They need well-drained soil and an open sunny position. Cultivars such as this only occasionally come true from seed. *A. vulgaris* has flowers of purple, white, pink and crimson on 3ft (90cm) stems.

Convallaria majalis *(below)* z 3
Lily-of-the-valley
An old favorite of cottage gardens, noted for its wonderfully scented flowers. The white bell-like flowers appear on arching stems during spring, emerging from a pair of broad, mid-green lance-shaped leaves. Plants grow to around 8in (20cm) tall and spread quickly. They prefer moist soil with plenty of organic matter added, and are ideal for carpeting a small bed or the ground below shrubs. Increase by replanting sections of the rhizome.

Euphorbia polychroma *(below)* z 4
Dappled shade is perfect for this early-flowering spurge, which emerges in spring reaching a height of 18in (45cm). The sulphur-yellow flower heads are held above fresh green leaves, most of the color being provided by the yellowish bracts. During summer the heads fade to green and finally to reddish-brown. This species associates well with *Brunnera macrophylla* or red tulips. Plant it in moist well-drained soil. Divide plants during autumn or take cuttings in summer. Avoid skin contact with the plant's white latex.

***Geum* 'Borisii'** z 5
The bright orange flowers of this avens have striking yellow stamens and add a touch of warmth to a border in spring. A clump-forming perennial, its leaves are broad and unevenly lobed, forming a loose clump at the base of the 1ft (30cm)-tall flowering stems. The stems are hairy and each one carries several single flowers. This perennial is at its best in full sun and needs moist but free-draining soil. Increase by seed sown during autumn or by division.

***Heuchera sanguinea* cvs** z 3
A number of fine cultivars have arisen from crossing this species with *H. americana*. 'Palace Purple' is an evergreen perennial hybrid with large clumps of deeply purple-bronze leaves, against which are set creamy flowers in spring and summer. 'Red Spangles' has silver-marbled leaves and spikes of bright crimson, bell-shaped flowers in summer. Both these make good ground cover and need moist soil, in sun or light shade. The flowering stems grow to 18in (45cm) tall and should be cut back as they fade. Divide the plants in spring or autumn.

Omphalodes verna z 5
Verna means early, in this case the early-flowering of this semi-evergreen perennial which is decked in spring with sprays of white-eyed, bright blue flattish flowers. Plants form clumps of mid-green oval-shaped leaves and grow to 8in (20cm) high. They make good ground cover for a shaded or semi-shaded border and need well-drained but moist soil. Similar, but with heart-shaped deeply-veined leaves, is *O. cappadocica*, which carries clear blue flowers above its leaves during spring. Plants can be divided in spring or raised from seed.

***Paeonia officinalis* 'Rubra Plena'** z 2
The deep velvety-red flowers of this old-fashioned, European herbaceous peony are fully double and are carried in great, sometimes unwieldy clusters. Plants form large 3ft (90cm)-wide clumps of glossy foliage which lasts for the entire season. This species does not like being moved, but will survive under adverse conditions for many years. Cultivars with single flowers include 'Phyllis Pritchard' and 'J.C.Weguelin'. Increase by root cuttings in winter or division in late autumn or early spring.

Papaver orientale *(above)* z 3
Great oriental poppy
With its enormous papery-petalled flowers on gently curving 3ft (90cm)-tall stems, this poppy is a spectacular spring-flowering plant for the border. Plants form rather loose clumps of long basal leaves. They thrive in dryer borders and must have full sun. 'Marcus Perry' has red petals with a black blotch and those of 'Perry's Pink' are gray-white. Plants will self-seed, but cultivars must be increased by root cuttings during winter.

Symphytum* × *uplandicum z 3
Russian comfrey
A tough herbaceous perennial which grows to 3ft (90cm) in height and carries spectacular cymes of pinkish-blue flowers in late spring and early summer. Plants grow best in deep moist soil and go well with yellow-flowered azaleas and rhododendrons. 'Variegatum' has similar flowers plus gray-green leaves broadly margined with pale cream. Plants will self-seed, although 'Variegata' must be increased by division in spring. Because of their deep roots, they can be difficult to eradicate.

Trollius europaeus *(above)* z 3
Globeflower
In spring this relative of the common buttercup produces large, globe-like lemon-yellow flowers on 2ft (60cm)-tall shoots. For best results grow it in moist soil next to a stream or pool, in sun or shade. Plants form clumps 18in (45cm) across of mid-green deeply-divided leaves. Hybrids are usually listed as cultivars of *T.* × *cultorum*, including the lovely 'Alabaster' with its yellowish-white blooms. Propagate cultivars by division in early autumn, and species from seed sown in summer or autumn.

Veronica gentianoides z 4
A pretty and dainty perennial which forms mats of broad dark green leaves from which rise spikes of washed-out blue flowers in spring. It is ideal for the front of borders and for mixing in with red or orange companions such as *Geum* × *borisii*. On strong plants the flowering stems grow to 18in (45cm), less if grown on poor dry soils. 'Variegata' has the added interest of cream splashed leaves. Propagate by division or softwood summer cuttings. Plants love a sunny spot in well-drained light soil.

Summer flowering

Acanthus spinosus *(below)* z 7
This species of bear's breeches is very variable but tends to be somewhat smaller than the commonly grown *A. mollis*. Both are prized for their architectural qualities. The shiny dark green leaves achieve 2-3ft (60-90cm) in length and form spiky clumps at the base of the 4ft (1.2m) flowering stems. The stems are clothed almost to the top in hooded purple and white flowers in late summer. Plants grow best in full sun. They can become invasive. Divide plants in autumn or spring, or take winter root cuttings.

Campanula lactiflora *(below)* z 4
An easily grown perennial bellflower needing moist soil to succeed, this species produces 4ft (1.2m)-tall stems which are clothed in pointed leaves. Bell-shaped mauve flowers appear in large branching heads at the top of the stems. 'Loddon Anna' is taller with pale pink flowers. To extend the flowering season cut back some of the stems in late spring. Plants need sun or light shade. Propagate by division in late autumn or spring, or through softwood or basal cuttings during the growing season. Stake on windy sites.

***Delphinium* hybrids** *(above)* z 3
Delphiniums form large and, if not supported, unwieldy clumps of growth up to 2ft (60cm) across, and tall flowering stems up to 6ft (1.8m) high. The flowers appear in narrow racemes, in vibrant tones of blue, white and purple, or now in reds in the University Hybrids. Plants need deep humus-rich soil, sun and shelter from wind for the taller types. Common hybrids are the Pacific Giants and Blue Fountains Series. Increase plants by division or by taking cuttings from young basal shoots during spring.

Digitalis × mertonensis *(above)* z 4
A clump-forming perennial, this attractive foxglove has 2½ft (75cm)-long spikes of nodding, tubular, rose-pink to coppery flowers, held all around the flowering stems. The basal rosette of soft, hairy oval leaves grows to 1ft (30cm) across. Plants should be divided after flowering in autumn. For best results plant in moist fertile soil in light shade. If seed sets this can be sown when it ripens in the autumn. *D. ferruginea* is best treated as a biennial and has pale orange-brown flowers.

Echinops ritro *(below)* z 3
Globe thistle
Any cottage-garden-style border is incomplete without the beautiful globe thistle. In summer its rounded bright blue flowers attract hordes of bees and butterflies. The flowers are held well above the jaggedly lobed leaves, which are fresh green on their upper sides and white-felted below. The flowers stay open for many weeks, while the seed heads carry interest into autumn. Strong plants reach 3-4ft (90-120cm). To propagate, sow seed in spring, or divide or take root cuttings in autumn.

***Euphorbia griffithii* 'Fireglow'** z 5
The massed flower heads of this beautiful spurge look like glowing embers in a fire when seen against a dark green background. The lance-shaped leaves appear all along the length of the 2-3ft (60-90cm) flowering stems and have a prominent pinkish-red midrib. Plants spread to 20in (50cm). After autumn frosts the foliage takes on attractive tints. 'Dixter' is similar but more compact. Divide in spring or autumn. The white sap can cause skin irritation and can damage the eyes.

***Geranium* 'Johnson's Blue'** z 3
A lovely hybrid cranesbill resulting from a cross between *G. pratense* and *G. himalayense*, which grows to a height of 1ft (30cm). The large flowers appear throughout the height of summer and are of a deep lavender-blue with distinct darker veining on the petals. The deeply lobed rounded leaves appear in spring before the blooms and will sometimes take on attractive reddish tints in autumn. Cut back in late summer for late flowers. Plants work well beneath pale yellow or apricot roses. Divide in spring or autumn.

***Hemerocallis* cvs** z 3
Daylily
This robust border perennial can survive drought, large amounts of watering and being transplanted at any time of the year. Plants look good both in flower and foliage, and with careful choice of cultivars continuous flowering is possible throughout the summer. 'Pink Damask' has pinkish flowers; *H. flava* has fragrant yellow blooms; while those of *H. fulva* are tawny-orange. Both of these species can be invasive. Newer hybrids need only be split when flowering begins to diminish. Plants grow in sun or light shade, need feeding in spring and reach a height of 1-4ft (30-120cm) depending on cultivar.

Hibiscus moscheutos z 4
Swamp rose mallow
A native of the eastern United States, this lovely plant has spectacularly large, rounded satiny flowers of crimson, white or pink. It needs fertile moist soil in full sun for best results, although it will grow in dryer conditions. Plants reach 3ft (90cm) in height with a similar spread. Raise plants from seed sown during spring.

Inula magnifica *(above)* z 3
For a splash of late summer cheer in the border, this herbaceous perennial is an ideal choice. Huge 6ft (1.8m)-tall stems appear from a basal clump of oval leaves 1ft (30cm) long. They are crowned with large flower heads containing numerous bright yellow, narrow petals which give them a shaggy appearance. Where space is limited, the more modest *I. hookeri* can be grown. Plant both in well-drained moist soil and propagate by division in spring or autumn. They look really good when seen against a dark green backdrop such as a yew hedge.

***Kniphofia* 'Little Maid'** *(below)* z 6
This is one of the more discreet and tasteful of the red hot pokers, providing color in the late summertime. It has narrow bluey-green foliage and flowering stems 2ft (60cm) high, carrying spikes of pale lemon-yellow flowers which fade to cream from the base up as they age. Other cultivars have flowers ranging from deep red to bright yellow. Grow plants in free-draining soil in a warm sunny spot. During winter tie up the leaves to keep the crowns dry. Divide in spring.

***Ligularia dentata* 'Desdemona'** z 4
A lightly shaded position at the back of a border, where the soil is cool and moist, is perfect for this majestic clump-forming perennial. It looks wonderful in front of *Gunnera manicata*. The large rounded kidney-shaped leaves are dark green on their upper sides and deep red-purple below. In late summer the foliage is topped by bunches of up to 12 large, daisy-like, bright orange flowers, carried on reddish-purple stems 3-4ft (1-1.2m) tall. 'The Rocket' has palmate, strongly dentate leaves and pale yellow flowers. Divide plants in spring.

Lychnis × arkwrightii z 6
The electric scarlet flowers of this hybrid maltese cross make it stand out in any border. A clump-forming perennial, it spreads to 18in (45cm) and has dark green oval leaves all the way up its quite weak, 18in (45cm)-tall stems. The stems carry clusters of brilliant orange-red, five-petaled flowers. *L. coronaria* has gray-furry leaves in great clumps, studded with bright purple-cerise flowers. Plants are often treated as biennials. They need sun and well-drained soil. Self-seeds freely; alternatively, divide plants.

***Lythrum salicaria* 'Firecandle'** *(above)* z 3
Purple loosestrife
Oval 3in (8cm)-long leaves are held in opposite pairs all the way up the 3ft (90cm)-tall stems of this handsome plant. The stems carry terminal spikes of deep rose-red flowers opening in mid-summer. For pink blooms lasting from early summer to early autumn, try 'Morden's Pink'. The species is invasive in the northeastern and central United States, colonizing roadsides and watercourses. Named cultivars are less vigorous, although they can hybridize.

***Monarda* 'Cambridge Scarlet'** *(above)* z 4
Bee balm, bergamot or oswego tea
The flowers are peculiar, borne in circular heads at the top of stiff erect stems, each being strangely hooded and of great attraction to hummingbirds and bees: deadhead regularly through the summer. The sharply-pointed oval leaves release a scent when rubbed or crushed. Other good cultivars include the compact 'Adam' with cerise flowers, 'Snow White', and the brownish-red 'Mahogany'. Grow in moist soil in sun. Divide every three to four years for the best results.

Oenothera tetragona z 4
Evening primrose
Carried on stems 1-2ft (30-60cm) tall, the reddish fragrant flowers begin opening in the late afternoon and by the evening are fully open, only to fade the next day. The bright yellow, cup-shaped flowers are held well above the broadly oval, dark green leaves which are bluish on their undersides. 'Fireworks' ('Fyrverkeri') has deep red buds and greenish-purple young foliage. Best in light, well-drained soils and sun. Divide the clumps during early spring or in autumn.

***Phlox paniculata* cvs** z 3
A popular border plant which flowers over a long period in summer, and again in early autumn if the first display is cut back as it fades. Plant in deep, free-draining humus-rich soil and water throughout the growing season as necessary. Pinch back weak shoots in spring. Plants reach 2-4ft (60-120cm) in height and are best grown in bold drifts, in sun or light shade. Always choose mildew-resistant cultivars. 'Eva Cullum' has bright pink flowers with red eyes. Divide in autumn.

Physostegia virginiana z 3
Obedient plant
If you bend the flowers of this plant to one side they will stay there. This late-flowering perennial adds interest to a summer border with its slender, pink snapdragon-like flowers arranged neatly on 2½ft (75cm)-tall stems. The lance-shaped mid-green leaves grow on the stems up to the first flowers. 'Vivid' has rich pink flowers; 'Alba' is white; 'Variegata' has white-edged foliage. Plant in a moist well-drained spot in full sun, but avoid highly alkaline soils. Divide in spring.

Platycodon grandiflorus z 3
Balloon plant
The buds appear in summer and look like clusters of small blue-purple balloons. They open to become cup-shaped flowers with dark veins. This perennial grows up to 2ft (60cm) tall and spreads to 18in (45cm). The leaves are greenish-blue, forming a tuft at the base of the plant, and also clothing the stems. Grow plants on light sandy soil in full sun. To propagate, detach non-flowering basal shoots with a piece of root attached during the summer, or sow seed in autumn.

***Polygonum bistorta* 'Superbum'** z 3
(above)
One of the finest bistorts for the perennial border, this plant forms spreading clumps of leathery basal leaves. From these rise the 2½ft (75cm)-tall flowering stems which are topped with bottlebrush-like spikes of small pale pink flowers from early to late summer. Plant in sun or light shade, in moist conditions. *P. amplexicaule* 'Atrosanguineum' has rich crimson flowers. Divide in spring or autumn, watering them well until established.

Romneya coulteri *(above)* z 8
Tree poppy
For the best results grow this plant in the shelter of a south- or west-facing wall. It detests being moved and must be planted in light, very free-draining soil to flourish, where it will produce a summer display of huge flowers, which have pure white, crinkled petals around a cluster of yellow stamens. The deeply-divided leaves are a beautiful bluish sea-green. Plants reach 6ft (1.8m) in height. Cut the stems to ground level in autumn and protect with mulch. To increase, cut away root pieces in spring.

***Rudbeckia fulgida* 'Goldsturm'** z 3
(below)
Coneflower or black-eyed susan
This easily grown perennial has distinctive cone-shaped flowers with black velvety centers in late summer. This cultivar's flowers are 3-4in (8-10cm) across with thin golden-yellow petals. The flowers are carried on 2ft (60cm)-tall stems which have numerous oval leaves at the base. These long-lived plants need moist soil in sun or light shade. Divide the spreading rhizomes in autumn or spring.

Salvia × superba z 4
This herbaceous perennial can reach a height of 3ft (90cm) or more and is a relative of the culinary sage *S. officinalis*. It has the characteristic stiff, square stems and oval dull-green leaves with toothed margins. The stems branch out in summer to form numerous narrow spikes of ½in (1cm)-long flowers of a deep violet-blue, surrounded by red-purple bracts from the base up. Cut right back as the flowers fade for a second flush in early autumn; this also prevents legginess. Some staking is advisable. Well-drained soil and full sun are essential. Divide in spring or take summer cuttings.

***Sidalcea* hybrids** z 5
These plants, which make neat rounded clumps of long-stalked weed-smothering leaves, are like miniature versions of hollyhocks. The flowering stems are 3-4ft (90-120cm) tall, have deeply-lobed leaves, and end in elegant branching spikes of pink cup-shaped flowers. Flower color ranges from the deep red of 'Croftway Red' to the pale pink in 'Elsie Heugh'. Grow in moisture-retentive but well-drained soil, in full sun or light shade. Divide in spring.

Autumn flowering

Aster novi-belgii *(above)* z 4
Michaelmas daisies are variable in both habit and color but they are always invaluable additions to the autumn garden. Anything from 1-4ft (30-120cm) in height, flowers range from deep crimson to white through every shade of purple, mauve, pink, red and blue ('Sheena' is illustrated). Quickly spreads to 18in (45cm); benefits from frequent splitting – retain the outside and discard the center. Thrives in moist fertile soil. Mildew can be a problem.

Catananche caerulea z 4
Cupid's dart or blue cupidone
Once used in love potions, this plant produces crisp blue flowers in a papery calyx on wiry 2ft (60cm)-high stems. Its grass-like thin foliage is gray-green, forming a tufted crown 1ft (30cm) across. Plants withstand drought well. Superior cultivars are 'Major', 'Perry's White' and 'Bicolor'. Split the crown every few years, discarding the old center and replanting the vigorous outer sections. Root cuttings can be taken in winter. The flowers can be dried.

Chelone obliqua z 4
Turtle's head or shell flower
An intriguing plant on account of its deep-lilac flowers, which are curiously-shaped, hooded and weather-resistant. They stand out well against the dark green, clearly-veined lance-shaped leaves held in opposite pairs all along the 3ft (90cm)-tall stems. This upright perennial is occasionally found in its two rarer forms: *C. alba* with its white flowers and the dwarf clone 'Praecox Nana'. Plants need moist soil in light shade to do well. Propagation is through spring or autumn division, seed or soft tip cuttings taken during the summer.

Echinacea purpurea *(below)* z 3
Purple or hedgehog coneflower
A native of the central and eastern United States, this sturdy plant has single daisy flowers with raised mahogany-colored discs surrounded by purplish-pink to palest pink drooping rays. They can reach 6in (15cm) across on stems 2-5ft (60cm-1.5m) high. The best cultivars include 'Robert Bloom', with deep crimson rays and orange discs, and 'White Swan', with pure white rays. They are useful for flower arrangements and attractive to bees and butterflies. Need a sunny position.

Eupatorium purpureum z 3
Joe Pye weed
Not the showiest of plants but useful for the back of a border or in a damp position where space is not restricted. The dark, dull green lanceolate leaves are up to 1ft (30cm) long and are held in whorls of three or five. The stiff stems stand 4-6ft (1.2-1.8m) and are topped by large panicles of pink to purple flowers that last from mid-summer well into autumn. Fertile, moist soil is most suitable although clumps can become very large in ideal conditions and need splitting regularly.

Tricyrtis hirta **'Variegata'** z 5
Hairy toad lily
The golden edged leaves of this plant make it attractive for much of the year but it is most striking in autumn when strange upright flowers appear in clusters in the axils of the top leaves. They are spotted and speckled with dark purple and last for up to three weeks. It reaches 1-3ft (30-90cm) with a spread of 18in (45cm). Grow in partial shade. Prefers moist, humus-rich deep soil on the acid side which never allows the rhizomatous roots to dry out.

Winter flowering

Bergenia **'Abendglut'** z 4
Elephant's ears
Also known as 'Evening Glow', this hardy evergreen perennial will flower in late winter if the weather is mild. It makes good ground cover, forming rosettes of crinkly, shiny purple-tinted leaves, with the tinting becoming more pronounced during winter. This cultivar reaches a height of 9in (23cm) and spreads to 1ft (30cm). The deep crimson-magenta, semi-double flowers appear in dense heads on stout stalks. Plants will grow in sun or shade and can be divided in spring.

Erica carnea *(below)* z 6
The winter-flowering heather is a woody evergreen perennial which can flower from early winter to spring. To achieve this choose reliable cultivars such as 'Springwood Pink' and 'Springwood White', both of which have large sweetly-scented flowers; for deeper red-mauve blooms grow 'Vivellii' and 'Ruby Glow'. Plants form dense mats of dark evergreen foliage which set off the bright papery flowers. They grow to 6-12in (15-30cm) high, spreading to 2ft (60cm); excellent for raised beds.

Erysimum **'Bowles' Mauve'** z 6
Also listed as *Cheiranthus* 'Bowles' Mauve', in a warm spot this bushy, evergreen perennial wallflower will flower from early spring to summer. It produces shoots up to 2½ft (75cm) high, which are topped with spikes of small, deep mauve flowers. The leaves are dark green, narrow and lance-shaped, some plants having a gray-green hue. Plants will not survive severe winters, so propagate by taking softwood cuttings in summer and overwintering them in a frame or cold greenhouse. They succeed best in alkaline soil.

For foliage

Helleborus niger z 3
Christmas rose
Protection from winter rains and wind is needed to get the best from this plant. It will flourish in a shaded position in moist soil which never dries out. Flowers appear in winter, if the weather is not severe, but are easily spoiled by bad weather. Each one is creamy-white, made up of an intermediate whorl of petal-like tepals surrounding a central cluster of yellow stamens. They grow on 1ft (30cm)-tall stems above clumps of dark green, leathery evergreen leaves. Divide plants in spring or sow the seed.

Iris unguicularis *(above)* z 8
Winter iris
Also listed as *I. stylosa*, the winter iris will produce flowers continuously from late autumn until spring. The delicate flowers are lilac with yellow centers and smell of primroses. Plants form a dense carpet of grassy evergreen leaves. They grow best at the base of a south- or west-facing wall, forming quite large clumps, 8in (20cm) tall. Two good cultivars are 'Walter Butt' and 'Mary Barnard'. To propagate, lift and divide the rhizomes. Plants take a few seasons to become established.

Sarcococca ruscifolia z 7
This frost-hardy sarcococca has shiny green leaves which somewhat resemble those of camellias. The extremely fragrant white flowers cover the stem and branches in late winter and early spring. They are followed by red fruits. A very slow-growing plant, it will eventually make 3 × 3ft (90 × 90cm). A single cut branch will perfume a whole room. Propagate by semi-ripe cuttings in summer. This evergreen, upright, arching plant is a great asset in the winter gardening.

Acorus calamus **'Variegatus'** z 7
Sweet flag
The sword-like leaves of this marginal water plant smell like oranges when crushed. A semi-evergreen perennial, it forms thick clumps of tough leaves which are green with creamy-white margins. Early in the season the young leaves are often tinged with pink. Clumps grow to 2½ft (75cm) tall and spread to around 2ft (60cm). Plants need to be in 10in (25cm) or more of water, in sun. To prevent them becoming invasive, lift and divide them every three to four years in autumn.

Alchemilla mollis *(below)* z 3
Lady's mantle
Beaded with droplets of glistening water around their crinkled edges, the pale green leaves can be a beautiful sight early in the morning. This low-growing perennial makes good ground cover, reaching a height and spread of 20in (50cm), less on poor soils. In summer the plants are covered in a haze of tiny lime green flowers which have large conspicuous calyces. Plants grow well in all but the wettest soils. Trim after flowering; divide in spring or autumn.

Anthericum liliago z 3
St Bernard's lily
An upright-growing perennial with long, narrow grayish-green leaves in tight clumps. Plants grow to a height of around 2ft (60cm), spreading to 1ft (30cm). In early summer they produce tall racemes of white trumpet-shaped flowers like tiny lilies. The seed heads are attractive in autumn, while the foliage adds color to a border through the entire season. Plants need full sun and moist fertile soil which does not dry out. Increase by transplanting self-sown seedlings or by division in spring.

Artemisia absinthium **'Lambrook Silver'** *(below)* z 4
A lovely cultivar derived from *A. absinthium*, which has masses of finely dissected, aromatic silvery-gray leaves. Plants grow as bushy perennials, needing protection during winter in exposed gardens. Vigorous bushes can reach 2½ft (75cm) in height and spread to 2ft (60cm), making a bold silver statement in the summer border. The flowers are insignificant. Give these plants a warm sunny spot in fertile soil, trimming them to shape in early spring. To increase, take cuttings in summer.

Athyrium filix-femina z 3
Lady fern
Although this fern prefers moist soil, it will grow in dryer conditions. It dies back to a scaly crown during winter; new fresh green fronds unfold in spring and have a fine lacy appearance. Plants reach 3 × 2ft (90 × 60cm) and continue to look good until late summer when the foliage withers. Remove fronds as they die back. Increase by division of larger crowns in autumn and winter. Add humus-rich material before planting in a shady spot in a border.

Euphorbia characias wulfenii z 8
In their first season plants produce clusters of gray-green leaves, followed in their second season by enormous dense spikes of yellow-green flowers with collar-like, pale green bracts. These impressive heads are carried on 5ft (1.5m)-tall stems. Through winter the foliage takes on a bluish tinge. Best planted in full sun in moist but free-draining soil, plants will tolerate light shade. Take basal cuttings in summer, allowing the cut end to dry before insertion, or divide in spring or autumn. Avoid skin contact with the sap.

Bellis perennis
For carpet bedding, edging, or for filling in gaps along borders the English daisy is ideal. Flowers appear from mid-spring onwards and can be rosy red, bright pink, white or crimson. Blooms last for many weeks. Plants are grown as hardy biennials, although they are actually perennial and can be replanted when taken from bedding displays. Sow seed in early summer outdoors and transplant to beds in autumn. Deadhead to maintain vigor. For large flowers grow 'Monstrosa' and 'Super Enorma', and for daintier plants 'Pomponette'.

Cheiranthus cheiri *(above)*
Wallflower
A wonderfully scented hardy biennial for a spring bedding scheme. The narrow, dark green leaves are topped by clusters of four-petaled flowers in shades of yellow, orange and red which open during spring into early summer. Raise plants from seed sown outdoors in summer and move to their flowering positions in autumn. They are susceptible to club root disease and should be grown in fertile well-limed soil. 'Orange Bedder' and 'Scarlet Bedder' are trusted cultivars.

Kochia scoparia tricophylla
Burning bush or summer cypress
Used widely as a dot plant for its striking summer foliage, the leaves of this half-hardy annual are feathery and mature plants resemble a conifer in shape. In autumn the foliage turns bronze-red. Plants can grow to 3ft (90cm) and need sun; well-drained sandy soil is best. They are rapid growers which can be clipped over if they become too large. Raise plants under glass planting out after spring frosts, 2ft (60cm) apart.

Mesembryanthemum criniflorum *(above)*
Livingstone daisy
More correctly named *Dorotheanthus bellidiformis*, there are few summer-flowering bedding plants to rival the large, glistening daisy-like flowers of this half-hardy succulent annual. In addition, the narrow fleshy leaves and stems have an attractive sparkling coating. Seeds are usually bought as mixtures – red, white, yellow, orange and many intermediates. Plant after frosts, 8in (20cm) apart. Plants love dry, sunny positions.

***Mimulus* cvs** *(above)*
Monkey flower
Its strength as a bedding plant is being able to provide red and yellow color in shaded or dark spots such as on patios which face north; it also suits hanging baskets. Plants are raised under glass in spring and planted out after frosts. They will flower in as little as seven weeks from sowing, producing blotched and spotted trumpet-like flowers. Plants can be up to 1ft (30cm) tall and should be spaced around 9in (22cm) apart in damp soil. 'Yellow velvet' is illustrated.

Tagetes patula*; *T. erecta
French marigold; African marigold
T. patula carries a mass of single flowers on plants growing up to 9in (22cm) high, while *T. erecta* is a larger plant, up to 2ft (60cm) high, with fewer but much larger, usually double flowers. The flowers appear throughout the summer and are bright orange or yellow in color. The mid-green pinnate leaves have a strong pungent aroma when rubbed. Plant in spring after frosts and remove all flower buds for a few weeks after that. *T. patula* 'Naughty Marietta' is an old trusted favorite.

Salvia splendens *(above)*
Scarlet sage
One of the most reliable summer bedding plants for red flowers. This tender perennial is grown as a half-hardy annual and is planted after frosts. The dense racemes of tubular scarlet flowers appear from mid-summer providing color right into autumn. Plants grow to 1ft (30cm) in height and should be spaced 1-1½ft (30-45cm) apart. 'Blaze of Fire' is a popular scarlet cultivar, while 'Laser Purple' has mauve flowers. White strains are also available. Plants grow well in most soils in sun.

Viola × wittrockiana
With careful planning pansies can be in flower in every season. All the modern strains and hybrids come from this species. Universal, Multiflora and Floral Dance are the hardiest and most reliable strains. Plants are treated either as hardy annuals or biennials. Sow plants for winter and spring bedding displays in early summer and plant out in autumn. Colors include blue, purple, yellow, white, orange and red, with bicolored and blotched forms. The petals are edible. Protect from slugs.

For cutting

Asperula azurea setosa
Most asperulas are perennial plants, this dainty hardy annual being a welcome exception. Seed is best sown where the plants are to flower, and the young seedlings not disturbed by transplanting. Autumn sowing is usual, for an early spring flowering. Plants grow to a height of 2in (5cm), and being quite small fit easily into any bare patches in borders or on rock gardens. The small green narrow leaves are studded with clusters of tiny four-petaled pale blue flowers which have the scent of new-mown hay.

Callistephus chinensis
Annual aster or China aster
This plant can provide a welcome crop of flowers for cutting in late summer. The flowers come in many forms; some are the typical daisy-type, others are double or have plumed petals, while still others resemble small chrysanthemums. Treat plants as half-hardy annuals, planting after the most severe frosts. They grow to ½-3ft (15-90cm) depending on cultivar. Never grow asters in the same spot year after year to avoid aster wilt, a soil disease.

Cosmos bipinnatus
Cosmos
With its large blooms and delicate feathery foliage, cosmos is an easy annual to grow, providing a useful supply of flowers for cutting through the summer. Plants will bloom until the first frosts if deadheaded regularly. Tall cultivars (up to 3ft (90cm) in height) may need staking, but all will grow well on poor but well-drained, preferably sandy soil. Seed is usually sold as mixtures; Sensation is a tall mixture with white, red and pink flowers.

Helichrysum bracteatum
Straw flower
This is one of the most popular "everlasting" flowers grown for its papery heads. What appear to be petals are in fact bracts which come in a range of colors including pinks, mauve, red, yellow and white. Cut the stems just before the flowers are fully open and hang to dry. Easy to grow, this hardy annual can be sown outdoors in spring or raised earlier under glass and planted out. Hot Bikini and Bright Bikini are good mixtures. Plants grow to 1-3ft (30-90cm) at a spacing of 1ft (30cm) apart.

Gilia capitata
With its feathery leaves and rounded heads of pale lavender flowers, this branching hardy annual is ideal for cutting. Twiggy supports may help the more lax-growing plants on windy sites. Seed can be sown *in situ* in autumn or in spring, or under glass for planting out later into rich, fertile soil in full sun. Flowers will continue to be produced into early autumn on well-grown plants if cut regularly. Space or thin plants to 8in (20cm) apart. They will grow up to 18in (45cm) tall. Plants do not respond well to high humidity.

Moluccella laevis *(above)*
Bells of Ireland or shell flower
The most conspicuous part of this plant is the large, pale green, bell-like calyx surrounding the small white, tubular flowers. These cluster all the way up the attractive, erect stems along with the rounded leaves. As the flowers fade, interest is maintained by the green calyces, making this a much sought after cut flower for summer. Plants are half-hardy and fast-growing, needing rich soil and full sun. Sow seed under glass in early spring or *in situ* after frosts, planting 1ft (30cm) apart.

Nigella damascena
Love-in-a-mist
The flowers of this hardy annual emerge through its finely divided foliage. Most seed gives rise to plants with a mixture of pink, white, blue and lavender flowers, and sowing should be staggered because the flowering season is short. The stems are useful as a fresh cut flower in summer, and the seed heads can be used as dried flowers. Enrich the soil with compost before sowing, which can take place in autumn or spring. Plants grow up to 2ft (60cm) tall.

Ornamental Grasses
What they lack in color, ornamental grasses make up for in fine textures and sounds. Quaking grass, *Briza maxima*, is perhaps the most popular with its papery lanterns rustling in the breeze; while the half-hardy Job's tears, *Coix lacryma-jobi*, has pearly seeds which appear among the reed-like foliage. Other species include hare's tail, *Lagurus ovatus*, and cloud grass, *Agrostis nebulosa*. Sow or plant in full sun in well-drained soil, with 1ft (30cm) between plants, or sow small patches to fill gaps. Plants self-seed freely.

Scabiosa
Sweet scabious or pincushion flower
Similar to the cornflower and useful as a summer cut flower, most modern strains of sweet scabious are derived from *S. atropurpurea* which is a hardy annual. Most flowers are double and available in pinks, reds, mauves and white. Plants suffer in prolonged wet weather. Sow the seed outdoors in autumn or spring, or raise under glass and plant out 1ft (30cm) apart. Plants reach up to 3ft (1m) in height if grown in slightly alkaline well-drained soil. Single color varieties are avilable.

Zinnia *(above)*
The modern types of *Zinnia* have complex parentage giving rise to flowers which can be as large as dahlias or small and button-like (Lilliput miniatures are shown). The flowers are daisy-like, single, semi-double or double, and come in a huge range of colors. A compost-enriched soil and full sun are vital. Plants grow to ½-2ft (15-60cm). Space plants 1ft (30cm) apart when planting out the young plants raised in spring under glass. They will not stand frosts or prolonged, cool wet weather.

BULBS AND CORMS

Bulbs are often associated with the dramatic and vibrantly colorful displays seen in public open spaces, but they can also be enjoyed in the garden where they can be put to many different uses. Bulbs reliably come into flower within one season and associate well with bedding plants and in a mixed border, either in the bright sunshine or light shade, throughout much of the year. As a group, they are versatile and reliable.

All bulbs require an annual resting period. This may be during the summer, as is the case for the spring-flowering species which most commonly originate from areas with a Mediterranean climate. In the winter many tender summer-flowering species, which require hot-house conditions to grow out of their natural habitat (or must be lifted in the autumn before the frosts and kept in a cool, dark frost-free place throughout the winter), are dormant. Other bulbs, such as the sweetly scented *Acidanthera murielae*, are usually cheap enough to be able to be replanted annually, after the risk of frost has passed, as one would bedding plants from the garden center.

Throughout the resting period the bulbs disappear under ground, leaving gaps which need to be furnished with other plants. This is most noticeable with

Left: The pink *Cyclamen hederifolium* and the white variety *album* do well in dry shade, as here at the base of a blue atlantic cedar. The cyclamen, which flowers in autumn and self-seeds readily, has the peculiarity of sending out roots from the top of the corm. It benefits from a mulch of leaf mold after flowering.

hardy late winter- and spring-flowering species. There are several different techniques of covering the spaces while allowing the bulbs to proceed through their cycle without damage and to increase steadily.

Many winter- and spring-flowering bulbs look at home in a border that is shaded by tall deciduous trees or shrubs, where they come into flower before the leaf canopy becomes too dense. Here, daffodils, winter aconites, snowdrops, cyclamen, bluebells and trilliums will thrive along with shade-loving herbaceous foliage plants such as hostas, geraniums and alchemilla which gradually cover the dying foliage, or evergreen ground cover plants such as ivy, erythronium and pachysandra. As a rule, in permanent bulb plantings it is useful to plant them very deep so that they are not damaged by any weeding or lifting of herbaceous plants that need dividing.

On a grander scale, all these plants can be naturalized in a woodland setting in great drifts. Alternatively it is possible to grow many species of daffodils, crocuses, the summer snowflake and snake's head fritillary in rough grass. The important thing to remember is that the flowers must rise above the grass to have any effect (so the later they bloom, the taller they

Left: Early-flowering narcissi and chionodoxas brighten an acid border that is suitably planted with heathers and rhododendrons.

Right: Bulbs are ideal for creating large drifts of color in spring. These squills flourish in the shade of a winter-flowering cherry (*Prunus* × *subhirtella* 'Autumnalis'). Recommended precursors for them are winter aconites, snowdrops and *Arum italicum* mormoratum.

Galanthus nivalis *(above)* z 5
Common snowdrop
Along with *Eranthis hyemalis*, this early-flowering bulb signals the start of spring. The flowers hang like small white drops on green stalks. It is best seen in bold drifts and benefits from being in the shade cast by trees or shrubs, especially if they are deciduous. It can push up through low-growing ground cover plants. For unusual yellow and white coloring grow 'Lutescens'. Ideally, plant snowdrops in heavy soil straight after flowering.

***Ipheion uniflorum* 'Wisley Blue'** z 5
(above)
A South American bulb needing a sunny position and freely-draining soil: it does best at the base of a south- or west-facing wall, or at the front of a border. The soft blue flowers are star-shaped and face straight up to the sky, having a sweet soapy fragrance. The pale green grassy leaves flop loosely below the flowers and smell of garlic if rubbed. Plant bulbs 2in (5cm) deep in autumn or lift and divide large clumps. Plants reach a height of 5-8in (13-20cm) and make useful ground cover.

Ornithogalum umbellatum z 6
Star of Bethlehem
This plant is grown for its white flowers, which are star-shaped and appear some time after the narrow basal leaves are formed. Each flower is translucent and up to 1¼in (3cm) long, held on spikes 6-14in (15-35cm) tall. Plants will form drifts when established in grassed areas so long as the soil is well drained. They prefer partial shade and the bulbs should be planted in autumn. For best effect grow on grassy banks where the flowers can be seen. They may be invasive.

Scilla peruviana *(above)* z 7
This native of the Mediterranean needs a warm sunny spot and moist soil. The conical flowers heads appear in early summer, each with up to 50 flattish blue-violet flowers. Each head is ¾-1¼in (2-3cm) across on a stem 4-10in (10-25cm) tall. At the base are a cluster of narrow leaves. Propagate by division in late summer; plant bulbs shallowly in autumn or spring. *S. tubergeniana* flowers in early spring with pale blue, dark-veined flowers and *S. siberica* has bell-shaped, deep blue flowers.

Tulips z 7
Apart from spring bedding displays, tulips can be put to good use in mixed borders, where they provide a bold splash of color early in the season interplanted with other early perennials or spring-flowering shrubs. Many of the older types look good at the base of a stone wall and will blend in well in borders containing wall-trained fruit. For double flowers choose the yellow 'Monte Carlo' or for white, 'Snow Queen'; while for flowers with crested and ruffled petals 'Red Parrot' and 'Flaming Parrot' are ideal.

Mixed border

Acidanthera murielae z 8
Also listed as *Gladiolus callianthus*, this beautiful plant adds a touch of elegance to any border. The exotic-looking flowers have six white petals with deep purple throats and are carried in groups of about ten on stems up to 3ft (90cm) tall. They appear in early autumn. Plant the corms in soil-based potting compost in autumn and keep in a cold frame, planting them out in a warm, sunny position the following spring. They must be lifted again before the first frosts in the autumn, or new bulbs must be bought in each year.

Allium giganteum z 5
A member of the ornamental onion family, this plant will reach 4ft (1.2m) in height and has large rounded heads of densely packed lilac-pink flowers. The attractive gray-blue leaves are susceptible to damage by late spring frosts, so a warm sheltered spot is desirable. The large size of the flower heads makes a bold statement in a purple, blue or gray border. Plants need well-drained soil and the large bulbs need a handful of coarse grit scattered around them at planting time.

Crinum × powellii *(above)* z 7
Although winter frosts will cut back the leaves of this South African native, the bulbs can be left planted outdoors year round in warm climates. Plant the bulbs with their necks just above soil level in a warm and sunny position, ideally at the base of a west- or south-facing wall. The strong, 3ft (90cm)-tall stems emerge in late summer with up to ten trumpet-shaped fragrant flowers. 'Roseum' has pink flowers, 'Album' white. Cover the leaves if late frosts are likely. Plants spread to 2ft (60cm). Plant fresh bulbs in spring in well-drained soil.

***Crocosmia* 'Lucifer'** *(below)* z 7
Montbretia
This hybrid will create an eye-catching display of large fire-red flowers during late summer and autumn. Other hybrids include 'Spitfire', with its large fiery orange flowers, and the darker orange 'Emberglow'. Plants grow to 1-3ft (60-90cm) high and have stiff sword-like leaves. Plant corms in spring in well-drained soil in an open sunny position. Divide large clumps every few years, just after flowering or in early spring. Plants go well with late-flowering perennials, such as *Helenium autumnale*.

Curtonus paniculatus z 8
Also listed as *Antholyza paniculata* and *Cyrtonus paniculata*, this close relative of the crocosmias has been hybridized with *Crocosmia masonorum* to produce many fine cultivars which are usually listed under *Crocosmia*. However, it is a fine plant in its own right, reaching a height of 4ft (1.2m) with attractive zig-zagging sprays of tubular scarlet flowers. The leaves are erect, sword-shaped and pleated along their length. Plants need a well-drained soil and a sunny position.

Eremurus stenophyllus bungei z 6
Foxtail lily or king's spear
Prized as a border plant for its elegant spikes of cup-shaped flowers held on a 5-6ft (1.5-1.8m)-tall flowering stem, this perennial needs a sunny growing position and well-drained soil to succeed. The flowers are yellow, turning darker at the base of the spike as they fade. The leaves are linear and form a loose basal rosette. The roots are fleshy and finger-like. It is necessary to protect early growth from frost with straw or sacking. In winter, the crown of the bulb should be mounded over with sharp sand or ash to keep it dry.

Fritillaria imperialis *(above)* z 5
Crown imperial
A truly majestic spring-flowering bulb. The flowers appear on stems up to 3ft (90cm) tall and hang like bells below an apical tuft of green leafy bracts. 'Aurora' has orange flowers and 'Rubra' bronze-red. The stems are partly clothed with mid-green leaves. Plant the tubers on their sides in spring, 8in (20cm) deep, in humus-rich but well-drained soil. Propagate by division of clumps after the foliage has died away or by removal of offsets.

Gladiolus byzantinus *(above)* z 7
Sword lily
This gladiolus is a native of the Mediterranean and has striking reddish-purple flowers carried on slightly arching stems which grow up to 3ft (90cm) tall. The flowers are set against bright green, narrow leaves. Plants rarely require staking and may even be naturalized in grass providing it is not too vigorous. Plant corms in autumn in fertile but well-drained soil. The sword lily never fails to look good when grown in the company of *Cistus* × *purpurea* or *Rosmarinus officinalis*.

Lilium candidum z 6
Madonna lily
Succeeding on alkaline soil, this beautiful plant grows to 3ft (90cm) and has strongly fragrant, pure white flowers. It benefits from soil that has been enriched with compost or well rotted manure, the bulbs being planted shallowly and away from other lilies if possible. Growth begins in the autumn, the crown of basal leaves staying green through winter but then dying away as the flowering shoots emerge. The flowers are funnel-shaped, 2-3in (5-8cm) long, with five to twenty flowers on each stem in summer. The lance-shaped leaves are scattered along the stems.

Narcissus z 5
These bulbous plants can be guaranteed to add early color to a mixed border. While the smaller species narcissi tend to be lost in larger borders, many of the newer cultivars are perfectly suited to them. It is best to plant the bulbs in clumps, preferably in the spaces that will be covered by herbaceous plants later in the season. Underplanting of deciduous shrubs can also work well. 'February Gold' has large, slightly reflexed petals; those of 'Thalia' are creamy-white.

Triteleia laxa z 8
Also known as *Brodiaea laxa*, this tender plant produces its funnel-shaped flowers in early summer. The flowers are carried in a large loose umbel, ranging from pale to deep purplish-blue, with each one being held erect and growing up to 2in (5cm) in length. The stem will reach a height of 20in (50cm) on a vigorous plant. Plant the corms during autumn in a sunny spot. The soil should be very well drained and dry out during summer. Propagate plants by seed or division. *T. hyacinthina* has white flowers which are sometimes tinged purple on thin stems.

Tulips z 5
Like daffodils, tulips are very useful early-flowering bulbs. For bright bold patches of color consider the larger flowered cultivars. However, there are several species of tulips which should not be overlooked because of their smaller size. For a clump of graceful flowers (red and white flushed with pink) grow the lady tulip, *Tulipa clusiana*. *T. tarda* has yellow and white flowers.

ROCK GARDEN PLANTS

The rock garden reached its apogee, in England, in the period spanning the latter part of the nineteenth century through to the First World War. At this time labor, in comparison to materials and transport, was inexpensive and large amounts of money were expended on creating monumental rock gardens. Rocks were imported from mountainous regions and as many gardeners as necessary were employed to carry out the weeding needed to prevent the establishment of perennial weeds which can be very difficult to remove from between the rocks. The subsequent demise of the monumental rock garden was due in large part to the increase in the cost of labor: unkempt growth went against the spirit of precision and order inherent in rockery design.

The advent of environment-friendly non-persistent herbicides (sold under various trade names), that are deactivated as soon as they hit the ground, have made the control of weeds in a rock garden less of a problem. While taking extreme care not to touch the cultivated plants, weeds can be painted with one of these herbicides which kills them off *in situ* without running the risk of leaving bits of root behind or disturbing the root system of the rock plants. This should be done in conjuction with ensuring that the soil used is free

Right: A naturally sloping and open site is ideal for a rock garden. Dwarf shrubs, such as hebes and some willows, add weight to a planting of geraniums, hypericums, pinks, rock roses, saxifrages, sedums and other perennials that thrive in sunny and free-draining conditions.

Left: The cool, moist cracks at the base of a rockery have been colonized by a mauve campanula, creeping jenny, a lungwort and a pink sedum.

Below: On an impressive limestone rockery the pale yellow of a large broom at the back with the vibrant, spring colors of alyssum, purple aubrieta and saxifrage.

from perennial weeds before planting and that it is covered with plants or mulch as quickly as possible to prevent new seeds from germinating.

Rock gardens are best suited to informally designed gardens and look most convincing on a large scale. Unfortunately the cost of construction and the lack of space in many modern gardens often leads to very awkward-looking mounds of inferior stones appearing in the middle of a carefully kept lawn. However, there are many ways of creating the right environment for growing rock garden plants, which are for the most part alpines, in a restricted space whether in a formal or informal setting.

In the smallest spaces sinks and troughs can be easily accommodated and are particularly well suited in areas devoid of soil such as patios. Small rocks can be incorporated to create a miniature landscape and dwarf conifers can be used to give structure to the composition while the rock garden plants spill over the edge of the container.

Raised beds are another possibility and can be constructed to any shape. Large numbers of plants can be grown, both in the soil within the bed and in the cracks of the walls around it. By including miniature bulbs in the planting schemes it is possible to have color throughout most of the season. In addition, cultivation and appreciation of the plants is possible with a minimum of bending and backache.

Dry stone walls or the top of brick walls, whether boundary or retaining walls, can also be the home for many trailing rock garden plants, as can the interstices between paving slabs of patios and courtyards, provided these have been laid on sand. In all these situations the planting will be most effective if the plants are allowed to find their own niche and self-seed, colonizing the structure or surface.

All these growing environments have one characteristic in common. They all drain freely which is essential to all plants that have their natural habitat in mountainous regions. Whatever the situation it is advisable to incorporate coarse drainage material in the base of the container or rock garden, followed by a layer of inverted blocks of sod and finally a mix of two parts soil to one each of sharp sand and coarse peat. An open site with plenty of light is also necessary for successful cultivation as is keeping the plants dry when they are dormant, a period in nature when they are either protected, in winter, by a layer of dry snow or, in summer, baked by the sun. In the latter case it is best to grow the most difficult and sensitive plants in a scree or even under glass.

Above: A dicentra and a dwarf geranium are among the plants that have seeded themselves at the base of these rocks. Great patience is needed to get plants to seed where they are wanted as tiny plants are easily washed away before they are fully established. Often the best strategy is to position the first plants on flat ground nearby and let them self-seed naturally among the adjacent cracks.

Left: Diascias, rock roses and violas are among the plants clothing the large blocks of stone in this garden. Large pieces of rock can be costly and need to be positioned carefully if they are to look natural. A free-draining compost needs to be incorporated during building.

For flowers

Adonis amurensis z 3

The flowers of this charming perennial open from late winter onwards: often the bronze-green shoots can be seen pushing through the snow. Each bloom resembles a buttercup and is borne singly at the end of a shoot. After flowering, the finely cut leaves expand, giving the plant an eventual height of 1ft (30cm), before it dies away at the end of summer. Plant in well-drained humus-rich soil in late summer away from baking sun. To avoid mud splash on the flowers, surround the plant with stone chippings. Very hardy.

Alyssum saxatile *(above)* z 6

Gold dust

Sometimes known as *Aurinia saxatile*, this hardy evergreen perennial forms low mounds of growth with small, hairy gray-green leaves. In spring it is covered by bright golden-yellow flowers, and is the natural partner to *Aubrieta*. Plants reach a height of 8-12in (20-30cm) and should be clipped over after flowering to stop them becoming too large. They need full sun and well-drained soil. Increase by sowing seed in autumn or from softwood cuttings.

Androsace sempervivoides z 5

A fully hardy, compact and cushion-forming evergreen perennial with leathery, oblong leaves. In spring smallish heads of four to ten flowers appear, which are flat, pinkish with yellow eyes turning red. The plants need sun and well-drained soil, and grow up to 3in (8cm) high with a spread of about 1ft (30cm). Propagate in summer by taking tip cuttings or by removing young stolons, or in autumn by sowing seed. *A. sarmentosa* (z 3) has bright pink flowers with yellow eyes and is good for all but the wettest areas.

Anthemis cupaniana *(above)* z 8

With its finely cut, dense silvery foliage and small, daisy-like white flower heads with yellow centers, this evergreen perennial is an excellent choice in a warm climate. The flowers appear from early summer to autumn. The plants form spreading carpets, grow to a height of 1ft (30cm) with similar spread, and need clipping over after flowering. In winter the foliage turns green. Increase by taking basal cuttings from late summer through to spring. Plant in well-drained soil in full sun.

Arabis caucasica *(above)* z 3

An ideal choice for sturdy ground cover in a large rock garden, this evergreen mat-forming perennial is very hardy. It has small, oval mid-green leaves and four-petalled white or pink fragrant flowers in late spring and summer. Plants reach a height of 6in (15cm) and are at home on dry banks in thin soil. They should be trimmed over after the flowers have faded. 'Variegata' has cream-splashed leaf margins; 'Plena' has double white flowers; 'Rosabella' is deep pink. Propagate by seed in autumn or by softwood cuttings in summer.

Armeria maritima *(below)* z 3

Thrift, sea thrift or sea pink

In the wild, the evergreen hummocks (1ft (30cm) high) of this popular perennial cling to rocky outcrops along coastlines. In the rock garden, it should be sited in full sun, where the soil is very well drained. During spring and summer the hummocks are studded with globular flowers, ranging from lilac through pink to white: deadhead to prolong flowering. 'Vindictive' has rose-pink flowers. To propagate, divide plants in spring or take semi-hardwood cuttings in late summer.

Aubrieta deltoidea *(below)* z 7

Purple rock cress

In spring the dense mats of this evergreen plant are smothered in flowers – of varying shades of blue, red, purple or pink – which look supurb next to those of *Alyssum saxatile*. Its spreading foliage makes excellent ground cover. Plants will flourish on dry chalky soils and in walls and other crevices, so long as the drainage is good. After flowering, cut hard back to maintain shape and vigor. Propagate by taking tip cuttings in spring, or by layering the plants during the summer.

Campanula carpatica z 3
Bellflower
Ideal for the rock garden, this low-growing hardy perennial reaches a height of 3-4in (8-10cm) and spreads to 1ft (30cm). Its branching stems carry toothed, round-oval leaves, above which, during summer, the wide, bell-shaped, blue or white flowers appear. Named forms include the deep violet 'Jewel', 'Turbinata' which is lavender, and the pure white 'Bressingham White'. Plants need moist, well-drained soil, in sun or light shade. Divide in autumn or spring, or take softwood or basal cuttings in summer, or plant seed.

Chiastophyllum oppositifolium z 6
Also called *Cotyledon simplicifolia*, this succulent trailing perennial has an evergreen spreading habit and large, oblong, serrated fleshy leaves. During spring and early summer small yellow flowers open on very distinctive, arching sprays 6-8in (15-20cm) tall. It is at home in the cracks and crevices between rocks, but needs some shade and moist soil to do well. Take cuttings during summer using side shoots.

Dryas octopetala z 1
Mountain avens
The dark green, leathery leaves of this prostrate-growing evergreen perennial are held close to the ground. During late spring and early summer creamy-white, cup-shaped flowers appear just above the leaves, followed by attractive fluffy seed heads. Plants have a woody base, grow to only 2in (6cm) tall and make excellent ground cover, forming large patches in time. Choose a sunny spot and well-drained, gritty soil with some leaf mold added. Sow the seeds when fresh or take semi-ripe cuttings during the summer months. The fine *D.* × *suendermannii* is similar with pale cream flowers that open flat.

Erinus alpinus z 4
Fairy foxglove
Sow this dainty semi-evergreen perennial in spring, after which it will self-seed readily without becoming a problem. The plants need light, well-drained soil and a sunny position. They grow to only 6in (15cm) tall when in flower; clusters of pink, starry flowers rising above the small mid-green leaves. 'Albus' has white flowers, while those of 'Mrs Charles Boyle' are large and pink.

Gentiana sino-ornata z 6
A native of Tibet, the rich blue flowers of this hardy autumn-flowering gentian are a very impressive sight. They are borne singly above a cushion of fine grassy evergreen leaves, each 2in (5cm)-long trumpet having a green-striped throat. When in flower, the plants stand 2in (5cm) high and can spread to 1ft (30cm). Plant into moist, acid soil that is well charged with leaf mold, preferably in a spot that is shaded around midday. Propagate by dividing in spring every two to three years.

Helianthemum nummularium z 4
(above)
Sun rose or rock rose
One of the most colorful and reliable of all rock garden plants, this evergreen sub-shrub forms a spreading prostrate mat of growth covered in small, single rose-like flowers throughout the summer. Plants grow to 6in (15cm) high and spread to 2ft (60cm). They need full sun and free-draining, gritty soil that is not too rich. In autumn cut back to a few inches from the ground. For gray foliage and large pink flowers grow 'Wisley Pink'; 'Beech Park Red' has crimson blooms; 'Wisley Primrose' has yellow flowers. Propagate from non-flowering shoots in late summer.

Hedyotis michauxii z 3
Also listed as *Houstonia serpyllifolia*, this vigorous creeping perennial forms dense mats of spreading stems which root readily at the nodes. The mid-green foliage is dotted with violet-blue star-shaped flowers from spring to early summer. Plants reach a height of 3in (8cm), spreading to 1ft (30cm). Ideally, the soil should be sandy with added leaf mold, to hold moisture, and shaded. Divide in spring or sow seed in autumn.

Lewisia cotyledon *(above)* z 6
A gem among rock garden plants, *Lewisia* needs the morning sun to show off its bright flowers that close soon after lunch, but must be shaded from the midday sun. The rosettes of evergreen spatulate leaves set off the 1ft (30cm)-tall panicles of pink to salmon flowers that age rose-red. It requires excellent drainage to thrive, particularly around the neck which is apt to wilt during the winter when growth stops, and even during wet periods in the summer; cracks in walls are ideal.

Saxifraga longifolia *(above)* z 6
This hardy saxifrage is a rosette-forming perennial with long, narrow leaves encrusted with lime, which makes them especially attractive. When the rosettes reach three to four years old they produce long, arching flowering shoots smothered in panicles of white flowers. The flowers appear in spring and summer, and then the rosettes die without leaving any offspring. For this reason plants must be raised from seed, sown in spring or autumn. They are ideal for cracks and crevices, and need well-drained, alkaline soil and full sun.

For foliage

Asplenium trichomanes *(below)* z 6
A dainty little fern suited to a limestone rock garden, where it will thrive in crannies, or planted in soil. It will tolerate full sun. It has slender tapering fronds (which should be removed once faded) with brown midribs carrying the bright green, rounded pinnae. The plant is semi-evergreen, often retaining most of its leaves through the winter. Plants grow to a height of 6in (15cm) spreading up to 1ft (30cm). Increase is by spores or more reliably by carefully dividing those clumps which have several crowns.

Bolax gummifera *(below)* z 4
Prized for its hard cushions of foliage made up of evergreen blue-green leaves held in tight rosettes, this plant rarely produces its insignificant yellow flowers. Plants reach a height of only 1in (2.5cm), spread slowly to 6in (15cm) and need humus-rich but well-drained soil in full sun. They are very hardy and most at home in a gritty scree garden. Propagate by rooting rosettes during summer. Work plenty of sharp stone chippings in around the crown to prevent rotting. *Sagina boydii* is similar, growing to only ½in (1cm).

Dryopteris cristata *(above)* z 5
Crested buckler fern
Moist conditions, such as are found next to a pond, suit this plant. It has light to mid-green fronds of two distinct types: sterile fronds which grow to 18in (45cm) in length and spread, and fertile spore-bearing fronds which can be 3ft (90cm) tall and stand fully erect. The latter, which have been likened to large shuttlecocks, give the fern a very distinctive appearance when planted in a group. Plants need some shade. Fading fronds should be removed regularly.

Sedum sieboldii **'Variegatum'** z 5
(above)
Also called *S. sieboldii* 'Foliis Medio-variegatis', this tuberous perennial has rounded fleshy leaves in whorls of three. They are blue-green splashed with cream, sometimes with reddish edges. The flowers are pink and star-shaped, opening during late summer. Plants reach a height of 4in (10cm) and spread to 8in (20cm). It is also a useful plant for the front of a mixed border. Needs fertile well-drained soil and full sun. Propagate by division or through softwood cuttings in summer.

Sedum spathulifolium **'Purpureum'** z 6
(below)
A purple-leaved form of the stonecrop, the leaves of this succulent perennial are spoon-shaped forming tight rosettes packed together on the plant. It produces mats or hummocks of growth to a height of 3in (8cm) and spreads up to 2ft (60cm). In summer, tiny yellow flowers appear in clusters: remove the flower heads in the following spring. Plants will tolerate some shade but prefer sun. Plant in well-drained soil and propagate by carefully detaching rooted rosettes.

Sempervivum tectorum *(below)* z 4
Houseleek
Traditionally grown on the tiled roofs of houses to give protection from lightning and witchcraft, this plant grows as tight rosettes of succulent leaves, each rosette being anything from ½-8in (1-20cm) across. The leaves are normally green, but can be flushed with shades of red, pink and purple. Pinkish flowers appear in summer. Plants need good drainage and full sun to thrive. 'Triste' has green leaves tipped with reddish-brown. Increase plants by detaching rooted rosettes and replanting.

PAVED GARDEN PLANTS

In both large and small gardens it is often appropriate to have a paved area, such as a patio, terrace or flight of steps. Here, container-grown plants can contribute significantly to the success of the garden, introducing splashes of color, architectural features, focal points and seasonal emphasis. They have the advantage that they can be moved around according to the mood and prevailing display of the moment.

There are also a number of plants that thrive in conditions where the soil is limited, poor and well drained, such as in the cracks between paving stones or in walls. For example, creeping thyme and chamomile can be used to soften the geometry of a paved area, as they will tolerate some walking on, while saxifrage and acaena are useful creeping around the edges. Erigeron and corydalis are suitable for colonizing cracks in walls and between steps, and tall plants such as verbascum make bold vertical statements.

Pots can be used to allow the inclusion of plants not suited to the soil in the garden (for example, camellias and rhododendrons in a garden where the soil is alkaline) or ones that have to be kept in frost-free conditions during the winter such as the sweetly-scented spidery-flowered bulbous hymenocallis.

Right: This decked courtyard contains numerous pot-grown, shade-tolerant plants, including impatiens, lamium and gardener's garters. Taller plants include a ginkgo, a willow (*Salix matsudana* 'Tortuosa') and a fig tree.

Left: Tender and hardy plants in carefully placed clusters of pots and individual containers do not obscure the decorative surface of bricks laid in a variety of patterns.

Below: Thymes and other tough, creeping plants occupy niches in the irregular paving of a sun-baked terrace on which a stone sink makes an attractive feature.

The importance of choosing the right container cannot be overstressed as it can make or break any aesthetic contribution the plant may bring to the garden. First, there is the style of the pot to consider, which should fit in with the chosen style of the garden. In a cottage garden, a mass of clay pots brimming over with flowering annuals and colorful bulbs will mingle happily with the exuberance of honeysuckles, roses, hollyhocks, phloxes and feverfew. In contrast, the recreation of a formal seventeenth-century garden will call for substantial containers of evergreen standards and topiary specimens displayed symmetrically about the main axes of the garden.

The containers may be of lead, stone or terracotta. There are many other materials available and much depends on the available resources, but it is better to have a few, well chosen containers than a host of second rate ones. Plastic pots may be light and cheap but should be hidden in wooden containers: marine ply stained dark green, black (which makes the vegetation stand out against it) or greeny-blue all work well. Alternatively, glazed containers created individually by potters that are in themselves pieces of art are an excellent choice as they would adorn the garden on their own or planted up.

The size of the container depends, within reason, on the size of the plant that is to be grown in it. It is

Left: Pansies and petunias form an underplanting beneath a mixture of shrubs – including trained cypresses, maples, pittosporums, roses and a yucca – grown in containers and raised beds that surround a small courtyard paved with stone.

Below: Pot-grown plants, including elaborately trained ivy, have been used as accents and focal points within the formal geometry of this garden, in which the beds are divided by gravel paths.

important to remember that any container-grown plant requires sufficient nutrients to keep it growing healthily throughout the season without becoming so vigorous that it outgrows the container. Most good quality proprietary composts should contain enough nutrients, but at the height of the season it may be necessary to supplement this once a week with some liquid fertilizer. Watering is the single most important task when looking after pot-grown plants. During the main growing period, when evaporation is at its height, this usually needs doing twice a day.

Bearing these growing requirements in mind, it can be said that almost anything can be grown in a pot as long as it is accepted that it may not be as long-lived as normal, or, in time, will outgrow the container. So small trees (or larger ones grown as bonsai), shrubs, fruit trees and climbers can be included in a scheme of container-grown plants. Those that in their natural habitat tolerate drought are often best adapted to pot conditions; for example, many Mediterranean plants including bays, box, *Rhamnus alaternus* and pyracantha. Many species that need moist, shady conditions, such as rhododendrons and camellias, often fail through lack of watering. Usually, the most successful container displays are mixes of annuals and/or bulbs, newly planted as the seasons change.

Between the paving

Acaena microphylla z 7
This charming native of New Zealand is prized more for its soft, burr-like scarlet seed heads, which glisten in the sun, than for its flowers. The plants form spreading evergreen mats of bronzed leaves, 1-2in (2.5-5cm) high. They prefer light soils in sun, needing only a few rooted shoots to establish quick-growing colonies. 'Blue Haze' grows slightly taller, with wonderful blue-gray foliage and reddish seed heads. Underplant with dwarf spring bulbs.

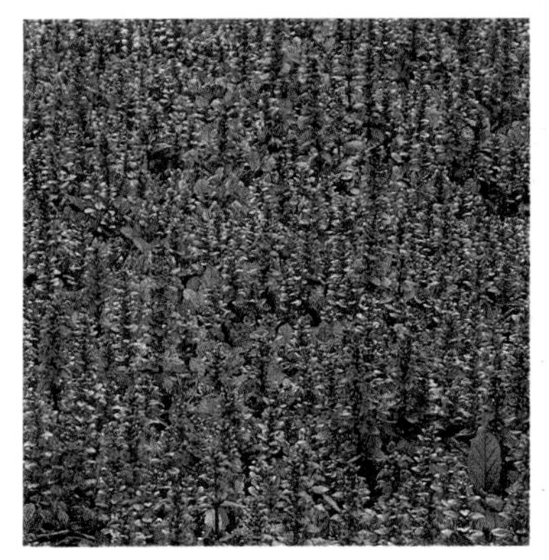

Ajuga reptans *(above)* z 4
Bugle
For paved areas in light shade where the soil is moist the bugle is perfect. Plants form an evergreen mat of dark green, glossy foliage with blue-purple flowers on elegant flower spikes in spring. In flower, the plants are up to 1ft (30cm) high and spread indefinitely unless checked. 'Burgundy Glow' has leaves variegated pink, purple, cream and green; 'Purpurea' has deep purple-bronze foliage. Bugles associate well with the small-flowered erigerons and blue-leaved grasses such as *Festuca glauca*. Remove rooted pieces of shoot to increase stocks.

Campanula portenschlagiana z 5
A vigorous bellflower which thrives in shade, needing moist soil. Plants produce a carpet of heart-shaped leaves covered from early summer to autumn with clusters of upright, open blue-violet flowers. At flowering the plants are 6in (15cm) tall, spreading up to 2ft (60cm). They are evergreen and hardy, but prone to slug damage in a wet spring. Plants self-seed and can become a pest in a sunny situation. Propagate by softwood cuttings of non-flowering shoots during summer.

Chamaemelum nobile **'Treneague'** z 6
A patch of this wonderfully fragrant, evergreen perennial releases the well-known "chamomile" scent when walked on or rubbed: a delight on warm summer evenings. It grows best on well-drained soils in full sun. Because the plant sets no seed it must be propagated by cuttings or division. The straight species is more vigorous and has white flowers with yellow centers; it grows to a height of 4in (10cm).

Corydalis lutea *(below)* z 5
The yellow corydalis produces its small, snapdragon-like yellow flowers nearly year-round above rounded mounds of finely divided, delicate gray-green leaves. The mounds grow to 1ft (30cm) high, with a similar spread, and are ideal between paving stones or spilling from crevices in walls. It self-seeds with ease, or the ripe seeds can be scattered by hand as required. A superb partner for early bulbs such as *Chionodoxa*. Plants do well on poor soils, especially in the sun. At the end of summer cut straggly plants to the ground.

Erigeron karvinskianus z 9/annual
A lovely fleabane with spreading loose stems carrying masses of daisy-like flower heads which open white, then turn pink, finally fading to purple. Flowers appear from summer through into autumn. The three-tone color on established plants is quite eye-catching, especially when seen along the edge of garden steps. The stems also bear small, lance-shaped bristly leaves which are mid-green. Plants only grow 6in (15cm) tall, but spread widely, and should be clipped back in spring before new growth begins. Propagate by softwood cuttings in summer. Needs well-drained soil and full sun.

Helxine soleirolii z 8
Also listed as *Soleirolia soleirolii*, this plant can become a nuisance in the wrong place. It is very tolerant and will fill the gaps between paving slabs or stones, especially if laid on cool moist soil in a shaded spot; but it is too delicate to withstand constant treading. Normally an evergreen perennial, it forms a dense carpet of tiny rounded green leaves which can be burned off by severe winter frosts. Plants never exceed 2in (5cm) in height. To propagate tease away small clumps and replant. Makes a good pot or greenhouse plant.

Lobularia maritima *(above)* annual
Sweet alyssum
Formerly known as *Alyssum maritimum*. During spring, scatter the seeds of this quick-growing plant in the gaps between paving for a show of tiny white, scented flowers in small heads in the summer and autumn. Deadhead the flowers regularly to maintain the display. Plants have small, narrow grayish-green leaves, grow to a height of 6in (15cm) and spread to 1ft (30cm). They are hardy and need fertile soil and full sun to give of their best. 'Wonderland' has pink-purple blooms.

Mazus reptans z 5
With some shelter (from frosts), moist soil and full sun, this creeping perennial will produce an abundance of purple flowers in spring. The flowers have a large, three-lobed whitish lower lip, spotted with red and yellow, and a small, slightly hooded top lip. Plants grow to no more than 2in (5cm) high, spread to 12in (30cm), and have narrow toothed leaves held in pairs along the stems. Divide plants in spring and replant vigorous tufts; alternatively, collect seed and sow in autumn.

Container plants

Saxifraga moschata *(below)* z 6
Plant this evergreen perennial where there is some shade from the midday sun and where the soil is constantly moist. It will form a tight hummock 4in (10cm) high, made up of rosettes of small, lance-shaped green leaves. From these grow thin stems during summer, each carrying up to five creamy-white or yellowish star-shaped flowers. 'Cloth of Gold' has bright golden-yellow leaves and is ideal for shade. 'Elf' is shown. Propagate by detaching and rooting vigorous rosettes.

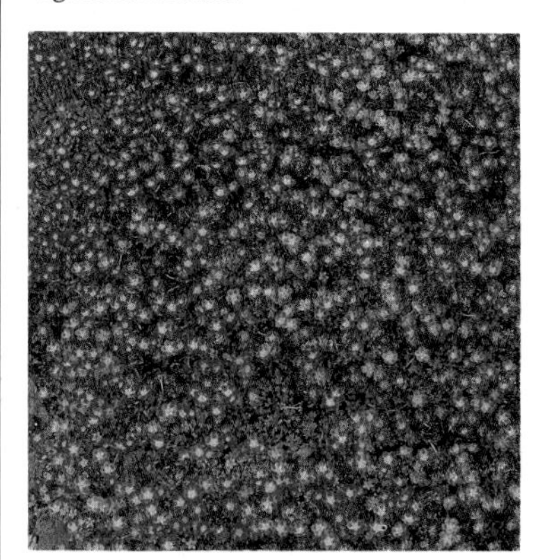

Thymus herba-barona z 4
Caraway thyme
The common name of this evergreen sub-shrub comes from its small, dark green, caraway-scented leaves. The fragrance is released when the leaves are brushed against, but the plant will not tolerate trampling. Plants reach a height of 2-4in (5-10cm) and in summer are covered in small, lilac-pink flowers borne in clusters at the ends of the shoots. An ideal setting is among sand-colored paving, especially if in tones of blue, gray and purple. Plants do best in full sun, where the soil is moist but free-draining. Take softwood or semi-ripe cuttings in summer.

Verbascum bombyciferum z 5/biennial
There are few more dramatic sights than this silver-leaved biennial mullein shooting up its tall racemes of densely-packed yellow flowers to a height of 4-6ft (1.2-1.8m). This it does in its second season, remaining evergreen through the previous winter. Both the large, oval basal leaves and the flower stems are covered in soft silvery hairs. Either allow to self-seed or scatter fresh seed, thinning in the following spring to produce strong plants.

***Agapanthus* Headbourne hybrids** z 7
(above)
Although the agapanthus is a native of South Africa, these hybrids originated in England and so tolerate cooler conditions. They are clump-forming perennials, evergreen in the mildest winters, with large, dark green strap-shaped leaves. In late summer the large, striking rounded heads of flowers rise to a height of up to 3ft (90cm). They range from deep blue to almost white. Plants need full sun, moist well-drained compost and protection during winter. Large plants can be divided.

Argyranthemum frutescens z 9/annual
Marguerite
Also known as *Chrysanthemum frutescens*, this tender bushy perennial is perfect for growing as a standard in containers. It has delicate, blue-gray leaves and numerous daisy-like flower heads – yellow, pink or white depending on the form grown – during summer. It may take several seasons to form a 3ft (90cm)-high standard but it is well worth the effort. Plants thrive in a sunny spot with fertile moist soil and can be moved indoors during winter for protection.

Ballota pseudodictamnus z 8
For a hot and sunny spot, this mound-forming sub-shrub provides considerable interest. It has gray-green rounded leaves covered in woolly hairs. During summer, small pink flowers emerge which have large, pale green calyces. The calyces remain long after the flowers have faded. Plants reach 2ft (60cm) in height and can spread rapidly to 3ft (90cm). To check growth cut back in early spring. Semi-ripe cuttings can be taken during summer. Needs well drained compost.

Felicia amelloides annual
Blue marguerite
A South African native, this attractive member of the daisy family is grown as a half-hardy annual, being raised from seed under glass in spring. The myriad delicate blue daisies with yellow centers are borne singly on virtually leafless stems. The foliage is lacy and bright green. Plants bloom prolifically all summer if deadheaded regularly as the flowers fade. They look charming in terracotta or white containers. May also be grown in the ground in hot summers.

Fuchsia *(above)* z 10/annual
The range of cultivars available of this popular garden plant is staggering. Most are tender and need overwintering where the temperature does not drop below 6°C (43°F) for some or 1°C (34°F) for others. They are often grown in containers and put out after the last frosts. The flower is prized for its great beauty. All fuchsias grow with a shrubby habit, being easily trained into standards. They need good, rich soil and a sunny position. For containers, bushy plants up to 2ft (60cm) tall are ideal. 'Morning Light' is shown.

Helichrysum petiolare z 8/annual
Grown primarily for its soft, silver-felted foliage, this rather tender sub-shrub is perfect for a mixed container planting. As the plant develops the shoots will trail and drape over the sides. It is best treated as an annual, young plants being overwintered from cuttings taken the previous season. Other cultivars well worth seeking are 'Limelight', with greenish-yellow leaves, and 'Variegata' which has cream variegation. Plants should be in sun and need well drained compost to produce their best displays.

Hydrangea macrophylla (*above*) z 6
With care, hydrangeas will grow well in a good-sized container. Position them in a lightly shaded spot, as excessive sunlight will scorch the foliage, out of the path of strong cold winds. Use a free-draining humus-rich mixture when planting up. The flowers are produced either in large mop-like heads or in flattish clusters, known as lacecaps. 'Blue Wave' is a lacecap with blue-pink heads; the mophead 'Madame Emile Mouillière' has white flowers with pink or blue centers. The dead flower heads add interest in winter.

Lilium regale (*above*) z 5
The regal lily
In summer, nothing can equal a grouping of weathered terracotta pots of this beautiful lily. The flowers appear on stems up to 6ft (2m) tall on really vigorous plants. Each stem can produce up to 25 funnel-shaped fragrant flowers, with petals that are whitish on the inside with a yellow base and tinted pink on the outside. The scaly bulbs can be repotted in fresh rich compost each spring. A few strong twigs are usually needed to support the flowers.

Lobelia erinus (*below*) annual
Few containers would be complete without the annual lobelia. The plants are raised under glass and planted out after the last frosts. They grow as spreading or pendulous mats, reaching a height of 8in (20cm), forming large clumps which cascade over the edge of the container. The flowers are two-lipped, small, and appear throughout summer into early autumn. 'Red Cascade' and 'Cambridge Blue' are notable; a mixed display is shown.

Osteospermum ecklonis z 9/annual
This evergreen semi-woody perennial must be planted in full sun in well-drained soil. It is ideal for pots or tubs as a central dot planting, reaching a height and spread of 18in (45cm). The main flush of the white daisy-like flowers with blue centers is in summer; they open to their maximum on sunny days. Take cuttings of non-flowering shoots in summer. Plants tend to become straggly and need some cutting back in late spring. In the ideal climate of subtropical areas they will flower almost all year round.

Pelargonium z 10/annual
Ideal for summer containers, the best types of these perennials are the ivy-leaved, Swiss Balcony and zonals. All these have bright red to white flowers with numerous pink, mauve and salmon intermediates. Repot plants in late autumn and cut down by half before overwintering in a frost-free place. In spring cut back to healthy buds as growth starts. Alternatively, take cuttings in late summer and overwinter ready for spring planting. The zonals are usually raised as half-hardy annuals from seed, preferably in fairly poor and dry conditions.

Petunia annual
The modern strains of this popular half-hardy summer bedding plant are available as grandifloras (with large, trumpet-shaped flowers) or multifloras (where the flowers are smaller and more numerous). Flower color ranges from white, through red, pink, purple and yellow, and they can be double, striped or frilly. For best results plant in sheltered containers in full sun, where the plants will adopt a trailing habit. Allow 9in (23cm) between the plants, which can grow up to 16in (40cm) high. Wet summers tend to spoil the flowers. Raise from seed in early spring.

Tropaeolum majus (*below*) annual
A very easy to grow hardy trailing annual. Sow the large seeds after the last frosts, choosing trailing varieties which soon produce vigorous, spreading shoots. During summer these are decked with large bright flowers in shades of red, orange and yellow. This plant will thrive in the poorest of soils and clamber through other container plants with ease, and off into nearby hedges and shrubs if allowed. Both the flowers and leaves can be used in salads.

Verbena annual
Most forms of vervain are descended from *V.* × *hybrida*, which is grown as a half-hardy bushy annual reaching a height of 6-18in (15-45cm) with similar spread. The plants have oval, rough-haired leaves and bright flowers held in tight clusters of pink, red, mauve, salmon or white from early summer onwards. They need full sun and well-drained soil. Selected forms are raised from cuttings taken in late summer and overwintered, the mixed types (such as 'Showtime') from seed raised under glass in spring.

WATER PLANTS

Water in a garden is an undisputed asset to its design and attractiveness. The introduction of water plants not only helps to keep the water clean by natural means, but also helps to support a whole range of wildlife, including tadpoles and frogs, dragonflies, snails and fish. The position of a pond in the garden is important as most water plants require plenty of light to prosper. The shade cast by their leaves is welcomed by fish and other wildlife and reduces the growth rate of vigorous plants, such as duckweed and pondweed.

Regularly-shaped formal pools are well suited to the area adjacent to the house, where they will make an immediate impact and provide a focal point. In the smallest gardens they can be reduced to the size of a barrel (at least 1-2ft/30-60 cm deep), stone trough or tank, and planted with a single plant or two or three small-leaved species such as *Juncus effusus* 'Spiralis', frogbit (*Hydrocharis morsus-ranae*) and *Nymphaea pygmaea alba*. The depth of the water and the vigor of plants can be regulated by planting each one in a basket that is supported by bricks so that it is immersed to the right depth. Larger pools call for simple treatments using only water lilies in a single striking color or a subtle association of two colors.

Right: Astilbes, azaleas and ferns enjoy a cool, moist atmosphere, generated by a cascade and pool in a shady position. This well planned, established planting scheme looks completely natural.

Left: Yellow flags and arum lilies make a harmonious combination of white, cream and yellow that blends with the rockwork surrounding this sunny pool.

Below right: Although many waterside plants die down in winter, the foliage of some persists and can be very decorative. Here, the strap-shaped leaves of phormiums stand up stiffly behind irises and reeds.

An irregularly shaped informal pool looks most realistic if placed at the lowest point in a wild or informal garden, where water would naturally gather, and a path should lead the visitor down to discover it. A variety of plants will be appropriate here. The center of the pool is suitable for deep-water plants, some of which root in the mud at the bottom of the pool or in specially designed baskets, while others, called floaters, are not rooted and have a tendency to spread very fast. Particularly fast-growing floaters are the oxygenators, which are essential to the ecology of the pool, but often need constant curbing. A common recommendation is that they should at the most take up a third of the pool's volume. Some suppliers still sell the common duckweed, *Lemna minor*, and Canadian pondweed, *Elodea canadensis*, both of which can grow very quickly as the summer heat increases, choking all around them. They cannot be recommended because of their invasive nature. However, *Myriophyllum spicatum*, the water milfoil, and *Cabomba caroliniana* are more desirable, being equally good purifiers and much less invasive.

For the edges of an informal pool, where the water is the shallowest, there is a wealth of "marginals" to choose from. With these, as with all other groups of plants, the art in designing is to select species of varying sizes and leaf shapes that harmonize and contrast with one another. In addition, they should complement the reflective quality of the water and the season, color and habit of the flowers needs to be taken into account. These considerations should also be extended to the area immediately surrounding the pool, which can be made into a bog garden. For example, the upright heart-shaped leaves of *Peltandra virginica* and the diamond-shaped, serrated leaves of *Trapa natans* contrast well with the strap-like leaves of *Iris laevigata* and tall, leafless stems of the variegated sedge *Scirpus tabernaemontani* 'Zebrinus'. The shapes and habits of these marginals can then be echoed in the boggy surroundings of the pool with the tall leaves of the American skunk cabbage, *Lysichiton americanum*, the great clumps of *Hosta fortunei*, the straps of *Iris kaempferi* and ferny foliage of *Osmunda regalis*.

Bog garden

Sagittaria sagittifolia z 5
Common arrowhead
Ideally suited to shallow water conditions, this deciduous perennial grows to a height of 18in (45cm) with a spread of 1ft (30cm). It has upright mid-green leaves shaped like arrows and in summer flowers are borne in spikes, each with three white petals and a purple center. In *S. latifolia* the flower center is yellow. Plants need full sun. Propagate by dividing in spring or summer, or by detaching young scaly shoots known as turions.

***Scirpus tabernaemontani* 'Zebrinus'** (*above*) z 5
Zebra rush
Also listed as *S. lacustris* sub-species *tabernaemontani* 'Zebrinus', this tall and handsome rush is useful in areas where the water is brackish. The leafless stems of this evergreen perennial sedge are striped markedly with white in horizontal bands. In summer, brown spikelets appear part way up the stems; these are the flowers. Remove any shoots that are all green to stop the plant reverting to the plain green form. Shoots reach a height of 5ft (1.5m) and spread indefinitely. Divide in spring.

Stratiotes aloides z 5
Water soldier
Characterized by its rosettes of spiny, olive green leaves, this free-floating semi-evergreen perennial is commonly found in alkaline water. It spends most of its time submerged, rising up to 10in (25cm) above the surface during summer when the whitish-pink cup-shaped flowers appear. The leaves are sharp and edged with spines. Plants spread to 12in (30cm) in diameter and need deep water. Propagate by small buds which develop on the plants' base.

Trapa natans z 6
Jesuit's nut or water chestnut
Grown primarily for its attractive foliage, the mid-green leaves are diamond-shaped with deeply toothed edges and grow in beautiful neat rosettes. The center of each leaf is often marked with deep purple blotches. White flowers are produced in summer. Each floating plant can spread to 9in (23cm) and looks best if part of a group in shallow water. To propagate this annual, collect seed in autumn, overwinter in water or wet moss and plant in spring.

Typha latifolia variegata z 3
Reed mace
The vigorous and invasive reed mace should be considered for planting only in larger ponds, in sun or shade. This deciduous perennial forms huge clumps of growth from which emerge green leathery leaves and spikes of brownish flowers in late summer. The flowers are followed by dark brown torpedo-shaped seed heads, which split open to release masses of fluffy airborne seeds and are very decorative through autumn and winter. Plants can reach 8ft (2.5m) in height. *T. minima* is more dainty. Propagate by seed or division in spring.

Utricularia vulgaris z 4
Greater bladderwort
With tiny, bladder-like, bronze-green modified leaves on its submerged roots, this carnivorous perennial traps water-dwelling organisms. Only the flower stems rise above the surface to a height of 16in (40cm), carrying bright yellow flowers in summer. Plants spread to 12in (30cm), grow in deep water and are deciduous. They form large clumps which should be thinned when overcrowded. Propagate by division.

Zantedeschia aethiopica z 8
Arum lily
This South African native grows well in shallow water. It flowers throughout the summer, with the erect funnel-shaped spathes being held well above the arrow-shaped glossy, deep green leaves. Each spathe surrounds a central yellow spadix. The leaves and flowering stems arise from a tuber. Plants can reach up to 3ft (90cm) in height, spreading to 18in (45cm). Ensure they are bedded deeply in the soil below water level. Propagate from seed or by division in spring.

***Carex stricta* 'Aurea'** z 5
Bowles' golden sedge
Also listed as *C. elata* 'Aurea', this evergreen hardy perennial has golden, lime-green striped leaves which create a splash of color in summer, fading to greener shades later in the season. It grows equally well at the waters' edge as in a bog garden. Plants have a tufted habit, need moist soil and a sunny spot to color well. They grow to 16in (40cm) in height and spread up to 6in (15cm). Dark brown flower spikes appear in summer. Propagate the plant by division in spring.

Hosta fortunei (*above*) z 3
Unlike many hostas, this species is prized more for its flowers than its foliage: tall mauve flower spikes appear around mid-summer, towering above the soft gray-green leaves. This hardy herbaceous perennial forms large clumps and grows to a height of 3ft (90cm) with an equal or greater spread. It needs a moist fertile soil and light shade. 'Albopicta' has yellow leaves edged with light green which become two-tone green in summer; 'Marginato-alba' has leaves margined with white and violet flowers. Protect against slugs and snails. Propagate by dividing the crowns in early spring.

Iris ensata z 5
Japanese flag iris
Also listed as *I. kaempferi.* Plant this iris in partial shade, ensuring that the soil is rich in humus. Its flowering stems reach 2-3ft (60-90cm) in height and are branched, carrying up to 15 reddish-purple flowers, each some 6in (15cm) across. There are many forms in a variety of colors. The rhizomes will spread indefinitely. To propagate plants, divide them in late summer.

Kirengeshoma palmata z 5
Even in the height of summer, this lovely herbaceous perennial exudes a coolness that is rarely matched by any other plants. An upright grower, it reaches a height of 3ft (90cm) with similar spread, and the stems carry lobed bright green leaves, topped by clusters of soft cream-yellow flowers from late summer to autumn. Prefers a lightly shaded position and moist, acid soil. Plants can be raised from seed or divided in autumn or spring.

Lysichiton americanus (*below*) z 3
Yellow skunk cabbage
The large, bright yellow spathes emerge before the leaves, from early spring onwards, surrounding a central yellowish-green spadix which are the true flowers. Space must be made for the huge, fresh green leaves which can be up to 4ft (1.2m) long, 30in (75cm) in *L. camtschatcense*, which has flowers with pure white spathes. These vigorous herbaceous perennials form large impressive clumps in full sun and will grow near still or running water, or in wet mud. Propagate through freshly collected seed or division in spring.

Mentha aquatica z 3
A wonderfully aromatic bog plant which releases a cool peppermint-like fragrance when crushed. It grows as a hairy purplish perennial, the flowers appearing in rounded heads on 30in (75cm)-tall stems above oval toothed leaves. The pinkish-lilac flowers have hairy sepals. Divide plants using pieces of the creeping rootstock which can be invasive but is easily contained in a deep open-bottomed container sunk in the ground. One of the parents of the cultivated peppermint, *M. × piperata*, which is used as a culinary herb.

Mimulus guttatus z 5
Monkey flower
With a height and spread of 2ft (60cm), this mat-forming perennial carries bright yellow snapdragon-like flowers which are spotted with brownish red. They appear throughout the summer until autumn. The mid-green leaves are oval. *M. luteus* (z 7) is similar but smaller and has large reddish blotches on the petals; rather more spectacular is *M. cardinalis* with its scarlet-orange flowers held on stems 2ft (60cm) tall. Propagate by division, through soft tip cuttings in summer, or by seed.

Osmunda regalis (*above*) z 3
Royal fern
The thick mat of roots produced by this majestic fern is excellent at stabilizing the soil in very wet areas or near the edge of water. This deciduous perennial is tolerant of sun and can grow to 6ft (2m) in a season, with a spread of 3ft (1m). The young fronds are pinkish as they emerge in spring, turning a bright green as they mature. On established plants the ends of taller fronds terminate in a rusty-red, spore-bearing female spike, like a tassel. Propagate by division in autumn or winter.

Pontederia cordata z 3
Pickerel weed
In late summer, blue flower spikes emerge from glossy, dark green leaves, which are narrow and lance-shaped. Plants form large clumps in time and grow best at the wet edges of a bog garden or in shallow water. They reach a height of 30in (75cm) and can spread to 18in (45cm). This deciduous perennial needs full sun to succeed and the flowers should be removed once they have faded. Increase in spring by seed or division.

Primula pulverulenta (*above*) z 5
Candelabra primula
The common name derives from the appearance of the flower stems, which carry striking crimson-red flowers with deep purple eyes. The main flowering stem and the flower stalks are covered in beautiful white farina. Plants seed themselves readily, forming clumps of upright growth, 2-3ft (60-100cm) in height and 18in (45cm) across. 'Bartley' has pale-pink flowers with carmine eyes and mid-green, toothed lance-shaped leaves. Plants need moist fertile soil in sun or shade. Divide plants or lift self-sown seedlings to increase numbers.

***Rheum palmatum* 'Atrosanguineum'** z 6
Consider this large ornamental form of the rhubarb only where its height and spread of 6ft (2m) can be accommodated with ease. This herbaceous perennial has deeply cut, five-lobed leaves of reddish-purple, with darker veins. Each leaf can grow to 2ft (60cm) across. In early summer, upright panicles of crimson flowers rise above the leaves. Propagate by division of the thick rootstock with a spade in spring.

Rodgersia aesculifolia z 5
Choose a spot away from strong winds to prevent damage to the large, crinkled bronze foliage (similar to that of the horse chestnut *Aesculus*), in sun or part-shade. Plants also grow well beside water. The rhizomes of this perennial form large clumps. Plants grow to 3ft (90cm) in height with similar spread. During mid-summer, plume-like, fragrant pink flowers appear from the foliage, held in rather flattish clusters. *R. pinnata* 'Superba' has bronze foliage, while 'Alba' has white flowers. Divide plants in spring.

Acid A term applied to soil or water with a pH value of below 7.

Aerial root A root growing above the soil from the stem of a plant.

Aggregate Small pebbles or gravel mixed with cement.

Alkaline A term applied to soil or water with a pH value of above 7.

Annual A plant that completes its life cycle within one growing season.

Anther The terminal part of a stamen that contains pollen.

Aril A covering on some seeds that is often brightly colored and fleshy.

Batter The profile of a hedge or a dry-stone wall with sides that slope inwards towards the top, making the top narrower than the base.

Bent Any perennial grass which has spreading panicles of tiny flowers; ideal for garden lawns.

Bract A modified, usually reduced, leaf that grows just below the flower head.

Breastwood Shoots that grow outwards from a plant that is trained against a support such as a fence or wall.

Calcareous Containing, or resembling, carbonate of lime or limestone; chalky or limy in nature.

Calyx The outer whorl of a flower, consisting of sepals that may be free to the base or partially joined.

Catkin An inflorescence consisting of a hanging spike of much reduced flowers occurring in trees like hazel and birch.

Cement Fine gray powder, a mixture of limestone and clay, used with water and sand to make mortar, or with water, sand and aggregate to make concrete.

Chlorosis A condition in which leaves become unnaturally pallid, whitish or yellow. The disease is usually due to lack of essential minerals.

Compost (seed or potting) A mixture of materials consisting chiefly of loam, peat, sand and fertilizers. It is used as a medium for sowing seeds, planting on seedlings and potting plants.

Compound leaf A leaf composed of two or more similar parts.

Concrete Sand, cement and aggregate, mixed with water to form a hard building material for paving and foundations.

Coniferous Relating to the group of plants that typically bear cones. Most are evergreen with linear leaves.

Container-grown A plant in a container as opposed to a bare-rooted one that is lifted from the open ground.

Corymb An inflorescence with a flat-topped flower cluster.

Crown The basal part of a plant from which roots and shoots grow.

Cultivar A cultivated, as distinct from a botanical, variety.

Cutting A separated piece of stem, root or leaf taken from a plant in order to propagate a new plant.

Deadhead To remove the spent flowers or the unripe seed-pods from a plant.

Deciduous A plant that loses all its leaves at one time of the year, usually during late autumn.

Desiccating wind A wind that dries plants, soil and organic material.

Digitate Describes a compound leaf that resembles a spread hand.

Division Propagation by means of dividing a single plant into smaller portions; also a way of thinning plants.

Dormancy The resting period of a plant, usually in winter.

Double (flower head) A flower with a double or multiple rows of petals.

Dressing A top covering like pea gravel, applied to the surface of the soil.

English bond In brickwork, this consists of three or five courses of stretchers to one of headers.

Evergreen A plant that retains its leaves throughout the year.

Fescue Any grass of the genus *Festuca*; ideal for garden lawns.

Flemish bond In brickwork, this consists of three or five stretchers to one header per course.

Floret A small flower making up the head of a composite flower.

Form (concrete) The timber frame into which concrete is poured.

Former A wood or metal frame used to train in growth for topiary; also a guide for trimming a hedge or building a dry-stone wall with a batter.

Germination The development of a seed into a seedling.

Glaucous A bluish-white, bluish-green or bluish-gray waxy bloom.

Gravel board A piece of timber fixed horizontally to the bottom of a fence to protect it from rot.

Grout A thin mortar for filling joints between tiles and masonry.

Habit The natural mode of growth and consequent shape of a plant.

Half-hardy A plant that is unable to survive the prevailing winter temparatures without some sort of protection but does not need to be kept in a greenhouse all the year round.

Harden off To gradually acclimatize plants raised in warm conditions to cooler conditions.

Hardy A plant capable of surviving the prevailing winter weather in the open, without protection.

Header A brick laid across a wall so that its ends are flush with the vertical faces.

Humus Fertile, partially decomposed organic matter in soil.

Hybrid A plant that is produced by the cross-fertilization of two species or variants of species.

Indumentum A hairy covering on leaves and other plant parts.

Inflorescence The flowering part of a plant.

Joist A beam made of timber, steel or reinforced concrete.

Lanceolate Describes the shape of a narrow, tapering leaf.

Lenticel One of many pores in the bark of woody plants through which gaseous exchange takes place.

Loam Any reasonably fertile soil that contains a free-draining mixture of clay, sand and organic material.

Microclimate A climate particular to a specific situation which differs from the overall climate of the garden or region.

Mortar A mixture of cement or lime or both with sand and water, used as a bond between bricks or stones or as a wall covering.

Mulch A soil covering that protects plants, reduces evaporation, suppresses weeds, prevents erosion and, in the case of organic mulch, enriches the soil.

Paling A fence made primarily of upright wooden posts.

Panicle A branched flower head, each branch having several stalked flowers.

Papery (petals) The term given to petals with a thin, paper-like texture.

Perennial A plant that lives for at least three seasons.

Petiole The stalk of a leaf.

pH The scale by which acidity or alkalinity is measured.

Pier A pillar, rectangular or otherwise, that bears heavy loads.

Plantlet A young plant produced naturally by the parent plant as a method of propagation.

Pleaching A technique for forming a dense hedge by interweaving the branches of well-spaced plants, usually trees such as limes or hornbeams, and often leaving bare trunks as stilts.

Plumb line A string with a metal weight attached, used to determine verticality.

Pointing The method of finishing joints in paving or brickwork with mortar.

Pricking out The transplanting of a seedling from a seed tray to a pot or another tray.

Propagation The production of a new plant from an existing one, either sexually by seed or asexually by cuttings.

Raceme An inflorescence in which the stalkless flowers are borne along the main stem.

Rhizome An undergroung creeping stem, sometimes thick as in irises, other times thin as in grasses, and usually horizontal.

Riser The vertical part of a step or stair.

Rootstock The underground part of a plant from which roots and shoots grow.

Rosette A circular cluster of leaves growing from the base of a shoot.

Runner A trailing stem that grows along the surface, takes root and forms new growth at nodes or the tip.

Running bond In brickwork, this consists of stretcher courses with alternate rows staggered by half a brick.

Scarify To rub or scratch the surface of a seed to increase water absorption in order to speed up germination.

Seedling A very young plant with few leaves, raised from seed.

Semi-evergreen Describes a plant intermediate between evergreen and deciduous. It bears some foliage throughout the year, but also loses some leaves during winter.

Sepal The outermost, leaf-like structures of a flower.

Sessile A flower or leaf with no stalk, growing directly from the stem.

Single (flower head) A flower with a single layer of petals.

Spacers small pieces of wood inserted between paving stones to ensure an even surface is laid.

Species A group of closely related organisms within a genus.

Spikes (flower) An inflorescence consisting of stalkless flowers arranged along a stem.

Stamens The male reproductive organ of a flower, consisting of a stalk bearing an anther.

Standard Any tree which has a main stem or trunk 4-6 ft (1.2-1.8m) in height with a large head; most commonly applied to fruit trees, roses and fuchsias.

Stigma The terminal part of the ovary, (the female reproductive organ of a flower) where pollen is deposited.

Stipule (leaf) Out-growths, usually paired, at the base of the leaf stalks in some plants that protect the young leaves.

Stooled Cut to the ground periodically and allowed to regrow, to encourage the growth of new whip-like stems.

Stretcher A brick that is laid horizontally so that its length is exposed.

Sub-shrub A plant with a woody base and herbaceous tips.

Subsoil The layer of soil below the topsoil. It is lighter in color than the topsoil.

Tamp To firmly pack down a material such as soil or concrete.

Tender A plant unable to withstand the coldest prevailing weather conditions.

Tepal The outer part of a flower resembling a petal.

Thin To reduce the number of seedlings.

Tilth The fine crumbly surface layer of soil. The ideal tilth for a seedbed is about the consistency of coarse breadcrumbs.

Tomentum A felt-like covering of hairs on leaves and other parts of a plant.

Topsoil The upper layer of soil, the darkest and most fertile part, in which plants grow.

Tread The top surface of a step or stair.

Trifoliate Leaves that are divided into three, as in clover.

Umbel A flat-topped or dome-shaped flower head in which the flowers are borne on stalks arising from the top of the main stem.

Variegated Leaves with attractive colored markings.

Variety A distinct variant of a species, either a cultivated form (a cultivar) or one that occurs naturally.

Watering in To water around the stem of a newly transplanted plant to settle soil around the roots.

Whorl Three or more flowers, buds, leaves or shoots arising from the same place on a plant stem.

CONSERVATORIES & GREENHOUSES

A conservatory is generally considered to be a liveable room where plants grow, either in permanent beds or in pots; a greenhouse is a simpler structure devoted mainly to plant propagation and care. All of these companies have catalogs for which you can write or call.

Amdega Conservatories
for local distributor call
(800) 922-0110
English wooden conservatories – mostly Victorian in style.

Everlite Greenhouses, Inc.
9515 Gerwig Lane
Suite 115
Columbia
MD 21046
(301) 381-3881
Greenhouses, sunrooms and conservatories.

Four Seasons Greenhouses
5005 Veterans
Memorial Highway
Holbrook
NY 11741-4516
(516) 694-4400 or
(800) 645-9527
Greenhouses and sunrooms.

Gothic Arch Greenhouses
PO Box 1564
Mobile
AL 36633
(205) 432-7529 or
(800) 628-4974
Wooden greenhouses and conservatories; supplies.

Janco Greenhouses
9390 Davis Avenue
Laurel
MD 20707-1993
(301) 498-5700 or
(800) 323-6933
Greenhouses and sunrooms.

Lord & Burnham
PO Box 1074
Falls Station
Niagara Falls
NY 14303
Greenhouses, attached and detached.

Machin Conservatories
For local distributor call (800) 622-4464
English metal conservatories in several styles.

Northwest Eden Sales, Inc.
15103 N.E. 68th Street
Redmond, WA 98052
(800) 545-3336
Greenhouses and supplies.

Pacific Coast Greenhouse Manufacturing Co.
8360 Industrial Avenue
Cotati, CA 94931
(707) 795-2164 or
(415) 492-8812
Redwood greenhouses and sunrooms.

Pella
P.O. Box 308
Moline, IL 61265-0308
(800) 524-3700
Sunrooms in a variety of styles.

Progressive Building Products
P.O. Box 453
Route 125 (Brentwood)
Exeter, NH 03833
(603) 679-1208 or
(800) 776-2534
Greenhouses and solariums.

Santa Barbara Greenhouses
1115-J Avenida Acaso
Camarillo, CA 93010
(805) 482-3765
Prefabricated and custom greenhouses in fiberglass or redwood.

Sturdi-built Greenhouse Manufacturing Co.
11304 SW Boones
Ferry Road
Portland, OR 97219
(503) 244-4100 or
(800) 722-4115
Redwood greenhouses, either detached or lean-to.

Sun Room Company, Inc.
322 East Main Street
Leola, PA 17540
(717) 656-8018 or
(800) 426-2737
Sunrooms.

Sun-Porch
Sunbeam Structures
Division
Vegetable Factory, Inc.
P.O. Box 1353
Stamford
CT 06904-1353
Sunrooms.

Sunglo Solar Greenhouses
4441 – 26th Avenue
West
Seattle, WA 98199
(206) 284-8900
Greenhouses in kit form.

FENCING

Standard wooden post-and-rail, picket and palisade fences are available at lumber-yards nationwide. Some special kinds of fencing may be ordered from companies which have catalogs, or can be commissioned from craftspeople.

Architectural Iron Company
Box 126, Route 6 West
Milford, PA 18337
(717) 296-7722 or
(212) 243-2664
Wrought and cast iron fences and restoration.

Bamboo Fencer
31 Germania St.
Jamaica Plain
MA 02130
(617) 524-6137
Design, manufacture and install bamboo fencing and structures.

Bufftech
2525 Walden Avenue
Buffalo, NY 14225
(800) 333-0569
Vinyl fencing resembling traditional wood.

Cassidy Bros. Forge, Inc.
U.S. Route 1
Rowley
MA 01969-1796
(508) 948-7303
Custom architectural ironwork.

Jerith Manufacturing Co., Inc.
3939 G Street
Philadelphia
PA 19124
Aluminum rustproof fencing.

Materials Unlimited
2 West Michigan
Avenue
Ypsilanti, MI 48197
(313) 483-6980
Cast iron fences, posts and gates. Custom work.

Monte Haberman
1202 East Pine Street
Placentia
CA 92670
(714) 993-4766
Hand-forged fence parts, lamps, etc.

Moultrie Manufacturing Company
PO Drawer 1179
Moultrie
GA 31768
(800) 841-8674 or
(912) 985-1312
Metal fences, furniture, fountains, statuary.

Mike Shaffer, Blacksmith
Mountain Forge
1155 Dantel Court
Stone Mountain
GA 30083
(404) 469-2680
Custom ornamental iron work, hand forgings.

Stewart Iron Works Co.
20 West 18th Street
Covington
KY 41012-2612
(606) 431-1985
Fences and gates in Victorian/Edwardian styles.

Walpole Woodworkers
767 East Street (Rt. 27)
Walpole, MA 02081
(508) 668-2800 or
(800) 343-6948
Cedar fences in many classic styles.

GARDEN FURNITURE

Furnishings for the garden come in a vast selection of styles and materials. Many of them are available at garden centers and furniture stores. Others, such as most of those below, may be ordered from catalogs.

Alsto's Handy Helpers
PO Box 1267
Galesburg, IL 61401
(309) 343-6181 or
(800) 447-0048
Cedar patio furniture and swings, metal lawn chairs and gliders.

Ballard Designs
1670 DeFoor Ave. NW
Atlanta
GA 30318-7528
(404) 351-5099
Catalog of metal and glass chairs, benches and tables; cast architectural ornaments suitable for use as tables.

Barlow Tyrie, Inc.
1263/230 Glen Ave.
Moorestown, NJ 08067
(609) 273-1631
English teak furniture.

Brown-Jordan
9860 Gidley St.
El Monte, CA 91731
(818) 443-8971
Many styles of aluminum-framed furniture. Sold in furniture stores.

Charleston Battery Bench, Inc.
191 King St.
Charleston, SC 29401
(803) 722-3842

Authentic reproductions of historic wood and metal benches.

Country Casual
17317 Germantown Road
Germantown
MD 20874-2999
(301) 540-0040
Imported teak garden furniture and trellis.

David Robinson
106 East Delaware Ave.
Pennington
NJ 08534
(609) 737-8996
Rustic architcture and furniture.

David Kay Garden & Gift Catalog
1 Jenni Lane
Peoria
IL 61614-3198
(800) 535-9917
Outdoor furniture in wood, plastic and metal by mail.

Garden Concepts
PO Box 241233
Memphis
TN 38124-1233
(901) 756-1649
Handcrafted furniture, structures and accessories in wood.

Gardeners Eden
PO Box 7307
San Francisco
CA 94120-7307
Catalog of metal, wood, wicker and twig furniture and garden ornaments.

Green Enterprises
43 South Rogers St.
Hamilton
VA 22068
(703) 338-3606
Oak Victorian swings, gliders, tables, benches.

Hemlock Shop
RD #1, Box 273
Olyphant, PA 18447
(717) 586-8809
Folding wooden Adirondack chairs.

Kingsley-Bate
5587B Guinea Road
Fairfax, VA 22032
(703)978-7222
Traditional teak garden furniture.

New Happy Centerville
Swing Bench & Rocker Shoppe
PO Box 211
Valencia, PA 16059
(800) 875-3724
Wooden swings, gliders and traditional garden furniture.

Park Place
2251 Wisconsin Ave. N.W.
Washington
DC 20007
(202) 342-6294
Classic furnishings in solid teak.

Reed Bros.
Turner Station
Sebastopol, CA 95472
(707) 795-6261
One-of-a-kind carved redwood furniture for indoors and outdoors.

Renovator's Supply
Millers Falls
MA 01349
(800) 659-2211
Inexpensive classic teak furniture and home renovation products.

Richardson Allen
PO Box 701
Cape Porpoise
ME 04014
(207) 967-8482
Wooden outdoor furniture in traditional styles.

Smith & Hawken
25 Corte Madera
Mill Valley, CA 94941
(415) 383-2000
Chairs, benches and tables, mostly traditional English styles in wood, sold mainly by catalog.

Sloan Designs
Route 1 – Box 183-A
Linden, VA 22642
(703) 636-1626
Jefferson benches and Adirondack chairs in wood; Deco and original designs in metal.

Telescope Casual Furniture, Inc.
85 Church St.
Granville, NY 12832
(518) 642-1100
Metal, mesh and glass garden and patio furniture. Sold through stores.

Wetherend Estate Furniture
PO Box 648
Rockland, ME 04841
(207) 596-6483
Fine traditional wooden outdoor furniture.

Willsboro Wood Products
PO Box 509
South Ausable St.
Keesville, NY 12944
(518) 834-5200 or
(800) 342-3373
Furniture, picnic tables and benches in cedar.

Windsor Designs
37 Great Valley Parkway
Malvern, PA 19355
(215) 640-5896 or
(800) 722-5434
Traditional designs in teak, hardwood and cast aluminum.

Wood Classics
Box 205
Gardiner, NY 12525
(914) 255-7871
Classic teak and mahogany garden furniture.

Woodbrook
PO Box 175
Trussville, AL 35173
(800) 828-3607
Distinctive wooden garden furniture.

LIGHTING AND PAVING MATERIALS

Simple garden lighting systems which turn on automatically at sunset are available at most garden centers, but more elaborate or sculptural lights may be ordered from a number of companies which have catalogs or photographs. Architectural salvage yards often have rich collections of old lighting.

Paving material such as brick or stone, too, is purchased locally, but certain special materials may be ordered from suppliers who will ship them.

Classic & Country Crafts
5100-1B Clayton Road
Suite 291
Concord, CA 94521
(510) 672-4337
Copper and bronze landscape accent lights.

Conn Stone Supplies
311 Post Road
Orange
CT 06477
(203) 795-9767
Cobblestones in two sizes and colors.

Doner Design, Inc.
2175 Beaver Valley Pike
New Providence
PA 17560
(717) 786-8891
Handcrafted copper landscape lights in five designs.

Great American Salvage Co.
34 Cooper Square
New York
NY 10003
(212) 505-0070
All architectural salvage plus reproduction lighting, etc.

Hanover Lanterns Terralight
470 High Street
Hanover
PA 17331
(717) 632-6464
Landscape lighting fixtures, regular or low voltage.

Liteform Designs
PO Box 3316
Portland, OR 97208
(503) 257-8464
Residential and commercial landscape lighting in wood, metal and ceramic.

Lost City Arts
275 Lafayette Street
New York, NY 10012
(212) 941-8025
Architectural lighting, advertising signs, elements of demolished buildings.

Popovitch Associates, Inc.
346 Ashland Avenue
Pittsburgh
PA 15228
(412) 344-6097
Ornamental garden lighting – in plant forms, for instance.

Buddy Rhodes Designs
725 18th Street
San Francisco
CA 94107
(415) 641-8070
Tinted pavers of textured concrete which may resemble weathered granite.

Stonelight Corporation
2701 Gulf Shore Boulevard, N.
Naples
FL 33940
(813) 263-2208
Contemporary lighting fixtures in Vermont gray granite.

GARDEN ORNAMENTS

Garden ornamentation begins with pots, planters and urns and continues through statuary, columns and gazebos, to the wilder shores of architectural fragments that may be used to convey a sense of history or romantic ruin. It is also possible to commission sculpture – often life-size portraits of pets or family members cunningly positioned near pools or tucked into a wooded landscape.

Architectural Artifacts, Inc.
4325 North Ravenswood
Chicago
IL 60613
(312) 863-1895
Architectural salvage such as sculptural decorations suitable for use in gardens.

Architectural Salvage Warehouse
337 Berry Street
Brooklyn
NY 11211
(718) 388-4527
All architectural elements from New York buildings.

The Bank
1824 Felicity Street
New Orleans
LA 70113-1321
(504) 523-2702
Southern architectural elements.

Chadsworth Incorporated
PO Box 53260
Atlanta, GA 30355
(404) 876-5410
Architectural wooden columns in many styles.

Dalton Pavilions
7260 Oakley Street
Philadelphia, PA 19111
(215) 342-9804
Gazebos in Victorian style made of western red cedar.

Design Toscano
7 East Campbell Street
Arlington Heights
IL 60005
(800) 525-0733
Gargoyles, replicas of medieval originals, in enriched cement or outdoor resin.

Eleganza, Ltd.
Magnolia Village
3217 West Smith #919
Seattle, WA 98199
(206) 283-0609
Statues in marble, bonded marble, bronze and terracotta. Pedestals and reproductions of Greek vases.

Elizabeth Street
210 Elizabeth Street
New York
NY 10012
(212) 941-4800
Outdoor and garden objects, fountains.

Florentine Craftsmen, Inc.
46-24 28th Street
Long Island City
NY 11101
(718) 937-7632
Garden ornaments, statuary, fountains, furniture in lead, bronze, iron, aluminum or stone.

French Wyres
PO Box 131655
Tyler, TX 75713
(903) 597-8322
Trellis, topiary frames, urns, plant stands in wire.

Garden Accents
4 Union Hill Road
Consohocken
PA 19428
(215) 825-5525
Antique and modern garden ornaments, statuary, lighting, urns in stone and metal.

Haddonstone (USA) Ltd.
201 Heller Place
Interstate Business Park
Bellmawr, NJ 08031
(609) 931-7011
Classically-inspired statuary, temples, balustrading and temples in reconstructed stone.

Hen-Feathers & Company
10 Balligomingo Road
Gulph Mills, PA 19428
(800) 282-1910
Urns, planters, fountains and garden statuary made of bonded marble resin finished in hand-rubbed patinas of lead, verdigris, rust and antique white.

Heritage Garden Houses
City Visions, Inc.
311 Seymour
Lansing, MI 48933
(517) 372-3385
Garden structures for use as garden retreat, pool house, tool shed, etc., in 15 styles from Japanese to Victorian.

Ink Pot Design
PO Box 26278
Los Angeles, CA 90026
(213) 664-5181
Red cedar planters for vines.

Kinsman Company
River Road
Point Pleasant
PA 18950
(800)733-5613
Victorian reproduction arches, gazebos, obelisks and screens in steel tubing coated with black nylon. Also planters and general garden equipment.

Kenneth Lynch & Sons
84 Danbury Road
Wilton
CT 06897
(203) 762-8363
Classic achitectural ornamental metal and stone work and ornaments – fountains, sculpture, urns, weather vanes.

Materials Unlimited
2 West Michigan Ave.
Ypsilanti
MI 48197
(313) 483-6980
Salvage plus new architectural materials, antique furniture and accessories.

New England Garden Ornaments
38 East Brookfield Road
North Brookfield
MA 01535
(508) 867-4474
Cast stone ornaments and garden temples, lead ornaments, balustrades and antique garden sculpture.

W.F. Norman Corp.
PO Box 323
Nevada, MO 64772
(800) 641-4038 or
(417) 667-5552
Sheet metal ornamentation, urns, capitals.

Old World Garden Troughs
PO Box 1253
Carmel, IN 46032
(317) 848-4490
Planters like English garden sinks in several sizes.

Pompeian Studios
90 Rockledge Road
Bronxville, NY 10708
(914) 337-5661
Marble or bronze sculptures, temples and ornaments made in Italy.

Sculpture Cast Editions
PO Box 426
15 Tamara Drive
Roosevelt, NJ 08555
(609) 426-0942
Cast stone and bronze garden statues.

A.F. Schwerd Manufacturing Company
3215 McClure Avenue
Pittsburgh, PA 15212
(412) 766-6322
Wooden columns in all classical and modern orders with ventilated aluminum bases.

Dennis Smith Sculptures
c/o Scott Kenney
1105 Gambol Oak Circle
Highland, UT 84003
(801) 756-6404
Limited edition and personally commissioned bronze sculptures – often portraits.

Greg Speiss
228-230 East Washington Street
Joliet, IL 60433
(815) 722-5639
Architectural elements from old buildings.

Stone Forest
Box 2840
Santa Fe, NM 87504
(505) 986-8883
Fountains, Japanese lanterns, stone basins, birdbaths in hand-carved granite.

Tom Torrens Sculpture Design, Inc.
PO Box 1819
Gig Harbor, WA 98335
(206) 857-5831
Functional sculpture (gongs, tables) for home or garden.

Urban Archaeology
285 Lafayette Street
New York, NY 10012
(212) 431-6969
Salvaged doors, windows, exterior ornament.

Vixen Hill Gazebos
Elverson
PA 19520
(800) 423-2766
Cedar gazebos in Victorian style, pre-engineered for easy assembly.

Wind & Weather
PO Box 2320
Mendocino, CA 95460
(707) 964-1284
Weathervanes, sundials and garden ornaments in metal.

Windleaves Weathervanes
7560 Morningside Drive
Indianapolis, IN 46240
(317) 251-1381
Metal weathervanes in the shape of various sorts of leaves.

Wood Garden
11 Fitzrandolph Street
Green Brook
NJ 08812
(201) 968-4325
Planters, barrels, tubs made of chestnut as well as a gazebo kit.

Worthington Group, Ltd.
PO Box 53101
Atlanta, GA 30355
(404) 872-1608
Columns and balustrades for outdoor use.

NURSERIES

All of the nurseries below have catalogs, usually free. Some charge a nominal fee which is almost always deducted from the price of the order. This is a representative, though not complete, list of suppliers of plants, seeds and bulbs throughout the country.

Abundant Life Seed Foundation
PO Box 772
Port Townsend
WA 98368
(206) 385-5660
Seeds. Vegetables, herbs, trees, annuals, perennials, wild flowers, books.

Ambergate Gardens
8015 Krey Avenue
Waconia
MN 55387
(612) 443-2248
Plants. Perennials, specializing in martagon lilies; grasses.

The Antique Rose Emporium
Rt. 5, Box 143
Brenham
TX 77833
(800) 441-0002
Plants. Old rose varieties, many collected by the Texas "rose rustlers". Perennials to accompany the roses.

Berthold Nursery
434 East Devon Ave.
Elk Grove Village
IL 60007
(708) 439-2600
Plants. Trees and shrubs for landscaping. Wholesale and retail.

Kurt Bluemel, Inc., Nurseries
2740 Greene Lane
Baldwin
MD 21013-9523
(410) 557-7229
Plants. Grasses, water and bog plants.

Bluestone Perennials
7211 Middle Ridge Road
Madison, OH 44057
(216) 428-5243 or
(800) 852-5243
Plants. Perennials, grasses, shrubs of small size and very small price. A few larger plants and bulbs in the fall.

Borbaleta Gardens
15980 Canby Avenue
Faribault, MN 55021
(507) 334-2807
Plants. Daylilies, iris and asiatic lilies, many new varieties.

Botanicals
219 Concord Road
Wayland, MA 01778
(508) 358-4846
Plants. Perennials adapted to difficult situations, especially dry spots.

Breck's
US Reservation Center
6523 North Galena Road
Peoria, IL 61632
(309) 691-4616
Bulbs. The most widely distributed catalog. Fairly limited selection.

Burpee Gardens
300 Park Avenue
Warminster
PA 18991-0001
(215) 674-9633
Seeds and plants. Seeds of perennial and annual flowers, vegetables. Plants of perennials, bedding annuals, fruit trees, shrubs and vines.

Busse Gardens
Rt. 2, Box 238
Cokato
MN 55321-9426
(612) 286-2654
Plants. Perennials, specializes in extensive lists of hostas, Siberian irises, peonies and daylilies.

Camellia Forest Nursery
125 Carolina Forest Road
Chapel Hill, NC 27516
(919) 967-5529
Plants. Camellias of all varieties, also camellia seeds. Other trees, emphasizing oriental varieties, a few perennials.

Canyon Creek Nursery
3527 Dry Creek Road
Oroville, CA 95965
(916) 533-2166
Plants. Perennials, many unusual – including rare varieties of salvia.

Caprilands Herb Farm
534 Silver Street
Coventry, CT 06238
(203) 742-7244
Plants. Herbs and supplies for herb gardeners.

Carlson's Gardens
Box 305
South Salem
NY 10590
(914) 763-5958
Plants. Azaleas, rhododendrons and their kin. Enormous selection.

Cold Stream Farm
2030 Free Soil Road
Free Soil
MN 49411-9752
(616) 464-5809
Plants. Hybrid poplars and other trees in quantity for landscaping and wildlife habitat.

The Country Garden
Rt. 2, Box 455A
Crivitz, WI 54114
(755) 757-2045
Seeds and plants. Seeds of annuals and perennials, plants and bulbs of other perennials.

Crownsville Nursery
PO Box 797
Crownsville
MD 21032
(410) 923-2212
Plants. Perennials, extensive list. Some shrubs.

The Daffodil Mart
Rt. 3, Box 794
Gloucester, VA 23061
(804) 693-3966
Bulbs. Big selection, both wholesale and retail.

Dutch Gardens
PO Box 200
Adelphia, NJ 07710
(908) 780-2713
Bulbs and plants. Enormous selection of Dutch bulbs in autumn, lilies, dahlias and perennials in spring, all at wholesale prices.

Forestfarm
990 Tetherow Road
Williams
OR 97544-9599
(503) 846-7269 (9am to 3pm Pacific time)
Plants. Wide selection of trees and shrubs, some perennials and books.

The Fragrant Path
PO Box 328
Fort Calhoun
NE 68023
Seeds. Annuals, perennials, herbs, climbers, trees and shrubs with the emphasis on fragrance.

French's Bulb Importer
Box 565
Pittsfield
VT 05762-0562
(802) 746-8148
Bulbs. Many prepared for forcing. Cyclamen and a few greenhouse plants.

The Garden Place
6780 Heisley Road
PO Box 388
Mentor
OH 44061-0388
(216) 255-3705
Plants. Perennials, extensive list.

Heard Gardens Ltd.
5355 Merle Hay Road
Johnston, IA 50131
(515) 276-4533
Plants. Specializing in lilacs and flowering crabapples. Some other trees and shrubs.

Heirloom Garden Seeds
PO Box 138
Guerneville, CA 95446
Seeds. Flowers and herbs. The catalog gives a history of each plant.

Heirloom Old Garden Roses
24062 NE Riverside Drive
St. Paul, OR 97137
(503) 538-1576
Plants. Hardy roses of old garden and English types.

High Country Rosarium
1717 Downing Street
Denver, CO 80218
(303) 832-4026
Plants. Shrub, climbing and rambling roses, grown for hardiness. Many old varieties.

Jackson & Perkins
PO Box 1028
Medford, OR 97501
(800) 292-4769
Plants. Famous for roses, which they breed in many varieties. Perennials, too.

Peter de Jager Bulb Co.
188 Asbury Street
PO Box 2010
South Hamilton
MA 01982
(508) 468-4707
Bulbs. Small or landscaping quantities.

Thomas Jefferson Center for Historic Plants
Monticello
PO Box 318
Charlottesville
VA 22902
(804) 979-5283
Seeds. Historic varieties of annuals and a few perennials, many harvested at Monticello.

Jung Quality Seeds
Randolph, WI 53957
(414) 326-3123
Seeds. Vegetables and annuals. Also perennial and fruit tree plants.

Klehm Nursery
Rte. 5
197 Penny Road
South Barrington
IL 60010
(312) 551-3715
Plants. Peonies, daylilies,

hostas and iris are the specialties – other perennials are sold as companion plants.

Lamb Nurseries
E. 101 Sharp Avenue
Spokane
WA 99202
(509) 328-7956
Plants. Hardy perennials and rock plants.

Lee Bristol Nursery
Box 5
Gaylordsville
CT 06755-0005
(203) 354-6951
Plants. Daylily specialist.

Lilypons Water Gardens
6800 Lilypons Road
PO Box 10
Buckeystown
MD 21717-0010
(301) 428-0686
Plants and equipment. Everything needed for water gardening from flowers, hardy and tender, to fish. Installation available, informative catalog.

Logee's Greenhouses
141 North Street
Danielson
CT 06239
(203) 774-8038
Plants. Very large selection of greenhouse rarities, annuals and tropical plants, orchids.

Thurman Maness
The Wildwood Flower
Rt. 3, Box 165
Pittsboro, NC 27312
(919) 542-4344
(evening only)
Plants. Hybrid lobelias, Japanese painted fern, special woodland perennials and shrubs.

McClure & Zimmerman
108 W. Winnebago
PO Box 368
Friesland
WI 53935
(414) 326-4220
Bulbs. Extensive list including many rarities.

Mellinger's
2310 W. South Range Road
North Lima
OH 44452
(216) 549-9861
Plants and seeds. A big catalog with some of everything – trees, annuals, perennials, fruit, etc. Also gardening supplies.

Milaeger's Gardens
4838 Douglas Avenue
Racine
WI 53402-2371
(414) 639-2371
Plants. Wide selection of perennials and grasses.

Miller Nurseries
Canandaigua
NY 14424
(800) 836-9630
Plants. Fruit and landscape trees, vegetables, some perennials.

Montrose Nursery
PO Box 957
Hillsborough
NC 27278
(919) 732-7787
Plants. Perennials, many suited to rock gardens. A specialty is hardy cyclamen.

Musser Forests, Inc.
PO Box 340
Indiana
PA 15701-0340
(412) 465-5685
Plants, mostly seedlings. Trees and shrubs for landscaping.

The New Peony Farm
PO Box 18235
St. Paul, MN 55118
(612) 457-8994
Plants. Literally hundreds of varieties of peony, of all strains (fernleaf, for instance).

Paradise Water Gardens
672 May Street
Whitman, MA 02382
(716) 447-4711
Plants. Lilies and bog plants as well as supplies and books.

Park Seed Co.
Cokesbury Road
Greenwood
SC 29647-0001
(800) 845-3369
Seeds. Perennials, annuals, vegetables. Also bulbs.

Perry's Water Gardens
191 Leatherman Gap Road
Franklin, NC 28734
(704) 524-3264
Plants. All water and bog plants, fish and equipment.

Prairie Nursery
PO Box 306
Westfield, WI 53964
(608) 296-3679
Seeds and plants. Wildflowers, seed mixes and garden designs.

Roses of Yesterday and Today
Watsonville
CA 95076-0398
(408) 724-3537
Plants. Old, rare and unusual roses as well as selected modern ones. Shrubs, ramblers and climbers.

Sandy Mush Herb Nursery
Rt. 2
Surret Cove Road
Leicester
NC 28748-9622
(704) 683-2014
(Thursday, Friday and Saturday only)
Plants. Herbs, shrubs and perennials, including many unusual varieties of salvia, scented geranium, thyme, grasses and ivies. Herb seeds.

John Scheepers, Inc.
PO Box 700
Bantam
CT 06750
(203) 567-0838
Bulbs. Well-illustrated catalog, large quantities available.

Schreiner's Iris Gardens
3628 Quinaby Road
Salem, OR 97303
(800) 525-2367
Plants. An enormous collection of bearded iris in the colors of the rainbow and more.

Schumacher Co., Inc.
36 Spring Hill Road
Sandwich
MA 02563-1023
(508) 888-0659
Seeds. Forest and fruit trees, azalea and rhododendrons, books.

Seeds Blüm
Idaho City Stage
Boise, ID 83706
(208) 342-0858
Seeds. Heirloom varieties as well as modern vegetables, herbs, edible flowers, annuals, wildflowers, perennials. Extraordinary illustrated catalog with cultural advice, recommendations, books.

Shady Oaks Nursery
700 - 19th Avenue, NE
Waseca, MN 56093
(507) 835-5055
Plants. Hostas and other shade-loving perennials, ferns, wildflowers and shrubs.

Shepherds Garden Seeds
30 Irene Street
Torrington, CT 06790
(203) 482-3638
Seeds. Vegetables, herbs, annuals. Many old-fashioned and unusual varieties.

Siskiyou Rare Plant Nursery
2825 Cummings Road
Medford, OR 97501
(503) 772-6846
Plants. Extremely extensive list of rock garden plants, many very rare. A few trees and shrubs, mostly dwarf.

Slocum Water Gardens
Cypress Gardens Road
Winter Haven
FL 33880
(813) 293-7151
Plants. Water lilies, lotus, aquarium plants and supplies.

Smith & Hawken
25 Corte Madera
Mill Valley
CA 94941
(415) 383-2000
Bulbs. Wide selection, including lilies.

Spring Hill Nurseries
110 West Elm Street
Tipp City, OH 45371
(309) 691-4616
Plants. Perennials, climbers, shrubs, roses, gladioli. Pre-planned garden schemes.

Sunsweet Bulb Company
Box Z
Sumner, GA 31789
(912) 386-2211
Bulbs and plants. Canna, crinums, palms for hot climates.

Thompson & Morgan
PO Box 1308
Jackson
NJ 08527-0308
(201) 363-2225
Seeds. Enormous list of perennials, vegetables, annuals including the Swiss trailing balcony geraniums.

William Tricker, Inc.
7125 Tanglewood Drive
Independence
OH 44131
(216) 524-3491
Plants. Water lilies, other water plants, fish and pool equipment.

TyTy Plantation Bulb Co.
Box 159
TyTy
GA 31795
(912) 382-0404
Plants, bulbs and corms. Tropical plants such as canna, crinum, ginger, as well as lilies and perennials for hot climates or for use as annuals in the North.

Van Bourgondien
245 Farmingdale Road
PO Box 1000
Babylon, NY 11702
(800) 622-9997
Bulbs, perennial plants.

Van Engelen, Inc.
Stillbrook Farm
313 Maple Street
Litchfield, CT 06759
(203) 567-8734
Bulbs. Wholesale quantities and prices for Dutch bulbs.

Van Ness Water Gardens
2460 North Euclid
Upland
CA 91786-1199
(714) 982-2425
Plants. Water and bog plants as well as products for water gardens.

Mary Walker Bulb Company
PO Box 256
Omega, GA 31775
(912) 386-1919
Bulbs, corms and plants. Canna, crinum, caladium, poinsettia in retail and wholesale quantities for tropical climates.

Waterford Gardens
74 East Allendale Road
Saddle River, NJ 07458
(201) 327-0721
Plants. Water lilies and other aquatic and bog plants. Water garden supplies.

Wayside Gardens
1 Garden Lane
Hodges
SC 29695-0001
(800) 845-1124
Plants. Enormous catalog of landscape and fruit trees, flowering shrubs, perennials, climbers. Distributors of new English shrub roses as well as old-fashioned ones and hybrid teas. Many unusual plants.

White Flower Farm
Litchfield
CT 06759-0050
(800) 888-7756
Plants, bulbs. Perennials from the nursery that made America perennial-conscious.

Winterthur Museum and Gardens
Winterthur
DE 19735
(800) 767-0500
Plants. A few choice trees, shrubs and perennials from the famous museum gardens.

Woodlanders, Inc.
1128 Colleton Avenue
Aiken, SC 29801
(803) 648-7522
Plants. Trees, shrubs, vines, perennials, grasses with emphasis on maintaining biodiversity.

HOW TO FIND OUT

Many publications and associations exist to share information about gardening. Books and magazines on the subject abound; every preoccupation from general gardening to specialization in one particular genus of plants has its own enthusiasts and newsletter. A few of the largest and most generalized ones are listed here; they will lead you to others.

Magazines

The widely distributed home magazines all have regular articles on gardens, especially ***Architectural Digest, House & Garden, House Beautiful, Metropolitan Home, Home, Colonial Homes, Country Living***, and ***Country Home***.

There are also specialist magazines such as ***Horticulture***, ***Garden Design***, ***Flower & Garden***, and ***Fine Gardening***; and an excellent newsletter which tracks new developments in horticulture, ***The Avant Gardener*** (Box 489, New York, NY 10028).

Another essential publication for anyone who wishes to grow roses – it tells you where to get any and every rose variety available here, in Canada or abroad – is ***The Combined Rose List*** (published annually by Beverly R. Dobson and Peter Schneider, PO Box 16035, Rocky River, OH 44116).

Books

New books on gardening are published every day. Many are notable more for their pretty pictures than for useful information. One of the continuing problems in this country is that many gardening classics are British in origin. Interesting as they may be, it is important to remember that North America is a sub-continent with many climates, few of which (excepting only parts of the Pacific Northwest) resemble the temperate and steady English climate. Many plant combinations common in Britain are impossible on this side of the Atlantic. Therefore, the wise American gardener owns both general and regional books on North American horticulture and reads British books for inspiration. When buying a garden book, inspect the title page to be sure that the book is either American in origin or, like this one, has been thoroughly Americanized as to plants as well as spelling.

To get an idea of what is available, look at book lists and reviews in the above magazines and join the following organizations:

The American Horticultural Society
7931 East Boulevard Drive
Alexandria
VA 22308-1300
(703) 768-5700
A national association of horticulturists and gardeners. The newsletter offers the members information on current garden matters as well as books at a discount. An enormous seed exchange shares both common and rare plants from members' gardens.

The Garden Book Club
3000 Cindel Drive
Delran, NJ 08370-0001
Offers a wide selection of books at a discount to members.

The Garden Conservancy
PO Box 219
Cold Spring
NY 10516
(914) 265-2045
A rapidly growing group devoted to preservation of important American gardens. Newsletter and tours of private gardens not normally open to the public.

The National Trust for Historic Preservation
1785 Massachusetts Avenue, NW
Washington, DC
20036
(202) 673-4000
Devoted to the preservation of houses and gardens with historic and architectural importance throughout the country. ***Historic Preservation*** *is the excellent magazine of the organization.*

Garden clubs and botanical gardens exist in every part of the coutry, and are well worth joining.

Garden Design

How can you find the right person to help with your own garden? The work of garden designers is showcased in all of the above magazines. Ask members of the local garden organizations for recommendations, and look at gardens designed by the people you are considering. Botanical gardens may maintain lists of local garden designers. You can also contact the

American Society of Landscape Architects
1733 Connecticut Avenue, NW
Washington, DC
20009
(202) 466-7730
The trade association of registered landscape architecture professionals. The local chapters have membership lists which may be consulted by potential clients.

However, many expert garden designers are not landscape architects, whose qualifications may have more to do with grading, zoning and construction than with horticulture.

Page numbers in *italics* refer to illustrations and captions

The publishers would like to thank the following people for allowing Sue Atkinson and Paul Barker to photograph their gardens for the book:

Mr and Mrs Anderson, C.H. Bagot, Mr and Mrs B. Balmer, Lady Barbirolli, the Duke and Duchess of Beaufort, Mr and Mrs W.R. Benyon, Mr Bond, Dr and Mrs David Boyd, Roger Brook, Mr and Mrs C. Caplin, Mr Carver, Major and Mrs J.W. Chandos-Pole, Mr H.T.C Christie, Lady Clarissa Collin, Mr and Mrs N. Coote, Brigadier and Mrs C.F. Cox, Elizabeth Dorling, Mrs M. Dormer, Mr and Mrs P. Drysdale, Mr Honour, Mr and Mrs Denys Fraser, Lucy Gent, Dr. and Mrs F.W. Gifford, Mr and Mrs R. Goode, Mrs Grey, Joan and Robin Grout, Mrs Diana Guy, Mr and Mrs Handslip, Mr and Mrs David Hellewell, Paul and Kay Henderson, Mr and Mrs D.Heyward, Mr and Mrs John Heyward, Mrs Louise Hill, Adrian Hornsey, Mr R. Howard, John Hubbard, Dr. and Mrs Frank Hytten, Rosalind Ingrams, Mrs J. Joyce, Mr and Mrs E.C.B. Knight, Mr and Mrs C.R. Kruger, Mrs C.G. Lancaster, Dr. Sylvia Landsberg, Mrs M.D. Laverack, Mrs C. Lea, Mr and Mrs N. Lindsay-Fynn, Mrs C.M. Luke, Mrs McBurnie, Mr and Mrs R.R. Merton, Mrs Joan Moss, Mrs D.B. Nicholson, Mr and Mrs W.E. Ninniss, Mr and Mrs Norton, Paul O'Prey , Mr and Mrs A.J. Parsons, Mr Michael and the Hon. Mrs Payne, Mr and Mrs Alan Peck, M.R. Puddle, Mr and Mrs J. Pumfrey, Mr and Mrs P.A. Randall, Mr and Mrs Michael Redgrave, Mr and Mrs Simon Relph, Lord and Lady Remnant, Mr and Mrs W. Roxburgh, Mrs L. Rutherford, Colin Sanders, Mr and Mrs Ray Scott, Mr and Mrs C. Scroggs, Peter Sharp, Mrs Pauline Sheppey, Dr and Mrs Malcolm Slade, Mrs Betty Smith, Mrs Rosalind Squire, Mr and Mrs Michael Stanley, Miss Elizabeth Stephenson, Leonard Stocks, Dr. and Mrs Storrow, Arthur J. Thomas, Mr and Mrs Thomson, Mrs S. Tidd, Mr and Mrs Michael Todhunter, Mr and Mrs Derek Tolman, Lady Anne Tree, Mr and Mrs K. Wilkins.

The publishers would also like to thank the many organizations and individuals who allowed them to reproduce their photographs in this book. Page numbers are followed by codes denoting left (l), right (r), top (t), center (c) and bottom (b); the location, owner and designer (D) of the garden are given in brackets where relevant.

Stephen Anderton: 83 r, 93 b; **Sue Atkinson/Mitchell Beazley**: 14, 28, 32, 34, 36 tl, tr, b, 40, 41 b, 43 b, 44 l, 45 bl, 47 br, 48 t, 49 t, 51 tr, 52 l, 54 l, 55 r, 57 b, 58, 59 tr, bl, br, 61 tr, 62 l, 63 r, 64 t, bl, br, 65 bl, 66-67, 68 tr, bl, 68-69 b, 70 l, 72 br, 73 tr, 78 l, 78-79, 82-3, 86 l, 90-91, 92 t, 93 t, 106 t, 109 cl, 111 r, 112 l, r, 113 bl, 114 r, 116 bc, 119 br, 121 t, 125 cl, b, 126, 128 r, 130 b, 131 l, 133 bl, 135, 136 l, 137 tl, 138 tl, tr, 141 t, 142 br, 143 l, 144 br, 145 tr, 146 t, bl, br, 147 r, 152 t, c, 156 r, 157 cr, 158, 159 cl, b, 160 r, 161 tr, b, 162 l, 163 t, 164 r, 165 tr, 167 tr, 169 bl, r, 173 t, 176 tl, r, 177 cl, bl, 184 t, bc, 185 l, r, 186 cl, bl, 190 t, bl, br, 191 cr, br, 193 cl, bl, br, 198 l, r, 200 r, 201 t, 202 l, tr, 204 t, c, bl, br, 205 c, 206 l, 210 t, 218 c, 219 tl, 221 t, bl, br, 224 tl, 227 cr, bl, 229 br, 230 br, 231 t, 232 bl, 236; **Paul Barker/Mitchell Beazley**: jacket insert, 6, 8-9, 13, 17, 30 tr, 35 t, c, b, 37 b, 41 tl, 42, 47 tl, bl, 48-49 b, 50 bl, 52-53 b, 54 t, 54-55 b, 55 t, 57 tl, tr, 59 tl, 62-3, 65 t, 67 t, b, 69 br, 70-71, 71 r, 72 bl, 72-73 t, 73 cr, bl, br, 82 l, 91 r, 99 r, 104, 106 br, 107 t, b, 109 b, 115 t, 117 r, 119 c, bl, 123 tl, 125 t, c, 129 l, 130 tr, 134 l, r, 138 bl, 142 t, bl, 145 tl, 146 c, 147 l, 153 cl, br, 156 l, 157 bl, br, 159 cr, 160 l, 161 tl, 162 r, 163 cr, b, 165 tl, 167 c, 170 tl, 171 t, cr, br, 172 l, 177 cr, 178 t, 180 bl, 184 bl, 187 tl, br, 192 tl, tr, 195 bl, 197 tr, br, 199 br, 201 b, 207 tr, 208 tr, 214 tl, bl, 215 r, 216 tl, b, 217 tr, 219 tr, 220 r, 222, 223 tr, c, 224 br, 227 br, 229 bl, 230 t, 233 t, 237 b; **Tommy Candler**: 85 t, 116 c, 121 cl, 129 r, 130 tl, 131 r, 142 tr, 150 r, 166 r, 172 r, 173 cl, 180 tl, 186 br, 192 br, 197 bl, 199 bl, 205 b, 206 r, 208 bl, br, 210 c, 211 bl, br, 212 r, 214 br, 217 bl, 219 bl, 225 b, 231 b, 232 tr; **Eric Crichton**: jacket background, 38 l, r, 41 tr, 43 t, 45 t, br, 48 bl, 50-1 t, 53 r, 60 t, b, 68 tl, 80 t, bl, 81 c, 87 r, 88 b, 88-9, 89 t, 100 tr, 105 l, 108 l, 127 r, 157 cl, 163 cl, 171 bl, 180 br, 182 r, 183 t, b, 184 br, 186 tr, 187 tr, 191 tl, 194 r, 203 l, r, 223 b, 225 t, 237 t, 238 b; **The Garden Picture Library**: **Jerry Pavia** 76 tl, b, 121 cr; **Brian Carter** 232 br; **Clay Perry** 232 tl, 233 b, **Ron Sutherland** 61 tl; **John Glover**: 128 l, 148 t, 216 tr, 217 c; **Jerry Harpur**: half title (D: Claus Scheinert, Alpes Maritimes), title (Heale House, Middle Woodford, Wilts), 4 (Arbigland, Kirkbean, Dumfries), 11 (Philip Watson, Fredericksburg, Virginia), 19 (D: Claus Scheinert, Alpes Maritimes), 26-27 (D: Claus Scheinert, Alpes Maritimes), 30 tl, b (D: Claus Scheinert, Alpes Maritimes), 31 (D: Claus Scheinert, Alpes Maritimes), 33 t, b (D: Claus Scheinert, Alpes Maritimes), 39 b (D: Claus Scheinert, Alpes Maritimes), 50-51 b (D: Susie Ranicar, Tasmania), 61 b (Meadowbrook Farm, Philadelphia), 74 l (Polly Park, Canberra, Australia), 74-75 (D: Patrick Miller, San Francisco), 75 r (D: Gary Orr, San Francisco), 76 tr (D: Keyes Landscape, Camden, London), 77 t (D: Garrett Eckbo, San Francisco), 81 t (D: Bruce Kelly, New York), 86-87 (Japanese Stroll Garden, Long Island), 88 tl (D: John Patrick, Melbourne, Victoria), 100 tl (D: Ann Alexander-Sinclair), 101 t, br (D: Edwina von Gal, New York), 102-3 (Wentworth, Sydney), 105 r (Dreamthorpe, Macedon, Victoria), 109 t (D: John Brooks, Denmans, Fontwell, Sussex), 110 t (Hazelbury Manor, Box, Wilts.), cl (D: Mark Laurence), cr (Wycken Hall, Stanton, Suffolk) b (Stonecrop, Coldspring, New York State), 111 l (D: Patrick Miller, San Francisco), 113 top (D: Oehme & van Sweden, Washington DC), 114 l (Panmure, Stirling, Western Australia), 116 t (D: Oehme & van Sweden, Washington DC), 116 bl (D: Michael Balston, Patney, Wilts.) r (D: Christopher Masson, London), 117 l (D: Ron Simple, Philadelphia), 118 t, c (Contractor: Berry's Garden Construction Co.), 119 t (D: Ruth Shellhorn, Los Angeles), 120 l (D: Chris Rosmini, Los Angeles) r (D: Michael Branch, Wantage, Berks.), 122 l (D: Topher Delaney, San Francisco), 123 b (D: Claus Scheinert, Alpes Maritimes), 124 cl (D: Fred Watson, New Hampshire), 127 l (D: Edwina von Gal, New York), 132 l (D: Claus Scheinert, Alpes Maritimes), 133 t (Ladew Garden, Maryland) br (Dumbarton Oaks, Georgetown, Washington DC), 136 r (D: Gos Lieber), 137 bl (D: Ann Griot, Los Angeles) r (Mr. and Mrs. Klok, Hobart, Tasmania), 139 (Mr. and Mrs. Potts, Chiffchaffs Nursery, Bourton, Dorset), 140 l (Lower Hall, Worfield, Shropshire), r, 144 bl (D: Jan Martinez, Alkam, Kent), 145 cl (Bradenham Hall, Norfolk), cr (House of Pitmuies, Guthrie by Forfar, Tayside), 148 c, bl (D: Bruce Kelly, New York), br (D: Oehme & van Sweden, Washington DC), 149 t (D: Bruce Kelly, New York), cl (Dumbarton Oaks, Georgetown, Washington DC), cr (Williamsburg, Virginia), 150 l (House of Pitmuies, Guthrie by Forfar, Tayside), 151 tl (D: Peter Wooster, Roxbury, Connecticut), tr (Ballarat, Victoria), bl (Heale House, Middle Woodford, Wilts.), br (D: Anne Griot, Los Angeles), 153 tr (D: Bruce Kelly, New York), bl (House of Pitmuies, Guthrie by Forfar, Tayside), 154-155 (D: Simon Fraser, Fulham, London), 157 t (D: Fred Watson, New Hampshire), 159 t (Kay Purvis, Cairns, Queensland), 164 l (D: Keith Corlett, New York), 165 c (D: Edwina von Gal, New York), 166 l (D: Claus Scheinert, Alpes Maritimes), 167 tl (D: Ragna Goddard, Higganum, Connecticut), 171 cl (Dumbarton Oaks, Georgetown, Washington DC), 174 (Lower Hall, Worfield, Shropshire), 175 r (Hazleby House, North End, Newbury, Berks.), 176 br (D: Claus Scheinert, Alpes Maritimes), 178 b (D: Joe Eck and Wayne Winterrowd, Readsboro, Vermont), 179 l (Heale House, Middle Woodford, Wilts.), r (Arbigland, Kirkbean, Dumfries), 180 tr (Lower Hall, Worfield, Shropshire), 181 tr (Olivers, Colchester, Essex) and b (Heale House, Middle Woodford, Wilts.), 191 tr (King Henry's Hunting Lodge, Odiham, Hants.), 195 t (Red Hill Farm, Deloraine, Tasmania), 196 tl (D: Claus Scheinert, Alpes Maritimes), bl (Jardin des Colombieres, Menton, Alpes Maritimes), 208 tl (D: Ragna Goddard, Higganum, Connecticut), 209 l (Ladew Garden, Maryland), 214 tr (Newry, Longford, Tasmania), 220 l (D: Keith Corlett, New York), 224 bl (D: Claus Scheinert, Alpes Maritimes), 226 b (D: Claus Scheinert, Alpes Maritimes), 227 tl (Ladew Garden, Maryland), 229 tl (D: Michael Wayman, Sydney, New South Wales), 230 cl (D: Bob Dash, Sagaponack, Long Island, NY), 231 c (D: Keith Corlett, New York); **John Heseltine**: 77 bl, 113 br, 124 br; **Marijke Heuff**: 65 br (Mrs. M. van Bennekom-Scheffer), 69 tl(Mr. J. van den Brink), 81 b, 84 t (Mr. L.J.Ph Groeneveld) and b (Jaap Nieuwenhuis and Paula Thies), 88 tr, 115 c, 138 br, 141 cl, 210 b (Mr. J. van den Brink), 219 br (Mrs. M. van Bennekom-Scheffer), 224 tr (Mrs. M. van Bennekom-Scheffer), 226 tl (Mrs. L. Goossenaerts-Miedema), 227 tr (Jaap Nieuwenhuis and Paula Thies); **Hozelock Ltd.**: 221 c; **Andrew Lawson**: 44 r, 122 r, 124 bl, 141 cr, 173 br, 209 r; **James Merrell/Mitchell Beazley**: 213 b; **Clive Nichols**: 29 t, 46, 47 tr, 80 br, 85 b, 98 l, 100 b (D: Anthony Noel), 106 bl, 108 r, 109 cr, 123 tr, 138 cr (D: Anthony Noel), 143 r, 168 l, r, 169 c, 170 c, 175 l, 177 t, 178 c, 189 l, 194 l (D: Anthony Noel), 195 br (D: Anthony Noel), 200 l, 202 br, 205 tl, tr, 207 tl, 215 l, 217 br (D: Anthony Noel), 218 t, b (D: Anthony Noel), 223 tl, 226 tr (D: Anthony Noel), 238 t, 239; **Hugh Palmer**: 39 t, 52-53 t, 69 tr, 77 br, 79 r, 92 b, 98-9, 101 bl, 137 top r, 144 t, 153 tl, 170 tr, 182 l, 188, 189 r, 191 bl, 192 bl, 193 tl, tr, 196 tr, br, 199 tl, 207 b, 208 cr, 211 tl, 212 l, 213 tl, tr, 228, 229 tr, 234-235; **Photos Horticultural**: 51 br; **Reed Consumer Books Picture Library**: 29 b, 37 t, 49 br, 56, 90 l, 132 r, 181 tl.

From p. 240 to p.347 (Directory section) all photographs are by **Andrew Lawson,** with the following exceptions:
A-Z Botanical Collection 274 tr, 275 tc, cl, 276 cl, 278 tr, 279 bl, 285 tr, 286 tl, bl; **Sue Atkinson/ Mitchell Beazley** 257, 258 b, 343 b; **Paul Barker/Mitchell Beazley** 256, 268, 270, 331 t, 332 t, 343 t; **Eric Crichton** 254 tc, 255 b, 259 t, 261 bc, 264 tr, 272 cr, 274 b, 277 tl, 278 bc, 279 br, 283 cl, 284 tc, 285 tl, 287 bl, bc, 291 bl, 292 bc, 308 t, c, 309 tr, 310 tr, 312 tr, 313 bl, 318 br, 319 tl, bl, 324 t, 325 cl, 331 b, 335 bc, 338 t, 340 l, 341 tl; **Garden Picture Library (Linda Burgess)** 314, **(John Glover)** 316 b; **John Glover** 250 c, 253 tc, 315 t, b, 316 t; **Derek Gould** 253 cr, 267 tl, 272 b, 275 bc; **Jerry Harpur** 259 b (Home Farm, Balscote, Oxfordshire), 269 b (Dreamthorpe, Macedon, Victoria), 288 ('Churchill', Campania, Tasmania), 324 b (D: Philip Watson, Fredericksburg, Virginia), 332 b (Royal Horticultural Society, Wisley, Surrey), 336 (D: Ann Griot, Los Angeles), 337 t (D: Victor Nelson, New York) and b, 338 b (Meadowbrook Farm, Philadelphia), 342 (D: Claus Scheinert, Alpes Maritimes); **Marijke Heuff** 258 t (Mrs. L. Goossenaerts-Miedema), 281 t (Mr. and Mrs. Bremmer-Smit), 282 t, b, 289 (Mr. and Mrs. Bremmer-Smit); **Clive Nichols** 269 t, 271 tl, 280, 294, 322, 323 t, b, 330; **Hugh Palmer** 296; **Photos Horticultural** 250 tl, 254 bl, 262 tc, 275 tl, 284 bl, 285 br, 291 cr, 292 tc, 293 bc, 298 tr, bl, 299 tc, 313 tc, tr, 318 tr, 334 tr, 335 tc, 339 r, 341 c; **Reed Consumer Books Picture Library**: 261 tc, 265 bl, 305 tl, tc, 340 tc; **Harry Smith Horticultural Collection** 275 cr, 279 tr, 293 tl, 303 bl, 312 tc, 335 bl, 346 br, 347 b.